STATISTICAL METHODS I

STA 2023

Taken from:
Statistics, Tenth Edition
by James T. McClave and Terry Sincich

PEARSON
Custom
Publishing

PEARSON
Prentice
Hall

Cover Art: *Tangerine*, by Jan Lhormer.

Taken from:

Statistics, Tenth Edition
by James T. McClave and Terry Sincich
Copyright © 2006, 2003 by Pearson Education, Inc.
Published by Prentice-Hall, Inc.
Upper Saddle River, New Jersey 07458

This special edition published in cooperation with Pearson Custom Publishing.

Printed in the United States of America

10 9 8 7 6 5 4 3 2 1

ISBN 0-536-94425-3

2005360146

CS

Please visit our web site at *www.pearsoncustom.com*

PEARSON CUSTOM PUBLISHING
75 Arlington Street, Suite 300, Boston, MA 02116
A Pearson Education Company

Contents

CHAPTER 1   Statistics, Data, and Statistical Thinking   2

1.1   The Science of Statistics   4
1.2   Types of Statistical Applications   4
1.3   Fundamental Elements of Statistics   6
1.4   Types of Data   12
1.5   Collecting Data   14
1.6   The Role of Statistics in Critical Thinking   17

Statistics in Action: *USA Weekend* Teen Surveys–Are Boys Really from Mars and Girls from Venus?   3

Using Technology: Creating and Listing Data Using MINITAB   24

CHAPTER 2   Methods for Describing Sets of Data   28

2.1   Describing Qualitative Data   30
2.2   Graphical Methods for Describing Quantitative Data   41
2.3   Summation Notation   54
2.4   Numerical Measures of Central Tendency   55
2.5   Numerical Measures of Variability   67
2.6   Interpreting the Standard Deviation   72
2.7   Numerical Measures of Relative Standing   81
2.8   Methods for Detecting Outliers (Optional)   85
2.9   Graphing Bivariate Relationships (Optional)   95
2.10   Distorting the Truth with Descriptive Techniques   101

Statistics in Action: The "Eye Cue" Test: Does Experience Improve Performance?   29

Using Technology: Describing Data Using MINITAB   114

CHAPTER 3   **Probability   118**

3.1   Events, Sample Spaces, and Probability   120

3.2   Unions and Intersections   133

3.3   Complementary Events   137

3.4   The Additive Rule and Mutually Exclusive Events   139

3.5   Conditional Probability   145

3.6   The Multiplicative Rule and Independent Events   148

3.7   Random Sampling   161

3.8   Some Additional Counting Rules (Optional)   165

3.9   Bayes's Rule (Optional)   174

Statistics in Action: **Lotto Buster!   119**

Using Technology: Generating a Random Sample Using MINITAB   186

CHAPTER 4   **Discrete Random Variables   188**

4.1   Two Types of Random Variables   190

4.2   Probability Distributions for Discrete Random Variables   193

4.3   Expected Values of Discrete Random Variables   198

4.4   The Binomial Random Variable   204

4.5   The Poisson Random Variable (Optional)   218

4.6   The Hypergeometric Random Variable (Optional)   224

Statistics in Action: **Probability in a Reverse Cocaine Sting   189**

**Using Technology: Binomial, Poisson, and Hypergeometric Probabilities
Using MINITAB   234**

CHAPTER 5   **Continuous Random Variables   236**

5.1   Continuous Probability Distributions   238

5.2   The Uniform Distribution   238

5.3   The Normal Distribution   243

5.4   Descriptive Methods for Assessing Normality   261

5.5   Approximating a Binomial Distribution with a Normal Distribution
(Optional)   269

5.6   The Exponential Distribution (Optional)   276

Statistics in Action: **Super Weapons Development—Optimizing the Hit Ratio   237**

**Using Technology: Cumulative Probabilities for Continuous Random Variables
and Normal Probability Plots Using MINITAB   286**

CHAPTER 6   Sampling Distributions   290

6.1   The Concept of a Sampling Distribution?   292

6.2   Properties of Sampling Distributions: Unbiasedness and Minimum Variance   298

6.3   The Sampling Distribution of $\bar{x}$ and the Central Limit Theorem   303

Statistics in Action: **The Insomnia Pill**   **291**

Using Technology: **Simulating a Sampling Distribution Using MINITAB**   **317**

CHAPTER 7   Inferences Based on a Single Sample: *Estimation with Confidence Intervals*   320

7.1   Identifying the Target Parameter   321

7.2   Large-Sample Confidence Interval for a Population Mean   322

7.3   Small-Sample Confidence Interval for a Population Mean   332

7.4   Large-Sample Confidence Interval for a Population Proportion   343

7.5   Determining the Sample Size   350

Statistics in Action: **Speed—Improving the Sprint Times of High School Football Players**   **321**

Using Technology: **Confidence Intervals Using MINITAB**   **364**

CHAPTER 8   Inferences Based on a Single Sample: *Tests of Hypothesis*   368

8.1   The Elements of a Test of Hypothesis   369

8.2   Large-Sample Test of Hypothesis About a Population Mean   376

8.3   Observed Significance Levels: *p*-Values   383

8.4   Small-Sample Test of Hypothesis About a Population Mean   390

8.5   Large-Sample Test of Hypothesis About a Population Proportion   397

8.6   Calculating Type II Error Probabilities: More About β (Optional)   404

8.7   Test of Hypothesis About a Population Variance (Optional)   412

Statistics in Action: **Diary of a Kleenex® User**   **369**

Using Technology: **Tests of Hypothesis Using MINITAB**   **424**

CHAPTER 9

Inferences Based on a Two Samples: *Confidence Intervals and Tests of Hypotheses* 428

9.1   Identifying the Target Parameter   430

9.2   Comparing Two Population Means: Independent Sampling   430

9.3   Comparing Two Population Means: Paired Difference Experiments   453

9.4   Comparing Two Population Proportions: Independent Sampling   468

9.5   Determining the Sample Size   479

9.6   Comparing Two Population Variances: Independent Sampling (Optional)   483

Statistics in Action: **Detection of Rigged Milk Prices   429**

Using Technology: **Two Sample Inferences Using MINITAB   508**

APPENDICES

Appendix A   Tables   881

Table I	Random Numbers 882
Table II	Binomial Probabilities 885
Table III	Poisson Probabilities 889
Table IV	Normal Curve Areas 894
Table V	Exponentials 895
Table VI	Critical Values of t 896
Table VII	Critical Values of X^2 897
Table VIII	Percentage Points of the F-Distribution, $\alpha = .10$ 899
Table IX	Percentage Points of the F-Distribution, $\alpha = .05$ 901
Table X	Percentage Points of the F-Distribution, $\alpha = .025$ 903
Table XI	Percentage Points of the F-Distribution, $\alpha = .01$ 905
Table XII	Critical Values of T_L and T_U for the Wilcoxon Rank Sum Test: Independent Samples 907
Table XIII	Critical Values of T_0 in the Wilcoxon Paired Difference Signed Rank Test 908
Table XIV	Critical Values of Spearman's Rank Correlation Coefficient 909
Table XV	Critical Values of the Studentized Range, $\alpha = .05$ 910
Table XVI	Critical Values of the Studentized Range, $\alpha = .01$ 912

Appendix B   Calculation Formulas for Analysis of Variance   914

Short Answers to Selected Odd-Numbered Exercises   918

Index   927

Statistics

1

Statistics, Data, and Statistical Thinking

Contents

1.1 The Science of Statistics

1.2 Types of Statistical Applications

1.3 Fundamental Elements of Statistics

1.4 Types of Data

1.5 Collecting Data

1.6 The Role of Statistics in Critical Thinking

Statistics in Action

USA Weekend Teen Survey:
Are Boys Really from Mars and
Girls from Venus?

Using Technology

Creating and Listing Data
Using MINITAB

Where We're Going

- Introduce the field of statistics.
- Demonstrate how statistics applies to real-world problems.
- Establish the link between statistics and data.
- Identify the different types of data and data collection methods.
- Differentiate between population and sample data.
- Differentiate between descriptive and inferential statistics.

Statistics in *ACTION*

USA WEEKEND Teen Survey: Are Boys Really from Mars and Girls from Venus?

Welcome to USA WEEKEND, the magazine that makes a difference.

www.usaweekend.com

USA Weekend is a magazine supplement in approximately 600 United States newspapers, with an estimated 50 million readers. Each year, the magazine conducts a Teen Survey in which America's teenagers give opinions on a wide variety of topics, including their views of the opposite sex (2003 survey) and their use of newspapers (2004 survey). The surveys are made available in print in the magazine supplement, at the www.usaweekend.com Web site, and via the mail using newspaper subscriber lists.

Each survey is typically sponsored by a special interest group. For example, the American Society of Newspaper Editors and the Newspaper Association of America Foundation were sponsors of the 2004 survey, while *YM Magazine* and John Gray (author of the best-selling book *Men are from Mars, Women are from Venus*) sponsored the 2003 survey. The number of teens responding to the survey varies as well (37,000 teenagers in 2003 and 65,000 in 2004).

Some of the questions (and corresponding results) for the 2003 and 2004 Teen Surveys are shown in the following table.

2004 Survey: Teens & Newspapers

1. Where do you get most of your news?

Television:	48%
Newspaper:	18%
Word of Mouth:	14%
Online:	9%
Radio:	7%
Magazines:	4%

2. How relevant is the newspaper to your life?

Very relevant:	18%
Somewhat relevant:	53%
Not very relevant:	23%
Not at all relevant:	6%

3. How many days a week do you read the newspaper?

Average = 3.1

4. Do you think newspapers will become obsolete because of other media?

Yes:	24%
No:	50%
Don't know:	26%

2003 Survey: Teens & the Opposite Sex

1. Which quality first catches your attention in the opposite sex?

	Boys	Girls
Looks:	58%	40%
Personality:	27%	36%
Athleticism:	1%	2%
Confidence:	2%	3%
Sense of Humor:	9%	16%
Intelligence:	2%	2%
Popularity:	1%	1%

2. Which quality of your sex first catches the attention of the opposite sex?

	Boys	Girls
Looks:	56%	79%
Personality:	16%	11%
Athleticism:	6%	0%
Confidence:	3%	3%
Sense of Humor:	12%	3%
Intelligence:	2%	1%
Popularity:	5%	3%

3. Do you think it's OK for girls in your grade to call guys?

	Boys	Girls
Yes:	96%	95%
No:	4%	5%

4. Do you think it's OK for girls in your grade to ask guys out?

	Boys	Girls
Yes:	90%	80%
No:	10%	20%

5. What part of the newspaper do you read first?	
Front page:	36%
Comics:	19%
Sports:	15%
Other:	30%

5. Is it possible to have a good friend of the opposite sex?	Boys	Girls
No:	6%	3%
Yes, but only if part of a group:	8%	7%
Yes, anytime:	86%	90%

In the following *Statistics in Action Revisited* sections, we discuss several key statistical concepts covered in this chapter that are relevant to the *USA Weekend* Annual Teen Surveys.

Statistics in Action Revisited for Chapter 1

- Identifying the population, sample, and inference (p. 12)
- Identifying the data collection method and data type (p. 16)
- Critically assessing the ethics of a statistical study (p. 18)

1.1 The Science of Statistics

What does statistics mean to you? Does it bring to mind batting averages, Gallup polls, unemployment figures, numerical distortions of facts (lying with statistics!)? Or is it simply a college requirement you have to complete? We hope to persuade you that statistics is a meaningful, useful science whose broad scope of applications to business, government, and the physical and social sciences is almost limitless. We also want to show that statistics can lie only when they are misapplied. Finally, we wish to demonstrate the key role statistics plays in critical thinking — whether in the classroom, on the job, or in everyday life. Our objective is to leave you with the impression that the time you spend studying this subject will repay you in many ways.

The *Random House College Dictionary* defines *statistics* as "the science that deals with the collection, classification, analysis, and interpretation of information or data." Thus, a statistician isn't just someone who calculates batting averages at baseball games or tabulates the results of a Gallup Poll. Professional statisticians are trained in *statistical science*. That is, they are trained in collecting numerical information in the form of **data**, evaluating it, and drawing conclusions from it. Furthermore, statisticians determine what information is relevant in a given problem and whether the conclusions drawn from a study are to be trusted.

> **DEFINITION 1.1**
>
> **Statistics** is the science of data. This involves collecting, classifying, summarizing, organizing, analyzing, and interpreting numerical information.

In the next section, you'll see several real-life examples of statistical applications that involve making decisions and drawing conclusions.

1.2 Types of Statistical Applications

Statistics means "numerical descriptions" to most people. Monthly housing starts, the failure rate of liver transplants, and the proportion of African-Americans who feel brutalized by local police all represent statistical descriptions of large sets of data collected on some phenomenon. Often the data are selected from

Biography

FLORENCE NIGHTINGALE (1820–1910)— The Passionate Statistician

In Victorian England, the "Lady of the Lamp" had a mission to improve the squalid field hospital conditions of the British army during the Crimean War. Today, most historians consider Florence Nightingale to be the founder of the nursing profession. To convince members of the British Parliament of the need for supplying nursing and medical care to soldiers in the field, Nightingale compiled massive amounts of data from the army files. Through a remarkable series of graphs (which included the first pie chart), she demonstrated that most of the deaths in the war were due to illnesses contracted outside the battlefield or long after battle action from wounds that went untreated. Florence Nightingale's compassion and self-sacrificing nature, coupled with her ability to collect, arrange, and present large amounts of data, led some to call her the Passionate Statistican.

some larger set of data whose characteristics we wish to estimate. We call this selection process *sampling*. For example, you might collect the ages of a sample of customers at a video store to estimate the average age of *all* customers of the store. Then you could use your estimate to target the store's advertisements to the appropriate age group. Notice that statistics involves two different processes: (1) describing sets of data and (2) drawing conclusions (making estimates, decisions, predictions, etc.) about the sets of data based on sampling. So, the applications of statistics can be divided into two broad areas: *descriptive statistics* and *inferential statistics*.

DEFINITION 1.2

Descriptive statistics utilizes numerical and graphical methods to look for patterns in a data set, to summarize the information revealed in a data set, and to present that information in a convenient form.

DEFINITION 1.3

Inferential statistics utilizes sample data to make estimates, decisions, predictions, or other generalizations about a larger set of data.

Although we'll discuss both descriptive and inferential statistics in the following chapters, the primary theme of the text is **inference**.

Let's begin by examining some studies that illustrate applications of statistics.

Study 1 "Speed Training Program for High School Football Players" (*The Sport Journal*, Winter 2004)

Michael Gray and Jessica Sauerbeck, researchers at Northern Kentucky University, designed and tested a speed training program for junior varsity and varsity high school football players. Each participant was timed in a 40-yard sprint prior to the start of the training program and timed again after completing the program. Based on these sprint times, each participant was classified as having an "improved" time, "no change" in time, or a "decrease" in time. The results are summarized in Figure 1.1. From the graph, you can clearly see that nearly 87% of the players improved their sprint times and only about 3% had decreased times.

Same 10.5%

Decrease 2.6%

Improve 86.8%

Figure 1.1

Success Rate of a Speed Training Program for High School Football Players

Since Figure 1.1 describes the categories of improvement in sprint times for players who participate in a speed training program, the graphic is an example of descriptive statistics.

Study 2 "Does Height Influence Progression through Primary School Grades?" (*The Archives of Disease in Childhood*, April 2000)

Researchers from the University of Melbourne (Australia) analyzed the heights of over 2,800 students in primary school (grades 1 through 6). After dividing the students into three equal groups based on age (youngest third, middle third, and oldest third) within each grade level, the researchers found that the oldest group of students were the shortest in height, on average — and that this phenomenon was mostly due to the 133 children (mostly boys) who had been held back a grade level. From the analysis, the researchers inferred "that older boys within grades were relatively shorter than their younger peers" and that "when boys experienced school difficulties, height [is] one factor influencing the final decision to [hold back the student a grade level]." Thus, inferential statistics was applied to arrive at this conclusion.

Study 3 "The Significance of Belief and Expectancy Within the Spiritual Healing Encounter" (*Social Science & Medicine*, July 1995)

"Spiritual healing techniques have been a fundamental component of the healing rituals of virtually all societies since the advent of man," says researcher Daniel P. Wirth. What effect, if any, do spiritual healing encounters have on the mental and physical health of patients in today's society? And do the effects depend on the patient's expectations? To answer these questions, Wirth conducted a scientific study of 48 individuals residing in a northern California suburb. The mental and physical health of each subject was determined via a battery of standardized tests. Each individual then underwent a spiritual healing encounter that involved a "magnetic laying-on-of-hands approach." One week following the healing session, subjects were retested.

An analysis of the data revealed a significant difference between the pretest and posttest health scores for the subjects. Further analysis led Wirth to conclude that "high healer and patient expectancy [are] important . . . predictors as well as facilitators of the healing process."

Like Study 2, this study is an example of the use of inferential statistics. Wirth used data from 48 individuals to make inferences about the beliefs and health improvements of all patients who experience a spiritual healing encounter.

These studies provide three real-life examples of the uses of statistics. Notice that each involves an analysis of data, either for the purpose of describing the data set (Study 1) or for making inferences about a data set (Studies 2 and 3).

1.3 Fundamental Elements of Statistics

Statistical methods are particularly useful for studying, analyzing, and learning about *populations* of *experimental units*.

DEFINITION 1.4

An **experimental unit** is an object (e.g., person, thing, transaction, or event) upon which we collect data.

DEFINITION 1.5

A **population** is a set of units (usually people, objects, transactions, or events) that we are interested in studying.

For example, populations may include (1) *all* employed workers in the United States, (2) *all* registered voters in California, (3) *everyone* who is afflicted with AIDS, (4) *all* the cars produced last year by a particular assembly line, (5) the entire stock of spare parts available at United Airlines' maintenance facility, (6) *all* sales made at the drive-in window of a McDonald's restaurant during a given year, and (7) the set of *all* accidents occurring on a particular stretch of interstate highway during a holiday period. Notice that the first three population examples (1–3) are sets (groups) of people, the next two (4–5) are sets of objects, the next (6) is a set of transactions, and the last (7) is a set of events. Also notice that *each set includes all the units in the population*.

In studying a population, we focus on one or more characteristics or properties of the units in the population. We call such characteristics *variables*. For example, we may be interested in the variables age, gender, and/or the number of years of education of the people currently unemployed in the United States.

DEFINITION 1.6

A **variable** is a characteristic or property of an individual population unit.

The name *variable* is derived from the fact that any particular characteristic may vary among the units in a population.

In studying a particular variable it is helpful to be able to obtain a numerical representation for it. Often, however, numerical representations are not readily available, so the process of measurement plays an important supporting role in statistical studies. **Measurement** is the process we use to assign numbers to variables of individual population units. We might, for instance, measure the performance of the President by asking a registered voter to rate it on a scale from 1 to 10. Or we might measure workforce age simply by asking each worker, "How old are you?" In other cases, measurement involves the use of instruments such as stopwatches, scales, and calipers.

If the population you wish to study is small, it is possible to measure a variable for every unit in the population. For example, if you are measuring the GPA for all incoming first-year students at your university, it is at least feasible to obtain every GPA. When we measure a variable for every unit of a population, it is called a **census** of the population. Typically, however, the populations of interest in most applications are much larger, involving perhaps many thousands or even an infinite number of units. Examples of large populations are those following Definition 1.5, as well as all graduates of your university or college, all potential buyers of a new fax machine, and all pieces of first-class mail handled by the U.S. Post Office. For such populations conducting a census would be prohibitively time-consuming and/or costly. A reasonable alternative would be to select and study a *subset* (or portion) of the units in the population.

DEFINITION 1.7

A **sample** is a subset of the units of a population.

For example, instead of polling all 120 million registered voters in the United States during a presidential election year, a pollster might select and question a sample of just 1,500 voters (see Figure 1.2). If he is interested in the variable "presidential preference," he would record (measure) the preference of each sampled vote.

After the variable(s) of interest for every unit in the sample (or population) are measured, the data are analyzed, either by descriptive or inferential statistical methods. The pollster, for example, may be interested only in *describing* the voting patterns of the sample of 1,500 voters. More likely, however, he will want to use the information in the sample to make inferences about the population of all 120 million voters.

> **DEFINITION 1.8**
>
> A **statistical inference** is an estimate, prediction, or some other generalization about a population based on information contained in a sample.

That is, *we use the information contained in the smaller sample to learn about the larger population.** Thus, from the sample of 1,500 voters, the pollster may estimate

Figure 1.2
A Sample of Voter Registration Cards for All Registered Voters

Population   Sample

120 million
voter ID cards

1,500 voter ID cards

---

*The terms *population* and *sample* are often used to refer to the sets of measurements themselves, as well as to the units on which the measurements are made. When a single variable of interest is being measured, this usage causes little confusion. But when the terminology is ambiguous, we'll refer to the measurements as *population data sets* and sample data sets, respectively.

the percentage of all the voters who would vote for each presidential candidate if the election were held on the day the poll was conducted, or he might use the results to predict the outcome on election day.

EXAMPLE 1.1   KEY ELEMENTS OF A STATISTICAL PROBLEM

Problem   According to the *Atlanta Journal-Constitution* (Nov. 4, 2003), the average age of viewers of MSNBC cable television news programming is 58 years. Suppose a rival network executive hypothesizes that the average age of MSNBC news viewers is less than 58. To test her hypothesis, she samples 500 MSNBC news viewers and determines the age of each.

   a.   Describe the population.

   b.   Describe the variable of interest.

   c.   Describe the sample.

   d.   Describe the inference.

Solution   **a.**   The population is the set of units of interest to the cable TV executive, which is the set of all MSNBC news viewers.

   b.   The age (in years) of each viewer is the variable of interest.

   c.   The sample must be a subset of the population. In this case, it is the 500 MSNBC news viewers selected by the executive.

   d.   The inference of interest involves the *generalization* of the information contained in the sample of 500 viewers to the population of all MSNBC viewers. In particular, the executive wants to *estimate* the average age of the viewers in order to determine whether it is less than 58 years. She might accomplish this by calculating the average age in the sample and using the sample average to estimate the population average.

Look Back   A key to diagnosing a statistical problem is to identify the data set collected (in this example, the ages of the 500 cable viewers) as a population or sample.

■ ■ ■

EXAMPLE 1.2   KEY ELEMENTS OF A STATISTICAL PROBLEM

Problem   "Cola wars" is the popular term for the intense competition between Coca-Cola and Pepsi displayed in their marketing campaigns. Their campaigns have featured movie and television stars, rock videos, athletic endorsements, and claims of consumer preference based on taste tests. Suppose, as part of a Pepsi marketing campaign, 1,000 cola consumers are given a blind taste test (i.e., a taste test in which the two brand names are disguised). Each consumer is asked to state a preference for brand A or brand B.

   a.   Describe the population.

   b.   Describe the variable of interest.

   c.   Describe the sample.

   d.   Describe the inference.

Solution
a. Since we are interested in the responses of cola consumers in a taste test, a cola consumer is the experimental unit. Thus, the population of interest is the collection or set of all consumers.

b. The characteristic that Pepsi wants to measure is the consumer's cola preference as revealed under the conditions of a blind taste test, so *cola preference* is the variable of interest.

c. The sample is the 1,000 cola consumers selected from the population of all cola consumers.

d. The inference of interest is the *generalization* of the cola preferences of the 1,000 sampled consumers to the population of all cola consumers. In particular, the preferences of the consumers in the sample can be used to *estimate* the percentage of all cola consumers who prefer each brand.

Look Back In determining whether the study is inferential or descriptive, we assess whether Pepsi is interested in the responses of only the 1,000 sampled customers (descriptive statistics) or in the responses for the entire population of consumers (inferential statistics).

Now Work   *Exercise 1.14b*

■ ■ ■

The preceding definitions and examples identify four of the five elements of an inferential statistical problem: a population, one or more variables of interest, a sample, and an inference. But making the inference is only part of the story. We also need to know its **reliability** — that is, how good the inference is. The only way we can be certain that an inference about a population is correct is to include the entire population in our sample. However, because of *resource constraints* (i.e., insufficient time and/or money), we usually can't work with whole populations, so we base our inferences on just a portion of the population (a sample). Thus, we introduce an element of *uncertainty* into our inferences. Consequently, whenever possible, it is important to determine and report the reliability of each inference made. Reliability, then, is the fifth element of inferential statistical problems.

The measure of reliability that accompanies an inference separates the science of statistics from the art of fortune-telling. A palm reader, like a statistician, may examine a sample (your hand) and make inferences about the population (your life). However, unlike statistical inferences, the palm reader's inferences include no measure of reliability.

Suppose, like the cable TV executive in Example 1.1, we are interested in the *error of estimation* (i.e., the difference between the average age of a population of cable TV viewers and the average age of a sample of viewers). Using statistical methods, we can determine a *bound on the estimation error*. This bound is simply a number that our estimation error is not likely to exceed. We'll see in later chapters that this bound is a measure of the uncertainty of our inference. The reliability of statistical inferences is discussed throughout this text. For now, we simply want you to realize that an inference is incomplete without a measure of its reliability.

DEFINITION 1.9

A **measure of reliability** is a statement (usually quantified) about the degree of uncertainty associated with a statistical inference.

Let's conclude this section with a summary of the elements of both descriptive and inferential statistical problems and an example to illustrate a measure of reliability.

Four Elements of Descriptive Statistical Problems

1. The population or sample of interest
2. One or more variables (characteristics of the population or sample units) that are to be investigated
3. Tables, graphs, or numerical summary tools
4. Identification of patterns in the data

Five Elements of Inferential Statistical Problems

1. The population of interest
2. One or more variables (characteristics of the population units) that are to be investigated
3. The sample of population units
4. The inference about the population based on information contained in the sample
5. A measure of reliability for the inference

EXAMPLE 1.3   RELIABILITY OF AN INFERENCE

Problem   Refer to Example 1.2, in which the cola preferences of 1,000 consumers were indicated in a taste test. Describe how the reliability of an inference concerning the preferences of all cola consumers in the Pepsi bottler's marketing region could be measured.

Solution   When the preferences of 1,000 consumers are used to estimate those of all consumers in the region, the estimate will not exactly mirror the preferences of the population. For example, if the taste test shows that 56% of the 1,000 consumers preferred Pepsi, it does not follow (nor is it likely) that exactly 56% of all cola drinkers in the region prefer Pepsi. Nevertheless, we can use sound statistical reasoning (which we'll explore later in the text) to ensure that the sampling procedure will generate estimates that are almost certainly within a specified limit of the true percentage of all consumers who prefer Pepsi. For example, such reasoning might assure us that the estimate of the preference for Pepsi is almost certainly within 5% of the actual population preference. The implication is that the actual preference for Pepsi is between 51% [i.e., $(56 - 5)$%] and 61% [i.e., $(56 + 5)$%] — that is, (56 ± 5)%. This interval represents a measure of reliability for the inference.

Look Back   The interval 56 ± 5 is called a *confidence interval*, since we are confident that the true percentage of customers that prefer Pepsi in a taste test falls into the range $(51, 61)$. In Chapter 7, we learn how to assess the degree of confidence (e.g., 90% or 95% level of confidence) in the interval.

■ ■ ■

Statistics in Action Revisited

Identifying the Population, Sample, and Inference

Consider the 2003 Teen Survey conducted by *USA Weekend* magazine. One of the survey questions is, "Which quality of your sex first catches the attention of the opposite sex?" The experimental unit for the study is a teenager (the person answering the question), and the variable measured is the response ("looks," "personality," "athleticism," "confidence," "sense of humor," "intelligence," or "popularity") to the question. The magazine reported that approximately 37,000 teens participated in the study. Obvi-

ously, this is not all of the teenagers in the United States. Consequently, the 37,000 responses represent a sample selected from the much larger population of all American teenagers.

USA Weekend reported that 79% of the girls felt that their "Looks" is the quality that first catches the attention of teenage boys, while only 56% of the boys felt that their "Looks" was the first thing noticed by girls. This large discrepancy in percentages (as well as some others) led the magazine to infer that "boys are from Mars, girls are from Venus."

1.4 Types of Data

You have learned that statistics is the science of data and that data are obtained by measuring the values of one or more variables on the units in the sample (or population). All data (and hence the variables we measure) can be classified as one of two general types: *quantitative data* and *qualitative data*.

Quantitative data are data that are measured on a naturally occurring numerical scale.* The following are examples of quantitative data:

1. The temperature (in degrees Celsius) at which each in a sample of 20 pieces of heat-resistant plastic begins to melt

2. The current unemployment rate (measured as a percentage) for each of the 50 states

3. The scores of a sample of 150 law school applicants on the LSAT, a standardized law school entrance exam administered nationwide

4. The number of convicted murderers who receive the death penalty each year over a 10-year period

> **DEFINITION 1.10**
>
> **Quantitative data** are measurements that are recorded on a naturally occurring numerical scale.

In contrast, qualitative data cannot be measured on a natural numerical scale; they can only be classified into categories.† Examples of qualitative data include

1. The political party affiliation (Democrat, Republican, or Independent) in a sample of 50 voters

2. The defective status (defective or not) of each of 100 computer chips manufactured by Intel

---

*Quantitative data can be subclassified as either *interval data* or *ratio data*. For ratio data, the origin (i.e., the value 0) is a meaningful number. But the origin has no meaning with interval data. Consequently, we can add and subtract interval data, but we can't multiply and divide them. Of the four quantitative data sets listed above, (1) and (3) are interval data, while (2) and (4) are ratio data.

†Qualitative data can be subclassified as either *nominal data* or *ordinal data*. The categories of an ordinal data set can be ranked or meaningfully ordered, but the categories of a nominal data set can't be ordered. Of the four qualitative data sets listed above, (1) and (2) are nominal and (3) and (4) are ordinal.

3. The size of a car (subcompact, compact, mid-size, or full-size) rented by each of a sample of 30 business travelers

4. A taste-tester's ranking (best, worst, etc.) of four brands of barbecue sauce for a panel of 10 testers

Often, we assign arbitrary numerical values to qualitative data for ease of computer entry and analysis. But these assigned numerical values are simply codes: They cannot be meaningfully added, subtracted, multiplied, or divided. For example, we might code Democrat = 1, Republican = 2, and Independent = 3. Similarly, a taste tester might rank the barbecue sauces from 1 (best) to 4 (worst). These are simply arbitrarily selected numerical codes for the categories and have no utility beyond that.

> **DEFINITION 1.11**
>
> **Qualitative data** are measurements that cannot be measured on a natural numerical scale; they can only be classified into one of a group of categories.

EXAMPLE 1.4   DATA TYPES

Problem Chemical and manufacturing plants often discharge toxic-waste materials such as DDT into nearby rivers and streams. These toxins can adversely affect the plants and animals inhabiting the river and the river bank. The U.S. Army Corps of Engineers conducted a study of fish in the Tennessee River (in Alabama) and its three tributary creeks: Flint Creek, Limestone Creek, and Spring Creek. A total of 144 fish were captured, and the following variables were measured for each:

1. River/creek where each fish was captured
2. Species (channel catfish, largemouth bass, or smallmouth buffalofish)
3. Length (centimeters)
4. Weight (grams)
5. DDT concentration (parts per million)

Classify each of the five variables measured as quantitative or qualitative.

Solution The variables length, weight, and DDT concentration are quantitative because each is measured on a numerical scale: length in centimeters, weight in grams, and DDT in parts per million. In contrast, river/creek and species cannot be measured quantitatively: They can only be classified into categories (e.g., channel catfish, largemouth bass, and smallmouth buffalofish for species). Consequently, data on river/creek and species are qualitative.

Look Back It is essential that you understand whether data is quantitative or qualitative in nature, since the statistical method appropriate for describing, reporting, and analyzing the data depends on the data type (quantitative or qualitative).

Now Work *Exercise 1.12*

■ ■ ■

We demonstrate many useful methods for analyzing quantitative and qualitative data in the remaining chapters of the text. But first, we discuss some important ideas on data collection.

1.5 Collecting Data

Once you decide on the type of data — quantitative or qualitative — appropriate for the problem at hand, you'll need to collect the data. Generally, you can obtain data in four different ways:

1. Data from a *published source*
2. Data from a *designed experiment*
3. Data from a *survey*
4. Data from an *observational study*

Sometimes, the data set of interest has already been collected for you and is available in a **published source**, such as a book, journal, or newspaper. For example, you may want to examine and summarize the divorce rates (i.e., number of divorces per 1,000 population) in the 50 states of the United States. You can find this data set (as well as numerous other data sets) at your library in the *Statistical Abstract of the United States*, published annually by the U.S. government. Similarly, someone who is interested in monthly mortgage applications for new home construction would find this data set in the *Survey of Current Business*, another government publication. Other examples of published data sources include *The Wall Street Journal* (financial data) and *The Sporting News* (sports information). The Internet (World Wide Web) now provides a medium by which data from published sources are readily obtained.*

A second method of collecting data involves conducting a **designed experiment**, in which the researcher exerts strict control over the units (people, objects, or things) in the study. For example, a recent medical study investigated the potential of aspirin in preventing heart attacks. Volunteer physicians were divided into two groups — the *treatment* group and the *control* group. In the treatment group, each physician took one aspirin tablet a day for one year, while each physician in the control group took an aspirin-free placebo made to look like an aspirin tablet. The researchers, not the physicians under study, controlled who received the aspirin (the treatment) and who received the placebo. As you'll learn in Chapter 10, a properly designed experiment allows you to extract more information from the data than is possible with an uncontrolled study.

Surveys are a third source of data. With a **survey**, the researcher samples a group of people, asks one or more questions, and records the responses. Probably the most familiar type of survey is the political poll conducted by any one of a number of organizations (e.g., Harris, Gallup, Roper, and CNN) and designed to predict the outcome of a political election. Another familiar survey is the Nielsen survey, which provides the major networks with information on the most watched programs on television. Surveys can be conducted through the mail, with telephone interviews, or with in-person interviews. Although in-person surveys are more expensive than mail or telephone surveys, they may be necessary when complex information is to be collected.

Finally, observational studies can be employed to collect data. In an **observational study**, the researcher observes the experimental units in their natural setting and records the variable(s) of interest. For example, a child psychologist might observe and record the level of aggressive behavior of a sample of fifth graders playing on a school playground. Similarly, a zoologist may observe and measure the weights of newborn elephants born in captivity. Unlike a designed experiment, an observational study is one in which the researcher makes no attempt to control any aspect of the experimental units.

---

*With published data, we often make a distinction between the *primary source* and a *secondary source*. If the publisher is the original collector of the data, the source is primary. Otherwise, the data is secondary source data.

Regardless of which data collection method is employed, it is likely that the data will be a sample from some population. And if we wish to apply inferential statistics, we must obtain a *representative sample*.

DEFINITION 1.12

A **representative sample** exhibits characteristics typical of those possessed by the target population.

For example, consider a political poll conducted during a presidential election year. Assume the pollster wants to estimate the percentage of all 120 million registered voters in the United States who favor the incumbent President. The pollster would be unwise to base the estimate on survey data collected for a sample of voters from the incumbent's own state. Such an estimate would almost certainly be *biased* high; consequently, it would not be very reliable.

The most common way to satisfy the representative sample requirement is to select a random sample. A **random sample** ensures that every subset of fixed size in the population has the same chance of being included in the sample. If the pollster samples 1,500 of the 120 million voters in the population so that every subset of 1,500 voters has an equal chance of being selected, he has devised a random sample. The procedure for selecting a random sample is discussed in Chapter 3. Here, we look at two examples involving actual sampling studies.

DEFINITION 1.13

A **random sample** of n experimental units is a sample selected from the population in such a way that every different sample of size n has an equal chance of selection.

EXAMPLE 1.5　　　METHOD OF DATA COLLECTION

Problem　What percentage of Web users are addicted to the Internet? To find out, a psychologist designed a series of 10 questions based on a widely used set of criteria for gambling addiction and distributed them through the website *ABCNews.com*. (A sample question: "Do you use the Internet to escape problems?") A total of 17,251 Web users responded to the questionnaire. If participants answered "yes" to at least half of the questions, they were viewed as addicted. The findings, released at the 1999 annual meeting of the American Psychological Association, revealed that 990 respondents, or 5.7%, are addicted to the Internet (*Tampa Tribune*, Aug. 23, 1999).

    a. Identify the data collection method.

    b. Identify the target population.

    c. Are the sample data representative of the population?

Solution　**a.** The data collection method is a survey: 17,251 Internet users responded to the questions posed at the *ABCNews.com* website.

    b. Since the website can be accessed by anyone surfing the Internet, presumably the target population is *all* Internet users.

    c. Because the 17,251 respondents clearly make up a subset of the target population, they do form a sample. Whether or not the sample is representative is unclear, since we are given no information on the 17,251 respondents. However, a survey like this one in which the respondents are *self-selected* (i.e., each Internet user who saw the survey chose whether or not to respond to it) often suffers from *nonresponse bias*. It is possible that many Internet users who chose not to respond (or who never saw the survey) would have answered the questions differently, leading to a higher (or lower) percentage of affirmative answers.

Look Back Any inferences based on survey samples that employ self-selection are suspect due to potential nonresponse bias.

■ ■ ■

EXAMPLE 1.6   METHOD OF DATA COLLECTION

Problem Psychologists at the University of Tennessee carried out a study of the susceptibility of people to hypnosis (*Psychological Assessment*, Mar. 1995). In a random sample of 130 undergraduate psychology students at the university, each experienced both traditional hypnosis and computer-assisted hypnosis. Approximately half were randomly assigned to undergo the traditional procedure first, followed by the computer-assisted procedure. The other half were randomly assigned to experience computer-assisted hypnosis first, then traditional hypnosis. Following the hypnosis episodes, all students filled out questionnaires designed to measure a student's susceptibility to hypnosis. The susceptibility scores of the two groups of students were compared.

a. Identify the data collection method.

b. Is the sample data representative of the target population?

Solution **a.** Here, the experimental units are the psychology students. Since the researchers controlled which type of hypnosis — traditional or computer assisted — the students experienced first (through random assignment), a designed experiment was used to collect the data.

b. The sample of 130 psychology students was randomly selected from all psychology students at the University of Tennessee. If the target population is *all University of Tennessee psychology students*, it is likely that the sample is representative. However, the researchers warn that the sample data should not be used to make inferences about other, more general, populations.

Look Back By using randomization in a designed experiment, the researcher is attempting to eliminate different types of bias, including self-selection bias.

Now Work   *Exercise 1.15*

■ ■ ■

Statistics in Action Revisited

Identifying the Data Collection Method and Data Type

In the *USA Weekend* Annual Teen Survey, American teenagers are asked to respond to a variety of questions on topics such as newspapers usage (2004 survey) and the opposite sex (2003 survey). The title of the study implies that the data are collected using a survey of teenagers. The *USA Weekend* surveys were made available using printed forms in the magazine, in an online survey form, and through the mail using newspaper subscriber lists.

Both quantitative and qualitative data were collected in the surveys. For example, the survey question "Do you think its OK for girls in your grade to call guys?" is phrased to elicit a "yes" or "no" response. Since the responses produced for this question are categorical in nature, the data are qualitative. However, the question "How many days a week do you read the newspaper?" will give meaningful numerical responses such as one, two, or three days. Thus, this data is quantitative.

1.6 The Role of Statistics in Critical Thinking

According to H. G. Wells, author of such science-fiction classics as *The War of the Worlds* and *The Time Machine*, "*Statistical thinking* will one day be as necessary for efficient citizenship as the ability to read and write." Written more than a hundred years ago, Wells's prediction is proving true today.

Biography

**H. G. WELLS
(1866–1946)—
Writer and Novelist**

English-born Herbert George Wells published his first novel, *The Time Machine*, in 1895 as a parody of the English class division and as a satirical warning that human progress is inevitable. Although most famous as a science-fiction novelist, Wells was a prolific writer as a journalist, sociologist, historian, and philosopher. Wells's prediction about statistical thinking (see Definition 1.14) is just one of a plethora of observations he made about life on this

world. Here are a few more of H. G. Wells's more famous quotes:

"Advertising is legalized lying."

"Crude classification and false generalizations are the curse of organized life."

"The crisis of today is the joke of tomorrow."

"Fools make researchers and wise men exploit them."

"The only true measure of success is the ration between what we might have done and what we might have been on the one hand, and the thing we have made and the things we have made of ourselves on the other."

The growth in data collection associated with scientific phenomena, business operations, and government activities (quality control, statistical auditing, forecasting, etc.) has been remarkable in the past several decades. Every day the media present us with published results of political, economic, and social surveys. In increasing government emphasis on drug and product testing, for example, we see vivid evidence of the need to be able to evaluate data sets intelligently. Consequently, each of us has to develop a discerning sense — an ability to use rational thought to interpret the meaning of data. This ability can help you make intelligent decisions, inferences, and generalizations; that is, it helps you *think critically* using statistics.

> **DEFINITION 1.14**
>
> **Statistical thinking** involves applying rational thought and the science of statistics to critically assess data and inferences.

To gain some insight into the role statistics plays in critical thinking, let's look at a *New York Times* (June 17, 1995) article titled "The Case for No Helmets." The article, written by the editor of a magazine for Harley-Davidson bikers, lists several reasons why motorcyclists should not be required by law to wear helmets. First, he argued that helmets may actually kill, since in collisions at speeds greater than 15 miles an hour, the heavy helmet may protect the head but snap the spine. Second, the editor cited a "study" that claimed "nine states without helmet laws had a lower fatality rate (3.05 deaths per 10,000 motorcycles) than those that mandated helmets (3.38)." Finally, he reported that "in a survey of 2,500 [at a rally], 98% of the respondents opposed such laws."

You can use "statistical thinking" to help you critically evaluate the arguments presented in this article. For example, before you accept the 98% estimate, you would want to know how the data were collected for the study cited by the editor of the biker magazine. If a survey was conducted, it's possible that the 2,500 bikers in the sample were not selected at random from the target population of all bikers, but rather were "self-selected." (Remember, they were all attending a rally — maybe even a rally for bikers who oppose the law.) If the respondents were likely to have strong opinions regarding the helmet law (e.g., strongly oppose the law), the resulting estimate is probably biased high. Also, if the biased sample was intentional, with the sole purpose to mislead the public, the researcher would be guilty of **unethical statistical practice**.

You'd also want more information about the study comparing the motorcycle fatality rate of the nine states without a helmet law to those states that mandate helmets: Were the data obtained from a published source? Were all 50 states included in the study? That is, are you seeing sample data or population data? Furthermore, do the helmet laws vary among states? If so, can you really compare the fatality rates?

These questions actually led to the discovery of two scientific and statistically sound studies on helmets. The first, a UCLA study of nonfatal injuries, disputed the charge that helmets shift injuries to the spine. The second study reported a dramatic *decline* in motorcycle crash deaths after California passed its helmet law.

As in the motorcycle helmet study, many statistical studies are based on survey data. Most of the problems with these surveys result from the use of *nonrandom* samples. These samples are subject to potential errors, such as *selection bias, nonresponse bias* (recall Example 1.6), and *measurement error*. Researchers who are aware of these problems and continue to use the sample data to make inferences are practicing unethical statistics.

> **DEFINITION 1.15**
>
> **Selection bias** results when a subset of the experimental units in the population is excluded so that these units have no chance of being selected in the sample.

> **DEFINITION 1.16**
>
> **Nonresponse bias** results when the researchers conducting a survey or study are unable to obtain data on all experimental units selected for the sample.

> **DEFINITION 1.17**
>
> **Measurement error** refers to inaccuracies in the values of the data recorded. In surveys, the error may be due to ambiguous or leading questions and the interviewer's effect on the respondent.

Statistics in Action Revisited

Critically Assessing the Ethics of a Statistical Study

The results from the *USA Weekend* Teen Surveys led the magazine to make conclusions such as "boys are from Mars, girls are from Venus" when relating to the opposite sex (2003 survey) and "America's teens read newspapers . . . and find them relevant and reliable" (2004 survey). Both surveys were based on a large sample of teen respondents — 37,000 in 2003 and 65,000 in 2004. However, several problems lead a critical thinker to cast doubt on the validity of the inferences.

First, are the samples representative of all American teens? *USA Weekend* admits that its annual teen survey is "unscientific," meaning that the teens are not randomly selected from all teens in the United States. In fact, the teens who responded are "self-selected," choosing to respond to the survey via the printed copy in the magazine, the Internet survey, or the copy mailed to their home. Therefore, there is a strong selection bias in the survey results. Second, because not all American teens receive the magazine, were aware of the Internet survey, or were on the magazine subscriber mailing list, the potential for non-response bias is extremely high.

Finally, the wording in several of the survey questions is ambiguous or leading. This can occur when the survey is designed to support a specific point of view or organization (such as the Newspaper Association of America Foundation). For example, the question "How relevant is the news-paper to your life?" is likely to lead to the responses "very relevant" or "somewhat relevant" since the phrase "relevant ... to your life" has different meanings to different people. (A teenager who delivers papers every afternoon after school but never reads the paper would likely answer "very relevant.") Ambiguities such as these will likely result in measurement error in the data.

In the remaining chapters of the text, you'll become familiar with the tools essential for building a firm foundation in statistics and statistical thinking.

Quick Review

Key Terms

Census 8
Data 4
Descriptive statistics 5
Designed experiment 14
Experimental unit 7
Inference 5
Inferential statistics 5
Measure of reliability 11
Measurement 7

Measurement error 18
Nonresponse bias 18
Observational study 14
Population 7
Published source 14
Qualitative data 13
Quantitative data 12
Random sample 15
Reliability 10
Representative sample 15

Sample 8
Selection bias 18
Statistical inference 9
Statistical thinking 17
Statistics 4
Survey 14
Unethical Statistical Practice 18
Variable 7

Chapter Summary

- Two types of statistical applications: **descriptive** and **inferential**
- Fundamental elements of statistics: **population**, **experimental units**, **variable**, **sample**, **inference**, **measure of reliability**

- Two types of data: **quantitative** and **qualitative**
- Data collection methods: **published source**, **designed experiment**, **survey**, and **observationally**
- Potential problems with nonrandom samples: **selection bias**, **nonresponse bias**, **measurement error**.

Exercises 1.1–1.32

Understanding the Principles

1.1 What is statistics?

1.2 Explain the difference between descriptive and inferential statistics.

1.3 List and define the five elements of an inferential statistical analysis.

1.4 List the four major methods of collecting data and explain their differences.

1.5 Explain the difference between quantitative and qualitative data.

1.6 Explain how populations and variables differ.

1.7 Explain how populations and samples differ.

1.8 What is a representative sample? What is its value?

1.9 Why would a statistician consider an inference incomplete without an accompanying measure of its reliability?

1.10 Define statistical thinking.

1.11 Suppose you're given a data set that classifies each sample unit into one of four categories: A, B, C, or D. You plan to create a computer database consisting of these data, and you decide to code the data as A = 1, B = 2, C = 3, and D = 4. Are the data consisting of the classifications A, B, C, and D qualitative or quantitative? After the data are input as 1, 2, 3, or 4, are they qualitative or quantitative? Explain your answers.

Applying the Concepts—Basic

1.12 College application. Colleges and universities are requiring an increasing amount of information about applicants before making acceptance and financial aid decisions. Classify each of the following types of data required on a college application as quantitative or qualitative.
a. High school GPA
b. High school class rank
c. Applicant's score on the SAT or ACT
d. Gender of applicant
e. Parents' income
f. Age of applicant

1.13 Miscellaneous data. Classify the following examples of data as either qualitative or quantitative:
a. The bacteria count in the water at each of 30 city swimming pools
b. The occupation of each of 200 shoppers at a supermarket
c. The marital status of each person living on a city block
d. The time (in months) between auto maintenance for each of 100 used cars

1.14 Sprint speed training. Refer to *The Sport Journal* (Winter, 2004) study of a speed training program for high school football players in Section 1.2 (Study 1, p. 5). Recall that each participant was timed in a 40-yard sprint both before and after training. The researchers measured two variables: (1) the difference between the before and after sprint times (in seconds), and (2) the category of improvement ("improved," "no change," and "worse") for each player.
a. Identify the type (quantitative or qualitative) of each variable measured.
b. A total of 14 high school football players participated in the speed training program. Does the data set collected represent a population or a sample? Explain.

1.15 Iraq War poll. A poll is to be conducted in which 2,000 individuals are asked whether the United States was justified in invading Iraq in 2003. The 2,000 individuals are selected by random-digit telephone dialing and asked the question over the phone.
a. What is the relevant population?
b. What is the variable of interest? Is it quantitative or qualitative?
c. What is the sample?
d. What is the inference of interest to the pollster?
e. What method of data collection is employed?

f. How likely is the sample to be representative?

1.16 Student GPAs. Consider the set of all students enrolled in your statistics course this term. Suppose you're interested in learning about the current grade point averages (GPAs) of this group.
a. Define the population and variable of interest.
b. Is the variable qualitative or quantitative?

c. Suppose you determine the GPA of every member of the class. Would this represent a census or a sample?
d. Suppose you determine the GPA of 10 members of the class. Would this represent a census or a sample?
e. If you determine the GPA of every member of the class and then calculate the average, how much reliability does this have as an "estimate" of the class average GPA?
f. If you determine the GPA of 10 members of the class and then calculate the average, will the number you get necessarily be the same as the average GPA for the whole class? On what factors would you expect the reliability of the estimate to depend?
g. What must be true in order for the sample of 10 students you select from your class to be considered a random sample?

1.17 The Executive Compensation Scoreboard. Each year, *Business Week* publishes its "Executive Compensation Scoreboard." Data are collected for a sample of chief executive officers and the following variables are measured for each CEO: (1) the industry type of the CEO's company (e.g., banking, consumer products, etc.), (2) the CEO's total compensation (in $ millions) for the year, (3) the CEO's total compensation (in $ millions) over the previous three years, and (4) the return (in dollars) on a $100 investment in the CEO's company made in three years earlier.
a. Describe the population of interest to *Business Week*.
b. Identify the type (quantitative or qualitative) of each variable measured.
c. In 2003, *Business Week* surveyed 370 CEOs from the top-ranked companies listed in the *Business Week 1000*. Discuss any biases that may exist in the sample.

1.18 Extinct birds. Biologists at the University of California (Riverside) are studying the patterns of extinction in the New Zealand bird population. (*Evolutionary Ecology Research*, July 2003.) At the time of the Maori colonization of New Zealand (prior to European contact), the following variables were measured for each bird species. Identify each variable as quantitative or qualitative.
a. Flight capability (volant or flightless)
b. Habitat type (aquatic, ground terrestrial, or aerial terrestrial)
c. Nesting site (ground, cavity within ground, tree, cavity above ground)
d. Nest density (high or low)
e. Diet (fish, vertebrates, vegetables, or invertebrates)

f. Body mass (grams)
g. Egg length (millimeters)
h. Extinct status (extinct, absent from island, present)

1.19 E-commerce survey. The Cutter Consortium surveyed 154 U.S. companies to determine the extent of their involvement in electronic commerce (called *e-commerce*). Four of the questions they asked follow. (*Internet Week*, Sept. 6, 1999.)

1. Do you have an overall e-commerce strategy?
2. If you don't already have an e-commerce plan, when will you implement one?
3. Are you delivering products over the Internet?
4. What was your company's total revenue in the last fiscal year?
    a. For each question, determine the variable of interest and classify it as quantitative or qualitative.
    b. Do the data collected for the 154 companies represent a sample or a population? Explain.

Applying the Concepts—Intermediate

1.20 Herbal Medicines. *The American Association of Nurse Anesthetists Journal* (Feb. 2000) published the results of a study on the use of herbal medicines before surgery. Of 500 surgical patients that were randomly selected for the study, 51% used herbal or alternative medicines (e.g., garlic, ginkgo, kava, fish oil) against their doctor's advice prior to surgery.
a. Do the 500 surgical patients represent a population or a sample? Explain.
b. If your answer was sample in part **a**, is the sample representative of the population? If you answered population in part **a**, explain how to obtain a representative sample from the population.
c. For each patient, what variable is measured? Is the data collected quantitative or qualitative?

1.21 National Bridge Inventory. All highway bridges in the United States are inspected periodically for structural deficiency by the Federal Highway Administration (FHWA). Data from the FHWA inspections are compiled into the National Bridge Inventory (NBI). Several of the nearly 100 variables maintained by the NBI are listed below. Classify each variable as quantitative or qualitative.
a. Length of maximum span (feet)
b. Number of vehicle lanes
c. Toll bridge (yes or no)
d. Average daily traffic
e. Condition of deck (good, fair, or poor)
f. Bypass or detour length (miles)
g. Route type (interstate, U.S., state, county, or city)

1.22 Structurally deficient bridges. Refer to Exercise 1.21. The most recent NBI data were analyzed, and the results published in the *Journal of Infrastructure Systems* (June 1995). Using the FHWA inspection ratings, each of the 470,515 highway bridges in the United States was categorized as structurally deficient, functionally obsolete, or safe. About 26% of the bridges were found to be structurally deficient, while 19% were functionally obsolete.
a. What is the variable of interest to the researchers?
b. Is the variable of part **a** quantitative or qualitative?
c. Is the data set analyzed a population or a sample? Explain.
d. How did the researchers obtain the data for their study?

1.23 CT scanning for lung cancer. According to the American Lung Association, lung cancer accounts for 28% of all cancer deaths in the United States. A new type of screening for lung cancer, computed tomography (CT), has been developed. Medical researchers believe CT scans are more sensitive than regular X-rays in pinpointing small tumors. The H. Lee Moffitt Cancer Center at the University of South Florida is currently conducting a clinical trial of 50,000 smokers nationwide to compare the effectiveness of CT scans with X-rays for detecting lung cancer. (*Todays' Tomorrows*, Fall 2002.) Each participating smoker is randomly assigned to one of two screening methods, CT or chest X-ray, and their progress tracked over time. The age at which the scanning method first detects a tumor is the variable of interest.
a. Identify the data collection method used by the cancer researchers.
b. Identify the experimental units of the study.
c. Identify the type (quantitative or qualitative) of the variable measured.
d. Identify the population and sample.
e. What is the inference that will ultimately be drawn from the clinical trial?

1.24 Gallup poll of teenagers. A Gallup Youth Poll was conducted to determine the topics that teenagers most want to discuss with their parents. The findings show that 46% would like more discussion about the family's financial situation, 37% would like to talk about school, and 30% would like to talk about religion. The survey was based on a national sampling of 505 teenagers, selected at random from all U.S. teenagers.
a. Describe the sample.
b. Describe the population from which the sample was selected.
c. Is the sample representative of the population?
d. What is the variable of interest?
e. How is the inference expressed?
f. Newspaper accounts of most polls usually give a *margin of error* (i.e., plus or minus 3%) for the survey result. What is the purpose of the margin of error and what is its interpretation?

1.25 Massage vs. rest in boxing. Does a massage enable the muscles of tired athletes to recover from exertion faster than usual? To answer this question, researchers recruited eight amateur boxers to participate in an experiment. (*British Journal of Sports Medicine*, April 2000.) After a 10-minute workout in which each boxer threw 400 punches, half the boxers were given a 20-minute massage and half just rested for 20 minutes. Before returning to the ring for a second workout, the heart rate (beats per minute) and blood lactate level (micromoles) were recorded for each boxer. The researchers found no difference in the means of the two groups of boxers for either variable.
a. Identify the data collection method used by the researchers.
b. Identify the experimental units of the study.

c. Identify the variables measured and their type (quantitative or qualitative).

d. What is the inference drawn from the analysis?

e. Comment on whether this inference can be made about all athletes.

1.26 Acid neutralizer experiment. A first-year chemistry student conducts an experiment to determine the amount of hydrochloric acid necessary to neutralize 2 milliliters (ml) of a basic solution. The student prepares five 2-ml portions of the solution and adds a known concentration of hydrochloric acid to each. The amount of acid necessary to achieve neutrality of the solution is recorded for each of the five portions.

a. Describe the population of interest to the student.

b. What is the variable of interest? Is it quantitative or qualitative?

c. Describe the sample.

d. Describe the data collection method.

1.27 Blood loss in burn patients. A group of University of South Florida surgery researchers believe that the drug aprotinin is effective in reducing the blood loss of burn patients who undergo skin replacement surgery. (*USF Office of Research Annual Report, 1997–1998.*) In a clinical trial of 14 burn patients, half were randomly assigned to receive the drug and half a placebo (no drug). A preliminary analysis of the patients' blood loss revealed that the group with the drug had a significant reduction of bleeding.

a. Identify the data collection method used for this study.

b. Does the study involve descriptive or inferential statistics? Explain.

c. What is the population (or sample) of interest to the researchers?

Applying the Concepts—Advanced

1.28 Object recall study. Are men or women more adept at remembering where they leave misplaced items (like car keys)? According to University of Florida psychology professor Robin West, women show greater competence in actually finding these objects (*Explore*, Fall 1998). Approximately 300 men and women from Gainesville, Florida, participated in a study in which each person placed 20 common objects in a 12-room "virtual" house represented on a computer screen. Thirty minutes later, the subjects were asked to recall where they put each of the objects. For each object, a recall variable was measured as "yes" or "no."

a. Identify the population of interest to the psychology professor.

b. Identify the sample.

c. Does the study involve descriptive or inferential statistics? Explain.

d. Are the variables measured in the study quantitative or qualitative?

1.29 Soccer "headers" and IQ. *USA Today* (Aug. 14, 1995) reported on a study that suggests "frequently 'heading' the ball in soccer lowers players' IQs." A psychologist tested 60 male soccer players, ages 14–29, who played up to five times a week. Players who averaged 10 or more headers a game had an average IQ of 103, while players who headed one or fewer times per game had an average IQ of 112.

a. Describe the population of interest to the psychologist.

b. Identify the variables of interest.

c. Identify the type (qualitative or quantitative) of the variables, part **b**.

d. Describe the sample.

e. What is the inference made by the psychologist?

f. Discuss possible reasons why the inference, part **e**, may be misleading.

Critical Thinking Challenges

1.30 "20/20" survey exposés. The popular prime-time ABC television program "20/20" presented several misleading (and possibly unethical) surveys in a segment titled "Facts or Fiction? — Exposés of So-Called Surveys" (March 31, 1995). The information reported from four of these surveys, conducted by businesses or special interest groups with specific objectives in mind, are given. (Actual survey facts are provided in parentheses.)

Quaker Oats Study: Eating oat bran is a cheap and easy way to reduce your cholesterol count. (*Fact*: Diet must consist of nothing but oat bran to achieve a slightly lower cholesterol count.)

March of Dimes Report: Domestic violence causes more birth defects than all medical issues combined. (*Fact*: No study — false report.)

American Association of University Women (AAUW) study: Only 29% of high school girls are happy with themselves, compared to 66% of elementary school girls. (*Fact*: Of 3,000 high school girls, 29% responded "Always true" to the statement, "I am happy the way I am." Most answered, "Sort of true" and "Sometimes true.")

Food Research and Action Center study: One in four American children under age 12 is hungry or at risk of hunger. (*Fact*: Based on responses to questions: "Do you ever cut the size of meals?", "Do you ever eat less than you feel you should?", "Did you ever rely on limited numbers of foods to feed your children because you were running out of money to buy food for a meal?")

a. Refer to the Quaker Oats study relating oat bran to cholesterol levels. Discuss why it is unethical to report the results as stated.

b. Consider the false March of Dimes report on domestic violence and birth defects. Discuss the type of data required to investigate the impact of domestic violence on birth defects. What data collection method would you recommend?

c. Refer to the AAUW study of self-esteem of high school girls. Explain why the results of the study are likely to be misleading. What data might be appropriate for assessing the self-esteem of high school girls?

d. Refer to the Food Research and Action Center study of hunger in America. Explain why the results of the study are likely to be misleading. What data would provide insight into the proportion of hungry American children?

1.31 Roper poll on the Holocaust. The Holocaust — the Nazi Germany extermination of the Jews during World War II — has been well documented through film, books, and interviews with the concentration camp survivors. But a recent Roper poll found that one in five U.S. residents doubted the Holocaust really occurred. A national sample of more than 1,000 adults and high school students were asked, "Does it seem possible or does it seem impossible to you that the Nazi extermination of the Jews never happened?" Twenty-two percent of the adults and 20% of the high school students responded "Yes." (*New York Times*, May 16, 1994.) Discuss reasons for doubting the reliability of the inference.

1.32 Poll on alien spacecraft. "Have you ever seen anything that you believe was a spacecraft from another planet?" This was the question put to 1,500 American adults in a national poll conducted by ABC News and *The Washington Post*. The pollsters used random-digit telephone dialing to contact adult Americans, until 1,500 responded. Ten percent (i.e., 150) of the respondents answered that they had, in fact, seen an alien spacecraft. (*Chance*, Summer 1997.) No information was provided on how many adults were called and, for one reason or another, did not answer the question.
a. Identify the data collection method.
b. Identify the target population.
c. Comment on the validity of the survey results.

Student Projects

Scan your daily newspaper or weekly news magazine or search the Internet for articles that contain numerical data. The data might be a summary of the results of a public opinion poll, the results of a vote by the U.S. Senate, or a list of crime rates, birth or death rates, etc. For each article you find, answer the following questions:

a. Do the data constitute a sample or an entire population? If a sample has been taken, clearly identify both the sample and the population; otherwise, identify the population.

b. What type of data (quantitative or qualitative) has been collected?

c. What is the data source?

d. If a sample has been observed, is it likely to be representative of the population?

e. If a sample has been observed, does the article present an explicit (or implied) inference about the population of interest? If so, state the inference made in the article.

f. If an inference has been made, has a measure of reliability been included? What is it?

g. Use your answers to questions d–f to critically evaluate the article.

REFERENCES

Brochures about Survey Research, Section on Survey Research Methods, American Statistical Association, 2004. (www.amstat.org)

Careers in Statistics, American Statistical Association, Biometric Society, Institute of Mathematical Statistics and Statistical Society of Canada, 2004. (www.amstat.org)

Cochran, W. G. *Sampling Techniques*, 3rd ed. New York: Wiley, 1977.

Deming, W. E. *Sample Design in Business Research*. New York: Wiley, Inc., 1963.

Ethical Guidelines for Statistical Practice. American Statistical Association, 1995.

Hansen, M. H., Hurwitz, W. N., and Madow, W. G. *Sample Survey Methods and Theory*, Vol. 1. New York: Wiley, 1953.

Kirk, R. E., ed. *Statistical Issues: A Reader for the Behavioral Sciences*. Monterey, Calif.: Brooks/Cole, 1972.

Kish, L. *Survey Sampling*. New York: Wiley, 1965.

Scheaffer, R., Mendenhall, W., and Ott, R. L. *Elementary Survey Sampling*, 2nd ed. Boston: Duxbury, 1979.

Tanur, J. M., Mosteller, F., Kruskal, W. H., Link, R. E., Pieters, R. S., and Rising, G. R. *Statistics: A Guide to the Unknown* (E. L. Lehmann, special editor). San Francisco: Holden-Day, 1989.

Yamane, T. *Elementary Sampling Theory*, 3rd ed. Englewood Cliffs, N.J.: Prentice Hall, 1967.

Using Technology

Creating and Listing Data Using MINITAB

Upon entering into a MINITAB session, you will see a screen similar to Figure 1.M.1. The bottom portion of the screen is an empty spreadsheet — called a MINITAB worksheet — with columns representing variables and rows representing observations (or cases). The very top of the screen is the MINITAB main menu bar, with buttons for the different functions and procedures available in MINITAB. Once you have entered data into the spreadsheet, you can analyze the data by clicking the appropriate menu buttons. The results will appear in the Session window.

Figure 1.M.1
Initial Screen Viewed by
MINITAB User

Figure 1.M.2
Data Entered into the
MINITAB Worksheet

You can create a MINITAB data file by entering data directly into the worksheet. Figure 1.M.2 shows data entered for a variable called "Ratio". The variables (columns) can be named by typing in the name of each variable in the box below the column number.

If the data are saved in an external data file, you can access it using the options available in MINITAB. Click the "File" button on the menu bar, then click "Open Worksheet", as shown in Figure 1.M.3. The dialog box shown in Figure 1.M.4 will appear.

Specify the disk drive and folder that contain the external data file and the file type, then click on the file name, as shown in Figure 1.M.4. If the data set contains qualitative data or data with special characters, click on the "Options" button as shown in Figure 1.M.4. The Options dialog box, shown in Figure 1.M.5, will appear. Specify the appropriate options for the data set, then click "OK" to return

Figure 1.M.3
MINITAB Options for
Reading Data from an
External File

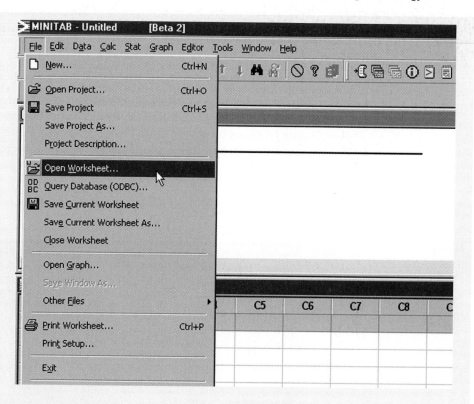

to the "Open Worksheet" dialog box (Figure 1.M.4). Click "Open" and the
MINITAB worksheet will appear with the data from the external data file, as
shown in Figure 1.M.6.

Figure 1.M.4
Selecting the External
Data File

Reminder. The variables (columns) can be named by typing in the name of each variable in the box under the column number.

To obtain a listing (printout) of your data, click on the "Data" button on the MINITAB main menu bar, then click on "Display Data" (see Figure 1.M.7). The resulting menu, or dialog box, appears as in Figure 1.M.8. Enter the names of the variables you want to print in the "Columns constants and matrices to display" box (you can do this by simply clicking on the variables), then click "OK". The printout will show up on your MINITAB session screen.

Figure 1.M.5
Selecting the Data
Input Options

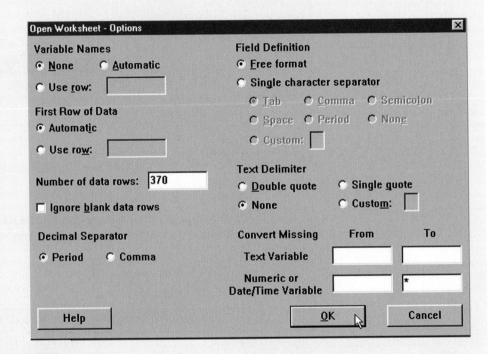

Figure 1.M.6
The MINITAB Worksheet
with the Imported Data

	C1-T	C2-T	C3-T	C4-T	C5	C6	C7	C8	C9	C10
1	AEROSPACE	IHT	Boeing	P.M.Condit	4145	27794	83	3		
2	AEROSPACE	IHT	GeneralDynamics	N.D.Chabraja	15245	31367	157	4		
3	AEROSPACE	IHT	Goodrich	D.L.Burner	2884	7449	77	4		
4	AEROSPACE	IHT	LockheedMartin	V.D.Coffman	25337	47702	274	4		
5	AEROSPACE	IHT	NorthropGrumman	K.Kresa	9222	23927	190	4		
6	AEROSPACE	IHT	Raytheon	D.P.Burnham	8922	19591	125	4		
7	AEROSPACE	IHT	UnitedTech.	G.David	9664	51136	99	3		
8	AIRLINES	TRAN	DeltaAirLines	L.F.Mullin	4688	9931	25	1		
9	APPLIANCES	CP	Leggett&Platt	F.E.Wright	1096	5017	112	4		
10	APPLIANCES	CP	Maytag	R.F.Hake	1703	0	63	0		
11	APPLIANCES	CP	Whirlpool	D.R.Whitwam	4819	11381	86	3		
12	AUTOMOTIVE	CP	Dana	J.M.Magliochetti	1433	4416	44	3		

bwecstest.dat ***

Figure 1.M.7

MINITAB Menu Options
for Obtaining a List of
Your Data

Figure 1.M.8

Display Data Dialog Box

2 Methods for Describing Sets of Data

Contents

2.1 Describing Qualitative Data

2.2 Graphical Methods for Describing Quantitative Data

2.3 Summation Notation

2.4 Numerical Measures of Central Tendency

2.5 Numerical Measures of Variability

2.6 Interpreting the Standard Deviation

2.7 Numerical Measures of Relative Standing

2.8 Methods for Detecting Outliers (Optional)

2.9 Graphing Bivariate Relationships (Optional)

2.10 Distorting the Truth with Descriptive Techniques

Statistics in Action

The "Eye Cue" Test: Does Experience Improve Performance?

Using Technology

Describing Data Using MINITAB

Where We've Been

- Examined the difference between inferential and descriptive statistics
- Described the key elements of a statistical problem
- Learned about the two types of data—quantitative and qualitative
- Discussed the role of statistical thinking in managerial decision making

Where We're Going

- Describe data using graphs.
- Describe data using numerical measures.

Statistics
in *ACTION*

The "Eye Cue" Test: Does Experience Improve Performance?

In 1948, famous child psychologist Jean Piaget devised a test of basic perceptual and conceptual skills dubbed the "water-level task." Subjects were shown a drawing of a glass being held perfectly still (at a 45° angle) by an invisible hand so that any water in it had to be at rest (see Figure SIA2.1).

The task for the subject was to draw a line representing the surface of the water — a line that would touch the black dot pictured on the right side of the glass. Piaget found that young children typically failed the test. Fifty years later, research psychologists still use the water-level task to test the perception of both adults and children. Surprisingly, about 40% of the adult population also fail. In addition, males tend to do better than females, and younger adults tend to do better than older adults.

Will people with experience handling liquid-filled containers perform better on this "eye cue" test? This question was the focus of research conducted by psychologists Heiko Hecht (NASA) and Dennis R. Proffitt (University of Virginia) and published in *Psychological Science* (Mar. 1995). The researchers presented the task to each of six different groups: (1) male college students, (2) female college students, (3) professional waitresses, (4) housewives, (5) male bartenders, and (6) male bus drivers. A total of 120 subjects

(20 per group) participated in the study. Two of the groups, waitresses and bartenders, were assumed to have considerable experience handling liquid-filled glasses.

After each subject completed the drawing task, the researchers recorded the deviation* (in angle degrees) of the judged line from the true line. If the deviation was within 5° of the true water surface angle, the answer was considered correct. Deviations of more than 5° in either direction were considered incorrect answers.

The data for the water-level task (simulated based on summary results presented in the journal article) are provided in the **EYECUE** file. For each of the 120 subjects in the experiment, the following variables (in the order they appear on the data file) were measured:

 ## EYECUE

Variables

GENDER (F or M)

GROUP (Student, Waitress, Wife, Bartender, or Busdriver)

DEVIATION (angle, in degrees, of the judged line from the true line)

JUDGE (Within5, More5Above, More5Below)

The researchers are interested in testing several theories concerning performance on the water-level task, including (1) males perform better than females, (2) younger adults perform better than older adults, and (3) experience improves task performance.

In the following *Statistics in Action Revisited* sections, we apply the graphical and numerical descriptive techniques of this chapter to the **EYECUE** data to answer some of the researchers questions.

Statistics in Action Revisited for Chapter 2

- Interpreting a Pie Chart (p. 35)
- Interpreting a Histogram (p. 49)
- Interpreting Descriptive Statistics (p. 78)
- Detecting Outliers (p. 93)

Figure SIA2.1
Drawing of the Water-Level Task

*The true surface line is perfectly parallel to the table top.

Suppose you wish to evaluate the mathematical capabilities of a class of 1,000 first-year college students based on their quantitative Scholastic Aptitude Test (SAT) scores. How would you describe these 1,000 measurements? Characteristics of interest include the typical or most frequent SAT score, the variability in the scores, the highest and lowest scores, the "shape" of the data, and whether or not the data set contains any unusual scores. Extracting this information isn't easy. The 1,000 scores provide too many bits of information for our minds to comprehend. Clearly we need some method for summarizing and characterizing the information in such a data set. Methods for describing data sets are also essential for statistical inference. Most populations are large data sets. Consequently, we need methods for describing a data set that let us make descriptive statements (inferences) about a population based on information contained in a sample.

Two methods for describing data are presented in this chapter, one *graphical* and the other *numerical*. Both play an important role in statistics. Section 2.1 presents both graphical and numerical methods for describing qualitative data. Graphical methods for describing quantitative data are illustrated in Sections 2.2, 2.8, and 2.9; numerical descriptive methods for quantitative data are presented in Sections 2.3–2.7. We end this chapter with a section on the *misuse* of descriptive techniques.

2.1 Describing Qualitative Data

Consider a study of aphasia published in the *Journal of Communication Disorders* (Mar. 1995). Aphasia is the "impairment or loss of the faculty of using or understanding spoken or written language." Three types of aphasia have been identified by researchers: Broca's, conduction, and anomic. They wanted to determine whether one type of aphasia occurs more often than any other, and, if so, how often. Consequently, they measured aphasia type for a sample of 22 adult aphasiacs. Table 2.1 gives the type of aphasia diagnosed for each aphasiac in the sample.

For this study, the variable of interest, aphasia type, is qualitative in nature. Qualitative data are nonnumerical in nature; thus, the value of a qualitative variable can only be classified into categories called *classes*. The possible aphasia types — Broca's, conduction, and anomic — represent the classes for this qualitative variable. We can summarize such data numerically in two ways: (1) by computing the *class frequency* — the number of observations in the data set that fall into each class; or (2) by computing the *class relative frequency* — the proportion of the total number of observations falling into each class.

 APHASIA

TABLE 2.1   Data on 22 Adult Aphasiacs

Subject	Type of Aphasia	Subject	Type of Aphasia
1	Broca's	12	Broca's
2	Anomic	13	Anomic
3	Anomic	14	Broca's
4	Conduction	15	Anomic
5	Broca's	16	Anomic
6	Conduction	17	Anomic
7	Conduction	18	Conduction
8	Anomic	19	Broca's
9	Conduction	20	Anomic
10	Anomic	21	Conduction
11	Conduction	22	Anomic

Source: Li, E. C., Williams, S. E., and Volpe, R. D., "The effects of topic and listener familiarity of discourse variables in procedural and narrative discourse tasks." *Journal of Communication Disorders,* Vol. 28, No. 1, Mar. 1995, p. 44 (Table 1).

A **class** is one of the categories into which qualitative data can be classified.

The **class frequency** is the number of observations in the data set falling in a particular class.

The **class relative frequency** is the class frequency divided by the total number of observations in the data set; that is,

$$\text{class relative frequency} = \frac{\text{class frequency}}{n}$$

The **class percentage** is the class relative frequency multiplied by 100; that is,

$$\text{class percentage} = (\text{class relative frequency}) \times 100$$

Examining Table 2.1, we observe that 5 aphasiacs in the study were diagnosed as suffering from Broca's aphasia, 7 from conduction aphasia, and 10 from anomic aphasia. These numbers — 5, 7, and 10 — represent the class frequencies for the three classes and are shown in the summary table, Figure 2.2, produced using SPSS.

Figure 2.2 also gives the relative frequency of each of the three aphasia classes. From Definition 2.3, we know that we calculate the relative frequency by dividing the class frequency by the total number of observations in the data set. Thus, the relative frequencies for the three types of aphasia are

$$\text{Broca's:} \quad \frac{5}{22} = .227$$

$$\text{Conduction:} \quad \frac{7}{22} = .318$$

$$\text{Anomic:} \quad \frac{10}{22} = .455$$

These values, expressed as a percent, are shown in the SPSS summary table, Figure 2.1. From these relative frequencies we observe that nearly half (45.5%) of the 22 subjects in the study are suffering from anomic aphasia.

Although the summary table of Figure 2.1 adequately describes the data of Table 2.1, we often want a graphical presentation as well. Figures 2.2 and 2.3 show two of the most widely used graphical methods for describing qualitative data — bar

Figure 2.1

SPSS Summary Table for Types of Aphasia

TYPE

		Frequency	Percent	Valid Percent	Cumulative Percent
Valid	Anomic	10	45.5	45.5	45.5
	Brocas	5	22.7	22.7	68.2
	Conduction	7	31.8	31.8	100.0
	Total	22	100.0	100.0	

FREQUENCY

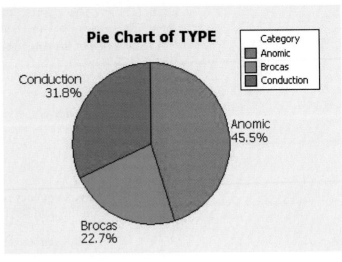

Figure 2.3
MINITAB Pie Chart for Aphasia Type

Figure 2.2
SAS Bar Graph for
Aphasia Type

graphs and pie charts. Figure 2.2 shows the frequencies of aphasia types in a **bar graph** produced with SAS. Note that the height of the rectangle, or "bar," over each class is equal to the class frequency. (Optionally, the bar heights can be proportional to class relative frequencies.)

In contrast, Figure 2.3 shows the relative frequencies of the three types of aphasia in a **pie chart** generated with MINITAB. Note that the pie is a circle (spanning 360°) and the size (angle) of the "pie slice" assigned to each class is proportional to the class relative frequency. For example, the slice assigned to anomic aphasia is 45.5% of 360°, or $(.455)(360°) = 163.8°$.

Before leaving the data set in Table 2.1, consider the bar graph shown in Figure 2.4, produced using SPSS. Note that the bars for types of aphasia are arranged in descending order of height from left to right across the horizontal axis. That is, the tallest bar (Anomic) is positioned at the far left and the shortest bars (Broca's) are

Figure 2.4

SPSS Pareto Diagram for
Type of Aphasia

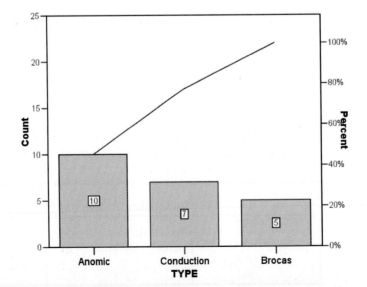

at the far right. This rearrangement of the bars in a bar graph is called a **Pareto diagram**. One goal of a Pareto diagram (named for the Italian economist, Vilfredo Pareto) is to make it easy to locate the "most important" categories — those with the largest frequencies.

Biography

VILFREDO PARETO (1843–1923)— The Pareto Principle

Born in Paris to an Italian aristocratic family, Vilfredo Pareto was educated at the University of Turin, where he studied engineering and mathematics. After the death of his parents, Pareto quit his job as an engineer and began writing and lecturing on the evils of the economic policies of the Italian government. While at the University of Lausanne in Switzerland in 1896, he published his first paper, *Cours d'economie politique*. In the paper, Pareto derived a complicated mathematical formula to prove that the distribution of income and wealth in society is not random but that a consistent pattern appears throughout history in all societies. Essentially, Pareto showed that approximately 80% of the total wealth in a society lies with only 20% of the families. This famous law about the "vital few and the trivial many" is widely known as the Pareto principle in economics.

Summary of Graphical Descriptive Methods for Qualitative Data

Bar Graph: The categories (classes) of the qualitative variable are represented by bars, where the height of each bar is either the class frequency, class relative frequency, or class percentage.

Pie Chart: The categories (classes) of the qualitative variable are represented by slices of a pie (circle). The size of each slice is proportional to the class relative frequency.

Pareto Diagram: A bar graph with the categories (classes) of the qualitative variable (i.e., the bars) arranged by height in descending order from left to right.

Now Work *Exercise 2.4*

Let's look at a practical example that requires interpretation of the graphical results.

EXAMPLE 2.1   GRAPHING AND SUMMARIZING QUALITATIVE DATA

Problem   A group of cardiac physicians in southwest Florida have been studying a new drug designed to reduce blood loss in coronary bypass operations. Blood loss data for 114 coronary bypass patients (some who received a dosage of the drug and others who did not) are saved in the **BLOODLOSS** file. Although the drug shows promise in reducing blood loss, the physicians are concerned about possible side effects and complications. So their data set includes not only the qualitative variable DRUG, which indicates whether or not the patient received the drug, but also the qualitative variable COMP, which specifies the type (if any) of complication experienced by the patient. The four values of COMP are (1) redo surgery, (2) post-op infection, (3) both, or (4) none.

BLOODLOSS

a. Figure 2.5, generated using SAS, shows summary tables for the two qualitative variables, DRUG and COMP. Interpret the results.

b. Interpret the MINITAB and SPSS printouts shown in Figures 2.6 and 2.7, respectively.

Figure 2.5

SAS Summary Tables for DRUG and COMP

The FREQ Procedure

DRUG	Frequency	Percent	Cumulative Frequency	Cumulative Percent
NO	57	50.00	57	50.00
YES	57	50.00	114	100.00

COMP	Frequency	Percent	Cumulative Frequency	Cumulative Percent
BOTH	6	5.26	6	5.26
INFECT	15	13.16	21	18.42
NONE	79	69.30	100	87.72
REDO	14	12.28	114	100.00

Figure 2.6

MINITAB Side-by-Side Bar Graphs for COMP by Value of DRUG

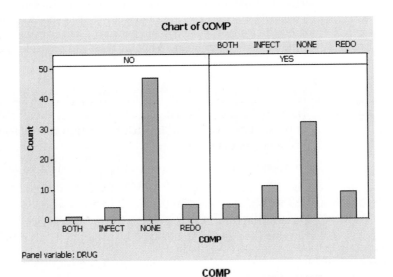

Figure 2.7

SPSS Summary Tables for COMP by Value of Drug

COMP

DRUG			Frequency	Percent	Valid Percent	Cumulative Percent
NO	Valid	BOTH	1	1.8	1.8	1.8
		INFECT	4	7.0	7.0	8.8
		NONE	47	82.5	82.5	91.2
		REDO	5	8.8	8.8	100.0
		Total	57	100.0	100.0	
YES	Valid	BOTH	5	8.8	8.8	8.8
		INFECT	11	19.3	19.3	28.1
		NONE	32	56.1	56.1	84.2
		REDO	9	15.8	15.8	100.0
		Total	57	100.0	100.0	

Solution   **a.** The top table in Figure 2.5 is a summary frequency table for DRUG. Note that exactly half (57) of the 114 coronary bypass patients received the drug and half did not. The bottom table in Figure 2.5 is a summary frequency table for COMP. The class relative frequencies are given in the Percent column. We see that about 69% of the 114 patients had no complications, leaving about 31% who experienced either a redo surgery, a post-op infection, or both.

b. Figure 2.6 is a MINITAB side-by-side bar graph for the data. The four bars in the left-side graph represent the frequencies of COMP for the 57 patients who did not receive the drug; the four bars in the right-side graph represent the frequencies of COMP for the 57 patients who did receive a dosage of the drug. The graph clearly shows that patients who did not receive the drug suffered fewer complications. The exact percentages are displayed in the SPSS summary tables of Figure 2.8. Over 56% of the patients who got the drug had no complications, compared to about 83% for the patients who got no drug.

Look Back Although these results show that the drug may be effective in reducing blood loss, Figures 2.6 and 2.7 imply that patients on the drug may have a higher risk of complications. But before using this information to make a decision about the drug, the physicians will need to provide a measure of reliability for the inference. That is, the physicians will want to know whether the difference between the percentages of patients with complications observed in this sample of 114 patients is generalizable to the population of all coronary bypass patients.

Now Work *Exercise 2.17*

■ ■ ■

Statistics in Action Revisited

Interpreting Pie Charts

In the *Psychological Science* "water-level task" experiment, the researchers measured three qualitative variables: *Gender* (F or M), *Subject Group* (student, waitress, wife, bartender, or bus driver), and *Judged Task Performance* (within 5° of the line, more than 5° above the line, or more than 5° below the line). Pie charts and bar graphs can be used to summarize and describe the responses in these variables are categories. Recall that the data is saved in the **EYECUE** file. These variables are named GENDER, GROUP, and JUDGE in the data file. We created pie charts for these variables using MINITAB.

Figure SIA2.2 is a pie chart for the JUDGE variable. Clearly, the large slice for "Within5" indicates that a majority of subjects (52.5%) were judged to be within 5° of the correct line. The researchers want to know if the water-level task

performance will vary across gender. Figure SIA2.3 shows side-by-side pie charts of the JUDGE variable for each level of GENDER. You can see that 65% of the male subjects (right-side chart) were judged to be within 5° of the line, compared to only 40% for female subjects (left-side chart). These graphs support the prevailing theory that men will perform better than women on the task.

We produced a similar set of side-by-side pie charts to compare the performances of the different groups of subjects in Figure SIA2.4. These charts again show that bus drivers (75% judged to be within 5° of the correct line) and college students (72.5%) perform the best, while bartenders (40%), wives (30%) and (surprisingly) waitresses (25%) perform the worst. These graphs do not seem to support the researchers' theory that experience improves task performance.

Figure SIA2.2

MINITAB Pie Chart for
Judged Task Performance

Pie Chart of Judged Line

Category
■ More5Above
■ More5Below
■ Within5

Within5
52.5%

More5Above
44.2%

More5Below
3.3%

Figure SIA2.3
MINITAB Pie Charts for Judged Task Performance — Females versus Males

Figure SIA2.4
MINITAB Pie Charts for Judged Task Performance — Group Comparisons

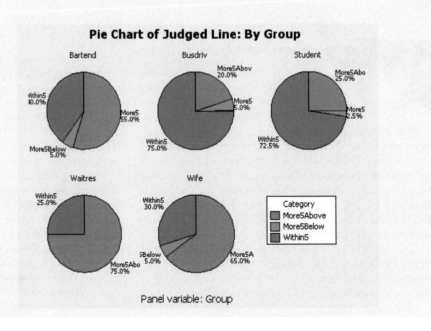

Exercises 2.1–2.20

Understanding the Principles

2.1 Explain the difference between class frequency, class relative frequency, and class percentage for a qualitative variable.

2.2 Explain the difference between a bar graph and a pie chart.

2.3 Explain the difference between a bar graph and a Pareto diagram.

Learning the Mechanics

2.4 Complete the following table.

Grade on Statistics Exam	Frequency	Relative Frequency
A: 90–100		.08
B: 80–89	36	
C: 65–79	90	
D: 50–64	30	
F: Below 50	28	
Total	200	1.00

2.5 A qualitative variable with three classes (X, Y, and Z) is measured for each of 20 units randomly sampled from a target population. The data (observed class for each unit) are listed below.

Y X X Z X Y Y Y X X Z X
Y Y X Z Y Y Y X

a. Compute the frequency for each of the three classes.
b. Compute the relative frequency for each of the three classes.
c. Display the results, part **a**, in a frequency bar graph.
d. Display the results, part **b**, in a pie chart.

Applying the Concepts—Basic

2.6 Types of cancer treated. The Moffitt Cancer Center at the University of South Florida treats over 25,000 patients a year. The graphic below describes the types of cancer treated in Moffitt's patients during fiscal year 2002.

a. What type of graph is portrayed?
b. Which type of cancer is treated most often at Moffitt?

c. What percentage of Moffitt's patients are treated for melanoma, lymphoma, or leukemia?

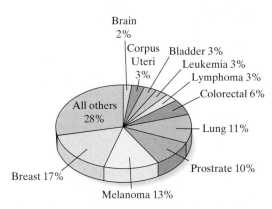

Source: Today's Tomorrows, Annual Report, H. Lee Moffitt Cancer Center & Research Institute, Winter 2002–2003.

2.7 Japanese reading levels. University of Hawaii language professors C. Hitosugi and R. Day incorporated a 10-week extensive reading program into a second semester Japanese course in an effort to improve students' Japanese reading comprehension. (*Reading in a Foreign Language*, Apr. 2004.) The professors collected 266 books originally written for Japanese children and required their students to read at least 40 of them as part of the grade in the course. The books were categorized into reading levels (color coded for easy selection) according to length and complexity. The reading levels for the 266 books are summarized in the table.

Reading Level	Number
Level 1 (Red)	39
Level 2 (Blue)	76
Level 3 (Yellow)	50
Level 4 (Pink)	87
Level 5 (Orange)	11
Level 6 (Green)	3
Total	266

Source: Hitosugi, C. I. and Day, R. R. "Extensive reading in Japanese," *Reading in a Foreign Language*, Vol. 16, No. 1. Apr. 2004 (Table 2).

a. Calculate the proportion of books at reading level 1 (red).
b. Repeat part **a** for each of the remaining reading levels.
c. Verify that the proportions in parts **a** and **b** sum to 1.
d. Use the previous results to form a bar graph for the reading levels.
e. Construct a Pareto diagram for the data. Use the diagram to identify the reading level that occurs most often.

2.8 Dates of pennies. *Chance* (Spring 2000) reported on a study to estimate the number of pennies required to fill a coin collectors album. The data used in the study were obtained by noting the mint date on each in a sample of 2,000 pennies. The distribution of mint dates are summarized in the following table.

Mint Date	Number
Pre-1960	18
1960s	125
1970s	330
1980s	727
1990s	800

Source: Lu, S., and Skiena, S. "Filling a penny album," *Chance*, Vol. 13, No. 2, Spring 2000, p. 26 (Table 1).

a. Identify the experimental unit for the study.
b. Identify the variable measured.
c. What proportion of pennies in the sample have mint dates in the 1960s?
d. Construct a pie chart to describe the distribution of mint dates for the 2,000 sampled pennies.

2.9 Estimating the rhino population. The International Rhino Federation estimates that there are 17,470 rhinoceroses living in the wild in Africa and Asia. A breakdown of the number of rhinos of each species is reported in the accompanying table.

Rhino Species	Population Estimate
African Black	3,610
African White	11,100
(Asian) Sumatran	300
(Asian) Javan	60
(Asian) Indian	2,400
Total	17,470

Source: International Rhino Federation, Sep. 2004.

a. Construct a relative frequency table for the data.
b. Display the relative frequencies in a bar graph.
c. What proportion of the 17,470 rhinos are African rhinos? Asian?

2.10 **Role importance for the elderly.** In *Psychology and Aging* (Dec. 2000), University of Michigan School of Public Health researchers studied the roles that elderly people feel are the most important to them in late life. The accompanying table summarizes the most salient roles identified by each in a national sample of 1,102 adults, 65 years or older.

Most Salient Role	Number
Spouse	424
Parent	269
Grandparent	148
Other relative	59
Friend	73
Homemaker	59
Provider	34
Volunteer, club, church member	36
Total	1,102

Source: Krause, N., and Shaw, B. A. "Role-specific feelings of control and mortality," *Psychology and Aging*, Vol. 15, No. 4, Dec. 2000 (Table 2).

a. Describe the qualitative variable summarized in the table. Give the categories associated with the variable.
b. Are the numbers in the table frequencies or relative frequencies?
c. Display the information in the table in a bar graph.
d. Which role is identified by the highest percentage of elderly adults? Interpret the relative frequency associated with this role.

2.11 **Switching off air bags.** Driver-side and passenger-side air bags are installed in all new cars to prevent serious or fatal injury in an automobile crash. However, air bags have been found to cause deaths in children and small people or people with handicaps in low-speed crashes. Consequently, in 1998 the federal government began allowing vehicle owners to request installation of an on-off switch for air bags. The table describes the reasons for requesting the installation of passenger-side on-off switches given by car owners in 1998 and 1999.

Reason	Number of Requests
Infant	1,852
Child	17,148
Medical	8,377
Infant & Medical	44
Child & Medical	903
Infant & Child	1,878
Infant & Child & Medical	135
Total	30,337

Source: National Highway Transportation Safety Administration. Sept. 2000.

a. What type of variable, quantitative or qualitative, is summarized in the table? Give the values that the variable could assume.
b. Calculate the relative frequencies for each reason.
c. Display the information in the table in an appropriate graph.
d. What proportion of the car owners who requested on-off air bag switches gave Medical as one of the reasons?

Applying the Concepts—Intermediate

2.12 **Excavating ancient pottery.** Archaeologists excavating the ancient Greek settlement at Phylakopi classified the pottery found in trenches (*Chance*, Fall 2000). The accompanying table describes the collection of 837 pottery pieces uncovered in a particular layer at the excavation site. Construct and interpret a graph that will aid the archaeologists in understanding the distribution of the pottery types found at the site.

Pot Category	Number Found
Burnished	133
Monochrome	460
Slipped	55
Painted in curvilinear decoration	14
Painted in geometric decoration	165
Painted in naturalistic decoration	4
Cycladic white clay	4
Conical cup clay	2
Total	837

Source: Berg, I., and Bliedon, S. "The Pots of Phylakopi: Applying Statistical Techniques to Archaeology," *Chance,* Vol. 13, No. 4, Fall 2000.

2.13 **"Made in the USA" survey.** "Made in the USA" is a claim stated in many product advertisements or on product labels. Advertisers want consumers to believe that the product is manufactured with 100% U.S. labor and materials — which is often not the case. What does "Made in the USA" mean to the typical consumer? To answer this question, a group of marketing professors conducted an experiment at a shopping mall in Muncie, Indiana. (*Journal of Global Business*, Spring 2002.) They asked every fourth adult entrant to the mall to participate in the study. A total of 106 shoppers agreed to answer the question, "'Made in the USA' means what percentage of US labor and materials?" The responses of the 106 shoppers are summarized in the table.

Response to "Made in the USA"	Number of Shoppers
100%	64
75 to 99%	20
50 to 74%	18
Less than 50%	4

Source: "'Made in the USA': Consumer perceptions, deception and policy alternatives," *Journal of Global Business,* Vol. 13, No. 24, Spring 2002 (Table 3).

a. What type of data collection method was used?

b. What type of variable, quantitative or qualitative, is measured?

c. Present the data in the table in graphical form. Use the graph to make a statement about the percentage of consumers who believe "Made in the USA" means 100% U.S. labor and materials.

2.14 Hearing loss in senior citizens. Audiologists have recently developed a rehabilitation program for hearing-impaired patients in a Canadian home for senior citizens. (*Journal of the Academy of Rehabilitative Audiology*, 1994.) Each of the 30 residents of the home were diagnosed for degree and type of sensorineural hearing loss, coded as follows: 1 = hear within normal limits, 2 = high-frequency hearing loss, 3 = mild loss, 4 = mild-to-moderate loss, 5 = moderate loss, 6 = moderate-to-severe loss, and 7 = severe-to-profound loss. The data are listed in the next table. Use a graph to portray the results. Which type of hearing loss appears to be the most prevalent among nursing home residents?

⊙ **HEARLOSS**

6	7	1	1	2	6	4	6	4	2	5	2	5
1	5	4	6	6	5	5	5	2	5	3	6	4
6	6	4	2								

Source: Jennings, M. B., and Head, B. G. "Development of an ecological audiologic rehabilitation program in a home-for-the-aged." *Journal of the Academy of Rehabilitative Audiology,* Vol. 27, 1994, p. 77 (Table 1).

2.15 Best-paid CEOs. *Forbes* magazine periodically conducts a salary survey of chief executive officers. In addition to salary information, *Forbes* collects and reports personal data on the CEOs, including level of education and age. Do most CEOs have advanced degrees, such as masters degrees or doctorates? The data in the table below represent the highest degree obtained for each of the top 25 best-paid CEOs of 2003. Use a graphical method to summarize the highest degree obtained for these CEOs. What is your opinion about whether most CEOs have advanced degrees?

⊙ **DDT**

2.16 Species of Contaminated Fish. Refer to Example 1.4 (p. 13) and the U.S. Army Corps of Engineers data on fish contaminated from the toxic discharges of a chemical plant located on the banks of the Tennessee River in Alabama. The engineers determined the species (channel catfish, largemouth bass, or smallmouth buffalofish) for each of the 144 captured fish. The data on species are saved in the DDT file. Use a graphical method to describe the frequency of occurrence of the three fish species in the 144 captured fish.

⊙ **FORBES25**

CEO	Company	Degree	Age
1. Jeffry C. Barbakow	Tenet Healthcare	Masters	59
2. Dwight C. Schar	NVR	Bachelors	61
3. Michael S. Dell	Dell Computer	None	38
4. Irwin M. Jacobs	Qualcomm	Masters	69
5. Barry Diller	USA Interactive	None	61
6. Dan M. Palmer	Concord EFS	Bachelors	60
7. Charles T. Fote	First Data	None	54
8. Orin C. Smith	Starbucks	Masters	60
9. Richard S. Fuld, Jr.	Lehman Bros Holding	Masters	57
10. Maurice R. Greenberg	American Int Group	Law	78
11. Charles M. Cawley	MBNA	Bachelors	62
12. James E. Cayne	Bear Stearns	None	69
13. Scott G. McNealy	Sun Microsystems	Masters	48
14. Philip J. Purcell	Morgan Stanley	Masters	59
15. Vance D. Coffman	Lockheed Martin	PhD	59
16. Lee R. Raymond	ExxonMobil	PhD	64
17. Richard J. Kogan	Schering-Plough	Masters	61
18. Kenneth W. Freeman	Quest Diagnostics	Masters	52
19. Leonard D. Schaeffer	WellPoint Health	Bachelors	57
20. Stuart A. Miller	Lennar	Law	45
21. Robert L. Tillman	Lowe's	Bachelors	59
22. Sumner M. Redstone	Viacom	Law	79
23. Peter Cartwright	Calpine	Masters	73
24. David D. Halbert	Advance PCS	Bachelors	47
25. Craig R. Barrett	Intel	PhD	63

Source: Forbes, April 23, 2003.

2.17 Unauthorized computer use. The Computer Security Institute (CSI) conducts an annual survey of computer crime at United States businesses. CSI sends survey questionnaires to computer security personnel at all U.S. corporations and government agencies. In 2001, 64% of the respondents admitted unauthorized use of computer systems at their firms during the year. (*Computer Security Issues & Trends*, Spring 2001.) One survey question asked, "If your business website suffered unauthorized use, where did the attack come from, inside or outside the company?" The responses for those business websites that did, in fact, experience unauthorized use are summarized in the table for two survey years, 1999 (125 reported attacks) and 2001 (163 reported attacks). Compare the responses for the two years using side-by-side bar charts. What inference can be made from the charts?

WWW Site Attack	Percentage in 1999	Percentage in 2001
Inside	7	4
Outside	38	47
Both	41	22
Don't Know	14	26
Totals	100	100

Source: "2001 CSI/FBI Computer Crime and Security Survey," *Computer Security Issues & Trends,* Vol. 7, No. 1, Spring 2001.

Applying the Concepts—Advanced

NZBIRDS

2.18 Extinct New Zealand birds. Refer to the *Evolutionary Ecology Research* (July 2003) study of the patterns of extinction in the New Zealand bird population, Exercise 1.18 (p. 20). Data on flight capability (volant or flightless), habitat (aquatic, ground terrestrial, or aerial terrestrial), nesting site (ground, cavity within ground, tree, cavity above ground), nest density (high or low), diet (fish, vertebrates, vegetables, or invertebrates), body mass (grams), egg length (millimeters), and extinct status (extinct, absent from island, present) for 132 bird species at the time of the Maori colonization of New Zealand are saved in the NZBIRDS file. Use a graphical method to investigate the theory that extinct status is related to flight capability, habitat, and nest density.

2.19 Whistling dolphins. Marine scientists who study dolphin communication have discovered that bottlenose dolphins exhibit an individualized whistle contour known as the *signature whistle*. A study was conducted to categorize the signature whistles of ten captive adult bottlenose dolphins in socially interactive contexts. (*Ethology*, July 1995.) A total of 185 whistles were recorded during the study period; each whistle contour was analyzed and assigned to a category using a contour similarity (CS) technique. The results are reported in the accompanying table. Use a graphical method to summarize the results. Do you detect any patterns in the data that might be helpful to marine scientists?

DOLPHIN

Whistle Category	Number of Whistles
Type a	97
Type b	15
Type c	9
Type d	7
Type e	7
Type f	2
Type g	2
Type h	2
Type i	2
Type j	4
Type k	13
Other types	25

Source: McCowan, B., and Reiss, D. "Quantitative comparison of whistle repertoires from captive adult bottlenose dolphins (Delphiniae, Tursiops truncatus): A re-evaluation of the signature whistle hypothesis." *Ethology*, Vol. 100, No. 3, July 1995, p. 200 (Table 2).

2.20 Benford's Law of Numbers. According to *Benford's Law*, certain digits $(1, 2, 3, \ldots, 9)$ are more likely to occur as the first significant digit in a randomly selected number than other digits. For example, the law predicts that the number "1" is the most likely to occur (30% of the time) as the first digit. In a study reported in the *American Scientist* (July–Aug. 1998) to test Benford's Law, 743 first-year college students were asked to write down a six-digit number at random. The first significant digit of each number was recorded and its distribution summarized in the following table.

DIGITS

First Digit	Number of Occurrences
1	109
2	75
3	77
4	99
5	72
6	117
7	89
8	62
9	43
Total	743

Source: Hill, T. P. "The First Digit Phenomenon." *American Scientist*, Vol. 86, No. 4, July–Aug. 1998, p. 363 (Figure 5).

a. Describe the first digit of the "random guess" data with an appropriate graph.

b. Does the graph support Benford's Law? Explain.

2.2 Graphical Methods for Describing Quantitative Data

Recall from Section 1.4 that quantitative data sets consist of data that are recorded on a meaningful numerical scale. For describing, summarizing, and detecting patterns in such data, we can use three graphical methods: *dot plots, stem-and-leaf displays,* and *histograms*. Since most statistical software packages can be used to construct these displays, we'll focus here on their interpretation rather than their construction.

For example, the Environmental Protection Agency (EPA) performs extensive tests on all new car models to determine their mileage ratings. Suppose that the 100 measurements in Table 2.2 represent the results of such tests on a certain new car model. How can we summarize the information in this rather large sample?

 EPAGAS

TABLE 2.2   EPA Mileage Ratings on 100 Cars

36.3	41.0	36.9	37.1	44.9	36.8	30.0	37.2	42.1	36.7
32.7	37.3	41.2	36.6	32.9	36.5	33.2	37.4	37.5	33.6
40.5	36.5	37.6	33.9	40.2	36.4	37.7	37.7	40.0	34.2
36.2	37.9	36.0	37.9	35.9	38.2	38.3	35.7	35.6	35.1
38.5	39.0	35.5	34.8	38.6	39.4	35.3	34.4	38.8	39.7
36.3	36.8	32.5	36.4	40.5	36.6	36.1	38.2	38.4	39.3
41.0	31.8	37.3	33.1	37.0	37.6	37.0	38.7	39.0	35.8
37.0	37.2	40.7	37.4	37.1	37.8	35.9	35.6	36.7	34.5
37.1	40.3	36.7	37.0	33.9	40.1	38.0	35.2	34.8	39.5
39.9	36.9	32.9	33.8	39.8	34.0	36.8	35.0	38.1	36.9

A visual inspection of the data indicates some obvious facts. For example, most of the mileages are in the 30s, with a smaller fraction in the 40s. But it is difficult to provide much additional information on the 100 mileage ratings without resorting to some method of summarizing the data. One such method is a dot plot.

Dot Plots

A MINITAB **dot plot** for the 100 EPA mileage ratings is shown in Figure 2.8. The horizontal axis of Figure 2.8 is a scale for the quantitative variable in miles per gallon (mpg). The numerical value of each measurement in the data set is located on the

Figure 2.8
MINITAB Dot Plot for 100 EPA Mileage Ratings

horizontal scale by a dot. When data values repeat, the dots are placed above one another, forming a pile at that particular numerical location. As you can see, this dot plot verifies that almost all of the mileage ratings are in the 30s, with most falling between 35 and 40 miles per gallon.

Stem-and-Leaf Display

Another graphical representation of these same data, a MINITAB **stem-and-leaf display**, is shown in Figure 2.9. In this display the *stem* is the portion of the measurement (mpg) to the left of the decimal point, while the remaining portion to the right of the decimal point is the *leaf*.

Figure 2.9
MINITAB Stem-and-Leaf
Display for 100 Mileage
Ratings

```
Stem-and-leaf of MPG  N   = 100
Leaf Unit = 0.10


  1     30   0
  2     31   8
  6     32   5799
 12     33   126899
 18     34   024588
 29     35   01235667899
 49     36   01233445566777888999
(21)    37   000011122334456677899
 30     38   0122345678
 20     39   00345789
 12     40   0123557
  5     41   002
  2     42   1
  1     43
  1     44   9
```

In Figure 2.9, the stems for the data set are listed in the second column from the smallest (30) to the largest (44). Then the leaf for each observation is listed to the right in the row of the display corresponding to the observation's stem. For example, the leaf 3 of the first observation (36.3) in Table 2.2 appears in the row corresponding to the stem 36. Similarly, the leaf 7 for the second observation (32.7) in Table 2.2 appears in the row corresponding to the stem 32, while the leaf 5 for the third observation (40.5) appears in the row corresponding to the stem 40. (The stems and leaves for these first three observations are highlighted in Figure 2.9.) Typically, the leaves in each row are ordered as shown in the MINITAB stem-and-leaf display.

The stem-and-leaf display presents another compact picture of the data set. You can see at a glance that the 100 mileage readings were distributed between 30.0 and 44.9, with most of them falling in stem rows 35 to 39. The six leaves in stem row 34 indicate that six of the 100 readings were at least 34.0 but less than 35.0. Similarly, the eleven leaves in stem row 35 indicate that eleven of the 100 readings were at least 35.0 but less than 36.0. Only five cars had readings equal to 41 or larger, and only one was as low as 30.

The definitions of the stem and leaf for a data set can be modified to alter the graphical description. For example, suppose we had defined the stem as the tens digit for the gas mileage data, rather than the ones and tens digits. With this definition, the stems and leaves corresponding to the measurements 36.3 and 32.7 would be as follows:

Stem	Leaf	Stem	Leaf
3	6	3	2

Note that the decimal portion of the numbers has been dropped. Generally, only one digit is displayed in the leaf.

If you look at the data, you'll see why we didn't define the stem this way. All the mileage measurements fall in the 30s and 40s, so all the leaves would fall into just two stem rows in this display. The resulting picture would not be nearly as informative as Figure 2.9.

Now Work   *Exercise 2.25*

Biography

JOHN TUKEY (1915–2000)— The Picasso of Statistics

Like the legendary artist Pablo Picasso, who mastered and revolutionized a variety of art forms during his lifetime, John Tukey is recognized for his contributions to many subfields of statistics. Born in Massachusetts, Tukey was home-schooled, graduated with his bachelor's and master's degrees in chemistry from Brown University, and received his Ph.D. in mathematics from Princeton University. While at Bell Telephone Laboratories in the 1960s and early 1970s, Tukey developed exploratory data analysis, a set of graphical descriptive methods for summarizing and presenting huge amounts of data. Many of these tools, including the stem-and-leaf display and the box plot, are now standard features of modern statistical software packages. (In fact, it was Tukey himself who coined the term *software* for computer programs.)

Histograms

An SPSS **histogram** for these 100 EPA mileage readings is shown in Figure 2.10. The horizontal axis of Figure 2.10, which gives the miles per gallon for a given automobile, is divided into **class intervals** commencing with the interval from 30.0–31.5 and proceeding in intervals of equal size to 43.5–45.0 mpg. The vertical axis gives the

Figure 2.10
SPSS Histogram for 100 EPA Mileage Ratings

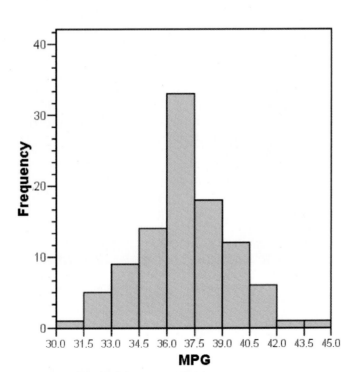

number (or *frequency*) of the 100 readings that fall in each interval. It appears that about 33 of the 100 cars, or 33%, obtained a mileage between 36.0 and 37.5. This class interval contains the highest frequency, and the intervals tend to contain a smaller number of the measurements as the mileages get smaller or larger.

Histograms can be used to display either the frequency or relative frequency of the measurements falling into the class intervals. The class intervals, frequencies, and relative frequencies for the EPA car mileage data are shown in the summary table, Table 2.3.*

TABLE 2.3   Class Intervals, Frequencies, and Relative Frequencies for the Car Mileage Data

Class Interval	Frequency	Relative Frequency
30.0–31.5	1	.01
31.5–33.0	5	.05
33.0–34.5	9	.09
34.5–36.0	14	.14
36.0–37.5	33	.33
37.5–39.0	18	.18
39.0–40.5	12	.12
40.5–42.0	6	.06
42.0–43.5	1	.01
43.5–45.0	1	.01
Totals	100	1.00

By summing the relative frequencies in the intervals 34.5–36.0, 36.0–37.5, and 37.5–39.0, you can see that 65% of the mileages are between 34.5 and 39.0. Similarly, only 2% of the cars obtained a mileage rating over 42.0. Many other summary statements can be made by further study of the histogram and accompanying summary table. Note that the sum of all class frequencies will always equal the sample size, n.

When interpreting a histogram consider two important facts. First, the proportion of the total area under the histogram that falls above a particular interval on the x-axis is equal to the relative frequency of measurements falling in the interval. For example, the relative frequency for the class interval 36.0–37.5 in Figure 2.10 is .33. Consequently, the rectangle above the interval contains .33 of the total area under the histogram.

Second, imagine the appearance of the relative frequency histogram for a very large set of data (say, a population). As the number of measurements in a data set is increased, you can obtain a better description of the data by decreasing the width of the class intervals. When the class intervals become small enough, a relative frequency histogram will (for all practical purposes) appear as a smooth curve (see Figure 2.11).

Figure 2.11

The Effect of the Size of a Data Set on the Outline of a Histogram

a. Small data set   b. Larger data set   c. Very large data set

*SPSS, like many software packages, will classify an observation that falls on the borderline of a class interval into the next highest interval. For example, the gas mileage of 37.5, which falls on the border between the class intervals 36.0–37.5 and 37.5–39.0, is classified into the 37.5–39.0 class. The frequencies in Table 2.3 reflect this convention.

Some recommendations for selecting the number of intervals in a histogram for smaller data sets are given in the following box.

Determining the Number of Classes in a Histogram

Number of Observations in Data Set	Number of Classes
Less than 25	5–6
25–50	7–14
More than 50	15–20

While histograms provide good visual descriptions of data sets — particularly very large ones — they do not let us identify individual measurements. In contrast, each of the original measurements is visible to some extent in a dot plot and clearly visible in a stem-and-leaf display. The stem-and-leaf display arranges the data in ascending order, so it's easy to locate the individual measurements. For example, in Figure 2.9 we can easily see that two of the gas mileage measurements are equal to 36.3, but can't see that fact by inspecting the histogram in Figure 2.10. However, stem-and-leaf displays can become unwieldy for very large data sets. A very large number of stems and leaves causes the vertical and horizontal dimensions of the display to become cumbersome, diminishing the usefulness of the visual display.

EXAMPLE 2.2

GRAPHING A QUANTITATIVE VARIABLE

Problem The data in Table 2.4 give, by state, the percentages of the total number of college or university student loans that are in default.

NW **a.** Create a histogram for these data. Where do most of the default rates lie?

b. Create a stem-and-leaf display for these data. Locate Wyoming's default rate of 2.7 on the graph.

Solution **a.** We used SAS to generate a relative frequency histogram in Figure 2.12. Note that 7 classes were formed. The classes are identified by their *midpoints* rather than their endpoints. Thus, the first interval has a midpoint of 1.5, the second of 4.5, and so on. The corresponding class intervals based on these midpoints are therefore 1.0–3.0, 3.0–5.0, etc. Note that the classes with midpoints of 7.5, and 10.5 (ranging from 6.0 to 12.0) contain approximately 60% of the 51 default measurements.

LOANDEFAULT

TABLE 2.4 Percentage of Student Loans (per State) in Default

State	%	State	%	State	%	State	%
Ala.	12.0	Ill.	9.3	Mont.	6.4	R.I.	8.8
Alaska	19.7	Ind.	6.7	Nebr.	4.9	S.C.	14.1
Ariz.	12.1	Iowa	6.2	Nev.	10.1	S. Dak.	5.5
Ark.	12.9	Kans.	5.7	N.H.	7.9	Tenn.	12.3
Calif.	11.4	Ky.	10.3	N.J.	12.0	Tex.	15.2
Colo.	9.5	La.	13.5	N. Mex.	7.5	Utah	6.0
Conn.	8.8	Maine	9.7	N.Y.	11.3	Vt.	8.3
Del.	10.9	Md.	16.6	N.C.	15.5	Va.	14.4
D.C.	14.7	Mass.	8.3	N. Dak.	4.8	Wash.	8.4
Fla.	11.8	Mich.	11.4	Ohio	10.4	W Va.	9.5
Ga.	14.8	Minn.	6.6	Okla.	11.2	Wis.	9.0
Hawaii	12.8	Miss.	15.6	Oreg.	7.9	Wyo.	2.7
Idaho	7.1	Mo.	8.8	Pa.	8.7		

Source: National Direct Student Loan Coalition.

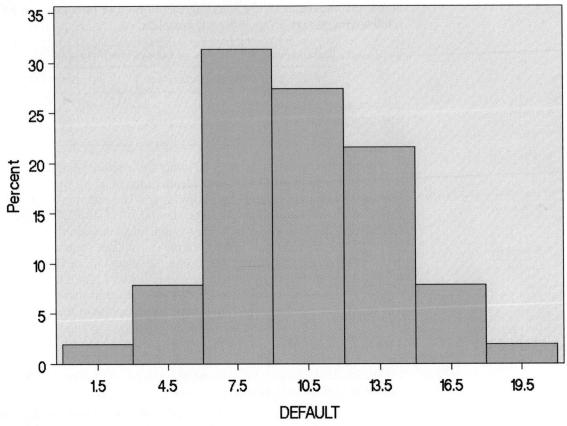

Figure 2.12
SAS Relative Frequency Histogram for Student Loan Default Rate Data

b. We used MINITAB to generate the stem-and-leaf display in Figure 2.13. Note that the stem, (the *second* column in the printout) has been defined as the number *two* places to the left of the decimal. The leaf (the third column in the printout) is the number one place to the left of the decimal.* (The digit to the right of the decimal is not shown.) Thus, the leaf 2 in the stem 0 row (the first row of the printout) represents the default rate of 2.7 for Wyoming.

Figure 2.13
MINITAB Stem-and-Leaf
Display for Student Loan
Default Rate Data

```
Stem-and-leaf of DEFAULT   N  = 51
Leaf Unit = 1.0


    1     0   2
    5     0   4455
   14     0   666667777
  (12)    0   888888899999
   25     1   000011111
   16     1   2222223
    9     1   4444555
    2     1   6
    1     1   9
```

*The first column of the MINITAB stem-and-leaf display represents the cumulative number of measurements from the class interval to the nearest extreme class interval.

Look Back As is usually the case for data sets that are not too large (say, fewer than 100 measurements), the stem-and-leaf display provides more detail than the histogram without being unwieldy. For instance, the stem-and-leaf display in Figure 2.13 clearly indicates the values of the individual measurements in the data set. For example, the highest default rate (representing the measurement 19.7 for Alaska) is shown in the last stem row. Histograms are most useful for displaying very large data sets when the overall shape of the distribution of measurements is more important than the identification of individual measurements.

Now Work	*Exercise 2.30*

■ ■ ■

Most statistical software packages can be used to generate histograms, stem-and-leaf displays, and dot plots. All three are useful tools for graphically describing data sets. We recommend that you generate and compare the displays whenever you can. You'll find that histograms are generally more useful for very large data sets, while stem-and-leaf displays and dot plots provide useful detail for smaller data sets.

Summary of Graphical Descriptive Methods for Quantitative Data

Dot Plot: The numerical value of each quantitative measurement in the data set is represented by a dot on a horizontal scale. When data values repeat, the dots are placed above one another vertically.

Stem-and-Leaf Display: The numerical value of the quantitative variable is partitioned into a "stem" and a "leaf." The possible stems are listed in order in a column. The leaf for each quantitative measurement in the data set is placed in the corresponding stem row. Leaves for observations with the same stem value are listed in increasing order horizontally.

Histogram: The possible numerical values of the quantitative variable are partitioned into class intervals, where each interval has the same width. These intervals form the scale of the horizontal axis. The frequency or relative frequency of observations in each class interval is determined. A vertical bar is placed over each class interval with height equal to either the class frequency or class relative frequency.

Histograms

Using the TI-83 Graphing Calculator

Making a Histogram from Raw Data

Step 1 *Enter the data*
Press **STAT** and select **1:Edit**
Note: If the list already contains data, clear the old data. Use the up arrow to highlight 'L1'. Press **CLEAR ENTER**.
Use the arrow and **ENTER** keys to enter the data set into **L1**.

Step 2 *Set up the histogram plot*
Press **2nd** and Press **Y** = for **STAT PLOT**
Press **1** for **Plot 1**

Set the cursor so that **ON** is flashing.

For **Type**, use the arrow and Enter keys to highlight and select the histogram.

For **Xlist**, choose the column containing the data (in most cases, L1).

Note: Press **2nd 1** for **L1**

Freq should be set to 1.

Step 3   *Select your window settings*

Press **WINDOW** and adjust the settings as follows:

Xmin = lowest class boundary

Xmax = highest class boundary

Xscl = class width

Ymin = 0

Ymax ≥ greatest class frequency

Yscl = 1

Xres = 1

Step 4   *View the graph*

Press **GRAPH**

Optional   *Read class frequencies and class boundaries*

Step   You can press **TRACE** to read the class frequencies and class boundaries. Use the arrow keys to move between bars.

Example   The figures below show TI-83 window settings and histogram for the following sample data:

86, 70, 62, 98, 73, 56, 53, 92, 86, 37, 62, 83, 78, 49, 78, 37, 67, 79, 57

II Making a Histogram from a Frequency Table

Step 1   *Enter the data*

Press **STAT** and select **1:Edit**

Note: If a list already contains data, clear the old data. Use the up arrow to highlight the list name, '**L1**' or '**L2**'.

Press **CLEAR ENTER**.

Enter the midpoint of each class into **L1**

Enter the class frequencies or relative frequencies into **L2**

Step 2   *Set up the histogram plot*

Press **2nd** and **Y =** for **STAT PLOT**

Press **1** for **Plot 1**

Set the cursor so that **ON** is flashing.

For **Type**, use the arrow and Enter keys to highlight and select the histogram.
For **Xlist**, choose the column containing the midpoints.
For **Freq**, choose the column containing the frequencies or relative frequencies.

Step 3–4 *Follow steps 3–4 given above.*
Note: To set up the Window for relative frequencies, be sure to set **Ymax**
to a value that is greater than or equal to the largest relative frequency.

Statistics in Action Revisited

Interpreting Histograms

A quantitative variable measured in the *Psychological Science* "water-level task" experiment was *Deviation angle* (measured in degrees) of the judged line from the true surface line (parallel to the table top). The smaller the deviation, the better the task performance. Recall that the researchers want to test the prevailing theory that males will do better than females on judging the correct water level. To check this theory, we accessed the **EYECUE** data file in MINITAB and created two frequency histograms for deviation angle — one for male subjects and one for female subjects. These side-by-side histograms are displayed in Figure SIA2.5.

From the histograms, there is some support for the theory. The histogram for males (the histogram on the right in Figure SIA2.5) shows the center of the distribution at about 0°, with most (about 70%) of the deviation values falling between −10° and 10°. In general, the male subjects tended to perform fairly well on the water-level task. Alternatively, the histogram for females (the histogram on the left in Figure SIA2.5) is centered at about 10°, with most (about 70%) of the deviation values falling above 0°. Thus, the histogram for females shows a tendency for female subjects to have greater deviations (and, thus, poorer performances) in the water-level task than males. In later chapters, we'll learn how to attach a measure of reliability to such an inference.

Figure SIA2.5
MINITAB Histograms for Deviation Angle in the Water-Level Task — Males versus Females

Exercises 2.21–2.41

Understanding the Principles

2.21 Explain the difference between a dot plot and a stem-and-leaf display.

2.22 Explain the difference between the stem and the leaf in a stem-and-leaf display.

2.23 In a histogram, what are the class intervals?

2.24 How many classes are recommended in a histogram for a data set with more than 50 observations?

Learning the Mechanics

2.25 Consider the stem-and-leaf display shown here.

NW

Stem	Leaf
5	1
4	457
3	00036
2	1134599
1	2248
0	012

a. How many observations were in the original data set?

b. In the bottom row of the stem-and-leaf display, identify the stem, the leaves, and the numbers in the original data set represented by this stem and its leaves.

c. Re-create all the numbers in the data set and construct a dot plot.

Learning the Mechanics

2.26 Graph the relative frequency histogram for the 500 measurements summarized in the accompanying relative frequency table.

Class Interval	Relative Frequency
.5–2.5	.10
2.5–4.5	.15
4.5–6.5	.25
6.5–8.5	.20
8.5–10.5	.05
10.5–12.5	.10
12.5–14.5	.10
14.5–16.5	.05

2.27 Refer to Exercise 2.26. Calculate the number of the 500 measurements falling into each of the measurement classes. Then graph a frequency histogram for these data.

2.28 Consider the following histogram:

a. Is this a frequency histogram or a relative frequency histogram? Explain.

b. How many class intervals were used in the construction of this histogram?

c. How many measurements are there in the data set described by this histogram?

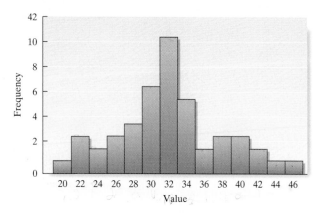

Applying the Concepts—Basic

2.29 **Earthquake magnitudes.** The strength of an earthquake — called magnitude — is measured quantitatively using the Richter scale. A magnitude below 3.0 is considered a very minor earthquake, while a magnitude of 7.0 or above is considered a major earthquake. The National Earthquake Information Center located 31,366 earthquakes worldwide in 2003. The magnitudes (on the Richter scale) of these earthquakes are summarized in the accompanying table. Display the data in a graph.

Magnitude	Number of Earthquakes
8.0 to 9.9	1
7.0 to 7.9	14
6.0 to 6.9	140
5.0 to 5.9	1,160
4.0 to 4.9	8,419
3.0 to 3.9	7,705
2.0 to 2.9	7,723
1.0 to 1.9	2,471
0.1 to 0.9	128
No Magnitude	3,605
Total	31,366

Source: National Earthquake Information Center, Department of Interior, U.S. Geological Survey.

2.30 **Aggressiveness scores.** The graph on p. 25 summarizes the scores obtained by 100 students on a questionnaire designed to measure aggressiveness. (Scores are integer values that range from 0 to 20. A high score indicates a high level of aggression.)

a. Which measurement class contains the highest proportion of test scores?

b. What is the proportion of scores that lie between 3.5 and 5.5?

c. What is the proportion of scores that are higher than 11.5?

d. How many students scored less than 5.5?

Source: United States Chess Federation, Jan. 1998.

2.31 Reading Japanese books. Refer to the *Reading in a Foreign Language* (Apr. 2004) experiment to improve the Japanese reading comprehension levels of University of Hawaii students, Exercise 2.7 (p. 37). Fourteen students participated in a 10-week extensive reading program in a second semester Japanese course. The number of books read by each student and the student's course grade are listed in the table.

JAPANESE

Number of Books	Course Grade	Number of Books	Course Grade
53	A	30	A
42	A	28	B
40	A	24	A
40	B	22	C
39	A	21	B
34	A	20	B
34	A	16	B

Source: Hitosugi, C. I., and Day, R. R. "Extensive reading in Japanese," *Reading in a Foreign Language,* Vol. 16, No. 1, Apr. 2004 (Table 4).

a. Construct a stem-and-leaf display for the number of books read by the students.

b. Highlight (or circle) the leaves in the display that correspond to students who earned an A grade in the course. What inference can you make about these students?

2.32 Ratings of chess players. The United States Chess Federation (USCF) establishes a numerical rating for each competitive chess player. The USCF rating is a number between 0 and 4,000 that changes over time depending on the outcome of tournament games. The higher the rating, the better (more successful) the player. The next graph describes the rating distribution of 27,563 players who were active competitors in 1997.

a. What type of graph is displayed?

b. Is the variable displayed on the graph quantitative or qualitative?

c. What percentage of players has a USCF rating above 1,000?

Applying the Concepts—Intermediate

DDT

2.33 Contaminated fish. Refer to Exercise 2.16 (p. 39) and the U.S. Army Corps of Engineers data on contaminated fish saved in the DDT file. In addition to species (channel catfish, largemouth bass, or smallmouth buffalofish), the length (in centimeters), weight (in grams), and DDT level (in parts per million) were measured for each of the 144 captured fish.

a. Use a graphical method to describe the distribution of the 144 fish lengths.

b. Use a graphical method to describe the distribution of the 144 fish weights.

c. Use a graphical method to describe the distribution of the 144 DDT measurements.

2.34 Radioactive lichen. Lichen has a high absorbance capacity for radiation fallout from nuclear accidents. Since lichen is a major food source for Alaskan caribou, and caribou are, in turn, a major food source for many Alaskan villagers, it is important to monitor the level of radioactivity in lichen. Researchers at the University of Alaska, Fairbanks collected data on 9 lichen specimens at various locations for this purpose. The amount of the radioactive element cesium-137 was measured (in microcuries per milliliter) for each specimen. The data values, converted to logarithms, are given in the table. (Note that the closer the value is to zero, the greater the amount of cesium in the specimen.)

LICHEN

Location			
Bethel	−5.50	−5.00	
Eagle Summit	−4.15	−4.85	
Moose Pass	−6.05		
Turnagain Pass	−5.00		
Wickersham Dome	−4.10	−4.50	−4.60

Source: Lichen Radionuclide Baseline Research Project, 2003.

a. Construct a dot plot for the nine measurements.

b. Construct a stem-and-leaf display for the nine measurements.

c. Construct a histogram plot for the nine measurements.

d. Which of the three graphs, parts **a–c**, is more informative?

e. What proportion of the measurements have a radioactivity level of −5.00 or lower?

2.35 College protests of labor exploitation. The United Students Against Sweatshops (USAS) was formed by students on American college campuses in 1999 to protest labor exploitation in the apparel industry. Clark University sociologist Robert Ross analyzed the USAS movement in the *Journal of World-Systems Research* (Winter 2004). Between 1999 and 2000 there were 18 student "sit-ins" for a "sweat free campus" organized at several universities. The table gives the duration (in days) of each sit-in as well as the number of student arrests.

SITIN

Sit-in	Year	University	Duration (days)	Number of Arrests	Tier Ranking
1	1999	Duke	1	0	1st
2	1999	Georgetown	4	0	1st
3	1999	Wisconsin	1	0	1st
4	1999	Michigan	1	0	1st
5	1999	Fairfield	1	0	1st
6	1999	North Carolina	1	0	1st
7	1999	Arizona	10	0	1st
8	2000	Toronto	11	0	1st
9	2000	Pennsylvania	9	0	1st
10	2000	Macalester	2	0	1st
11	2000	Michigan	3	0	1st
12	2000	Wisconsin	4	54	1st
13	2000	Tulane	12	0	1st
14	2000	SUNY Albany	1	11	2nd
15	2000	Oregon	3	14	2nd
16	2000	Purdue	12	0	2nd
17	2000	Iowa	4	16	2nd
18	2000	Kentucky	1	12	2nd

Source: Ross, R. J. S. "From antisweatshop to global justice to antiwar: How the new new left is the same and different from the old new left." *Journal of World-Systems Research,* Vol. X, No. 1, Winter 2004 (Tables 1 and 3).

a. Summarize the data on sit-in duration using a stem-and-leaf display.

b. Highlight (or circle) the leaves in the display that correspond to sit-ins where at least one arrest was made. Does the pattern revealed support the theory that sit-ins of longer duration are more likely to lead to arrests?

2.36 Fluid loss in spiders. A group of University of Virginia biologists studied nectivory (nectar drinking) in crab spiders to determine if adult males were feeding on nectar to prevent fluid loss. (*Animal Behavior,* June 1995.) Nine male spiders were weighed and then placed on the flowers of Queen Anne's lace. One hour later, the spiders were removed and reweighed. The evaporative fluid loss (in milligrams) of each of the nine male spiders is given in the next table.

SPIDERS

Male Spider	Fluid Loss
A	.018
B	.020
C	.017
D	.024
E	.020
F	.024
G	.003
H	.001
I	.009

Source: Pollard, S. D., et al. "Why do male crab spiders drink nectar?" *Animal Behavior,* Vol. 49, No. 6, June 1995, p.1445 (Table II).

a. Summarize the fluid losses of male crab spiders with a stem-and-leaf display.

b. Of the nine spiders, only three drank any nectar from the flowers of Queen Anne's lace. These three spiders are identified as G, H, and I in the table. Locate and circle these three fluid losses on the stem-and-leaf display. Does the pattern depicted in the graph give you any insight into whether feeding on flower nectar reduces evaporative fluid loss for male crab spiders? Explain.

2.37 Research on brain specimens. *Postmortem interval* (PMI) is defined as the elapsed time between death and an autopsy. Knowledge of PMI is considered essential when conducting medical research on human cadavers. The data in the table are the PMIs of 22 human brain specimens obtained at autopsy in a recent study. (*Brain and Language,* June 1995.) Graphically describe the PMI data with a dot plot. Based on the plot, make a summary statement about the PMI of the 22 human brain specimens.

BRAINPMI

Postmortem Intervals for 22 Human Brain Specimens

5.5	14.5	6.0	5.5	5.3	5.8	11.0	6.1
7.0	14.5	10.4	4.6	4.3	7.2	10.5	6.5
3.3	7.0	4.1	6.2	10.4	4.9		

Source: Hayes, T. L., and Lewis, D. A. "Anatomical specialization of the anterior motor speech area: Hemispheric differences in magnopyramidal neurons." *Brain and Language,* Vol. 49, No. 3, June 1995, p. 292 (Table 1).

2.38 Research on eating disorders. Data from a psychology experiment were reported and analyzed in *The American Statistician* (May 2001). Two samples of female students participated in the experiment. One sample consisted of 11 students known to suffer from the eating disorder bulimia; the other sample consisted of 14 students with normal eating habits. Each student completed a questionnaire from which a "fear of negative evaluation" (FNE) score was produced. (The higher the score, the greater the fear of negative evaluation.) The data are displayed in the table on p. 53.

a. Construct a dot plot or stem-and-leaf display for the FNE scores of all 25 female students.
b. Highlight the bulimic students on the graph, part **a**. Does it appear that bulimics tend to have a greater fear of negative evaluation? Explain.
c. Why is it important to attach a measure of reliability to the inference made in part **b**?

BULIMIA

Bulimic
students: 21 13 10 20 25 19 16 21 24 13 14
Normal
students: 13 6 16 13 8 19 23 18 11 19 7 10 15 20

Source: Randles, R. H. "On neutral responses (zeros) in the sign test and ties in the Wilcoxon-Mann-Whitney test," *The American Statistician,* Vol. 55, No. 2, May 2001 (Figure 3).

2.39 Eclipses and occults. Saturn has five satellites that rotate around the planet. *Astronomy* (Aug. 1995) lists 19 different events involving eclipses or occults of Saturnian satellites during the month of August. For each event, the percent of light lost by the eclipsed or occulted satellite at midevent is recorded in the table.

SATURN

Date	Event	Light Loss (%)
Aug. 2	Eclipse	65
4	Eclipse	61
5	Occult	1
6	Eclipse	56
8	Eclipse	46
8	Occult	2
9	Occult	9
11	Occult	5
12	Occult	39
14	Occult	1
14	Eclipse	100
15	Occult	5
15	Occult	4
16	Occult	13
20	Occult	11
23	Occult	3
23	Occult	20
25	Occult	20
28	Occult	12

Source: ASTRONOMY magazine, Aug. 1995, p. 60.

a. Construct a stem-and-leaf display for light loss percentage of the 19 events.
b. Locate on the stem-and-leaf plot, part **a**, the light losses associated with eclipses of Saturnian satellites. (Circle the light losses on the plot.)
c. Based on the marked stem-and-leaf display, part **b**, make an inference about which event type (eclipse or occult) is more likely to lead to a greater light loss.

Applying the Concepts—Advanced

2.40 Comparing SAT scores. Educators are constantly evaluating the efficacy of public schools in the education and training of American students. One quantitative assessment of change over time is the difference in scores on the SAT, which has been used for decades by colleges and universities as one criterion for admission. The SATSCORES file contains the average SAT scores for each of the 50 states and District of Columbia for 1990 and 2000. Selected observations are shown below.

SATSCORES (First five and last two deservations)

State	1990	2000
Alabama	1079	1114
Alaska	1015	1034
Arizona	1041	1044
Arkansas	1077	1117
California	1002	1015
⋮	⋮	⋮
Wisconsin	1111	1181
Wyoming	1072	1090

Source: College Entrance Examination Board, 2001.

a. Use graphs to display the two SAT score distributions. How have the distributions of average state scores changed over the last decade?
b. As another method of comparing the 1990 and 2000 average SAT scores, compute the **paired difference** by subtracting the 1990 score from the 2000 score for each state. Summarize these differences with a graph.
c. Interpret the graph, part **b**. How do your conclusions compare to those you reached when comparing the two graphs in part **a**?
d. What is the largest improvement in the average score between 1990 and 2000 as indicated on the graph, part **b**? With which state is this improvement associated in the table of data?

2.41 Speech listening study. The role that listener knowledge plays in the perception of imperfectly articulated speech was investigated in the *American Journal of Speech–Language Pathology* (Feb. 1995). Thirty female college students, randomly divided into three groups of ten, participated as listeners in the study. All subjects were required to listen to a 48-sentence audiotape of a Korean woman with cerebral palsy and asked to transcribe her entire speech. For the first group of students (the *control group*), the speaker used her normal manner of speaking. For the second group (the *treatment group*), the speaker employed a learned breathing pattern (called breath-group strategy) to improve speech efficiency. The third group (the *familiarity group*) also listened to the tape with the breath-group strategy, but only after they had practiced listening twice to another tape in which they were told exactly what the speaker was saying. At the end of the listening/transcribing session, two quantitative variables were measured for each listener: (1) the total number of words transcribed (called the rate of response) and (2) the percentage of words correctly transcribed (called the accuracy score). The data for all 30 subjects are provided in the table on p. 54.

a. Use a graphical method to describe the differences in the distributions of response rates among the three groups.
b. Use a graphical method to describe the distribution of accuracy scores for the three listener groups.

◎ LISTEN

Control Group		Treatment Group		Familiarization Group	
Rate of Response	Percent Correct	Rate of Response	Percent Correct	Rate of Response	Percent Correct
250	23.6	254	26.0	193	36.0
230	26.0	178	32.6	223	41.0
197	26.0	139	32.6	232	43.0
238	26.7	249	33.0	214	44.0
174	29.2	236	34.4	269	44.0
263	29.5	231	36.5	256	46.0
275	31.3	161	38.5	224	46.0
193	32.9	255	40.0	225	48.0
204	35.4	275	41.7	288	49.0
168	29.2	181	44.8	244	52.0

Source: Tjaden, K., and Liss, J. M. "The influence of familiarity on judgments of treated speech." *American Journal of Speech–Language Pathology,* Vol. 4, No. 1, Feb. 1995, p. 43 (Table 1).

2.3 Summation Notation

Now that we've examined some graphical techniques for summarizing and describing quantitative data sets, we turn to numerical methods for accomplishing this objective. Before giving the formulas for calculating numerical descriptive measures, let's look at some shorthand notation that will simplify our calculation instructions. Remember that such notation is used for one reason only — to avoid repeating the same verbal descriptions over and over. If you mentally substitute the verbal definition of a symbol each time you read it, you'll soon get used to it.

We denote the measurements of a quantitative data set as

$$x_1, x_2, x_3, \ldots, x_n$$

where x_1 is the first measurement in the data set, x_2 is the second measurement in the data set, x_3 is the third measurement in the data set, $\ldots$, and x_n is the nth (and last) measurement in the data set. Thus, if we have five measurements in a set of data, we will write x_1, x_2, x_3, x_4, x_5 to represent the measurements. If the actual numbers are 5, 3, 8, 5, and 4, we have $x_1 = 5, x_2 = 3, x_3 = 8, x_4 = 5$, and $x_5 = 4$.

Most of the formulas we use require a summation of numbers. For example, one sum we'll need to obtain is the sum of all the measurements in the data set, or $x_1 + x_2 + x_3 + \cdots + x_n$. To shorten the notation, we use the symbol $\sum$ for the summation. That is, $x_1 + x_2 + x_3 + \cdots + x_n = \sum_{i=1}^{n} x_i$. Verbally translate $\sum_{i=1}^{n} x_i$ as follows: "The sum of the measurements, whose typical member is x_i, beginning with the member x_1 and ending with the member x_n."

Suppose, as in our earlier example, $x_1 = 5, x_2 = 3, x_3 = 8, x_4 = 5$, and $x_5 = 4$. Then the sum of the five measurements, denoted $\sum_{i=1}^{5} x_i$ is obtained as follows:

$$\sum_{i=1}^{5} x_i = x_1 + x_2 + x_3 + x_4 + x_5$$

$$= 5 + 3 + 8 + 5 + 4 = 25$$

Another important calculation requires that we square each measurement and then sum the squares. The notation for this sum is $\sum_{i=1}^{n} x_i^2$. For the five measurements, we have

$$\sum_{i=1}^{5} x_i^2 = x_1^2 + x_2^2 + x_3^2 + x_4^2 + x_5^2$$

$$= 5^2 + 3^2 + 8^2 + 5^2 + 4^2$$

$$= 25 + 9 + 64 + 25 + 16 = 139$$

In general, the symbol following the summation sign $\sum$ represents the variable (or function of the variable) that is to be summed.

The Meaning of Summation Notation $\sum_{i=1}^{n} x_i$

Sum the measurements on the variable that appears to the right of the summation symbol, beginning with the 1st measurement and ending with the nth measurement.

Exercises 2.42–2.45

Learning the Mechanics

Note: In all exercises, $\sum$ represents $\sum_{i=1}^{n}$.

2.42 A data set contains the observations 5, 1, 3, 2, 1. Find
   a. $\sum x$ **b.** $\sum x^2$ **c.** $\sum(x - 1)$
   d. $\sum(x - 1)^2$ **e.** $\left(\sum x\right)^2$

2.43 Suppose a data set contains the observations 3, 8, 4, 5, 3, 4, 6. Find
   a. $\sum x$ **b.** $\sum x^2$ **c.** $\sum(x - 5)^2$
   d. $\sum(x - 2)^2$ **e.** $\left(\sum x\right)^2$

2.44 Refer to Exercise 2.42. Find
   a. $\sum x^2 - \dfrac{\left(\sum x\right)^2}{5}$ **b.** $\sum(x - 2)^2$ **c.** $\sum x^2 - 10$

2.45 A data set contains the observations 6, 0, -2, -1, 3. Find
   a. $\sum x$ **b.** $\sum x^2$ **c.** $\sum x^2 - \dfrac{\left(\sum x\right)^2}{5}$

2.4 Numerical Measures of Central Tendency

When we speak of a data set, we refer to either a sample or to a population. If statistical inference is our goal, we'll wish ultimately to use sample **numerical descriptive measures** to make inferences about the corresponding measures for a population.

As you'll see, a large number of numerical methods are available to describe quantitative data sets. Most of these methods measure one of two data characteristics:

1. The **central tendency** of the set of measurements — that is, the tendency of the data to cluster, or center, about certain numerical values (see Figure 2.14a).

2. The **variability** of the set of measurements — that is, the spread of the data (see Figure 2.14b).

In this section we concentrate on **measures of central tendency**. In the next section, we discuss measures of variability.

The most popular and best understood measure of central tendency for a quantitative data set is the *arithmetic mean* (or simply the *mean*) of a data set.

Figure 2.14
Numerical Descriptive
Measures

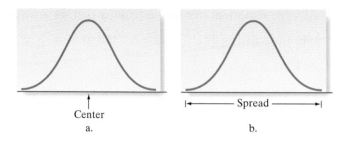

Center
a.

|←——— Spread ———→|
b.

> **DEFINITION 2.5**
>
> The **mean** of a set of quantitative data is the sum of the measurements divided by the number of measurements contained in the data set.

In everyday terms, the mean is the average value of the data set and is often used to represent a "typical" value. We denote the **mean of a sample** of measurements by $\bar{x}$ (read "*x*-bar"), and represent the formula for its calculation as shown in the box:

> **Formula for a Sample Mean**
>
> $$\bar{x} = \frac{\sum\limits_{i=1}^{n} x_i}{n}$$

EXAMPLE 2.3   COMPUTING THE SAMPLE MEAN

Problem Calculate the mean of the following five sample measurements: 5, 3, 8, 5, 6.

Solution Using the definition of sample mean and the summation notation, we find

$$\bar{x} = \frac{\sum\limits_{i=1}^{5} x_i}{5} = \frac{5 + 3 + 8 + 5 + 6}{5} = \frac{27}{5} = 5.4$$

Thus, the mean of this sample is 5.4.

Look Back There is no specific rule for rounding when calculating $\bar{x}$ because $\bar{x}$ is specifically defined to be the sum of all measurements divided by n; that is, it is a specific fraction. When $\bar{x}$ is used for descriptive purposes, it is often convenient to round the calculated value of $\bar{x}$ to the number of significant figures used for the original measurements. When $\bar{x}$ is to be used in other calculations, however, it may be necessary to retain more significant figures.

Now Work   *Exercise 2.55*

EXAMPLE 2.4   FINDING THE MEAN ON A PRINTOUT

Problem Calculate the sample mean for the 100 EPA mileages given in Table 2.2.

Solution The mean gas mileage for the 100 cars is denoted

$$\bar{x} = \frac{\sum\limits_{i=1}^{100} x_i}{100}$$

Rather than compute $\bar{x}$ by hand (or calculator), we employed SAS to compute the mean. The SAS printout is shown in Figure 2.15. The sample mean, highlighted on the printout, is $\bar{x} = 36.9940$.

The MEANS Procedure

Analysis Variable : MPG

Mean	Std Dev	Variance	N	Minimum	Maximum	Median
36.9940000	2.4178971	5.8462263	100	30.0000000	44.9000000	37.0000000

Figure 2.15

SAS Numerical Descriptive Measures for 100 EPA Gas Mileages

Look Back Given this information, you can visualize a distribution of gas mileage readings centered in the vicinity of $\bar{x} \approx 37$. An examination of the relative frequency histogram (Figure 2.10) confirms that $\bar{x}$ does in fact fall near the center of the distribution.

■ ■ ■

The sample mean $\bar{x}$ will play an important role in accomplishing our objective of making inferences about populations based on sample information. For this reason we need to use a different symbol for the *mean of a population* — the mean of the set of measurements on every unit in the population. We use the Greek letter μ (mu) for the population mean.

Symbols for the Sample Mean and the Population Mean

In this text, we adopt a general policy of using Greek letters to represent numerical descriptive measures for the population and Roman letters to represent corresponding descriptive measures for the sample. The symbols for the mean are

$\bar{x}$ = Sample mean μ = Population mean

We'll often use the sample mean, $\bar{x}$, to estimate (make an inference about) the population mean, μ. For example, the EPA mileages for the population consisting of *all* cars has a mean equal to some value, μ. Our sample of 100 cars yielded mileages with a mean of $\bar{x} = 36.9940$. If, as is usually the case, we don't have access to the measurements for the entire population, we could use $\bar{x}$ as an estimator or approximator for μ. Then we'd need to know something about the reliability of our inference. That is, we'd need to know how accurately we might expect $\bar{x}$ to estimate μ. In Chapter 7, we'll find that this accuracy depends on two factors:

1. The *size of the sample*. The larger the sample, the more accurate the estimate will tend to be.

2. The *variability, or spread, of the data*. All other factors remaining constant, the more variable the data, the less accurate the estimate.

Another important measure of central tendency is the **median**.

DEFINITION 2.6

The **median** of a quantitative data set is the middle number when the measurements are arranged in ascending (or descending) order.

The median is of most value in describing large data sets. If the data set is characterized by a relative frequency histogram (Figure 2.16), the median is the point on the *x*-axis such that half the area under the histogram lies above the medi-

Figure 2.16
Location of the Median

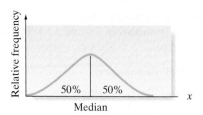

an and half lies below. [*Note*: In Section 2.2 we observed that the relative frequency associated with a particular interval on the *x*-axis is proportional to the amount of area under the histogram that lies above the interval.] We denote the *median* of a *sample* by M.

Calculating a Sample Median, M

Arrange the *n* measurements from the smallest to the largest.

1. If *n* is odd, *M* is the middle number.
2. If *n* is even, *M* is the mean of the middle two numbers.

EXAMPLE 2.5   COMPUTING THE MEDIAN

Problem   Consider the following sample of *n* = 7 measurements: 5, 7, 4, 5, 20, 6, 2

    a.   Calculate the median *M* of this sample.

    b.   Eliminate the last measurement (the 2) and calculate the median of the remaining *n* = 6 measurements.

Solution   **a.**   The seven measurements in the sample are ranked in ascending order: 2, 4, 5, 5, 6, 7, 20. Because the number of measurements is odd, the median is the middle measurement. Thus, the median of this sample is *M* = 5.

    b.   After removing the 2 from the set of measurements, we rank the sample measurements in ascending order as follows: 4, 5, 5, 6, 7, 20. Now the number of measurements is even, so we average the middle two measurements. The median is $M = (5 + 6)/2 = 5.5$.

Look Back When the sample size *n* is even (as in part **b**), exactly half of the measurements will fall below the calculated median *M*. However, when *n* is odd (as in part **a**), the percentage of measurements that fall below *M* is approximately 50%. The approximation improves as *n* increases.

Now Work   *Exercise 2.52*

In certain situations, the median may be a better measure of central tendency than the mean. In particular, the median is less sensitive than the mean to extremely large or small measurements. Note, for instance, that all but one of the measurements in part **a** of Example 2.5 center about *x* = 5. The single relatively large measurement, *x* = 20, does not affect the value of the median, 5, but it causes the mean, $\bar{x} = 7$, to lie to the right of most of the measurements.

As another example of data for which the central tendency is better described by the median than the mean, consider the household incomes of a community being studied by a sociologist. The presence of just a few households with very high incomes will affect the mean more than the median. Thus, the median will provide a more accurate picture of the typical income for the community. The mean could exceed the vast majority of the sample measurements (household incomes), making it a misleading measure of central tendency.

EXAMPLE 2.6 FINDING THE MEDIAN ON A PRINTOUT

Problem Calculate the median for the 100 EPA mileages given in Table 2.2. Compare the median to the mean computed in Example 2.4.

Solution For this large data set, we again resort to a computer analysis. The median is highlighted on the SAS printout displayed in Figure 2.15 (p. 57). You can see that the median is 37.0. This value implies that half of the 100 mileages in the data set fall below 37.0 and half lie above 37.0. Note that the median, 37.0, and the mean, 36.9940, are almost equal. This fact indicates a lack of **skewness** in the data — that is, the tendency to have as many measurements in the left tail of the distribution as in the right tail (recall the histogram, Figure 2.10).

Look Back In general, extreme values (large or small) affect the mean more than the median since these values are used explicitly in the calculation of the mean. On the other hand, the median is not affected directly by extreme measurements since only the middle measurement (or two middle measurements) is explicitly used to calculate the median. Consequently, if measurements are pulled toward one end of the distribution, the mean will shift toward that tail more than the median.

DEFINITION 2.7

A data set is said to be **skewed** if one tail of the distribution has more extreme observations than the other tail.

A comparison of the mean and median gives us a general method for detecting skewness in data sets, as shown in the next box.

Detecting Skewness by Comparing the Mean and the Median

If the data set is skewed to the right, then the median is less than the mean.

Rightward skewness

If the data set is symmetric, the mean equals the median.

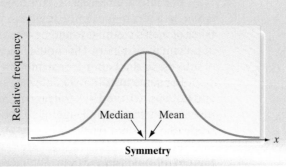

Symmetry

If the data set is skewed to the left, the mean is less than (to the left of) the median.

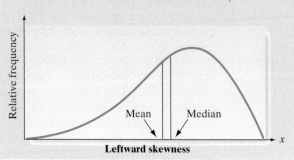

Now Work   *Exercise 2.51*

A third measure of central tendency is the **mode** of a set of measurements.

DEFINITION 2.8

The **mode** is the measurement that occurs most frequently in the data set.

Therefore, the mode shows where the data tend to concentrate.

EXAMPLE 2.7   FINDING THE MODE

Problem   Each of ten taste testers rated a new brand of barbecue sauce on a 10-point scale, where 1 = awful and 10 = excellent. Find the mode for the ten ratings shown below.

8   7   9   6   8   10   9   9   5   7

Solution   Since 9 occurs most often (three times), the mode of the ten taste ratings is 9.

Look Back Note that the data are actually qualitative in nature (e.g., "awful," "excellent"). The mode is particularly useful for describing qualitative data. The modal category is simply the category (or class) that occurs most often.

Now Work   *Exercise 2.53*

■ ■ ■

Because it emphasizes data concentration, the mode is also used with quantitative data sets to locate the region in which much of the data is concentrated. A retailer of men's clothing would be interested in the modal neck size and sleeve length of potential customers. The modal income class of the laborers in the United States is of interest to the Labor Department.

For some quantitative data sets, the mode may not be very meaningful. For example, consider the EPA mileage ratings in Table 2.2. A reexamination of the data reveals that the gas mileage of 37.0 occurs most often (four times). However, the mode of 37.0 is not particularly useful as a measure of central tendency.

A more meaningful measure can be obtained from a relative frequency histogram for quantitative data. The measurement class containing the largest relative frequency is called the **modal class**. Several definitions exist for locating the position of the mode within a modal class, but the simplest is to define the mode as the midpoint of the modal class. For example, examine the frequency histogram for the EPA mileage ratings, in Figure 2.10 (p. 43). You can see that the modal class is the interval 36.0–37.5. The mode (the midpoint) is 36.75. This modal class (and the mode itself) identifies the area in which the data are most concentrated, and in that sense it is a measure of central tendency. However, for most applications involving quantitative data, the mean and median provide more descriptive information than the mode.

EXAMPLE 2.8   COMPARING THE MEAN, MEDIAN, AND MODE

Problem   Each year, *Business Week* magazine compiles its "Executive Compensation Scoreboard" based on a survey of approximately 350 executives at U.S. companies. The 2003 scoreboard contains the total annual pay for each CEO as well as the dollar value of a $100 investment in the CEO's company stock made three years earlier. If the ratio of shareholder return to total pay is high, *Business Week* deems the CEO "worth his/her pay." Based on the return-to-pay ratio, each CEO was assigned a rating of 1 to 5, where 1 represents a "low" ratio and 5 represents a "high" ratio. (*Business Week*, April 21, 2003.) The data for the 2003 scoreboard, saved in the **BWECS** file, includes the variables "shareholder return" and "rating." Find the mean, median, and mode for both of these variables. Which measure of central tendency is better for describing the distribution of shareholder returns? Ratings?

Solution   Measures of central tendency for the two variables were obtained using SPSS. The means, medians, and modes are displayed at the top of the SPSS printout, Figure 2.17.

For "shareholder return," the mean, median, and mode are $111.80, $103.50, and $125, respectively. Note that the mean is greater than the median, indicating that the data is skewed right. This rightward skewness (graphically shown on the histogram for the returns in the middle of Figure 2.17) is due to a few exceptionally high shareholder return values. Consequently, we would probably want to use the median, $103.50, as the "typical" value for shareholder return. The mode of $125 is the return value that occurs most often in the data set, but it is not very descriptive of the "center" of the return distribution.

For "Rating," the mean, median, and mode are 3.16, 3, and 3, respectively. The rating value assigned by *Business Week* is really categorical in nature (low return-to-pay ratios are assigned the "low" rating of 1, high return-to-pay ratios are assigned the "high" rating of 5). Consequently, the more meaningful measure of central tendency would be the mode of 3—it is the most frequently occurring category, as shown in the histogram at the bottom of Figure 2.17. The mean of 3.16 would not be very descriptive of this type of data.

Look Back The choice of which measure of central tendency to use will depend on the properties of the data set analyzed and the application. Consequently, it is vital that you understand how the mean, median, and mode are computed.

Now Work   *Exercise 2.66 a,b*

■ ■ ■

Figure 2.17
SPSS Analysis of Return-on-Investment and Rating for CEOs in Executive Compensation Scoreboard

Statistics

		return	rating
N	Valid	350	330
	Missing	13	33
Mean		111.80	3.16
Median		103.50	3.00
Mode		125	3

One-Variable Descriptive Statistics

Using the TI-83 Graphing Calculator

Step 1 Enter the data
Press STAT and select 1:Edit
Note: If the list already contains data, clear the old data. Use the up arrow to highlight 'L1'. Press CLEAR ENTER.
Use the arrow and ENTER keys to enter the data set into L1.

Step 2 Calculate descriptive statistics
Press STAT
Press the right arrow key to highlight CALC
Press ENTER for 1-Var Stats
Enter the name of the list containing your data.
Press 2nd 1 for L1 (or 2nd 2 for L2 etc.)
Press ENTER

You should see the statistics on your screen. Some of the statistics are off the bottom of the screen. Use the down arrow to scroll through to see the remaining statistics. Use the up arrow to scroll back up.

Example The descriptive statistics for the sample data set

86, 70, 62, 98, 73, 56, 53, 92, 86, 37, 62, 83, 78, 49, 78, 37, 67, 79, 57

The output screens for this example are shown below.

```
1-Var Stats
 x̄=68.57894737
 Σx=1303
 Σx²=94897
 Sx=17.54142966
 σx=17.07357389
↓n=19
```

```
1-Var Stats
↑n=19
 minX=37
 Q₁=56
 Med=70
 Q₃=83
 maxX=98
■
```

Sorting Data

The descriptive statistics do not include the mode. To find the mode, sort your data as follows:

Press STAT
Press 2 for SORTA(
Enter the name of the list your data is in. If your data is in L1, press 2nd 1

Press ENTER
The screen will say: DONE
To see the sorted data, press STAT and select 1:Edit
Scroll down through the list and locate the data value that occurs most frequently.

Exercises 2.46–2.68

Understanding the Principles:

2.46 Explain the difference between a measure of central tendency and a measure of variability.

2.47 Give three different measures of central tendency.

2.48 What is the symbol used to represent the sample mean? The population mean?

2.49 What two factors impact the accuracy of the sample mean as an estimate of the population mean?

2.50 Explain the concept of a skewed distribution.

2.51 Describe how the mean compares to the median for a distribution as follows:
a. Skewed to the left
b. Skewed to the right
c. Symmetric

Learning the Mechanics

2.52 Calculate the mean and median of the following grade
NW point averages:

$$3.2 \quad 2.5 \quad 2.1 \quad 3.7 \quad 2.8 \quad 2.0$$

2.53 Calculate the mode, mean, and median of the following
NW data:

$$18 \quad 10 \quad 15 \quad 13 \quad 17 \quad 15 \quad 12 \quad 15 \quad 18 \quad 16 \quad 11$$

2.54 Construct one data set consisting of five measurements and another consisting of six measurements for which the medians are equal.

2.55 Calculate the mean for samples where
a. $n = 10, \sum x = 85$
NW b. $n = 16, \sum x = 400$
c. $n = 45, \sum x = 35$
d. $n = 18, \sum x = 242$

2.56 Calculate the mean, median, and mode for each of the following samples:
a. $7, -2, 3, 3, 0, 4$
b. $2, 3, 5, 3, 2, 3, 4, 3, 5, 1, 2, 3, 4$
c. $51, 50, 47, 50, 48, 41, 59, 68, 45, 37$

Applying the Concepts

2.57 Reading Japanese Books. Refer to the *Reading in a Foreign Language* (Apr. 2004) experiment to improve the Japanese reading comprehension levels of 14 University of Hawaii students, Exercise 2.31 (p. 51). The number of books read by each student and the student's course grade are repeated in the table.

JAPANESE

Number of Books	Course Grade	Number of Books	Course Grade
53	A	30	A
42	A	28	B
40	A	24	A
40	B	22	C
39	A	21	B
34	A	20	B
34	A	16	B

Source: Hitosugi, C. I., and Day, R. R. "Extensive reading in Japanese," *Reading in a Foreign Language*, Vol. 16, No. 1, Apr. 2004 (Table 4).

a. Find the mean, median, and mode of the number of books read. Interpret these values.

b. What do the mean and median indicate about the skewness of the distribution of the data?

2.58 Most powerful women in American *Fortune* (Oct. 14, 2002) published a list of the 50 most powerful women in America. The data on age (in years) and title of each of these 50 women are stored in the **WPOWER50** file. The first five and last two observations of the data are listed in the accompanying table.
a. Find the mean, median, and modal age of these 50 women.
b. What do the mean and median indicate about the skewness of the age distribution?
c. Construct a relative frequency histogram for the age data. What is the modal age class?

WPOWER50 (Selected observations)

Rank	Name	Age	Company	Title
1	Carly Fiorina	48	Hewlet-Packard	CEO
2	Betsy Holden	46	Kraft Foods	CEO
3	Meg Whitman	46	eBay	CEO
4	Indra Nooyi	46	PepsiCo	CFO
5	Andrea Jung	44	Avon Products	CEO
.	.	.		
.	.	.		
.	.	.		
49	Fran Keeth	56	Royal Dutch Petrol.	CEO
50	Heidi Miller	49	Bank One	EVP

Source: Fortune, Oct. 14, 2002.

2.59 Ammonia in car exhaust. Three-way catalytic converters have been installed in new vehicles in order to reduce pollutants from motor vehicle exhaust emissions. However, these converters unintentionally increase the level of ammonia in the air. *Environmental Science & Technology* (Sept. 1, 2000) published a study on the ammonia levels near the exit ramp of a San Francisco highway tunnel. The data in the table represent daily ammonia concentrations (parts per million) on eight randomly selected days during afternoon drive-time in the summer of a recent year,

AMMONIA

1.53	1.50	1.37	1.51	1.55	1.42	1.41	1.48

a. Find the mean daily ammonia level in air in the tunnel.

b. Find the median ammonia level.
c. Interpret the values obtained in parts **a** and **b**.

DDT

2.60 Contaminated fish. Refer to Exercise 2.33 (p. 51) and the U.S. Army Corps of Engineers data on contaminated fish saved in the **DDT** file. Consider the quantitative variables length (in centimeters), weight (in grams), and DDT level (in parts per million).
a. Find three numerical measures of central tendency for the 144 fish lengths. Interpret these values.

b. Find three numerical measures of central tendency for the 144 fish weights. Interpret these values.

c. Find three numerical measures of central tendency for the 144 DDT measurements. Interpret these values.

d. Use the results, part **a**, and the graph of the data from Exercise 2.33a to make a statement about the type of skewness in the fish length distribution.

e. Use the results, part **b**, and the graph of the data from Exercise 2.33b to make a statement about the type of skewness in the fish weight distribution.

f. Use the results, part **c**, and the graph of the data from Exercise 2.33c to make a statement about the type of skewness in the fish DDT distribution.

2.61 Radioactive lichen. Refer to the University of Alaska study to monitor the level of radioactivity in lichen, Exercise 2.34 (p. 51). The amount of the radioactive element cesium-137 (measured in microcuries per milliliter) for each of nine lichen specimens is repeated in the table.

LICHEN

Location			
Bethel	−5.50	−5.00	
Eagle Summit	−4.15	−4.85	
Moose Pass	−6.05		
Turnagain Pass	−5.00		
Wickersham Dome	−4.10	−4.50	−4.60

Source: Lichen Radionuclide Baseline Research Project, 2003.

a. Find the mean, median, and mode of the radioactivity levels.
b. Interpret the value of each measure of central tendency, part **a**.

Applying the Concepts—Intermediate

2.62 Recommendation letters for professors. Applicants for an academic position (e.g., assistant professor) at a college or university are usually required to submit at least three letters of recommendation. A study of 148 applicants for an entry-level position in experimental psychology at the University of Alaska Anchorage revealed that many did not meet the three-letter requirement. (*American Psychologist*, July 1995.) Summary statistics for the number of recommendation letters in each application are given below. Interpret these summary measures.

Mean = 2.28   Median = 3   Mode = 3

2.63 Training zoo animals. "The Training Game" is an activity used in psychology in which one person shapes an arbitrary behavior by selectively reinforcing the movements of another person. A group of 15 psychology students at Georgia Institute of Technology played "The Training Game" at Zoo Atlanta while participating in an experimental psychology laboratory in which they assisted in the training of ani-

mals. (*Teaching of Psychology*, May 1998.) At the end of the session, each student was asked to rate the statement: "'The Training Game' is a great way for students to understand the animal's perspective during training." Responses were recorded on a 7-point scale ranging from 1 (strongly disagree) to 7 (strongly agree). The 15 responses were summarized as follows:

mean = 5.87, mode = 6.

a. Interpret the measures of central tendency in the words of the problem.
b. What type of skewness (if any) is likely to be present in the distribution of student responses? Explain.

2.64 Symmetric or skewed? Would you expect the data sets described below to possess relative frequency distributions that are symmetric, skewed to the right, or skewed to the left? Explain.
a. The salaries of all persons employed by a large university
b. The grades on an easy test
c. The grades on a difficult test
d. The amounts of time students in your class studied last week
e. The ages of automobiles on a used-car lot
f. The amounts of time spent by students on a difficult examination (maximum time is 50 minutes)

2.65 Children's use of pronouns. Clinical observations suggest that specifically language-impaired (SLI) children have great difficulty with the proper use of pronouns. This phenomenon was investigated and reported in the *Journal of Communication Disorders* (Mar. 1995). Thirty children, all from low-income families, participated in the study. Ten were 5-year-old SLI children, ten were younger (3-year-old) normally developing (YND) children, and ten were older (5-year-old) normally developing (OND) children. The table contains the gender, deviation intelligence quotient (DIQ), and percentage of pronoun errors observed for each of the 30 subjects.

SLI

Subject	Gender	Group	DIQ	Pronoun Errors (%)
1	F	YND	110	94.40
2	F	YND	92	19.05
3	F	YND	92	62.50
4	M	YND	100	18.75
5	F	YND	86	0
6	F	YND	105	55.00
7	F	YND	90	100.00
8	M	YND	96	86.67
9	M	YND	90	32.43
10	F	YND	92	0
11	F	SLI	86	60.00
12	M	SLI	86	40.00
13	M	SLI	94	31.58
14	M	SLI	98	66.67
15	F	SLI	89	42.86
16	F	SLI	84	27.27

SLI (Continued)

Subject	Gender	Group	DIQ	Pronoun Errors (%)
17	M	SLI	110	33.33
18	F	SLI	107	0
19	F	SLI	87	0
20	M	SLI	95	0
21	M	OND	110	0
22	M	OND	113	0
23	M	OND	113	0
24	F	OND	109	0
25	M	OND	92	0
26	F	OND	108	0
27	M	OND	95	0
28	F	OND	87	0
29	F	OND	94	0
30	F	OND	98	0

Source: Moore, M. E. "Error analysis of pronouns by normal and language-impaired children." *Journal of Communication Disorders,* Vol. 28, No. 1, Mar. 1995, p. 62 (Table 2), p. 67 (Table 5).

a. Identify the variables in the data set as quantitative or qualitative.
b. Why is it nonsensical to compute numerical descriptive measures for qualitative variables?
c. Compute measures of central tendency for DIQ for the ten SLI children.
d. Compute measures of central tendency for DIQ for the ten YND children.
e. Compute measures of central tendency for DIQ for the ten OND children.
f. Use the results, parts c–e, to compare the DIQ central tendencies of the three groups of children. Is it reasonable to use a single number (e.g., mean or median) to describe the center of the DIQ distribution? Or should three "centers" be calculated, one for each of the three groups of children? Explain.
g. Repeat parts c–f for the percentage of pronoun errors.

2.66 **Mongolian desert ants.** The *Journal of Biogeography* **NW** (Dec. 2003) published an article on the first comprehensive study of ants in Mongolia (Central Asia).

Botanists placed seed baits at 11 study sites and observed the ant species attracted to each site. Some of the data recorded at each study site are provided in the table at the bottom of the page.

a. Find the mean, median, and mode for the number of ant species discovered at the 11 sites. Interpret each of these values.
b. Which measure of central tendency would you recommend to describe the center of the number of ant species distribution? Explain.
c. Find the mean, median, and mode for the total plant cover percentage at the 5 Dry Steppe sites only.
d. Find the mean, median, and mode for the total plant cover percentage at the 6 Gobi Desert sites only.
e. Based on the results, parts c and d, does the center of the total plant cover percentage distribution appear to be different at the two regions?

Applying the Concepts — Advanced

2.67 **Eye refractive study.** The conventional method of measuring the refractive status of an eye involves three quantities: (1) sphere power, (2) cylinder power, and (3) axis. Optometric researchers studied the variation in these three measures of refraction. (*Optometry and Vision Science*, June 1995.) Twenty-five successive refractive measurements were obtained on the eyes of over 100 university students. The cylinder power measurements for the left eye of one particular student (ID #11) are listed in the table. [*Note:* All measurements are negative values.]

LEFTEYE

.08	.08	1.07	.09	.16	.04	.07	.17	.11
.06	.12	.17	.20	.12	.17	.09	.07	.16
.15	.16	.09	.06	.10	.21	.06		

Source: Rubin, A., and Harris, W. F. "Refractive variation during autorefraction: Multivariate distribution of refractive status." *Optometry and Vision Science,* Vol. 72, No. 6, June 1995, p. 409 (Table 4).

GOBIANTS

Site	Region	Annual Rainfall (mm)	Max. Daily Temp. (°C)	Total Plant Cover (%)	Number of Ant Species	Species Diversity Index
1	Dry Steppe	196	5.7	40	3	.89
2	Dry Steppe	196	5.7	52	3	.83
3	Dry Steppe	179	7.0	40	52	1.31
4	Dry Steppe	197	8.0	43	7	1.48
5	Dry Steppe	149	8.5	27	5	.97
6	Gobi Desert	112	10.7	30	49	.46
7	Gobi Desert	125	11.4	16	5	1.23
8	Gobi Desert	99	10.9	30	4	
9	Gobi Desert	125	11.4	56	4	.76
10	Gobi Desert	84	11.4	22	5	1.26
11	Gobi Desert	115	11.4	14	4	.69

Source: Pfeiffer, M., et al. "Community organization and species richness of ants in Mongolia along an ecological gradient from steppe to Gobi desert," *Journal of Biogeography,* Vol. 30, No. 12, Dec. 2003 (Tables 1 and 2).

a. Find measures of central tendency for the data and interpret their values.

b. Note that the data contains one unusually large (negative) cylinder power measurement relative to the other measurements in the data set. Find this measurement. (In Section 2.8, we call this value an **outlier**).

c. Delete the outlier, part **b**, from the data set and recalculate the measures of central tendency. Which measure is most affected by the deletion of the outlier?

2.68 Active nuclear power plants. The U.S. Energy Information Administration monitors all nuclear power plants operating in the United States. The table lists the number of active nuclear power plants operating in each of a sample of 20 states.

a. Find the mean, median, and mode of this data set.

b. Eliminate the largest value from the data set and repeat part **a**. What effect does dropping this measurement have on the measures of central tendency found in part **a**?

c. Arrange the 20 values in the table from lowest to highest. Next, eliminate the lowest two values and the highest two values from the data set and find the mean of the remaining data values. The result is called a *10% trimmed mean*, since it is calculated after removing the highest 10% and the lowest 10% of the data values. What advantages does a trimmed mean have over the regular arithmetic mean?

⊚ **NUCLEAR**

State	Number of Power Plants
Alabama	5
Arizona	3
California	4
Florida	5
Georgia	4
Illinois	13
Kansas	1
Louisiana	2
Massachusetts	1
Mississippi	1
New Hampshire	1
New York	6
North Carolina	5
Ohio	2
Pennsylvania	9
South Carolina	7
Tennessee	3
Texas	4
Vermont	1
Wisconsin	3

Source: Statistical Abstract of the United States, 2000 (Table 966). U.S. Energy Information Administration, *Electric Power Annual.*

2.5 Numerical Measures of Variability

Measures of central tendency provide only a partial description of a quantitative data set. The description is incomplete without a **measure of the variability**, or **spread**, of the data set. Knowledge of the data set's variability along with its center can help us visualize the shape of a data set as well as its extreme values.

If you examine the two histograms in Figure 2.18, you'll notice that both hypothetical data sets are symmetric with equal modes, medians, and means. However, data set 1 (Figure 2.18a) has measurements spread with almost equal relative frequency over the measurement classes, while data set 2 (Figure 2.18b) has most of its measurements clustered about its center. Thus, data set 2 is *less variable* than data set 1. Consequently, you can see that we need a measure of variability as well as a measure of central tendency to describe a data set.

Perhaps the simplest measure of the variability of a quantitative data set is its *range*.

a. Data set 1

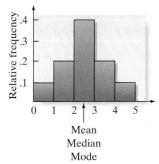

b. Data set 2

Figure 2.18
Hypothetical Data Sets

> **DEFINITION 2.9**
>
> The **range** of a quantitative data set is equal to the largest measurement minus the smallest measurement.

The range is easy to compute and easy to understand, but it is a rather insensitive measure of data variation when the data sets are large. This is because two data sets can have the same range and be vastly different with respect to data variation. This phenomenon is demonstrated in Figure 2.18. Both distributions of data shown in the figure have the same range, but most of the measurements in data set 2 tend to concentrate near the center of the distribution. Consequently, the data are much less variable than the data in set 1. Thus, you can see that the range does not always detect differences in data variation for large data sets.

Let's see if we can find a measure of data variation that is more sensitive than the range. Consider the two samples in Table 2.5: Each has five measurements. (We have ordered the numbers for convenience.) Note that both samples have a mean of 3 and that we have also calculated the distance between each measurement and the mean. What information do these distances contain? If they tend to be large in magnitude, as in sample 1, the data are spread out, or highly variable. If the distances are mostly small, as in sample 2, the data are clustered around the mean, $\bar{x}$, and therefore do not exhibit much variability. You can see that these distances, displayed graphically in Figure 2.19, provide information about the variability of the sample measurements.

TABLE 2.5   Two Hypothetical Data Sets

	Sample 1	Sample 2
Measurements	$1, 2, 3, 4, 5$	$2, 3, 3, 3, 4$
Mean	$\bar{x} = \dfrac{1 + 2 + 3 + 4 + 5}{5} = \dfrac{15}{5} = 3$	$\bar{x} = \dfrac{2 + 3 + 3 + 3 + 4}{5} = \dfrac{15}{5} = 3$
Distances of measurement values from $\bar{x}$	$(1 - 3), (2 - 3), (4 - 3),$ $(5 - 3)$ or $-2, -1, 0, 1, 2$	$(2 - 3), (3 - 3), (3 - 3), (3 - 3),$ $(4 - 3)$ or $-1, 0, 0, 0, 1$

Figure 2.19
Dot Plots for Two Data Sets

a. Sample 1   b. Sample 2

The next step is to condense the information in these distances into a single numerical measure of variability. Averaging the distances from $\bar{x}$ won't help because the negative and positive distances cancel; that is, the sum of the deviations (and thus the average deviation) is always equal to zero.

Two methods come to mind for dealing with the fact that positive and negative distances from the mean cancel. The first is to treat all the distances as though they were positive, ignoring the sign of the negative distances. We won't pursue this line of thought because the resulting measure of variability (the mean of the absolute values of the distances) presents analytical difficulties beyond the scope of this text. A second method of eliminating the minus signs associated with the distances is to square them. The quantity we can calculate from the squared distances will provide a meaningful description of the variability of a data set and presents fewer analytical difficulties in inference making.

To use the squared distances calculated from a data set, we first calculate the *sample variance*.

DEFINITION 2.10

The **sample variance** for a sample of n measurements is equal to the sum of the squared distances from the mean divided by $(n - 1)$. The symbol, s^2 is used to represent the sample variance.

Formula for the Sample Variance:

$$s^2 = \frac{\sum_{i=1}^{n}(x_i - \bar{x})^2}{n-1}$$

Note: A shortcut formula for calculating s^2 is

$$s^2 = \frac{\sum_{i=1}^{n}x_i^2 - \frac{\left(\sum_{i=1}^{n}x_i\right)^2}{n}}{n-1}$$

Referring to the two samples in Table 2.5, you can calculate the variance for sample 1 as follows:

$$s^2 = \frac{(1-3)^2 + (2-3)^2 + (3-3)^2 + (4-3)^2 + (5-3)^2}{5-1}$$

$$= \frac{4+1+0+1+4}{4} = 2.5$$

The second step in finding a meaningful measure of data variability is to calculate the *standard deviation* of the data set:

DEFINITION 2.11

The **sample standard deviation**, s, is defined as the positive square root of the sample variance, s^2. Thus,

$$s = \sqrt{s^2}$$

The population variance, denoted by the symbol σ^2 (sigma squared), is the average of the squared distances of the measurements on *all* units in the population from the mean, μ, and σ (sigma) is the square root of this quantity.

Symbols for Variance and Standard Deviation

s^2 = Sample variance

s = Sample standard deviation

σ^2 = Population variance

σ = Population standard deviation

Notice that, unlike the variance, the standard deviation is expressed in the original units of measurement. For example, if the original measurements are in dollars, the variance is expressed in the peculiar units "dollar squared," but the standard deviation is expressed in dollars.

You may wonder why we use the divisor $(n-1)$ instead of n when calculating the sample variance. Wouldn't using n seem more logical, so that the sample variance would be the average squared distance from the mean? The trouble is, using n tends to produce an underestimate of the population variance, σ^2. So we use $(n-1)$ in the denominator to provide the appropriate correction for this tendency.* Since sample statistics like s^2 are primarily used to estimate population parameters like σ^2, $(n-1)$ is preferred to n when defining the sample variance.

*_Appropriate_ here means that s^2 with a divisor of $(n-1)$ is an *unbiased estimator* of σ^2. We define and discuss unbiasedness of estimators in Chapter 6.

EXAMPLE 2.9   COMPUTING MEASURES OF VARIATION

Problem   Calculate the variance and standard deviation of the following sample: 2, 3, 3, 3, 4.

Solution   As the number of measurements increases, calculating s^2 and s becomes very tedious. Fortunately, as we show in Example 2.10, we can use a statistical software package (or calculator) to find these values. If you must calculate these quantities by hand, it is advantageous to use the shortcut formula provided in Definition 2.10.

To do this, we need two summations: $\sum x$ and $\sum x^2$. These can easily be obtained from the following type of tabulation:

x	x^2
2	4
3	9
3	9
3	9
4	16
$\sum x = 15$	$\sum x^2 = 47$

Then we use*

$$s^2 = \frac{\sum_{i=1}^{n} x_i^2 - \frac{\left(\sum_{i=1}^{n} x_i\right)^2}{n}}{n-1} = \frac{47 - \frac{(15)^2}{5}}{5-1} = \frac{2}{4} = .5$$

$$s = \sqrt{.5} = .71$$

Look Back   As the sample size n increases, these calculations can become very tedious. As the next example shows, we can use the computer to find s^2 and s.

Now Work   *Exercise 2.76a*

EXAMPLE 2.10   FINDING MEASURES OF VARIATION ON A PRINTOUT

Problem   Use the computer to find the sample variance s^2 and the sample standard deviation s for the 100 gas mileage readings given in Table 2.2.

Solution   The SAS printout describing the gas mileage data is reproduced in Figure 2.20. The variance and standard deviation, highlighted on the printout, are (rounded) $s^2 = 5.85$ and $s = 2.42$.

■ ■ ■

You now know that the standard deviation measures the variability of a set of data and how to calculate it. The larger the standard deviation, the more variable the data are. The smaller the standard deviation, the less variation in the data. But how can we practically interpret the standard deviation and use it to make inferences? This is the topic of Section 2.6.

*When calculating s^2, how many decimal places should you carry? Although there are no rules for the rounding procedure, it is reasonable to retain twice as many decimal places in s^2 as you ultimately wish to have in s. If you wish to calculate s to the nearest hundredth (two decimal places), for example, you should calculate s^2 to the nearest ten-thousandth (four decimal places).

The MEANS Procedure

Analysis Variable : MPG

Mean	Std Dev	Variance	N	Minimum	Maximum	Median
36.9940000	2.4178971	5.8462263	100	30.0000000	44.9000000	37.0000000

Figure 2.20

Reproduction of SAS Numerical Descriptive Measures for 100 EPA Mileages

Exercises 2.69–2.85

Understanding the Principles

2.69 What is the range of a data set?

2.70 What is the primary disadvantage of using the range to compare the variability of data sets?

2.71 Describe the sample variance using words rather than a formula. Do the same with the population variance.

2.72 Can the variance of a data set ever be negative? Explain. Can the variance ever be smaller than the standard deviation? Explain.

2.73 If the standard deviation increases, does this imply that the data are more variable or less variable?

Learning the Mechanics

2.74 Calculate the variance and standard deviation for samples where
a. $n = 10$, $\sum x^2 = 84$, $\sum x = 20$
b. $n = 40$, $\sum x^2 = 380$, $\sum x = 100$
c. $n = 20$, $\sum x^2 = 18$, $\sum x = 17$

2.75 Calculate the range, variance, and standard deviation for the following samples:
a. 39, 42, 40, 37, 41
b. 100, 4, 7, 96, 80, 3, 1, 10, 2
c. 100, 4, 7, 30, 80, 30, 42, 2

2.76 Calculate the range, variance, and standard deviation
NW for the following samples:
a. 4, 2, 1, 0, 1
b. 1, 6, 2, 2, 3, 0, 3
c. 8, −2, 1, 3, 5, 4, 4, 1, 3
d. 0, 2, 0, 0, −1, 1, −2, 1, 0, −1, 1, −1, 0, −3, −2, −1, 0, 1

2.77 Using only integers between 0 and 10, construct two data sets with at least 10 observations each so that the two sets have the same mean but different variances. Construct dot plots for each of your data sets, and mark the mean of each data set on its dot plot.

2.78 Using only integers between 0 and 10, construct two data sets with at least 10 observations each that have the same range but different means. Construct a dot plot for each of your data sets, and mark the mean of each data set on its dot plot.

2.79 Consider the following sample of five measurements: 2, 1, 1, 0, 3.

a. Calculate the range, s^2, and s.
b. Add 3 to each measurement and repeat part **a**.
c. Subtract 4 from each measurement and repeat part **a**.
d. Considering your answers to parts **a**, **b**, and **c**, what seems to be the effect on the variability of a data set by adding the same number to or subtracting the same number from each measurement?

2.80 Compute s^2, and s for each of the following data sets. If appropriate, specify the units in which your answer is expressed.
a. 3, 1, 10, 10, 4
b. 8 feet, 10 feet, 32 feet, 5 feet
c. −1, −4, −3, 1, −4, −4
d. 1/5 ounce, 1/5 ounce, 1/5 ounce, 2/5 ounce, 1/5 ounce, 4/5 ounce

Applying the Concepts—Basic

⊘ **JAPANESE**

2.81 **Reading Japanese books.** Refer to the *Reading in a Foreign Language* (Apr. 2004) experiment to improve the Japanese reading comprehension levels of 14 University of Hawaii students, Exercises 2.31 and 2.57 (p. 64). The data on number of books read and grade for each student is saved in the JAPANESE file.
a. Find the range, variance, and standard deviation of the number of books read by students who earned an A grade.
b. Find the range, variance, and standard deviation of the number of books read by students who earned either a B or C grade.
c. Refer to parts **a** and **b**. Which of the two groups of students has a more variable distribution for number of books read?

⊘ **DDT**

2.82 **Contaminated fish.** Refer to Exercise 2.60 (p. 64) and the U.S. Army Corps of Engineers data on contaminated fish saved in the DDT file. Consider the quantitative variables length (in centimeters), weight (in grams), and DDT level (in parts per million).
a. Find three different measures of variation for the 144 fish lengths. Give the units of measurement for each.

b. Find three different measures of variation for the 144 fish weights. Give the units of measurement for each.

c. Find three different measures of variation for the 144 DDT values. Give the units of measurement for each.

2.83 Ammonia in car exhaust. Refer to the *Environmental Science & Technology* (Sept. 1, 2000) study on the ammonia levels near the exit ramp of a San Francisco highway tunnel, Exercise 2.59 (p. 54). The data (in parts per million) for 8 days during afternoon drive-time are reproduced in the table.

⊙ AMMONIA

1.53	1.50	1.37	1.51	1.55	1.42	1.41	1.48

a. Find the range of the ammonia levels.
b. Find the variance of the ammonia levels.
c. Find the standard deviation of the ammonia levels.
d. Suppose the standard deviation of the daily ammonia levels during morning drive-time at the exit ramp is 1.45 ppm. Which time, morning or afternoon drive-time, has more variable ammonia levels?

Applying the Concepts—Intermediate

⊙ WPOWER50

2.84 Most powerful women in America. Refer to Exercise 2.58 (p. 54) and *Fortune's* (Oct. 14, 2002) list of the 50 most powerful women in America. The data are stored in the WPOWER50 file.

a. Find the range of the ages for these 50 women.
b. Find the variance of the ages for these 50 women.

c. Find the standard deviation of the ages for these 50 women.
d. Suppose the standard deviation of the ages of the most powerful women in Europe is 10 years. For which location, the United States or Europe, is the age data more variable?
e. If the largest age in the data set is omitted, would the standard deviation increase or decrease? Verify your answer.

⊙ NUCLEAR

2.85 Active nuclear power plants. Refer to Exercise 2.68 (p. 67) and the U.S. Energy Information Administration's data on the number of nuclear power plants operating in each of 20 states. The data are saved in the NUCLEAR file.

a. Find the range, variance, and standard deviation of this data set.
b. Eliminate the largest value from the data set and repeat part **a**. What effect does dropping this measurement have on the measures of variation found in part **a**?
c. Eliminate the smallest and largest value from the data set and repeat part **a**. What effect does dropping both of these measurements have on the measures of variation found in part **a**?

2.6 Interpreting the Standard Deviation

We've seen that if we are comparing the variability of two samples selected from a population, the sample with the larger standard deviation is the more variable of the two. Thus, we know how to interpret the standard deviation on a relative or comparative basis, but we haven't explained how it provides a measure of variability for a single sample.

To understand how the standard deviation provides a measure of variability of a data set, consider a specific data set and answer the following questions: How many measurements are within 1 standard deviation of the mean? How many measurements are within 2 standard deviations? For example, look at the 100 mileage per gallon readings given in Table 2.2. Recall that $\bar{x} = 36.99$ and $s = 2.42$. Then

$$\bar{x} - s = 34.57 \qquad \bar{x} + s = 39.41$$

$$\bar{x} - 2s = 32.15 \qquad \bar{x} + 2s = 41.83$$

If we examine the data, we find that 68 of the 100 measurements, or 68%, are in the interval

$$\bar{x} - s \text{ to } \bar{x} + s$$

Similarly, we find that 96, or 96%, of the 100 measurements are in the interval

$$\overline{x} - 2s \text{ to } \overline{x} + 2s$$

We usually write these intervals as

$$(\overline{x} - s, \overline{x} + s) \text{ and } (\overline{x} - 2s, \overline{x} + 2s)$$

Such observations identify criteria for interpreting a standard deviation that apply to *any* set of data, whether a population or a sample. The criteria, expressed as a mathematical theorem and as a rule of thumb, are presented in Tables 2.6 and 2.7. In these tables we give two sets of answers to the questions of how many measurements fall within 1, 2, and 3 standard deviations of the mean. The first, which applies to *any* set of data, is derived from a theorem proved by the Russian mathematician P. L. Chebyshev (1821–1894). The second, which applies to **mound-shaped, symmetric, distributions** of data (where the mean, median, and mode are all about the same), is based upon empirical evidence that has accumulated over the years. However, the percentages given for the intervals in Table 2.7 provide remarkably good approximations even when the distribution of the data is slightly skewed or asymmetric. Note that the rules apply to either population or sample data sets.

TABLE 2.6   Interpreting the Standard Deviation: Chebyshev's Rule

Chebyshev's Rule applies to any data set, regardless of the shape of the frequency distribution of the data.

a. It is possible that very few of the measurements will fall within 1 standard deviation of the mean, i.e., within the interval $(\overline{x} - s, \overline{x} + s)$ for samples and $(\mu - \sigma, \mu + \sigma)$ for populations.

b. At least $\frac{3}{4}$ of the measurements will fall within 2 standard deviations of the mean, i.e., within the interval $(\overline{x} - 2s, \overline{x} + 2s)$ for samples and $(\mu - 2\sigma, \mu + 2\sigma)$ for populations.

c. At least $\frac{8}{9}$ of the measurements will fall within 3 standard deviations of the mean, i.e., within the interval $(\overline{x} - 3s, \overline{x} + 3s)$ for samples and $(\mu - 3\sigma, \mu + 3\sigma)$ for populations.

d. Generally, for any number k greater than 1, at least $(1 - 1/k^2)$ of the measurements will fall within k standard deviations of the mean, i.e., within the interval $(\overline{x} - ks, \overline{x} + ks)$ for samples and $(\mu - k\sigma, \mu + k\sigma)$ for populations.

Biography

PAFNUTY L. CHEBYSHEV (1821–1894)— The Splendid Russian Mathematician

P. L. Chebyshev was educated in mathematical science at Moscow University, eventually earning his master's degree. Following his graduation, Chebyshev joined St. Petersburg (Russia) University as a professor, becoming part of the well-known "Petersburg mathematical school." It was here that Chebyshev proved his famous theorem about the probability of a measurement being within k standard deviations of the mean (Table 2.6). His fluency in French allowed him to gain international recognition in probability theory. In fact, Chebyshev once objected to being described as a "splendid Russian mathematician," saying he surely was a "world-wide mathematician." One student remembered Chebyshev as "a wonderful lecturer" who "was always prompt for class," and "as soon as the bell sounded, he immediately dropped the chalk, and, limping, left the auditorium."

TABLE 2.7   Interpreting the Standard Deviation: The Empirical Rule

The **Empirical Rule** is a rule of thumb that applies to data sets with frequency distributions that are mound shaped and symmetric, as shown below.

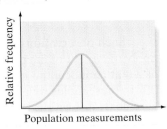

a. Approximately 68% of the measurements will fall within 1 standard deviation of the mean, i.e., within the interval $(\bar{x} - s, \bar{x} + s)$ for samples and $(\mu - \sigma, \mu + \sigma)$ for populations.
b. Approximately 95% of the measurements will fall within 2 standard deviations of the mean, i.e., within the interval $(\bar{x} - 2s, \bar{x} + 2s)$ for samples and $(\mu - 2\sigma, \mu + 2\sigma)$ for populations.
c. Approximately 99.7% (essentially all) of the measurements will fall within 3 standard deviations of the mean, i.e., within the interval $(\bar{x} - 3s, \bar{x} + 3s)$ for samples and $(\mu - 3\sigma, \mu + 3\sigma)$ for populations.

EXAMPLE 2.11   INTERPRETING THE STANDARD DEVIATION

Problem   Thirty students in an experimental psychology class use various techniques to train a rat to move through a maze. At the end of the course, each student's rat is timed through the maze. The results (in minutes) are listed in Table 2.8. Determine the fraction of the 30 measurements in the intervals $\bar{x} \pm s$, $\bar{x} \pm 2s$, and $\bar{x} \pm 3s$, and compare the results with those predicted in Tables 2.6 and 2.7.

⊚ RATMAZE

TABLE 2.8   Times (in Minutes) of 30 Rats Running Through a Maze

1.97	.60	4.02	3.20	1.15	6.06	4.44	2.02	3.37	3.65
1.74	2.75	3.81	9.70	8.29	5.63	5.21	4.55	7.60	3.16
3.77	5.36	1.06	1.71	2.47	4.25	1.93	5.15	2.06	1.65

Solution   First, we entered the data into the computer and used MINITAB to produce summary statistics. The mean and standard deviation of the sample data, highlighted on the printout shown in Figure 2.21, are (rounded)

$$\bar{x} = 3.74 \text{ minutes} \qquad s = 2.20 \text{ minutes}$$

Figure 2.21
MINITAB Descriptive
Statistics for Rat Maze
Times

Descriptive Statistics: RUNTIME

Variable	N	Mean	StDev	Minimum	Median	Maximum
RUNTIME	30	3.744	2.198	0.600	3.510	9.700

Now, we form the interval

$$(\bar{x} - s, \bar{x} + s) = (3.74 - 2.20, 3.74 + 2.20) = (1.54, 5.94)$$

A check of the measurements shows that 23 of the times are within this 1 standard deviation interval around the mean. This number represents 23/30, or ≈77% of the sample measurements.

The next interval of interest is

$$(\bar{x} - 2s, \bar{x} + 2s) = (3.74 - 4.40, 3.74 + 4.40) = (-.66, 8.14)$$

All but two of the times are within this interval, so 28/30, or approximately 93%, are within 2 standard deviations of $\bar{x}$.

Finally, the 3-standard-deviation interval around $\bar{x}$ is

$$(\bar{x} - 3s, \bar{x} + 3s) = (3.74 - 6.60, 3.74 + 6.60) = (-2.86, 10.34)$$

All of the times fall within 3 standard deviations of the mean.

These 1-, 2-, and 3-standard-deviation percentages (77%, 93%, and 100%) agree fairly well with the approximations of 68%, 95%, and 100% given by the Empirical Rule (Table 2.7).

Look Back If you look at the MINITAB frequency histogram for this data set in Figure 2.22, you'll note that the distribution is not really mound shaped, nor is it extremely skewed. Thus, we get reasonably good results from the mound-shaped approximations. Of course, we know from Chebyshev's Rule (Table 2.6) that no matter what the shape of the distribution, we would expect at least 75% and at least 89% of the measurements to lie within 2 and 3 standard deviations of $\bar{x}$, respectively.

Figure 2.22
MINITAB Histogram of Rat Maze Times

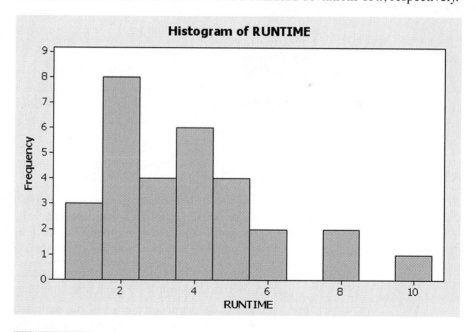

Now Work   *Exercise 2.90*

EXAMPLE 2.12   CHECKING THE CALCULATION OF THE SAMPLE STANDARD DEVIATION

Problem   Chebyshev's Rule and the Empirical Rule are useful as a check on the calculation of the standard deviation. For example, suppose we calculated the standard deviation for the gas mileage data (Table 2.2) to be 5.85. Are there any "clues" in the data that enable us to judge whether this number is reasonable?

Solution   The range of the mileage data in Table 2.2 is $44.0 - 30.0 = 14.9$. From Chebyshev's Rule and the Empirical Rule we know that most of the measurements (approximately 95% if the distribution is mound shaped) will be within 2 standard deviations of the mean. And, regardless of the shape of the distribution and the number of measurements, almost all of them will fall within 3 standard deviations of the mean. Consequently, we would expect the range of the measurements to be between 4 (i.e., $\pm 2s$) and 6 (i.e., $\pm 3s$) standard deviations in length (see Figure 2.23). For the car mileage data, this means that s should fall between

Figure 2.23
The Relation Between the Range and the Standard Deviation

$$\frac{\text{Range}}{6} = \frac{14.9}{6} = 2.48 \quad \text{and} \quad \frac{\text{Range}}{4} = \frac{14.9}{4} = 3.73$$

In particular, the standard deviation should not be much larger than 1/4 of the range, particularly for the data set with 100 measurements. Thus, we have reason to believe that the calculation of 5.85 is too large. A check of our work reveals that 5.85 is the variance s^2, not the standard deviation s (see Example 2.10). We "forgot" to take the square root (a common error); the correct value is $s = 2.42$. Note that this value is slightly smaller than the range divided by 6 (2.48). The larger the data set, the greater the tendency for very large or very small measurements (extreme values) to appear, and when they do, the range may exceed 6 standard deviations.

Look Back In examples and exercises we'll sometimes use $s \approx \text{range}/4$ to obtain a crude, and usually conservatively large, approximation for s. However, we stress that this is no substitute for calculating the exact value of s when possible.

Now Work   *Exercise 2.91*

In the next example, we use the concepts in Chebyshev's Rule and the Empirical Rule to build the foundation for statistical inference-making.

EXAMPLE 2.13   MAKING A STATISTICAL INFERENCE

Problem   A manufacturer of automobile batteries claims that the average length of life for its grade A battery is 60 months. However, the guarantee on this brand is for just 36 months. Suppose the standard deviation of the life length is known to be 10 months, and the frequency distribution of the life-length data is known to be mound shaped.

a. Approximately what percentage of the manufacturer's grade A batteries will last more than 50 months, assuming the manufacturer's claim is true?

b. Approximately what percentage of the manufacturer's batteries will last less than 40 months, assuming the manufacturer's claim is true?

c. Suppose your battery lasts 37 months. What could you infer about the manufacturer's claim?

Solution   If the distribution of life length is assumed to be mound shaped with a mean of 60 months and a standard deviation of 10 months, it would appear as shown in Figure 2.24. Note that we can take advantage of the fact that mound-shaped distributions are (approximately) symmetric about the mean, so that the percentages given by the Empirical Rule can be split equally between the halves of the distribution on each side of the mean.

Figure 2.24

Battery Life-Length
Distribution: Manufacturer's
Claim Assumed True

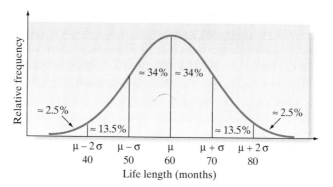

For example, since approximately 68% of the measurements will fall within 1 standard deviation of the mean, the distribution's symmetry implies that approximately $(1/2)(68\%) = 34\%$ of the measurements will fall between the mean and 1 standard deviation on each side. This concept is illustrated in Figure 2.24. The figure also shows that 2.5% of the measurements lie beyond 2 standard deviations in each direction from the mean. This result follows from the fact that if approximately 95% of the measurements fall within 2 standard deviations of the mean, then about 5% fall outside 2 standard deviations; if the distribution is approximately symmetric, then about 2.5% of the measurements fall beyond 2 standard deviations on each side of the mean.

   a. It is easy to see in Figure 2.24 that the percentage of batteries lasting more than 50 months is approximately 34% (between 50 and 60 months) plus 50% (greater than 60 months). Thus, approximately 84% of the batteries should have life length exceeding 50 months.

   b. The percentage of batteries that last less than 40 months can also be easily determined from Figure 2.24. Approximately 2.5% of the batteries should fail prior to 40 months, assuming the manufacturer's claim is true.

   c. If you are so unfortunate that your grade A battery fails at 37 months, you can make one of two inferences: Either your battery was one of the approximately 2.5% that fail prior to 40 months, or something about the manufacturer's claim is not true. Because the chances are so small that a battery fails before 40 months, you would have good reason to have serious doubts about the manufacturer's claim. A mean smaller than 60 months and/or a standard deviation longer than 10 months would both increase the likelihood of failure prior to 40 months.*

Look Back The approximations given in Figure 2.24 are more dependent on the assumption of a mound-shaped distribution than those given by the Empirical Rule (Table 2.7), because the approximations in Figure 2.24 depend on the (approximate) symmetry of the mound-shaped distribution. We saw in Example 2.11 that the Empirical Rule can yield good approximations even for skewed distributions. This will *not* be true of the approximations in Figure 2.24; the distribution *must* be mound shaped and (approximately) symmetric.

---

*The assumption that the distribution is mound shaped and symmetric may also be incorrect. However, if the distribution were skewed to the right, as life-length distributions often tend to be, the percentage of measurements more than 2 standard deviations below the mean would be even less than 2.5%.

Example 2.13 is our initial demonstration of the statistical inference-making process. At this point you should realize that we'll use sample information (in Example 2.13, your battery's failure at 37 months) to make inferences about the population (in Example 2.13, the manufacturer's claim about the life length for the population of all batteries). We'll build on this foundation as we proceed.

Statistics in Action Revisited
Interpreting Descriptive Statistics

We return to the analysis of data from the *Psychological Science* "water-level task" experiment. The quantitative variable of interest is *Deviation angle* (measured in degrees) of the judged line from the true surface line (parallel to the table top). Recall that the researchers want to test the theory that males will do better than females on judging the correct water level (i.e., that males, in general, have deviation angles closer to 0 than females). The MINITAB descriptive statistics printout for the EYECUE data is displayed in Figure SIA2.6, with the means and standard deviations highlighted.

The sample mean for females is 6.57 degrees and the mean for males is 2.92 degrees. Our interpretation is that males' judged lines have smaller deviation angles from the true surface line (2.92 degrees, on average) than females' judged lines (6.57 degrees, on average), supporting the theory stated by the researchers.

To interpret the standard deviation, we substitute into the formula, Mean $\pm$ 2(Standard deviation), to obtain the intervals:

Females: $6.57 \pm 2(7.82) = 6.57 \pm 15.64 = (-9.07, 22.21)$
Males: $2.92 \pm 2(7.54) = 2.92 \pm 15.08 = (-12.16, 18.00)$

From the Chebyshev's Rule (Table 2.6), we know that at least 75% of the females who perform the water task will have deviation angles anywhere between -9.07 and 22.21 degrees. Similarly, we know that at least 75% of the males will have deviation angles anywhere from -12.16 to 18.00 degrees. Note that these ranges indicate that there is very little difference in the spread of the deviation angle distributions of the two groups. However, the intervals indicate that a male subject is more likely to judge the water line below the actual surface (i.e., with a greater negative deviation angle) than a female, while a female subject is more likely to judge the water line above the actual surface (i.e., with a greater positive deviation angle) than a male.

Descriptive Statistics: Deviation

Variable	Gender	N	Mean	StDev	Variance	Minimum	Median	Maximum
Deviation	Female	60	6.57	7.82	61.10	-15.00	7.00	35.00
	Male	60	2.917	7.543	56.891	-18.000	2.000	27.000

Figure SIA2.6
MINITAB Analysis of Deviation Angle in the Water-Level Task — Males versus Females

Exercises 2.86–2.102

Understanding the Principles

2.86 To what kind of data sets can Chebyshev's Rule be applied? The Empirical Rule?

2.87 The output from a statistical computer program indicates that the mean and standard deviation of a data set consisting of 200 measurements are $1,500 and $300, respectively.

a. What are the units of measurement of the variable of interest? Based on the units, what type of data is this: quantitative or qualitative?

b. What can be said about the number of measurements between $900 and $2,100? Between $600 and $2,400? Between $1,200 and $1,800? Between $1,500 and $2,100?

2.88 For any set of data, what can be said about the percentage of the measurements contained in each of the following intervals?
  a. $\bar{x} - s$ to $\bar{x} + s$
  b. $\bar{x} - 2s$ to $\bar{x} + 2s$
  c. $\bar{x} - 3s$ to $\bar{x} + 3s$

2.89 For a set of data with a mound-shaped relative frequency distribution, what can be said about the percentage of the measurements contained in each of the intervals specified in Exercise 2.88?

Learning the Mechanics

2.90 The following is a sample of 25 measurements:

LM 2-90

7	6	6	11	8	9	11	9	10	8	7	7	5
9	10	7	7	7	7	9	12	10	10	8	6	

  a. Compute $\bar{x}$, s^2, and s for this sample.

  b. Count the number of measurements in the intervals $\bar{x} \pm s$, $\bar{x} \pm 2s$, and $\bar{x} \pm 3s$. Express each count as a percentage of the total number of measurements.

  c. Compare the percentages found in part **b** to the percentages given by the Empirical Rule and Chebyshev's Rule.

  d. Calculate the range and use it to obtain a rough approximation for s. Does the result compare favorably with the actual value for s found in part **a**?

2.91 Given a data set with a largest value of 760 and a smallest value of 135, what would you estimate the standard deviation to be? Explain the logic behind the procedure you used to estimate the standard deviation. Suppose the standard deviation is reported to be 25. Is this feasible? Explain.

Applying the Concepts—Basic

WPOWER50

2.92 Most powerful women in America. Refer to the *Fortune* (Oct. 14, 2002) list of the 50 most powerful women in America, saved in the WPOWER file. In Exercise 2.58 (p. 64) you found the mean age of the 50 women in the data set and in Exercise 2.84 (p. 72) you found the standard deviation. Use the mean and standard deviation to form an interval that will contain at least 75% of the ages in the data set.

2.93 Sanitation inspection of cruise ships. To minimize the potential for gastrointestinal disease outbreaks, all passenger cruise ships arriving at U.S. ports are subject to unannounced sanitation inspections. Ships are rated on a 100-point scale by the Centers for Disease Control and Prevention. A score of 86 or higher indicates that the ship is providing an accepted standard of sanitation. The May 2004 sanitation scores for 174 cruise ships are saved in the SHIPSANIT file. The first five and last five observations in the data set are listed in the accompanying table.

  a. Find the mean and standard deviation of the sanitation scores.
  b. Calculate the intervals $\bar{x} \pm s$, $\bar{x} \pm 2s$, $\bar{x} \pm 3s$.
  c. Find the percentage of measurements in the data set that fall within each of the intervals, part **b**. Do these percentages agree with either Chebyshev's Theorem or the Empirical Rule?

SHIPSANIT (Selected observations)

Ship Name	Sanitation Score
Adonia	99
Adventure of the Seas	97
AIDAAura	99
AIDAAvita	98
Albatross	96
.	.
.	.
Volendam	97
Voyager of the Seas	97
Wind Spirit	97
Wind Surf	98
World Discoverer	89

Source: National Center for Environmental Health, Centers for Disease Control and Prevention, May 24, 2004.

2.94 Recommendation letters for professors. Refer to the *American Psychologist* (July 1995) study of 148 applicants for a position in experimental psychology, Exercise 2.62 (p. 65). Recall that the mean number of recommendation letters included in each application packet was $\bar{x} = 2.28$. The standard deviation was also reported in the article; it's value was $s = 1.48$.

  a. Sketch the relative frequency distribution for the number of recommendation letters included in each application for the experimental psychology position. (Assume the distribution is mound-shaped and relatively symmetric.)

  b. Locate an interval on the distribution, part **a**, that captures approximately 95% of the measurements in the sample.

  c. Locate an interval on the distribution, part **a**, that captures almost all the sample measurements.

2.95 Dentists' use of anesthetics. A study published in *Current Allergy & Clinical Immunology* (Mar. 2004) investigated allergic reactions of dental patients to local anesthetics (LA). Based on a survey of dental practitioners, the study reported that the mean number of units (ampoules) of LA used per week by dentists was 79 with a standard deviation of 23. Suppose we want to determine the percentage of dentists that use less than 102 units of LA per week.

  a. Assuming nothing is known about the shape of the distribution for the data, what percentage of dentists use less than 102 units of LA per week?

  b. Assuming the data has a mound-shaped distribution, what percentage of dentists use less than 102 units of LA per week?

Applying the Concepts—Intermediate

NZBIRDS

2.96 Extinct New Zealand birds. Refer to the *Evolutionary Ecology Research* (July 2003) study of the patterns of extinction in the New Zealand bird population, Exercise 2.18 (p. 40). Consider the data on the egg length (measured in millimeters) for the 132 bird species saved in the NZBIRDS file.

a. Find the mean and standard deviation of the egg lengths.

b. Form an interval that can be used to predict the egg length of a bird species found in New Zealand.

2.97 Handwashing versus handrubbing. In hospitals, handwashing with soap is emphasized as the single most important measure to prevent infections. As an alternative to handwashing, some hospitals allow health workers to rub their hands with an alcohol-based antiseptic. The *British Medical Journal* (Aug. 17, 2002) reported on a study to compare the effectiveness of handwashing with soap and handrubbing with alcohol. One group of health care workers used handrubbing, while a second group used handwashing to clean their hands. The bacterial count (number of colony forming units) on the hand of each worker was recorded. The table gives descriptive statistics on bacteria counts for the two groups of health care workers.

	Mean	Standard Deviation
Handrubbing	35	59
Handwashing	69	106

a. For handrubbers, form an interval that contains about 95% of the bacterial counts. (*Note*: The bacterial count cannot be less than 0.)

b. Repeat part **a** for handwashers.

c. Based on the results, parts **a** and **b**, make an inference about the effectiveness of the two hand cleaning methods.

2.98 Sentence complexity study. A study published in *Applied Psycholinguistics* (June 1998) compared the language skills of young children (16–30 months old) from low income and middle income families. A total of 260 children — 65 in the low income and 195 in the middle income group — completed the Communicative Development Inventory (CDI) exam. One of the variables measured on each child was sentence complexity score. Summary statistics for the scores of the two groups are reproduced in the table. Use this information to sketch a graph of the sentence complexity score distribution for each income group. (Assume the distributions are mound-shaped and symmetric.) Compare the distributions. What can you infer?

	Low Income	Middle Income
Sample Size	65	195
Mean	7.62	15.55
Median	4	14
Standard Deviation	8.91	12.24
Minimum	0	0
Maximum	36	37

Source: Arriaga, R. I. et al. "Scores on the MacArthur Communicative Development Inventory of children from low-income and middle-income families." *Applied Psycholinguistics*, Vol. 19, No. 2, June 1998, p. 217 (Table 7).

2.99 Velocity of Winchester bullets. The *American Rifleman* (June 1993) reported on the velocity of ammunition fired from the FEG P9R pistol, a 9mm gun manufactured in Hungary. Field tests revealed that Winchester bullets fired from the pistol had a mean velocity (at 15 feet) of 936 feet per second and a standard deviation of 10 feet per second. Tests were also conducted with Uzi and Black Hills ammunition.

a. Describe the velocity distribution of Winchester bullets fired from the FEG P9R pistol.

b. A bullet, brand unknown, is fired from the FEG P9R pistol. Suppose the velocity (at 15 feet) of the bullet is 1,000 feet per second. Is the bullet likely to be manufactured by Winchester? Explain.

2.100 Speed of light from galaxies. Astronomers theorize that cold dark matter (CDM) caused the formation of galaxies and clusters of galaxies in the universe. The theoretical CDM model requires an estimate of the velocity of light emitted from the galaxy cluster. *The Astronomical Journal* (July 1995) published a study of observed velocities for galaxies in four different galaxy clusters. Galaxy velocity was measured in kilometers per second (km/s) using a spectrograph and high-power telescope.

a. The observed velocities of 103 galaxies located in the cluster named A2142 are summarized in the

Source: Oegerle, W. R., Hill, J. M., and Fitchett, M. J. "Observations of high dispersion clusters of galaxies: Constraints on cold dark matter." *The Astronomical Journal*, Vol. 110, No. 1, July 1995, p. 37 (Figure 1).

accompanying histogram. Comment on whether the Empirical Rule is applicable for describing the velocity distribution for this cluster.

b. The mean and standard deviation of the 103 velocities observed in galaxy cluster A2142 were reported as $\bar{x} = 27,117$ km/s and $s = 1,280$ km/s, respectively. Use this information to construct an interval that captures approximately 95% of the galaxy velocities in the cluster.

c. Recommend a single velocity value to be used in the CDM model for galaxy cluster A2142. Explain your reasoning

Applying the Concepts — Advanced

2.101 Improving SAT scores. The National Education Longitudinal Survey (NELS) tracks a nationally representative sample of U.S. students from eighth grade through high school and college. Research published in *Chance* (Winter 2001) examined the Standardized Admission Test (SAT) scores of 265 NELS students who paid a private tutor to help them improve their scores. The table summarizes the changes in both the SAT-Mathematics and SAT-Verbal scores for these students.

	SAT-Math	SAT-Verbal
Mean change in score	19	7
Standard deviation of score changes	65	49

a. Suppose one of the 265 students who paid a private tutor is selected at random. Give an interval that is likely to contain this student's change in the SAT-Math score.

b. Repeat part **a** for the SAT-Verbal score.

c. Suppose the selected student's score increased on one of the SAT tests by 140 points. Which test, the SAT-Math or SAT-Verbal, is the one most likely to have the 140-point increase? Explain.

2.102 Land purchase decision. A buyer for a lumber company must decide whether to buy a piece of land containing 5,000 pine trees. If 1,000 of the trees are at least 40 feet tall, the buyer will purchase the land; otherwise, he won't. The owner of the land reports that the height of the trees has a mean of 30 feet and a standard deviation of 3 feet. Based on this information, what is the buyer's decision?

2.7 Numerical Measures of Relative Standing

We've seen that numerical measures of central tendency and variability describe the general nature of a quantitative data set (either a sample or a population). In addition, we may also be interested in describing the *relative* quantitative location of a particular measurement within a data set. Descriptive measures of the relationship of a measurement to the rest of the data are called **measures of relative standing**.

One measure of the relative standing of a measurement is its *percentile ranking*. For example, suppose you scored an 80 on a test and you want to know how you fared in comparison with others in your class. If the instructor tells you that you scored at the 90th percentile, it means that 90% of the grades were lower than yours and 10% were higher. Thus, if the scores were described by the relative frequency histogram in Figure 2.25, the 90th percentile would be located at a point such that 90% of the total area under the relative frequency histogram lies below the 90th percentile and 10% lies above. If the instructor tells you that you scored in the 50th percentile (the median of the data set), 50% of the test grades would be lower than yours and 50% would be higher.

Percentile rankings are of practical value only for large data sets. Finding them involves a process similar to the one used in finding a median. The measurements are ranked in order and a rule is selected to define the location of each percentile. Since we are primarily interested in interpreting the percentile rankings of measurements (rather than finding particular percentiles for a data set), we define the *p*th *percentile* of a data set as shown in Definition 2.12.

Figure 2.25

Location of 90th Percentile for Test Grades

DEFINITION 2.12

For any set of n measurements (arranged in ascending or descending order), the *p***th percentile** is a number such that $p\%$ of the measurements fall below the *p*th percentile and $(100 - p)\%$ fall above it.

EXAMPLE 2.14

FINDING AND INTERPRETING PERCENTILES

Problem   Refer to the student default rates of the 50 states (and District of Columbia) in Table 2.4. An SPSS printout describing the data is shown in Figure 2.26. Locate the 25th percentile and 95th percentile on the printout and interpret these values.

Figure 2.26

SPSS Percentiles for Student Default Rate Data

Statistics

DEFAULT

N	Valid	51
	Missing	0
Percentiles	5	4.860
	10	5.760
	25	7.900
	50	9.700
	75	12.300
	90	15.120
	95	16.000

Solution   Both the 25th percentile and 95th percentile are highlighted on the SPSS printout, Figure 2.26. These values are 7.9 and 16.0, respectively. Our interpretations are as follows: 25% of the 51 default rates fall below 7.9 and 95% of the default rates fall below 16.0.

Look Back The method for computing percentiles with small data sets varies according to the software used. As the sample size increases, the percentiles from the different software packages will converge to a single number.

Now Work   *Exercise 2.103*

■ ■ ■

Another measure of relative standing in popular use is the *z-score*. As you can see in Definition 2.13, the *z*-score makes use of the mean and standard deviation of the data set in order to specify the relative location of the measurement.

Note that the *z*-score is calculated by subtracting $\bar{x}$ (or μ) from the measurement x and then dividing the result by s (or σ). The final result, the **z-score**, represents the distance between a given measurement x and the mean, expressed in standard deviations.

> **DEFINITION 2.13**
>
> The **sample z-score** for a measurement x is
> $$z = \frac{x - \bar{x}}{s}$$
> The **population z-score** for a measurement x is
> $$z = \frac{x - \mu}{\sigma}$$

EXAMPLE 2.15

FINDING A Z-SCORE

Problem   Suppose a sample of 2,000 high school seniors' verbal SAT scores is selected. The mean and standard deviation are

$$\bar{x} = 550 \quad s = 75$$

Suppose Joe Smith's score is 475. What is his sample *z*-score?

Solution Joe Smith's Verbal SAT score lies below the mean score of the 2,000 seniors; as shown in Figure 2.27.

Figure 2.27
Verbal SAT Scores of High School Seniors

$$
\begin{array}{cccc}
325 & 475 & 550 & 775 \\
\bar{x} - 3s & \text{Joe Smith's} & \bar{x} & \bar{x} + 3s \\
 & \text{score} & &
\end{array}
$$

We compute

$$
z = \frac{x - \bar{x}}{s} = \frac{475 - 550}{75} = -1.0
$$

which tells us that Joe Smith's score is 1.0 standard deviation *below* the sample mean; in short, his sample z-score is -1.0.

Look Back The numerical value of the z-score reflects the relative standing of the measurement. A large positive z-score implies that the measurement is larger than almost all other measurements, whereas a large negative z-score indicates that the measurement is smaller than almost every other measurement. If a z-score is 0 or near 0, the measurement is located at or near the mean of the sample or population.

Now Work   *Exercise 2.106*

■ ■ ■

We can be more specific if we know that the frequency distribution of the measurements is mound shaped. In this case, the following interpretation of the z-score can be given:

Interpretation of z-Scores for Mound-Shaped Distributions of Data

1. Approximately 68% of the measurements will have a z-score between -1 and 1.

2. Approximately 95% of the measurements will have a z-score between -2 and 2.

3. Approximately 99.7% (almost all) of the measurements will have a z-score between -3 and 3.

Note that this interpretation of z-scores is identical to that given by the Empirical Rule for mound-shaped distributions (Table 2.7). The statement that a measurement falls in the interval $(\mu - \sigma)$ to $(\mu + \sigma)$ is equivalent to the statement that a measurement has a population z-score between -1 and 1, since all measurements between $(\mu - \sigma)$ and $(\mu + \sigma)$ are within 1 standard deviation of μ. These z-scores are displayed in Figure 2.28.

Figure 2.28
Population z-Scores for a Mound-Shaped Distribution

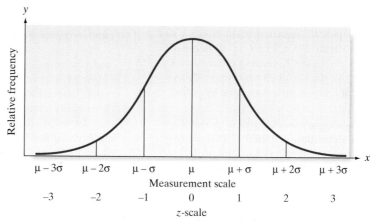

Exercises 2.103–2.117

Understanding the Principles

2.103 Give the percentage of measurements in a data set
NW that are above and below each of the following percentiles:
  a. 75th percentile
  b. 50th percentile
  c. 20th percentile
  d. 84th percentile

2.104 What is the 50th percentile of a quantitative data set called?

2.105 For mound-shaped data, what percentage of measurements have a z-score between -2 and 2?

Learning the Mechanics

2.106 Compute the z-score corresponding to each of the fol-
NW lowing values of x:
  a. $x = 40$, $s = 5$, $\bar{x} = 30$
  b. $x = 90$, $\mu = 89$, $\sigma = 2$
  c. $\mu = 50$, $\sigma = 5$, $x = 50$
  d. $s = 4$, $x = 20$, $\bar{x} = 30$
  e. In parts **a–d**, state whether the z-score locates x within a sample or a population.
  f. In parts **a–d**, state whether each value of x lies above or below the mean and by how many standard deviations.

2.107 Compare the z-scores to decide which of the following x values lie the greatest distance above the mean and the greatest distance below the mean.
  a. $x = 100$, $\mu = 50$, $\sigma = 25$
  b. $x = 1$, $\mu = 4$, $\sigma = 1$
  c. $x = 0$, $\mu = 200$, $\sigma = 100$
  d. $x = 10$, $\mu = 5$, $\sigma = 3$

2.108 Suppose that 40 and 90 are two elements of a population data set and that their z-scores are -2 and 3, respectively. Using only this information, is it possible to determine the population's mean and standard deviation? If so, find them. If not, explain why it's not possible.

Applying the Concepts — Basic

2.109 **Drivers stopped by police.** According to the Bureau of Justice Statistics (March 2002), 73.5% of all licensed drivers stopped by police are 25 years or older. Give a percentile ranking for the age of 25 years in the distribution of all ages of licensed drivers stopped by police.

2.110 **Math scores of eighth graders.** According to the National Center for Education Statistics (2000), scores on a mathematics assessment test for United States eighth graders have a mean of 500, a 5th percentile of 356, a 25th percentile of 435, a 75th percentile of 563, and a 95th percentile of 653. Interpret each of these numerical descriptive measures.

SHIPSANIT

2.111 **Sanitation inspection of cruise ships.** Refer to the sanitation levels of cruise ships, Exercise 2.93 (p. 79), saved in the SHIPSANIT file.
  a. Give a measure of relative standing for the Nautilus Explorer's score of 74. Interpret the result.
  b. Give a measure of relative standing for the Rotterdam's score of 93. Interpret the result.

JAPANESE

2.112 **Reading Japanese books.** Refer to the *Reading in a Foreign Language* (Apr. 2004) experiment to improve the Japanese reading comprehension levels of 14 University of Hawaii students, Exercises 2.57 and 2.81 (p. 71). The data on number of books read and grade for each student are saved in the JAPANESE file.
  a. Find the mean and standard deviation of the number of books read by students who earned an A grade. Find the z-score for an A student who read 40 books. Interpret the result.
  b. Find the mean and standard deviation of the number of books read by students who either earned either a B or C grade. Find the z-score for a B or C student who read 40 books. Interpret the result.
  c. Refer to parts **a** and **b**. Which of the two groups of students is more likely to have read 40 books? Explain.

Applying the Concepts — Intermediate

NZBIRDS

2.113 **Extinct New Zealand birds.** Refer to the *Evolutionary Ecology Research* (July 2003) study of the patterns of extinction in the New Zealand bird population, Exercise 2.96 (p. 80). Again, consider the data on the egg length (measured in millimeters) for the 132 bird species saved in the NZBIRDS file.
  a. Find the 10th percentile for the egg length distribution and interpret its value.
  b. The *Moas, P. australis* bird species has an egg length of 205 millimeters. Find the z-score for this species of bird and interpret its value.

Applying the Concepts — Intermediate

2.114 **Lead in drinking water.** The US. Environmental Protection Agency (EPA) sets a limit on the amount of lead permitted in drinking water. The EPA *Action Level* for lead is .015 milligrams per liter (mg/L) of water. Under EPA guidelines, if 90% of a water system's study samples have a lead concentration less than .015 mg/L, the water is considered safe for drinking. I (co-author Sincich) received a report on a study of lead levels in the drinking water of homes in my subdivision. The 90th percentile of the study sample had a lead concentration of .00372 mg/L. Are water customers in my subdivision at risk of drinking water with unhealthy lead levels? Explain.

2.115 Eye refractive study. Refer to the *Optometry and Vision Science* (June 1995) study of refractive variation in eyes, Exercise 2.67 (p. 66). The 25 cylinder power measurements are saved in the LEFTEYE file.

    a. Find the 10th percentile of cylinder power measurements. Interpret the result.

    b. Find the 95th percentile of cylinder power measurements. Interpret the result.

    c. Calculate the *z*-score for the cylinder power measurement of 1.07. Interpret the result.

2.116 Blue versus red exam study. In a study of how external clues influence performance, psychology professors at the University of Alberta and Pennsylvania State University gave two different forms of a midterm examination to a large group of introductory psychology students. The questions on the exam were identical and in the same order, but one exam was printed on blue paper and the other on red paper. (*Teaching Psychology*, May 1998.) Grading only the difficult questions on the exam, the researchers found that scores on the blue exam had a distribution with a mean of 53% and a standard deviation of 15%, while scores on the red exam had a distribution with a mean of 39% and a standard deviation of 12%. (Assume that both distributions are approximately mound-shaped and symmetric.)

    a. Give an interpretation of the standard deviation for the students who took the blue exam.

    b. Give an interpretation of the standard deviation for the students who took the red exam.

    c. Suppose a student is selected at random from the group of students who participated in the study and the student's score on the difficult questions is 20%. Which exam form is the student more likely to have taken, the blue or the red exam? Explain.

Applying the Concepts—Advanced

2.117 GPAs of students. At one university, the students are given *z*-scores at the end of each semester rather than the traditional GPAs. The mean and standard deviation of all students' cumulative GPAs, on which the *z*-scores are based, are 2.7 and .5, respectively.

    a. Translate each of the following *z*-scores to corresponding GPA scores: $z = 2.0$, $z = -1.0$, $z = .5$, $z = -2.5$.

    b. Students with *z*-scores below -1.6 are put on probation. What is the corresponding probationary GPA?

    c. The president of the university wishes to graduate the top 16% of the students with *cum laude* honors and the top 2.5% with *summa cum laude* honors. Where (approximately) should the limits be set in terms of *z*-scores? In terms of GPAs? What assumption, if any, did you make about the distribution of the GPAs at the university?

2.8 Methods for Detecting Outliers (Optional)

Sometimes it is important to identify inconsistent or unusual measurements in a data set. An observation that is unusually large or small relative to the data values we want to describe is called an **outlier**.

    Outliers are often attributable to one of several causes. First, the measurement associated with the outlier may be invalid. For example, the experimental procedure used to generate the measurement may have malfunctioned, the experimenter may have misrecorded the measurement, or the data might have been coded incorrectly in the computer. Second, the outlier may be the result of a misclassified measurement. That is, the measurement belongs to a population different from that from which the rest of the sample was drawn. Finally, the measurement associated with the outlier may be recorded correctly and from the same population as the rest of the sample, but represents a rare (chance) event. Such outliers occur most often when the relative frequency distribution of the sample data is extremely skewed, because such a distribution has a tendency to include extremely large or small observations relative to the others in the data set.

> **DEFINITION 2.14**
>
> An observation (or measurement) that is unusually large or small relative to the other values in a data set is called an **outlier**. Outliers typically are attributable to one of the following causes:
>
> **1.** The measurement is observed, recorded, or entered into the computer incorrectly.
>
> **2.** The measurement comes from a different population.
>
> **3.** The measurement is correct, but represents a rare (chance) event.

Two useful methods for detecting outliers, one graphical and one numerical, are **box plots** and z-scores. The box plot is based on the *quartiles* of a data set. **Quartiles** are values that partition the data set into four groups, each containing 25% of the measurements. The *lower quartile* Q_L is the 25th percentile, the *middle quartile* is the median M (the 50th percentile), and the *upper quartile* Q_U is the 75th percentile (see Figure 2.29).

Figure 2.29
The Quartiles for a Data Set

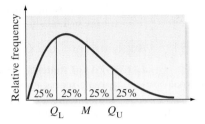

DEFINITION 2.15

The **lower quartile** Q_L is the 25th percentile of a data set. The **middle quartile** M is the median. The **upper quartile** Q_U is the 75th percentile.

A box plot is based on the *interquartile range (IQR)*, the distance between the lower and upper quartiles:

$$IQR = Q_U - Q_L$$

DEFINITION 2.16

The **interquartile range (IQR)** is the distance between the lower and upper quartiles:

$$IQR = Q_U - Q_L$$

An annotated MINITAB box plot for the gas mileage data (Table 2.2) is shown in Figure 2.30.* Note that a rectangle (the *box*) is drawn, with the bottom and top of the rectangle (the **hinges**) drawn at the quartiles Q_L and Q_U, respectively.

Figure 2.30
Annotated MINITAB Box Plot for EPA Gas Mileages

*Although box plots can be generated by hand, the amount of detail required makes them particularly well suited for computer generation. We use computer software to generate the box plots in this section.

By definition, then, the "middle" 50% of the observations — those between Q_L and Q_U — fall inside the box. For the gas mileage data, these quartiles are at 35.625 and 38.375. Thus,

$$IQR = 38.375 - 35.625 = 2.75$$

The median is shown at 37 by a horizontal line within the box.

To guide the construction of the "tails" of the box plot, two sets of limits, called **inner fences** and **outer fences**, are used. Neither set of fences actually appears on the box plot. Inner fences are located at a distance of 1.5(IQR) from the hinges. Emanating from the hinges of the box are vertical lines called the **whiskers**. The two whiskers extend to the most extreme observation inside the inner fences. For example, the inner fence on the lower side of the gas mileage box plot is

$$\text{Lower inner fence} = \text{Lower hinge} - 1.5(\text{IQR})$$

$$= 35.625 - 1.5(2.75)$$

$$= 35.625 - 4.125 = 31.5$$

The smallest measurement *inside* this fence is the second smallest measurement, 31.8. Thus, the lower whisker extends to 31.8. Similarly, the upper whisker extends to 42.1, the largest measurement inside the upper inner fence

$$\text{Upper inner fence} = \text{Upper hinge} + 1.5(\text{IQR})$$

$$= 38.375 + 1.5(2.75)$$

$$= 38.375 + 4.125 = 42.5$$

Values that are beyond the inner fences are deemed *potential outliers* because they are extreme values that represent relatively rare occurrences. In fact, for mound-shaped distributions, fewer than 1% of the observations are expected to fall outside the inner fences. Two of the 100 gas mileage measurements, 30.0 and 44.9, fall beyond the inner fences, one on each end of the distribution. Each of these potential outliers is represented by a common symbol (an asterisk in MINITAB).

The other two imaginary fences, the outer fences, are defined at a distance 3(IQR) from each end of the box. Measurements that fall beyond the outer fences (also represented by an asterisk in MINITAB) are very extreme measurements that require special analysis. Since less than one-hundredth of 1% (.01% or .0001) of the measurements from mound-shaped distributions are expected to fall beyond the outer fences, these measurements are considered to be *outliers*. Since there are no measurements of gas mileage beyond the outer fences, there are no outliers.

Recall that outliers may be incorrectly recorded observations, members of a population different from the rest of the sample, or, at the least, very unusual measurements from the same population. The box plot of Figure 2.30 detected two potential outliers — the two gas mileage measurements beyond the inner fences. When we analyze these measurements, we find that they are correctly recorded. Perhaps they represent mileages that correspond to exceptional models of the car being tested or to unusual gas mixtures. Outlier analysis often reveals useful information of this kind and therefore plays an important role in the statistical inference-making process.

In addition to detecting outliers, box plots provide useful information on the variation in a data set. The elements (and nomenclature) of box plots are summarized in the next box. Some aids to the interpretation of box plots are also given.

Elements of a Box Plot

1. A rectangle (the **box**) is drawn with the ends (the **hinges**) drawn at the lower and upper quartiles (Q_L and Q_U). The median of the data is shown in the box, usually by a line.

2. The points at distances 1.5(IQR) from each hinge mark the **inner fences** of the data set. Lines (the **whiskers**) are drawn from each hinge to the most extreme measurement inside the inner fence.

$$\text{Lower inner fence} = Q_L - 1.5(\text{IQR})$$

$$\text{Upper inner fence} = Q_U + 1.5(\text{IQR})$$

3. A second pair of fences, the **outer fences**, appear at a distance of 3 interquartile ranges, 3(IQR), from the hinges. One symbol (e.g., "*") is used to represent measurements falling between the inner and outer fences, and another (e.g., "0") is used to represent measurements beyond the outer fences. Thus, outer fences are not shown unless one or more measurements lie beyond them.

$$\text{Lower outer fence} = Q_L - 3(\text{IQR})$$

$$\text{Upper outer fence} = Q_U + 3(\text{IQR})$$

4. The symbols used to represent the median and the extreme data points (those beyond the fences) will vary depending on the software you use to construct the box plot. (You may use your own symbols if you are constructing a box plot by hand.) You should consult the program's documentation to determine exactly which symbols are used.

Aids to the Interpretation of Box Plots

1. Examine the length of the box. The IQR is a measure of the sample's variability and is especially useful for the comparison of two samples (see Example 2.16).

2. Visually compare the lengths of the whiskers. If one is clearly longer, the distribution of the data is probably skewed in the direction of the longer whisker.

3. Analyze any measurements that lie beyond the fences. Fewer than 5% should fall beyond the inner fences, even for very skewed distributions. Measurements beyond the outer fences are probably outliers, with one of the following explanations:
   a. The measurement is incorrect. It may have been observed, recorded, or entered into the computer incorrectly.
   b. The measurement belongs to a population different from the population that the rest of the sample was drawn from (see Example 2.17).
   c. The measurement is correct *and* from the same population as the rest. Generally, we accept this explanation only after carefully ruling out all others.

EXAMPLE 2.16   BOX PLOTS USING THE COMPUTER

Problem   Use a statistical software package to draw a box plot for the student loan default data, Table 2.4. Identify any outliers in the data set.

Solution   The MINITAB box plot for the student loan default rates is shown in Figure 2.32. Note that the median appears to be about 9.5, and, with the exception of a single extreme observation, the distribution appears to be symmetrically distributed between approximately 3% and 17%. The single outlier is beyond the inner fence but inside the outer fence. Examination of the data reveals that this observation corresponds to Alaska's default rate of 19.7%.

Figure 2.31

MINITAB Box Plot for
Student Loan Default Rates

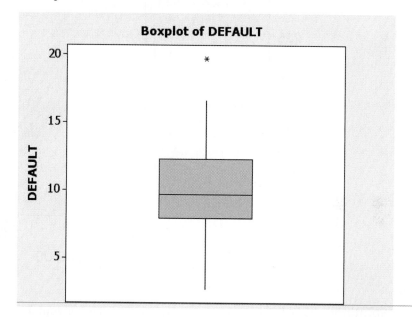

Look Back Before removing the outlier from the data set, a good analyst will make a concerted effort to find the cause of the outlier.

Now Work   *Exercise 2.125*

EXAMPLE 2.17   COMPARING BOX PLOTS

Problem   A Ph.D. student in psychology conducted a stimulus reaction experiment as a part of her dissertation research. She subjected 50 subjects to a threatening stimulus and 50 to a nonthreatening stimulus. The reaction times of all 100 students, recorded to the nearest tenth of a second, are listed in Table 2.9. Box plots of the two resulting samples of reaction times, generated using SAS, are shown in Figure 2.32. Interpret the box plots.

REACTION

TABLE 2.9   Reaction Times of Students

Nonthreatening Stimulus									
2.0	1.8	2.3	2.1	2.0	2.2	2.1	2.2	2.1	2.1
2.0	2.0	1.8	1.9	2.2	2.0	2.2	2.4	2.1	2.0
2.2	2.1	2.2	1.9	1.7	2.0	2.0	2.3	2.1	1.9
2.0	2.2	1.6	2.1	2.3	2.0	2.0	2.0	2.2	2.6
2.0	2.0	1.9	1.9	2.2	2.3	1.8	1.7	1.7	1.8

Threatening Stimulus									
1.8	1.7	1.4	2.1	1.3	1.5	1.6	1.8	1.5	1.4
1.4	2.0	1.5	1.8	1.4	1.7	1.7	1.7	1.4	1.9
1.9	1.7	1.6	2.5	1.6	1.6	1.8	1.7	1.9	1.9
1.5	1.8	1.6	1.9	1.3	1.5	1.6	1.5	1.6	1.5
1.3	1.7	1.3	1.7	1.7	1.8	1.6	1.7	1.7	1.7

Figure 2.32
SAS Box Plots for Reaction
Time Data

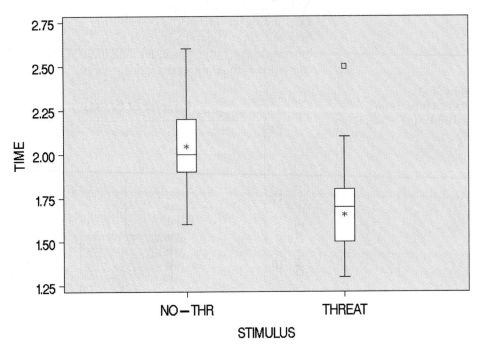

Box Plots of Time by Stimulus

Solution   In SAS, the median is represented by the horizontal line through the box, while the asterisk (*) symbol represents the mean. Analysis of the box plots on the same numerical scale reveals that the distribution of times corresponding to the threatening stimulus lies below that of the nonthreatening stimulus. The implication is that the reaction times tend to be faster to the threatening stimulus. Note, too, that the upper whiskers of both samples are longer than the lower whiskers, indicating that the reaction times are positively skewed.

No observations in the two samples fall between the inner and outer fences. However, there is one outlier — the observation of 2.5 seconds corresponding to the threatening stimulus that is beyond the outer fence (denoted by the square symbol in SAS). When the researcher examined her notes from the experiments, she found that the subject whose time was beyond the outer fence had mistakenly been given the nonthreatening stimulus. You can see in Figure 2.32 that his time would have been within the upper whisker if moved to the box plot corresponding to the nonthreatening stimulus. The box plots should be reconstructed since they will both change slightly when this misclassified reaction time is moved from one sample to the other.

Look Back The researcher concluded that the reactions to the threatening stimulus were faster than those to the nonthreatening stimulus. However, she was asked by her Ph.D. committee whether the results were *statistically significant*. Their question addresses the issue of whether the observed difference between the samples might be attributable to chance or sampling variation rather than to real differences between the populations. To answer their question, the researcher must use inferential statistics rather than graphical descriptions. We discuss how to compare two samples using inferential statistics in Chapter 9.

■ ■ ■

The following example illustrates how z-scores can be used to detect outliers and make inferences.

EXAMPLE 2.18   INFERENCE USING Z-SCORES

Problem   Suppose a female bank employee believes that her salary is low as a result of sex discrimination. To substantiate her belief, she collects information on the salaries of her male counterparts in the banking business. She finds that their salaries have a mean of $54,000 and a standard deviation of $2,000. Her salary is $47,000. Does this information support her claim of sex discrimination?

Solution   The analysis might proceed as follows: First, we calculate the z-score for the woman's salary with respect to those of her male counterparts. Thus,

$$z = \frac{\$47{,}000 - \$54{,}000}{\$2{,}000} = -3.5$$

The implication is that the woman's salary is 3.5 standard deviations *below* the mean of the male salary distribution. Furthermore, if a check of the male salary data shows that the frequency distribution is mound shaped, we can infer that very few salaries in this distribution should have a z-score less than −3, as shown in Figure 2.33. Clearly, a z-score of −3.5 represents an outlier. Either her salary is from a distribution different from the male salary distribution or it is a very unusual (highly improbable) measurement from a salary distribution no different from the male distribution.

Figure 2.33
Male Salary Distribution

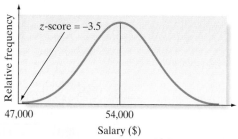

Look Back Which of the two situations do you think prevails? Statistical thinking would lead us to conclude that her salary does not come from the male salary distribution, lending support to the female bank employee's claim of sex discrimination. However, the careful investigator should require more information before inferring sex discrimination as the cause. We would want to know more about the data collection technique the woman used and more about her competence at her job. Also, perhaps other factors such as length of employment should be considered in the analysis.

Now Work   *Exercise 2.123*

------   ■ ■ ■   ------

Examples 2.17 and 2.18 exemplify an approach to statistical inference that might be called the **rare-event approach**. An experimenter hypothesizes a specific frequency distribution to describe a population of measurements. Then a sample of measurements is drawn from the population. If the experimenter finds it unlikely that the sample came from the hypothesized distribution, the hypothesis is concluded to be false. Thus, in Example 2.18 the woman believes her salary reflects discrimination. She hypothesizes that her salary should be just another measurement in the distribution of her male counterparts' salaries if no discrimination exists. However, it is so unlikely that the sample (in this case, her salary) came from the male frequency distribution that she rejects that hypothesis, concluding that the distribution from which her salary was drawn is different from the distribution for the men.

This rare-event approach to inference-making is discussed further in later chapters. Proper application of the approach requires a knowledge of probability, the subject of our next chapter.

We conclude this section with some rules of thumb for detecting outliers.

Rules of Thumb for Detecting Outliers*

	Suspect Outliers	Highly Suspect Outliers
Box Plots:	Data points between inner & outer fences	Data points beyond outer fences
z-Scores:	$2 < |z| < 3$	$|z| > 3$

Box Plots

Using the T1-83 Graphing Calculator

Making a Box Plot

Step 1 Enter the data
Press STAT and select 1:Edit
Note: If the list already contains data, clear the old data. Use the up arrow to highlight 'L1'. Press CLEAR ENTER.
Use the arrow and ENTER keys to enter the data set into L1.

Step 2 Set up the box plot

Press 2nd **Y** = for STAT PLOT
Press 1 for Plot 1

Set the cursor so that 'ON' is flashing.
For TYPE, use the right arrow to scroll through the plot icons and select the boxplot in the middle of the second row.
For XLIST, choose L1.
Set FREQ to 1.

Step 3 View the graph
Press ZOOM and select 9:ZoomStat

Optional *Read the five number summary*
Step Press TRACE
Use the left and right arrow keys to move between minX, Q1, Med, Q3, and maxX.

Example Make a box plot for the given data,
86, 70, 62, 98, 73, 56, 53, 92, 86, 37, 62, 83, 78, 49, 78, 37, 67, 79, 57

The output screen for this example is shown below.

*The z-score and box plot methods both establish rule-of-thumb limits outside of which a measurement is deemed to be an outlier. Usually, the two methods produce similar results. However, the presence of one or more outliers in a data set can inflate the computed value of s. Consequently, it will be less likely that an errant observation would have a z-score larger than 3 in absolute value. In contrast, the values of the quartiles used to calculate the intervals for a box plot are not affected by the presence of outliers.

Statistics in Action Revisited
Detecting Outliers

In the *Psychological Science* "water-level task" experiment, the quantitative variable of interest is *Deviation angle* (measured in degrees) of the judged line from the true surface line (parallel to the table top). Are there any unusual values of this variable in the **EYECUE** data set? We will employ both the box plot and z-score methods to aid in identifying outliers in the data.

Descriptive statistics for the deviation angles of all 120 experimental subjects, produced using MINITAB, are shown in Figure SIA2.7. To employ the z-score method, we need the mean and standard deviation. These values are highlighted on Figure SIA2.7. Then, the 3-standard deviation interval is

$$4.742 \pm 3(7.865) = 4.742 \pm 23.595 = (-18.853, 28.337)$$

If you examine the deviation angles in the **EYECUE** data set, you find that only one of these values, 35, falls beyond

the 3-standard deviation interval. Thus, the data for the subject whose judged line had a deviation angle of 35° (z-score = 3.85) is considered a highly suspect outlier using the z-score approach.

A box plot for the data is shown in Figure SIA2.8. Although there are several suspect outliers (asterisks) shown on the box plot, there are no highly suspect outliers (zeros) shown. That is, there are no data points that fall beyond the outer fences. Thus, the box plot method does not identify the value of 35 as a highly suspect outlier, only as a suspect outlier.

Before any type of inference is made concerning the population of deviation angles for subjects performing the water-level task, we should consider whether this potential outlier is a legitimate observation (in which case it will remain in the data set for analysis) or is associated with a subject that is not a member of the population of interest (in which case it will be removed from the data set).

Descriptive Statistics: Deviation

Variable	N	Mean	StDev	Minimum	Q1	Median	Q3	Maximum	IQR
Deviation	120	4.742	7.865	-18.000	0.000	4.000	9.000	35.000	9.000

Figure SIA2.7
MINITAB Descriptive Statistics for Deviation Angle of Judged Water Level

Figure SIA2.8
MINITAB Box Plot for
Deviation Angle of Judged
Water Level

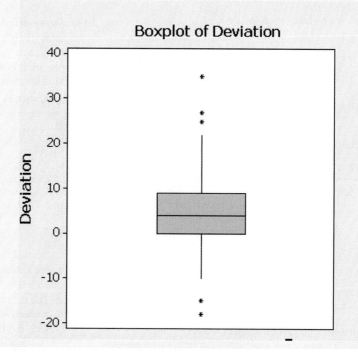

Exercises 2.118–2.135

Understanding the Principles:

2.118 Define an outlier.

2.119 Define the 25th, 50th, and 75th percentiles of a data set.

2.120 What is the interquartile range?

2.121 What are the hinges of a box plot?

2.122 With mound-shaped data, what proportion of the measurements have z-scores between -3 and 3?

Learning the Mechanics

2.123 A sample data set has a mean of 57 and a standard
NW deviation of 11. Determine whether each of the following sample measurements are outliers.
   a. 65   **b.** 21   **c.** 72   **d.** 98

2.124 Suppose a data set consisting of exam scores has a lower quartile $Q_L = 60$, a median $M = 75$, and an upper quartile $Q_U = 85$. The scores on the exam range from 18 to 100. Without having the actual scores available to you, construct as much of the box plot as possible.

2.125 Consider the horizontal box plot shown below.
NW **a.** What is the median of the data set (approximately)?

   b. What are the upper and lower quartiles of the data set (approximately)?
   c. What is the interquartile range of the data set (approximately)?
   d. Is the data set skewed to the left, skewed to the right, or symmetric?
   e. What percentage of the measurements in the dataset lie to the right of the median? To the left of the upper quartile?
   f. Identify any outliers in the data.

2.126 Consider the following two sample data sets:

   ⊙ **LM2_126**

Sample A			Sample B		
121	171	158	171	152	170
173	184	163	168	169	171
157	85	145	190	183	185
165	172	196	140	173	206
170	159	172	172	174	169
161	187	100	199	151	180
142	166	171	167	170	188

   a. Construct a box plot for each data set.
   b. Identify any outliers that may exist in the two data sets.

Applying the Concepts—Basic

⊙ **PMI**

2.127 **Research on brain specimens.** Refer to the *Brain and Language* data on postmortem intervals (PMIs) of 22 human brain specimens, Exercise 2.37 (p. 52). The mean and standard deviation of the PMI values are 7.3 and 3.18, respectively.
   a. Find the z-score for the PMI value of 3.3.
   b. Is the PMI value of 3.3 considered an outlier? Explain.

2.128 **Dentists' use of anesthetics.** Refer to the *Current Allergy & Clinical Immunology* (Mar. 2004) study of the use of local anesthetics (LA) in dentistry, Exercise 2.95 (p. 79). Recall that the mean number of units (ampoules) of LA used per week by dentists was 79 with a standard deviation of 23. Consider a dentist who used 175 units of LA in a week.
   a. Find the z-score for this measurement.
   b. Would you consider this measurement to be an outlier? Explain.
   c. Give several reasons why the outlier may occur.

⊙ **SATSCORES**

2.129 **Comparing SAT Scores.** Refer to Exercise 2.40 (p. 53) in which we compared states' average SAT scores in 1990 and 2000. The data is saved in the SATSCORES file.
   a. Construct side-by-side box plots of the SAT scores for the two years.
   b. Compare the variability of the SAT scores for the two years.
   c. Are any states' SAT scores outliers in either year? If so, identify them.

2.130 **Salary offers to MBAs.** The table contains the top salary offer (in thousands of dollars) received by each member of a sample of 50 MBA students who recently graduated from the Graduate School of Management at Rutgers University.

   ⊙ **MBASAL**

61.1	48.5	47.0	49.1	43.5
50.8	62.3	50.0	65.4	58.0
53.2	39.9	49.1	75.0	51.2
41.7	40.0	53.0	39.6	49.6
55.2	54.9	62.5	35.0	50.3
41.5	56.0	55.5	70.0	59.2
39.2	47.0	58.2	59.0	60.8
72.3	55.0	41.4	51.5	63.0
48.4	61.7	45.3	63.2	41.5
47.0	43.2	44.6	47.7	58.6

Source: Career Services Office, Graduate School of Management, Rutgers University.

   a. The mean and standard deviation are 52.33 and 9.22, respectively. Find and interpret the z-score associated with the highest salary offer, the lowest salary offer, and the mean salary offer. Would you consider the highest offer to be unusually high? Why or why not?

b. Construct a box plot for this data set and identify any outliers.

Applying the Concepts—Intermediate

2.131 Speech listening study. Refer to the *American Journal of Speech–Language Pathology* (Feb. 1995) study, Exercise 2.41 (p. 53). Recall that three groups of college students listened to an audio tape of a woman with imperfect speech. The groups were called *control, treatment,* and *familiarity.* At the end of the session, each student transcribed the spoken words.

   a. Construct box plots for the percentage of words correctly transcribed (i.e., accuracy rate) for each group.

   b. How do the median accuracy rates compare for the three groups?

   c. How do the variabilities of the accuracy rates compare for the three groups?

   d. The standard deviations of the accuracy rates are 3.56 for the control group, 5.45 for the treatment group, and 4.46 for the familiarity group. Do the standard deviations agree with the interquartile ranges (part **c**) with regard to the comparison of the variabilities of the accuracy rates?

   e. Is there evidence of outliers in any of the three distributions?

⊙ WPOWER50

2.132 Most powerful woman in America. Refer to the *Fortune* (Oct. 14, 2002) ranking of the 50 most powerful women in America, Exercise 2.92 (p. 79). Create box plots to compare the ages of the women in three groups based on their position within the firm: Group 1 (CEO, CFO, CIO, or COO); Group 2 (Chairman, President, or Director); and Group 3 (Vice President, Vice Chairman, or General Manager).

⊙ SHIPSANIT

2.133 Sanitation inspection of cruise ships. Refer to the data on sanitation levels of cruise ships, Exercise 2.93 (p. 53).

   a. Use the box plot method to detect any outliers in the data.

   b. Use the z-score method to detect any outliers in the data.

   c. Do the two methods agree? If not, explain why.

Applying the Concepts—Advanced

2.134 Library book checkouts. A city librarian claims that books have been checked out an average of seven (or more) times in the last year. You suspect he has exaggerated the checkout rate (book usage) and that the mean number of checkouts per book per year is, in fact, less than seven. Using the computerized card catalog, you randomly select one book and find that it has been checked out four times in the last year. Assume that the standard deviation of the number of checkouts per book per year is approximately 1.

   a. If the mean number of checkouts per book per year really is seven, what is the z-score corresponding to four?

   b. Considering your answer to part **a**, do you have reason to believe that the librarian's claim is incorrect?

   c. If you knew that the distribution of the number of checkouts were mound shaped, would your answer to part **b** change? Explain.

   d. If the standard deviation of the number of checkouts per book per year were 2 (instead of 1), would your answers to parts **b** and **c** change? Explain.

2.135 Zinc phosphide in sugarcane. A chemical company produces a substance composed of 98% cracked corn particles and 2% zinc phosphide for use in controlling rat populations in sugarcane fields. Production must be carefully controlled to maintain the 2% zinc phosphide because too much zinc phosphide will cause damage to the sugarcane and too little will be ineffective in controlling the rat population. Records from past production indicate that the distribution of the actual percentage of zinc phosphide present in the substance is approximately mound-shaped, with a mean of 2.0% and a standard deviation of .08%. Suppose one batch chosen randomly actually contains 1.80% zinc phosphide. Does this indicate that there is too little zinc phosphide in today's production? Explain your reasoning.

2.9 Graphing Bivariate Relationships (Optional)

The claim is often made that the crime rate and the unemployment rate are "highly correlated." Another popular belief is that smoking and lung cancer are "related." Some people even believe that the Dow Jones Industrial Average and the lengths of fashionable skirts are "associated." The words *correlated, related,* and *associated* imply a relationship between two variables — in the examples above, two *quantitative* variables.

One way to describe the relationship between two quantitative variables — called a **bivariate relationship** — is to plot the data in a **scattergram** (or **scatterplot**). A scattergram is a two-dimensional plot, with one variable's values plotted along the vertical axis and the other along the horizontal axis. For example, Figure 2.34 is a scattergram relating (1) the cost of mechanical work (heating, ventilating, and

Figure 2.34

Scattergram of cost vs. floor area

plumbing) to (2) the floor area of the building for a sample of 26 factory and warehouse buildings. Note that the scattergram suggests a general tendency for mechanical cost to increase as building floor area increases.

When an increase in one variable is generally associated with an increase in the second variable, we say that the two variables are "positively related" or "positively correlated."* Figure 2.34 implies that mechanical cost and floor area are positively correlated. Alternatively, if one variable has a tendency to decrease as the other increases, we say the variables are "negatively correlated." Figure 2.35 shows several hypothetical scattergrams that portray a positive bivariate relationship (Figure 2.35a), a negative bivariate relationship (Figure 2.35b), and a situation where the two variables are unrelated (Figure 2.35c).

Figure 2.35

Hypothetical Bivariate Relationship

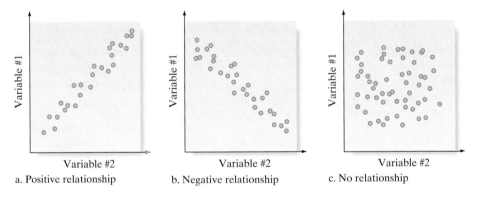

a. Positive relationship   b. Negative relationship   c. No relationship

EXAMPLE 2.19   GRAPHING BIVARIATE DATA

Problem   A medical item used to administer to a hospital patient is called a *factor*. For example, factors can be intravenous (IV) tubing, IV fluid, needles, shave kits, bedpans, diapers, dressings, medications, and even code carts. The coronary care unit at Bayonet Point Hospital (St. Petersburg, Florida) recently investigated the relationship between the number of factors administered per patient and the patient's length of stay (in days). Data on these two variables for a sample of 50 coronary care patients are given in Table 2.10. Use a scattergram to describe the relationship between the two variables of interest, number of factors, and length of stay.

*A formal definition of correlation is given in Chapter 11. We will learn that correlation measures the strength of the linear (or straight-line) relationship between two quantitative variables.

◉ **MEDFACTORS**

TABLE 2.10   Data on Patient's Factors and Length of Stay

Number of Factors	Length of Stay (days)	Number of Factors	Length of Stay (days)
231	9	354	11
323	7	142	7
113	8	286	9
208	5	341	10
162	4	201	5
117	4	158	11
159	6	243	6
169	9	156	6
55	6	184	7
77	3	115	4
103	4	202	6
147	6	206	5
230	6	360	6
78	3	84	3
525	9	331	9
121	7	302	7
248	5	60	2
233	8	110	2
260	4	131	5
224	7	364	4
472	12	180	7
220	8	134	6
383	6	401	15
301	9	155	4
262	7	338	8

Source: Bayonet Point Hospital, Coronary Care Unit.

Solution   Rather than construct the plot by hand, we resort to a statistical software package. The SPSS plot of the data in Table 2.10, with length of stay (LOS) on the horizontal axis and number of factors (FACTORS) on the vertical axis, is shown in Figure 2.36.

Figure 2.36
SPSS Scatterplot of Data
in Table 2.10

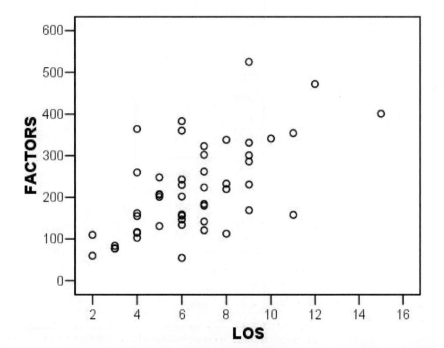

Although the plotted points exhibit a fair amount of variation, the scattergram clearly shows an increasing trend. It appears that a patient's length of stay is positively correlated with the number of factors administered to the patient.

Look Back If hospital administrators can be confident that the sample trend shown in Figure 2.36 accurately describes the trend in the population, then they may use this information to improve their forecasts of lengths of stay for future patients.

Now Work   *Exercise 2.139*

The scattergram is a simple but powerful tool for describing a bivariate relationship. However, keep in mind that it is only a graph. No measure of reliability can be attached to inferences made about bivariate populations based on scattergrams of sample data. The statistical tools that enable us to make inferences about bivariate relationships are presented in Chapter 11.

Scatterplots

Using the T1-83 Graphing Calculator

Making Scatterplots

Step 1   Enter the data
Press STAT and select 1:Edit
Note: If a list already contains data, clear the old data. Use the up arrow to highlight the list name, 'L1' or 'L2'.
Press CLEAR ENTER
Enter your x-data in L1 and your y-data in L2.

Step 2   Set up the scatterplot
Press 2nd **Y =** for STAT PLOT
Press 1 for Plot1
Set the cursor so that ON is flashing.
For Type, use the arrow and Enter keys to highlight and select the scatterplot (first icon in the first row).
For Xlist, choose the column containing the x-data.
For Freq, choose the column containing the y-data.

Step 3   View the scatterplot
Press ZOOM 9 for ZoomStat

Example   The figures below show a table of data entered on the T1-83 and the scatterplot of the data obtained using the steps given above.

Exercises 2.136–2.148

Understanding the Principles

2.136 For what types of variables, quantitative or qualitative, are scatterplots useful?

2.137 Define a bivariate relationship.

2.138 What is the difference between positive association and negative association when describing the relationship between two variables?

Learning the Mechanics

2.139 Construct a scatterplot for the data in the following table. Do you detect a trend?
NW

Variable #1:	5	3	−1	2	7	6	4	0	8
Variable #2:	14	3	10	1	8	5	3	2	12

2.140 Construct a scatterplot for the data in the following table. Do you detect a trend?

Variable #1:	.5	1	1.5	2	2.5	3	3.5	4	4.5	5
Variable #2:	2	1	3	4	6	10	9	12	17	17

Applying the Concepts—Basic

2.141 Baseball batting averages versus wins. Baseball wisdom says if you can't hit, you can't win. Is the number of games won by a major league baseball team in a season related to the team's batting average? The information in the table, found in the *Baseball Almanac* (2003), shows the number of games won and the batting averages for the 14 teams in the American League for the 2002 Major League Baseball season. Construct a scatterplot for the data. Do you observe a trend?

⊚ ALWINS

Team	Games Won	Batting Ave.
New York	103	.275
Toronto	78	.261
Baltimore	67	.246
Boston	93	.277
Tampa Bay	55	.253
Cleveland	74	.249
Detroit	55	.248
Chicago	81	.268
Kansas City	62	.256
Minnesota	94	.272
Anaheim	99	.282
Texas	72	.269
Seattle	93	.275
Oakland	103	.261

Source: Baseball Almanac, 2003.

2.142 Feeding behavior of fish. Zoologists at the University of Western Australia conducted a study of the feeding behavior of blackbream fish spawned in aquariums. (*Brain and Behavior Evolution*, April 2000.) In one experiment, the zoologists recorded the number of aggressive strikes of two blackbream fish feeding at the bottom of the aquarium in the 10-minute period following the addition of food. The number of strikes and age of the fish (in days) was recorded approximately each week for nine weeks, as shown in the table.

⊚ BLACKBREAM

Week	Number of Strikes	Age of Fish (days)
1	85	120
2	63	136
3	34	150
4	39	155
5	58	162
6	35	169
7	57	178
8	12	184
9	15	190

Source: J. Shand, et al. "Variability in the location of the retinal ganglion cell area centralis is correlated with ontogenetic changes in feeding behavior in the Blackbream, Acanthopagrus 'butcher'," Brain and Behavior, Vol. 55, No. 4, April 2000 (Figure H).

a. Construct a scattergram for the data, with number of strikes on the y-axis and age of the fish on the x-axis.
b. Examine the scattergram of part **a**. Do you detect a trend?

2.143 Walking study. A "self-avoiding walk" describes a path in which you never retrace your steps or cross your own path. An "unrooted walk" is a path in which it is impossible to distinguish between the starting point and ending point of the path. The *American Scientist* (July–Aug. 1998) investigated the relationship between self-avoiding and unrooted walks. The table gives the number of unrooted walks and possible number of self-avoiding walks of various lengths, where length is measured as number of steps.

⊚ WALK

Walk Length (Number of Steps)	Unrooted Walks	Self-Avoiding Walks
1	1	4
2	2	12
3	4	36
4	9	100
5	22	284
6	56	780
7	147	2,172
8	388	5,916

Source: Hayes, B. "How to avoid yourself." American Scientist, Vol. 86, No. 4, July–Aug.1998, p. 317 (Figure 5).

a. Construct a plot to investigate the relationship between total possible number of self-avoiding walks and walk length. What pattern (if any) do you observe?

b. Repeat part **a** for unrooted walks.

DDT

2.144 Contaminated fish. Refer to the U.S. Army Corps of Engineers data on contaminated fish saved in the DDT file. Three quantitative variables are measured for each of the 144 captured fish: length (in centimeters), weight (in grams), and DDT level (in parts per million). Form a scatterplot for each pair of these variables. What trends, if any, do you detect?

Applying the Concepts—Intermediate

SITIN

2.145 College protests of labor exploitation. Refer to the *Journal of World-Systems Research* (Winter 2004) study of 14 student "sit-ins" for a "sweat free campus" at universities in 1999 and 2000, Exercise 2.35 (p. 52). The SITIN file contains data on the duration (in days) of each sit-in as well as the number of student arrests.

a. Use a scatterplot to graph the relationship between duration and number of arrests. Do you detect a trend?

b. Repeat part **a**, but only graph the data for sit-ins where there was at least one arrest. Do you detect a trend?

c. Comment on the reliability of the trend you detected in part **b**.

2.146 Short-term memory study. Research published in the *American Journal of Psychiatry* (July 1995) attempted to establish a link between hippocampal (brain) volume and short-term verbal memory of patients with combat-related post-traumatic stress disorder (PTSD). A sample of 21 Vietnam veterans with a history of combat-related PTSD participated in the study. Magnetic resonance imaging was used to measure the volume of the right hippocampus (in cubic millimeters) of each subject. Verbal memory retention of each subject was measured by the percent retention subscale of the Wechsler Memory Scale. The data for the 21 patients are plotted in the scattergram. The researchers "hypothesized that smaller hippocampal volume would be associated with deficits in short-term verbal memory in patients with PTSD." Does the scattergram provide visual evidence to support this theory?

GOBIANTS

2.147 Mongolian desert ants. Refer to the *Journal of Biogeography* (Dec. 2003) study of ants in Mongolia, Exercise 2.66 (p. 66). Data on annual rainfall, maximum daily temperature, plant cover percentage, number of ant species, and species diversity index recorded at each of 11 study sites are saved in the GOBIANTS file.

a. Construct a scatterplot to investigate the relationship between annual rainfall and maximum daily temperature. What type of trend (if any) do you detect?

b. Use scatterplots to investigate the relationship that annual rainfall has with each of the other four variables in the data set. Are the other variables positively or negatively related to rainfall?

2.148 Forest fragmentation study. Ecologists classify the cause of forest fragmentation as either anthropogenic (i.e., due to human development activities such as road construction or logging) or natural in origin (e.g., due to wetlands or wildfire). *Conservation Ecology* (Dec. 2003) published an article on the causes of fragmentation for 54 South American forests. Using advanced high resolution satellite imagery, the researchers developed two fragmentation indices for each forest — one index for anthropogenic fragmentation and one for fragmentation from natural causes. The values of these two indices (where higher values indicate more fragmentation) for five of the forests in the sample are shown in the accompanying table. The data for all 54 forests are saved in the FORFRAG file.

FORFRAG (Selected observations)

Ecoregion (forest)	Anthropogenic Index	Natural Origin Index
Araucaria moist forests	34.09	30.08
Atlantic Coast restingas	40.87	27.60
Bahia coastal forests	44.75	28.16
Bahia interior forests	37.58	27.44
Bolivian Yungas	12.40	16.75

Source: Wade, T. G., et al. "Distribution and causes of global forest fragmentation," *Conservation Ecology*, Vol. 72, No. 2, Dec. 2003 (Table 6).

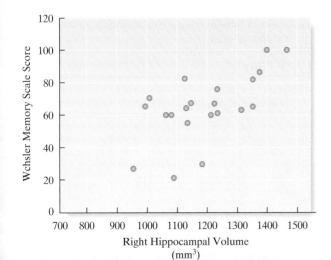

a. Ecologists theorize that an approximately linear (straight-line) relationship exists between the two fragmentation indices. Graph the data for all 54 forests. Does the graph support the theory?

b. Delete the data for the three forests with the largest anthropogenic indices and reconstruct the graph, part **a.** Comment on the ecologists' theory.

2.10 Distorting the Truth with Descriptive Techniques

A picture may be "worth a thousand words," but pictures can also color messages or distort them. In fact, the pictures in statistics — histograms, bar charts, and other graphical descriptions — are susceptible to distortion, so we have to examine each of them with care. We'll mention a few of the pitfalls to watch for when interpreting a chart or graph.

One common way to change the impression conveyed by a graph is to change the scale on the vertical axis, the horizontal axis, or both. For example, Figure 2.37 is a bar graph that shows the market share of sales for a company for each of the years 2000 to 2005. If you want to show that the change in firm A's market share over time is moderate, you should pack in a large number of units per inch on the vertical axis. That is, make the distance between successive units on the vertical scale small, as shown in Figure 2.37. You can see that a change in the firm's market share over time is barely apparent.

Figure 2.37

Firm A's Market Share: Packed Vertical Axis

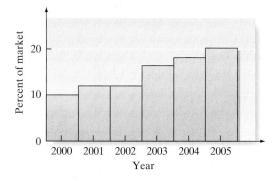

If you want to use the same data to make the changes in firm A's market share appear large, you should increase the distance between successive units on the vertical axis. That is, stretch the vertical axis by graphing only a few units per inch as in Figure 2.38. A telltale sign of stretching is a long vertical axis, but this is often hidden by starting the vertical axis at some point above 0. The same effect can be achieved by using a broken line — called a *scale break* — for the vertical axis, as shown in Figure 2.39.

Figure 2.38

Firm A's Market Share: Stretched Vertical Axis

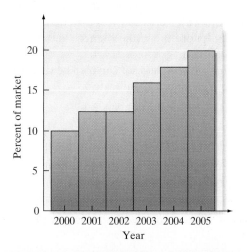

Figure 2.39
Firm A's Market Share:
Scale Break

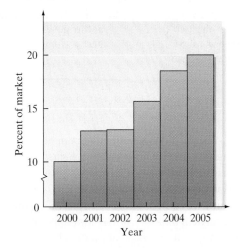

The changes in categories indicated by a bar graph can also be emphasized or deemphasized by stretching or shrinking the vertical axis. Another method of achieving visual distortion with bar graphs is by making the width of the bars proportional to height. For example, look at the bar chart in Figure 2.40a, which depicts the percentage of the total number of motor vehicle deaths in a year that occurred on each of four major highways. Now suppose we make both the width and the height grow as the percentage of fatal accidents grows. This change is shown in Figure 2.40b. The reader may tend to equate the *area* of the bars with the percentage of deaths occurring at each highway. But in fact, the true relative frequency of fatal accidents is proportional only to the *height* of the bars.

Figure 2.40
Relative Frequency of
Fatal Motor Vehicle
Accidents on Each of Four
Major Highways

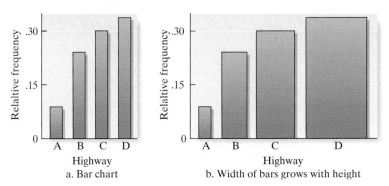

Although we've discussed only a few of the ways that graphs can be used to convey misleading pictures of phenomena, the lesson is clear. Look at all graphical descriptions of data with a critical eye. Particularly, check the axes and the size of the units on each axis. Ignore the visual changes and concentrate on the actual numerical changes indicated by the graph or chart.

The information in a data set can also be distorted by using numerical descriptive measures, as Example 2.20 indicates.

EXAMPLE 2.20   MISLEADING DESCRIPTIVE STATISTICS

Problem   Suppose you're considering working for a small law firm — one that currently has a senior member and three junior members. You inquire about the salary you could expect to earn if you join the firm. Unfortunately, you receive two answers:

Answer A: The senior member tells you that an "average employee" earns $87,500

Answer B: One of the junior members later tells you that an "average employee" earns $75,000

Which answer can you believe?

Solution The confusion exists because the phrase "average employee" has not been clearly defined. Suppose the four salaries paid are $75,000 for each of the three junior members and $125,000 for the senior member. Thus,

$$\bar{x} = \frac{3(\$75,000) + \$125,000}{4} = \frac{\$350,000}{4} = \$87,500$$

$$\text{Median} = \$75,000$$

You can now see how the two answers were obtained. The senior member reported the mean of the four salaries, and the junior member reported the median. The information you received was distorted because neither person stated which measure of central tendency was being used.

Look Back Based on our earlier discussion of the mean and median, we would probably prefer the median as the number that best describes the salary of the "average" employee.

Another distortion of information in a sample occurs when *only* a measure of central tendency is reported. Both a measure of central tendency and a measure of variability are needed to obtain an accurate mental image of a data set.

Suppose you want to buy a new car and are trying to decide which of two models to purchase. Since energy and economy are both important issues, you decide to purchase model A because its EPA mileage rating is 32 miles per gallon in the city, whereas the mileage rating for model B is only 30 miles per gallon in the city.

However, you may have acted too quickly. How much variability is associated with the ratings? As an extreme example, suppose that further investigation reveals that the standard deviation for model A mileages is 5 miles per gallon, whereas that for model B is only 1 mile per gallon. If the mileages form a mound-shaped distribution, they might appear as shown in Figure 2.41. Note that the larger amount of variability associated with model A implies that more risk is involved in purchasing model A. That is, the particular car you purchase is more likely to have a mileage rating that will greatly differ from the EPA rating of 32 miles per gallon if you purchase model A, while a model B car is not likely to vary from the 30 miles per gallon rating by more than 2 miles per gallon.

We conclude this section with another example on distorting the truth with numerical descriptive measures.

Figure 2.41

Mileage Distributions for Two Car Models

EXAMPLE 2.21   MORE MISLEADING DESCRIPTIVE STATISTICS

Problem   *Children Out of School in America* is a report on delinquency of school-age children by the Children's Defense Fund (CDF). Consider the following three reported results of the CDF survey.

- Reported result: 25% of the 16- and 17-year-olds in the Portland, Maine, Bayside East Housing Project were out of school. Actual data: *Only eight children were surveyed; two were found to be out of school.*

- Reported result: Of all the secondary school students who had been suspended more than once in census tract 22 in Columbia, South Carolina, 33% had been suspended two times and 67% had been suspended three or more times. Actual data: *CDF found only three children in that entire census tract who had been suspended; one child was suspended twice and the other two children, three or more times.*

- Reported result: In the Portland Bayside East Housing Project, 50% of all the secondary school children who had been suspended more than once had been suspended three or more times. Actual data: *The survey found two secondary school children had been suspended in that area; one of them had been suspended three or more times.*

Identify the potential distortions in the results reported by the CDF.

Solution   In each of these examples the reporting of percentages (i.e., relative frequencies) instead of the numbers themselves is misleading. No inference we might draw from the cited examples would be reliable. (We'll see how to measure the reliability of estimated percentages in Chapter 7.) In short, either the report should state the numbers alone instead of percentages, or, better yet, it should state that the numbers were too small to report by region. If several regions were combined, the numbers (and percentages) would be more meaningful.

Look Back If several regions were combined, the numbers (and percentages) would be more meaningful.

Quick Review

Key Terms

Note: Starred (*) terms are from the optional sections to this chapter

Bar graph   32
Bivariate relationship*   95
Box plots*   88
Central tendency   55
Chebyshev's Rule   73
Class   31
Class percentage   31
Class interval   38
Class frequency   31
Class relative frequency   31
Dot plot   41
Empirical Rule   74
Hinges*   87

Histogram   43
Inner fences*   87
Interquartile range*   86
Lower quartile*   86
Mean   56
Measures of central tendency   55
Measures of relative standing   71
Measures of variation or spread   67
Median   57
Middle quartile*   86
Modal class   51
Mode   50
Mound-shaped distribution   73
Numerical descriptive measures   55
Outer fences*   87
Outlier*   85
Pareto diagram   33

Percentile   81
Pie chart   86
Quartiles*   86
Range   67
Rare-event approach*   91
Scattergram*   95
Scatterplot*   95
Skewness   59
Standard deviation   69
Stem-and-leaf display   52
Symmetric distribution   59
Upper quartile*   86
Variability   55
Variance   68
Whiskers*   88
z-score   82

Key Formulas

$$\frac{\text{Class frequency}}{n}$$ Class relative frequency   31

$$\left(\frac{\text{Class frequency}}{n}\right) \times 100$$ Class percentage   31

$$\overline{x} = \frac{\sum_{i=1}^{n} x_i}{n}$$ Sample mean   56

$$s^2 = \frac{\sum_{i=1}^{n}(x_i - \overline{x})^2}{n-1} = \frac{\sum_{i=1}^{n} x_i^2 - \dfrac{\left(\sum_{i=1}^{n} x_i\right)^2}{n}}{n-1}$$ Sample variance   69

$$s = \sqrt{s^2}$$ Sample standard deviation   69

$$z = \frac{x - \overline{x}}{s}$$ Sample z-score   82

$$z = \frac{x - \mu}{\sigma}$$ Population z-score   82

$$\text{IQR} = Q_U - Q_L$$ Interquartile range   86

$$Q_L - 1.5(\text{IQR})$$ *Lower inner fence   88

$$Q_U + 1.5(\text{IQR})$$ *Upper inner fence   88

$$Q_L - 3(\text{IQR})$$ *Lower outer fence   88

$$Q_U + 3(\text{IQR})$$ *Upper outer fence   88

Chapter Summary

- Graphical methods for qualitative data: **pie chart, bar graph,** and **Pareto diagram**
- Graphical methods for quantitative data: **dot plot, stem-and-leaf display,** and **histogram**
- Numerical measures of central tendency: **mean, median,** and **mode**
- Numerical measures of variation: **range, variance,** and **standard deviation**

- Rules for determining the percentage of measurements in the interval (mean) $\pm$ 2(std. dev.): **Chebyshev's Rule** (at least 75%) and **Empirical Rule** (approximately 95%)
- Measures of relative standing: **percentile score** and **z-score**
- Methods for detecting outliers: box plots and z-scores
- Method for graphing the relationship between two quantitative variables: **scatterplot**

Language Lab

Symbol	Pronunciation	Description
$\sum$	sum of	Summation notation; $\sum_{i=1}^{n} x_i$ represents the sum of the measurements $x_1, x_2, \ldots, x_n,$
μ	mu	Population mean
$\overline{x}$	x-bar	Sample mean
σ^2	sigma-squared	Population variance
σ	sigma	Population standard deviation
s^2		Sample variance
s		Sample standard deviation
z		z-score for a measurement

M	Median (middle quartile) of a sample data set
Q_L	Lower quartile (25th percentile)
Q_U	Upper quartile (75th percentile)
IQR	Interquartile range

Supplementary Exercises 2.149–2.187

Note: Starred (*) exercises refer to the optional sections in this chapter.

Understanding the Principles

2.149 Discuss conditions under which the median is preferred to the mean as a measure of central tendency.

2.150 Explain why we generally prefer the standard deviation to the range as a measure of variation.

2.151 Give a situation where we will prefer using a stem-and-leaf display over a histogram when graphically describing quantitative data.

2.152 Give a situation where we will prefer using a box plot over z-scores to detect an outlier.

2.153 Give a technique that is used to distort information shown on a graph.

Learning the Mechanics

2.154 Construct a relative frequency histogram for the data summarized in the table below.

Measurement Class	Relative Frequency	Interval Class	Relative Frequency
.00–.75	.02	5.25–6.00	.15
.75–1.50	.01	6.00–6.75	.12
1.50–2.25	.03	6.75–7.50	.09
2.25–3.00	.05	7.50–8.25	.05
3.00–3.75	.10	8.25–9.00	.04
3.75–4.50	.14	9.00–9.75	.01
4.50–5.25	.19		

2.155 Consider the following three measurements: 50, 70, 80. Find the z-score for each measurement if they are from a population with a mean and standard deviation equal to

  a. $\mu = 60, \sigma = 10$
  b. $\mu = 60, \sigma = 5$
  c. $\mu = 40, \sigma = 10$
  d. $\mu = 40, \sigma = 100$

*2.156 Refer to Exercise 2.155. For parts **a**–**d**, determine whether the three measurements 50, 70, and 80 are outliers.

2.157 Compute s^2 for data sets with the following characteristics:

  a. $\sum_{i=1}^{n} x_i^2 = 246, \sum_{i=1}^{n} x_i = 63, n = 22$

  b. $\sum_{i=1}^{n} x_i^2 = 666, \sum_{i=1}^{n} x_i = 106, n = 25$

  c. $\sum_{i=1}^{n} x_i^2 = 76, \sum_{i=1}^{n} x_i = 11, n = 7$

2.158 If the range of a set of data is 20, find a rough approximation to the standard deviation of the data set.

2.159 For each of the following data sets, compute $\bar{x}$, s^2, and s. If appropriate, specify the units in which your answers are expressed.

  a. 4, 6, 6, 5, 6, 7
  b. −\$1, \$4, −\$3, \$0, −\$3, −\$6
  c. 3/5%, 4/5%, 2/5%, 1/5%, 1/16%
  d. Calculate the range of each data set in parts **a**–**c**.

2.160 For each of the following data sets, compute $\bar{x}$, s^2, and s:

  a. 13, 1, 10, 3, 3
  b. 13, 6, 6, 0
  c. 1, 0, 1, 10, 11, 11, 15
  d. 3, 3, 3, 3
  e. For each data set in parts **a**–**d**, form the interval $\bar{x} \pm 2s$ and calculate the percentage of the measurements that fall in the interval.

*2.161 Construct a scatterplot for the data listed here. Do you detect any trends?

Variable #1:	174	268	345	119	400	520	190	448	307	252
Variable #2:	8	10	15	7	22	31	15	20	11	9

2.162 The following data sets have been invented to demonstrate that the lower bounds given by Chebyshev's Rule are appropriate. Notice that the data are contrived and would not be encountered in a real-life problem.

  a. Consider a data set that contains ten 0s, two 1s, and ten 2s. Calculate $\bar{x}$, s^2, and s. What percentage of the measurements are in the interval $\bar{x} \pm s$? Compare this result to Chebyshev's Rule.

  b. Consider a data set that contains five 0s, thirty-two 1s, and five 2s. Calculate $\bar{x}$, s^2, and s. What percentage of the measurements are in the interval $\bar{x} \pm 2s$? Compare this result to Chebyshev's Rule.

  c. Consider a data set that contains three 0s, fifty 1s, and three 2s. Calculate $\bar{x}$, s^2, and s. What percentage of the measurements are in the interval $\bar{x} \pm 3s$? Compare this result to Chebyshev's Rule.

d. Draw a histogram for each of the data sets in parts **a**, **b**, and **c**. What do you conclude from these graphs and the answers to parts **a**, **b**, and **c**?

Applying the Concepts—Basic

2.163 Gallup poll on smoking. *USA Today* (Dec. 31, 1999) reported on a Gallup Survey which asked: "Do you think cigarette smoking is one of the causes of lung cancer?" The accompanying table shows the results of the 1999 survey compared to the results of a similar survey conducted 45 years earlier.

Is Smoking a Cause of Lung Cancer?	1954 Survey	1999 Survey
Yes	41%	92%
No	31%	6%
No opinion	28%	2%

a. Construct a pie chart for the 1954 survey results.
b. Construct a pie chart for the 1999 survey results.
c. Compare the two graphs. Do the graphs show a dramatic shift in people's opinion on whether smoking causes lung cancer?

CRASH

2.164 Crash tests on new cars. Each year, the National Highway Traffic Safety Administration (NHTSA) crash tests new car models to determine how well they protect the driver and front-seat passenger in a head-on collision. The NHTSA has developed a "star" scoring system for the frontal crash test, with results ranging from one star (*) to five stars (*****). The more stars in the rating, the better the level of crash protection in a head-on collision. The NHTSA crash test results for 98 cars in a recent model year are stored in the data file named CRASH. The driver-side star ratings for the 98 cars are summarized in the accompanying MINITAB printout. Use the information in the printout to form a pie chart. Interpret the graph.

Tally for Discrete Variables: DRIVSTAR

```
DRIVSTAR   Count   Percent
      2        4      4.08
      3       17     17.35
      4       59     60.20
      5       18     18.37
    N=        98
```

2.165 Crash Tests on New Cars. Refer to Exercise 2.164 and the NHTSA crash test data. One quantitative variable recorded by the NHTSA is driver's severity of head injury (measured on a scale from 0 to 1,500). The mean and standard deviation for the 98 driver head-injury ratings in the CRASH file are displayed in the

MINITAB printout at the bottom of the page. Use these values to find the *z*-score for a driver head-injury rating of 408. Interpret the result.

2.166 Competition for bird nest holes. *The Condor* (May 1995) published a study of competition for nest holes among collared flycatchers, a bird species. The authors collected the data for the study by periodically inspecting nest boxes located on the island of Gotland in Sweden. The nest boxes were grouped into 14 discrete locations (called plots). The accompanying table gives the number of flycatchers killed and the number of flycatchers breeding at each plot.

CONDOR

Plot Number	Number Killed	Number of Breeders
1	5	30
2	4	28
3	3	38
4	2	34
5	2	26
6	1	124
7	1	68
8	1	86
9	1	32
10	0	30
11	0	46
12	0	132
13	0	100
14	0	6

Source: Merilä, J., and Wiggins, D. A. "Interspecific competition for nest holes causes adult mortality in the collared flycatcher." *The Condor*, Vol. 97, No. 2, May 1995, p. 447 (Table 4). Cooper Ornithological Society.

a. Calculate the mean, median, and mode for the number of flycatchers killed at the 14 study plots.
b. Interpret the measures of central tendency, part **a**.
***c.** Graphically examine the relationship between number killed and number of breeders. Do you detect a trend?

2.167 Beanie Babies. Beanie Babies are toy stuffed animals that have become valuable collector's items. *Beanie World Magazine* provided the age, retired status, and value of 50 Beanie Babies. The data one saved in the BEANIE file, with several of the observations shown in the table on p. 82.
a. Summarize the retried/current status of the 50 Beanie Babies with an appropriate graph. Interpret the graph.
b. Summarize the values of the 50 Beanie Babies with an appropriate graph. Interpret the graph.
***c.** Use a graph to portray the relationship between a Beanie Baby's value and its age. Do you detect a trend?

Descriptive Statistics: DRIVHEAD

```
Variable    N    Mean   StDev  Minimum      Q1   Median      Q3  Maximum
DRIVHEAD   98   603.7   185.4    216.0   475.0    605.0   724.3   1240.0
```

BEANIE (Selected observations)

Name	Age (Months) as of Sept. 1998	Retired (R) Current (C)	Value ($)
1. Ally the Alligator	52	R	55.00
2. Batty the Bat	12	C	12.00
3. Bongo the Brown Monkey	28	R	40.00
4. Blackie the Bear	52	C	10.00
5. Bucky the Beaver	40	R	45.00
⋮	⋮	⋮	⋮
46. Stripes the Tiger (Gold/Black)	40	R	400.00
47. Teddy the 1997 Holiday Bear	12	R	50.00
48. Tuffy the Terrier	17	C	10.00
49. Tracker the Basset Hound	5	C	15.00
50. Zip the Black Cat	28	R	40.00

Source: Beanie World Magazine, Sept. 1998.

d. According to Chebyshev's Rule, what percentage of the age measurements would you expect to find in the intervals $\bar{x} \pm .75s$, $\bar{x} \pm 2.5s$, $\bar{x} \pm 4s$?

e. What percentage of the age measurements actually fall in the intervals of part **e**? Compare your results with those of part

f. Repeat parts **d** and **e** for value.

2.168 Public image of mental illness. A survey was conducted to investigate the impact of the mass media on the public's perception of mental illness. (*Health Education Journal,* Sept. 1994.) The media coverage for each of 562 items related to mental health in Scotland was classified into one of five categories: violence to others, sympathetic coverage, harm to self, comic images, and criticism of accepted definitions of mental illness. A summary of the results is provided in the accompanying table.

Media Coverage	Number of Items
Violence to others	373
Sympathetic	102
Harm to self	71
Comic images	12
Criticism of definitions	4
Total	**562**

Source: Philo, G., et al. "The impact of the mass media on public images of mental illness: Media content and audience belief." *Health Education Journal,* Vol. 53, No. 3, Sept. 1994, p.274 (Table 1).

a. Construct a relative frequency table for the data.

b. Display the relative frequencies in a graph.

c. Discuss the findings.

2.169 Computer anxiety of teachers. The extent of computer anxiety among secondary technical education teachers in West Virginia was examined in the *Journal of Studies in Technical Careers* (Vol. 15, 1995). Level of computer anxiety was measured by the Computer Anxiety Scale (COMPAS), with scores ranging from 10 to 50. (Lower scores reflect a higher degree of anxiety.) One objective was to compare the computer anxiety levels of male and female secondary technical education teachers in West Virginia. The data for the 116 teachers who participated in the survey are summarized in the following table.

	Male Teachers	Female Teachers
n	68	48
$\bar{x}$	26.4	24.5
s	10.6	11.2

Source: Gordon, H. R. D. "Analysis of the computer anxiety levels of secondary technical education teachers in West Virginia." *Journal of Studies in Technical Careers,* Vol. 15, No. 2, 1995, pp. 26–27 (Table 1).

a. Interpret the mean COMPAS score for male teachers.

b. Repeat part **a** for female teachers.

c. Give an interval that contains about 95% of the COMPAS scores for male teachers. (Assume the distribution of scores for males is symmetric and mound shaped.)

d. Repeat part **c** for female teachers.

2.170 Achievement test scores. The distribution of scores on a nationally administered college achievement test has a median of 520 and a mean of 540.

a. Explain why it is possible for the mean to exceed the median for this distribution of measurements.

b. Suppose you are told that the 90th percentile is 660. What does this mean?

c. Suppose you are told that you scored at the 94th percentile. Interpret this statement.

Applying the Concepts—Intermediate

2.171 New book reviews. *Choice* magazine provides new-book reviews each issue. A random sample of 375 *Choice* book reviews in American history, geography, and area studies was selected and the "overall opinion" of the book stated in each review was ascertained. (*Library Acquisitions: Practice and Theory*, Vol. 19, 1995.) Overall opinion was coded as follows: 1 = would not recommend, 2 = cautious or very little recommendation, 3 = little or no preference, 4 = favorable/recommended, 5 = outstanding/significant contribution. A summary table for the data is provided below.

Opinion Code	Number of Reviews
1	19
2	37
3	35
4	238
5	46
Total	375

Source: Carlo, P. W., and Natowitz, A. "Choice book reviews in American history, geography, and area studies: An analysis for 1988–1993." *Library Acquisitions: Practice & Theory,* Vol. 19, No. 2, 1995, p. 159 (Figure 1).

a. Use a Pareto diagram to find the opinion that occurred most often. What proportion of the books reviewed had this opinion?

b. Do you agree with the following statement extracted from the study: "A majority (more than 75%) of books reviewed are evaluated favorably and recommended for purchase."?

2.172 Archaeologists study of ring diagrams. Archaeologists gain insight into the social life of ancient tribes by measuring the distance (in centimeters) of each artifact found at a site from the "central hearth" (i.e., the middle of an artifact scatter). A graphical summary of these distances, in the form of a histogram, is called a *ring diagram*. (*World Archaeology*, Oct. 1997.) Ring diagrams for two archaeological sites (A and G) in Europe follow.

a. Identify the type of skewness (if any) present in the data collected at the two sites.

b. Archaeologists have associated unimodal ring diagrams with open air hearths and multimodal ring diagrams with hearths inside dwellings. Can you identify the type of hearth (*open air or inside dwelling*) that was most likely present at each site?

2.173 Golf handicaps. The United States Golf Association (USGA) Handicap System is designed to allow golfers of differing abilities to enjoy fair competition. The handicap index is a measure of a player's potential scoring ability on an 18-hole golf course of standard difficulty. For example, on a par-72 course, a golfer with a handicap of 7 will typically have a score of 79 (seven strokes over par). Over 4.5 million golfers have an official USGA Handicap index. The handicap indexes for both male and female golfers were obtained from the USGA and are summarized in the two histograms shown below.

a. What percentage of male USGA golfers have a handicap greater than 20?

b. What percentage of female USGA golfers have a handicap greater than 20?

c. Which group of golfers, male or female, tend to have the greater handicap?

2.174 Control of life perception study. The Locus of Control (LOC) is a measure of one's perception of control over factors affecting one's life. In one study, the LOC was measured for two groups of individuals undergoing weight-reduction for treatment of obesity. (*Journal of Psychology*, Mar. 1991.) The LOC mean and standard deviation for a sample of 46 adults were 6.45 and 2.89, respectively, while the LOC mean and standard deviation for a sample of 19 adolescents were 10.89 and 2.48, respectively. A lower score on the LOC scale indicates a perception that internal factors are in control, while a higher score indicates a perception that external factors are in control.

a. Calculate the 1- and 2-standard-deviation intervals around the means for each group. Plot these intervals on a line graph using different colors or symbols to represent each group.

b. Assuming that the distributions of LOC scores are approximately mound-shaped, estimate the numbers of individuals within each interval.

c. Based on your answers to parts **a** and **b**, do you think an inference can be made that *all* adults and adolescents undergoing weight-reduction treatment differ with respect to LOC? What factors did you consider in making this inference? (We'll reconsider this exercise in Chapter 9 to show how to measure the reliability of this inference.)

2.175 Road use study. For each day of last year, the number of vehicles passing through a certain intersection was recorded by a city engineer. One objective of this study was to determine the percentage of days that more than 425 vehicles used the intersection. Suppose the mean for the data was 375 vehicles per day and the standard deviation was 25 vehicles.

a. What can you say about the percentage of days that more than 425 vehicles used the intersection? Assume you know nothing about the shape of the relative frequency distribution for the data.

b. What is your answer to part **a** if you know that the relative frequency distribution for the data is mound-shaped?

2.176 Chinese herbal drugs. Platelet-activating factor (PAF) is a potent chemical that occurs in patients suffering from shock, inflammation, hypotension, respiratory, and cardiovascular disorders. A bioassay was undertaken to investigate the potential of 17 traditional Chinese herbal drugs in PAF inhibition. (*Progress in Natural Science*, June 1995.) The prevention of the PAF binding process, measured as a percentage, for each drug is provided in the accompanying table.

a. Construct a stem-and-leaf display for the data.

⊙ **PAF**

Drug	PAF Inhibition (%)
Hai-feng-teng (Fuji)	77
Hai-feng-teng (Japan)	33
Shan-ju	75
Zhang-yiz-hu-jiao	62
Shi-nan-teng	70
Huang-hua-hu-jiao	12
Hua-nan-hu-jiao	0
Xiao-yie-pa-ai-xiang	0
Mao-ju	0
Jia-ju	15
Xie-yie-ju	25
Da-yie-ju	0
Bian-yie-hu-jiao	9
Bi-bo	24
Duo-mai-hu-jiao	40
Yan-sen	0
Jiao-guo-hu-jiao	31

Source: Guiqiu, H. "PAF receptor antagonistic principles from Chinese traditional drugs." *Progress in Natural Science,* Vol. 5, No. 3, June 1995, p. 301 (Table 1).

b. Compute the mean, median, and mode of the inhibition percentages for the 17 herbal drugs. Interpret the results.

c. Locate the median, mean, and mode on the stem-and-leaf display, part **a**. Do these measures of central tendency appear to locate the center of the data?

d. Compute the range, variance, and standard deviation for the inhibition percentages.

e. Form an interval that is highly likely to capture the inhibition percentage of a Chinese herbal drug.

*2.177 Computer system down time study. A manufacturer of minicomputers is investigating the down time of its systems. The 40 most recent customers were surveyed to determine the amount of down time (in hours) they had experienced during the previous month. These data are listed in the table.

⊙ **DOWNTIME**

Customer Number	Down Time	Customer Number	Down Time	Customer Number	Down Time
230	12	244	2	258	28
231	16	245	11	259	19
232	5	246	22	260	34
233	16	247	17	261	26
234	21	248	31	262	17
235	29	249	10	263	11
236	38	250	4	264	64
237	14	251	10	265	19
238	47	252	15	266	18
239	0	253	7	267	24
240	24	254	20	268	49
241	15	255	9	269	50
242	13	256	22		
243	8	257	18		

a. Use a statistical software package to construct a box plot for these data. Use the information reflected in the box plot to describe the frequency distribution of the data set. Your description should address central tendency, variation, and skewness.

b. Use your box plot to determine which customers are having unusually lengthy down times.

c. Find and interpret the z-scores associated with customers you identified in part **b**.

SLI

*2.178 Childrens use of pronouns. Refer to the *Journal of Communication Disorders* data on deviation intelligence quotient (DIQ) and percent pronoun errors for 30 children, Exercise 2.65 (p. 65). The data are saved in the SLI file.

a. Plot all the data to investigate a possible trend between DIQ and proper use of pronouns. What do you observe?

b. Plot the data for the ten SLI children only. Is there a trend between DIQ and proper use of pronouns?

2.179 Oil spill impact on seabirds. The *Journal of Agricultural, Biological, and Environmental Statistics* (Sept. 2000) published a study on the impact of the *Exxon Valdez* tanker oil spill on the seabird population in Prince William Sound, Alaska. A subset of the data analyzed is stored in the EVOS file. Data were collected on 96 shoreline locations (called transects) of constant width but variable length. For each transect, the number of seabirds found is recorded as well as the length (in kilometers) of the transect and whether or not the transect was in an oiled area. (The first five and last five observations in the EVOS file are listed in the table.)

a. Identify the variables measured as quantitative or qualitative.

EVOS (Selected observations)

Transect	Seabirds	Length	Oil
1	0	4.06	No
2	0	6.51	No
3	54	6.76	No
4	0	4.26	No
5	14	3.59	No
⋮	⋮	⋮	⋮
92	7	3.40	Yes
93	4	6.67	Yes
94	0	3.29	Yes
95	0	6.22	Yes
96	27	8.94	Yes

Source: McDonald, T. L., Erickson, W. P, and McDonald, L. L. "Analysis of count data from before–after control-impact studies," *Journal of Agricultural, Biological, and Environmental Statistics,* Vol. 5, No. 3, Sept. 2000, pp. 277–8 (Table A.1).

b. Identify the experimental unit.

c. Use a pie chart to describe the percentage of transects in oiled and unoiled areas.

d. Use a graphical method to examine the relationship between observed number of seabirds and transect length.

e. Observed seabird density is defined as the observed count divided by the length of the transect. MINITAB descriptive statistics for seabird densities in unoiled and oiled transects are displayed in the printout shown at the bottom of the page. Assess whether the distribution of seabird densities differs for transects in oiled and unoiled areas.

f. For unoiled transects, give an interval of values that is likely to contain at least 75% of the seabird densities.

g. For oiled transects, give an interval of values that is likely to contain at least 75% of the seabird densities.

h. Which type of transect, an oiled or unoiled one, is more likely to have a seabird density of 16? Explain.

Applying the Concepts—Advanced

2.180 Standardized test "average." *US News & World Report* reported on many factors contributing to the breakdown of public education. One study mentioned in the article found that over 90% of the nation's school districts reported that their students were scoring "above the national average" on standardized tests. Using your knowledge of measures of central tendency, explain why the schools' reports are incorrect. Does your analysis change if the term "average" refers to the mean? To the median? Explain what effect this misinformation might have on the perception of the nation's schools.

2.181 Speed of light from galaxies. Refer to *The Astronomical Journal* study of galaxy velocities, Exercise 2.100 (p. 80). A second cluster of galaxies, named A1775, is thought to be a *double cluster*; that is, two clusters of galaxies in close proximity. Fifty-one velocity observations (in kilometers per second, km/s) from cluster A1775 are listed in the table.

GALAXY2

22922	20210	21911	19225	18792	21993	23059
20785	22781	23303	22192	19462	19057	23017
20186	23292	19408	24909	19866	22891	23121
19673	23261	22796	22355	19807	23432	22625
22744	22426	19111	18933	22417	19595	23408
22809	19619	22738	18499	19130	23220	22647
22718	22779	19026	22513	19740	22682	19179
19404	22193					

Source: Oegerle, W. R., Hill, J. M., and Fitchett, M. J. "Observations of high dispersion clusters of galaxies: Constraints on cold dark matter." *The Astronomical Journal,* Vol. 110, No. 1, July 1995, p. 34 (Table 1), p. 37 (Figure 1).

Descriptive Statistics: Density

Variable	Oil	N	Mean	StDev	Minimum	Q1	Median	Q3	Maximum
Density	no	36	3.27	6.70	0.000	0.000	0.890	3.87	36.23
	yes	60	3.495	5.968	0.0000	0.000	0.700	5.233	32.836

a. Use a graphical method to describe the velocity distribution of galaxy cluster A1775.

b. Examine the graph, part **a**. Is there evidence to support the double cluster theory? Explain.

c. Calculate numerical descriptive measures (e.g., mean and standard deviation) for galaxy velocities in cluster A1775. Depending on your answer to part **b**, you may need to calculate two sets of numerical descriptive measures, one for each of the clusters (say, A1775A and A1775B) within the double cluster.

d. Suppose you observe a galaxy velocity of 20,000 km/s. Is this galaxy likely to belong to cluster A1775A or A1775B? Explain.

OILSPILL

2.182 Hull failures of oil tankers. Owing to several major ocean oil spills by tank vessels, Congress passed the 1990 Oil Pollution Act, which requires all tankers to be designed with thicker hulls. Further improvements in the structural design of a tank vessel have been proposed since then, each with the objective of reducing the likelihood of an oil spill and decreasing the amount of outflow in the event of a hull puncture. To aid in this development, *Marine Technology* (Jan. 1995) reported on the spillage amount (in thousands of metric tons) and cause of puncture for 50 recent major oil spills from tankers and carriers. [*Note*: Cause of puncture is classified as either collision (C), fire/explosion (FE), hull failure (HF) or grounding (G).] The data are saved in the OILSPILL file.

a. Use a graphical method to describe the cause of oil spillage for the 50 tankers. Does the graph suggest that any one cause is more likely to occur than any other? How is this information of value to the design engineers?

b. Find and interpret descriptive statistics for the 50 spillage amounts. Use this information to form an interval that can be used to predict the spillage amount of the next major oil spill.

2.183 Risk of jail suicides. Suicide is the leading cause of death of Americans incarcerated in correctional facilities. To determine what factors increase the risk of suicide in urban jails, a group of researchers collected data on all 37 suicides that occurred over a 15-year period in the Wayne County Jail, Detroit, Michigan (*American Journal of Psychiatry*, July 1995). The data for each suicide victim are saved in the SUICIDE file. Selected observations are shown in the accompanying table.

a. Identify the type (quantitative or qualitative) of each variable measured.

b. Are suicides at the jail more likely to be committed by inmates charged with murder/manslaughter or with lesser crimes? Illustrate with a graph.

c. Are suicides at the jail more likely to be committed at night? Illustrate with a graph.

d. What is the mean length of time an inmate is in jail before committing suicide? What is the median? Interpret these two numbers.

e. Is it likely that a future suicide at the jail will occur after 200 days? Explain.

*f. Have suicides at the jail declined over the years? Support your answer with a graph.

Critical Thinking Challenges

2.184 Grades in statistics. The final grades given by two professors in introductory statistics courses have been carefully examined. The students in the first professor's class had a grade point average of 3.0 and a standard deviation of .2. Those in the second professor's class had grade points with an average of 3.0 and a standard deviation of 1.0. If you had a choice, which professor would you take for this course?

2.185 Salaries of professional athletes. The salaries of superstar professional athletes receive much attention in the media. The multimillion-dollar long-term contract is now commonplace among this elite group. Nevertheless, rarely does a season pass without negotiations between one or more of the players' associations and team owners for additional salary and fringe benefits for *all* players in their particular sports.

a. If a players' association wanted to support its argument for higher "average" salaries, which measure of central tendency do you think it should use? Why?

b. To refute the argument, which measure of central tendency should the owners apply to the players' salaries? Why?

2.186 No Child Left Behind Act. According to the government, federal spending on K–12 education has increased dramatically over the past 20 years, but student performance has essentially stayed the same. Hence, in 2002, President George Bush signed into law the No

SUICIDE (Selected Observations)

Victim	Days in Jail Before Suicide	Marital Status	Race	Murder/Manslaughter Charge	Time of Suicide	Year
1	3	Married	W	Yes	Night	1972
2	4	Single	W	Yes	Night	1987
3	5	Single	NW	Yes	Afternoon	1975
4	7	Widowed	NW	Yes	Night	1981
5	10	Single	NW	Yes	Afternoon	1982
⋮	⋮	⋮	⋮	⋮	⋮	⋮
36	41	Single	NW	No	Night	1985
37	86	Married	W	No	Night	1968

Source: DuRand, C. J., et al. "A quarter century of suicide in a major urban jail: Implications for community psychiatry." *American Journal of Psychiatry,* Vol. 152, No. 7, July 1995, p. 1078 (Table 1).

Federal Spending on
K-12 Education
(Elementary and Secondary
Education Act)

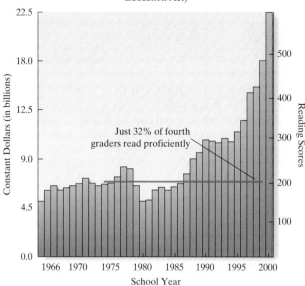

U.S. Department of Education $$$

average of 250 with a standard deviation of 50, and (3) the reading test scores of seventh and twelfth grades and the mathematics scores of fourth graders did improve substantially over the past 20 years.

2.187 The new Hite Report. In 1968 researcher Shere Hite shocked conservative America with her famous Hite Report on the permissive sexual attitudes of American men and women. Some 20 years later, Hite was surrounded by controversy again with her book, *Women and Love: A Cultural Revolution in Progress* (Knopf Press, 1988). In this book, Hite reveals some startling statistics describing how women feel about contemporary relationships:

- Eighty-four percent are not emotionally satisfied with their relationship.
- Ninety-five percent report "emotional and psychological harassment" from their men.
- Seventy percent of those married 5 years or more are having extramarital affairs.
- Only 13% of those married more than 2 years are "in love."

Hite conducted the survey by mailing out 100,000 questionnaires to women across the country over a 7-year period. These questionnaires were mailed to a wide variety of organizations, including church groups, women's voting and political groups, women's rights organizations, and counseling and walk-in centers for women. Organizational leaders were asked to circulate the questionnaires to their members. Hite also relied on volunteer respondents who wrote in for copies of the questionnaire. Each questionnaire consisted of 127 open-ended questions, many with numerous subquestions and follow-ups. Hite's instructions read, "It is not necessary to answer every question! Feel free to skip around and answer those questions you choose." Approximately 4,500 completed questionnaires were returned for a response rate of 4.5%, and they form the data set from which the percentages above were determined. Hite claims that these 4,500 women are a representative sample of all women in the United States and, therefore, the survey results imply that vast numbers of women are "suffering a lot of pain in their love relationships with men." Critically assess the survey results. Do you believe they are reliable?

Child Left Behind Act, a bill that promised improved student achievement for all U.S. children. *Chance* (Fall 2003) reported on a graphic obtained from the U.S. Department of Education Web site (www.ed.gov) that was designed to support the new legislation. The graphic is reproduced above. The bars in the graph represent annual federal spending on education, in billions of dollars (left-side vertical axis). The horizontal line represents the annual average fourth grade children's reading ability score (right-side vertical axis). Critically assess the information portrayed in the graph. Does it, in fact, support the government's position that our children are not making classroom improvements despite federal spending on education? Use the following facts (divulged in the *Chance* article) to help you frame your answer: (1) The U.S. student population has also increased dramatically over the past 20 years, (2) fourth-grade reading test scores are designed to have an

Student Project

We list here several sources of real-life data sets (many in the list have been obtained from Wasserman and Bernero's *Statistics Sources* and many can be accessed via the Internet). This index of data sources is very complete and is a useful reference for anyone interested in finding almost any type of data. First we list some almanacs:

CBS News Almanac
Information Please Almanac
World Almanac and Book of Facts

United States Government publications are also rich sources of data:

Agricultural Statistics
Digest of Educational Statistics
Handbook of Labor Statistics
Housing and Urban Development Yearbook
Social Indicators
Uniform Crime Reports for the United States

Vital Statistics of the United States
Business Conditions Digest
Economic Indicators
Monthly Labor Review
Survey of Current Business
Bureau of the Census Catalog
Statistical Abstract of the United States

Main data sources are published on an annual basis:

Commodity Yearbook
Facts and Figures on Government Finance
Municipal Yearbook
Standard and Poor's Corporation, Trade and Securities: Statistics

Some sources contain data that are international in scope:

Compendium of Social Statistics
Demographic Yearbook
United Nations Statistical Yearbook
World Handbook of Political and Social Indicators

Utilizing the data sources listed, sources suggested by your instructor, or your own resourcefulness, find one real-life quantitative data set that stems from an area of particular interest to you.

a. Describe the data set by using a relative frequency histogram, stem-and-leaf display, or dot plot.

b. Find the mean, median, variance, standard deviation, and range of the data set.

c. Use Chebyshev's Rule and the Empirical Rule to describe the distribution of this data set. Count the actual number of observations that fall within 1, 2, and 3 standard deviations of the mean of the data set and compare these counts with the description of the data set you developed in part **b**.

References

Hoff, D. *How to Lie with Statistics*. New York: Norton, 1954.

Mendenhall, W., Beaver, R. J., and Beaver, B. M. *Introduction to Probability and Statistics*, 10th ed. North Scituate, Mass.: Duxbury, 1999.

Tufte, E. R. *Envisioning Information*. Cheshire, Conn.: Graphics Press, 1990.

Tufte, E.R. *Visual Explanations*. Cheshire, Conn.: Graphics Press, 1997.

Tufte, E. R. *Visual Display of Quantitative Information*. Cheshire, Conn.: Graphics Press, 1983.

Tukey, J. *Exploratory Data Analysis*. Reading, Mass.: Addison-Wesley, 1977.

Using Technology

Describing Data Using MINITAB

Graphing Data

To obtain graphical descriptions of your data, click on the "Graph" button on the MINITAB menu bar. The resulting menu list appears as shown in Figure 2.M.1. Several of the options covered in this text are "Bar Chart," "Pie Chart", "Scatter Plot," "Histogram," "Dotplot," and "Stem-and-Leaf (display)." Click on the graph of your choice to view the appropriate dialog box. For example, the dialog box for a histogram is shown in Figure 2.M.2. Make the appropriate variable selections and click "OK" to view the graph.

Numerical Descriptive Statistics

To obtain numerical descriptive measures for a quantitative variable (e.g., mean, standard deviation, etc.), click on the "Stat" button on the main menu bar, then click on "Basic Statistics, then click on "Display Descriptive Statistics" (see Figure 2.M.3). The resulting dialog box appears in Figure 2.M.4.

Figure 2.M.1
MINITAB Menu Options for Graphing Your Data

Select the quantitative variables you want to analyze and place them in the "Variables" box. You can control which particular descriptive statistics appear by clicking the "Statistics" button on the dialog box and making your selections. (As an option, you can create histograms and dot plots for the data by clicking the "Graphs" button and making the appropriate selections.) Click on "OK" to view the descriptive statistics printout.

Figure 2.M.2
Histogram Dialog Box

Figure 2.M.3
MINITAB Options for Obtaining Descriptive Statistics

Figure 2.M.4
Descriptive Statistics Dialog Box

3

Probability

Contents

3.1 Events, Sample Spaces, and Probability

3.2 Unions and Intersections

3.3 Complementary Events

3.4 The Additive Rule and Mutually Exclusive Events

3.5 Conditional Probability

3.6 The Multiplicative Rule and Independent Events

3.7 Random Sampling

3.8 Some Additional Counting Rules (Optional)

3.9 Bayes's Rule (Optional)

Statistics in Action

Lotto Buster!

Using Technology

Generating a Random Sample Using MINITAB

Where We've Been

- Identified the objective of inferential statistics— to make inferences about a population based on information in a sample

- Introduced graphical and numerical descriptive measures for both quantitative and qualitative data

Where We're Going

- Develop probability as a measure of uncertainty.

- Introduce basic rules for finding probabilities.

- Use a probability as a measure of reliability for an inference.

Statistics in *ACTION*

Lotto Buster!

"Welcome to the Wonderful World of Lottery Bus$ters." So began the premier issue of *Lottery Buster*, a monthly publication for players of the state lottery games. *Lottery Buster* provides interesting facts and figures on the 37 state lotteries currently operating in the United States and, more importantly, tips on how to increase a player's odds of winning the lottery.

New Hampshire, in 1963, was the first state in modern times to authorize a state lottery as an alternative to increasing taxes. (Prior to this time, beginning in 1895, lotteries were banned in America because of corruption.) Since then, lotteries have become immensely popular for two reasons. First, they lure you with the opportunity to win millions of dollars with a $1 investment, and second, when you lose, at least you believe your money is going to a good cause. Many state lotteries, like Florida, designate a high percentage of lottery revenues to fund state education.

The popularity of the state lottery has brought with it an avalanche of "experts" and "mathematical wizards" (such as the editors of *Lottery Buster*) who provide advice on how to win the lottery — for a fee, of course! Many offer guaranteed "systems" of winning through computer software products with catchy names such as Lotto Wizard, Lottorobics, Win4D, and Loto-Luck.

For example, most knowledgeable lottery players would agree that the "golden rule" or "first rule" in winning lotteries is *game selection*. State lotteries generally offer three types of games: Instant (scratch-off tickets or online) games, Daily Numbers (Pick-3 or Pick-4), and the weekly Pick-6 Lotto game.

One version of the Instant game involves scratching off the thin opaque covering on a ticket with the edge of a coin to determine whether you have won or lost. The cost of a ticket ranges from 50¢ to $1, and the amount won ranges from $1 to $100,000 in most states and to as much as $1 million in others. *Lottery Buster* advises against playing the Instant game because it is "a pure chance play, and you can win only by dumb luck. No skill can be applied to this game."

The Daily Numbers game permits you to choose either a three-digit (Pick-3) or four-digit (Pick-4) number at a cost of $1 per ticket. Each night, the winning number is drawn. If your number matches the winning number, you win a large sum of money, usually $100,000. You do have some control over the Daily Numbers game (since you pick the numbers that you play) and, consequently, there are strategies available to increase your chances of winning. However, the Daily Numbers game, like the Instant game, is not available for out-of-state play.

To play Pick-6 Lotto, you select six numbers of your choice from a field of numbers ranging from 1 to N, where N depends on which state's game you are playing. For example, Florida's current Lotto game involves picking six numbers ranging from 1 to 53. (See Figure SIA3.1.) The cost of a ticket is $1, and the payoff, if your six numbers match the winning numbers drawn, is $7 million or more, depending on the number of tickets purchased. (To date, Florida has had the largest state weekly payoff of over $200 million.) In addition to the grand prize, you can win second-, third-, and fourth-prize payoffs by matching five, four, and three of the six numbers drawn, respectively. And you don't have to be a resident of the state to play the state's Lotto game.

In this chapter, several Statistics In Action Revisited examples demonstrate how to use the basic concepts of probability to compute the odds of winning a state lottery game and to assess the validity of the strategies suggested by lottery "experts."

Figure SIA3.1

Statistics in Action Revisited for Chapter 3

- Computing and Understanding the Probability of Winning Lotto (p. 130)

- The Probability of Winning Lotto with a Wheel System (p. 141)
- The Probability of Winning Daily Cash 3 or Play 4 (p. 155)

Recall that one branch of statistics is concerned with decisions about a population based on sample information. You can see how this is accomplished more easily if you understand the relationship between population and sample — a relationship that becomes clearer if we reverse the statistical procedure of making inferences from sample to population. In this chapter we assume the population is *known* and calculate the chances of obtaining various samples from the population. Thus, we show that probability is the reverse of statistics: In probability, we use the population information to infer the probable nature of the sample.

Probability plays an important role in inference making. Suppose, for example, you have an opportunity to invest in an oil exploration company. Past records show that out of ten previous oil drillings (a sample of the company's experiences), all ten came up dry. What do you conclude? Do you think the chances are better than 50 : 50 that the company will hit a gusher? Should you invest in this company? Chances are, your answer to these questions will be an emphatic No. If the company's exploratory prowess is sufficient to hit a producing well 50% of the time, a record of ten dry wells out of ten drilled is an event that is just too improbable.

Or suppose you're playing poker with what your opponents assure you is a well-shuffled deck of cards. In three consecutive five-card hands, the person on your right is dealt four aces. Based on this sample of three deals, do you think the cards are being adequately shuffled? Again, your answer is likely to be No because dealing three hands of four aces is just too improbable if the cards were properly shuffled.

Note that the decisions concerning the potential success of the oil drilling company and the adequacy of card shuffling both involve knowing the chance — or probability — of a certain sample result. Both situations were contrived so that you could easily conclude that the probabilities of the sample results were small. Unfortunately, the probabilities of many observed sample results aren't so easy to evaluate intuitively. For these cases we need the assistance of a theory of probability.

3.1 Events, Sample Spaces, and Probability

Let's begin our treatment of probability with straightforward examples that are easily described. With the aid of simple examples, we can introduce important definitions that will help us develop the notion of probability more easily.

Suppose a coin is tossed once and the up face is recorded. The result we see is called an *observation*, or *measurement*, and the process of making an observation is called an *experiment*. Notice that our definition of experiment is broader than the one used in the physical sciences, where you tend to picture test tubes, microscopes, and other laboratory equipment. Among other things, statistical experiments may include recording an Internet user's preference for a Web browser, recording a voter's opinion on an important political issue, measuring the amount of dissolved oxygen in a polluted river, observing the level of anxiety of a test taker, counting the number of errors in an inventory, and observing the fraction of insects killed by a new insecticide. The point is that a statistical experiment can be almost any act of observation as long as the outcome is uncertain.

DEFINITION 3.1

An **experiment** is an act or process of observation that leads to a single outcome that cannot be predicted with certainty.

Consider another simple experiment consisting of tossing a die and observing the number on the up face. The six possible outcomes to this experiment are:

1. Observe a 1
2. Observe a 2
3. Observe a 3
4. Observe a 4
5. Observe a 5
6. Observe a 6

Note that if this experiment is conducted once, *you can observe one and only one of these six basic outcomes, and the outcome cannot be predicted with certainty*. Also, these possibilities cannot be decomposed into more basic outcomes. Because observing the outcome of an experiment is similar to selecting a sample from a population, the basic possible outcomes to an experiment are called **sample points**.*

DEFINITION 3.2

A **sample point** is the most basic outcome of an experiment.

EXAMPLE 3.1

LISTING SAMPLE POINTS

Problem Two coins are tossed, and their up faces are recorded. List all the sample points for this experiment.

Solution Even for a seemingly trivial experiment, we must be careful when listing the sample points. At first glance, we might expect three basic outcomes: Observe two heads; Observe two tails; or Observe one head and one tail. However, further reflection reveals that the last of these, Observe one head and one tail, can be decomposed into two outcomes: Head on coin 1, Tail on coin 2; and Tail on coin 1, Head on coin 2. Thus, we have four sample points:

1. Observe *HH*
2. Observe *HT*
3. Observe *TH*
4. Observe *TT*

where *H* in the first position means "Head on coin 1," *H* in the second position means "Head on coin 2," and so on.

Look Back Even if the coins are identical in appearance they are, in fact, two distinct coins. Thus, the sample points must account for this distinction.

Now Work *Exercise 3.15a*

■ ■ ■

*Alternatively, the term *simple event* can be used.

TABLE 3.1 Experiments and Their Sample Spaces

Experiment: Observe the up face on a coin.
Sample Space: 1. Observe a head
2. Observe a tail

This sample space can be represented in set notation as a set containing two sample points:

$$S: \{H, T\}$$

where H represents the sample point Observe a head and T represents the sample point Observe a tail.

Experiment: Observe the up face on a die.
Sample Space: 1. Observe a 1
2. Observe a 2
3. Observe a 3
4. Observe a 4
5. Observe a 5
6. Observe a 6

This sample space can be represented in set notation as a set of six sample points:

$$S: \{1, 2, 3, 4, 5, 6\}$$

Experiment: Observe the up faces on two coins.
Sample Space: 1. Observe HH
2. Observe HT
3. Observe TH
4. Observe TT

This sample space can be represented in set notation as a set of four sample points:

$$S: \{HH, HT, TH, TT\}$$

We often wish to refer to the collection of all the sample points of an experiment. This collection is called the *sample space* of the experiment. For example, there are six sample points in the sample space associated with the die-toss experiment. The sample spaces for the experiments discussed thus far are shown in Table 3.1.

> **DEFINITION 3.3**
>
> The **sample space** of an experiment is the collection of all its sample points.

Just as graphs are useful in describing sets of data, a pictorial method for presenting the sample space will often be useful. Figure 3.1 shows such a representation for each of the experiments in Table 3.1. In each case, the sample space is shown as a closed figure, labeled **S**, containing all possible sample points. Each sample point is represented by a solid dot (i.e., a "point") and labeled accordingly. Such graphical representations are called **Venn diagrams**.

$\circ H$ $\circ T$

S

a. Experiment: Observe the up face on a coin

$\circ 1$ $\circ 2$ $\circ 3$
$\circ 4$ $\circ 5$ $\circ 6$

S

b. Experiment: Observe the up face on a die

$\circ HH$ $\circ HT$
$\circ TH$ $\circ TT$

S

c. Experiment: Observe the up faces on two coins

Figure 3.1
Venn Diagrams for the Three Experiments from Table 3.1

Biography

JOHN VENN (1834–1923)— The English Logician

Born in Hull, England, John Venn is probably best known for his pictorial representation of unions and intersections (the Venn diagram). While lecturing in Moral Science at Cambridge University, Venn wrote *The Logic of Chance* and two other treatises on logic. In these works, Venn probably had his greatest contribution to the field of probability and statistics — the notion that the probability of an event is simply the long-run proportion of times the event occurs. Besides being a well-known mathematician, Venn was also a historian, philosopher, priest, and skilled machine builder. (His machine for bowling cricket balls once beat a top star on the Australian cricket team.)

Now that we know that an experiment will result in *only one* basic outcome — called a sample point — and that the sample space is the collection of all possible sample points, we're ready to discuss the probabilities of the sample points. You have undoubtedly used the term *probability* and have some intuitive idea about its meaning. Probability is generally used synonymously with "chance," "odds," and similar concepts. For example, if a fair coin is tossed, we might reason that both the sample points, Observe a head and Observe a tail, have the same *chance* of occurring. Thus, we might state that "the probability of observing a head is 50%" or "the odds of seeing a head are 50 : 50." Both these statements are based on an informal knowledge of probability. We'll begin our treatment of probability by using such informal concepts and then solidify what we mean later.

The probability of a sample point is a number between 0 and 1 that measures the likelihood that the outcome will occur when the experiment is performed. This number is usually taken to be the relative frequency of the occurrence of a sample point in a very long series of repetitions of an experiment.* For example, if we are assigning probabilities to the two sample points in the coin-toss experiment (Observe a head and Observe a tail), we might reason that if we toss a balanced coin a very large number of times, the sample points Observe a head and Observe a tail will occur with the same relative frequency of .5.

Our reasoning is supported by Figure 3.2. The figure plots the relative frequency of the number of times that a head occurs when simulating (by computer) the toss of a coin N times, where N ranges from as few as 25 tosses to as many as 1,500 tosses of the coin. You can see that when N is large (i.e., $N = 1,500$), the relative frequency is converging to .5. Thus, the probability of each sample point in the coin tossing experiment is .5.

For some experiments, we may have little or no information on the relative frequency of occurrence of the sample points; consequently, we must assign probabilities

Figure 3.2

Proportion of Heads in N Tosses of a Coin

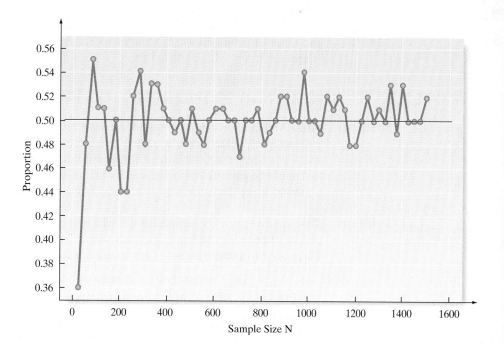

*The result derives from an axiom in probability theory called the *Law of Large Numbers*. Phrased informally, the law states that the relative frequency of the number of times that an outcome occurs when an experiment is replicated over and over again (i.e., a large number of times) approaches the true (or theoretical) probability of the outcome.

Figure 3.3
Experiment: Invest in a
Business Venture and
Observe Whether It
Succeeds (S) or Fails (F)

to the sample points based on general information about the experiment. For example, if the experiment is to invest in a business venture and to observe whether it succeeds or fails, the sample space would appear as in Figure 3.3.

We are unlikely to be able to assign probabilities to the sample points of this experiment based on a long series of repetitions since unique factors govern each performance of this kind of experiment. Instead, we may consider factors such as the personnel managing the venture, the general state of the economy at the time, the rate of success of similar ventures, and any other information deemed pertinent. If we finally decide that the venture has an 80% chance of succeeding, we assign a probability of .8 to the sample point Success. This probability can be interpreted as a measure of our degree of belief in the outcome of the business venture; that is, it is a subjective probability. Notice, however, that such probabilities should be based on expert information that is carefully assessed. If not, we may be misled on any decisions based on these probabilities or based on any calculations in which they appear. [*Note:* For a text that deals in detail with the subjective evaluation of probabilities, see Winkler (1972) or Lindley (1985).]

No matter how you assign the probabilities to sample points, the probabilities assigned must obey two rules:

> **Probability Rules for Sample Points**
>
> Let p_i represent the probability of sample point i.
>
> **1.** All sample point probabilities *must* lie between 0 and 1 (i.e., $0 \leq p_i \leq 1$).
> **2.** The probabilities of all the sample points within a sample space *must* sum to 1 (i.e., $\Sigma p_i = 1$).

Assigning probabilities to sample points is easy for some experiments. For example, if the experiment is to toss a fair coin and observe the face, we would probably all agree to assign a probability of $\frac{1}{2}$ to the two sample points, Observe a head and Observe a tail. However, many experiments have sample points whose probabilities are more difficult to assign.

EXAMPLE 3.2   ASSIGNING PROBABILITIES TO SAMPLE POINTS

Problem   Many American hotels offer complimentary shampoo in their guest rooms. Suppose you randomly select one hotel from a registry of all hotels in the United States and check whether or not the hotel offers complimentary shampoo. Show how this problem might be formulated in the framework of an experiment with sample points and a sample space. Indicate how probabilities might be assigned to the sample points.

Solution   The experiment can be defined as the selection of an American hotel and the observation of whether or not complimentary shampoo is offered in the hotel's guest rooms. There are two sample points in the sample space corresponding to this experiment:

S: {The hotel offers complimentary shampoo}
N: {No complimentary shampoo is offered by the hotel}

The difference between this and the coin-toss experiment becomes apparent when we attempt to assign probabilities to the two sample points. What probability should we assign to the sample point S? If you answer .5, you are assuming that the events S and N should occur with equal likelihood, just like the sample points Heads and Tails in the coin-toss experiment. But assignment of sample point probabilities for the hotel-shampoo experiment is not so easy. In fact, a recent survey of American hotels found that 80% now offer complimentary shampoo to guests. Then it might be reasonable to approximate the probability of the sample point S as .8 and that of the sample point N as .2.

Look Back Here we see that the sample points are not always equally likely, so assigning probabilities to them can be complicated — particularly for experiments that represent real applications (as opposed to coin- and die-toss experiments).

Now Work   *Exercise 3.20*

■ ■ ■

Although the probabilities of sample points are often of interest in their own right, it is usually probabilities of collections of sample points that are important. Example 3.3 demonstrates this point.

EXAMPLE 3.3

FINDING THE PROBABILITY OF A COLLECTION OF SAMPLE POINTS

Problem A fair die is tossed, and the up face is observed. If the face is even, you win $1. Otherwise, you lose $1. What is the probability that you win?

Solution Recall that the sample space for this experiment contains six sample points:

$$S: \{1, 2, 3, 4, 5, 6\}$$

Since the die is balanced, we assign a probability of $\frac{1}{6}$ to each of the sample points in this sample space. An even number will occur if one of the sample points, Observe a 2, Observe a 4, or Observe a 6, occurs. A collection of sample points such as this is called an *event*, which we denote by the letter A. Since the event A contains three sample points — all with probability $\frac{1}{6}$ — and since no sample points can occur simultaneously, we reason that the probability of A is the sum of the probabilities of the sample points in A. Thus, the probability of A is $\frac{1}{6} + \frac{1}{6} + \frac{1}{6} = \frac{1}{2}$.

Look Back Based on our notion of probability, this implies that, *in the long run*, you will win $1 half the time and lose $1 half the time.

Now Work   *Exercise 3.14*

■ ■ ■

Figure 3.4
Die-Toss Experiment with Event A: Observe an Even Number

Figure 3.4 is a Venn diagram depicting the sample space associated with a die-toss experiment and the event A, Observe an even number. The event A is represented by the closed figure inside the sample space **S**. This closed figure A contains all the sample points that comprise it.

To decide which sample points belong to the set associated with an event A, test each sample point in the sample space **S**. If event A occurs, then that sample point is in the event A. For example, the event A, Observe an even number, in the die-toss experiment will occur if the sample point Observe a 2 occurs. By the same reasoning, the sample points Observe a 4 and Observe a 6 are also in event A.

To summarize, we have demonstrated that an event can be defined in words, or it can be defined as a specific set of sample points. This leads us to the following general definition of an *event*:

DEFINITION 3.4

An **event** is a specific collection of sample points.

EXAMPLE 3.4   FINDING THE PROBABILITY OF AN EVENT

Problem   Consider the experiment of tossing two *unbalanced* coins. Because the coins are *not* balanced, their outcomes (*H* or *T*) are not equiprobable. Suppose the correct probabilities associated with the sample points are given in the accompanying table. [*Note:* The necessary properties for assigning probabilities to sample points are satisfied.]
Consider the events:

$$A: \{\text{Observe exactly one head}\}$$
$$B: \{\text{Observe at least one head}\}$$

Calculate the probability of *A* and the probability of *B*.

Sample Point	Probability
HH	$\frac{4}{9}$
HT	$\frac{2}{9}$
TH	$\frac{2}{9}$
TT	$\frac{1}{9}$

Solution   Event *A* contains the sample points *HT* and *TH*. Since two or more sample points cannot occur at the same time, we can easily calculate the probability of event *A* by summing the probabilities of the two sample points. Thus, the probability of observing exactly one head (event *A*), denoted by the symbol $P(A)$, is

$$P(A) = P(\text{Observe } HT) + P(\text{Observe } TH) = \frac{2}{9} + \frac{2}{9} = \frac{4}{9}$$

Similarly, since *B* contains the sample points *HH, HT,* and *TH,*

$$P(B) = \frac{4}{9} + \frac{2}{9} + \frac{2}{9} = \frac{8}{9}$$

Look Back   Again, these probabilities should be interpreted *in the long run.* For example, $P(B) = \frac{8}{9} \approx .89$ implies that if we were to toss two coins an infinite number of times, we would observe at least two heads on about 89% of the tosses.

Now Work   *Exercise 3.11*

■ ■ ■

The preceding example leads us to a general procedure for finding the probability of an event *A*:

Probability of an Event

The probability of an event *A* is calculated by summing the probabilities of the sample points in the sample space for *A*.

Thus, we can summarize the steps for calculating the probability of any event, as indicated in the next box.

Steps for Calculating Probabilities of Events

1. Define the experiment, that is, describe the process used to make an observation and the type of observation that will be recorded.

2. List the sample points.

3. Assign probabilities to the sample points.

4. Determine the collection of sample points contained in the event of interest.

5. Sum the sample point probabilities to get the event probability.

EXAMPLE 3.5   **APPLYING THE FIVE STEPS**

Problem   The American Association for Marriage and Family Therapy (AAMFT) is a group of professional therapists and family practitioners that treats many of the nation's couples and families. The AAMFT released the findings of a study that tracked the post-divorce history of 100 pairs of former spouses with children. Each divorced couple was classified into one of four groups, nicknamed "perfect pals (PP)," "cooperative colleagues (CC)," "angry associates (AA)," and "fiery foes (FF)." The proportions classified into each group are shown in Table 3.2.

Suppose one of the 100 couples is selected at random.

a. Define the experiment that generated the data in Table 3.2, and list the sample points.

b. Assign probabilities to the sample points.

c. What is the probability that the former spouses are "fiery foes?"

d. What is the probability that the former spouses have at least some conflict in their relationship?

TABLE 3.2   Results of AAMFT Study of Divorced Couples

Group	Proportion
Perfect Pals (PP) (Joint-custody parents who get along well)	.12
Cooperative Colleagues (CC) (Occasional conflict, likely to be remarried)	.38
Angry Associates (AA) (Cooperate on children-related issues only, conflicting otherwise)	.25
Fiery Foes (FF) (Communicate only through children, hostile toward each other)	.25

Solution   **a.** The experiment is the act of classifying the randomly selected couple. The sample points, the simplest outcomes of the experiment, are the four groups (categories) listed in Table 3.2. They are shown in the Venn diagram in Figure 3.5.

b. If, as in Example 3.1, we were to assign equal probabilities in this case, each of the response categories would have a probability of one-fourth (1/4), or .25. But, by examining Table 3.2 you can see that equal probabilities are not reasonable in this case because the response percentages are not all the same in the four categories. It is more reasonable to assign a probability equal to the response proportion in each class, as shown in Table 3.3.*

Figure 3.5
Venn Diagram for
AAMFT Survey

*Since the response percentages were based on a sample of divorced comples, these assigned probabilities are estimates of the true population response percentages. You will learn how to measure the reliability of probability estimates in Chapter 7.

TABLE 3.3   Sample Point Probabilities
for AAMFT Survey

Sample Point	Probability
PP	.12
CC	.38
AA	.25
FF	.25

c. The event that the former spouses are "fiery foes" corresponds to the sample point FF. Consequently, the probability of the event is the probability of the sample point. From Table 3.3, we find $P(FF) = .25$. Therefore, there is a .25 probability (or one-fourth chance) that the couple we select are "fiery foes."

d. The event that the former spouses have at least some conflict in their relationship, call it event C, is not a sample point because it consists of more than one of the response classifications (the sample points). In fact, as shown in Figure 3.5, the event C consists of three sample points: CC, AA, and FF. The probability of C is defined to be the sum of the probabilities of the sample points in C:

$$P(C) = P(CC) + P(AA) + P(FF) = .38 + .25 + .25 = .88$$

Thus, the chance that we observe a divorced couple with some degree of conflict in their relationship is .88 — a fairly high probability.

Look Back The key to solving this problem is to follow the steps outlined in the box. We defined the experiment (Step 1) and listed the sample points (Step 2) in part **a**. The assignment of probabilities to the sample points (Step 3) was done in part **b**. For each probability in parts c and d, we identified the collection of sample points in the event (Step 4) and summed their probabilities (Step 5).

Now Work   *Exercise 3.23*

■ ■ ■

The preceding examples have one thing in common: The number of sample points in each of the sample spaces was small; hence, the sample points were easy to identify and list. How can we manage this when the sample points run into the thousands or millions? For example, suppose you wish to select five marines for a dangerous mission from a division of 1,000. Then each different group of five marines would represent a sample point. How can you determine the number of sample points associated with this experiment?

One method of determining the number of sample points for a complex experiment is to develop a counting system. Start by examining a simple version of the experiment. For example, see if you can develop a system for counting the number of ways to select two marines from a total of four. If the marines are represented by the symbols M_1, M_2, M_3, and M_4, the sample points could be listed in the following pattern:

(M_1, M_2) (M_2, M_3) (M_3, M_4)
(M_1, M_3) (M_2, M_4)
(M_1, M_4)

Note the pattern and now try a more complex situation — say, sampling three marines out of five. List the sample points and observe the pattern. Finally, see if you can deduce the pattern for the general case. Perhaps you can program a computer to produce the matching and counting for the number of samples of 5 selected from a total of 1,000.

A second method of determining the number of sample points for an experiment is to use **combinatorial mathematics**. This branch of mathematics is concerned with developing counting rules for given situations. For example, there is a simple rule for finding the number of different samples of five marines selected from 1,000. This rule, called the **Combinations Rule**, is given in the box.

Combinations Rule

A sample of n elements is to be drawn from a set of N elements. Then, the number of different samples possible is denoted by $\binom{N}{n}$ and is equal to

$$\binom{N}{n} = \frac{N!}{n!(N-n)!}$$

where the factorial symbol (!) means that

$$n! = n(n-1)(n-2)\cdots(3)(2)(1)$$

For example, $5! = 5 \cdot 4 \cdot 3 \cdot 2 \cdot 1$. [*Note:* The quantity 0! is defined to be equal to 1.]

EXAMPLE 3.6   USING THE COMBINATIONS RULE

Problem   Consider the task of choosing 2 marines from a platoon of 4 to send on a dangerous mission. Use the combinations counting rule to determine how many different selections can be made.

Solution   For this example, $N = 4$, $n = 2$, and

$$\binom{4}{2} = \frac{4!}{2!2!} = \frac{4 \cdot 3 \cdot 2 \cdot 1}{(2 \cdot 1)(2 \cdot 1)} = 6$$

Look Back You can see that this agrees with the number of sample points listed on p. 128.

Now Work   *Exercise 3.13*

■ ■ ■

EXAMPLE 3.7   USING THE COMBINATIONS RULE

Problem   Suppose you plan to invest equal amounts of money in each of five business ventures. If you have 20 ventures from which to make the selection, how many different samples of five ventures can be selected from the 20?

Solution   For this example, $N = 20$ and $n = 5$. Then the number of different samples of 5 that can be selected from the 20 ventures is

$$\binom{20}{5} = \frac{20!}{5!(20-5)!} = \frac{20!}{5!15!}$$

$$= \frac{20 \cdot 19 \cdot 18 \cdot \cdots \cdot 3 \cdot 2 \cdot 1}{(5 \cdot 4 \cdot 3 \cdot 2 \cdot 1)(15 \cdot 14 \cdot 13 \cdot \cdots \cdot 3 \cdot 2 \cdot 1)} = 15,504$$

Look Back You can see that attempting to list all the sample points for this experiment would be an extremely tedious and time consuming, if not practically impossible, task.

■ ■ ■

The Combinations Rule is just one of a large number of counting rules that have been developed by combinatorial mathematicians. This counting rule applies to situations in which the experiment calls for selecting n elements from a total of N elements, without replacing each element before the next is selected. Several other basic counting rules are presented in optional Section 3.8.

Statistics in Action Revisited

Computing and Understanding the Probability of Winning Lotto

In Florida's state lottery game, called Pick-6 Lotto, you select six numbers of your choice from a set of numbers ranging from 1 to 53. We can apply the Combinations Rule to determine the total number of combinations of 6 numbers selected from 53 (i.e., the total number of sample points [or possible winning tickets]). Here, $N = 53$ and $n = 6$; therefore, we have

$$\binom{N}{n} = \frac{N!}{n!(N-n)!} = \frac{53!}{6!47!}$$
$$= \frac{(53)(52)(51)(50)(49)(48)(47!)}{(6)(5)(4)(3)(2)(1)(47!)}$$
$$= 22,957,480$$

Now, since the Lotto balls are selected at random, each of these 22,957,480 combinations is equally likely to occur. Therefore, the probability of winning Lotto is

$$P(\text{Win 6/53 Lotto}) = 1/(22,957,480) = .00000004356$$

This probability is often stated as follows: The odds of winning the game with a single ticket are 1 in 22,957,480, or, 1 in approximately 23 million. For all practical purposes, this probability is 0, implying that you have almost no chance of winning the lottery with a single ticket. Yet each week there is almost always a winner in the Florida Lotto. This apparent contradiction can be explained with the following analogy.

Suppose there is a line of minivans, front-to-back, from New York City to Los Angeles, California. Based on the distance between the two cities and the length of a standard minivan, there would be approximately 23 million minivans in line. Lottery officials will select, at random, one of the minivans and put a check for $10 million dollars in the glove compartment. For a cost of $1, you may roam the country and select one (and only one) minivan and check the glove compartment. Do you think you will find $10 million in the minivan you choose? You can be almost certain that you won't. But now permit anyone to enter the lottery for $1 and suppose that 50 million people do so. With such a large number of participants, it is very likely that someone will find the minivan with the $10 million — but it almost certainly won't be you! (This example illustrates an axiom in statistics called the Law of Large Numbers. See the footnote at the bottom of p. 123.)

Exercises 3.1–3.32

Understanding the Principles

3.1 What is an experiment?

3.2 What are the most basic outcomes of an experiment called?

3.3 Define the sample space.

3.4 What is a Venn diagram?

3.5 Give two probability rules for sample points.

3.6 What is an event?

3.7 How do you find the probability of an event made up of several sample points?

3.8 Give a scenario where the combinations rule is appropriate for counting the number of sample points.

Learning the Mechanics

3.9 An experiment results in one of the following sample points: E_1, E_2, E_3, E_4, or E_5.
   a. Find $P(E_3)$ if $P(E_1) = .1$, $P(E_2) = .2$, $P(E_4) = .1$, and $P(E_5) = .1$
   b. Find $P(E_3)$ if $P(E_1) = P(E_3)$, $P(E_2) = .1$, $P(E_4) = .2$, and $P(E_5) = .1$

   c. Find $P(E_3)$ if $P(E_1) = P(E_2) = P(E_4) = P(E_5) = .1$

3.10 The accompanying Venn diagram describes the sample space of a particular experiment and events A and B.

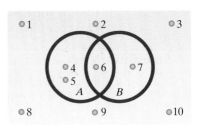

a. Suppose the sample points are equally likely. Find $P(A)$ and $P(B)$

b. Suppose $P(1) = P(2) = P(3) = P(4) = P(5) = \frac{1}{20}$ and $P(6) = P(7) = P(8) = P(9) = P(10) = \frac{3}{20}$. Find $P(A)$ and $P(B)$.

3.11 The sample space for an experiment contains five sam-
NW ple points with probabilities as shown in the table. Find
the probability of each of the following events:

    A: {Either 1, 2, or 3 occurs}
    B: {Either 1, 3, or 5 occurs}
    C: {4 does not occur}

Sample Points	Probabilities
1	.05
2	.20
3	.30
4	.30
5	.15

3.12 Compute each of the following:

a. $\binom{9}{4}$ **b.** $\binom{7}{2}$ **c.** $\binom{4}{4}$

d. $\binom{5}{0}$ **e.** $\binom{6}{5}$

3.13 Compute the number of ways you can select n elements
NW from N elements for each of the following:
    a. $n = 2, N = 5$ **b.** $n = 3, N = 6$
    c. $n = 5, N = 20$

3.14 Two fair dice are tossed, and the up face on each die is
NW recorded.
    a. List the 36 sample points contained in the sample
space.
    b. Assign probabilities to the sample points.
    c. Find the probability of observing each of the fol-
lowing events:

    A: {A 3 appears on each of the two dice}
    B: {The sum of the numbers is even}
    C: {The sum of the numbers is equal to 7}
    D: {A 5 appears on at least one of the dice}
    E: {The sum of the numbers is 10 or more}

3.15 Two marbles are drawn at random and without replacement from a box containing two blue marbles and three
red marbles.
    a. List the sample points.
    b. Assign probabilities to the sample points.
    c. Determine the probability of observing each of the
following events:

    A: {Two blue marbles are drawn}
    B: {A red and a blue marble are drawn}
    C: {Two red marbles are drawn}

3.16 Simulate the experiment described in Exercise 3.15
using any five identically shaped objects, two of which
are one color and three, another. Mix the objects,
draw two, record the results, and then replace the
objects. Repeat the experiment a large number of
times (at least 100). Calculate the proportion of times
events A, B, and C occur. How do these proportions
compare with the probabilities you calculated in

Exercise 3.8? Should these proportions equal the
probabilities? Explain.

Applying the Concepts—Basic

3.17 **Post office violence.** *The Wall Street Journal* (Sept. 1,
2000) reported on an independent study of postal
workers and violence at post offices. In a sample of
12,000 postal workers, 600 of them were physically
assaulted on the job in the past year. Use this information to estimate the probability that a randomly
selected postal worker will be physically assaulted on
the job during the year.

3.18 **International Nanny Association.** According to *USA
Today* (Sept. 19, 2000), there are 650 members of
the International Nanny Association (INA). Of these,
only three are men. Find the probability that a randomly selected member of the INA is a man.

3.19 **USDA chicken inspection.** The United States Department of Agriculture (USDA) reports that, under its standard inspection system, one in every 100 slaughtered
chickens pass inspection with fecal contamination.
(*Tampa Tribune*, Mar. 31, 2000.)
    a. If a slaughtered chicken is selected at random, what
is the probability that it passes inspection with fecal
contamination?
    b. The probability of part **a** was based on a USDA study
that found that 306 of 32,075 chicken carcasses passed
inspection with fecal contamination. Do you agree
with the USDA's statement about the likelihood of a
slaughtered chicken passing inspection with fecal
contamination?

3.20 **African rhinos.** Two species of rhinoceros native to
NW Africa are black rhinos and white rhinos. The International Rhino Federation estimates that the African
rhinoceros population consists of 2,600 white rhinos
and 8,400 black rhinos. Suppose one rhino is selected at
random from the African rhino population and its
species (black or white) is observed.
    a. List the sample points for this experiment.
    b. Assign probabilities to the sample points based
on the estimates made by the International Rhino
Federation.

3.21 **Fungi in beech forest trees.** Beechwood forests in East
Central Europe are being threatened by dynamic
changes in land ownership and economic upheaval. The
current status of the beech tree species in this area was
evaluated by Hungarian university professors in
Applied Ecology and Environmental Research (Vol. 1,
2003). Of 188 beech trees surveyed, 49 of the trees had
been damaged by fungi. Depending on the species of
fungi, damage will occur either on the trunk, branches,
or leaves of the tree. In the damaged trees, the trunk
was affected 85% of the time, the leaves 10% of the
time, and the branches 5% of the time.
    a. Give a reasonable estimate of the probability of a
beech tree in East Central Europe being damaged
by fungi.

b. A fungi-damaged beech tree is selected at random and the area (trunk, leaf, or branch) affected is observed. List the sample points for this experiment and assign a reasonable probability to each sample point.

3.22 Chance of rain. Answer the following question posed in the *Atlanta Journal-Constitution* (Feb. 7, 2000): When a meteorologist says that "the probability of rain this afternoon is .4," does it mean that 40% of the time during the afternoon, it will be raining?

Applying the Concepts—Intermediate

3.23 Benford's Law of numbers. Refer to the *American Scientist* (July–Aug.1998) study of *Benford's Law*, Exercise 2.14 (p. 51). Recall that *Benford's Law* states that the integer 1 is more likely to occur as the first significant digit in a randomly selected number than the other integers. The table summarizes the results of a study where 743 college freshmen selected a six-digit number at random. Assume that one of these 743 numbers is selected and the first significant digit is observed.

⊙ DIGITS

First Digit	Number of Occurrences
1	109
2	75
3	77
4	99
5	72
6	117
7	89
8	62
9	43
Total	**743**

Source: Hill, T. P. "The first digit phenomenon." *American Scientist*, Vol. 86, No. 4, July–Aug. 1998, p. 363 (Figure 5).

a. List the sample points for this experiment.
b. Explain why the sample points are not equally likely to occur.
c. Assign reasonable probabilities to the sample points. Verify that the probabilities sum to 1.
d. What is the probability that the first significant digit is 1 or 2?
e. What is the probability that the first significant digit is greater than 5?

3.24 Sex composition patterns of children in families. When having children, is there a genetic factor that causes some families to favor one sex over the other? That is, does having boys or girls "run in the family?" This was the question of interest in *Chance* (Fall 2001). Using data collected on children's sex for over 4,000 American families that had at least 2 children, the researchers compiled the following table. An American family with at least 2 children is selected, and the sex composition of the first two children is observed.

Sex Composition of First Two Children	Frequency
Boy-Boy	1,085
Boy-Girl	1,086
Girl-Boy	1,111
Girl-Girl	926
TOTAL	4,208

Source: Rodgers, J. L., and Doughty, D. "Does having boys or girls run in the family?" *Chance*, Vol. 14, No. 4, Fall 2001, Table 3.

a. List the sample points for this experiment.
b. If having a boy is no more likely than having a girl and vice versa, assign a probability to each sample point.
c. Use the information in the table to estimate the sample point probabilities. Do these estimates agree (to a reasonable degree of approximation) with the probabilities, part **b**?
d. Make an inference about whether having boys or girls "runs in the family."

3.25 Choosing portable grill displays. University of Maryland marketing professor R. W. Hamilton studied how people attempt to influence the choices of others by offering undesirable alternatives. (*Journal of Consumer Research*, Mar. 2003.) Such a phenomenon typically occurs when family members propose a vacation spot, friends recommend a restaurant for dinner, and realtors show the buyer potential home sites. In one phase of the study, the researcher had each of 124 college students select showroom displays for portable grills. Five different displays (representing five different sized grills) were available, but only three displays would be selected. The students were instructed to select the displays to maximize purchases of Grill #2 (a smaller-sized grill).

a. In how many possible ways can the 3-grill displays be selected from the 5 displays? List the possibilities.
b. The table shows the grill display combinations and number of each selected by the 124 students. Use this information to assign reasonable probabilities to the different display combinations.
c. Find the probability that a student who participated in the study selected a display combination involving Grill #1.

Grill Display Combination	Number of Students
1-2-3	35
1-2-4	8
1-2-5	42
2-3-4	4
2-3-5	1
2-4-5	34

Source: Hamilton, R. W. "Why do people suggest what they do not want? Using context effects to influence others' choices," *Journal of Consumer Research*, Vol. 29, Mar. 2003, Table 1.

3.26 Perfect SAT scores. The maximum score possible on the Standardized Admission Test (SAT) is 1600. According to the test developers, the chance that a student scores a perfect 1600 on the SAT is 5 in 10,000.

a. Find the probability that a randomly selected student scores a 1600 on the SAT.

b. In a recent year, 545 students scored a perfect 1600 on the SAT. How is this possible given the probability calculated in part **a**?

3.27 **Jai-alai quinella bet.** The Quinella bet at the paramutual game of jai-alai consists of picking the jai-alai players that will place first and second in a game *irrespective* of order. In jai-alai, eight players (numbered $1, 2, 3, \ldots, 8$) compete in every game.

a. How many different Quinella bets are possible?

b. Suppose you bet the Quinella combination of 2-7. If the players are of equal ability, what is the probability that you win the bet?

3.28 **Alzheimer's gene study.** Scientists have already discovered two genes (on chromosomes 19 and 21) that mutate to cause the early onset of Alzheimer's disease. *Science News* (July 8, 1995) reported on a search for a third gene that causes Alzheimer's. An international team of scientists gathered genetic information from 21 families afflicted by the early-onset form of the disease. In six of these families, mutations in the S182 gene on chromosome 14 accounted for the early onset of Alzheimer's.

a. Consider a family afflicted by the early onset of Alzheimer's disease. Find the approximate probability that the researchers will find mutations in the S182 gene on chromosome 14 for this family

b. Discuss the reliability of the probability, part **a**. How could a more accurate estimate of the probability be obtained?

Applying the Concepts—Advanced

3.29 **Odd Man Out.** Three people play a game called "Odd Man Out." In this game, each player flips a fair coin until the outcome (heads or tails) for one of the players is not the same as the other two players. This player is then "the odd man out" and loses the game. Find the probability that the game ends (i.e., either exactly one of the coins will fall heads or exactly one of the coins will fall tails) after only one toss by each player. Suppose one of the players, hoping to reduce his chances of being the odd man, uses a two-headed coin. Will this ploy be successful? Solve by listing the sample points in the sample space.

3.30 **Matching socks.** Consider the following question posed to Marilyn vos Savant in her weekly newspaper column "Ask Marilyn":

I have two pairs of argyle socks, and they look nearly identical — one navy blue and the other black. [When doing the laundry] my wife matches the socks incorrectly much more often than she does correctly.... If all four socks are in front of her, it seems to me that her chances are 50% for a wrong match and 50% for a right match. What do you think?

  Source: *Parade Magazine*, Feb. 27, 1994.

Use your knowledge of probability to answer this question. [*Hint:* List the sample points in the experiment.]

3.31 **Post-op nausea study.** Nausea and vomiting after surgery are common side effects of anesthesia and painkillers. Six different drugs, varying in cost, were compared for their effectiveness in preventing nausea and vomiting. (*New England Journal of Medicine*, June 10, 2004.) The medical researchers looked at all possible combinations of the drugs as treatments, including a single drug, as well as 2-drug, 3-drug, 4-drug, 5-drug, and 6-drug combinations.

a. How many 2-drug combinations of the six drugs are possible?

b. How many 3-drug combinations of the six drugs are possible?

c. How many 4-drug combinations of the six drugs are possible?

d. How many 5-drug combinations of the six drugs are possible?

e. The researchers stated that a total of 64 drug combinations were tested as treatments for nausea. Verify that there are 64 ways that the six drugs can be combined. (Remember to include the 1-drug and 6-drug combinations, as well as the control treatment of no drugs.)

3.32 **Dominant versus recessive traits.** An individual's genetic makeup is determined by the genes obtained from each parent. For every genetic trait, each parent possesses a gene pair, and each contributes one-half of this gene pair, with equal probability, to their offspring, forming a new gene pair. The offspring's traits (eye color, baldness, etc.) come from this new gene pair, where each gene in this pair possesses some characteristic.

  For the gene pair that determines eye color, each gene trait may be one of two types: dominant brown (*B*) or recessive blue (*b*). A person possessing the gene pair *BB* or *Bb* has brown eyes, whereas the gene pair *bb* produces blue eyes.

a. Suppose both parents of an individual are brown-eyed, each with a gene pair of the type *Bb*. What is the probability that a randomly selected child of this couple will have blue eyes?

b. If one parent has brown eyes, type *Bb*, and the other has blue eyes, what is the probability that a randomly selected child of this couple will have blue eyes?

c. Suppose one parent is brown-eyed, type *BB*. What is the probability that a child has blue eyes?

3.2 Unions and Intersections

An event can often be viewed as a composition of two or more other events. Such events, which are called **compound events**, can be formed (composed) in two ways, as defined and illustrated here.

The **union** of two events A and B is the event that occurs if either A or B or both occur on a single performance of the experiment. We denote the union of events A and B by the symbol $A \cup B$. $A \cup B$ consists of all the sample points that belong to A *or* B *or both*. (See Figure 3.6a.)

The **intersection** of two events A and B is the event that occurs if both A and B occur on a single performance of the experiment. We write $A \cap B$ for the intersection of A and B. $A \cap B$ consists of all the sample points belonging to *both* A *and* B. (See Figure 3.6b.)

Figure 3.6
Venn Diagrams for Union
and Intersection

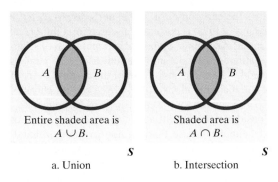

Entire shaded area is
$A \cup B$.

a. Union

Shaded area is
$A \cap B$.

b. Intersection

EXAMPLE 3.8   UNION AND INTERSECTION OF TWO EVENTS

Problem   Consider the die-toss experiment. Define the following events:

A: {Toss an even number}
B: {Toss a number less than or equal to 3}

a. Describe $A \cup B$ for this experiment.

b. Describe $A \cap B$ for this experiment.

c. Calculate $P(A \cup B)$ and $P(A \cap B)$ assuming the die is fair.

Solution   Draw the Venn diagram as shown in Figure 3.7.

a. The union of A and B is the event that occurs if we observe either an even number, a number less than or equal to 3, or both on a single throw of the die. Consequently, the sample points in the event $A \cup B$ are those for which A occurs, B occurs, or both A and B occur. Checking the sample points in the entire sample space, we find that the collection of sample points in the union of A and B is

$$A \cup B = \{1, 2, 3, 4, 6\}$$

Figure 3.7
Venn Diagram for
Die Toss

b. The intersection of A and B is the event that occurs if we observe *both* an even number and a number less than or equal to 3 on a single throw of the die. Checking the sample points to see which imply the occurrence of *both* events A and B, we see that the intersection contains only one sample point:

$$A \cap B = \{2\}$$

In other words, the intersection of A and B is the sample point Observe a 2.

c. Recalling that the probability of an event is the sum of the probabilities of the sample points of which the event is composed, we have

$$P(A \cup B) = P(1) + P(2) + P(3) + P(4) + P(6)$$

$$= \frac{1}{6} + \frac{1}{6} + \frac{1}{6} + \frac{1}{6} + \frac{1}{6} = \frac{5}{6}$$

and

$$P(A \cap B) = P(2) = \frac{1}{6}$$

Look Back Since the 6 sample points are equally likely, then the probabilities in part c are simply the number of sample points in the event of interest divided by 6.

Now Work *Exercise 3.43a–d*

■ ■ ■

Unions and intersections can be defined for more than two events. For example, the event $A \cup B \cup C$ represents the union of three events — A, B, and C. This event, which includes the set of sample points in A, B, or C, will occur if any one or more of the events A, B, or C occurs. Similarly, the intersection $A \cap B \cap C$ is the event that all three of the events A, B, and C occur. Therefore, $A \cap B \cap C$ is the set of sample points that are in all three of the events A, B, and C.

EXAMPLE 3.9   **UNION AND INTERSECTION OF THREE EVENTS**

Problem   Refer to Example 3.6 and define the event

$$C: \{\text{Toss a number greater than 1}\}$$

Find the sample points in

a. $A \cup B \cup C$
b. $A \cap B \cap C$

where

$$A: \{\text{Toss an even number}\}$$
$$B: \{\text{Toss a number less than or equal to 3}\}$$

Solution   **a.** Event C contains the sample points corresponding to tossing a 2, 3, 4, 5, or 6; event A contains the sample points 2, 4, and 6; and event B contains the sample points 1, 2, and 3. Therefore, the event that either A, B, or C occurs contains all six sample points in S — that is, those corresponding to tossing a 1, 2, 3, 4, 5, or 6.

b. You will observe all of the events A, B, and C only if you observe a 2. Therefore, the intersection $A \cap B \cap C$ contains the single sample point Toss a 2.

Look Back Again, the probability of the two events can be found by dividing the number of sample points in the event by 6.

Now Work *Exercise 3.46a*

■ ■ ■

EXAMPLE 3.10

FINDING PROBABILITIES FROM A TWO-WAY TABLE

Problem　*Family Planning Perspectives* reported on a study of over 200,000 births in New Jersey over a recent two-year period. The study investigated the link between the mother's race and the age at which she gave birth (called maternal age). The percentages of the total number of births in New Jersey are given by the maternal age and race classifications in Table 3.4.

　　　　　This table is called a **two-way table** since responses are classified according to two variables, maternal age (rows) and race (columns).

TABLE 3.4　Percentage of New Jersey Birth Mothers in Age–Race Classes

Maternal Age (years)	Race	
	White	Black
≤17	2%	2%
18–19	3%	2%
20–29	41%	12%
≥30	33%	5%

Source: Reichman, N. E., and Pagnini, D. L. "Maternal age and birth outcomes: Data from New Jersey." *Family Planning Perspectives*, Vol. 29, No. 6, Nov./Dec. 1997, p. 269 (adapted from Table 1).

Define the following events:

A: {A New Jersey birth mother is white}
B: {A New Jersey mother was a teenager when giving birth}

a. Find $P(A)$ and $P(B)$.

b. Find $P(A \cup B)$.

c. Find $P(A \cap B)$.

Solution　Following the steps for calculating probabilities of events, we first note that the objective is to characterize the race and maternal age distribution of New Jersey birth mothers. To accomplish this, we define the experiment to consist of selecting a birth mother from the collection of all New Jersey birth mothers during the two-year period and observing her race and maternal age class. The sample points are the eight different age-race classifications:

E_1:　{≤17 yrs., white}　　　　E_5:　{≤17 yrs., black}
E_2:　{18–19 yrs., white}　　　E_6:　{18–19 yrs., black}
E_3:　{20–29 yrs., white}　　　E_7:　{20–29 yrs., black}
E_4:　{≥30 yrs., white}　　　　E_8:　{≥30 yrs., black}

　　　　　Next, we assign probabilities to the sample points. If we blindly select one of the birth mothers, the probability that she will occupy a particular age–race classification is just the proportion, or relative frequency, of birth mothers in the classification. These proportions (as percentages) are given in Table 3.4. Thus,

$P(E_1) =$ Relative frequency of birth mothers in age–race class {≤17 yrs., white} $= .02$
$P(E_2) = .03$
$P(E_3) = .41$
$P(E_4) = .33$

$$P(E_5) = .02$$
$$P(E_6) = .02$$
$$P(E_7) = .12$$
$$P(E_8) = .05$$

You may verify that the sample point probabilities add to 1.

a. To find $P(A)$, we first determine the collection of sample points contained in event A. Since A is defined as {white}, we see from Table 3.4 that A contains the four sample points represented by the first column of the table. In words, the event A consists of the race classification {white} in all four age classifications. The probability of A is the sum of the probabilities of the sample points in A:

$$P(A) = P(E_1) + P(E_2) + P(E_3) + P(E_4) = .02 + .03 + .41 + .33 = .79$$

Similarly, $B = $ {teenage mother, age ≤ 19 years} consists of the four sample points in the first and second rows of Table 3.4:

$$P(B) = P(E_1) + P(E_2) + P(E_5) + P(E_6) = .02 + .03 + .02 + .02 = .09$$

b. The union of events A and B, $A \cup B$, consists of all sample points in *either A or B or both*. That is, the union of A and B consists of all birth mothers who are white *or* who gave birth as a teenager. In Table 3.4 this is any sample point found in the first column *or* the first two rows. Thus,

$$P(A \cup B) = .02 + .03 + .41 + .33 + .02 + .02 = .83$$

c. The intersection of events A and B, $A \cap B$, consists of all sample points in *both A and B*. That is, the intersection of A and B consists of all birth mothers who are white *and* who gave birth as a teenager. In Table 3.4 this is any sample point found in the first column *and* the first two rows. Thus,

$$P(A \cap B) = .02 + .03 = .05.$$

Look Back As with previous problems, the key to finding the probabilities of parts **b** and **c** is to identify the sample points that comprise the event of interest. In a two-way table like Table 3.4, the total number of sample points will be equal to the number of rows times the number of columns.

Now Work   *Exercise 3.45f–g*

■ ■ ■

3.3 Complementary Events

A very useful concept in the calculation of event probabilities is the notion of **complementary events**:

DEFINITION 3.7

The **complement** of an event A is the event that A does *not* occur — that is, the event consisting of all sample points that are not in event A. We denote the complement of A by A^c.

An event A is a collection of sample points, and the sample points included in A^c are those not in A. Figure 3.8 demonstrates this idea. Note from the figure that all sample points in S are included in *either* A or A^c and that *no* sample point is in both A

Figure 3.8
Venn Diagram of
Complementary Events

and A^c. This leads us to conclude that the probabilities of an event and its comple-ment *must sum to 1*:

> **Rule of Complements**
>
> The sum of the probabilities of complementary events equals 1; that is,
> $P(A) + P(A^c) = 1.$

In many probability problems calculating the probability of the complement of the event of interest is easier than calculating the event itself. Then, because

$$P(A) + P(A^c) = 1$$

we can calculate $P(A)$ by using the relationship

$$P(A) = 1 - P(A^c).$$

EXAMPLE 3.11   FINDING THE PROBABILITY OF A COMPLEMENTARY EVENT

Problem   Consider the experiment of tossing two fair coins. (The sample space for this exper-iment is shown in Figure 3.9.) Calculate the probability of event A: {Observing at least one head}.

Solution   We know that the event A: {Observing at least one head} consists of the sample points

$$A: \{HH, HT, TH\}$$

The complement of A is defined as the event that occurs when A does not occur. Therefore,

$$A^c: \{\text{Observe no heads}\} = \{TT\}$$

This complementary relationship is shown in Figure 3.9. Assuming the coins are balanced,

$$P(A^c) = P(TT) = \frac{1}{4}$$

and

$$P(A) = 1 - P(A^c) = 1 - \frac{1}{4} = \frac{3}{4}.$$

Figure 3.9
Complementary Events
in the Toss of Two Coins

Look Back   Note that we can find $P(A)$ by summing the probabilities of the sample points, HH, HT, and TH, in A. Many times, it is easier to find $P(A^c)$ using the Rule of Complements.

| Now Work | *Exercise 3.43e–f* |

■ ■ ■

EXAMPLE 3.12   APPLYING THE RULE OF COMPLEMENTS

Problem   A fair coin is tossed 10 times, and the up face is recorded after each toss. What is the probability of event A: {Observe at least one head}?

Solution   We solve this problem by following the five steps for calculating probabilities of events (see Section 3.1).

Step 1 Define the experiment. The experiment is to record the results of the 10 tosses of the coin.

Step 2 List the sample points. A sample point consists of a particular sequence of ten heads and tails. Thus, one sample point is *HHTTTHTHTT*, which denotes head on first toss, head on second toss, tail on third toss, etc. Others are *HTHHHTTTTT* and *THHTHTHTTH*. Obviously, the number of sample points is very large — too many to list. It can be shown (see Section 3.8) that there are $2^{10} = 1,024$ sample points for this experiment.

Step 3 Assign probabilities. Since the coin is fair, each sequence of heads and tails has the same chance of occurring, and therefore all the sample points are equally likely. Then

$$P(\text{Each sample point}) = \frac{1}{1,024}$$

Step 4 Determine the sample points in event A. A sample point is in A if at least one H appears in the sequence of 10 tosses. However, if we consider the complement of A, we find that

$$A^c = \{\text{No heads are observed in 10 tosses}\}$$

Thus, A^c contains only one sample point:

$$A^c: \quad \{TTTTTTTTTT\}$$

and $P(A^c) = \dfrac{1}{1,024}$

Step 5 Now we use the relationship of complementary events to find $P(A)$:

$$P(A) = 1 - P(A^c) = 1 - \frac{1}{1,024} = \frac{1,023}{1,024} = .999$$

Look Back With such a high probability, we are virtually certain of observing at least one head in 10 tosses of the coin.

■ ■ ■

3.4   The Additive Rule and Mutually Exclusive Events

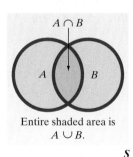

$A \cap B$

A B

Entire shaded area is
$A \cup B$.

S

Figure 3.10
Venn Diagram of Union

In Section 3.2 we saw how to determine which sample points are contained in a union and how to calculate the probability of the union by adding the probabilities of the sample points in the union. It is also possible to obtain the probability of the union of two events by using the *additive rule of probability*.

By studying the Venn diagram in Figure 3.10, you can see that the probability of the union of two events, A and B, can be obtained by summing $P(A)$ and $P(B)$ and subtracting $P(A \cap B)$. We must subtract $P(A \cap B)$ because the sample point probabilities in $A \cap B$ have been included twice — once in $P(A)$ and once in $P(B)$.

The formula for calculating the probability of the union of two events is given in the next box.

Additive Rule of Probability

The probability of the union of events A and B is the sum of the probability of events A and B minus the probability of the intersection of events A and B, that is

$$P(A \cup B) = P(A) + P(B) - P(A \cap B)$$

EXAMPLE 3.13

APPLYING THE ADDITIVE RULE

Problem   Hospital records show that 12% of all patients are admitted for surgical treatment, 16% are admitted for obstetrics, and 2% receive both obstetrics and surgical treatment. If a new patient is admitted to the hospital, what is the probability that the patient will be admitted either for surgery, obstetrics, or both?

Solution   Consider the following events:

A: {A patient admitted to the hospital receives surgical treatment}
B: {A patient admitted to the hospital receives obstetrics treatment}

Then, from the given information

$$P(A) = .12$$
$$P(B) = .16$$

and the probability of the event that a patient receives both obstetrics and surgical treatment is

$$P(A \cap B) = .02$$

The event that a patient admitted to the hospital receives either surgical treatment, obstetrics treatment, or both is the union $A \cup B$. The probability of $A \cup B$ is given by the additive rule of probability:

$$P(A \cup B) = P(A) + P(B) - P(A \cap B)$$
$$= .12 + .16 - .02 = .26$$

Thus, 26% of all patients admitted to the hospital receive either surgical treatment, obstetrics treatment, or both.

Look Back From the information given, it is not possible to list and assign probabilities to all the sample points. Consequently, we cannot proceed through the 5-step process (p. 127) for finding $P(A \cup B)$ and must use the Additive Rule.

Now Work   *Exercise 3.41*

■ ■ ■

A very special relationship exists between events A and B when $A \cap B$ contains no sample points. In this case we call the events A and B *mutually exclusive events*.

DEFINITION 3.8

Events A and B are **mutually exclusive** if $A \cap B$ contains no sample points, that is, if A and B have no sample points in common. For mutually exclusive events,

$$P(A \cap B) = 0$$

Figure 3.11
Venn Diagram of
Mutually Exclusive
Events

Figure 3.11 shows a Venn diagram of two mutually exclusive events. The events A and B have no sample points in common, that is, A and B cannot occur simultaneously and $P(A \cap B) = 0$. Thus, we have the important relationship given in the box.

Probability of Union of Two Mutually Exclusive Events

If two events A and B are *mutually exclusive*, the probability of the union of A and B equals the sum of the probabilities of A and B; that is, $P(A \cup B) = P(A) + P(B)$.

Caution

The formula shown above is *false* if the events are *not* mutually exclusive. In this case (i.e., two nonmutually exclusive events), you must apply the general additive rule of probability.

EXAMPLE 3.14   UNION OF TWO MUTUALLY EXCLUSIVE EVENTS

Problem   Consider the experiment of tossing two balanced coins. Find the probability of observing *at least* one head.

Solution   Define the events

$$A: \{\text{Observe at least one head}\}$$
$$B: \{\text{Observe exactly one head}\}$$
$$C: \{\text{Observe exactly two heads}\}$$

Note that

$$A = B \cup C$$

and that $B \cap C$ contains no sample points (see Figure 3.12). Thus, B and C are mutually exclusive, so that

$$P(A) = P(B \cup C) = P(B) + P(C) = \frac{1}{2} + \frac{1}{4} = \frac{3}{4}$$

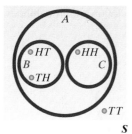

Figure 3.12
Venn Diagram for Coin Toss Experiment

Look Back   Although this example is very simple, it shows us that writing events with verbal descriptions that include the phrases "at least" or "at most" as unions of mutually exclusive events is very useful. This practice enables us to find the probability of the event by adding the probabilities of the mutually exclusive events.

■ ■ ■

Statistics in Action Revisited

The Probability of Winning Lotto with a Wheel System

Refer to Florida's Pick-6 Lotto game in which you select six numbers of your choice from a field of numbers ranging from 1 to 53. In Section 3.2, we learned that the probability of winning Lotto on a single ticket is only 1 in approximately 23 million. The "experts" at Lotto Buster recommend many strategies for increasing the odds of winning the lottery. One strategy is to employ a *wheeling system*. In a complete wheeling system, you select more than six numbers, say, seven, and play every combination of six of those seven numbers.

Suppose you choose to "wheel" the following seven numbers: 2, 7, 18, 23, 30, 32, and 51. Every combination of six of these seven numbers is listed in Table SIA3.1. You can see that there are 7 different possibilities. (Use the Combinations Rule with $N = 7$ and $n = 6$ to verify this.) Thus, we would purchase seven tickets (at a cost of $7) corresponding to these different combinations in a complete wheeling system.

To determine if this strategy does, in fact, increase our odds of winning, we need to find the probability that one of these seven combinations occurs during the 6/53 Lotto

TABLE SIA3.1	Wheeling the Six Numbers 2, 7, 18, 23, 30, 32, and 51				
Ticket #1	2	7	18	23	30	32
Ticket #2	2	7	18	23	30	51
Ticket #3	2	7	18	23	32	51
Ticket #4	2	7	18	30	32	51
Ticket #5	2	7	23	30	32	51
Ticket #6	2	18	23	30	32	51
Ticket #7	7	18	23	30	32	51

draw. That is, we need to find the probability that either Ticket #1 or Ticket #2 or Ticket #3 or Ticket #4 or Ticket #5 or Ticket #6 or Ticket #7 is the winning combination. Note that this probability is stated using the word *or*, implying a union of seven events. Letting T_1 represent the event that Ticket #1 wins, and defining $T_2, T_3, \ldots, T_7$ in a similar fashion, we want to find

$$P(T_1 \text{ or } T_2 \text{ or } T_3 \text{ or } T_4 \text{ or } T_5 \text{ or } T_6 \text{ or } T_7)$$

Recall (Section 3.2) that the 22,957,480 possible combinations in Pick-6 Lotto are mutually exclusive and equally likely to occur. Consequently, the probability of the union of the seven events is simply the sum of the probabilities of the individual events, where each event has probability of $1/(22,957,480)$:

$P($win Lotto with 7 Wheeled Numbers$)$
$= P(T_1$ or T_2 or T_3 or T_4 or T_5 or T_6 or $T_7)$
$= 7/(22,957,480) = .0000003$

In terms of odds, we now have 3 chances in 10 million of winning the Lotto with the complete wheeling system. The "experts" are correct — our odds of winning Lotto have increased (from 1 in 23 million). However, the probability of winning is so close to 0 we question whether the $7 spent on lottery tickets is worth the negligible increase in odds. In fact, it can be shown that to increase your chance of winning the 6/53 Lotto to 1 chance in 100 (i.e., .01) using a complete wheeling system, you would have to wheel 26 of your favorite numbers — a total of 230,230 combinations at a cost of $230,230!

Exercises 3.33–3.56

Understanding the Principles

3.33 Define the union of two events, in words.

3.34 Define the intersection of two events, in words.

3.35 Define the complement of an event, in words.

3.36 State the Rule of Complements.

3.37 State the Additive Rule of Probability for any two events.

3.38 Define mutually exclusive events, in words.

3.39 State the Additive Rule of Probability for mutually exclusive events.

Learning the Mechanics

3.40 Suppose $P(A) = .4$, $P(B) = .7$, and $P(A \cap B) = .3$. Find the following probabilities:
  a. $P(B^c)$ **b.** $P(A^c)$ **c.** $P(A \cup B)$

3.41 A fair coin is tossed three times and the events A and B are defined as follows:

  A: {At least one head is observed}
  B: {The number of heads observed is odd}

  a. Identify the sample points in the events A, B, $A \cup B$, A^c, and $A \cap B$.
  b. Find $P(A)$, $P(B)$, $P(A \cup B)$, $P(A^c)$, and $P(A \cap B)$ by summing the probabilities of the appropriate sample points.
  c. Find $P(A \cup B)$ using the additive rule. Compare your answer to the one you obtained in part **b**.
  d. Are the events A and B mutually exclusive? Why?

3.42 A pair of fair dice is tossed. Define the following events:

  A: {You will roll a 7 (i.e., the sum of the numbers of dots on the upper faces of the two dice is equal to 7)}
  B: {At least one of the two dice is showing a 4}

  a. Identify the sample points in the events A, B, $A \cap B$, $A \cup B$, and A^c.
  b. Find $P(A)$, $P(B)$, $P(A \cap B)$, $P(A \cup B)$, and $P(A^c)$ by summing the probabilities of the appropriate sample points.
  c. Find $P(A \cup B)$ using the additive rule. Compare your answer to that for the same event in part **b**.
  d. Are A and B mutually exclusive? Why?

3.43 Consider the Venn diagram, where $P(E_1) = P(E_2) = P(E_3) = \frac{1}{5}$, $P(E_4) = P(E_5) = \frac{1}{20}$, $P(E_6) = \frac{1}{10}$, and $P(E_7) = \frac{1}{5}$. Find each of the following probabilities.

  a. $P(A)$ **b.** $P(B)$ **c.** $P(A \cup B)$
  d. $P(A \cap B)$ **e.** $P(A^c)$ **f.** $P(B^c)$
  g. $P(A \cup A^c)$ **h.** $P(A^c \cap B)$

3.44 Consider the accompanying Venn diagram, where $P(E_1) = .10$, $P(E_2) = .05$, $P(E_3) = P(E_4) = .2$, $P(E_5) = .06$, $P(E_6) = .3$, $P(E_7) = .06$, and $P(E_8) = .03$. Find the following probabilities:

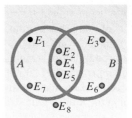

  a. $P(A^c)$ **b.** $P(B^c)$ **c.** $P(A^c \cap B)$
  d. $P(A \cup B)$ **e.** $P(A \cap B)$
  f. $P(A^c \cup B^c)$
  g. Are events A and B mutually exclusive? Why?

3.45 The outcomes of two variables are (Low, Medium, High) and (On, Off), respectively. An experiment is conducted in which the outcomes of each of the two variables are observed. The probabilities associated with each of the six possible outcome pairs are given in the accompanying table.

	Low	Medium	High
On	.50	.10	.05
Off	.25	.07	.03

Consider the following events:

A: {On}
B: {Medium or On}
C: {Off and Low}
D: {High}

a. Find $P(A)$.   **b.** Find $P(B)$.
c. Find $P(C)$.   **d.** Find $P(D)$.
e. Find $P(A^c)$.   **f.** Find $P(A \cup B)$.
g. Find $P(A \cap B)$.

h. Consider each possible pair of events A, B, C, and D. List the pairs of events that are mutually exclusive. Justify your choices.

3.46 Three fair coins are tossed. We wish to find the probability of the event A: {Observe at least one head}.
[NW]
a. Express A as the union of three mutually exclusive events. Find the probability of A using this expression.
b. Express A as the complement of an event. Find the probability of A using this expression.

Applying the Concepts — Basic

3.47 Mathematics achievement test. According to the National Center for Education Statistics (2002), only 5% of United States eighth graders score above 655 on a mathematics assessment test. Make a probability statement about the event that a randomly selected eighth grader has a score of 655 or below on the mathematics assessment test.

3.48 Binge alcohol drinking. A study of binge alcohol drinking by college students was published in the *American Journal of Public Health* (July 1995). Suppose an experiment consists of randomly selecting one of the undergraduate students who participated in the study. Consider the following events:

A: {The student is a binge drinker}
B: {The student is a male}
C: {The student lives in a coed dorm}

Describe each of the following events in terms of unions, intersections, and complements ($A \cup B$, $A \cap B$, A^c, etc.):
a. The student is male and a binge drinker.
b. The student is not a binge drinker.
c. The student is male or lives in a coed dorm.
d. The student is female and not a binge drinker.

3.49 Odds of winning roulette. *Roulette* is a very popular game in many American casinos. In Roulette, a ball spins on a circular wheel that is divided into 38 arcs of equal length, bearing the numbers 00, 0, 1, 2, ..., 35, 36. The number of the arc on which the ball stops is the outcome of one play of the game. The numbers are also colored in the manner shown in the table.

Red: 1, 3, 5, 7, 9, 12, 14, 16, 18, 19, 21, 23, 25, 27, 30, 32, 34, 36
Black: 2, 4, 6, 8, 10, 11, 13, 15, 17, 20, 22, 24, 26, 28, 29, 31, 33, 35
Green: 00, 0

Players may place bets on the table in a variety of ways, including bets on odd, even, red, black, high, low, etc. Consider the following events:

A: {Outcome is an odd number (00 and 0 are considered neither odd nor even)}
B: {Outcome is a black number}
C: {Outcome is a low number (1–18)}

a. Define the event $A \cap B$ as a specific set of sample points.
b. Define the event $A \cup B$ as a specific set of sample points.
c. Find $P(A)$, $P(B)$, $P(A \cap B)$, $P(A \cup B)$, and $P(C)$ by summing the probabilities of the appropriate sample points.
d. Define the event $A \cap B \cap C$ as a specific set of sample points.
e. Find $P(A \cup B)$ using the additive rule. Are events A and B mutually exclusive? Why?
f. Find $P(A \cap B \cap C)$ by summing the probabilities of the sample points given in part **d**.
g. Define the event $(A \cup B \cup C)$ as a specific set of sample points.
h. Find $P(A \cup B \cup C)$ by summing the probabilities of the sample points given in part **g**.

3.50 Abortion Provider Survey. The Alan Guttmacher Institute (AGI) Abortion Provider Survey is a survey of all 258 known nonhospital abortion providers in the United States (*Perspectives on Sexual and Reproductive Health*, Jan./Feb. 2003.) For one part of the survey, the 358 providers were classified according to caseload (number of abortions performed per year) and whether they permit their patient to take the abortion drug, misoprostol, at home or return to the abortion facility to receive the drug. The responses are summarized in the accompanying table. Suppose we select, at random, one of the 358 providers and observe the provider's caseload (less than 50, or, 50 or more) and home use of the drug (yes or no).

	Number of Abortions		
Permit Drug at Home	Less than 50	50 or More	Totals
Yes	170	130	300
No	48	10	58
Totals	218	140	358

Source: Henshaw, S. K., and Finer, L. B. "The accessibility of abortion services in the United States, 2001," *Perspectives on Sexual and Reproductive Health*, Vol. 35, No. 1, Jan./Feb. 2003 (Table 4).

a. List all the possible outcomes for this provider.
b. Based on the table, assign reasonable probabilities to the outcomes, part **a**.
c. Find the probability that the provider permits home use of the abortion drug.

d. Find the probability that the provider permits home use of the drug or has a caseload of less than 50 abortions.

e. Find the probability that the provider permits home use of the drug and has a caseload of less than 50 abortions.

Applying the Concepts—Intermediate

3.51 Federal civil trial appeals. The *Journal of the American Law and Economics Association* (Vol. 3, 2001) published the results of a study of appeals of Federal civil trials. The following table, extracted from the article, gives a break-down of 2,143 civil cases that were appealed by either the plaintiff or defendant. The outcome of the appeal, as well as the type of trial (judge or jury), was determined for each civil case. Suppose one of the 2,143 cases is selected at random and both the outcome of the appeal and type of trial are observed.

	Jury	Judge	Totals
Plaintiff trial win — reversed	194	71	265
Plaintiff trial win — affirmed/dismissed	429	240	669
Defendant trial win — reversed	111	68	179
Defendant trial win — affirmed/dismissed	731	299	1,030
Totals	1,465	678	2,143

a. List the sample points for this experiment.
b. Find $P(A)$, where A = {jury trial}.
c. Find $P(B)$, where B = {plaintiff trial win is reversed}.
d. Are A and B mutually exclusive events?
e. Find $P(A^c)$.
f. Find $P(A \cup B)$.
g. Find $P(A \cap B)$.

3.52 Stacking in the NBA. In professional sports, *stacking* is a term used to describe the practice of African-American players being excluded from certain positions because of race. To illustrate the stacking phenomenon, the *Sociology of Sport Journal* (Vol. 14, 1997) presented the table shown here. The table summarizes the race and positions of 368 National Basketball Association (NBA) players in 1993. Suppose an NBA player is selected at random from that year's player pool.

	POSITION			
	Guard	Forward	Center	Totals
White	26	30	28	84
Black	128	122	34	284
Totals	154	152	62	368

a. What is the probability that the player is white?
b. What is the probability that the player is a center?
c. What is the probability that the player is African-American and plays guard?

d. What is the probability that the player is not a guard?
e. What is the probability that the player is white or a center?

3.53 Elderly wheelchair user study. The *American Journal of Public Health* (Jan. 2002) reported on a study of elderly wheelchair users who live at home. A sample of 306 wheelchair users, age 65 or older, were surveyed about whether they had an injurious fall during the year and whether their home features any one of five struc-tural modifications: bathroom modifications, widened doorways/hallways, kitchen modifications, installed rail-ings, and easy-open doors. The responses are summa-rized in the accompanying table. Suppose we select, at random, one of the 306 surveyed wheelchair users.

Home Features	Injurious Fall(s)	No Falls	Totals
All 5	2	7	9
At least 1, but not all	26	162	188
None	20	89	109
Totals	48	258	306

Source: Berg, K., Hines, M., and Allen, S. "Wheelchair users at home: Few home modifications and many injurious falls," *American Journal of Public Health,* Vol. 92, No. 1, Jan. 2002 (Table 1).

a. Find the probability that the wheelchair user had an injurious fall.
b. Find the probability that the wheelchair user had all five features installed in the home.
c. Find the probability that the wheelchair user had no falls and none of the features installed in the home.

3.54 Gang research study. The National Gang Crime Re-search Center (NGCRC) has developed a six-level gang classification system for both adults and juveniles. The NGCRC collected data on approximately 7,500 confined offenders and assigned each a score using the gang classification system. (*Journal of Gang Research,* Winter 1997.) One of several other variables measured by the NGCRC was whether or not the offender has ever carried a homemade weapon (e.g., knife) while in custody. The table on p. 145 gives the number of con-fined offenders in each of the gang score and home-made weapon categories. Assume one of the confined offenders is randomly selected.

a. Find the probability that the offender has a gang score of 5.
b. Find the probability that the offender has carried a homemade weapon.
c. Find the probability that the offender has a gang score below 3.
d. Find the probability that the offender has a gang score of 5 and has carried a homemade weapon.
e. Find the probability that the offender has a gang score of 0 or has never carried a homemade weapon.
f. Are the events described in parts **a** and **b** mutually exclusive? Explain.
g. Are the events described in parts **a** and **c** mutually exclusive? Explain.

Applying the Concepts—Advanced

3.55 Buying men's dress pants. A buyer for a large metropolitan department store must choose two firms from the four available to supply the store's fall line of men's dress pants. The buyer has not dealt with any of the four firms before and considers their products equally attractive. Unknown to the buyer, two of the four firms are having serious financial problems that may result in their not being able to deliver the fall line of slacks as soon as promised. The four firms are identified as G_1 and G_2 (firms in good financial condition) and P_1 and P_2 (firms in poor financial condition). If the buyer selects the firms at random, find

  a. The probability that firm P_1 is selected.
  b. The probability that at least one of the selected firms is in good financial condition.

3.56 Galileo's Passedix game. Passedix is a game of chance played with three fair dice. Players bet whether the sum of the faces shown on the dice will be above or below 10. During the late sixteenth century, the astronomer and mathematician Galileo Galilei was asked by the Grand Duke of Tuscany to explain why "the chance of throwing a total 9 with three fair dice was less than that of throwing a total of 10." (*Interstat,* Jan. 2004.) The Grand Duke believed that the chance should be the same since "there are an equal number of partitions of the numbers 9 and 10." Find the flaw in the Grand Duke's reasoning and answer the question posed to Galileo.

	Weapon		
Gang Classification Score	Yes	No	Totals
0 (Never joined a gang, no close friends in a gang)	255	2,551	2,806
1 (Never joined a gang, 1–4 close friends in a gang)	110	560	670
2 (Never joined a gang, 5 or more friends in a gang)	151	636	787
3 (Inactive gang member)	271	959	1,230
4 (Active gang member, no position of rank)	175	513	688
5 (Active gang member, holds position of rank)	476	831	1,307
Totals	1,438	6,050	7,488

Source: Knox, G. W. et al. "A gang classification system for corrections," *Journal of Gang Research,* Vol. 4, No. 2, Winter 1997, p. 54 (Table 4).

3.5 Conditional Probability

Figure 3.13
Reduced Sample Space for the Die Toss Experiment: Given that Event B Has Occurred

The event probabilities we've been discussing give the relative frequencies of the occurrences of the events when the experiment is repeated a very large number of times. Such probabilities are often called **unconditional probabilities** because no special conditions are assumed, other than those that define the experiment.

Often, however, we have additional knowledge that might affect the outcome of an experiment, so we may need to alter the probability of an event of interest. A probability that reflects such additional knowledge is called the **conditional probability** of the event. For example, we've seen that the probability of observing an even number (event A) on a toss of a fair die is $1/2$. But suppose we're given the information that on a particular throw of the die the result was a number less than or equal to 3 (event B). Would the probability of observing an even number on that throw of the die still be equal to $1/2$? It can't be, because making the assumption that B has occurred reduces the sample space from six sample points to three sample points (namely, those contained in event B). This reduced sample space is as shown in Figure 3.13.

Because the sample points for the die-toss experiment are equally likely, each of the three sample points in the reduced sample space is assigned an equal *conditional probability* of $1/3$. Since the only even number of the three in the reduced sample space B is the number 2 and the die is fair, we conclude that the probability that A occurs *given that B occurs* is $1/3$. We use the symbol $P(A|B)$ to represent the probability of event A given that event B occurs. For the die-toss example

$$P(A|B) = \frac{1}{3}$$

To get the probability of event A given that event B occurs, we proceed as follows. We divide the probability of the part of A that falls within the reduced sample space B, namely $P(A \cap B)$, by the total probability of the reduced sample space, namely, $P(B)$. Thus, for the die-toss example with event A: {Observe an even number} and event B: {Observe a number less than or equal to 3}, we find

$$P(A|B) = \frac{P(A \cap B)}{P(B)} = \frac{P(2)}{P(1) + P(2) + P(3)} = \frac{1/6}{3/6} = \frac{1}{3}$$

The formula for $P(A|B)$ is true in general:

Conditional Probability Formula

To find the *conditional probability that event A occurs given that event B occurs*, divide the probability that *both A and B* occur by the probability that *B* occurs, that is,

$$P(A|B) = \frac{P(A \cap B)}{P(B)} \qquad \text{[We assume that } P(B) \neq 0.]$$

This formula adjusts the probability of $A \cap B$ from its original value in the complete sample space **S** to a conditional probability in the reduced sample space B. If the sample points in the complete sample space are equally likely, then the formula will assign equal probabilities to the sample points in the reduced sample space, as in the die-toss experiment. If, on the other hand, the sample points have unequal probabilities, the formula will assign conditional probabilities proportional to the probabilities in the complete sample space. This is illustrated by the following examples.

EXAMPLE 3.15   APPLYING THE CONDITIONAL PROBABILITY FORMULA

Problem   Many medical researchers have conducted experiments to examine the relationship between cigarette smoking and cancer. Consider an individual randomly selected from the adult male population. Let A represent the event that the individual smokes, and let A^c denote the complement of A (the event that the individual does not smoke). Similarly, let B represent the event that the individual develops cancer, and let B^c be the complement of that event. Then the four sample points associated with the experiment are shown in Figure 3.14, and their probabilities for a certain section of the United States are given in Table 3.5. Use these sample point probabilities to examine the relationship between smoking and cancer.

Solution   One method of determining whether these probabilities indicate that smoking and cancer are related is to compare the *conditional probability* that an adult male acquires cancer given that he smokes with the conditional probability that an adult male acquires cancer given that he does not smoke [i.e., compare $P(B|A)$ to $P(B|A^c)$].

Figure 3.14
Sample Space for
Example 3.15

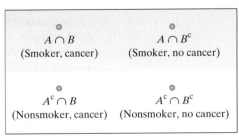

$A \cap B$
(Smoker, cancer)

$A \cap B^c$
(Smoker, no cancer)

$A^c \cap B$
(Nonsmoker, cancer)

$A^c \cap B^c$
(Nonsmoker, no cancer)

S

TABLE 3.5   Probabilities of Smoking and Developing Cancer

	Develops Cancer	
Smoker	Yes, B	No, B^c
Yes, A	.05	.20
No, A^c	.03	.72

First, we consider the reduced sample space A corresponding to adult male smokers. This reduced sample space is highlighted in Figure 3.14. The two sample points $A \cap B$ and $A \cap B^c$ are contained in this reduced sample space, and the adjusted probabilities of these two sample points are the two conditional probabilities:

$$P(B|A) = \frac{P(A \cap B)}{P(A)} \quad \text{and} \quad P(B^c|A) = \frac{P(A \cap B^c)}{P(A)}$$

The probability of event A is the sum of the probabilities of the sample points in A:

$$P(A) = P(A \cap B) + P(A \cap B^c) = .05 + .20 = .25$$

Then the values of the two conditional probabilities in the reduced sample space A are:

$$P(B|A) = \frac{.05}{.25} = .20 \quad \text{and} \quad P(B^c|A) = \frac{.20}{.25} = .80$$

These two numbers represent the probabilities that an adult male smoker develops cancer and does not develop cancer, respectively.

In a like manner, the conditional probabilities of an adult male nonsmoker developing cancer and not developing cancer are

$$P(B|A^c) = \frac{P(A^c \cap B)}{P(A^c)} = \frac{.03}{.75} = .04$$

$$P(B^c|A^c) = \frac{P(A^c \cap B^c)}{P(A^c)} = \frac{.72}{.75} = .96$$

Two of the conditional probabilities give some insight into the relationship between cancer and smoking: the probability of developing cancer given that the adult male is a smoker, and the probability of developing cancer given that the adult male is not a smoker. The conditional probability that an adult male smoker develops cancer (.20) is five times the probability that a nonsmoker develops cancer (.04). This does not imply that smoking *causes* cancer, but it does suggest a pronounced link between smoking and cancer.

Look Back   Notice that the conditional probabilities $P(B^c|A) = .80$ and $P(B|A) = .20$ are in the same 4 to 1 ratio as the original unconditional probabilities, .20 and .05. The conditional probability formula simply adjusts the unconditional probabilities so that they add to 1 in the reduced sample space, A, of adult male smokers. Similarly, the conditional probabilities $P(B^c|A^c) = .96$ and $P(B|A^c) = .04$ are in the same 24 to 1 ratio as the unconditional probabilities .72 and .03.

Now Work   *Exercise 3.63a-b*

■ ■ ■

EXAMPLE 3.16   FINDING A CONDITIONAL PROBABILITY

Problem   The investigation of consumer product complaints by the Federal Trade Commission (FTC) has generated much interest by manufacturers in the quality of their products. A manufacturer of an electromechanical kitchen utensil conducted an analysis of a large number of consumer complaints and found that they fell into the six categories shown in Table 3.6. If a consumer complaint is received, what is the probability that the cause of the complaint was product appearance given that the complaint originated during the guarantee period?

TABLE 3.6   Distribution of Product Complaints

	Reason for Complaint			
	Electrical	Mechanical	Appearance	Totals
During Guarantee Period	18%	13%	32%	63%
After Guarantee Period	12%	22%	3%	37%
Totals	30%	35%	35%	100%

Solution   Let A represent the event that the cause of a particular complaint is product appearance, and let B represent the event that the complaint occurred during the guarantee period. Checking Table 3.6, you can see that $(18 + 13 + 32)\% = 63\%$ of the complaints occur during the guarantee period. Hence, $P(B) = .63$. The percentage of complaints that were caused by appearance and occurred during the guarantee period (the event $A \cap B$) is 32%. Therefore, $P(A \cap B) = .32$.

Using these probability values, we can calculate the conditional probability $P(A|B)$ that the cause of a complaint is appearance given that the complaint occurred during the guarantee time:

$$P(A|B) = \frac{P(A \cap B)}{P(B)} = \frac{.32}{.63} = .51$$

Consequently, we can see that slightly more than half the complaints that occurred during the guarantee period were due to scratches, dents, or other imperfections in the surface of the kitchen devices.

Look Back   Note that the answer $\frac{.32}{.63}$ is the proportion for the event of interest A (.32) divided by the row total proportion for the given event B (.63). That is, it is the proportion of the time that A occurs within the given event B.

Now Work   *Exercise 3.77*

■ ■ ■

3.6 The Multiplicative Rule and Independent Events

The probability of an intersection of two events can be calculated using the *multiplicative rule*, which employs the conditional probabilities we defined in the previous section. Actually, we've already developed the formula in another context. Recall that the conditional probability of B given A is

$$P(B|A) = \frac{P(A \cap B)}{P(A)}$$

Multiplying both sides of this equation by $P(A)$, we obtain a formula for the probability of the intersection of events A and B. This is often called the **multiplicative rule of probability**.

> **Multiplicative Rule of Probability**
> $P(A \cap B) = P(A)P(B|A)$ or, equivalently, $P(A \cap B) = P(B)P(A|B)$

EXAMPLE 3.17   APPLYING THE MULTIPLICATIVE RULE

Problem An agriculturist, who is interested in planting wheat next year, is concerned with the following events:

$$B: \{\text{The production of wheat will be profitable}\}$$
$$A: \{\text{A serious drought will occur}\}$$

The agriculturist believes that the probability is .01 that production of wheat will be profitable *assuming* a serious drought will occur in the same year and that the probability is .05 that a serious drought will occur. That is,

$$P(B|A) = .01 \quad \text{and} \quad P(A) = .05$$

Based on the information provided, what is the probability that a serious drought will occur *and* that a profit will be made? That is, find $P(A \cap B)$, the probability of the intersection of events A and B.

Solution We want to calculate $P(A \cap B)$. Using the formula for the multiplicative rule, we obtain

$$P(A \cap B) = P(A)P(B|A) = (.05)(.01) = .0005$$

The probability that a serious drought occurs *and* the production of wheat is profitable is only .0005.

Look Back As we might expect, this intersection is a very rare event.

> Now Work *Exercise 3.72*

■ ■ ■

Intersections often contain only a few sample points. In this case, the probability of an intersection is easy to calculate by summing the appropriate sample point probabilities. However, the formula for calculating intersection probabilities is invaluable when the intersection contains numerous sample points, as the next example illustrates.

EXAMPLE 3.18   APPLYING THE MULTIPLICATIVE RULE

Problem A county welfare agency employs 10 welfare workers who interview prospective food stamp recipients. Periodically the supervisor selects, at random, the forms completed by two workers to audit for illegal deductions. Unknown to the supervisor, three of the workers have regularly been giving illegal deductions to applicants. What is the probability that both of the two workers chosen have been giving illegal deductions?

Solution Define the following two events:

$$A: \{\text{First worker selected gives illegal deductions}\}$$
$$B: \{\text{Second worker selected gives illegal deductions}\}$$

We want to find the probability of the event that both selected workers have been giving illegal deductions. This event can be restated as: {First worker gives illegal deductions *and* second worker gives illegal deductions}. Thus, we want to find the probability of the intersection, $A \cap B$. Applying the multiplicative rule, we have

$$P(A \cap B) = P(A)P(B|A)$$

Figure 3.15

Venn Diagram for Finding $P(A)$

To find $P(A)$ it is helpful to consider the experiment as selecting one worker from the 10. Then the sample space for the experiment contains 10 sample points (representing the 10 welfare workers), where the three workers giving illegal deductions are denoted by the symbol I (I_1, I_2, I_3), and the seven workers not giving illegal deductions are denoted by the symbol N ($N_1, \ldots, N_7$). The resulting Venn diagram is illustrated in Figure 3.15.

Since the first worker is selected at random from the 10, it is reasonable to assign equal probabilities to the 10 sample points. Thus, each sample point has a probability of $1/10$. The sample points in event A are {I_1, I_2, I_3} — the three workers who are giving illegal deductions. Thus,

$$P(A) = P(I_1) + P(I_2) + P(I_3) = \frac{1}{10} + \frac{1}{10} + \frac{1}{10} = \frac{3}{10}$$

Figure 3.16

Venn Diagram for Finding $P(B|A)$

To find the conditional probability, $P(B|A)$, we need to alter the sample space **S**. Since we know A has occurred (i.e., the first worker selected is giving illegal deductions), only two of the nine remaining workers in the sample space are giving illegal deductions. The Venn diagram for this new sample space is shown in Figure 3.16.

Each of these nine sample points is equally likely, so each is assigned a probability of $1/9$. Since the event $B|A$ contains the sample points {I_1, I_2}, we have

$$P(B|A) = P(I_1) + P(I_2) = \frac{1}{9} + \frac{1}{9} = \frac{2}{9}$$

Substituting $P(A) = 3/10$ and $P(B|A) = 2/9$ into the formula for the multiplicative rule, we find

$$P(A \cap B) = P(A)P(B|A) = \left(\frac{3}{10}\right)\left(\frac{2}{9}\right) = \frac{6}{90} = \frac{1}{15}$$

Thus, there is a 1 in 15 chance that both workers chosen by the supervisor have been giving illegal deductions to food stamp recipients.

Look Back The key words *both* and *and* in the statement "both A and B occur" imply an intersection of two events. This, in turn, implies that we should *multiply* probabilities to obtain the answer.

| Now Work | *Exercise 3.67d* |

■ ■ ■

The sample space approach is only one way to solve the problem posed in Example 3.18. An alternative method employs the concept of a **tree diagram**. Tree diagrams are helpful for calculating the probability of an intersection.

To illustrate, a tree diagram for Example 3.18 is displayed in Figure 3.17. The tree begins at the far left with two branches. These branches represent the two possible outcomes N (no illegal deductions) and I (illegal deductions) for the first worker selected. The unconditional probability of each outcome is given (in parentheses) on the appropriate branch. That is, for the first worker selected, $P(N) = 7/10$

Figure 3.17

Tree Diagram for
Example 3.18

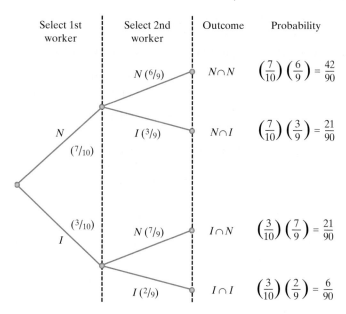

| Select 1st worker | Select 2nd worker | Outcome | Probability |

$N \cap N$ $\left(\frac{7}{10}\right)\left(\frac{6}{9}\right) = \frac{42}{90}$

$N \cap I$ $\left(\frac{7}{10}\right)\left(\frac{3}{9}\right) = \frac{21}{90}$

$I \cap N$ $\left(\frac{3}{10}\right)\left(\frac{7}{9}\right) = \frac{21}{90}$

$I \cap I$ $\left(\frac{3}{10}\right)\left(\frac{2}{9}\right) = \frac{6}{90}$

and $P(I) = \frac{3}{10}$. (These can be obtained by summing sample point probabilities as in Example 3.18.)

The next level of the tree diagram (moving to the right) represents the outcomes for the second worker selected. The probabilities shown here are conditional probabilities since the outcome for the first worker is assumed to be known. For example, if the first worker is giving illegal deductions (I), the probability that the second worker is also giving illegal deductions (I) is $\frac{2}{9}$ since of the nine workers left to be selected, only two remain who are giving illegal deductions. This conditional probability, $\frac{2}{9}$, is shown in parentheses on the bottom branch of Figure 3.17.

Finally, the four possible outcomes of the experiment are shown at the end of each of the four tree branches. These events are intersections of two events (outcome of first worker *and* outcome of second worker). Consequently, the multiplicative rule is applied to calculate each probability, as shown in Figure 3.17. You can see that the intersection $\{I \cap I\}$ — the event that both workers selected are giving illegal deductions — has probability $\frac{6}{90} = \frac{1}{15}$, which is the same value obtained in Example 3.18.

In Section 3.5 we showed that the probability of event A may be substantially altered by the knowledge that an event B has occurred. However, this will not always be the case. In some instances the assumption that event B has occurred will *not* alter the probability of event A at all. When this occurs, we say that the two events A and B are *independent events*.

DEFINITION 3.9

Events A and B are **independent events** if the occurrence of B does not alter the probability that A has occurred; that is, events A and B are independent if

$$P(A|B) = P(A)$$

When events A and B are independent, it is also true that

$$P(B|A) = P(B)$$

Events that are not independent are said to be **dependent**.

EXAMPLE 3.19   CHECKING FOR INDEPENDENCE

Problem   Consider the experiment of tossing a fair die and let

$$A = \{\text{Observe an even number}\}$$
$$B = \{\text{Observe a number less than or equal to 4}\}$$

Are events A and B independent?

Solution   The Venn diagram for this experiment is shown in Figure 3.18. We first calculate

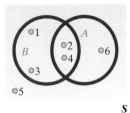

Figure 3.18
Venn Diagram for
Die-Toss Experiment

$$P(A) = P(2) + P(4) + P(6) = \frac{1}{2}$$

$$P(B) = P(1) + P(2) + P(3) + P(4) = \frac{4}{6} = \frac{2}{3}$$

$$P(A \cap B) = P(2) + P(4) = \frac{2}{6} = \frac{1}{3}$$

Now assuming B has occurred, the conditional probability of A given B is

$$P(A|B) = \frac{P(A \cap B)}{P(B)} = \frac{1/3}{2/3} = \frac{1}{2} = P(A)$$

Thus, assuming that event B occurs does not alter the probability of observing an even number — it remains $\frac{1}{2}$. Therefore, the events A and B are independent.

Look Back Note that if we calculate the conditional probability of B given A, our conclusion is the same:

$$P(B|A) = \frac{P(A \cap B)}{P(A)} = \frac{1/3}{1/2} = \frac{2}{3} = P(B)$$

■ ■ ■

Biography

**BLAISE PASCAL
(1623–1662)—
Solver of the Chevalier's
Dilemma**

As a precocious child growing up in France, Blaise Pascal showed an early inclination toward mathematics. Although his father would not permit Pascal to study mathematics before the age of 15 (removing all math texts from his house), at age 12 Blaise discovered on his own that the sum of the angles of a triangle are two right angles.

Pascal went on to become a distinguished mathematician, as well as a physicist, theologian, and the inventor of the first digital calculator. Most historians attribute the beginning of the study of probability to the correspondence between Pascal and Pierre de Fermat in 1654. The two solved The Chevalier's Dilemma — a gambling problem related to Pascal by his friend and Paris gambler the Chevalier de Mere. The problem involved determining the expected number of times one could roll two dice without throwing a double 6. (Pascal proved that the "break-even" point was 25 rolls.)

EXAMPLE 3.20   CHECKING FOR INDEPENDENCE

Problem   Refer to the consumer product complaint study in Example 3.16. The percentages of complaints of various types during and after the guarantee period are shown in Table 3.6 (p. 148). Define the following events:

A: {Cause of complaint is product appearance}
B: {Complaint occurred during the guarantee term}

Are A and B independent events?

Solution   Events A and B are independent if $P(A|B) = P(A)$. We calculated $P(A|B)$ in Example 3.16 to be .51, and from Table 3.6 we see that

$$P(A) = .32 + .03 = .35$$

Therefore, $P(A|B)$ is not equal to $P(A)$, and A and B are dependent events.

| Now Work | *Exercise 3.63c* |

■ ■ ■

To gain an intuitive understanding of independence, think of situations in which the occurrence of one event does not alter the probability that a second event will occur. For example, new medical procedures are often tested on laboratory animals. The scientists conducting the tests generally try to perform the procedures on the animals so the results for one animal do not affect the results for the others. That is, the event that the procedure is successful on one animal is *independent* of the result for another. In this way, the scientists can get a more accurate idea of the efficacy of the procedure than if the results were dependent, with the success or failure for one animal affecting the results for other animals.

As a second example, consider an election poll in which 1,000 registered voters are asked their preference between two candidates. Pollsters try to use procedures for selecting a sample of voters so that the responses are independent. That is, the objective of the pollster is to select the sample so the event that one polled voter prefers candidate A does not alter the probability that a second polled voter prefers candidate A.

Now consider the world of sports. Do you think the results of a batter's successive trips to the plate in baseball, or of a basketball player's successive shots at the basket, are independent? If a basketball player makes two successive shots, is the probability of making the next shot altered from its value if the result of the first shot is not known? If a player makes two shots in a row, the probability of a third successful shot is likely to be different from what we would assign if we knew nothing about the first two shots. Why should this be so? Research has shown that many such results in sports tend to be *dependent* because players (and even teams) tend to get on "hot" and "cold" streaks, during which their probabilities of success may increase or decrease significantly.

We will make three final points about independence. The first is that the property of independence, unlike the mutually exclusive property, cannot be shown on or gleaned from a Venn diagram. This means *you can't trust your intuition*. In general, the only way to check for independence is by performing the calculations of the probabilities in the definition.

The second point concerns the relationship between the mutually exclusive and independence properties. Suppose that events A and B are mutually exclusive, as shown in Figure 3.19, and both events have nonzero probabilities. Are these events independent or dependent? That is, does the assumption that B occurs alter the probability of the occurrence of A? It certainly does, because if we assume that B has occurred, it is impossible for A to have occurred simultaneously. That is, $P(A|B) = 0$. Thus, *mutually exclusive events are dependent events* since $P(A) \neq P(A|B)$.

The third point is that the probability of the intersection of independent events is very easy to calculate. Referring to the formula for calculating the probability of an intersection, we find

$$P(A \cap B) = P(A)P(B|A)$$

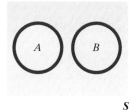

Figure 3.19
Mutually Exclusive
Events are Dependent
Events

Thus, since $P(B|A) = P(B)$ when A and B are independent, we have the following useful rule:

Probability of Intersection of Two Independent Events

If events A and B are independent, the probability of the intersection of A and B equals the product of the probabilities of A and B; that is

$$P(A \cap B) = P(A)P(B)$$

The converse is also true: If $P(A \cap B) = P(A)P(B)$, then events A and B are independent.

In the die-toss experiment, we showed in Example 3.19 that the two events A A: {Observe an even number} and B B: {Observe a number less than equal to 4} are independent if the die is fair. Thus,

$$P(A \cap B) = P(A)P(B) = \left(\frac{1}{2}\right)\left(\frac{2}{3}\right) = \frac{1}{3}$$

This agrees with the result that we obtained in the example:

$$P(A \cap B) = P(2) + P(4) = \frac{2}{6} = \frac{1}{3}$$

EXAMPLE 3.21   FINDING THE PROBABILITY OF INDEPENDENT EVENTS OCCURRING SIMULTANEOUSLY

Problem   Refer to Example 3.5 (p. 127). Recall that the American Association for Marriage and Family Therapy (AAMFT) found that 25% of divorced couples are classified as "fiery foes" (i.e., they communicate through their children and are hostile toward each other).

    a. What is the probability that in a sample of two divorced couples, both are classified as "fiery foes?"

    b. What is the probability that in a sample of ten divorced couples, all ten are classified as "fiery foes?"

Solution   **a.** Let F_1 represent the event that divorced couple 1 is classified as "fiery foes" and F_2 represent the event that divorced couple 2 are also "fiery foes." The event that *both* couples are "fiery foes" is the intersection of the two events, $F_1 \cap F_2$. Based on the AAMFT survey that found that 25% of divorced couples are "fiery foes," we could reasonably conclude that $P(F_1) = .25$ and $P(F_2) = .25$. However, in order to compute the probability of $F_1 \cap F_2$ from the multiplicative rule, we must make the assumption that the two events are independent. Since the classification of any divorced couple is not likely to affect the classification of another divorced couple, this assumption is reasonable. Assuming independence, we have

$$P(F_1 \cap F_2) = P(F_1)P(F_2) = (.25)(.25) = .0625$$

    b. To see how to compute the probability that ten of ten divorced couples will all be classified as "fiery foes," first consider the event that three of three couples are "fiery foes." If F_3 represents the event that the third divorced couple are "fiery foes," then we want to compute the probability of the intersection $F_1 \cap F_2 \cap F_3$. Again assuming independence of the classifications, we have

$$P(F_1 \cap F_2 \cap F_3) = P(F_1)P(F_2)P(F_3) = (.25)(.25)(.25) = .015625$$

Similar reasoning leads us to the conclusion that the intersection of ten such events can be calculated as follows:

$$P(F_1 \cap F_2 \cap F_3 \cap \ldots \cap F_{10}) = P(F_1)P(F_2)\cdots P(F_{10}) = (.25)^{10} = .000001$$

Thus, the probability that ten of ten sampled divorced couples are all classified as "fiery foes" is 1 in 1 million, assuming the probability of each couple being classified as "fiery foes" is .25 and the classification decisions are independent.

Look Back The very small probability in part b makes it extremely unlikely that ten of ten divorced couples are "fiery foes." If this event should actually occur, we should question the probability of .25 provided by the AAMFT and used in the calculation — it is likely to be much higher. (This conclusion is another application of the rare event approach to statistical inference.)

Now Work *Exercise 3.88a*

■ ■ ■

Statistics in Action Revisited
The Probability of Winning Cash 3 or Play 4

In addition to biweekly Lotto 6/53, the Florida Lottery runs several other games. Two popular daily games are Cash 3 and Play 4. In Cash 3, players pay $1 to select three numbers in sequential order, where each number ranges from 0 to 9. If the three numbers selected (e.g., 2-8-4) match exactly the order of the three numbers drawn, the player wins $500. Play 4 is similar to Cash 3, but players must match four numbers (each number ranging from 0 to 9). For a $1 Play 4 ticket (e.g., 3-8-3-0), the player will win $5,000 if the numbers match the order of the four numbers drawn.

During the official drawing for Cash 3, ten ping pong balls numbered 0, 1, 2, 3, 4, 5, 6, 7, 8, and 9 are placed into each of three chambers. The balls in the first chamber are colored pink, the balls in the second chamber are blue, and the balls in the third chamber are yellow. One ball of each color is randomly drawn, with the official order as pink-blue-yellow. In Play 4, a fourth chamber with orange balls is added, and the official order is pink-blue-yellow-orange. Since the draws of the colored balls are random and independent, we can apply an extension of the Probability Rule for the Intersection of Two Independent Events to find the odds of winning Cash 3 and Play 4. The probability of matching a numbered ball being drawn from a chamber is 1/10; therefore,

$$
\begin{aligned}
P(\text{Win Cash 3}) &= P(\text{match pink AND match blue} \\
&\quad \text{AND match yellow}) \\
&= P(\text{match pink}) \times P(\text{match blue}) \times \\
&\quad P(\text{match yellow}) \\
&= (1/10)(1/10)(1/10) = 1/1000 = .001 \\
P(\text{Win Play 4}) &= P(\text{match pink AND match blue AND} \\
&\quad \text{match yellow AND match orange}) \\
&= P(\text{match pink}) \times P(\text{match blue}) \times \\
&\quad P(\text{match yellow}) \times P(\text{match orange}) \\
&= (1/10)(1/10)(1/10)(1/10) \\
&= 1/10,000 = .0001
\end{aligned}
$$

Although the odds of winning one of these daily games is much better than the odds of winning Lotto 6/53, there is still only a 1 in 1,000 chance (for Cash 3) or 1 in 10,000 chance (for Play 4) of winning the daily game. And the payoffs ($500 or $5,000) are much smaller. In fact, it can be shown that you will lose an average of 50¢ every time you play either Cash 3 or Play 4!

Exercises 3.57–3.91

Understanding the Principles

3.57 Explain the difference between an unconditional probability and a conditional probability.

3.58 Give the formula for finding $P(B|A)$.

3.59 Give the Multiplicative Rule of Probability for any two events.

3.60 How are independent events different from dependent events?

3.61 Give the Multiplicative Rule of Probability for two independent events.

3.62 Defend or refute each of the following statements:
  a. Dependent events are always mutually exclusive.

b. Mutually exclusive events are always dependent.

c. Independent events are always mutually exclusive.

Learning the Mechanics

3.63 For two events, A and B, $P(A) = .4$, $P(B) = .2$, and $P(A \cap B) = .1$.
  a. Find $P(A|B)$.   **b.** Find $P(B|A)$.
  c. Are A and B independent events?

3.64 For two events, A and B, $P(A) = .4$, $P(B) = .2$, and $P(A|B) = .6$.
  a. Find $P(A \cap B)$.   **b.** Find $P(B|A)$.

3.65 For two independent events, A and B, $P(A) = .4$ and $P(B) = .2$.
  a. Find $P(A \cap B)$.   **b.** Find $P(A|B)$.
  c. Find $P(A \cup B)$.

3.66 An experiment results in one of three mutually exclusive events, A, B, or C. It is known that $P(A) = .30$, $P(B) = .55$, and $P(C) = .15$, Find each of the following probabilities:
  a. $P(A \cup B)$ **b.** $P(A \cap B)$
  c. $P(A|B)$ **d.** $P(B \cup C)$
  e. Are B and C independent events? Explain.

3.67 Consider the experiment defined by the accompany-
NW ing Venn diagram, with the sample space S containing five sample points. The sample points are assigned the following probabilities: $P(E_1) = .1$, $P(E_2) = .1$, $P(E_3) = .2$, $P(E_4) = .5$, $P(E_5) = .1$.

S

a. Calculate $P(A)$, $P(B)$, and $P(A \cap B)$.

b. Suppose we know event A has occurred, so the reduced sample space consists of the three sample points in A: E_1, E_2, and E_3. Use the formula for conditional probability to determine the probabilities of these three sample points given that A has occurred. Verify that the conditional probabilities are in the same ratio to one another as the original sample point probabilities and that they sum to 1.

c. Calculate the conditional probability $P(B|A)$, in two ways: First, sum $P(E_2|A)$ and $P(E_3|A)$ since these sample points represent the event that B occurs given that A has occurred. Second, use the formula for conditional probability:

$$P(B|A) = \frac{P(A \cap B)}{P(A)}$$

Verify that the two methods yield the same result.

3.68 An experiment results in one of five sample points with the following probabilities: $P(E_1) = .22$, $P(E_2) = .31$,

$P(E_3) = .15$, $P(E_4) = .22$, and $P(E_5) = .1$. The following events have been defined:

  A: $\{E_1, E_3\}$
  B: $\{E_2, E_3, E_4\}$
  C: $\{E_1, E_5\}$

Find each of the following probabilities:
  a. $P(A)$ **b.** $P(B)$ **c.** $P(A \cap B)$
  d. $P(A|B)$ **e.** $P(B \cap C)$ **f.** $P(C|B)$
  g. Consider each pair of events: A and B, A and C, and B and C. Are any of the pairs of events independent? Why?

3.69 Two fair dice are tossed, and the following events are defined:

  A: $\{$Sum of the numbers showing is odd$\}$
  B: $\{$Sum of the numbers showing is 9, 11, or 12$\}$

Are events A and B independent? Why?

3.70 A sample space contains six sample points and events A, B, and C as shown in the accompanying Venn diagram. The probabilities of the sample points are $P(1) = .20$, $P(2) = .05$, $P(3) = .30$, $P(4) = .10$, $P(6) = .25$.

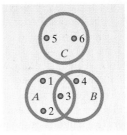

S

a. Which pairs of events, if any, are mutually exclusive? Why?

b. Which pairs of events, if any, are independent? Why?

c. Find $P(A \cup B)$ by adding the probabilities of the sample points and then by using the additive rule. Verify that the answers agree. Repeat for $P(A \cup C)$.

3.71 A box contains two white, two red, and two blue poker chips. Two chips are randomly chosen without replacement, and their colors are noted. Define the following events:

  A: $\{$Both chips are of the same color$\}$
  B: $\{$Both chips are red$\}$
  C: $\{$At least one chip is red or white$\}$

Find $P(B|A)$, $P(B|A^c)$, $P(B|C)$, $P(A|C)$, and $P(C|A^c)$.

Applying the Concepts—Basic

3.72 **Treating brain cancer.** According to the Children's
NW Oncology Group Research Data Center at the University of Florida, 20% of children with neuroblastoma (a form of brain cancer) undergo surgery

rather than the traditional treatment of chemotherapy or radiation. The surgery is successful in curing the disease 95% of the time. (*Explore*, Spring 2001.) Consider a child diagnosed with neuroblastoma. What are the chances that the child undergoes surgery and is cured?

3.73 Executives who cheat at golf. To develop programs for business travelers staying at convention hotels, Hyatt Hotels Corp. commissioned a study of executives who play golf. The study revealed that 55% of the executives admitted they had cheated at golf. Also, 20% of the executives admitted they had cheated at golf and had lied in business. Given an executive had cheated at golf, what is the probability that the executive also had lied in business?

3.74 Sterile couples in Jordan. A sterile family is a couple who has no children by their deliberate choice or because they are biologically infertile. Couples who are childless by chance are not considered to be sterile. Researchers at Yarmouk University (Jordan) estimated the proportion of sterile couples in Jordan to be .06. (*Journal of Data Science*, July 2003.) Also, 64% of the sterile couples in Jordan are infertile. Find the probability that a Jordanian couple is both sterile and infertile.

3.75 Testing a psychic's ability. Consider an experiment in which 10 identical small boxes are placed side-by-side on a table. A crystal is placed, at random, inside one of the boxes. A self-professed "psychic" is asked to pick the box that contains the crystal.

a. If the "psychic" simply guesses, what is the probability that she picks the box with the crystal?

b. If the experiment is repeated seven times, what is the probability that the "psychic" guesses correctly at least once?

c. A group called the Tampa Bay Skeptics recently tested a self-proclaimed "psychic" using the above test. The "psychic" failed to pick the correct box all seven times. (*Tampa Tribune*, Sept. 20, 1998.) What would you infer about this person's psychic ability?

3.76 Herbal medicines survey. Refer to *The American Association of Nurse Anesthetists Journal* (Feb. 2000) study on the use of herbal medicines before surgery, Exercise 1.20 (p. 21). Recall that 51% of surgical patients use herbal medicines against their doctor's advice prior to surgery.

a. What is the probability that a randomly selected surgical patient will use herbal medicines against his or her doctor's advice?

b. What is the probability that in a sample of two independently selected surgical patients, both will use herbal medicines against their doctor's advice?

c. What is the probability that in a sample of five independently selected surgical patients, all five will use herbal medicines against their doctor's advice?

d. Would you expect the event in part **c** to occur? Explain.

3.77 World Series winners. The New York Yankees, a member of the Eastern Division of the American League in Major League Baseball (MLB), recently won three consecutive World Series. The table summarizes the ten MLB World Series winners from 1990 to 2003 by division and league. (There was no World Series in 1994 due to a players' strike.) One of these 13 World Series winners is to be chosen at random.

a. Given that the winner is a member of the American League, what is the probability that the winner plays in the Eastern Division?

b. If the winner plays in the Central Division, what is the probability that the winner is a member of the National League?

c. If the winner is a member of the National League, what is the probability that the winner plays in either the Central or Western Division?

		League	
		National	American
Division	Eastern	3	6
	Central	1	1
	Western	1	1

Source: Major League Baseball.

3.78 Study of ancient pottery. Refer to the *Chance* (Fall 2000) study of ancient pottery found at the Greek settlement of Phylakopi, Exercise 2.12 (p. 40). Of the 837 pottery pieces uncovered at the excavation site, 183 were painted. These painted pieces included 14 painted in a curvilinear decoration, 165 painted in a geometric decoration, and 4 painted in a naturalistic decoration. Suppose one of the 837 pottery pieces is selected and examined.

a. What is the probability that the pottery piece is painted?

b. Given that the pottery piece is painted, what is the probability that it is painted in a curvilinear decoration?

Applying the Concepts—Intermediate

NZBIRDS

3.79 Extinct New Zealand birds. Refer to the *Evolutionary Ecology Research* (July 2003) study of the patterns of extinction in the New Zealand bird population, Exercise 2.18 (p. 42). Consider the data on extinct status (extinct, absent from island, present) for the 132 bird species saved in the **NZBIRDS** file. The data are summarized in the MINITAB printout on p. 158. Suppose you randomly select 10 of the 132 bird species (without replacement) and record the extinct status of each.

a. What is the probability that the first species you select is extinct? (*Note*: Extinct = Yes on the MINITAB printout.)

b. Suppose the first nine species you select are all extinct. What is the probability that the tenth species you select is extinct?

Tally for Discrete Variables: Extinct

Extinct	Count	Percent
Absent	16	12.12
No	78	59.09
Yes	38	28.79
N=	132	

3.80 Requirements for high school graduation. In Italy, all high school students must take a High School Diploma (HSD) exam and write a paper. In *Organizational Behavior and Human Decision Processes* (July 2000), University of Milan researcher L. Macchi provided the following information to a group of college undergraduates. *Fact 1*: In Italy, 360 out of every 1,000 students fail their HSD exam. *Fact 2*: Of those who fail the HSD, 75% also fail the written paper. *Fact 3*: Of those who pass the HSD, only 20% fail the written paper. Define events A and B as follows:

$$A = \{\text{Student fails the HSD exam}\}$$
$$B = \{\text{Student fails the written paper}\}$$

a. Write Fact 1 as a probability statement involving events A and/or B.
b. Write Fact 2 as a probability statement involving events A and/or B.
c. Write Fact 3 as a probability statement involving events A and/or B.
d. State $P(A \cap B)$ in the words of the problem.
e. Find $P(A \cap B)$.

3.81 Intrusion detection systems. A computer intrusion detection system (IDS) is designed to provide an alarm whenever an intrusion (e.g., unauthorized access) is being attempted into a computer system. A probabilistic evaluation of a system with two independently operating intrusion detection systems (a double IDS) was published in the *Journal of Research of the National Institute of Standards and Technology* (Nov.–Dec., 2003). Consider a double IDS with system A and system B. If there is an intruder, system A sounds an alarm with probability .9, and system B sounds an alarm with probability .95. If there is no intruder, the probability that system A sounds an alarm (i.e., a false alarm) is .2, and the probability that system B sounds an alarm is .1.

a. Express the four probabilities given above using symbols.
b. If there is an intruder, what is the probability that both systems sound an alarm?
c. If there is no intruder, what is the probability that both systems sound an alarm?
d. Given an intruder, what is the probability that at least one of the systems sounds an alarm?

3.82 Cigar smoking and cancer. The *Journal of the National Cancer Institute* (Feb. 16, 2000) published the results of a study that investigated the association between cigar smoking and death from tobacco-related cancers. Data were obtained for a national sample of 137,243 American men. The results are summarized in the table below. Each male in the study was classified according to his cigar-smoking status and whether or not he died from a tobacco-related cancer.

a. Find the probability that a randomly selected man never smoked cigars and died from cancer.
b. Find the probability that a randomly selected man was a former cigar smoker and died from cancer.
c. Find the probability that a randomly selected man was a current cigar smoker and died from cancer.
d. Given that a male was a current cigar smoker, find the probability that he died from cancer.
e. Given that a male never smoked cigars, find the probability that he died from cancer.

| | Died from Cancer | | |
Cigars	Yes	No	Totals
Never Smoked	782	120,747	121,529
Former Smoker	91	7,757	7,848
Current Smoker	141	7,725	7,866
Totals	1,014	136,229	137,243

Source: Shapiro, J. A., Jacobs, E. J., and Thun, M. J. "Cigar smoking in men and risk of death from tobacco-related cancers." *Journal of the National Cancer Institute,* Vol. 92, No. 4, Feb. 16, 2000 (Table 2).

3.83 Stacking in the NBA. Refer to the *Sociology of Sport Journal* (Vol. 14, 1997) study of "stacking" in the National Basketball Association (NBA), Exercise 3.52 (p. 144). Reconsider the table below, which summarizes the race and positions of 368 NBA players in 1993. Suppose an NBA player is selected at random from that year's player pool.

| | Position | | | |
	L Guard	*D* Forward	*E* Center	Totals
A **White**	26	30	28	84
B **Black**	128	122	34	284
Totals	154	152	62	368

a. Given the player is white, what is the probability that he is a center?
b. Given the player is African-American, what is the probability that he is a center?
c. Are the events {White player} and {Center} independent?
d. Recall that "stacking" refers to the practice of African-American players being excluded from certain positions because of race. Use your answers to parts **a–c** to make an inference about stacking in the NBA.

3.84 Refer to the *Conservation Ecology* (Dec. 2003) study of the causes of forest fragmentation, Exercise 2.148 (p. 102). Recall that the researchers used advanced high resolution satellite imagery to develop fragmentation indices for each forest. A 3 × 3 grid was superimposed over an aerial photo of the forest, and each square (pixel) of the grid was classified as forest (F), anthropogenic land use (A), or natural land cover (N). An example of one such grid is shown here. The edges of the grid (where an "edge" is an imaginary line that separates any two adjacent pixels) are classified as F-A, F-N, A-A, A-N, N-N, or F-F edges.

A	A	N
N	F	F
N	F	F

a. Refer to the grid shown. Note that there are 12 edges inside the grid. Classify each edge as F-A, F-N, A-A, A-N, N-N or F-F.

b. The researchers calculated the fragmentation index by considering only the F-edges in the grid. Count the number of F-edges. (These edges represent the sample space for the experiment.)

c. If an F-edge is selected at random, find the probability that it is an F-A edge. (This probability is proportional to the anthropogenic fragmentation index calculated by the researchers.)

d. If an F edge is selected at random, find the probability that it is an F-N edge. (This probability is proportional to the natural fragmentation index calculated by the researchers.)

3.85 **Speeding New Jersey drivers.** A certain stretch of highway on the New Jersey Turnpike has a posted speed limit of 60 mph. A survey of drivers on this portion of the turnpike revealed the following facts (reported in *The Washington Post*, Aug.16, 1998):

(1) 14% of the drivers on this stretch of highway were African Americans

(2) 98% of the drivers were exceeding the speed limit by at least 5 mph (and, thus, subject to being stopped by the state police)

(3) Of these violators, 15% of the drivers were African Americans

(4) Of the drivers stopped for speeding by the New Jersey state police, 35% were African Americans

a. Convert each of the reported percentages above into a probability statement.

b. Find the probability that a driver on this stretch of highway is African American and exceeding the speed limit.

c. Given a driver on this stretch of highway is exceeding the speed limit, what is the probability the driver is not African American?

d. Given that a driver on this stretch of highway is stopped by the New Jersey state police, what is the probability that the driver is not African American?

e. For this stretch of highway, are the events {African American driver} and {Driver exceeding the speed limit} independent (to a close approximation)? Explain.

f. Use the probabilities in *The Washington Post* report to make a statement about whether African Americans are stopped more often for speeding than expected on this stretch of turnpike.

3.86 **Antibiotic for blood infections.** Enterococci are bacteria that cause blood infections in hospitalized patients. One antibiotic used to battle enterococci is vancomycin. A study by the Federal Centers for Disease Control and Prevention revealed that 8% of all enterococci isolated in hospitals nationwide were resistant to vancomycin. (*New York Times*, Sept.12, 1995.) Consider a random sample of three patients with blood infections caused by the enterococci bacteria. Assume that all three patients are treated with the antibiotic vancomycin.

a. What is the probability that all three patients are successfully treated? What assumption did you make concerning the patients?

b. What is the probability that the bacteria resist the antibiotic for at least one patient?

3.87 **Cornmaize seeds.** The genetic origin and properties of maize (modern-day corn) was investigated in *Economic Botany* (Jan.–Mar. 1995). Seeds from maize ears carry either single spikelets or paired spikelets, but not both. Progeny tests on approximately 600 maize ears revealed the following information. Forty percent of all seeds carry single spikelets, while 60% carry paired spikelets. A seed with single spikelets will produce maize ears with single spikelets 29% of the time and paired spikelets 71% of the time. A seed with paired spikelets will produce maize ears with single spikelets 26% of the time and paired spikelets 74% of the time.

a. Find the probability that a randomly selected maize ear seed carries a single spikelet and produces ears with single spikelets.

b. Find the probability that a randomly selected maize ear seed produces ears with paired spikelets.

3.88 **Lie detector test.** A new type of lie detector — called the Computerized Voice Stress Analyzer (CVSA) — has been developed. The manufacturer claims that the CVSA is 98% accurate and, unlike a polygraph machine, will not be thrown off by drugs and medical factors. However, laboratory studies by the U.S. Defense Department found that the CVSA had an accuracy rate of 49.8% — slightly less than pure chance. (*Tampa Tribune*, Jan. 10, 1999.) Suppose the CVSA is used to test the veracity of four suspects. Assume the suspects' responses are independent.

NW a. If the manufacturer's claim is true, what is the probability that the CVSA will correctly determine the veracity of all four suspects?

b. If the manufacturer's claim is true, what is the probability that the CVSA will yield an incorrect result for at least one the four suspects?

c. Suppose that in a laboratory experiment conducted by the U.S. Defense Department on four suspects, the CVSA yielded incorrect results for two of the suspects. Use this result to make an inference about the true accuracy rate of the new lie detector.

Applying the Concepts—Advanced

3.89 Strategy in the game "Go." "Go" is one of the oldest and most popular strategic board games in the world, especially in Japan and Korea. The two-player game is played on a flat surface marked with 19 vertical and 19 horizontal lines. The objective is to control territory by placing pieces called "stones" on vacant points on the board. Players alternate placing their stones. The player using black stones goes first, followed by the player using white stones. [*Note:* The University of Virginia requires MBA students to learn Go to understand how the Japanese conduct business.] *Chance* (Summer 1995) published an article that investigated the advantage of playing first (i.e., using the black stones) in Go. The results of 577 games recently played by professional Go players were analyzed.

a. In the 577 games, the player with the black stones won 319 times, and the player with the white stones won 258 times. Use this information to estimate the probability of winning when you play first in Go.

b. Professional Go players are classified by level. Group C includes the top-level players, followed by Group B (middle-level) and Group A (low-level) players. The table describes the number of games won by the player with the black stones, categorized by level of the black player and level of the opponent. Estimate the probability of winning when you play first in Go for each combination of player and opponent level.

c. If the player with the black stones is ranked higher than the player with the white stones, what is the probability that black wins?

d. Given that the players are of the same level, what is the probability that the player with the black stones wins?

Black Player Level	Opponent Level	Number of Wins	Number of Games
C	A	34	34
C	B	69	79
C	C	66	118
B	A	40	54
B	B	52	95
B	C	27	79
A	A	15	28
A	B	11	51
A	C	5	39
	Totals	319	577

Source: Kim J., and Kim H. J., "The advantage of playing first in Go." *Chance*, Vol. 8, No. 3, Summer 1995, p. 26 (Table 3).

3.90 Patient medical instruction sheets. Physicians and pharmacists sometimes fail to inform patients ade-

quately about the proper application of prescription drugs and the precautions to take in order to avoid potential side effects. One method of increasing patients' awareness of the problem is for physicians to provide Patient Medication Instruction (PMI) sheets. The American Medical Association, however, has found that only 20% of the doctors who prescribe drugs frequently distribute PMI sheets to their patients. Assume that 20% of all patients receive the PMI sheet with their prescriptions and that 12% receive the PMI sheet and are hospitalized because of a drug-related problem. What is the probability that a person will be hospitalized for a drug-related problem given that the person has received the PMI sheet?

3.91 NBA draft lottery. The National Basketball Association (NBA) utilizes a lottery to determine the order in which teams draft amateur (high school and college) players. Teams with the poorest won-lost records have the best chance of obtaining the first selection (and, presumably, best player) in the draft. Under the current lottery system, 14 ping-pong balls numbered 1 through 14 are placed in a drum, and four balls are drawn. There are 1,001 possible combinations when four balls are drawn out of 14, without regard to their order of selection. Prior to the drawing, 1,000 combinations are assigned to the 13 teams with the worst records — the Lottery teams — based on their order of finish during the regular season. (The team with the worst record is assigned 250 of these combinations, the team with the second worst record is assigned 200 of these combinations, the team with the third worst record is assigned 157 of these combinations, etc. The table below gives the number combinations assigned to each Lottery team.) Once the four ping pong balls are drawn to the top of the drum to determine a four-digit combination, the team that has been assigned that combination will receive the first pick. The four balls are placed back in the drum and the process is repeated to determine the second, third, and subsequent draft picks. (*Note:* If the one unassigned combination is drawn, the balls are drawn to the top again.)

NBA Lottery Team	Number of Combinations
Worst record	250
2nd worst record	200
3rd worst record	157
4th worst record	120
5th worst record	89
6th worst record	64
7th worst record	44
8th worst record	29
9th worst record	18
10th worst record	11
11th worst record	7
12th worst record	6
13th worst record	5

Source: McCann, M. A. "Illegal defense: The irrational economics of banning high school players from the NBA draft," *Virginia Sports and Entertainment Law Journal*, Vol. 3, No. 2, Spring 2004, Table 5.

a. Demonstrate that there are 1,001 four-number combinations of the numbers 1 through 14.

b. For each of the 13 Lottery teams, find the probability that the team obtains the first pick in the draft.

c. Given that the team with the second worst record obtains the number 1 pick, find the probability that the team with the worst record obtains the second pick of the draft.

d. Calculate the conditional probability, part **c**, given that the team with the third worst record obtains the number 1 pick. Repeat these calculations for the remaining Lottery teams, assuming that Lottery team obtains the number 1 pick.

e. Find the probability that the team with the worst record obtains the second pick of the draft, assuming it did not obtain the first pick.

3.7 Random Sampling

How a sample is selected from a population is of vital importance in statistical inference because the probability of an observed sample will be used to infer the characteristics of the sampled population. To illustrate, suppose you deal yourself four cards from a deck of 52 cards and all four cards are aces. Do you conclude that your deck is an ordinary bridge deck, containing only four aces, or do you conclude that the deck is stacked with more than four aces? It depends on how the cards were drawn. If the four aces were always placed at the top of a standard bridge deck, drawing four aces is not unusual — it is certain. On the other hand, if the cards are thoroughly mixed, drawing four aces in a sample of four cards is highly improbable. The point, of course, is that in order to use the observed sample of four cards to draw inferences about the population (the deck of 52 cards), you need to know how the sample was selected from the deck.

One of the simplest and most frequently employed sampling procedures is implied in the previous examples and exercises. It produces what is known as a *random sample*. We learned in Section 1.5 (p. 14) that a random sample is likely to be *representative* of the population that it is selected from.

> **DEFINITION 3.10**
>
> If n elements are selected from a population in such a way that every set of n elements in the population has an equal probability of being selected, the n elements are said to be a **random sample.***

If a population is not too large and the elements can be numbered on slips of paper, poker chips, etc., you can physically mix the slips of paper or chips and remove n elements from the total. The numbers that appear on the chips selected would indicate the population elements to be included in the sample. Since it is often difficult to achieve a thorough mix, such a procedure only provides an approximation to random sampling. Most researchers rely on **random number generators** to automatically generate the random sample. These random number generators are available in table form, are built into most statistical software packages, and are available on the Internet (e.g., www.random.org).

EXAMPLE 3.22   SELECTING A RANDOM SAMPLE

Problem   Suppose you wish to randomly sample five households from a population of 100,000 households.

  a. How many different samples can be selected?

  b. Use a random number generator to select a random sample.

---

*Strictly speaking, this is a *simple random sample*. There are many different types of random samples. The simple random sample is the most common.

Solution

a. Since we want to select $n = 5$ objects (households) from $N = 100,000$, we apply the combinatorial rule, of Section 3.1:

$$\binom{N}{n} = \binom{100,000}{5} = \frac{100,000!}{5!\,99,995!}$$

$$= \frac{100,000 \cdot 99,999 \cdot 99,998 \cdot 99,997 \cdot 99,996}{5 \cdot 4 \cdot 3 \cdot 2 \cdot 1}$$

$$= 8.33 \times 10^{22}$$

Thus, there are 83.3 billion trillion different samples of five households that can be selected from 100,000.

b. To ensure that each of the possible samples has an equal chance of being selected, as required for random sampling, we can employ a **random number table**, as provided in Table I of Appendix A. Random number tables are constructed in such a way that every number occurs with (approximately) equal probability. Furthermore, the occurrence of any one number in a position is independent of any of the other numbers that appear in the table. To use a table of random numbers, number the N elements in the population from 1 to N. Then turn to Table I and select a starting number in the table. Proceeding from this number either across the row or down the column, remove and record n numbers from the table.

To illustrate, first we number the households in the population from 1 to 100,000. Then, we turn to a page of Table I, say the first page. (A partial reproduction of the first page of Table I is shown in Table 3.7.) Now, we arbitrarily select a starting number, say the random number appearing in the third row, second column. This number is 48,360. Then we proceed down the second column to obtain the remaining four random numbers. In this case we have selected five random numbers, which are highlighted in Table 3.7. Using the first five digits to represent households from 1 to 99,999 and the number 00000 to represent household 100,000, we can see that the households numbered

$$48,360 \quad 93,093 \quad 39,975 \quad 6,907 \quad 72,905$$

should be included in our sample.

Note: Use only the necessary number of digits in each random number to identify the element to be included in the sample. If, in the course of recording

Figure 3.20

MINITAB Worksheet with

	C1	C2	C3
	HouseID		
1	832		
2	4010		
3	4535		
4	5219		
5	5584		
6	6890		
7	8060		
8	8237		
9	11445		
10	12283		
11	12548		
12	14096		
13	17376		
14	22464		
15	24019		
16	24664		
17	26183		
18	27439		
19	28044		
20	31598		
21	32249		
22	33103		
23	37956		
24	45573		
25	48559		
26	48751		
27	51488		
28	52912		
29	53975		
30	54388		
31	54932		
32	60158		
33	60166		
34	61286		
35	62169		
36	68876		
37	70487		
38	70607		
39	78736		
40	82305		
41	83385		
42	84279		
43	85559		
44	88629		
45	92277		
46	93985		
47	94391		
48	95748		
49	96502		
50	97256		

TABLE 3.7   Partial Reproduction of Table I in Appendix A

Column Row	1	2	3	4	5	6
1	10480	15011	01536	02011	81647	91646
2	22368	46573	25595	85393	30995	89198
3	24130	48360	22527	97265	76393	64809
4	42167	93093	06243	61680	07856	16376
5	37670	39975	81837	16656	06121	91782
6	77921	06907	11008	42751	27756	53498
7	99562	72905	56420	69994	98872	31016
8	96301	91977	05463	07972	18876	20922
9	89579	14342	63661	10281	17453	18103
10	85475	36857	53342	53988	53060	59533
11	28918	69578	88231	33276	70997	79936
12	63553	40961	48235	03427	49626	69445
13	09429	93969	52636	92737	88974	33488

the *n* numbers from the table, you select a number that has already been selected, simply discard the duplicate and select a replacement at the end of the sequence. Thus, you may have to record more than *n* numbers from the table to obtain a sample of *n* unique numbers.

Look Back Can we be sure that all 83.3 billion trillion samples have an equal chance of being selected? The fact is, We can't; but to the extent that the random number table contains truly random sequences of digits, the sample should be very close to random.

| Now Work | *Exercise 3.96* |

■ ■ ■

Table I in Appendix A is just one example of a random number generator. For most scientific studies that require a large random sample, computers are used to generate the random sample. The SAS, MINITAB, and SPSS statistical software packages all have easy-to-use random number generators.

For example, suppose we required a random sample of *n* = 50 households from the population of 100,000 households in Example 3.22. Here, we might employ the MINITAB random number generator. Figure 3.20 shows a MINITAB printout listing 50 random numbers (from a population of 100,000). The households with these identification numbers would be included in the random sample.

Recall our discussion of designed experiments in Section 1.5 (p. 14). The notion of random selection and randomization is key to conducting good research with a designed experiment. The next example illustrates a basic application.

	C1	C2	C3
	Physician	Treatment	
1	1	3	
2	2	11	
3	3	10	
4	4	14	
5	5	2	
6	6	7	
7	7	6	
8	8	16	
9	9	17	
10	10	9	
11	11		
12	12		
13	13		
14	14		
15	15		
16	16		
17	17		
18	18		
19	19		
20	20		
21			

Figure 3.21

MINITAB Worksheet with Random Assignment of Physicians

EXAMPLE 3.23   RANDOMIZATION IN A DESIGNED EXPERIMENT

Problem   A designed experiment in the medical field involving human subjects is referred to as a *clinical trial*. One recent clinical trial was designed to determine the potential of using aspirin in preventing heart attacks. Volunteer physicians were randomly divided into two groups — the *treatment* group and the *control* group. Each physician in the treatment group took one aspirin tablet a day for one year, while the physicians in the control group took an aspirin-free placebo made to look identical to an aspirin tablet. Since the physicians did not know which group, treatment or control, they were assigned to, the clinical trial is called a *blind study*. Assume 20 physicians volunteered for the study. Use a random number generator to randomly assign half of the physicians to the treatment group and half to the control group.

Solution   Essentially, we want to select a random sample of 10 physicians from the 20. The first 10 selected will be assigned to the treatment group; the remaining 10 will be assigned to the control group. (Alternatively, we could randomly assign each physician, one by one, to either the treatment or control group. However, this would not guarantee exactly 10 physicians in each group.)

The MINITAB random sample procedure was employed, producing the printout shown in Figure 3.21. Numbering the physicians from 1 to 20, we see that physicians 3, 11, 10, 14, 2, 7, 6, 16, 17, and 9 are assigned to receive the aspirin (treatment). The remaining physicians are assigned the placebo (control).

■ ■ ■

Exercises 3.92–3.103

Understanding the Principles

3.92 Define a random sample.

3.93 How are random samples related to representative samples?

3.94 What is a random number generator?

3.95 Define a blind study.

Learning the Mechanics

3.96 Suppose you wish to sample $n = 2$ elements from a
NW total of $N = 10$ elements.
   a. Count the number of different samples that can be drawn, first by listing them, and then by using combinatorial mathematics.
   b. If random sampling is to be employed, what is the probability that any particular sample will be selected?
   c. Show how to use the random number table, Table I in Appendix A, to select a random sample of 2 elements from a population of 10 elements. Perform the sampling procedure 20 times. Do any two of the samples contain the same 2 elements? Given your answer to part **b**, did you expect repeated samples?

3.97 Suppose you wish to sample $n = 3$ elements from a total of $N = 600$ elements.
   a. Count the number of different samples by using combinatorial mathematics.
   b. If random sampling is to be employed, what is the probability that any particular sample will be selected?
   c. Show how to use the random number table, Table I in Appendix A, to select a random sample of three elements from a population of 600 elements. Perform the sampling procedure 20 times. Do any two of the samples contain the same three elements? Given your answer to part **b**, did you expect repeated samples?
   d. Use the computer to generate a random sample of three from the population of 600 elements.

3.98 Suppose that a population contains $N = 200{,}000$ elements. Use a computer or Table I of Appendix A to select a random sample of $n = 10$ elements from the population. Explain how you selected your sample.

Applying the Concepts—Basic

3.99 **Random-digit dialing.** To ascertain the effectiveness of their advertising campaigns, firms frequently conduct telephone interviews with consumers using *random-digit dialing*. With this method, a random number generator mechanically creates the sample of phone numbers to be called.
   a. Explain how the random number table (Table I of Appendix A) or a computer could be used to generate a sample of 7-digit telephone numbers.
   b. Use the procedure you described in part **a** to generate a sample of ten 7-digit telephone numbers.

   c. Use the procedure you described in part **a** to generate five 7-digit telephone numbers whose first three digits are 373.

3.100 **Census sampling.** In addition to its decennial enumeration of the population, the U.S. Bureau of the Census regularly samples the population for demographic information such as income, family size, employment, and marital status. Suppose the Bureau plans to sample 1,000 households in a city that has a total of 534,322 households. Show how the Bureau could use the random number table in Appendix A or a computer to generate the sample. Select the first 10 households to be included in the sample.

Applying the Concepts—Intermediate

3.101 **Study of the effect of songs with violent lyrics.** A series of designed experiments were conducted to examine the effects of songs with violent lyrics on aggressive thoughts and hostile feelings. (*Journal of Personality & Social Psychology*, May 2003.) In one of the experiments, college students were randomly assigned to listen to one of four types of songs: (1) humorous song with violent lyrics, (2) humorous song with nonviolent lyrics, (3) nonhumorous song with violent lyrics, and (4) nonhumorous song with nonviolent lyrics. Assuming 120 students participated in the study, use a random number generator to randomly assign 30 students to each of the four experimental conditions.

3.102 **Auditing an accounting system.** In auditing a firm's financial statements, an auditor is required to assess the operational effectiveness of the accounting system. In performing the assessment, the auditor frequently relies on a random sample of actual transactions. (Stickney and Weil, *Financial Accounting: An Introduction to Concepts, Methods, and Uses*, 1994.) A particular firm has 5,382 customer accounts that are numbered from 0001 to 5382.
   a. One account is to be selected at random for audit. What is the probability that account number 3,241 is selected?
   b. Draw a random sample of 10 accounts and explain in detail the procedure you used.
   c. Refer to part **b**. The following are two possible random samples of size 10. Is one more likely to be selected than the other? Explain.

Sample Number 1				
5011	0082	0963	0772	3415
2663	1126	0008	0026	4189

Sample Number 2				
0001	0003	0005	0007	0009
0002	0004	0006	0008	0010

Applying the Concepts—Advanced

3.103 Selecting archaeological dig sites. Archaeologists plan to perform test digs at a location they believe was inhabited several thousand years ago. The site is approximately 10,000 meters long and 5,000 meters wide. They first draw rectangular grids over the area, consisting of lines every 100 meters, creating a total of $100 \cdot 50 = 5,000$ intersections (not counting one of the outer boundaries). The plan is to randomly sample 50 intersection points and dig at the sampled intersections. Explain how you could use a random number generator to obtain a random sample of 50 intersections. Develop at least two plans: one that numbers the intersections from 1 to 5,000 prior to selection and another that selects the row and column of each sampled intersection (from the total of 100 rows and 50 columns).

3.8 Some Additional Counting Rules (Optional)

In Section 3.1 we pointed out that experiments sometimes have so many sample points that it is impractical to list them all. However, many of these experiments possess sample points with identical characteristics. If you can develop a **counting rule** to count the number of sample points for such an experiment, it can be used to aid in the solution of the problems. The Combinations Rule for selecting n elements from N elements without regard to order was presented in Section 3.1 (p. 129). In this optional section, we give three additional counting rules: the *Multiplicative Rule*, the *Permutations Rule*, and the *Partitions Rule*.

EXAMPLE 3.24   **APPLYING THE MULTIPLICATIVE RULE**

Problem   A product can be shipped by four airlines, and each airline can ship via three different routes. How many distinct ways exist to ship the product?

Solution   A pictorial representation of the different ways to ship the product will aid in counting them. The tree diagram (see Section 3.6) is useful for this purpose. Consider the tree diagram shown in Figure 3.22. At the starting point (stage 1), there are four choices — the different airlines — to begin the journey. Once we have chosen an airline (stage 2), there are three choices — the different routes — to complete the shipment and reach the final destination. Thus, the tree diagram clearly shows that there are $(4)(3) = 12$ distinct ways to ship the product.

Figure 3.22
Tree Diagram for Shipping Problem

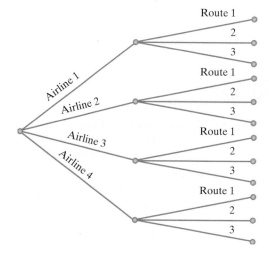

Look Back The method of solving this example can be generalized to any number of stages with sets of different elements. This method is given by the *Multiplicative Rule*.

Now Work   *Exercise 3.114*

> **The Multiplicative Rule**
>
> You have k sets of elements, n_1 in the first set, n_2 in the second set, $\ldots$, and n_k in the kth set. Suppose you wish to form a sample of k elements by *taking one element from each* of the k sets. The number of different samples that can be formed is the product
>
> $$n_1 n_2 n_3 \cdots n_k$$

EXAMPLE 3.25   APPLYING THE MULTIPLICATIVE RULE

Problem   There are 20 candidates for three different executive positions, E_1, E_2, and E_3. How many different ways could you fill the positions?

Solution   For this example, there are $k = 3$ sets of elements corresponding to

> Set 1: Candidates available to fill position E_1
> Set 2: Candidates remaining (after filling E_1) that are available to fill E_2
> Set 3: Candidates remaining (after filling E_1 and E_2) that are available to fill E_3

The number of elements in the sets are $n_1 = 20$, $n_2 = 19$, $n_3 = 18$. Therefore, the number of different ways of filling the three positions is given by the Multiplicative Rule as $n_1 n_2 n_3 = (20)(19)(18) = 6{,}840$.

■ ■ ■

EXAMPLE 3.26   APPLYING THE MULTIPLICATIVE RULE

Problem   Consider the experiment discussed in Example 3.12 of tossing a coin 10 times. Show how we found that there were $2^{10} = 1{,}024$ sample points for this experiment.

Solution   There are $k = 10$ sets of elements for this experiment. Each set contains two elements: a head and a tail. Thus, there are

$$(2)(2)(2)(2)(2)(2)(2)(2)(2)(2) = 2^{10} = 1{,}024$$

different outcomes (sample points) of this experiment.

■ ■ ■

EXAMPLE 3.27   APPLYING THE PERMUTATIONS RULE

Problem   Suppose there are five dangerous military missions, each requiring one soldier. In how many different ways can five soldiers from a squadron of 100 be assigned to these five missions?

Solution   We can solve this problem by using the Multiplicative Rule. The entire set of 100 soldiers is available for the first mission, and after the selection of one soldier for that mission, 99 are available for the second mission, etc. Thus, the total number of different ways of choosing five soldiers for the five missions is

$$n_1 n_2 n_3 n_4 n_5 = (100)(99)(98)(97)(96) = 9{,}034{,}502{,}400$$

Look Back   The arrangement of elements in a distinct order is called a **permutation**. Thus, there are more than 9 billion different *permutations* of five elements (soldiers) drawn from a set of 100 elements!

■ ■ ■

> **Permutations Rule**
>
> Given a *single set* of N distinctly different elements, you wish to select n elements from the N and *arrange* them within n positions. The number of different **permutations** of the N elements taken n at a time is denoted by P_n^N and is equal to
>
> $$P_n^N = N(N-1)(N-2) \cdot \cdots \cdot (N-n+1) = \frac{N!}{(N-n)!}$$
>
> where $n! = n(n-1)(n-2)\cdots(3)(2)(1)$ and is called n *factorial*. (Thus, for example, $5! = 5 \cdot 4 \cdot 3 \cdot 2 \cdot 1 = 120$.) The quantity $0!$ is defined to be 1.

EXAMPLE 3.28 APPLYING THE PERMUTATIONS RULE

Problem You wish to drive, in sequence, from a starting point to each of five cities, and you wish to compare the distances — and ultimately the costs — of the different routes. How many different routes would you have to compare?

Solution Denote the cities as $C_1, C_2, \ldots, C_5$. Then a route moving from the starting point to C_2 to C_1 to C_3 to C_4 to C_5 would be represented as $C_2 C_1 C_3 C_4 C_5$. The total number of routes would equal the number of ways you could rearrange the $N = 5$ cities in $n = 5$ positions. This number is

$$P_n^N = P_5^5 = \frac{5!}{(5-5)!} = \frac{5!}{0!} = \frac{5 \cdot 4 \cdot 3 \cdot 2 \cdot 1}{1} = 120$$

(Recall that $0! = 1$.)

| Now Work | *Exercise 3.113c* |

■ ■ ■

EXAMPLE 3.29 APPLYING THE PARTITIONS RULE

Problem You are supervising four construction workers. You must assign three to job 1 and one to job 2. In how many different ways can you make this assignment?

Solution To begin, suppose each worker is to be assigned to a distinct job. Then, using the multiplicative rule, you obtain $(4)(3)(2)(1) = 24$ ways of assigning the workers to four distinct jobs. The 24 ways are listed in four groups in Table 3.8 (where ABCD signifies that worker A was assigned the first distinct job, worker B the second, etc.).

Now suppose the first three positions represent job 1 and the last position represents job 2. You can now see that all the listings in group 1 represent the same outcome of the experiment of interest. That is, workers A, B, and C are assigned to job 1 and worker D to job 2. Similarly, group 2 listings are equivalent, as are group 3

TABLE 3.8 Workers Assigned to Four Jobs, Example 3.29

Group 1	Group 2	Group 3	Group 4
ABCD	ABDC	ACDB	BCDA
ACBD	ADBC	ADCB	BDCA
BACD	BADC	CADB	CBDA
BCAD	BDAC	CDAB	CDBA
CABD	DABC	DACB	DBCA
CBAD	DBAC	DCAB	DCBA

TABLE 3.9 Workers Assigned to Two Jobs, Example 3.29

Job 1	Job 2
ABC	D
ABD	C
ACD	B
BCD	A

and group 4 listings. Thus, there are only four different assignments of four workers to the two jobs. These are shown in Table 3.9.

Look Back To generalize this result, we point out that the final result can be found by

$$\frac{(4)(3)(2)(1)}{(3)(2)(1)(1)} = 4$$

The $(4)(3)(2)(1)$ is the number of different ways (*permutations*) the workers could be assigned four distinct jobs. The division by $(3)(2)(1)$ is to remove the duplicated permutations resulting from the fact that three workers are assigned the same jobs. And the division by 1 is associated with the worker assigned to job 2.

> Now Work   *Exercise 3.113b*

■ ■ ■

Partitions Rule

There exists a *single* set of N distinctly different elements. You wish to partition them into k sets, with the first set containing n_1 elements, the second containing n_2 elements, ..., and the kth set containing n_k elements. The number of different partitions is

$$\frac{N!}{n_1! n_2! \cdot \cdots \cdot n_k!} \quad \text{where } n_1 + n_2 + n_3 + \cdots + n_k = N$$

EXAMPLE 3.30   APPLYING THE PARTITIONS RULE

Problem   You have 12 construction workers. You wish to assign three to job site 1, four to job site 2, and five to job site 3. In how many different ways can you make this assignment?

Solution   For this example, $k = 3$ (corresponding to the $k = 3$ different job sites), $N = 12$, and $n_1 = 3, n_2 = 4$, and $n_3 = 5$. Then the number of different ways to assign the workers to the job sites is

$$\frac{N!}{n_1! n_2! n_3!} = \frac{12!}{3! 4! 5!} = \frac{12 \cdot 11 \cdot 10 \cdot \cdots \cdot 3 \cdot 2 \cdot 1}{(3 \cdot 2 \cdot 1)(4 \cdot 3 \cdot 2 \cdot 1)(5 \cdot 4 \cdot 3 \cdot 2 \cdot 1)} = 27,720$$

■ ■ ■

EXAMPLE 3.31   APPLYING THE COMBINATIONS RULE

Problem   Five soldiers from a squadron of 100 are to be chosen for a dangerous mission. In how many ways can groups of five be formed?

Solution   This problem is equivalent to sampling $n = 5$ elements from a set of $N = 100$ elements. Here, we apply the Combinations Rule from Section 3.1. The number of ways is the number of possible combinations of five soldiers selected from 100, or

$$\binom{100}{5} = \frac{100!}{(5!)(95!)} = \frac{100 \cdot 99 \cdot 98 \cdot 97 \cdot 96 \cdot 95 \cdot 94 \cdot \cdots \cdot 2 \cdot 1}{(5 \cdot 4 \cdot 3 \cdot 2 \cdot 1)(95 \cdot 94 \cdot \cdots \cdot 2 \cdot 1)}$$

$$= \frac{100 \cdot 99 \cdot 98 \cdot 97 \cdot 96}{5 \cdot 4 \cdot 3 \cdot 2 \cdot 1} = 75,287,520$$

Look Back Compare this result with that of Example 3.27, where we found that the number of permutations of five elements drawn from 100 was more than 9 billion. Because the order of the elements does not affect combinations, there are *fewer* combinations than permutations.

Now Work   *Exercise 3.113a*

━━━━━━━━━━   ■ ■ ■   ━━━━━━━━━━

When working a probability problem, you should carefully examine the experiment to determine whether you can use one or more of the rules we have discussed in this section. Let's see how these rules (summarized in the next box) can help solve a probability problem.

Summary of Counting Rules

1. *Multiplicative rule.* If you are drawing *one element from each of k sets of elements*, with the sizes of the sets $n_1, n_2, \ldots, n_k$, the number of different results is

$$n_1 n_2 n_3 \cdot \cdots \cdot n_k$$

2. *Permutations rule.* If you are drawing *n elements from a set of N elements and arranging the n elements in a distinct order*, the number of different results is

$$P_n^N = \frac{N!}{(N-n)!}$$

3. *Partitions rule.* If you are partitioning the *elements of a set of N elements into k groups consisting of* $n_1, n_2, \ldots, n_k$ *elements* $(n_1 + \cdots + n_k = N)$, the number of different results is

$$\frac{N!}{n_1! n_2! \cdot \cdots \cdot n_k!}$$

4. *Combinations rule.* If you are drawing *n elements from a set of N elements without regard to the order of the n elements*, the number of different results is

$$\binom{N}{n} = \frac{N!}{n!(N-n)!}$$

[*Note:* The combinations rule is a special case of the partitions rule when $k = 2$.]

EXAMPLE 3.32

APPLYING SEVERAL COUNTING RULES

Problem   A consumer testing service is commissioned to rank the top three brands of laundry detergent. A total of 10 brands are to be included in the study.

a. In how many different ways can the consumer testing service arrive at the final ranking?

b. If the testing service can distinguish no difference among the brands and therefore arrives at the final ranking by random selection, what is the probability that company Z's brand is ranked first? In the top three?

Solution   **a.** Since the testing service is drawing three elements (brands) from a set of 10 elements and arranging the three elements in a distinct order, we use the permutations rule to find the number of different results:

$$P_3^{10} = \frac{10!}{(10-3)!} = 10 \cdot 9 \cdot 8 = 720$$

b. The steps for calculating the probability of interest are as follows:

Step 1 The experiment is to select and rank three brands of detergent from 10 brands.

Step 2 There are too many sample points to list. However, we know from part **a** that there are 720 different outcomes (i.e., sample points) of this experiment.

Step 3 If we assume the testing service determines the rankings at random, each of the 720 sample points should have an equal probability of occurrence. Thus,

$$P(\text{Each sample point}) = \frac{1}{720}$$

Step 4 One event of interest to company Z is that their brand receives top ranking. We will call this event A. The list of sample points that result in the occurrence of event A is long, but the *number* of sample points contained in event A is determined by breaking event A into two parts:

Thus, event A can occur in 72 different ways.

Now define B as the event that company Z's brand is ranked in the top three. Since event B specifies only that brand Z appear in the top three, we repeat the calculations above, fixing brand Z in position 2 and then in position 3. We conclude that the number of sample points contained in event B is 3(72) = 216.

Step 5 The final step is to calculate the probabilities of events A and B. Since the 720 sample points are equally likely to occur, we find

$$P(A) = \frac{\text{Number of sample points in } A}{\text{Total number of sample points}} = \frac{72}{720} = \frac{1}{10}$$

Similarly,

$$P(B) = \frac{216}{720} = \frac{3}{10}$$

━━━━━ ■ ■ ■ ━━━━━

EXAMPLE 3.33   APPLYING SEVERAL COUNTING RULES

Problem   Refer to Example 3.32. Suppose the consumer testing service is to choose the top three laundry detergents from the group of 10 *but is not to rank the three.*

a. In how many different ways can the testing service choose the three to be designated as top detergents?

b. Assuming that the testing service makes its choice by a random selection and that company X has two brands in the group of 10, what is the probability that exactly one of the company X brands is selected in the top three? At least one?

Solution   **a.** The testing service is selecting three elements (brands) from a set of 10 elements *without regard to order*, so we can apply the combinations rule to determine the number of different results:

$$\binom{10}{3} = \frac{10!}{3!(10-3)!} = \frac{10 \cdot 9 \cdot 8}{3 \cdot 2 \cdot 1} = 120$$

b. The steps for calculating the probability of interest are as follows:

Step 1 The experiment is to select (*but not rank*) three brands from 10.
Step 2 There are 120 sample points for this experiment.
Step 3 Since the selection is made at random,

$$P(\text{Each sample point}) = \frac{1}{120}$$

Step 4 Define events A and B as follows:

A: {Exactly one company X brand is selected}
B: {At least one company X brand is selected}

Since each of the sample points is equally likely to occur, we need only know the number of sample points in A and B to determine their probabilities.

For event A to occur, exactly one company X brand must be selected, along with two of the remaining eight brands. We thus break A into two parts:

Note that the one company X brand can be selected in two ways, whereas the two other brands can be selected in 28 ways. (We use the combinations rule because the order of selection is not important.) Then, we use the multiplicative rule to combine one of the two ways to select a company X brand with one of the 28 ways to select two other brands, yielding a total of 56 sample points for event A.

To count the sample points contained in B, we first note that

$$B = A \cup C$$

where A is defined as before and

C: {Both company X brands are selected}

We have determined that A contains 56 sample points. Using the same method for event C, we find

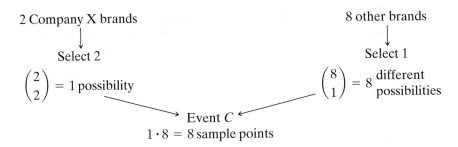

Thus, event C contains eight sample points and $P(C) = {}^8/_{120}$.

Step 5 Since all the sample points are equally likely,

$$P(A) = \frac{\text{Number of sample points in } A}{\text{Total number of sample points}} = \frac{56}{120} = \frac{7}{15}$$

$$P(B) = P(A \cup C) = P(A) + P(C) - P(A \cap C)$$

where $P(A \cap C) = 0$ because the testing service cannot select exactly one *and* exactly two of the company X brands; that is, A and C are mutually exclusive events. Thus,

$$P(B) = \frac{56}{120} + \frac{8}{120} = \frac{64}{120} = \frac{8}{15}$$

■ ■ ■

Learning how to decide whether a particular counting rule applies to an experiment takes patience and practice. If you wish to develop this skill, attempt to use the rules to solve the following exercises and especially the optional exercises (marked with an asterisk) at the end of this chapter. Proofs of the counting rules can be found in the text by W. Feller (1968, Chapter 3).

Exercises 3.104–3.125

Understanding the Principles

3.104 Give a scenario where the Multiplicative Rule applies.

3.105 Give a scenario where the Permutations Rule applies.

3.106 Give a scenario where the Partitions Rule applies.

3.107 What is the difference between the Permutations Rule and the Combinations Rule?

Learning the Mechanics

3.108 Find the numerical values of
a. $\binom{6}{3}$ **b.** P_2^5 **c.** P_2^4 **d.** $\binom{100}{98}$
e. $\binom{50}{50}$ **f.** $\binom{50}{0}$ **g.** P_3^5 **h.** P_0^{10}

3.109 Use the multiplicative rule to determine the number of sample points in the sample space corresponding to the experiment of tossing a coin the following number of times:
a. 2 times   **b.** 3 times   **c.** 5 times
d. n times

3.110 Determine the number of sample points contained in the sample space when you toss the following:
a. 1 die   **b.** 2 dice   **c.** 4 dice
d. n dice 6^n

3.111 An experiment consists of choosing objects without regard to order. How many sample points are there if you choose the following?
a. 3 objects from 7   **b.** 2 objects from 6
c. 2 objects from 30   **d.** 8 objects from 10
e. r objects from q

Applying the Concepts — Basic

3.112 **Selecting project teams.** Suppose you are managing 10 employees, and you need to form three teams to work on different projects. Assume that each employee may serve on any team. In how many different ways can the teams be formed if the number of members on each project team are as follows:
a. 3, 3, 4   **b.** 2, 3, 5   **c.** 1, 4, 5
d. 2, 4, 4

3.113 **Picking a basketball team.** Suppose you are to choose a basketball team (five players) from eight available athletes.
a. How many ways can you choose a team (ignoring positions)?
b. How many ways can you choose a team composed of two guards, two forwards, and a center?

c. How many ways can you choose a team composed of point guard, shooting guard, power forward, small forward, and center?

3.114 Air travel options. Flying into New York from a certain
NW city, you can choose one of three airlines and can travel either first class or coach. How many travel options do you have?

3.115 Traveling between cities. A salesperson living in city A wishes to visit four cities, B, C, D, and E.

a. If the cities are all connected by airlines, how many different travel plans could be constructed to visit each city exactly once and then return home?

b. Suppose all cities are connected except that B and C are not directly connected. How many different flight plans would be available to the salesperson?

3.116 U.S. Zip codes. The 9-digit Zip code has become an integral part of the U.S. postal system.

a. How many different Zip codes are available for use by the postal service? (Assume any 9-digit number can be used as a Zip code.)

b. The first three digits of a Chicago Zip code are 606. If no other city in the United States has these first three digits as part of its Zip, how many different Zip codes may possibly exist in Chicago?

Applying the Concepts—Intermediate

3.117 Multilevel marketing schemes. Successful companies such as Amway, Herbalife, and NuSkin employ multilevel marketing (MLM) schemes to distribute their products. In MLM, each distributor recruits several additional distributors to work at the first level. Each of these first-level distributors, in turn, recruits distributors to work at the second level. Distributors at any level continue to recruit distributors, forming additional levels. A distributor at any particular level makes a 5% commission on the sales of all distributors at lower levels in his or her "group." (*Success*, Dec. 1995.)

a. Elaine is a distributor for a MLM company. Elaine recruits six distributors to work for her at the first level. Each of these distributors recruits an additional five distributors to work at the second level. How many distributors are under Elaine?

b. Refer to part **a.** Suppose each distributor at Elaine's second level recruits seven third-level distributors, and each of these third-level distributors recruits five level-four distributors. Now, how many distributors are under Elaine? (Your answer should provide insight into why some MLM distributors can earn $100,000 in commissions per month!)

3.118 Mathematical Theory of Partitions. Mathematicians at the University of Florida solved a 30-year-old math problem using the theory of partitions. (*Explore*, Fall 2000.) In math terminology, a partition is a representation of an integer as a sum of positive integers. (For example, the number 3 has three possible partitions: 3, 2 + 1 and 1 + 1 + 1.) The researchers solved the problem by using "colored partitions" of a number,

where the colors correspond to the four suits—red hearts, red diamonds, black spades, and black clubs—in a standard 52-card bridge deck. Consider forming colored partitions of an integer.

a. How many colored partitions of the number 3 are possible? [*Hint:* One partition is 3♥; another is 2♦ + 1♣.]

b. How many colored partitions of the number 5 are possible?

3.119 Matching medical students with residencies. The National Resident Matching Program (NRMP) is a service provided by the Association of American Medical Colleges to match graduating medical students with residency appointments at hospitals. After students and hospitals have evaluated each other, they submit rank-order lists of their preferences to the NRMP. Using a matching algorithm, the NRMP then generates final, nonnegotiable assignments of students to the residency programs of hospitals (*Academic Medicine*, June 1995). Assume that three graduating medical students (#1, #2, and #3) have applied for positions at three different hospitals (A, B, and C), where each hospital has one and only one resident opening.

a. How many different assignments of medical students to hospitals are possible? List them.

b. Suppose student #1 prefers hospital B. If the NRMP algorithm is entirely random, what is the probability that the student is assigned to hospital B?

3.120 Florida license plates. In the mid-1980s the state of Florida ran out of combinations of letters and numbers for its license plates. Then, each license plate contained three letters of the alphabet followed by three digits selected from the 10 digits 0, 1, 2, ..., 9.

a. How many different license plates did this system allow?

b. New Florida tags were obtained by reversing the procedure, starting with three digits followed by three letters. How many new tags did the new system provide?

c. Since the new tag numbers were added to the old numbers, what is the total number of licenses available for registration in Florida?

3.121 Selecting committee members. The Republican governor of a state with no income tax is appointing a committee of five members to consider changes in the income tax law. There are 15 state representatives available for appointment to the committee, seven Democrats and eight Republicans. Assume that the governor selects the committee of five members randomly from the 15 representatives.

a. In how many different ways can the committee members be selected?

b. What is the probability that no Democrat is appointed to the committee? If this were to occur, what would you conclude about the assumption that the appointments were made at random? Why?

c. What is the probability that the majority of the committee members are Republican? If this were to occur, would you have reason to doubt that the governor made the selections randomly? Why?

3.122 Selecting new car options. A company sells midlevel models of automobiles in five different styles. A buyer can get an automobile in one of eight colors with either standard or automatic transmission. Would it be reasonable to expect a dealer to stock at least one automobile in every style, color, and transmission combination? At a minimum, how many automobiles would the dealer have to stock?

3.123 Studying exam questions. A college professor hands out a list of 10 questions, five of which will appear on the final examination for the course. One of the students taking the course is pressed for time and can prepare for only seven of the 10 questions. Suppose the professor chooses the five questions at random from the 10.
a. What is the probability that the student will be prepared for all five questions that appear on the final examination?
b. What is the probability that the student will be prepared for fewer than three questions?
c. What is the probability that the student will be prepared for exactly four questions?

3.124 Volleyball positions. Intercollegiate volleyball rules require that after the opposing team has lost its serve, each of the six members of the serving team must rotate into new positions on the court. Hence, each player must be able to play all six different positions. How many different team combinations by player and position are possible during a volleyball game? If players are initially assigned to the positions in a random manner, find the probability that the best server on the team is in the serving position.

Applying the Concepts—Advanced

3.125 A straight flush in poker. Consider five-card poker hands dealt from a standard 52-card bridge deck. Two important events are

A: {You draw a flush}
B: {You draw a straight}

[*Note:* A *flush* consists of any five cards of the same suit. A *straight* consists of any five cards with values in sequence. In a straight, the cards may be of any suit, and an ace may be considered as having a value of 1 or a value higher than a king.]
a. How many different five-card hands can be dealt from a 52-card bridge deck?
b. Find $P(A)$.
c. Find $P(B)$.
d. The event that both A and B occur, that is $A \cap B$, is called a *straight flush*. Find $P(A \cap B)$.

3.9 Bayes's Rule (Optional)

An early attempt to employ probability in making inferences is the basis for a branch of statistical methodology known as **Bayesian statistical methods**. The logic employed by the English philosopher, Thomas Bayes, in the mid-1700s, involves converting an unknown conditional probability, say $P(B|A)$, to one involving a known conditional probability, say $P(A|B)$. The method is illustrated in the next example.

EXAMPLE 3.34   APPLYING BAYES'S LOGIC

Problem   An unmanned monitoring system uses high-tech video equipment and microprocessors to detect intruders. A prototype system has been developed and is in use outdoors at a weapons munitions plant. The system is designed to detect intruders with a probability of .90. However, the design engineers expect this probability to vary with weather condition. The system automatically records the weather condition each time an intruder is detected. Based on a series of controlled tests, in which an intruder was released at the plant under various weather conditions, the following information is available: Given the intruder was, in fact, detected by the system, the weather was clear 75% of the time, cloudy 20% of the time, and raining 5% of the time. When the system failed to detect the intruder, 60% of the days were clear, 30% cloudy, and 10% rainy. Use this information to find the probability of detecting an intruder, given rainy weather conditions. (Assume that an intruder has been released at the plant.)

Solution   Define D to be the event that the intruder is detected by the system. Then D^c is the event that the system failed to detect the intruder. Our goal is to calculate the conditional probability, $P(D|\text{Rainy})$. From the statement of the problem, the following information is available:

$$P(D) = .90 \qquad\qquad P(D^c) = .10$$
$$P(\text{Clear}|D) = .75 \qquad P(\text{Clear}|D^c) = .60$$
$$P(\text{Cloudy}|D) = .20 \qquad P(\text{Cloudy}|D^c) = .30$$
$$P(\text{Rainy}|D) = .05 \qquad P(\text{Rainy}|D^c) = .10$$

Note that $P(D|\text{Rainy})$ is not one of the conditional probabilities that is known. However, we can find

$$P(\text{Rainy} \cap D) = P(D)P(\text{Rainy}|D) = (.90)(.05) = .045$$

and

$$P(\text{Rainy} \cap D^c) = P(D^c)P(\text{Rainy}|D^c) = (.10)(.10) = .01$$

using the Multiplicative Probability Rule. Now the event Rainy is the union of two mutually exclusive events, $(\text{Rainy} \cap D)$ and $(\text{Rainy} \cap D^c)$. Thus, applying the Additive Probability Rule, we have

$$P(\text{Rainy}) = P(\text{Rainy} \cap D) + P(\text{Rainy} \cap D^c) = .045 + .01 = .055$$

We now apply the formula for conditional probability to obtain

$$P(D|\text{Rainy}) = \frac{P(\text{Rainy} \cap D)}{P(\text{Rainy})} = \frac{P(\text{Rainy} \cap D)}{P(\text{Rainy} \cap D) + P(\text{Rainy} \cap D^c)}$$
$$= .045/.055 = .818$$

Therefore, under rainy weather conditions, the prototype system can detect the intruder with a probability of .818 — a value lower than the designed probability of .90.

The technique utilized in Example 3.34, called **Bayes's Rule**, can be applied when an observed event A occurs with any one of several mutually exclusive and exhaustive events, $B_1, B_2, \ldots, B_k$. The formula for finding the appropriate conditional probabilities is given in the box.

Bayes's Rule

Given k mutually exclusive and exhaustive events, $B_1, B_2, \ldots, B_k$, such that $P(B_1) + P(B_2) + \cdots + P(B_k) = 1$, and an observed event A, then

$$P(B_i|A) = P(B_i \cap A)/P(A)$$

$$= \frac{P(B_i)P(A|B_i)}{P(B_1)P(A|B_1) + P(B_2)P(A|B_2) + \cdots + P(B_k)P(A|B_k)}$$

In applying Bayes's rule to Example 3.34, the observed event $A = \{\text{Rainy}\}$ and the $k = 2$ mutually exclusive and exhaustive events are the complementary events $D = \{\text{intruder detected}\}$ and $D^c = \{\text{intruder not detected}\}$. Hence, the formula

$$P(D|\text{Rainy}) = \frac{P(D)P(\text{Rainy}|D)}{P(D)P(\text{Rainy}|D) + P(D^c)P(\text{Rainy}|D^c)}$$
$$= \frac{(.90)(.05)}{(.90)(.05) + (.10)(.10)} = .818$$

Biography

THOMAS BAYES
(1702–1761)
The Inverse Probabilist

The Reverend Thomas Bayes was an ordained English Presbyterian minister who became a Fellow of the Royal Statistical Society without benefit of any formal training in mathematics or any published

papers in science during his lifetime. His manipulation of the formula for conditional probability in 1761 is now known as Bayes's Theorem. At the time and for 200 years afterward, use of Bayes's Theorem (or inverse probability, as it was called) was controversial and, to some, considered an inappropriate practice. It was not until the 1960s that the power of the Bayesian approach to decision making began to be tapped.

Exercises 3.126–3.137

Understanding the Principles

3.126 Explain the difference between the two probabilities, $P(A|B)$ and $P(B|A)$.

3.127 Why is Bayes's Rule unnecessary for finding $P(B|A)$ if events A and B are independent?

3.128 Why is Bayes's Rule unnecessary for finding $P(B|A)$ if events A and B are mutually exclusive?

Learning the Mechanics

3.129 Suppose the events B_1 and B_2 are mutually exclusive and complementary events, such that $P(B_1) = .75$ and $P(B_2) = .25$. Consider another event A such that $P(A|B_1) = .3$ and $P(A|B_2) = .5$.
  a. Find $P(B_1 \cap A)$.   **b.** Find $P(B_2 \cap A)$.
  c. Find $P(A)$ using the results in parts a and b.
  d. Find $P(B_1|A)$.   **e.** Find $P(B_2|A)$.

3.130 Suppose the events B_1, B_2, and B_3 are mutually exclusive and complementary events, such that $P(B_1) = .2$, $P(B_2) = .15$, and $P(B_3) = .65$. Consider another event A such that $P(A|B_1) = .4$, $P(A|B_2) = .25$, and $P(A|B_3) = .6$. Use Bayes's Rule to find
  a. $P(B_1|A)$ **b.** $P(B_2|A)$
  c. $P(B_3|A)$

3.131 Suppose the events B_1, B_2, and B_3 are mutually exclusive and complementary events, such that $P(B_1) = .2$, $P(B_2) = .15$, and $P(B_3) = .65$. Consider another event A such that $P(A) = .4$. If A is independent of B_1, B_2, and B_3, use Bayes's Rule to show that $P(B_1|A) = P(B_1) = .2$.

Applying the Concepts—Basic

DDT
3.132 Contaminated fish. Refer to the U.S. Army Corps of Engineers' study on the DDT contamination of fish in the Tennessee River (Alabama), Example 1.4 (p. 00). Part of the investigation focused on how far upstream the contaminated fish have migrated. (A fish is considered to be contaminated if its measured DDT concentration is greater than 5.0 parts per million.)

a. Considering only the contaminated fish captured from the Tennessee River, the data reveal that 52% of the fish are found between 275 and 300 miles upstream, 39% are found 305 to 325 miles upstream, and 9% are found 330 to 350 miles upstream. Use these percentages to determine the probabilities, $P(275–300)$, $P(305–325)$, and $P(330–350)$.

b. Given a contaminated fish is found a certain distance upstream, the probability that it is a channel catfish (CC) is determined from the data as $P(CC|275–300) = .775$, $P(CC|305–325) = .77$, and $P(CC|330–350) = .86$. If a contaminated channel catfish is captured from the Tennessee River, what is the probability that it was captured 275–300 miles upstream?

3.133 Drug testing in athletes. Due to inaccuracies in drug testing procedures (e.g., false positives and false negatives), in the medical field the results of a drug test represent only one factor in a physician's diagnosis. Yet when Olympic athletes are tested for illegal drug use (i.e., doping), the results of a single test are used to ban the athlete from competition. In *Chance* (Spring 2004), University of Texas biostatisticians D. A. Berry and L. Chastain demonstrated the application of Bayes's Rule for making inferences about testosterone abuse among Olympic athletes. They used the following example. In a population of 1,000 athletes, suppose 100 are illegally using testosterone. Of the users, suppose 50 would test positive for testosterone. Of the nonusers, suppose 9 would test positive.

a. Given the athlete is a user, find the probability that a drug test for testosterone will yield a positive result. (This probability represents the *sensitivity* of the drug test.)

b. Given the athlete is a nonuser, find the probability that a drug test for testosterone will yield a negative result. (This probability represents the *specificity* of the drug test.)

c. If an athlete tests positive for testosterone, use Bayes's Rule to find the probability that the athlete is really doping. (This probability represents the *positive predictive value* of the drug test.)

3.134 Errors in estimating Job Costs. A construction company employs three sales engineers. Engineers 1, 2, and 3 estimate the costs of 30%, 20%, and 50%, respectively, of all jobs bid by the company. For $i = 1, 2, 3$, define E_i to be the event that a job is estimated by engineer i. The following probabilities describe the rates at which the engineers make serious errors in estimating costs:

$P(\text{error}|E_1) = .01$, $P(\text{error}|E_2) = .03$, and
$P(\text{error}|E_3) = .02$

a. If a particular bid results in a serious error in estimating job cost, what is the probability that the error was made by engineer 1?

b. If a particular bid results in a serious error in estimating job cost, what is the probability that the error was made by engineer 2?

c. If a particular bid results in a serious error in estimating job cost, what is the probability that the error was made by engineer 3?

d. Based on the probabilities, parts a–c, which engineer is most likely responsible for making the serious error?

Applying the Concepts—Intermediate

3.135 Intrusion detection systems. Refer to the *Journal of Research of the National Institute of Standards and Technology* (Nov.–Dec. 2003) study of a double intrusion detection system with independent systems, Exercise 3.81 (p. 158). Recall that if there is an intruder, system A sounds an alarm with probability .9 and system B sounds an alarm with probability .95. If there is no intruder, system A sounds an alarm with probability .2 and system B sounds an alarm with probability .1. Now, assume that the probability of an intruder is .4. If both systems sound an alarm, what is the probability that an intruder is detected?

3.136 Repairing a computer system. The local area network (LAN) for the College of Business computing system at a large university is temporarily shutdown for repairs. Previous shutdowns have been due to hardware failure, software failure, or power failure. Maintenance engineers have determined that the probabilities of hardware, software, and power problems are .01, .05, and .02, respectively. They have also determined that if the system experiences hardware problems, it shuts down 73% of the time. Similarly, if software problems occur, the system shuts down 12% of the time; and, if power failure occurs, the system shuts down 88% of the time. What is the probability that the current shutdown of the LAN is due to hardware failure? Software failure? Power failure?

3.137 Purchasing microchips. An important component of your desktop or laptop personal computer (PC) is a microchip. The table gives the proportions of microchips that a certain PC manufacturer purchases from seven suppliers.

Supplier	Proportion
S_1	.15
S_2	.05
S_3	.10
S_4	.20
S_5	.12
S_6	.20
S_7	.18

a. It is known that the proportions of defective microchips produced by the seven suppliers are .001, .0003, .0007, .006, .0002, .0002, and .001, respectively. If a single PC microchip failure is observed, which supplier is most likely responsible?

b. Suppose the seven suppliers produce defective microchips at the same rate, .0005. If a single PC microchip failure is observed, which supplier is most likely responsible?

Quick Review

Key Terms

[Note: Items marked with an asterisk (*)are from the optional sections in this chapter.]

Additive rule of probability   139
*Bayes's rule   175
*Bayesian statistical methods   174
Combinations rule   129
Combinatorial mathematics   129
Complementary events   137
Compound event   133
Conditional probability   145

*Counting rule   165
Dependent events   151
Event   125
Experiment   121
Independent events   151
Intersection   134
Law of large numbers   123
*Multiplicative counting rule   166
Multiplicative rule of probability   149
Mutually exclusive events   140
Odds   183
*Partitions rule   168
*Permutations rule   167

Probability rules (sample points)   124
Random number generator   161
Random number table   162
Random sample   161
Sample point   121
Sample space   122
Tree diagram   150
Two-way table   136
Unconditional probabilities   145
Union   134
Venn diagram   122

Key Formulas

$$\binom{N}{n} = \frac{N!}{n!(N-n)!}$$

where $N! = N(N-1)(N-2)\cdots(2)(1)$

$P(A) + P(A^c) = 1$

$P(A \cup B) = P(A) + P(B) - P(A \cap B)$

$P(A \cap B) = 0$

$P(A \cup B) = P(A) + P(B)$

$$P(A|B) = \frac{P(A \cap B)}{P(B)}$$

$P(A \cap B) = P(A)P(B|A) = P(B)P(A|B)$

$P(A|B) = P(A)$

$P(A \cap B) = P(A)P(B)$

$$P(B_i|A) = \frac{P(B_i)P(A|B_i)}{P(B_1)P(A|B_1) + P(B_2)P(A|B_2) + \cdots + P(B_k)P(A|B_k)}$$

Combinations rule   129
Rule of Complements   138
Additive rule of probability   139
Mutually exclusive events   140
Additive rule of probability for mutually exclusive events   140

Conditional probability   146

Multiplicative rule of probability   149
Independent events   151
Multiplicative rule of probability for independent events   154

*Bayes's rule   175

Note: For a summary of counting rules, see p. 169.

Language Lab

Symbol	Pronunciation	Description
S		Sample space
$S: \{1, 2, 3, 4, 5\}$		Set of sample points, 1,2,3,4,5, in sample space
$A: \{1, 2\}$		Set of sample points, 1,2, in event A
$P(A)$	Probability of A	Probability that event A occurs
$A \cup B$	A union B	Union of events A and B (either A or B or both occur)
$A \cap B$	A intersect B	Intersection of events A and B (both A and B occur)
A^c	A complement	Complement of event A (the event that A does not occur)
$P(A|B)$	Probability of A given B	Conditional probability that event A occurs given that event B occurs
$\binom{N}{n}$	N choose n	Number of combinations of N elements taken n at a time
$N!$	N factorial	Multiply $N(N-1)(N-2)\cdots(2)(1)$

Chapter Summary

Chapter Summary Notes

- Probability rules for k **sample points**:

  (1) $0 \le P(S_i) \le 1$ and (2) $\sum_{i=1}^{k} P(S_i) = 1$

- If $A = \{S_1, S_3, S_4\}$, then
  $P(A) = P(S_1) + P(S_3) + P(S_4)$

- The number of samples of size n that can be selected from N element is $\binom{N}{n}$

- **Union**: $(A \cup B)$ implies that either A or B will occur.
- **Intersection**: $(A \cap B)$ implies that both A and B will occur.
- **Complement**: A^c is all the sample points not in A.
- **Conditional**: $(A|B)$ is the event that A occurs, given B has occurred.
- **Independent**: B occurring does not change the probability that A occurs.
- **Random sample**: All possible samples have equal probability of being selected.

Supplementary Exercises 3.138–3.179

Note: Starred (*)exercises refer to the optional sections in this chapter.

Understanding the Principles

3.138 Which of the following pairs of events are mutually exclusive?
   a. A = {San Francisco Giants win the World Series next year}
   B = {Barry Bonds, Giants outfielder, hits 75 home runs next year}
   b. A = {Psychiatric patient Tony responds to a stimulus within 5 seconds}
   B = {Psychiatric patient Tony has the fastest stimulus response time of 2.3 seconds}
   c. A = {High school graduate Cindy enrolls at the University of South Florida next year}
   B = {High school graduate Cindy does not enroll in college next year}

3.139 Convert the following statements into compound events involving events A and B using the symbols $\cap$, $\cup$, and $|$, and ^{c}, where A = {You purchase an IBM notebook computer} and B = {you vacation in Europe}.
   a. You purchase an IBM notebook computer or vacation in Europe.
   b. You will not vacation in Europe.
   c. You purchase an IBM notebook computer and vacation in Europe.
   d. Given that you vacation in Europe, you will not purchase an IBM notebook computer.

Learning the Mechanics

3.140 A sample space consists of four sample points, where $P(S_1) = .2$, $P(S_2) = .1$, $P(S_3) = .3$, and $P(S_4) = .4$.
   a. Show that the sample points obey the two probability rules for a sample space.
   b. If an event $A = \{S_1, S_4\}$, find $P(A)$.

3.141 A and B are mutually exclusive events, with $P(A) = .2$ and $P(B) = .3$
   a. Find $P(A|B)$.
   b. Are A and B independent events?

3.142 For two events A and B, suppose $P(A) = .7$, $P(B) = .5$, and $P(A \cap B) = .4$. Find $P(A \cup B)$.

3.143 Given that $P(A \cap B) = .4$ and $P(A|B) = .8$, find $P(B)$.

Learning the Mechanics

3.144 The accompanying Venn diagram illustrates a sample space containing six sample points and three events, $A, B,$ and C. The probabilities of the sample points are $P(1) = .3$, $P(2) = .2$, $P(3) = .1$, $P(4) = .1$, $P(5) = .1$, and $P(6) = .2$.
   a. Find $P(A \cap B)$, $P(B \cap C)$, $P(A \cup C)$, $P(A \cup B \cup C)$, $P(B^c)$, $P(A^c \cap B)$, $P(B|C)$, and $P(B|A)$.

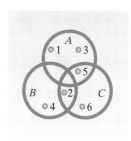

S

   b. Are A and B independent? Mutually exclusive? Why?
   c. Are B and C independent? Mutually exclusive? Why?

3.145 A fair die is tossed, and the up face is noted. If the number is even, the die is tossed again; if the number is odd, a fair coin is tossed. Define the events:
   A: {A head appears on the coin}
   B: {The die is tossed only one time}
   a. List the sample points in the sample space.
   b. Give the probability for each of the sample points.
   c. Find $P(A)$ and $P(B)$.
   d. Identify the sample points in A^c, B^c, $A \cap B$, and $A \cup B$.
   e. Find $P(A^c)$, $P(B^c)$, $P(A \cap B)$, $P(A \cup B)$, $P(A|B)$, and $P(B|A)$.
   f. Are A and B mutually exclusive events? Independent events? Why?

3.146 A balanced die is thrown once. If a 4 appears, a ball is drawn from urn 1; otherwise, a ball is drawn from urn 2. Urn 1 contains four red, three white, and three black balls. Urn 2 contains six red and four white balls.
   a. Find the probability that a red ball is drawn.
   b. Find the probability that urn 1 was used given that a red ball was drawn.

3.147 Two events, A and B, are independent, with $P(A) = .3$ and $P(B) = .1$.
   a. Are A and B mutually exclusive? Why?
   b. Find $P(A|B)$ and $P(B|A)$.
   c. Find $P(A \cup B)$.

*3.148 Find the numerical value of
   a. $6!$ **b.** $\binom{10}{9}$ **c.** $\binom{10}{1}$ **d.** P_2^6
   e. $\binom{6}{3}$ **f.** $0!$ **g.** P_4^{10} **h.** P_2^{50}

Applying the Concepts—Basic

CRASH

3.149 NHTSA new car crash testing. Refer to the National Highway Traffic Safety Administration (NHTSA) crash tests of new car models, Exercise 2.164 (p. 109). Recall that the NHTSA has developed a "star" scoring system, with results ranging from one star (*) to five stars (*****). The more stars in the rating, the better the level of crash protection in a head-on collision. A summary of the driver-side star ratings for 98 cars is reproduced in the accompanying MINITAB printout. Assume that one of the 98 cars is selected at random. State whether each of the following is true or false.

a. The probability that the car has a rating of two stars is 4.

b. The probability that the car has a rating of four or five stars is .7857.

c. The probability that the car has a rating of one star is 0.

d. The car has a better chance of having a 2-star rating than of having a 5-star rating.

Tally for Discrete Variables: DRIVSTAR

```
DRIVSTAR   Count   Percent
      2       4      4.08
      3      17     17.35
      4      59     60.20
      5      18     18.37
     N=      98
```

3.150 Selecting a sample. A random sample of five students is to be selected from 50 sociology majors for participation in a special program.

a. In how many different ways can the sample be drawn?

b. Show how the random number table, Table I of Appendix A, can be used to select the sample of students.

3.151 Forbes survey of companies. *Forbes* (July 26, 1999) conducted a survey of the 20 largest nondomestic public companies in the world. Of these 20 companies, 6 were trading companies based in Japan. A total of 11 Japanese companies were on the top 20 list. Suppose we select one of these 20 companies at random. Given the company is based in Japan, what is the probability that it is a trading company?

⚙ **EVOS**
3.152 Oilspill impact on seabirds. Refer to the *Journal of Agricultural, Biological, and Environmental Statistics* (Sept. 2000) study of the impact of the *Exxon Valdez* tanker oil spill on the seabird population in Prince William Sound, Alaska, Exercise 2.179 (p. 113). Recall that data were collected on 96 shoreline locations (called transects), and it was determined whether or not the transect was in an oiled area. The data are stored in the file called EVOS. From the data, estimate the probability that a randomly selected transect in Prince William Sound is contaminated with oil.

3.153 Education TV network. "Channel One" is an education television network for which participating secondary schools are equipped with TV sets in every classroom. According to *Educational Technology* (May–June 1995), 40% of all U.S. secondary schools subscribe to the Channel One Communications Network (CCN). Of these subscribers, 5% never use the CCN broadcasts, while 20% use CCN more than five times per week.

a. Find the probability that a randomly selected U.S. secondary school subscribes to CCN and never uses the CCN broadcasts.

b. Find the probability that a randomly selected U.S. secondary school subscribes to CCN and uses the broadcasts more than five times per week.

3.154 Carbon monoxide poisoning. The *American Journal of Public Health* (July 1995) published a study on unintentional carbon monoxide (CO) poisoning of Colorado residents. A total of 981 cases of CO poisoning were reported during a six-year period. Each case was classified as fatal or nonfatal and by source of exposure. The number of cases occurring in each of the categories is shown in the accompanying table. Assume that one of the 981 cases of unintentional CO poisoning is randomly selected.

Source of Exposure	Fatal	Nonfatal	Total
Fire	63	53	116
Auto exhaust	60	178	238
Furnace	18	345	363
Kerosene or spaceheater	9	18	27
Appliance	9	63	72
Other gas-powered motor	3	73	76
Fireplace	0	16	16
Other	3	19	22
Unknown	9	42	51
Total	174	807	981

Source: Cook, M. C., Simon P. A., and Hoffman, R. E., "Unintentional carbon monoxide poisoning in Colorado, 1986 through 1991." *American Journal of Public Health,* Vol. 85, No. 7, July 1995, p. 989 (Table 1).

a. List all sample points for this experiment.

b. What is the set of all sample points called?

c. Let A be the event that the CO poisoning is caused by fire. Find $P(A)$.

d. Let B be the event that the CO poisoning is fatal. Find $P(B)$.

e. Let C be the event that the CO poisoning is caused by auto exhaust. Find $P(C)$.

f. Let D be the event that the CO poisoning is caused by auto exhaust and is fatal. Find $P(D)$.

g. Let E be the event that the CO poisoning is caused by fire but is nonfatal. Find $P(E)$.

h. Given that the source of the poisoning is fire, what is the probability that the case is fatal?

i. Given that the case is nonfatal, what is the probability that it is caused by auto exhaust?

j. If the case is fatal, what is the probability that the source is unknown?

k. If the case is nonfatal, what is the probability that the source is not fire or a fireplace?

3.155 Media coverage of mental illness. Refer to the *Health Education Journal* (Sept. 1994) study of media coverage of stories involving mental illness in Scotland, Exercise 2.168 (p. 110). The media coverage of each of

562 stories was classified by type, with the results shown in the table. Assume that one of the 562 stories on mental illness is selected and the type of media coverage is noted.

Media Coverage	Number of Items
Violence to others	373
Sympathetic	102
Harm to self	71
Comic images	12
Criticism of definitions	4
Total	**562**

Source: Philo, G. et al. "The impact of the mass media on public images of mental illness: Media content and audience belief." *Health Education Journal,* Vol. 53, No. 3, Sept. 1994, p. 274 (Table 1).

a. List the sample points for this experiment.
b. Explain why the sample points, part **a**, are not equally likely to occur.
c. Assign reasonable probabilities to the sample points.
d. Find the probability that a randomly selected story on mental health is portrayed sympathetically or comically by the Scottish media.

3.156 Chemical insect attractant. An entomologist is studying the effect of a chemical sex attractant (pheromone) on insects. Several insects are released at a site equidistant from the pheromone under study and a control substance. If the pheromone has an effect, more insects will travel toward it rather than toward the control. Otherwise, the insects are equally likely to travel in either direction. Suppose the pheromone under study has no effect, so that it is equally likely that an insect will move toward either the pheromone or the control. Suppose five insects are released:
a. List or count the number of different way the insects can travel.
b. What is the chance that all five travel toward the pheromone?
c. What is the chance that exactly four travel toward the pheromone?
d. What inference would you make if the event in part **c** actually occurs? Explain.

3.157 Factors identifying urban counties. *Urban* and *rural* describe geographic areas upon which land zoning regulations, school district policy, and public service policy are often set. However, the characteristics of urban/rural areas are not clearly defined. Researchers at the University of Nevada (Reno) asked a sample of county commissioners to give their perception of the single most important factor in identifying urban counties. (*Professional Geographer,* Feb. 2000.) In all, five factors were mentioned by the commissioners: total population, agricultural change, presence of industry, growth, and population concentration. The survey results are displayed in the pie chart. Suppose one of the commissioners is selected at random, and the most important factor specified by the commissioner is recorded.

a. List the sample points for this experiment.
b. Assign reasonable probabilities to the sample points.
c. Find the probability that the most important factor specified by the commissioner is population-related.

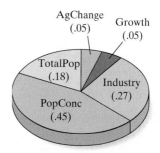

Applying the Concepts—Intermediate

3.158 Study of agressiveness and birth order. Psychologists tend to believe that there is a relationship between aggressiveness and order of birth. To test this belief, a psychologist chose 500 elementary school students at random and administered each a test designed to measure the student's aggressiveness. Each student was classified according to one of four categories. The percentages of students falling in the four categories are shown here.

	Firstborn	Not Firstborn
Aggressive	15%	15%
Not Aggressive	25%	45%

a. If one student is chosen at random from the 500, what is the probability that the student is firstborn?
b. What is the probability that the student is aggressive?
c. What is the probability that the student is aggressive, given the student was firstborn?
d. If

A: {Student chosen is aggressive}
B: {Student chosen is firstborn}

are A and B independent? Explain.

3.159 Elderly and their roles. Refer to the *Psychology and Aging* (Dec. 2000) study of elderly people and their roles, Exercise 2.10 (p. 40). The table summarizing the most salient roles identified by each in a national sample of 1,102 adults, 65 years or older, is reproduced on p. 182.
a. What is the probability that a randomly selected elderly person feels his/her most salient role is a spouse?
b. What is the probability that a randomly selected elderly person feels his/her most salient role is a parent or grandparent?
c. What is the probability that a randomly selected elderly person feels his/her most salient role does not involve a spouse or relative of any kind?

Most Salient Role	Number
Spouse	424
Parent	269
Grandparent	148
Other relative	59
Friend	73
Homemaker	59
Provider	34
Volunteer, club, church member	36
Total	1,102

Source: Krause, N., and Shaw, B. A. "Role-specific feelings of control and mortality." *Psychology and Aging,* Vol. 15, No. 4, Dec. 2000 (Table 2).

3.160 Mental health study. A Victoria University psychologist investigated whether Asian immigrants to Australia differed from Anglo-Australians in their attitudes toward mental illness. (*Community Mental Health Journal,* Feb. 1999.) Each in a sample of 139 Australian students was classified according to ethnic group and degree of contact with mentally ill people. The number in each category is displayed in the table. Suppose we randomly select one of the 139 students.

a. Find the probability that the student is an Anglo-Australian who has had little or no contact with mentally ill people.

b. Find the probability that the student has had close contact with mentally ill people.

c. Find the probability that the student is not an Anglo-Australian.

d. Find the probability that the student has had close contact with mentally ill people or is an Asian immigrant.

e. Given the student is an Asian immigrant, what is the probability that he or she has had little or no contact with mentally ill patients?

f. Given the student is Anglo-Australian, what is the probability that he or she has had little or no contact with mentally ill patients?

g. Which ethnic group, Anglo-Australians or Asian immigrants, is most likely to have had little or no contact with mentally ill patients?

Mental Illness	Contact			
	Little/None	Some	Close	Totals
Anglo-Australian	30	17	16	63
Short-Term Asian	17	5	0	22
Long-Term Asian	20	3	1	24
Other	15	11	4	30
Totals	82	36	21	139

Source: Fan, C. "A comparison of attitudes towards mental illness and knowledge of mental health services between Australian and Asian students." *Community Mental Health Journal,* Vol. 35, No. 1, Feb. 1999, p. 54 (Table 2).

3.161 Shooting free throws. In college basketball games a player may be afforded the opportunity to shoot two consecutive foul shots (free throws).

a. Suppose a player who makes (i.e., scores on) 80% of his foul shots has been awarded two free throws. If the two throws are considered independent, what is the probability that the player makes both shots? Exactly one? Neither shot?

b. Suppose a player who makes 80% of his first attempted foul shots has been awarded two free throws, and the outcome on the second shot is dependent on the outcome of the first shot. In fact, if this player makes the first shot, he makes 90% of the second shots; and if he misses the first shot, he makes 70% of the second shots. In this case, what is the probability that the player makes both shots? Exactly one? Neither shot?

c. In parts a and b, we considered two ways of *modeling* the probability a basketball player makes two consecutive foul shots. Which model do you think is a more realistic attempt to explain the outcome of shooting foul shots; that is, do you think two consecutive foul shots are independent or dependent? Explain.

3.162 Probability of making a sale. The probability that an Avon salesperson sells beauty products to a prospective customer on the first visit to the customer is .4. If the salesperson fails to make the sale on the first visit, the probability that the sale will be made on the second visit is .65. The salesperson never visits a prospective customer more than twice. What is the probability that the salesperson will make a sale to a particular customer?

3.163 Kidney transplant patients. Sandoz, a pharmaceutical firm, reports that kidney transplant patients who receive the drug cyclosporine have an 80% chance of surviving the first year. Suppose a hospital performs four kidney transplants, and all patients receive the drug cyclosporine. Assuming one patient's survival is independent of another's, what is the probability that

a. All four patients are alive at the end of 1 year?

b. None of the four patients is alive at the end of 1 year?

c. At least one of the patients is alive at the end of 1 year?

*3.164 Producing electronic fuses. A manufacturing operation utilizes two production lines to assemble electronic fuses. Both lines produce fuses at the same rate and generally produce 2.5% defective fuses. However, production line 1 recently suffered mechanical difficulty and produced 6.0% defectives during a three-week period. This situation was not known until several lots of electronic fuses produced in this period were shipped to customers. If one of the two fuses tested by a customer was found to be defective, what is the probability that the lot from which it came was produced on malfunctioning line 1? (Assume all the fuses in the lot were produced on the same line.)

3.165 Series and parallel systems. Consider two system shown in the schematics. System A operates properly

System A: Three Components in Series

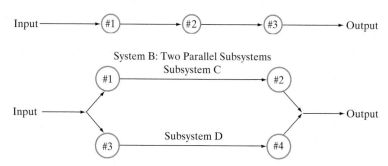

only if all three components operate properly. (The three components are said to operate *in series*.) The probability of failure for system A components 1, 2, and 3 are .12, .09 and .11 respectively. Assume the components operate independently of each other.

  System B comprises two subsystems said to operate *in parallel*. Each subsystem has two components that operate in series. System B will operate properly as long as at least one of the subsystems functions properly. The probability of failure for each component in the system is .1. Assume the components operate independently of each other.

a. Find the probability that System A operates properly.

b. What is the probability that at least one of the components in System A will fail and therefore that the system will fail?

c. Find the probability that System B operates properly.

d. Find the probability that exactly one subsystem in System B fails.

e. Find the probability that System B fails to operate properly.

f. How many parallel subsystems like the two shown here would be required to guarantee that the system would operate properly at least 99% of the time?

*3.166 Bottles produced at a brewery. A small brewery has two bottling machines. Machine A produces 75% of the bottles and machine B produces 25%. One out of every 20 bottles filled by A is rejected for some reason, while one out of every 30 bottles from B is rejected.

a. What proportion of bottles is rejected?

b. What is the probability that a randomly selected bottle comes from machine A, given that it is accepted?

*3.167 Allocating TVs to stores. Suppose a manufacturer of big-screen plasma television sets is prepared to send 20 new sets to three retail dealers. Dealer A is to get ten of the sets, dealer B six of the sets, and dealer C four of the sets.

a. In how many different ways can the 20 sets be divided among the dealers in the prescribed numbers?

b. Assuming the sets are randomly divided among the dealers and there are three defective sets among the 20, what is the probability that dealer A gets all three defective sets?

c. Making the assumptions given in part **b**, what is the probability that dealer A gets two defective sets and dealer B the other defective set?

*3.168 Dream experiment in psychology. A clinical psychologist is given tapes of 20 subjects discussing their recent dreams. The psychologist is told that 10 are high-anxiety individuals and 10 are low-anxiety individuals. The psychologist's task is to select the 10 high-anxiety subjects.

a. Count the number of sample points for this experiment.

b. Assuming that the psychologist is guessing, assign probabilities to each of the sample points.

c. Find the probability that the psychologist guesses all classifications correctly.

d. Find the probability that the psychologist guesses at least nine of the 10 high-anxiety subjects correctly.

Applying the Concepts—Advanced

3.169 Odds of winning a horse race. Handicappers for horse races express their belief about the probabilities of each horse winning a race in terms of **odds**. If the probability of event E is $P(E)$, then the *odds in favor of E* are $P(E)$ to $1 - P(E)$. Thus, if a handicapper assesses a probability of .25 that Smarty Jones will win the Belmont Stakes, the odds in favor of Smarty Jones are $^{25}/_{100}$ to $^{75}/_{100}$, or 1 to 3. It follows that the *odds against E* are $1 - P(E)$ to $P(E)$, or 3 to 1 against a win by Smarty Jones. In general, if the odds in favor of event E are a to b, then $P(E) = a/(a + b)$.

a. A second handicapper assesses the probability of a win by Smarty Jones to be $\frac{1}{3}$. According to the second handicapper, what are the odds in favor of a Smarty Jones win?

b. A third handicapper assesses the odds in favor of Smarty Jones to be 1 to 1. According to the third handicapper, what is the probability of a Smarty Jones win?

c. A fourth handicapper assesses the odds against Smarty Jones winning to be 3 to 2. Find this handicapper's assessment of the probability that Smarty Jones will win.

3.170 Effectiveness of an antipneumonia vaccine. Pneumovax is an antipneumonia vaccine designed especially for elderly or debilitated patients who are usually the most vulnerable to bacterial pneumonia. The vaccine is 90% effective in stimulating the production of antibodies to pneumonia-producing bacteria (i.e., it is 90% successful in preventing a person exposed to pneumonia-producing bacteria from acquiring the disease). Suppose the probability that an elderly or debilitated person is exposed to these bacteria is .40 (whether inoculated or not) and, after being exposed, the probability that the person will contract bacterial pneumonia if not inoculated with the vaccine is .95. Find the probability that an elderly or debilitated person inoculated with this new vaccine acquires pneumonia. What is the probability if this person has not been inoculated?

3.171 Finding an organ transplant match. One of the problems encountered in organ transplants is the body's rejection of the transplanted tissue. If the antigens attached to the tissue cells of the donor and receiver match, the body will accept the transplanted tissue. While the antigens in identical twins always match, the probability of a match in other siblings is .25 and that of a match in two people from the population at large is .001. Suppose you need a kidney, and you have two brothers and a sister.
  a. If one of your three siblings offers a kidney, what is the probability that the antigens will match?
  b. If all three siblings offer a kidney, what is the probability that all three antigens will match?
  c. If all three siblings offer a kidney, what is the probability that none of the antigens will match?

  d. Repeat parts **b** and **c**, this time assuming that the three donors were obtained from the population at large.

3.172 Chance of winning blackjack. Blackjack, a favorite game of gamblers, is played by a dealer and at least one opponent. At the outset of the game, two cards of a 52-card bridge deck are dealt to the player and two cards to the dealer. Drawing an ace and a face card is called *blackjack*. If the dealer does not draw a blackjack and the player does, the player wins. If both the dealer and player draw blackjack, a "push" (i.e., a tie) occurs.
  a. What is the probability that the dealer will draw a blackjack?
  b. What is the probability that the player wins with a blackjack?

3.173 Accuracy of pregnancy tests. Seventy-five percent of all women who submit to pregnancy tests are really pregnant. A certain pregnancy test gives a *false positive* result with probability .02 and a *valid positive result* with probability .99. If a particular woman's test is positive, what is the probability that she really is pregnant? [*Hint:* If A is the event that a woman is pregnant and B is the event that the pregnancy test is positive,

then B is the union of the two mutually exclusive events $A \cap B$ and $A^c \cap B$. Also, the probability of a false positive result may be written as $P(B|A^c) = .02$.]

3.174 Language impairment in children. Children who develop unexpected difficulties with acquisition of spoken language are often diagnosed with specific language impairment (SLI). A study published in the *Journal of Speech, Language, and Hearing Research* (Dec. 1997) investigated the incidence of SLI in kindergarten children. As an initial screen, each in a national sample of over 7,000 children was given a test for language performance. The percentages of children who passed and failed the screen were 73.8% and 26.2%, respectively. All children who failed the screen were tested clinically for SLI. About one-third of those who passed the screen were randomly selected and also tested for SLI. The percentage of children diagnosed with SLI in the "failed screen" group was 20.5%; the percentage diagnosed with SLI in the "pass screen" group was 2.8%.
  a. For this problem, let "pass" represent a child who passed the language performance screen, "fail" represent a child who failed the screen, and "SLI" represent a child diagnosed with SLI. Now find each of the following probabilities: $P(\text{Pass})$, $P(\text{Fail})$, $P(\text{SLI}|\text{Pass})$, and $P(\text{SLI}|\text{Fail})$.

  b. Use the probabilities, part **a**, to find $P(\text{Pass} \cap \text{SLI})$ and $P(\text{Fail} \cap \text{SLI})$. What probability law did you use to calculate these probabilities?
  c. Use the probabilities, part **b**, to find $P(\text{SLI})$. What probability law did you use to calculate this probability?

*3.175 The perfect bridge hand. According to a morning news program, a very rare event recently occurred in Dubuque, Iowa. Each of four women playing bridge was astounded to note that she had been dealt a perfect bridge hand. That is, one woman was dealt all 13 spades, another all 13 hearts, another all the diamonds, and another all the clubs. What is the probability of this rare event?

3.176 Chance of winning at "craps." A version of the dice game "craps" is played in the following manner: A player starts by rolling two dice. If the result is a 7 or 11, the player wins. For most other sums appearing on the dice, the player continues to roll the dice until that sums recurs (in which case the player loses). But if on any roll the outcome is 2 or 3 (called "craps"), the game is over, and the player loses.
  a. What is the probability that a player wins the game on the first roll of the dice? (Assume the dice are balanced.)
  b. What is the probability that a player loses the game on the first roll of the dice?
  c. If the player throws a total of 4 on the first roll, what is the probability that the game ends on the next roll?

Critical Thinking Challenges

3.177 Most likely coin flip sequence. In *Parade Magazine*'s (Nov. 26, 2000) column "Ask Marilyn," the following question was posed: "I have just tossed a [balanced] coin 10 times, and I ask you to guess which of the following three sequences was the result. One (and only one) of the sequences is genuine."

1. H H H H H H H H H H
2. H H T T H T T H H H
3. T T T T T T T T T T

Marilyn's answer to the question posed was, "Though the chances of the three specific sequences occurring randomly are equal … it's reasonable for us to choose sequence (2) as the most likely genuine result." Do you agree?

3.178 Flawed Pentium computer chip. In October 1994, a flaw was discovered in the Pentium microchip installed in personal computers. The chip produced an incorrect result when dividing two numbers. Intel, the manufacturer of the Pentium chip, initially announced that such an error would occur once in 9 billion divides, or "once in every 27,000 years" for a typical user; consequently, it did not immediately offer to replace the chip.

Depending on the procedure, statistical software packages (e.g., SAS) may perform an extremely large number of divisions to produce the required output.

For heavy users of the software, 1 billion divisions over a short time frame is not unusual. Will the flawed chip be a problem for a heavy SAS user? [*Note:* Two months after the flaw was discovered, Intel agreed to replace all Pentium chips free of charge.]

3.179 "Let's Make a Deal." Marilyn vos Savant, who is listed in *Guinness Book of World Records Hall of Fame* for "Highest IQ," writes a weekly column in the Sunday newspaper supplement, *Parade Magazine*. Her column, "Ask Marilyn," is devoted to games of skill, puzzles, and mind-bending riddles. (See Exercise 3.177.) In one issue (*Parade Magazine*, Feb. 24, 1991), vos Savant posed the following question:

Suppose you're on a game show, and you're given a choice of three doors. Behind one door is a car; behind the others, goats. You pick a door — say, #1 — and the host, who knows what's behind the doors, opens another door — say #3 — which has a goat. He then says to you, "Do you want to pick door #2?" Is it to your advantage to switch your choice?

Marilyn's answer: "Yes, you should switch. The first door has a $\frac{1}{3}$ chance of winning [the car], but the second has a $\frac{2}{3}$ chance [of winning the car]." Predictably, vos Savant's surprising answer elicited thousands of critical letters, many of them from Ph.D. mathematicians, who disagreed with her. Who is correct, the Ph.D.'s or Marilyn?

Student Projects

Obtain a standard deck of 52 playing cards (the kind commonly used for bridge, poker, or solitaire). An experiment will consist of drawing one card at random from the deck of cards and recording which card was observed. This random drawing will be simulated by shuffling the deck thoroughly and observing the top card. Consider the following two events:

    A: {Card observed is a heart}
    B: {Card observed is an ace, king, queen, or jack}

a. Find $P(A)$, $P(B)$, $P(A \cap B)$, and $P(A \cup B)$.

b. Conduct the experiment 10 times, and record the observed card each time. Be sure to return the observed card each time, and thoroughly shuffle the deck before making the draw. After you've observed 10 cards, calculate the proportion of observations that satisfy event *A*, event *B*, event $A \cap B$, and event $A \cup B$. Compare the observed proportions with the true probabilities calculated in part **a**.

c. Conduct the experiment 40 more times to obtain a total of 50 observed cards. Now calculate the proportion of observations that satisfy event *A*, event *B*, event $A \cap B$, and event $A \cup B$. Compare these proportions with those found in part **b** and the true probabilities found in part **a**.

d. Conduct the experiment 50 more times to obtain a total of 100 observations. Compare the observed proportions for the 100 trials with those found previously. What comments do you have concerning the different proportions found in parts **b**, **c**, and **d** as compared to the true probabilities found in part **a**? How do you think the observed proportions and true probabilities would compare if the experiment were conducted 1,000 times? 1 million times?

REFERENCES

Bennett, D. J. *Randomness.* Cambridge, Mass.: Harvard University Press, 1998.

Epstein, R. A. *The Theory of Gambling and Statistical Logic*, rev. ed. New York: Academic Press, 1977.

Feller, W. *An Introduction to Probability Theory and Its Applications*, 3rd ed., Vol. 1. New York: Wiley, 1968.

Lindley, D. V. *Making Decisions*, 2nd ed. London: Wiley, 1985.

Parzen, E. *Modern Probability Theory and Its Applications*. New York: Wiley, 1960.

Wackerly, D., Mendenhall, W., and Scheaffer, R. L. *Mathematical Statistics with Applications*, 6th ed. Boston: Duxbury, 2002.

Williams, B. *A Sampler on Sampling*. New York: Wiley, 1978.

Winkler, R. L. *An Introduction to Bayesian Inference and Decision*. New York: Holt, Rinehart and Winston, 1972.

Wright, G., and Ayton, P., eds. *Subjective Probability*. New York: Wiley, 1994.

Using Technology

Generating a Random Sample Using MINITAB

To obtain a random sample of observations (cases) from a data set stored in the MINITAB worksheet, click on the "Calc" button on the MINITAB menu bar, then click on "Random Data", and finally, click on "Sample from Columns", as shown in Figure 3.M.1. The resulting dialog box appears as shown in Figure 3.M.2. Specify the sample size (i.e., number of rows), the variable(s) to be sampled, and the column(s) where you want to save the sample. Click "OK" and the MINITAB worksheet will reappear with the values of the variable for the selected (sampled) cases in the column specified.

In MINITAB, you can also generate a sample of case numbers. From the MINITAB menu, click on the "Calc" button, then click on "Random Data" and finally, click on the "Uniform" option (see Figure 3.M.1). The resulting dialog box

Figure 3.M.1
MINITAB Menu Options for Sampling Your Data

Figure 3.M.2
MINITAB Options for
Selecting a Random Sample
from Worksheet Columns

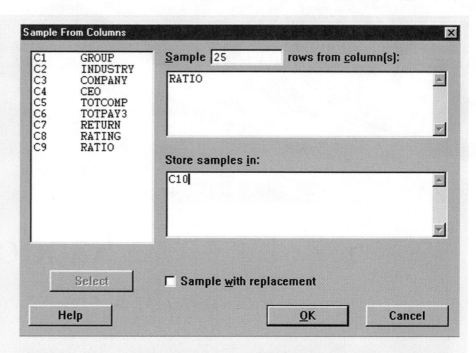

Figure 3.M.3
MINITAB Options for
Selecting a Random Sample
of Cases

appears as shown in Figure 3.M.3. Specify the number of cases (rows) (i.e., the sample size) and the column where the case numbers selected will be stored. Click "OK" and the MINITAB worksheet will reappear with the case numbers for the selected (sampled) cases in the column specified.

[*Note:* If you want the option of generating the same (identical) sample multiple times from the data set, then first click on the "Set Base" option shown in Figure 3.M.1. Specify an integer in the resulting dialog box. If you always select the same integer, MINITAB will select the same sample when you choose the random sampling options.]

4

Discrete Random Variables

Contents

4.1 Two Types of Random Variables

4.2 Probability Distributions for Discrete Random Variables

4.3 Expected Values of Discrete Random Variables

4.4 The Binomial Random Variable

4.5 The Poisson Random Variable (Optional)

4.6 The Hypergeometric Random Variable (Optional)

Statistics in Action

Probability in a Reverse Cocaine Sting

Using Technology

Binomial, Poisson, and Hypergeometric Probabilities Using MINITAB

Where We've Been

- Used probability to make an inference about a population from data in an observed sample
- Used probability to measure the reliability of the inference

Where We're Going

- Develop the notion of a random variable.
- Learn that many types of numerical data are observed values of discrete random variables.
- Study several important types of discrete random variables and their probability models.

Statistics in ACTION

Probability in a Reverse Cocaine Sting

The American Statistician (May 1991) described an interesting application of a discrete probability distribution in a case involving illegal drugs. It all started with a "bust" in a mid-sized Florida city. During the bust, police seized approximately 500 foil packets of a white, powdery substance, presumably cocaine. Since it is not a crime to buy or sell non-narcotic cocaine look-a-likes (e.g., inert powders), detectives had to prove that the packets contained genuine cocaine in order to convict their suspects of drug trafficking. When the police laboratory randomly selected and chemically tested four of the packets, all four tested positive for cocaine. This finding led to the conviction of the traffickers.

After the conviction, the police decided to use the remaining foil packets (i.e., those not tested) in reverse sting operations. Two of these packets were randomly selected and sold by undercover officers to a buyer. Between the sale and the arrest, however, the buyer disposed of the evidence. The key question is, Beyond a reasonable doubt, did the defendant really purchase cocaine?

In court, the defendant's attorney argued that his client should not be convicted because the police could not prove that the missing foil packets contained cocaine. The police contended, however, that since four of the original packets tested positive for cocaine, the two packets sold in the reverse sting were also highly likely to contain cocaine. In this chapter, two Statistics in Action Revisited examples demonstrate how to use probability models to solve the dilemma. (The case represented Florida's first cocaine-possession conviction without the actual physical evidence.)

Statistics in Action Revisited

- Using the Binomial Model to Solve the Cocaine Sting Case (p. 215)
- Using the Hypergeometric Model to Solve the Cocaine Sting Case (p. 226)

S

Figure 4.1
Venn Diagram for
Coin-Tossing Experiment

You may have noticed that many of the examples of experiments in Chapter 3 generated quantitative (numerical) observations. The unemployment rate, the percentage of voters favoring a particular candidate, the cost of textbooks for a school term, and the amount of pesticide in the discharge waters of a chemical plant are all examples of numerical measurements of some phenomenon. Thus, most experiments have sample points that correspond to values of some numerical variable.

To illustrate, consider the coin-tossing experiment of Chapter 3. Figure 4.1 is a Venn diagram showing the sample points when two coins are tossed and the up faces (heads or tails) of the coins are observed. One possible numerical outcome is the total number of heads observed. These values (0, 1, or 2) are shown in parentheses on the Venn diagram, one numerical value associated with each sample point. In the jargon of probability, the variable "total number of heads observed in two tosses of a coin" is called a *random variable*.

> ### DEFINITION 4.1
>
> A **random variable** is a variable that assumes numerical values associated with the random outcomes of an experiment, where one (and only one) numerical value is assigned to each sample point.

The term *random variable* is more meaningful than the term *variable* alone because the adjective *random* indicates that the coin-tossing experiment may result in one of the several possible values of the variable—0, 1, and 2—according to the *random* outcome of the experiment, *HH, HT, TH,* and *TT*. Similarly, if the experiment is to count the number of customers who use the drive-up window of a bank each day, the random variable (the number of customers) will vary from day to day, partly because of the random phenomena that influence whether customers use the drive-up window. Thus, the possible values of this random variable range from 0 to the maximum number of customers the window could possibly serve in a day.

We define two different types of random variables, *discrete* and *continuous*, in Section 4.1. Then we spend the remainder of this chapter discussing specific types of discrete random variables and the aspects that make them important to the statistician. We discuss continuous random variables in Chapter 5.

4.1 Two Types of Random Variables

Recall that the sample point probabilities corresponding to an experiment must sum to 1. Dividing one unit of probability among the sample points in a sample space and consequently assigning probabilities to the values of a random variable is not always as easy as the examples in Chapter 3 might lead you to believe. If the number of sample points can be completely listed, the job is straightforward. But if the experiment results in an infinite number of sample points that are impossible to list, the task of assigning probabilities to the sample points is impossible without the aid of a probability model. The next three examples demonstrate the need for different probability models depending on the number of values that a random variable can assume.

EXAMPLE 4.1   VALUES OF A DISCRETE RANDOM VARIABLE

Problem A panel of 10 experts for the *Wine Spectator* (a national publication) is asked to taste a new white wine and assign a rating of 0, 1, 2, or 3. A score is then obtained by adding together the ratings of the 10 experts. How many values can this random variable assume?

Solution A sample point is a sequence of 10 numbers associated with the rating of each expert. For example, one sample point is

$$\{1, 0, 0, 1, 2, 0, 0, 3, 1, 0\}.$$

The random variable assigns a score to each one of these sample points by adding the 10 numbers together. Thus, the smallest score is 0 (if all 10 ratings are 0) and the largest score is 30 (if all 10 ratings are 3). Since every integer between 0 and 30 is a possible score, the random variable denoted by the symbol x can assume 31 values. Note that the value of the random variable for the sample point above is $x = 8$.*

Look Back This is an example of a *discrete random variable*, since there is a finite number of distinct possible values. Whenever all the possible values a random variable can assume can be listed (or *counted*), the random variable is *discrete*.

EXAMPLE 4.2   VALUES OF A DISCRETE RANDOM VARIABLE

Problem Suppose the Environmental Protection Agency (EPA) takes readings once a month on the amount of pesticide in the discharge water of a chemical company. If the amount of pesticide exceeds the maximum level set by the EPA, the company is

---

*The standard mathematical convention is to use a capital letter (e.g., X) to denote the theoretical random variable. The possible values (or realizations) of the random variable are typically denoted with a lowercase letter (e.g., x). Thus, in Example 4.1, the random variable X can take on the values $x = 0, 1, 2, \ldots, 30$. Since this notation can be confusing for introductory statistics students, we simplify the notation by using the lowercase x to represent the random variable throughout.

forced to take corrective action and may be subject to penalty. Consider the random variable, number, x, of months before the company's discharge exceeds the EPA's maximum level. What values can x assume?

Solution   The company's discharge of pesticide may exceed the maximum allowable level on the first month of testing, the second month of testing, etc. It is possible that the company's discharge will *never* exceed the maximum level. Thus, the set of possible values for the number of months until the level is first exceeded is the set of all positive integers 1, 2, 3, 4, ...

   If we can list the values of a random variable x, even though the list is never-ending, we call the list *countable* and the corresponding random variable *discrete*. Thus, the number of months until the company's discharge first exceeds the limit is a *discrete random variable*.

[Now Work]   *Exercise 4.7*

■ ■ ■

EXAMPLE 4.3   VALUES OF A CONTINUOUS RANDOM VARIABLE.

Problem   Refer to Example 4.2. A second random variable of interest is the amount x of pesticide (in milligrams per liter) found in the monthly sample of discharge waters from the chemical company. What values can this random variable assume?

Solution   Unlike the *number* of months before the company's discharge exceeds the EPA's maximum level, the set of all possible values for the *amount* of discharge *cannot* be listed (i.e., is not countable). The possible values for the amount x of pesticide would correspond to the points on the interval between 0 and the largest possible value the amount of the discharge could attain, the maximum number of milligrams that could occupy 1 liter of volume. (Practically, the interval would be much smaller, say, between 0 and 500 milligrams per liter.)

Look Back When the values of a random variable are not countable but instead correspond to the points on some interval, we call it a *continuous random variable*. Thus, the *amount* of pesticide in the chemical plant's discharge waters is a *continuous random variable*.

[Now Work]   *Exercise 4.8*

■ ■ ■

DEFINITION 4.2

Random variables that can assume a *countable* number of values are called **discrete**.

DEFINITION 4.3

Random variables that can assume values corresponding to any of the points contained in one or more intervals are called **continuous**.

The following are examples of discrete random variables:

1. The number of seizures an epileptic patient has in a given week: $x = 0, 1, 2, \ldots$

2. The number of voters in a sample of 500 who favor impeachment of the president: $x = 0, 1, 2, \ldots, 500$

3. The number of students applying to medical schools this year: $x = 0, 1, 2, \ldots$

4. The change received for paying a bill: $x = 1\text{¢}, 2\text{¢}, 3\text{¢}, \ldots, \$1, \ldots$

5. The number of customers waiting to be served in a restaurant at a particular time: $x = 0, 1, 2, \ldots$

Note that several of the examples of discrete random variables begin with the words *The number of* .... This wording is very common, since the discrete random variables most frequently observed are counts. The following are examples of continuous random variables:

1. The length of time (in seconds) between arrivals at a hospital clinic: $0 \leq x \leq \infty$ (infinity)

2. The length of time (in minutes) it takes a student to complete a one-hour exam: $0 \leq x \leq 60$

3. The amount (in ounces) of carbonated beverage loaded into a 12-ounce can in a can-filling operation: $0 \leq x \leq 12$

4. The depth (in feet) at which a successful oil drilling venture first strikes oil: $0 \leq x \leq c$, where c is the maximum depth obtainable

5. The weight (in pounds) of a food item bought in a supermarket: $0 \leq x \leq 500$ [*Note:* Theoretically, there is no upper limit on x, but it is unlikely that it would exceed 500 pounds.]

Discrete random variables and their probability distributions are discussed in this chapter. Continuous random variables and their probability distributions are the topic of Chapter 5.

Exercises 4.1–4.8

Understanding the Principles

4.1 What is a random variable?

4.2 How do discrete and continuous random variables differ?

Applying the Concepts—Basic

4.3 **Type of Random Variable.** Classify the following random variables according to whether they are discrete or continuous:
a. The number of words spelled correctly by a student on a spelling test
b. The amount of water flowing through the Hoover Dam in a day
c. The length of time an employee is late for work
d. The number of bacteria in a particular cubic centimeter of drinking water
e. The amount of carbon monoxide produced per gallon of unleaded gas
f. Your weight

4.4 **Type of Random Variable.** Identify the following random variables as discrete or continuous:
a. The amount of flu vaccine in a syringe
b. The heart rate (number of beats per minute) of an American male
c. The time it takes a student to complete an examination
d. The barometric pressure at a given location

e. The number of registered voters who vote in a national election
f. Your score on the Scholastic Assessment Test (SAT)

4.5 **Type of Random Variable.** Identify the following variables as discrete or continuous:
a. The reaction time difference to the same stimulus before and after training
b. The number of violent crimes committed per month in your community
c. The number of commercial aircraft near-misses per month
d. The number of winners each week in a state lottery
e. The number of free throws made per game by a basketball team
f. The distance traveled by a school bus each day

4.6 **NHTSA crash tests.** The National Highway Traffic Safety Administration (NHTSA) has developed a driver-side "star" scoring system for crash-testing new cars. Each crash-tested car is given a rating ranging from one star (*) to five stars (*****); the more stars in the rating, the better the level of crash protection in a head-on collision. Suppose that a car is selected and its driver-side star rating is determined. Let x equal the number of stars in the rating. Is x a discrete or continuous random variable?

4.7 **Customers in line at a Subway shop.** The number of NW customers, x, waiting in line to order sandwiches at a Subway shop at noon is of interest to the store manager.

What values can x assume? Is x a discrete or continuous random variable?

⊚ **GOBIANTS**

4.8 Mongolian desert ants. Refer to the *Journal of*
NW *Biogeography* (Dec. 2003) study of ants in Mongolia,

Exercises 2.66 and 2.147 (pp. 66, 100). Two of the several variables recorded at each of 11 study sites were annual rainfall (in millimeters) and number of ant species. Identify these variables as discrete or continuous.

4.2 Probability Distributions for Discrete Random Variables

A complete description of a discrete random variable requires that we *specify the possible values the random variable can assume* and *the probability associated with each value.* To illustrate, consider Example 4.4.

EXAMPLE 4.4   FINDING A PROBABILITY DISTRIBUTION

Problem   Recall the experiment of tossing two coins (Section 4.1), and let x be the number of heads observed. Find the probability associated with each value of the random variable x, assuming the two coins are fair.

Solution   The sample space and sample points for this experiment are reproduced in Figure 4.2. Note that the random variable x can assume values 0, 1, 2. Recall (from Chapter 3) that the probability associated with each of the four sample points is $1/4$. Then, identifying the probabilities of the sample points associated with each of these values of x, we have

$$P(x = 0) = P(TT) = \frac{1}{4}$$

$$P(x = 1) = P(TH) + P(HT) = \frac{1}{4} + \frac{1}{4} = \frac{1}{2}$$

$$P(x = 2) = P(HH) = \frac{1}{4}$$

Thus, we now know the values the random variable can assume $(0, 1, 2)$ and how the probability is *distributed over* these values $\left(\frac{1}{4}, \frac{1}{2}, \frac{1}{4}\right)$. This completely describes the random variable and is referred to as the *probability distribution*, denoted by the symbol $p(x)$.* The probability distribution for the coin-toss example is shown in tabular form in Table 4.1 and in graphic form in Figure 4.3. Since the probability distribution for a discrete random variable is concentrated at specific points (values of x), the graph in Figure 4.3a represents the probabilities as the heights of vertical lines over the corresponding values of x. Although the representation of the probability distribution as a histogram, as in Figure 4.3b, is less precise (since the probability is spread over a unit interval), the histogram representation will prove useful when we approximate probabilities of certain discrete random variables in Section 4.4.

Figure 4.2
Venn Diagram for the Two-Coin-Toss Experiment

HH	HT
$x = 2$	$x = 1$
TH	TT
$x = 1$	$x = 0$

S

Look Back We could also present the probability distribution for x as a formula, but this would unnecessarily complicate a very simple example. We give the formulas for the probability distributions of some common discrete random variables later in this chapter.

TABLE 4.1   Probability Distribution for Coin-Toss Experiment: Tabular Form

x	$p(x)$
0	$1/4$
1	$1/2$
2	$1/4$

Now Work   *Exercise 4.15*

■ ■ ■

*In standard mathematical notation, the probability that a random variable X takes on a value x is denoted $P(X = x) = p(x)$. Thus, $P(X = 0) = p(0)$, $P(X = 1) = p(1)$, etc. In this text, we adopt the simpler $p(x)$ notation.

Figure 4.3
Probability Distribution
for Coin-Toss Experiment:
Graphical Form

a. Point representation of $p(x)$

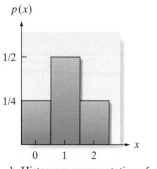

b. Histogram representation of $p(x)$

DEFINITION 4.4

The **probability distribution** of a discrete random variable is a graph, table, or formula that specifies the probability associated with each possible value the random variable can assume.

Two requirements must be satisfied by all probability distributions for discrete random variables.

Requirements for the Probability Distribution of a Discrete Random Variable x

1. $p(x) \geq 0$ for all values of x

2. $\sum p(x) = 1$

where the summation of $p(x)$ is over all possible values of x.*

| Now Work | *Exercise 4.12* |

Example 4.4 illustrates how the probability distribution for a discrete random variable can be derived, but for many practical situations the task is much more difficult. Fortunately, many experiments and associated discrete random variables observed in nature possess identical characteristics. Thus, you might observe a random variable in a psychology experiment that would possess the same probability distribution as a random variable observed in an engineering experiment or a social sample survey. We classify random variables according to type of experiment, derive the probability distribution for each of the different types, and then use the appropriate probability distribution when a particular type of random variable is observed in a practical situation. The probability distributions for most commonly occurring discrete random variables have already been derived. This fact simplifies the problem of finding the probability distributions for random variables, as the next example illustrates.

EXAMPLE 4.5

PROBABILITY DISTRIBUTION USING A FORMULA

Problem The distribution of parasites (tapeworms) found in Mediterranean brill fish was studied in the *Journal of Fish Biology* (Aug. 1990). The researchers showed that the distribution of x, the number of brill that must be sampled until a parasitic infection is found in the digestive tract, can be modeled using the formula $p(x) = (.6)(.4)^{x-1}$, $x = 1, 2, 3$, etc. Find the probability that exactly 3 brill fish must be sampled before a tapeworm is found in the digestive tract.

*Unless otherwise indicated, summations will always be over all possible values of x.

Solution   We want to find the probability that $x = 3$. Using the formula, we have

$$p(3) = (.6)(.4)^{3-1} = (.6)(.4)^2 = (.6)(.16) = .096$$

Thus, there is about a 10% chance that exactly 3 fish must be sampled before a tapeworm is found in the digestive tract.

Look Back   The probability of interest can also be derived using the principles of probability developed in Chapter 3. The event of interest is $N_1 N_2 P_3$, where N_1 represents no parasite found in the first sampled fish, N_2 represents no parasite found in the second sampled fish, and P_3 represents a parasite found in the third sampled fish. The researchers discovered that the probability of finding a parasite in any sampled fish is .6 (and consequently, the probability of not finding a parasite in any sampled fish is .4). Using the Multiplicative Law of Probability for independent events, the probability of interest is $(.4)(.4)(.6) = .096$.

■ ■ ■

In Sections 4.4 and 4.5, we describe two important types of discrete random variables, give their probability distributions, and explain where and how they can be applied in practice. (Mathematical derivations of the probability distributions will be omitted, but these details can be found in the chapter references.)

But first, in Section 4.3, we discuss some descriptive measures of these sometimes complex probability distributions. Since probability distributions are analogous to the relative frequency distributions of Chapter 2, it should be no surprise that the mean and standard deviation are useful descriptive measures.

Exercises 4.9–4.26

Understanding the Principles

4.9   Give three different ways of representing the probability distribution of a discrete random variable.

Learning the Mechanics

4.10   Consider the following probability distribution:

x	-4	0	1	3
$p(x)$	.1	.2	.4	.3

a. List the values that x may assume.
b. What value of x is most probable?
c. What is the probability that x is greater than 0?
d. What is the probability that $x = -2$?

4.11   A discrete random variable x can assume five possible values: 2, 3, 5, 8, and 10. Its probability distribution is shown here:

x	2	3	5	8	10
$p(x)$	.15	.10		.25	.25

a. What is $p(5)$?
b. What is the probability that x equals 2 or 10?
c. What is $P(x \le 8)$?

4.12   Explain why each of the following is or is not a
NW valid probability distribution for a discrete random variable x:

a.
x	0	1	2	3
$p(x)$	.2	.3	.3	.2

b.
x	-2	-1	0
$p(x)$	.25	.50	.20

c.
x	4	9	20
$p(x)$	-.3	1.0	.3

d.
x	2	3	5	6
$p(x)$	.15	.20	.40	.35

4.13   The random variable x has the following discrete probability distribution:

x	10	11	12	13	14
$p(x)$	.2	.3	.2	.1	.2

Since the values that x can assume are mutually exclusive events, the event $\{x \le 12\}$ is the union of three mutually exclusive events:

$$\{x = 10\} \cup \{x = 11\} \cup \{x = 12\}$$

a. Find $P(x \le 12)$.   **b.** Find $P(x > 12)$.
c. Find $P(x \le 14)$.   **d.** Find $P(x = 14)$.
e. Find $P(x \le 11 \text{ or } x > 12)$.

4.14 The random variable x has the discrete probability distribution shown here.

x	-2	-1	0	1	2
$p(x)$	.10	.15	.40	.30	.05

a. Find $P(x \le 0)$.
b. Find $P(x > -1)$.
c. Find $P(-1 \le x \le 1)$.
d. Find $P(x < 2)$.
e. Find $P(-1 < x < 2)$.
f. Find $P(x < 1)$.

4.15 Toss three fair coins and let x equal the number of heads
NW observed.

    a. Identify the sample points associated with this experiment and assign a value of x to each sample point.
    b. Calculate $p(x)$ for each value of x.
    c. Construct a probability histogram for $p(x)$.
    d. What is $P(x = 2$ or $x = 3)$?

Applying the Concepts—Basic

4.16 NHTSA crash tests. Refer to the National Highway Traffic Safety Administration (NHTSA) crash tests of new car models, Exercise 4.6 (p. 192). A summary of the driver-side star ratings for the 98 cars in the **CRASH** file is reproduced in the accompanying MINITAB printout. Assume that one of the 98 cars is selected at random, and let x equal the number of stars in the car's driver-side star rating.

    a. Use the information in the printout to find the probability distribution for x.
    b. Find $P(x = 5)$.
    c. Find $P(x \le 2)$.

Tally for Discrete Variables: DRIVSTAR

```
DRIVSTAR   Count   Percent
    2        4      4.08
    3       17     17.35
    4       59     60.20
    5       18     18.37
   N=       98
```

4.17 Dust mite allergies. A dust mite allergen level that exceeds 2 micrograms per gram (μg/g) of dust has been associated with the development of allergies. Consider a random sample of four homes and let x be the number of homes with a dust mite level that exceeds 2 μg/g. The probability distribution for x, based on a May 2000 study

by the National Institute of Environmental Health Sciences, is shown in the following table.

x	0	1	2	3	4
$p(x)$	.09	.30	.37	.20	.04

    a. Verify that the sum of the probabilities for x in the table sum to 1.
    b. Find the probability that three or four of the homes in the sample have a dust mite level that exceeds 2 μg/g.
    c. Find the probability that fewer than two homes in the sample have a dust mite level that exceeds 2 μg/g.

4.18 Customer arrivals at Wendy's. The probability distribution of x, the number of customer arrivals per 15-minute period, at a Wendy's restaurant in New Jersey is shown in the table at the bottom of the page.

    a. Does this distribution meet the two requirements for the probability distribution of a discrete random variable? Justify your answer.
    b. What is the probability that exactly 16 customers enter the restaurant in the next 15 minutes?
    c. Find $P(x \le 10)$.
    d. Find $P(5 \le x \le 15)$.

Applying the Concepts—Intermediate

4.19 Perfect SAT score. In Exercise 3.26 (p. 132) you learned that five in every 10,000 students who take the Scholastic Assessment Test (SAT) score a perfect 1,600. Consider a random sample of three students who take the SAT. Let x equal the number who score a perfect 1,600.

    a. Find $p(x)$ for $x = 0, 1, 2, 3$.
    b. Graph $p(x)$.   **c.** Find $P(x \le 1)$.

4.20 Contaminated gun cartridges. A weapons manufacturer uses a liquid propellant to produce gun cartridges. During the manufacturing process, the propellant can get mixed with another liquid to produce a contaminated cartridge. A University of South Florida statistician, hired by the company to investigate the level of contamination in the stored cartridges, found that 23% of the cartridges in a particular lot were contaminated. Suppose you randomly sample (without replacement) gun cartridges from this lot until you find a contaminated one. Let x be the number of cartridges sampled until a contaminated one is found. It is known that the probability distribution for x is given by the formula:

$$p(x) = (.23)(.77)^{x-1}, \qquad x = 1, 2, 3, \dots$$

Table for Exercise 4.18

x	5	6	7	8	9	10	11	12	13	14	15
$p(x)$	.01	.02	.03	.05	.08	.09	.11	.13	.12	.10	.08

x	16	17	18	19	20	21
$p(x)$	.06	.05	.03	.02	.01	.01

Source: Ford, R., Roberts, D., and Saxton, P. *Queuing Models.* Graduate School of Management, Rutgers University, 1992.

a. Find $p(1)$. Interpret this result.
b. Find $p(5)$. Interpret this result.
c. Find $P(x \geq 2)$. Interpret this result.

4.21 Federal civil trial appeals. Refer to the *Journal of the American Law and Economics Association* (Vol. 3, 2001) study of appeals of federal civil trials, Exercise 3.51 (p. 144). A breakdown of the 678 civil cases that were originally tried in front of a judge (rather than a jury) and appealed by either the plaintiff or defendant is reproduced in the table. Suppose each civil case is awarded points (positive or negative) based on the outcome of the appeal for the purpose of evaluating Federal judges. If the appeal is affirmed or dismissed, +5 points are awarded. If the appeal of a plaintiff trial win is reversed, −1 point is awarded. If the appeal of a defendant trial win is reversed, −3 points are awarded. Suppose one of the 678 cases is selected at random, and the number, x, of points awarded is determined. Find and graph the probability distribution for x.

Outcome of Appeal	Number of Cases
Plaintiff trial win—reversed	71
Plaintiff trial win—affirmed/dismissed	240
Defendant trial win—reversed	68
Defendant trial win—affirmed/dismissed	299
Total	**678**

4.22 Successful NFL running plays. In his article "American Football" (*Statistics in Sport*, 1998), Iowa State University statistician Hal Stern evaluates winning strategies of teams in the National Football League (NFL). In a section on estimating the probability of winning a game, Stern used actual NFL play-by-play data to approximate the probabilities associated with certain outcomes (e.g., running plays, short pass plays, and long pass plays). The following table gives the probability distribution for the yardage gained, x, on a running play. (A negative gain represents a loss of yards on the play.)

x, Yards	Probability	x, Yards	Probability
−4	.020	6	.090
−2	.060	8	.060
−1	.070	10	.050
0	.150	15	.085
1	.130	30	.010
2	.110	50	.004
3	.090	99	.001
4	.070		

a. Find the probability of gaining 10 yards or more on a running play.
b. Find the probability of losing yardage on a running play.

4.23 Reliability of a bridge network. A team of Chinese university professors investigated the reliability of several capacitated-flow networks in the journal *Networks* (May 1995). One network examined in the article and illus-

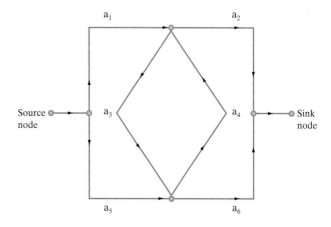

trated here is a bridge network with arcs a_1, a_2, a_3, a_4, a_5, and a_6. The probability distribution of the capacity x for each of the six arcs is provided in the table.

Arc	Capacity x	$p(x)$	Arc	Capacity x	$p(x)$
a_1	3	.60	a_4	1	.90
	2	.25		0	.10
	1	.10			
	0	.05			
a_2	2	.60	a_5	1	.90
	1	.30		0	.10
	0	.10			
a_3	1	.90	a_6	2	.70
	0	.10		1	.25
				0	.05

Source: Lin, J., et al. "On reliability evaluation of capacitated-flow network in terms of minimal pathsets." *Networks,* Vol. 25, No. 3, May 1995, p. 135 (Table 1).

a. Verify that the properties of discrete probability distributions are satisfied for each arc capacity distribution.
b. Find the probability that the capacity for arc a_1 will exceed 1.
c. Repeat part **b** for each of the remaining five arcs.

Applying the Concepts—Advanced

4.24 Bridge network reliability (cont'd). Refer to Exercise 4.23.
a. One path from the source node to the sink node is through arcs a_1 and a_2. Find the probability that the system maintains a capacity of more than 1 through the a_1–a_2 path. (Assume that the arc capacities are independent.)
b. Another path from the source node to the sink node is through a_1, a_3, and a_6. Find the probability that the system maintains a capacity of 1 through the a_1–a_3–a_6 path.

4.25 X and Y chromosomes. Every human possesses two sex chromosomes. A copy of one or the other (equally likely) is contributed to an offspring. Males have one X chromosome and one Y chromosome. Females have two X chromosomes. If a couple has three children, what is the probability that they have at least one boy?

4.26 Punnett square for earlobes. Geneticists use a grid—called a *Punnett square*—to display all possible gene combinations in genetic crosses. (The grid is named for Reginald Punnett, a British geneticist who developed the method in the early 1900s.) The accompanying figure is a Punnett square for a cross involving human earlobes. In humans, free earlobes (E) are dominant over attached earlobes (e). Consequently, the gene pairs EE and Ee will result in free earlobes, while the gene pair ee results in attached earlobes. Consider a couple with genes as shown in the Punnett square. Suppose the couple has seven children. Let *x* represent the number of children with attached earlobes (i.e., with the gene pair ee). Find the probability distribution of *x*.

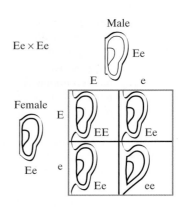

4.3 Expected Values of Discrete Random Variables

If a discrete random variable *x* were observed a very large number of times and the data generated were arranged in a relative frequency distribution, the relative frequency distribution would be indistinguishable from the probability distribution for the random variable. Thus, the probability distribution for a random variable is a theoretical model for the relative frequency distribution of a population. To the extent that the two distributions are equivalent (and we will assume they are), the probability distribution for *x* possesses a mean μ and a variance σ^2 that are identical to the corresponding descriptive measures for the population. This section explains how you can find the mean value for a random variable. We illustrate the procedure with an example.

Examine the probability distribution for *x* (the number of heads observed in the toss of two fair coins) in Figure 4.4. Try to locate the mean of the distribution intuitively. We may reason that the mean μ of this distribution is equal to 1 as follows: In a large number of experiments, $^1\!/_4$ should result in $x = 0$, $^1\!/_2$ in $x = 1$, and $^1\!/_4$ in $x = 2$ heads. Therefore, the average number of heads is

$$\mu = 0\left(^1\!/_4\right) + 1\left(^1\!/_2\right) + 2\left(^1\!/_4\right) = 0 + ^1\!/_2 + ^1\!/_2 = 1$$

Note that to get the population mean of the random variable *x*, we multiply each possible value of *x* by its probability $p(x)$, and then we sum this product over all possible values of *x*. The *mean of x* is also referred to as the *expected value of x*, denoted $E(x)$.

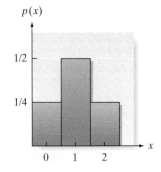

Figure 4.4
Probability Distribution for a Two-Coin Toss

> ### DEFINITION 4.5
>
> The **mean**, or **expected value**, of a discrete random variable *x* is
>
> $$\mu = E(x) = \Sigma x p(x)$$

The term *expected* is a mathematical term and should not be interpreted as it is typically used. Specifically, *a random variable might never be equal to its "expected value."* Rather, the expected value is the mean of the probability distribution, or a measure of its central tendency. You can think of μ as the mean value of *x* in a *very large* (actually, *infinite*) number of repetitions of the experiment, where the values of *x* occur in proportions equivalent to the probabilities of *x*.

EXAMPLE 4.6   FINDING AN EXPECTED VALUE

Problem   Suppose you work for an insurance company, and you sell a $10,000 1-year term insurance policy at an annual premium of $290. Actuarial tables show that the probability of death during the next year for a person of your customer's age, sex, health, etc., is .001. What is the expected gain (amount of money made by the company) for a policy of this type?

Solution   The experiment is to observe whether the customer survives the upcoming year. The probabilities associated with the two sample points, Live and Die, are .999 and .001, respectively. The random variable you are interested in is the gain x, which can assume the values shown in the following table.

Gain x	Sample Point	Probability
$290	Customer lives	.999
−$9,710	Customer dies	.001

If the customer lives, the company gains the $290 premium as profit. If the customer dies, the gain is negative because the company must pay $10,000, for a net "gain" of $(290 - 10,000) = -$9,710$. The expected gain is therefore

$$\mu = E(x) = \Sigma xp(x)$$
$$= (290)(.999) + (-9,710)(.001) = \$280$$

In other words, if the company were to sell a very large number of 1-year $10,000 policies to customers possessing the characteristics described above, it would (on the average) net $280 per sale in the next year.

Look Back   Note that $E(x)$ need not equal a possible value of x. That is, the expected value is $280, but x will equal either $290 or $-$9,710 each time the experiment is performed (a policy is sold and a year elapses). The expected value is a measure of central tendency—and in this case represents the average over a very large number of 1-year policies—but is not a possible value of x.

Now Work   *Exercise 4.34*

━━━━━ ■ ■ ■ ━━━━━

We learned in Chapter 2 that the mean and other measures of central tendency tell only part of the story about a set of data. The same is true about probability distributions. We need to measure variability as well. Since a probability distribution can be viewed as a representation of a population, we will use the population variance to measure its variability.

The *population variance* σ^2 is defined as the average of the squared distance of x from the population mean μ. Since x is a random variable, the squared distance, $(x - \mu)^2$, is also a random variable. Using the same logic used to find the mean value of x, we find the mean value of $(x - \mu)^2$ by multiplying all possible values of $(x - \mu)^2$ by $p(x)$ and then summing over all possible x values.* This quantity

$$E[(x - \mu)^2] = \sum_{\text{all } x} (x - \mu)^2 p(x)$$

is also called the *expected value of the squared distance from the mean;* that is, $\sigma^2 = E[(x - \mu)^2]$. The standard deviation of x is defined as the square root of the variance σ^2.

---

*It can be shown that $E[(x - \mu)^2] = E(x^2) - \mu^2$, where $E(x^2) = \Sigma x^2 p(x)$. Note the similarity between this expression and the shortcut formula $\Sigma(x - \bar{x})^2 = \Sigma x^2 - (\Sigma x)^2/n$ given in Chapter 2.

DEFINITION 4.6

The **variance** of a random variable x is

$$\sigma^2 = E[(x - \mu)^2] = \Sigma(x - \mu)^2 p(x) = \Sigma x^2 p(x) - \mu^2$$

DEFINITION 4.7

The **standard deviation** of a discrete random variable is equal to the square root of the variance, i.e., $\sigma = \sqrt{\sigma^2}$.

Knowing the mean μ and standard deviation σ of the probability distribution of x, in conjunction with Chebyshev's Rule (Table 2.6) and the Empirical Rule (Table 2.7), we can make statements about the likelihood of values of x falling within the intervals $\mu \pm \sigma$, $\mu \pm 2\sigma$, and $\mu \pm 3\sigma$. These probabilities are given in the box.

Chebyshev's Rule and Empirical Rule for a Discrete Random Variable

Let x be a discrete random variable with probability distribution $p(x)$, mean μ, and standard deviation σ. Then, depending on the shape of $p(x)$, the following probability statements can be made:

	Chebyshev's Rule	Empirical Rule
	Applies to any probability distribution (see Figure 4.5a)	Applies to probability distributions that are mound-shaped and symmetric (see Figure 4.5b)
$P(\mu - \sigma < x < \mu + \sigma)$	≥ 0	$\approx .68$
$P(\mu - 2\sigma < x < \mu + 2\sigma)$	$\geq 3/4$	$\approx .95$
$P(\mu - 3\sigma < x < \mu + 3\sigma)$	$\geq 8/9$	≈ 1.00

Figure 4.5
Shapes of Two Probability Distributions for a Discrete Random Variable x

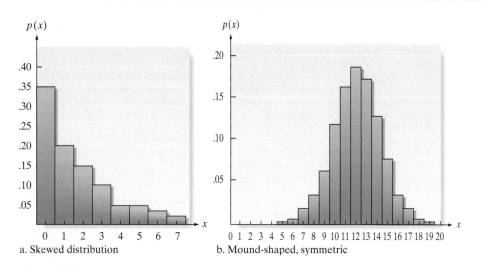

a. Skewed distribution

b. Mound-shaped, symmetric

EXAMPLE 4.7   FINDING μ AND σ

Problem   Medical research has shown that a certain type of chemotherapy is successful 70% of the time when used to treat skin cancer. Suppose five skin cancer patients are treated with this type of chemotherapy and let x equal the number of successful cures out of the five. The probability distribution for the number x of successful cures out of five is given in the table:

x	0	1	2	3	4	5
$p(x)$	.002	.029	.132	.309	.360	.168

a. Find $\mu = E(x)$. Interpret the result.

b. Find $\sigma = \sqrt{E[(x - \mu)^2]}$. Interpret the result.

c. Graph $p(x)$. Locate μ and the interval $\mu \pm 2\sigma$ on the graph. Use either Chebyshev's Rule or the Empirical Rule to approximate the probability that x falls in this interval. Compare this result with the actual probability.

d. Would you expect to observe fewer than two successful cures out of five?

Solution   **a.** Applying the formula

$$\mu = E(x) = \Sigma x p(x)$$
$$= 0(.002) + 1(.029) + 2(.132) + 3(.309) + 4(.360) + 5(.168) = 3.50$$

On average, the number of successful cures out of five skin cancer patients treated with chemotherapy will equal 3.5. Remember that this expected value only has meaning when the experiment—treating five skin cancer patients with chemotherapy—is repeated a large number of times.

b. Now we calculate the variance of x:

$$\sigma^2 = E[(x - \mu)^2] = \Sigma(x - \mu)^2 p(x)$$
$$= (0 - 3.5)^2(.002) + (1 - 3.5)^2(.029) + (2 - 3.5)^2(.132)$$
$$+ (3 - 3.5)^2(.309) + (4 - 3.5)^2(.360) + (5 - 3.5)^2(.168)$$
$$= 1.05$$

Thus, the standard deviation is

$$\sigma = \sqrt{\sigma^2} = \sqrt{1.05} = 1.02$$

This value measures the spread of the probability distribution of x, the number of successful cures out of five. A more useful interpretation is obtained by answering parts **c** and **d**.

c. The graph of $p(x)$ is shown in Figure 4.6 with the mean μ and the interval $\mu \pm 2\sigma = 3.50 \pm 2(1.02) = 3.50 \pm 2.04 = (1.46, 5.54)$ shown on the graph.

Figure 4.6
Graph of $p(x)$ for
Example 4.7

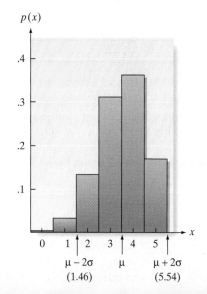

Note particularly that $\mu = 3.5$ locates the center of the probability distribution. Since this distribution is a theoretical relative frequency distribution that is moderately mound-shaped (see Figure 4.6), we expect (from Chebyshev's Rule) at least 75% and, more likely (from the Empirical Rule), approximately 95% of observed x values to fall between 1.46 and 5.54. You can see from Figure 4.6 that the actual probability that x falls in the interval $\mu \pm 2\sigma$ includes the sum of $p(x)$ for the values $x = 2$, $x = 3$, $x = 4$, and $x = 5$. This probability is $p(2) + p(3) + p(4) + p(5) = .132 + .309 + .360 + .168 = .969$. Therefore, 96.9% of the probability distribution lies within 2 standard deviations of the mean. This percentage is consistent with both Chebyshev's Rule and the Empirical Rule.

d. Fewer than two successful cures out of five implies that $x = 0$ or $x = 1$. Since both these values of x lie outside the interval $\mu \pm 2\sigma$, we know from the Empirical Rule that such a result is unlikely (approximate probability of .05). The exact probability, $P(x \le 1)$, is $p(0) + p(1) = .002 + .029 = .031$. Consequently, in a single experiment where five skin cancer patients are treated with chemotherapy, we would not expect to observe fewer than two successful cures.

Now Work   *Exercise 4.32*

■ ■ ■

Exercises 4.27–4.43

Understanding the Principles

4.27 What does the expected value of a random variable represent?

4.28 Will $E(x)$ always be equal to a specific value of the random variable, x?

4.29 For a mound-shaped, symmetric distribution, what is the probability that x falls in the interval $\mu \pm 2\sigma$?

Learning the Mechanics

4.30 Consider the probability distribution for the random variable x shown here.

x	10	20	30	40	50	60
$p(x)$	.05	.20	.30	.25	.10	.10

a. Find μ, σ^2, and σ.
b. Graph $p(x)$.
c. Locate μ and the interval $\mu \pm 2\sigma$ on your graph. What is the probability that x will fall within the interval $\mu \pm 2\sigma$?

4.31 Consider the probability distribution shown here.

x	1	2	4	10
$p(x)$	.2	.4	.2	.2

a. Find $\mu = E(x)$.
b. Find $\sigma^2 = E[(x - \mu)^2]$.
c. Find σ.

d. Interpret the value you obtained for μ.
e. In this case, can the random variable x ever assume the value μ? Explain.
f. In general, can a random variable ever assume a value equal to its expected value? Explain.

4.32 Consider the probability distribution shown here.
NW

x	−4	−3	−2	−1	0	1	2	3	4
$p(x)$	.02	.07	.10	.15	.30	.18	.10	.06	.02

a. Calculate μ, σ^2, and σ.
b. Graph $p(x)$. Locate μ, $\mu - 2\sigma$, and $\mu + 2\sigma$ on the graph.
c. What is the probability that x will fall in the interval $\mu \pm 2\sigma$?

4.33 Consider the probability distributions shown here.

x	0	1	2
$p(x)$	.3	.4	.3

y	0	1	2
$p(y)$	.1	.8	.1

a. Use your intuition to find the mean for each distribution. How did you arrive at your choice?
b. Which distribution appears to be more variable? Why?
c. Calculate μ and σ^2 for each distribution. Compare these answers to your answers in parts **a** and **b**.

Applying the Concepts—Basic

4.34 NHTSA car crash tests. Refer to Exercise 4.16 (p. 196),
NW where you found the probability distribution for x, the

number of stars in a randomly selected car's driver-side crash rating. Find $\mu = E(x)$ for this distribution and practically interpret the result.

4.35 Benford's Law of Numbers. Refer to the *American Scientist* (July–Aug. 1998) study of which integer is most likely to occur as the first significant digit in a randomly selected number (Benford's Law), Exercise 3.23 (p. 132). The table giving the frequency of each integer selected as the first digit in a six-digit random number is reproduced here.

First Digit	Frequency of Occurrence
1	109
2	75
3	77
4	99
5	72
6	117
7	89
8	62
9	43
Total	743

a. Construct a probability distribution for the first significant digit, x.
b. Find $E(x)$.
c. If possible, give a practical interpretation of $E(x)$.

4.36 Dust mite allergies. Exercise 4.17 (p. 196) gives the probability distribution for the number x of homes with high dust mite levels. The probability distribution is reproduced here.

Number of Homes, x	$p(x)$
0	.09
1	.30
2	.37
3	.20
4	.04

a. Find $E(x)$. Give a meaningful interpretation of the result.
b. Find σ.
c. Find the exact probability that x is in the interval $\mu \pm 2\sigma$. Compare to Chebyshev's Rule and the Empirical Rule.

4.37 Bridge-network reliabilities. A capacitated-bridge network with six arcs (*Networks*, May 1995) was presented in Exercise 4.23 (p. 197). The probability distributions for the capacities of the six arcs are reproduced here.
a. Compute the mean capacity of each arc and interpret its value.
b. Compute σ for each arc and interpret its value.

Applying the Concepts—Intermediate

4.38 Likelihood of flood damage. The National Weather Service issues precipitation forecasts that indicate the likelihood of measurable precipitation ($\geq .01$ inch) at a

Arc	Capacity x	$p(x)$	Arc	Capacity x	$p(x)$
a_1	3	.60	a_3	1	.90
	2	.25		0	.10
	1	.10			
	0	.05			
a_2	2	.60	a_4	1	.90
	1	.30		0	.10
	0	.10			
a_5	1	.90	a_6	2	.70
	0	.10		1	.25
				0	.05

Source: Lin, J., et al. "On reliability evaluation of capacitated-flow network in terms of minimal pathsets." *Networks*, Vol. 25, No. 3, May 1995, p. 135 (Table 1).

specific point—called the official rain gauge—during a given time period. Suppose that if a measurable amount of rain falls during the next 24 hours, an Ohio river will reach flood stage and a business will incur damages of $300,000. The National Weather Service has indicated that there is a 30% chance of a measurable amount of rain during the next 24 hours.
a. Construct the probability distribution that describes the potential flood damages.
b. Find the firm's expected loss due to flood damage. Interpret the result.

4.39 Expected winnings in roulette. In the popular casino game of roulette, you can bet on whether the ball will fall in an arc on the wheel colored red, black, or green. You showed (Exercise 3.49, p. 143) that the probability of a red outcome is 18/38, a black outcome is 18/38, and a green outcome is 2/38. Suppose you make a $5 bet on red. Find your expected net winnings for this single bet. Interpret the result.

4.40 Expected Lotto winnings. The chance of winning Florida's Pick-6 Lotto game is 1 in approximately 23 million. Suppose you buy a $1 Lotto ticket in anticipation of winning the $7 million grand prize. Calculate your expected net winnings for this single ticket. Interpret the result.

4.41 The Showcase Showdown. On the popular television game show, *The Price is Right*, contestants can play "The Showcase Showdown." The game involves a large wheel with twenty nickel values, 5, 10, 15, 20, ..., 95, 100, marked on it. Contestants spin the wheel once or twice, with the objective of obtaining the highest total score *without going over a dollar (100)*. [According to the *American Statistician* (Aug. 1995), the optimal strategy for the first spinner in a three-player game is to spin a second time only if the value of the initial spin is 65 or less.] Let x represent a single contestant playing "The Showcase Showdown." Assume a "fair" wheel (i.e., a wheel with equally likely outcomes). If the total of the player's spins exceeds 100, the total score is set to 0.
a. If the player is permitted only one spin of the wheel, find the probability distribution for x.

b. Refer to part **a**. Find $E(x)$ and interpret this value.

c. Refer to part **a**. Give a range of values within which x is likely to fall.

d. Suppose the player will spin the wheel twice, no matter what the outcome of the first spin. Find the probability distribution for x.

e. What assumption did you make to obtain the probability distribution, part **d**? Is it a reasonable assumption?

f. Find μ and σ for the probability distribution, part **d**, and interpret the results.

g. Refer to part **d**. What is the probability that in two spins the player's total score exceeds a dollar (i.e., is set to 0)?

h. Suppose the player obtains a 20 on the first spin and decides to spin again. Find the probability distribution for x.

i. Refer to part **h**. What is the probability that the player's total score exceeds a dollar?

j. Given the player obtains a 65 on the first spin and decides to spin again, find the probability that the player's total score exceeds a dollar.

k. Repeat part **j** for different first-spin outcomes. Use this information to suggest a strategy for the one-player game.

Applying the Concepts—Advanced

4.42 Parlay card betting. Odds makers try to predict which professional and college football teams will win and by how much (the *spread*). If the odds makers do this accurately, adding the spread to the underdog's score should make the final score a tie. Suppose a bookie will give you $6 for every $1 you risk if you pick the winners in three ballgames (adjusted by the spread) on a "parlay" card. What is the bookie's expected earnings per dollar wagered? Interpret this value.

4.43 Mastering a computer program. The number of training units that must be passed before a complex computer software program is mastered varies from one to five, depending on the student. After much experience, the software manufacturer has determined the probability distribution that describes the fraction of users mastering the software after each number of training units:

Number of Units	1	2	3	4	5
Probability of Mastery	.1	.25	.4	.15	.1

a. Calculate the mean number of training units necessary to master the program. Calculate the median. Interpret each.

b. If the firm wants to ensure that at least 75% of the students master the program, what is the minimum number of training units that must be administered? At least 90%?

c. Suppose the firm develops a new training program that increases the probability that only one unit of training is needed from .1 to .25, increases the probability that only two units are needed to .35, leaves the probability that three units are needed at .4, and completely eliminates the need for four or five units. How do your answers to parts **a** and **b** change for this new program?

4.4 The Binomial Random Variable

Many experiments result in *dichotomous* responses (i.e., responses for which there exist two possible alternatives, such as Yes–No, Pass–Fail, Defective–Nondefective, or Male–Female). A simple example of such an experiment is the coin-toss experiment. A coin is tossed a number of times, say 10. Each toss results in one of two outcomes, Head or Tail, and the probability of observing each of these two outcomes remains the same for each of the 10 tosses. Ultimately, we are interested in the probability distribution of x, the number of heads observed. Many other experiments are equivalent to tossing a coin (either balanced or unbalanced) a fixed number n of times and observing the number x of times that one of the two possible outcomes occurs. Random variables that possess these characteristics are called **binomial random variables**.

Public opinion and consumer preference polls (e.g., the CNN, Gallup, and Harris polls) frequently yield observations on binomial random variables. For example, suppose a sample of 100 students is selected from a large student body and each person is asked whether he or she favors (a Head) or opposes (a Tail) a certain campus issue. Suppose we are interested in x, the number of students in the sample who favor the issue. Sampling 100 students is analogous to tossing the coin 100 times. Thus, you can see that opinion polls that record the number of people who favor a certain issue are real-life equivalents of coin-toss experiments. We have been describing a **binomial experiment**; it is identified by the following characteristics.

> **Characteristics of a Binomial Random Variable**
>
> 1. The experiment consists of n identical trials.
> 2. There are only two possible outcomes on each trial. We will denote one outcome by S (for Success) and the other by F (for Failure).
> 3. The probability of S remains the same from trial to trial. This probability is denoted by p, and the probability of F is denoted by q. Note that $q = 1 - p$.
> 4. The trials are independent.
> 5. The binomial random variable x is the number of S's in n trials.

Biography

JACOB BERNOULLI (1654–1705)—The Bernoulli Distribution

Son of a magistrate and spice maker in Basel, Switzerland, Jacob Bernoulli completed a degree in theology at the University of Basel. While at the university, however, he studied mathematics secretly and against the will of his father. Jacob taught mathematics to his younger brother Johan, and they both went on to become distinguished European mathematicians. At first the brothers collaborated on the problems of the time (e.g., calculus); unfortunately, they later became bitter mathematical rivals. Jacob applied his philosophical training and mathematical intuition to probability and the theory of games of chance, where he developed the law of large numbers. In his book *Ars Conjectandi*, published in 1713 (eight years after his death), the binomial distribution was first proposed. Jacob showed that the binomial distribution was a sum of independent 0-1 variables, now known as Bernoulli random variables.

EXAMPLE 4.8   ASSESSING WHETHER X IS A BINOMIAL

Problem   For the following examples, decide whether x is a binomial random variable.

a. A university scholarship committee must select two students to receive a scholarship for the next academic year. The committee receives 10 applications for the scholarships—six from male students and four from female students. Suppose the applicants are all equally qualified, so that the selections are randomly made. Let x be the number of female students who receive a scholarship.

b. Before marketing a new product on a large scale, many companies will conduct a consumer-preference survey to determine whether the product is likely to be successful. Suppose a company develops a new diet soda and then conducts a taste-preference survey in which 100 randomly chosen consumers state their preferences among the new soda and the two leading sellers. Let x be the number of the 100 who choose the new brand over the two others.

c. Some surveys are conducted by using a method of sampling other than simple random sampling (defined in Chapter 3). For example, suppose a television cable company plans to conduct a survey to determine the fraction of households in the city that would use the cable television service. The sampling method is to choose a city block at random and then survey every household on that block. This sampling technique is called *cluster sampling*. Suppose 10 blocks are so sampled, producing a total of 124 household responses. Let x be the number of the 124 households that would use the television cable service.

Solution   a. In checking the binomial characteristics, a problem arises with independence (characteristic 4 in the preceding box). Given that the first student selected is female, the probability that the second chosen is female is $3/9$. On the other hand, given that the first selection is a male student, the probability that the second is female is $^4/_9$. Thus, the conditional probability of a Success (choosing a female student to receive a scholarship) on the second trial (selection) depends on the outcome of the first trial, and the trials are therefore dependent. Since the trials are *not independent*, this is not a binomial random variable. (This variable is actually a *hypergeometric* random variable, the topic of Optional Section 4.6.)

b. Surveys that produce dichotomous responses and use random sampling techniques are classic examples of binomial experiments. In our example, each randomly selected consumer either states a preference for the new diet soda or does not. The sample of 100 consumers is a very small proportion of the totality of potential consumers, so the response of one would be, for all practical purposes, independent of another.* Thus, x is a binomial random variable.

c. This example is a survey with dichotomous responses (Yes or No to the cable service), but the sampling method is not simple random sampling. Again, the binomial characteristic of independent trials would probably not be satisfied. The responses of households within a particular block would be dependent, since households within a block tend to be similar with respect to income, level of education, and general interests. Thus, the binomial model would not be satisfactory for x if the cluster sampling technique were employed.

Look Back Nonbinomial variables with two outcomes on every trial typically occur because they do not satisfy characteristics 3 or 4 of a binomial distribution.

Now Work *Exercise 4.56a*

— ▪ ▪ ▪ —

EXAMPLE 4.9
DERIVING THE BINOMIAL PROBABILITY DISTRIBUTION

Problem The Heart Association claims that only 10% of U.S. adults over 30 can pass the President's Physical Fitness Commission's minimum requirements. Suppose four adults are randomly selected, and each is given the fitness test.

a. Use the steps given in Chapter 3 (box on p. 127) to find the probability that none of the four adults passes the test.

b. Find the probability that three of the four adults pass the test.

c. Let x represent the number of the four adults who pass the fitness test. Explain why x is a binomial random variable.

d. Use the answers to parts **a** and **b** to derive a formula for $p(x)$, the probability distribution of the binomial random variable x.

Solution **a.** **1.** The first step is to define the experiment. Here we are interested in observing the fitness test results of each of the four adults: pass (S) or fail (F).

2. Next, we list the sample points associated with the experiment. Each sample point consists of the test results of the four adults. For example, $SSSS$ represents the sample point that all four adults pass, while $FSSS$ represents the sample point that adult 1 fails, while adults 2, 3, and 4 pass the test. The 16 sample points are listed in Table 4.2.

---

*In most real-life applications of the binomial distribution, the population of interest has a finite number of elements (trials), denoted N. When N is large and the sample size n is small relative to N, say $n/N \leq .05$, the sampling procedure, for all practical purposes, satisfies the conditions of a binomial experiment.

TABLE 4.2   Sample Points for Fitness Test of Example 4.9

SSSS	FSSS	FFSS	SFFF	FFFF
	SFSS	FSFS	FSFF	
	SSFS	FSSF	FFSF	
	SSSF	SFFS	FFFS	
		SFSF		
		SSFF		

3. We now assign probabilities to the sample points. Note that each sample point can be viewed as the intersection of four adults' test results and, assuming the results are independent, the probability of each sample point can be obtained using the multiplicative rule, as follows:

$$P(SSSS) = P[(\text{adult 1 passes}) \cap (\text{adult 2 passes})$$
$$\cap (\text{adult 3 passes}) \cap (\text{adult 4 passes})]$$
$$= P(\text{adult 1 passes}) \times P(\text{adult 2 passes})$$
$$\times P(\text{adult 3 passes}) \times P(\text{adult 4 passes})$$
$$= (.1)(.1)(.1)(.1) = (.1)^4 = .0001$$

All other sample point probabilities are calculated using similar reasoning. For example,

$$P(FSSS) = (.9)(.1)(.1)(.1) = .0009$$

You can check that this reasoning results in sample point probabilities that add to 1 over the 16 points in the sample space.

4. Finally, we add the appropriate sample point probabilities to obtain the desired event probability. The event of interest is that all four adults fail the fitness test. In Table 4.2 we find only one sample point, *FFFF*, contained in this event. All other sample points imply that at least one adult passes. Thus,

$$P(\text{All four adults fail}) = P(FFFF) = (.9)^4 = .6561$$

b. The event that three of the four adults pass the fitness test consists of the four sample points in the second column of Table 4.2: *FSSS, SFSS, SSFS,* and *SSSF*. To obtain the event probability we add the sample point probabilities:

$$P(3 \text{ of } 4 \text{ adults pass}) = P(FSSS) + P(SFSS) + P(SSFS) + P(SSSF)$$
$$= (.1)^3(.9) + (.1)^3(.9) + (.1)^3(.9) + (.1)^3(.9)$$
$$= 4(.1)^3(.9) = .0036$$

Note that each of the four sa.mple point probabilities is the same, because each sample point consists of three *S*'s and one *F*; the order does not affect the probability because the adults' test results are (assumed) independent.

c. We can characterize the experiment as consisting of four identical trials—the four test results. There are two possible outcomes to each trial, *S* or *F*, and the probability of passing, $p = .1$, is the same for each trial. Finally, we are assuming that each adult's test result is independent of all others, so that the four trials are independent. Then it follows that x, the number of the four adults who pass the fitness test, is a binomial random variable.

d. The event probabilities in parts **a** and **b** provide insight into the formula for the probability distribution $p(x)$. First, consider the event that three adults pass (part **b**). We found that

$$P(x = 3) = (\text{Number of sample points for which } x = 3) \times (.1)^{\text{Number of successes}} \times (.9)^{\text{Number of failures}}$$
$$= 4(.1)^3(.9)^1$$

In general, we can use combinatorial mathematics to count the number of sample points. For example,

Number of sample points for which $x = 3$
$= $ Number of different ways of selecting 3 successes of the 4 trials
$$= \binom{4}{3} = \frac{4!}{3!(4-3)!} = \frac{4 \cdot 3 \cdot 2 \cdot 1}{(3 \cdot 2 \cdot 1) \cdot 1} = 4$$

The formula that works for any value of x can be deduced as follows:

$$P(x = 3) = \binom{4}{3}(.1)^3(.9)^1 = \binom{4}{x}(.1)^x(.9)^{4-x}$$

The component $\binom{4}{x}$ counts the number of sample points with x successes, and the component $(.1)^x(.9)^{4-x}$ is the probability associated with each sample point having x successes.

For the general binomial experiment, with n trials and probability of Success p on each trial, the probability of x successes is

$$p(x) = \binom{n}{x} p^x (1 - p)^{n-x}$$

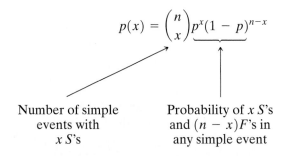

Number of simple events with x S's

Probability of x S's and $(n - x)F$'s in any simple event

Look Back In theory, you could always resort to the principles developed in this example to calculate binomial probabilities; list the sample points and sum their probabilities. However, as the number of trials (n) increases, the number of sample points grows very rapidly (the number of sample points is 2^n). Thus, we prefer the formula for calculating binomial probabilities, since its use avoids listing sample points.

■ ■ ■

The binomial distribution* is summarized in the box.

The Binomial Probability Distribution

$$p(x) = \binom{n}{x} p^x q^{n-x} \qquad (x = 0, 1, 2, \ldots, n)$$

where

$p = $ Probability of a success on a single trial
$q = 1 - p$
$n = $ Number of trials
$x = $ Number of successes in n trials
$$\binom{n}{x} = \frac{n!}{x!(n-x)!}$$

---

*The binomial distribution is so named because the probabilities, $p(x)$, $x = 0, 1, \ldots, n$, are terms of the binomial expansion, $(q + p)^n$.

As noted in Chapter 3, the symbol 5! means $5 \cdot 4 \cdot 3 \cdot 2 \cdot 1 = 120$. Similarly, $n! = n(n - 1)(n - 2) \cdots 3 \cdot 2 \cdot 1$; remember, $0! = 1$.

EXAMPLE 4.10 — APPLYING THE BINOMIAL DISTRIBUTION

Problem Refer to Example 4.9. Use the formula for a binomial random variable to find the probability distribution of x, where x is the number of adults who pass the fitness test. Graph the distribution.

Solution For this application, we have $n = 4$ trials. Since a success S is defined as an adult who passes the test, $p = P(S) = .1$ and $q = 1 - p = .9$. Substituting $n = 4$, $p = .1$, and $q = .9$ into the formula for $p(x)$, we obtain

$$p(0) = \frac{4!}{0!(4 - 0)!}(.1)^0(.9)^{4-0} = \frac{4 \cdot 3 \cdot 2 \cdot 1}{(1)(4 \cdot 3 \cdot 2 \cdot 1)}(.1)^0(.9)^4 = 1(1)^0(.9)^4 = .6561$$

$$p(1) = \frac{4!}{1!(4 - 1)!}(.1)^1(.9)^{4-1} = \frac{4 \cdot 3 \cdot 2 \cdot 1}{(1)(3 \cdot 2 \cdot 1)}(.1)^1(.9)^3 = 4(.1)(.9)^3 = .2916$$

$$p(2) = \frac{4!}{2!(4 - 2)!}(.1)^2(.9)^{4-2} = \frac{4 \cdot 3 \cdot 2 \cdot 1}{(2 \cdot 1)(2 \cdot 1)}(.1)^2(.9)^2 = 6(.1)^2(.9)^2 = .0486$$

$$p(3) = \frac{4!}{3!(4 - 3)!}(.1)^3(.9)^{4-3} = \frac{4 \cdot 3 \cdot 2 \cdot 1}{(3 \cdot 2 \cdot 1)(1)}(.1)^3(.9)^1 = 4(.1)^3(.9) = .0036$$

$$p(4) = \frac{4!}{4!(4 - 4)!}(.1)^4(.9)^{4-4} = \frac{4 \cdot 3 \cdot 2 \cdot 1}{(4 \cdot 3 \cdot 2 \cdot 1)(1)}(.1)^4(.9)^0 = 1(.1)^4(.9) = .0001$$

Look Back Note that these probabilities, listed in Table 4.3, sum to 1. A graph of this probability distribution is shown in Figure 4.7.

Now Work *Exercise 4.49*

■ ■ ■

TABLE 4.3 Probability Distribution for Physical Fitness Example: Tabular Form

x	p(x)
0	.6561
1	.2916
2	.0486
3	.0036
4	.0001

Figure 4.7

Probability Distribution for Physical Fitness Example: Graphical Form

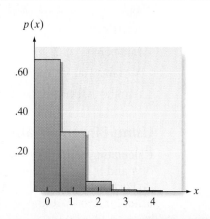

EXAMPLE 4.11   FINDING μ AND σ

Problem   Refer to Examples 4.9 and 4.10. Calculate μ and σ, the mean and standard deviation, respectively, of the number of the four adults who pass the test. Interpret the results.

Solution   From Section 4.3 we know that the mean of a discrete probability distribution is

$$\mu = \Sigma x p(x)$$

Referring to Table 4.3, the probability distribution for the number x who pass the fitness test, we find

$$\mu = 0(.6561) + 1(.2916) + 2(.0486) + 3(.0036) + 4(.0001) = .4$$
$$= 4(.1) = np$$

Thus, in the long run, the average number of adults (out of four) who pass the test is only .4. [*Note: The relationship* $\mu = np$ *holds in general for a binomial random variable.*]

    The variance is

$$\begin{aligned}
\sigma^2 &= \Sigma(x - \mu)^2 p(x) = \Sigma(x - .4)^2 p(x) \\
&= (0 - .4)^2(.6561) + (1 - .4)^2(.2916) + (2 - .4)^2(.0486) \\
&\quad + (3 - .4)^2(.0036) + (4 - .4)^2(.0001) \\
&= .104976 + .104976 + .124416 + .024336 + .001296 \\
&= .36 = 4(.1)(.9) = npq
\end{aligned}$$

[*Note: The relationship* $\sigma^2 = npq$ *holds in general for a binomial random variable.*]

    Finally, the standard deviation of the number who pass the fitness test is

$$\sigma = \sqrt{\sigma^2} = \sqrt{.36} = .6$$

    Applying the Empirical Rule, we know that approximately 95% of the x values will fall in the interval $\mu \pm 2\sigma = .4 \pm 2(.6) = (-.8, 1.6)$. Since x cannot be negative, we expect (i.e., in the long run) the number of adults out of four who pass the fitness test to be less than 1.6.

Look Back Examining Figure 4.7, you can see that all observations equal to 0 or 1 will fall within the interval $(-.8, 1.6)$. The probabilities corresponding to these values (from Table 4.3) are .6561 and .2916, respectively. Summing them, we obtain $.6561 + .2916 = .9477 \approx .95$. This result, again, supports the Empirical Rule.

■ ■ ■

    We emphasize that you need not use the expectation summation rules to calculate μ and σ^2 for a binomial random variable. You can find them easily using the formulas $\mu = np$ and $\sigma^2 = npq$.

Mean, Variance, and Standard Deviation for a Binomial Random Variable

Mean: $\mu = np$

Variance: $\sigma^2 = npq$

Standard deviation: $\sigma = \sqrt{npq}$

Using Binomial Tables

Calculating binomial probabilities becomes tedious when n is large. For some values of n and p, the binomial probabilities have been tabulated in Table II of Appendix A. Part of Table II is shown in Table 4.4; a graph of the binomial probability distribution for $n = 10$ and $p = .10$ is shown in Figure 4.8.

TABLE 4.4   Reproduction of Part of Table II of Appendix A: Binomial Probabilities for $n = 10$

k \ p	.01	.05	.10	.20	.30	.40	.50	.60	.70	.80	.90	.95	.99
0	.904	.599	.349	.107	.028	.006	.001	.000	.000	.000	.000	.000	.000
1	.996	.914	.736	.376	.149	.046	.011	.002	.000	.000	.000	.000	.000
2	1.000	.988	.930	.678	.383	.167	.055	.012	.002	.000	.000	.000	.000
3	1.000	.999	.987	.879	.650	.382	.172	.055	.011	.001	.000	.000	.000
4	1.000	1.000	.998	.967	.850	.633	.377	.166	.047	.006	.000	.000	.000
5	1.000	1.000	1.000	.994	.953	.834	.623	.367	.150	.033	.002	.000	.000
6	1.000	1.000	1.000	.999	.989	.945	.828	.618	.350	.121	.013	.001	.000
7	1.000	1.000	1.000	1.000	.998	.988	.945	.833	.617	.322	.070	.012	.000
8	1.000	1.000	1.000	1.000	1.000	.988	.989	.954	.851	.624	.264	.086	.004
9	1.000	1.000	1.000	1.000	1.000	1.000	.999	.994	.972	.893	.651	.401	.096

Table II actually contains a total of nine tables, labeled (**a**) through (**i**), one each corresponding to $n = 5, 6, 7, 8, 9, 10, 15, 20,$ and 25, respectively. In each of these tables the columns correspond to values of p, and the rows correspond to values of the random variable x. The entries in the table represent **cumulative binomial probabilities**. Thus, for example, the entry in the column corresponding to $p = .10$ and the row corresponding to $x = 2$ is .930 (highlighted), and its interpretation is

$$P(x \le 2) = P(x = 0) + P(x = 1) + P(x = 2) = .930$$

This probability is also highlighted in the graphical representation of the binomial distribution with $n = 10$ and $p = .10$ in Figure 4.8.

You can also use Table II to find the probability that x equals a specific value. For example, suppose you want to find the probability that $x = 2$ in the binomial distribution with $n = 10$ and $p = .10$. This is found by subtraction as follows:

$$P(x = 2) = [P(x = 0) + P(x = 1) + P(x = 2)] - [P(x = 0) + P(x = 1)]$$
$$= P(x \le 2) - P(x \le 1) = .930 - .736 = .194$$

The probability that a binomial random variable exceeds a specified value can be found using Table II and the notion of complementary events. For example, to find the probability that x exceeds 2 when $n = 10$ and $p = .10$, we use

$$P(x > 2) = 1 - P(x \le 2) = 1 - .930 = .070$$

Note that this probability is represented by the unhighlighted portion of the graph in Figure 4.8.

All probabilities in Table II are rounded to three decimal places. Thus, although none of the binomial probabilities in the table is exactly zero, some are small enough (less than .0005) to round to .000. For example, using the formula to find $P(x = 0)$ when $n = 10$ and $p = .6$, we obtain

$$P(x = 0) = \binom{10}{0}(.6)^0(.4)^{10-0} = .4^{10} = .00010486$$

but this is rounded to .000 in Table II of Appendix A (see Table 4.4).

Figure 4.8

Binomial Probability
Distribution for $n = 10$
and $p = .10$; $P(x \le 2)$
Highlighted

Similarly, none of the table entries is exactly 1.0, but when the cumulative probabilities exceed .9995, they are rounded to 1.000. The row corresponding to the largest possible value for x, $x = n$, is omitted, because all the cumulative probabilities in that row are equal to 1.0 (exactly). For example, in Table 4.4 with $n = 10$, $P(x \leq 10) = 1.0$, no matter what the value of p.

The following example further illustrates the use of Table II.

EXAMPLE 4.12   USING THE BINOMIAL TABLE

Problem   Suppose a poll of 20 voters is taken in a large city. The purpose is to determine x, the number who favor a certain candidate for mayor. Suppose that 60% of all the city's voters favor the candidate.

    a. Find the mean and standard deviation of x.

    b. Use Table II of Appendix A to find the probability that $x \leq 10$.

    c. Use Table II to find the probability that $x > 12$.

    d. Use Table II to find the probability that $x = 11$.

    e. Graph the probability distribution of x and locate the interval $\mu \pm 2\sigma$ on the graph.

Solution   **a.** The number of voters polled is presumably small compared with the total number of eligible voters in the city. Thus, we may treat x, the number of the 20 who favor the mayoral candidate, as a binomial random variable. The value of p is the fraction of the total voters who favor the candidate (i.e., $p = .6$). Therefore, we calculate the mean and variance:

$$\mu = np = 20(.6) = 12$$
$$\sigma^2 = npq = 20(.6)(.4) = 4.8$$
$$\sigma = \sqrt{4.8} = 2.19$$

    b. Looking in the $k = 10$ row and the $p = .6$ column of Table II (Appendix A) for $n = 20$, we find the value of .245. Thus,

$$P(x \leq 10) = .245$$

    c. To find the probability

$$P(x > 12) = \sum_{x=13}^{20} p(x)$$

we use the fact that for all probability distributions,

$$\sum_{\text{all } x} p(x) = 1.$$

Therefore,

$$P(x > 12) = 1 - P(x \leq 12) = 1 - \sum_{x=0}^{12} p(x)$$

Consulting Table II, we find the entry in row $k = 12$, column $p = .6$ to be .584. Thus,

$$P(x > 12) = 1 - .584 = .416$$

Figure 4.9

The Binomial Probability Distribution for x in Example 4.12: $n = 20$ and $p = .6$

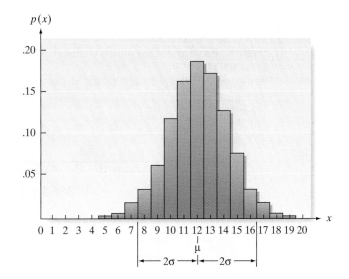

$p(x)$

d. To find the probability that exactly 11 voters favor the candidate, recall that the entries in Table II are cumulative probabilities and use the relationship

$$P(x = 11) = [p(0) + p(1) + \cdots + p(11)] - [p(0) + p(1) + \cdots + p(10)]$$
$$= P(x \le 11) - P(x \le 10)$$

Then

$$P(x = 11) = .404 - .245 = .159$$

e. The probability distribution for x is shown in Figure 4.9. Note that

$$\mu - 2\sigma = 12 - 2(2.2) = 7.6 \qquad \mu + 2\sigma = 12 + 2(2.2) = 16.4$$

The interval $\mu - 2\sigma$ to $\mu + 2\sigma$ is shown in Figure 4.9. The probability that x falls in the interval $\mu + 2\sigma$ is $P(x = 8, 9, 10, \ldots, 16) = P(x \le 16) - P(x \le 7)$ $.984 - .021 = .963$. Note that this probability is very close to the .95 given by the Empirical Rule. Thus, we expect the number of voters in the sample of 20 who favor the mayoral candidate to be between 8 and 16.

 Now Work *Exercise 4.52*

■ ■ ■

Binomial Probabilities

Using the TI-83 Graphing Calculator

I. $P(x = k)$

To compute the probability of k successes in n trials, where the p is probability of success for each trial, use the binompdf(command. Binompdf stands for "binomial probability density function." This command is under the DISTRibution menu and has the format binompdf(n, p, k).

Example Compute the probability of 5 successes in 8 trials where the probability of success for a single trial is 40%.

In this example, $n = 8$, $p = .4$, and $k = 5$.

Step 1   Enter the binomial parameters
Press 2nd VARS for DISTR
Press the down arrow key until 0:binompdf is highlighted
Press ENTER
After binompdf(,type 8, .4, 5) (Note: be sure to use the comma key between each parameter)
Press ENTER

You should see

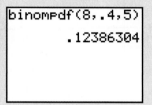

Thus, $P(x = 5)$ is about 12.4%.

II. $P(x \leq k)$

To compute the probability of k or fewer successes in n trials, where the p is probability of success for each trial, use the binomcdf(command. Binomcdf stands for "binomial *cumulative* probability density function." This command is under the DISTRibution menu and has the format binomcdf(n, p, k).

Example   Compute the probability of less than 5 successes in 8 trials where the probability of success for a single trial is 40%. In this example, $n = 8$, $p = .4$, and $k = 5$.

Step 1   Enter the binomial parameters
Press 2nd VARS for DISTR
Press down the arrow key until A:binomcdf is highlighted
Press ENTER
After binomcdf(,type 8, .4, 5)
Press ENTER

You should see

Thus, $P(x < 5)$ is about 95%.

III. $P(x < k)$, $P(x > k)$, $P(x \geq k)$

To find the probability of less than k successes $P(x < k)$, more than k successes $P(x > k)$, or at least k successes $P(x \geq k)$, variations of the binomcdf(command must be used as shown below.

$P(x < k)$ use **binomcdf** $(n, p, k - 1)$

$P(x > k)$ use **1–binomcdf** (n, p, k)

$P(x \geq k)$ use **1–binomcdf** $(n, p, k-1)$

Statistics in Action Revisited

Using the Binomial Model to Solve the Cocaine Sting Case

Refer to the reverse cocaine sting case described on p. 189. During a drug bust, police seized 496 foil packets of a white, powdery substance that appeared to be cocaine. The police laboratory randomly selected four packets and found that all four tested positive for cocaine. This finding led to the conviction of the drug traffickers. Following the conviction, the police used two of the remaining 492 foil packets (i.e., those not tested) in a reverse sting operation. The two randomly selected packets were sold by undercover officers to a buyer who disposed of the evidence before being arrested. Is there evidence beyond a reasonable doubt that the two packets contained cocaine?

To solve the dilemma, we will assume that of the 496 original packets confiscated, 331 contained genuine cocaine and 165 contained an inert (legal) powder. (A statistician, hired as an expert witness on the case, showed that the chance of the defendant being found not guilty is maximized when 331 packets contain cocaine and 165 do not.) First, we'll find the probability that four packets randomly selected from the original 496 will test positive for cocaine. Then we'll find the probability that the two packets sold in the reverse sting did not contain cocaine. Finally, we'll find the probability that both events occur (i.e., that the first four packets selected test positive for cocaine but that the next two packets selected do not). In each of these probability calculations, we will apply the binomial probability distribution to approximate the probabilities.

Let x be the number of packets that contain cocaine in a sample of n selected from the 496 packets. Here, we are defining a "success" as a packet that contains cocaine. If n is small, say $n = 2$ or $n = 4$, then x has an approximate binomial distribution with probability of success $p = 331/496 \approx .67$.

The probability that the first four packets selected contain cocaine [i.e., $P(x = 4)$] is obtained using the binomial formula with $n = 4$ and $p = .67$:

$$P(x = 4) = p(4) = \binom{4}{4}p^4(1 - p)^0 = \frac{4!(.67)^4(.33)^0}{4!0!}$$
$$= (.67)^4 = .201$$

Thus, there is about a 20% chance that all four of the randomly selected packets contain cocaine.

Given that four of the original packets tested positive for cocaine, the probability that the two packets randomly selected and sold in the reverse sting *do not* contain cocaine is approximated using a binomial distribution with $n = 2$ and $p = .67$. Since a "success" is a packet with cocaine, we find $P(x = 0)$:

$$P(x = 0) = p(0) = \binom{2}{0}p^0(1 - p)^2 = \frac{2!(.67)^0(.33)^2}{0!2!}$$
$$= (.33)^2 = .109$$

Finally, to compute the probability that of the original 496 foil packets, the first four selected (at random) test positive for cocaine and the next two selected (at random) test negative, we employ the Multiplicative Law of Probability. Let A be the event that the first four packets test positive. Let B be the event that the next two packets test negative. We want to find the probability of both events occurring [i.e., $P(A \text{ and } B) = P(A \cap B) = P(B|A)P(A)$]. Note that this probability is the product of the two previously calculated probabilities:

$$P(A \text{ and } B) = (.109)(.201) = .022$$

Consequently, there is only a .022 probability (i.e., about 2 chances in a hundred) that the first four packets will test positive for cocaine and the next two packets will test negative for cocaine. A reasonable jury would likely believe that an event with such a small probability is unlikely to occur and conclude that the two "lost" packets contained cocaine. In other words, most of us would infer that the defendant in the reverse cocaine sting was guilty of drug trafficking.

[*Epilogue:* Several of the defendant's lawyers believed that the .022 probability was too high for jurors to conclude guilt "beyond a reasonable doubt." The argument was made moot, however, when, to the surprise of the defense, the prosecution revealed that the remaining 490 packets had not been used in any other reverse sting operations and offered to test a sample of them. On the advice of the statistician, the defense requested that an additional 20 packets be tested. All 20 tested positive for cocaine! As a consequence of this new evidence, the defendant was convicted by the jury.]

Exercises 4.44–4.68

Understanding the Principles

4.44 Give the five characteristics of a binomial random variable.

4.45 Give the formula for $p(x)$ for a binomial random variable with $n = 7$ and $p = .2$.

4.46 Consider the following binomial probability distribution:

$$p(x) = \binom{5}{x}(.7)^x(.3)^{5-x} \quad (x = 0, 1, 2, \ldots, 5)$$

a. How many trials (n) are in the experiment?
b. What is the value of p, the probability of success?

Learning the Mechanics

4.47 Compute the following:

a. $\dfrac{6!}{2!(6-2)!}$ b. $\dbinom{5}{2}$ c. $\dbinom{7}{0}$

d. $\dbinom{6}{6}$ e. $\dbinom{4}{3}$

4.48 Refer to Exercise 4.46.

a. Graph the probability distribution.

b. Find the mean and standard deviation of x.

c. Show the mean and the 2-standard-deviation interval on each side of the mean on the graph you drew in part **a**.

4.49 If x is a binomial random variable, compute $p(x)$ for NW each of the following cases:

a. $n = 5, x = 1, p = .2$

b. $n = 4, x = 2, q = .4$

c. $n = 3, x = 0, p = .7$

d. $n = 5, x = 3, p = .1$

e. $n = 4, x = 2, q = .6$

f. $n = 3, x = 1, p = .9$

4.50 Suppose x is a binomial random variable with $n = 3$ and $p = .3$.

a. Calculate the value of $p(x)$, $x = 0, 1, 2, 3$, using the formula for a binomial probability distribution.

b. Using your answers to part **a**, give the probability distribution for x in tabular form.

4.51 If x is a binomial random variable, calculate μ, σ^2, and σ for each of the following:

a. $n = 25, p = .5$

b. $n = 80, p = .2$

c. $n = 100, p = .6$

d. $n = 70, p = .9$

e. $n = 60, p = .8$

f. $n = 1,000, p = .04$

4.52 If x is a binomial random variable, use Table II in NW Appendix A to find the following probabilities:

a. $P(x = 2)$ for $n = 10, p = .4$

b. $P(x \le 5)$ for $n = 15, p = .6$

c. $P(x > 1)$ for $n = 5, p = .1$

4.53 If x is a binomial random variable, use Table II, Appendix A to find the following probabilities:

a. $P(x < 10)$ for $n = 25, p = .7$

b. $P(x \ge 10)$ for $n = 15, p = .9$

c. $P(x = 2)$ for $n = 20, p = .2$

4.54 Suppose x is a binomial random variable with $n = 5$ and $p = .5$. Compute $p(x)$ for $x = 0, 1, 2, 3, 4$, and 5 using the following two methods:

a. List the sample points (using S for Success and F for Failure on each trial) corresponding to each value of x, assign probabilities to each sample point, and obtain $p(x)$ by adding sample point probabilities.

b. Use the formula for the binomial probability distribution to obtain $p(x)$.

4.55 The binomial probability distribution is a family of probability distributions with each single distribution depending on the values of n and p. Assume that x is a binomial random variable with $n = 4$.

a. Determine a value of p such that the probability distribution of x is symmetric.

b. Determine a value of p such that the probability distribution of x is skewed to the right.

c. Determine a value of p such that the probability distribution of x is skewed to the left.

d. Graph each of the binomial distributions you obtained in parts **a**, **b**, and **c**. Locate the mean for each distribution on its graph.

e. In general, for what values of p will a binomial distribution be symmetric? Skewed to the right? Skewed to the left?

Applying the Concepts—Basic

4.56 Mobile phones with Internet access. According to a Jupiter/NPD Consumer Survey of young adults (18–24 years of age) who shop online, 20% own a mobile phone with Internet access. (*American Demographics*, May 2002.) In a random sample of 200 young adults who shop online, let x be the number who own a mobile phone with Internet access.

NW a. Explain why x is a binomial random variable (to a reasonable degree of approximation).

b. What is the value of p? Interpret this value.

c. What is the expected value of x? Interpret this value.

4.57 Quit smoking program. According to the University of South Florida's Tobacco Research and Intervention Program, only 5% of the nation's cigarette smokers ever enter into a treatment program to help them quit smoking. (*USF Magazine*, Spring 2000.) In a random sample of 200 smokers, let x be the number who enter into a treatment program.

a. Explain why x is a binomial random variable (to a reasonable degree of approximation).

b. What is the value of p? Interpret this value.

c. What is the expected value of x? Interpret this value.

4.58 Caesarian births. The American College of Obstetricians and Gynecologists report that 22% of all births in the U.S. take place by Caesarian section each year. (*USA Today*, Sept. 19, 2000.)

a. In a random sample of 1,000 births, how many, on average will take place by Caesarian section?

b. What is the standard deviation of the number of Caesarian section births in a sample of 1,000 births?

c. Use your answers to parts **a** and **b** to form an interval that is likely to contain the number of Caesarian section births in a sample of 1,000 births.

4.59 Belief in an afterlife. A national poll conducted by *The New York Times* (May 7, 2000) revealed that 80% of Americans believe that after you die, some part of you lives on, either in a next life on earth or in heaven. Consider a random sample of 10 Americans and count x, the number who believe in life after death.

a. Find $P(x = 3)$.   b. Find $P(x \le 7)$.

c. Find $P(x > 4)$.

4.60 Parents who condone spanking. According to a nationwide survey, 60% of parents with young children condone spanking their child as a regular form of punishment. (*Tampa Tribune*, Oct. 5, 2000.) Consider a random sample of three people, each of whom is a parent with young children. Assume that x, the number in the sample that condone spanking, is a binomial random variable.

a. What is the probability that none of the three parents condones spanking as a regular form of punishment for their children?

b. What is the probability that at least one condones spanking as a regular form of punishment?

c. Give the mean and standard deviation of x. Interpret the results.

Applying the Concepts—Intermediate

4.61 Fungi in beech forest trees. Refer to the *Applied Ecology and Environmental Research* (Vol. 1, 2003) study of beech trees damaged by fungi, Exercise 3.21 (p. 131). The researchers found that 25% of the beech trees in East Central Europe have been damaged by fungi. Consider a sample of 20 beech trees from this area.

a. What is the probability that fewer than half are damaged by fungi?

b. What is the probability that more than 15 are damaged by fungi?

c. How many of the sampled trees would you expect to be damaged by fungi?

4.62 Countries that allow a free press. The degree to which democratic and nondemocratic countries attempt to control the news media was examined in the *Journal of Peace Research* (Nov. 1997). Between 1948 and 1996, 80% of all democratic regimes allowed a free press. In contrast, over the same time period, 10% of all nondemocratic regimes allowed a free press.

a. In a random sample of 50 democratic regimes, how many would you expect to allow a free press? Give a range that is highly likely to include the number of democratic regimes with a free press.

b. In a random sample of 50 nondemocratic regimes, how many would you expect to allow a free press? Give a range that is highly likely to include the number of nondemocratic regimes with a free press.

4.63 Victims of domestic abuse. According to researchers at Johns Hopkins University School of Medicine, one in every three women has been a victim of domestic abuse. (*Annals of Internal Medicine*, Nov. 1995.) This probability was obtained from a survey of nearly 2,000 adult women residing in Baltimore, Maryland. Suppose we randomly sample 15 women and find that four have been abused.

a. What is the probability of observing four or more abused women in a sample of 15 if the proportion p of women who are victims of domestic abuse is really $p = \frac{1}{3}$?

b. Many experts on domestic violence believe that the proportion of women who are domestically abused

is closer to $p = .10$. Calculate the probability of observing four or more abused women in a sample of 15 if $p = .10$.

c. Why might your answers to parts **a** and **b** lead you to believe that $p = \frac{1}{3}$?

4.64 Chickens with fecal contamination. The United States Department of Agriculture (USDA) reports that, under its standard inspection system, one in every 100 slaughtered chickens passes inspection with fecal contamination. (*Tampa Tribune*, Mar. 31, 2000.) In Exercise 3.19 (p. 141), you found the probability that a randomly selected slaughtered chicken passes inspection with fecal contamination. Now find the probability that, in a random sample of five slaughtered chickens, at least one passes inspection with fecal contamination.

4.65 Testing a psychic's ESP. Refer to Exercise 3.75 (p. 157) and the experiment conducted by the Tampa Bay Skeptics to see whether an acclaimed psychic has extrasensory perception (ESP). Recall that a crystal is placed, at random, inside one of 10 identical boxes lying side-by-side on a table. The experiment was repeated seven times, and x, the number of correct decisions, was recorded. (Assume that the seven trials are independent.)

a. If the psychic is guessing (i.e., if the psychic does *not* possess ESP) what is the value of p, the probability of a correct decision on each trial?

b. If the psychic is guessing, what is the expected number of correct decisions in seven trials?

c. If the psychic is guessing, what is the probability of no correct decisions in seven trials?

d. Now suppose the psychic has ESP and $p = .5$. What is the probability that the psychic guesses incorrectly in all seven trials?

e. Refer to part **d**. Recall that the psychic failed to select the box with the crystal on all seven trials. Is this evidence against the psychic having ESP? Explain.

Applying the Concepts—Advanced

4.66 Assigning a passing grade. A literature professor decides to give a 20-question true-false quiz to determine who has read an assigned novel. She wants to choose the passing grade such that the probability of passing a student who guesses on every question is less than .05. What score should she set as the lowest passing grade?

4.67 USGA golf ball specifications. According to the U.S. Golf Association (USGA), "The weight of the [golf] ball shall not be greater than 1.620 ounces avoirdupois (45.93 grams) .... The diameter of the ball shall not be less than 1.680 inches .... The velocity of the ball shall not be greater than 250 feet per second" (USGA, 2001). The USGA periodically checks the specifications of golf balls sold in the United States by randomly sampling balls from pro shops around the country. Two dozen of each kind are sampled, and if more than three do not meet size and/or velocity requirements, that kind of ball is removed from the USGA's approved-ball list.

a. What assumptions must be made and what information must be known in order to use the binomial probability distribution to calculate the probability that the USGA will remove a particular kind of golf ball from its approved-ball list?

b. Suppose 10% of all balls produced by a particular manufacturer are less than 1.680 inches in diameter, and assume that the number of such balls, x, in a sample of two dozen balls can be adequately characterized by a binomial probability distribution. Find the mean and standard deviation of the binomial distribution.

c. Refer to part **b**. If x has a binomial distribution, then so does the number, y, of balls in the sample that meet the USGA's minimum diameter. [*Note:* $x + y = 24$.] Describe the distribution of y. In particular, what are p, q, and n? Also, find $E(y)$ and the standard deviation of y.

4.68 Premature aging gene. Ataxia-telangiectasia (A-T) is a neurological disorder that weakens immune systems and causes premature aging. According to *Science News* (June 24, 1995), when both members of a couple carry the A-T gene, their children have a one in five chance of developing the disease.

a. Consider 15 couples in which both members of each couple carry the A-T gene. What is the probability that more than 8 of 15 couples have children that develop the neurological disorder?

b. Consider 10,000 couples in which both members of each couple carry the A-T gene. Is it likely that fewer than 3,000 will have children that develop the disease? [*Hint:* Calculate the mean and standard deviation of the distribution.]

4.5 The Poisson Random Variable (Optional)

A type of probability distribution that is often useful in describing the number of events that will occur in a specific period of time or in a specific area or volume is the **Poisson distribution** (named after the 18th-century physicist and mathematician, Siméon Poisson). Typical examples of random variables for which the Poisson probability distribution provides a good model are

1. The number of traffic accidents per month at a busy intersection
2. The number of noticeable surface defects (scratches, dents, etc.) found by quality inspectors on a new automobile
3. The parts per million of some toxin found in the water or air emission from a manufacturing plant
4. The number of diseased trees per acre of a certain woodland
5. The number of death claims received per day by an insurance company
6. The number of unscheduled admissions per day to a hospital

Characteristics of a Poisson Random Variable

1. The experiment consists of counting the number of times a certain event occurs during a given unit of time or in a given area or volume (or weight, distance, or any other unit of measurement).
2. The probability that an event occurs in a given unit of time, area, or volume is the same for all the units.
3. The number of events that occur in one unit of time, area, or volume is independent of the number that occur in other units.
4. The mean (or expected) number of events in each unit is denoted by the Greek letter lambda, λ.

The characteristics of the Poisson random variable are usually difficult to verify for practical examples. The examples given satisfy them well enough that the Poisson distribution provides a good model in many instances.* As with all probability models,

---

*The Poisson probability distribution also provides a good approximation to a binomial probability distribution with mean $\lambda = np$ when n is large and p is small (say, $np \leq 7$).

the real test of the adequacy of the Poisson model is in whether it provides a reasonable approximation to reality—that is, whether empirical data support it.

The probability distribution, mean, and variance for a Poisson random variable are shown in the next box.

Probability Distribution, Mean, and Variance for a Poisson Random Variable

$$p(x) = \frac{\lambda^x e^{-\lambda}}{x!} \qquad (x = 0, 1, 2, \dots)$$

$$\mu = \lambda \qquad \sigma^2 = \lambda$$

where

λ = Mean number of events during given unit of time, area, volume, etc.

Biography

SIMEON D. POISSON (1781–1840)—A Lifetime Mathematician

Growing up in France during the French Revolution, Simeon-Denis Poisson was sent away by his father to become an apprentice surgeon, but he lacked the manual dexterity to perform delicate procedures required and returned home. He eventually enrolled in École Polytechnique University to study mathematics. In his final year of study, Poisson wrote a paper on the theory of equations that was of such quality that he was allowed to graduate without taking the final examination. Two years later, Poisson was named a professor at the university. During his illustrious career, Poisson published between 300 and 400 mathematics papers. He is most known for his 1837 paper where the distribution of a rare event—the Poisson distribution—first appears. (In fact, the distribution was actually described years earlier by one of the Bernoulli brothers.) Poisson dedicated his life to mathematics, once stating that "Life is good for only two things: to study mathematics and to teach it."

The calculation of Poisson probabilities is made easier by the use of Table III in Appendix A, which gives the cumulative probabilities $P(x \leq k)$ for various values of λ. The use of Table III is illustrated in Example 4.13.

EXAMPLE 4.13   FINDING POISSON PROBABILITIES

Problem   Ecologists often use the number of reported sightings of a rare species of animal to estimate the remaining population size. For example, suppose the number, x, of reported sightings per week of blue whales is recorded. Assume that x has (approximately) a Poisson probability distribution. Furthermore, assume that the average number of weekly sightings is 2.6.

a. Find the mean and standard deviation of x, the number of blue whale sightings per week. Interpret the results.

b. Use Table III to find the probability that fewer than two sightings are made during a given week.

c. Use Table III to find the probability that more than five sightings are made during a given week.

d. Use Table III to find the probability that exactly five sightings are made during a given week.

Solution   **a.** The mean and variance of a Poisson random variable are both equal to λ. Thus, for this example,

$$\mu = \lambda = 2.6$$
$$\sigma^2 = \lambda = 2.6$$

Then the standard deviation of x is

$$\sigma = \sqrt{2.6} = 1.61$$

Remember that the mean measures the central tendency of the distribution and does not necessarily equal a possible value of x. In this example, the mean is 2.6 sightings, and although there cannot be 2.6 sightings during a given week, the average number of weekly sightings is 2.6. Similarly, the standard deviation of 1.61 measures the variability of the number of sightings per week. Perhaps a more helpful measure is the interval $\mu \pm 2\sigma$, which in this case stretches from $-.62$ to 5.82. We expect the number of sightings to fall in this interval most of the time—with at least 75% relative frequency (according to Chebyshev's Rule) and probably with more than 90% relative frequency (the Empirical Rule). The mean and the 2-standard-deviation interval around it are shown in Figure 4.10.

b. A partial reproduction of Table III is shown in Table 4.5. The rows of the table correspond to different values of λ, and the columns correspond to different values k of the Poisson random variable x. The entries in the table (like the binomial probabilities in Table II) give the cumulative probability $P(x \le k)$. To find the probability that fewer than two sightings are made during a given week, we first note that

$$P(x < 2) = P(x \le 1)$$

This probability is a cumulative probability and therefore is the entry in Table III in the row corresponding to $\lambda = 2.6$ and the column corresponding to $k = 1$. The entry is .267, shown highlighted in Table 4.5. This probability corresponds to the highlighted area in Figure 4.10 and may be interpreted as meaning that there is a 26.7% chance that fewer than two sightings will be made during a given week.

c. To find the probability that more than five sightings are made during a given week, we consider the complementary event

$$P(x > 5) = 1 - P(x \le 5) = 1 - .951 = .049$$

where .951 is the entry in Table III corresponding to $\lambda = 2.6$ and $k = 5$ (see Table 4.5). Note from Figure 4.10 that this is the area in the interval $\mu \pm 2\sigma$, or $-.62$ to 5.82. Then the number of sightings should exceed 5—or, equivalently, should be more than 2 standard deviations from the mean—during only about 4.9% of all weeks. Note that this percentage agrees remarkably well with that given by the Empirical Rule for mound-shaped distributions, which tells us to

Figure 4.10

Probability Distribution for Number of Blue Whale Sightings

TABLE 4.5   Reproduction of Part of Table III in Appendix A

λ \ k	0	1	2	3	4	5	6	7	8	9
2.2	.111	.355	.623	.819	.928	.975	.993	.998	1.000	1.000
2.4	.091	.308	.570	.779	.904	.964	.988	.997	.999	1.000
2.6	.074	.267	.518	.736	.877	.951	.983	.995	.999	1.000
2.8	.061	.231	.469	.692	.848	.935	.976	.992	.998	.999
3.0	.050	.199	.423	.647	.815	.916	.966	.988	.996	.999
3.2	.041	.171	.380	.603	.781	.895	.955	.983	.994	.998
3.4	.033	.147	.340	.558	.744	.871	.942	.977	.992	.997
3.6	.027	.126	.303	.515	.706	.844	.927	.969	.988	.996
3.8	.022	.107	.269	.473	.668	.816	.909	.960	.984	.994
4.0	.018	.092	.238	.433	.629	.785	.889	.949	.979	.992
4.2	.015	.078	.210	.395	.590	.753	.867	.936	.972	.989
4.4	.012	.066	.185	.359	.551	.720	.844	.921	.964	.985
4.6	.010	.056	.163	.326	.513	.686	.818	.905	.955	.980
4.8	.008	.048	.143	.294	.476	.651	.791	.887	.944	.975
5.0	.007	.040	.125	.265	.440	.616	.762	.867	.932	.968
5.2	.006	.034	.109	.238	.406	.581	.732	.845	.918	.960
5.4	.005	.029	.095	.213	.373	.546	.702	.822	.903	.951
5.6	.004	.024	.082	.191	.342	.512	.670	.797	.886	.941
5.8	.003	.021	.072	.170	.313	.478	.638	.771	.867	.929
6.0	.002	.017	.062	.151	.285	.446	.606	.744	.847	.916

expect approximately 5% of the measurements (values of the random variable) to lie farther than 2 standard deviations from the mean.

d. To use Table III to find the probability that *exactly* five sightings are made during a given week, we must write the probability as the difference between two cumulative probabilities:

$$P(x = 5) = P(x \le 5) - P(x \le 4) = .951 - .877 = .074$$

Now Work   *Exercise 4.75*

■ ■ ■

Note that the probabilities in Table III are all rounded to three decimal places. Thus, although in theory a Poisson random variable can assume infinitely large values, the values of k in Table III are extended only until the cumulative probability is 1.000. This does not mean that x *cannot* assume larger values, but only that the likelihood is less than .001 (in fact, less than .0005) that it will do so.

Finally, you may need to calculate Poisson probabilities for values of λ not found in Table III. You may be able to obtain an adequate approximation by interpolation, but if not, consult more extensive tables for the Poisson distribution.

Poisson Probabilities

Using the TI-83 Graphing Calculator

I. $P(x = k)$

To compute $P(x = k)$, the probability of exactly k successes in a specified interval where λ is the mean number of successes in the interval, use the poissonpdf(command. Poissonpdf stands for "Poisson probability density function." This command is under the DISTRibution menu and has the format poissonpdf( ).

Example   Suppose that the number, x, of reported sightings per week of blue whales is recorded. Assume that x has approximately a Poisson probability distribution, and that the average number of weekly sightings is 2.6.
Compute the probability that exactly five sightings are made during a given week. In this example, $\lambda = 2.6$ and $k = 5$.

Step 1   Enter the poisson parameters
Press 2nd VARS for DISTR
Press the down arrow key until B:poissonpdf is highlighted
Press ENTER
After poissonpdf(, type 2.6, 5) (Note: be sure to use the comma key between each parameter.)
Press ENTER

You should see

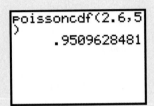

Thus, the $P(x = 5)$ is about 7.4%.

II. $P(x \leq k)$

To compute the probability of k or fewer successes in a specified interval, where λ is the mean number of successes in the interval, use the poissoncdf(command. Poissoncdf stands for "Poisson *cumulative* probability density function." This command is under the DISTRibution menu and has the format poissoncdf).

Example   In the example given above, compute the probability that five or fewer sightings are made during a given week. In this example, $\lambda = 2.6$ and $k = 5$.

Step 1   Enter the poisson parameters
Press 2nd VARS for DISTR
Press the down arrow key until C:poissoncdf is highlighted
Press ENTER
After poissoncdf(, type 2.6, 5)
Press ENTER

You should see

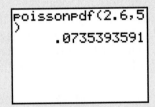

Thus, the $P(x \leq 5)$ is about 95.1%.

III. $P(x < k)$, $P(x > k)$, $P(x \geq k)$

To find the probability of less than k successes, more than k successes, or at least k successes variations of poissoncdf(command must be used as shown below.

$P(x < k)$ use **poissoncdf($\lambda, k - 1$)**
$P(x > k)$ use **1 − poissoncdf(λ, k)**
$P(x \geq k)$ use **1 − poissoncdf($\lambda, k - 1$)**

Exercises 4.69–4.87

Understanding the Principles

4.69 Give the four characteristics of a Poisson random variable.

4.70 Consider a Poisson random variable with probability distribution

$$p(x) = \frac{10^x e^{-10}}{x!} \qquad (x = 0, 1, 2, \dots)$$

What is the value of λ?

4.71 Consider the Poisson probability distribution shown here:

$$p(x) = \frac{3^x e^{-3}}{x!} \qquad (x = 0, 1, 2, \dots)$$

What is the value of λ?

Learning the Mechanics

4.72 Refer to Exercise 4.70.
  a. Graph the probability distribution.
  b. Find the mean and standard deviation of x.

4.73 Refer to Exercise 4.71.
  a. Graph the probability distribution.
  b. Find the mean and standard deviation of x.

4.74 Given that x is a random variable for which a Poisson probability distribution provides a good approximation, use Table III to compute the following:
  a. $P(x \le 2)$ when $\lambda = 1$
  b. $P(x \le 2)$ when $\lambda = 2$
  c. $P(x \le 2)$ when $\lambda = 3$
  d. What happens to the probability of the event $\{x \le 2\}$ as λ increases from 1 to 3? Is this intuitively reasonable?

4.75 Assume that x is a random variable having a Poisson **NW** probability distribution with a mean of 1.5. Use Table III to find the following probabilities:
  a. $P(x \le 3)$ **b.** $P(x \ge 3)$
  c. $P(x = 3)$ **d.** $P(x = 0)$
  e. $P(x > 0)$ **f.** $P(x > 6)$

4.76 Suppose x is a random variable for which a Poisson probability distribution with $\lambda = 1$ provides a good characterization.
  a. Graph $p(x)$ for $x = 0, 1, 2, \dots, 9$.
  b. Find μ and σ for x, and locate μ and the interval $\mu \pm 2\sigma$ on the graph.
  c. What is the probability that x will fall within the interval $\mu \pm 2\sigma$?

4.77 Suppose x is a random variable for which a Poisson probability distribution with $\lambda = 3$ provides a good characterization.
  a. Graph $p(x)$ for $x = 0, 1, 2, \dots, 9$.
  b. Find μ and σ for x, and locate μ and the interval $\mu \pm 2\sigma$ on the graph.
  c. What is the probability that x will fall within the interval $\mu \pm 2\sigma$?

4.78 As mentioned in Section 4.5, when n is large, p is small, and $np \le 7$, the Poisson probability distribution provides a good approximation to the binomial probability distribution. Since we provide exact binomial probabilities (Table II in Appendix A) for relatively small values of n, you can investigate the adequacy of the approximation for $n = 25$. Use Table II to find $p(0)$, $p(1)$, and $p(2)$ for $n = 25$ and $p = .05$. Calculate the corresponding Poisson approximations using $\lambda = \mu = np$. [*Note:* These approximations are reasonably good for n as small as 25, but to use the approximation in a practical situation we would prefer to have $n \ge 100$.]

Applying the Concepts—Basic

4.79 Eye fixation experiment. Cognitive scientists at the University of Massachusetts designed an experiment to measure x, the number of times a reader's eye fixated on a single word before moving past that word. (*Memory and Cognition*, Sept. 1997.) For this experiment, x was found to have a mean of 1. Suppose one of the readers in the experiment is randomly selected and assume that x has a Poisson distribution.
  a. Find $P(x = 0)$.
  b. Find $P(x > 1)$.
  c. Find $P(x \le 2)$.

4.80 Rare planet transits. The "Venus transit" describes a rare celestial event where the planet Venus appears to cross in front of the Sun as seen from Earth. The last "Venus transit" occurred more than a century ago, in 1882. (National Aeronautics and Space Administration, 2004.) When a planet crosses in front of a star, there is a noticeable dip in the star's brightness. These brightness dips allow NASA scientists to detect the presence of a planet even if the planet itself is not directly visible. In October 2007 NASA will launch its Kepler mission, measuring the brightness of 100,000 stars every 15 minutes in hopes of detecting extrasolar planet transits. The mission is expected to detect 5.6 extrasolar planets for every 10,000 stars. If the number of extrasolar planet transits for 10,000 stars follows a Poisson distribution with $\lambda = 5.6$, what is the probability that more than 10 transits will be seen?

4.81 Airline fatalities. U.S. airlines average about 3.8 fatalities per month. (*Statistical Abstract of the United States: 2000.*) Assume the probability distribution for x, the number of fatalities per month, can be approximated by a Poisson probability distribution.
  a. What is the probability that no fatalities will occur during any given month?
  b. What is the probability that one fatality will occur during any given month?
  c. Find $E(x)$ and the standard deviation of x.

4.82 Deep-draft vessel casualties. Economists at the University of New Mexico modeled the number of casualties (deaths or missing persons) experienced by a deep-draft U.S. flag vessel over a three-year period as a Poisson random variable, x. The researchers estimated $E(x)$ to be .03. (*Management Science*, Jan. 1999.)

a. Find the variance of x.

b. Discuss the conditions that would make the researchers' Poisson assumption plausible.

c. What is the probability that a deep-draft U.S. flag vessel will have no casualties in a three-year time period?

Applying the Concepts—Intermediate

4.83 Vinyl chloride emissions. The Environmental Protection Agency (EPA) limits the amount of vinyl chloride in plant air emissions to no more than 10 parts per million. Suppose the mean emission of vinyl chloride for a particular plant is 4 parts per million. Assume that the number of parts per million of vinyl chloride in air samples, x, follows a Poisson probability distribution.

a. What is the standard deviation of x for the plant?

b. Is it likely that a sample of air from the plant would yield a value of x that would exceed the EPA limit? Explain.

c. Discuss conditions that would make the Poisson assumption plausible.

4.84 Davey Crockett's use of words. Davey Crockett, a U.S. congressman during the 1830s, published *A Narrative of the Life of Davey Crockett, Written by Himself*. In a *Chance* (Spring 1999) article, researchers determined that x, the number of times (per 1,000 words) that the word *though* appears in the *Life* narrative, has a mean of .25. Assume that x has an approximate Poisson distribution.

a. Find the variance of x.

b. Calculate the interval $\mu \pm 2\sigma$. What proportion of the time will x fall in this interval?

c. In 1836, Davey Crockett died at the Alamo defending Texans from an attack by the Mexican general, Santa Anna. The following year, the narrative *Colonel Crockett's Exploits and Adventures in Texas* was published. Some historians have doubts whether Crockett was the actual author of this narrative. In the *Texas* narrative, "though" appears twice in the first 1,000 words. Use this information and your answer to part **b** to make an inference about whether Crockett actually wrote the *Texas* narrative. (Assume the *Life* narrative was really written by Davey Crockett.)

4.85 Customer arrivals at a bakery. As part of a project targeted at improving the services of a local bakery, a management consultant (L. Lei of Rutgers University) monitored customer arrivals for several Saturdays and Sundays. Using the arrival data, she estimated the average number of customer arrivals per 10-minute period on Saturdays to be 6.2. She assumed that arrivals per 10-minute interval followed the Poisson distribution shown at the bottom of the page, some of whose values are missing.

a. Compute the missing probabilities.

b. Graph the distribution.

c. Find μ and σ and show the intervals $\mu \pm \sigma$, $\mu \pm 2\sigma$, and $\mu \pm 3\sigma$ on your graph of part **b**.

d. The owner of the bakery claims that more than 75 customers per hour enter the store on Saturdays. Based on the consultant's data, is this likely? Explain.

4.86 Crime Watch neighborhood. In many cities, neighborhood Crime Watch groups are formed in an attempt to reduce the amount of criminal activity. Suppose one neighborhood that has experienced an average of 10 crimes per year organizes such a group. During the first year following the creation of the group, three crimes are committed in the neighborhood.

a. Use the Poisson distribution to calculate the probability that three or fewer crimes are committed in a year assuming the average number is still 10 crimes per year.

b. Do you think this event provides some evidence that the Crime Watch group has been effective in this neighborhood?

Applying the Concepts—Advanced

4.87 Waiting for a car wash. A certain automatic car wash takes exactly 5 minutes to wash a car. On the average, 10 cars per hour arrive at the car wash. Suppose that, 30 minutes before closing time, five cars are in line. If the car wash is in continuous use until closing time, is it likely anyone will be in line at closing time?

Table for Exercise 4.85

x	0	1	2	3	4	5	6	7	8	9	10	11	12	13
$p(x)$	.002	.013	—	.081	.125	.155	—	.142	.110	.076	—	.026	.014	.007

Source: Lei, L. *Dorsi's Bakery: Modeling Service Operations.* Graduate School of Management, Rutgers University, 1993.

4.6 The Hypergeometric Random Variable (Optional)

The **hypergeometric probability distribution** provides a realistic model for some types of enumerative (countable) data. The characteristics of the hypergeometric distribution are listed in the box.

Characteristics of a Hypergeometric Random Variable

1. The experiment consists of randomly drawing n elements without replacement from a set of N elements, r of which are S's (for Success) and $(N - r)$ of which are F's (for Failure).

2. The hypergeometric random variable x is the number of S's in the draw of n elements.

Note that both the hypergeometric and binomial characteristics stipulate that each draw, or trial, results in one of two outcomes. The basic difference between these random variables is that the hypergeometric trials are dependent, while the binomial trials are independent. The draws are dependent because the probability of drawing an S (or an F) is dependent on what occurred on preceding draws.

To illustrate the dependence between trials, we note that the probability of drawing an S on the first draw is r/N. Then the probability of drawing an S on the second draw depends on the outcome of the first. It will be either $(r - 1)/(N - 1)$, or $r/(N - 1)$, depending on whether the first draw was an S or an F. Consequently, the results of the draws represent dependent events.

For example, suppose we define x as the number of women hired in a random selection of three applicants from a total of six men and four women. This random variable satisfies the characteristics of a hypergeometric random variable with $N = 10$ and $n = 3$. The possible outcomes on each trial are either selection of a female (S) or selection of a male (F). Another example of a hypergeometric random variable is the number, x, of defective large-screen television picture tubes in a random selection of $n = 4$ from a shipment of $N = 8$ tubes. And, as a third example, suppose $n = 5$ stocks are randomly selected from a list of $N = 15$ stocks. Then, the number x of the five selected companies that pay regular dividends to stockholders is a hypergeometric random variable.

The hypergeometric probability distribution is summarized in the box.

Probability Distribution, Mean, and Variance of the Hypergeometric Random Variable

$$p(x) = \frac{\binom{r}{x}\binom{N - r}{n - x}}{\binom{N}{n}} \qquad [x = \text{Maximum } [0, n - (N - r)], \dots, \text{Minimum}(r, n)]$$

$$\mu = \frac{nr}{N} \qquad \sigma^2 = \frac{r(N - r)n(N - n)}{N^2(N - 1)}$$

where

$N = $ Total number of elements
$r = $ Number of S's in the N elements
$n = $ Number of elements drawn
$x = $ Number of S's drawn in the n elements

EXAMPLE 4.14   APPLYING THE HYPERGEOMETRIC DISTRIBUTION

Problem   Suppose a professor randomly selects three new teaching assistants from a total of 10 applicants, six male and four female students. Let x be the number of females who are hired.

  a. Find the mean and standard deviation of x.

  b. Find the probability that no females are hired.

Solution **a.** Since x is a hypergeometric random variable with $N = 10$, $n = 3$, and $r = 4$, the mean and variance are

$$\mu = \frac{nr}{N} = \frac{(3)(4)}{10} = 1.2$$

$$\sigma^2 = \frac{r(N - r)n(N - n)}{N^2(N - 1)} = \frac{4(10 - 4)3(10 - 3)}{(10)^2(10 - 1)}$$

$$= \frac{(4)(6)(3)(7)}{(100)(9)} = .56$$

The standard deviation is

$$\sigma = \sqrt{.56} = .75$$

b. The probability that no female students are hired by the professor, assuming the selection is truly random, is

$$P(x = 0) = p(0) = \frac{\binom{4}{0}\binom{10 - 4}{3 - 0}}{\binom{10}{3}}$$

$$= \frac{\dfrac{4!}{0!(4 - 0)!}\dfrac{6!}{3!(6 - 3)!}}{\dfrac{10!}{3!(10 - 3)!}} = \frac{(1)(20)}{120} = \frac{1}{6}$$

p(x)

Figure 4.11
Probability Distribution for x in Example 4.14

Look Back The entire probability distribution for x is shown in Figure 4.11. The mean $\mu = 1.2$ and the interval $\mu \pm 2\sigma = (-.3, 2.7)$ are indicated. You can see that if this random variable were to be observed over and over again a large number of times, most of the values of x would fall within the interval $\mu \pm 2\sigma$.

Now Work *Exercise 4.103*

■ ■ ■

Statistics in Action Revisited

Using the Hypergeometric Model to Solve the Cocaine Sting Case

The reverse cocaine sting case described on p. 189 and solved in Section 4.3 can also be solved by applying the hypergeometric distribution. In fact, the probabilities obtained using the hypergeometric distribuion are *exact* probabilities, as compared to the approximate probabilities obtained using the binomial distribution.

Our objective, you will recall, is to find the probability that four packets (randomly selected from 496 packets confiscated in a drug bust) will contain cocaine and two packets (randomly selected from the remaining 492) will not contain cocaine. We assumed that of the 496 original packets, 331 contained genuine cocaine and 165 contained an inert (legal) powder. Since we are sampling *without replacement* from the 496 packets, the probability of a "Success" (i.e., the probability of a packet containing cocaine) does not remain *exactly* the same from trial to trial. For example, for the first randomly selected packet, the probability of a "Success" is

$331/496 = .66734$. If we find that the first three packets selected contain cocaine, the probability of "Success" for the fourth packet selected is now $328/493 = .66531$. You can see that these probabilities are not exactly the same. Hence, the binomial distribution will only approximate the distribution of x, the number of packets that contain cocaine is a sample of size n.

To find the probability that four packets randomly selected from the original 496 will test positive for cocaine using the hypergeometric distribution, we first identify the parameters of the distribution:

$N = 496$ is the total number of packets in the population
$S = 331$ is the number of "successes" (cocaine packets) in the population
$n = 4$ is the sample size
$x = 4$ is the number of "successes" (cocaine packets) in the sample

Substituting into the formula for $p(x)$ (page 225), we obtain

$$P(x = 4) = p(4) = \frac{\binom{331}{4}\binom{165}{0}}{\binom{496}{4}} = \frac{\left(\frac{331!}{4!327!}\right)\left(\frac{165!}{0!165!}\right)}{\left(\frac{496!}{4!492!}\right)}$$

$$= .197$$

To find the probability that two packets randomly selected from the remaining 492 will test negative for cocaine *assuming that the first four packets tested positive*, we identify the parameters of the relevant hypergeometric distribution:

$N = 492$ is the total number of packets in the population

$S = 327$ is the number of "successes" (cocaine packets) in the population

$n = 2$ is the sample size

$x = 0$ is the number of "successes" (cocaine packets) in the sample

Again, we substitute into the formula for $p(x)$ (page 225) to obtain

$$P(x = 0) = p(0) = \frac{\binom{327}{0}\binom{165}{2}}{\binom{492}{2}} = \frac{\left(\frac{327!}{0!327!}\right)\left(\frac{165!}{2!163!}\right)}{\left(\frac{492!}{2!490!}\right)}$$

$$= .112$$

Using the Multiplicative Law of Probability, the probability that the first four packets test positive for cocaine and the next two packets test negative is the product of the two probabilities just given:

$$P(\text{first 4 positive and next 2 negative}) = (.112)(.197)$$
$$= .0221$$

Note that this exact probability is almost identical to the approximate probability computed using the binomial distribution in Section 4.3.

Exercises 4.88–4.105

Understanding the Principles

4.88 Give the characteristics of a hypergeometric distribution.

4.89 How do binomial and hypergeometric random variables differ? In what respects are they similar?

4.90 Explain the difference between sampling with replacement and sampling without replacement.

Learning the mechanics

4.91 Given that x is a hypergeometric random variable, compute $p(x)$ for each of the following cases:
a. $N = 5, n = 3, r = 3, x = 1$
b. $N = 9, n = 5, r = 3, x = 3$
c. $N = 4, n = 2, r = 2, x = 2$
d. $N = 4, n = 2, r = 2, x = 0$

4.92 Given that x is a hypergeometric random variable with $N = 8, n = 3$, and $r = 5$, compute the following:
a. $P(x = 1)$ **b.** $P(x = 0)$
c. $P(x = 3)$ **d.** $P(x \geq 4)$

4.93 Given that x is a hypergeometric random variable with $N = 12, n = 8$, and $r = 6$:
a. Display the probability distribution for x in tabular form.
b. Compute μ and σ for x.
c. Graph $p(x)$ and locate μ and the interval $\mu \pm 2\sigma$ on the graph.
d. What is the probability that x will fall within the interval $\mu \pm 2\sigma$?

4.94 Given that x is a hypergeometric random variable with $N = 10, n = 5$, and $r = 7$:
a. Display the probability distribution for x in tabular form.
b. Compute the mean and variance of x.
c. Graph $p(x)$ and locate μ and the interval $\mu \pm 2\sigma$ on the graph.

d. What is the probability that x will fall within the interval $\mu \pm 2\sigma$?

4.95 Suppose you plan to sample 10 items from a population of 100 items and would like to determine the probability of observing four defective items in the sample. Which probability distribution should you use to compute this probability under the following conditions? Justify your answers.
a. The sample is drawn without replacement.
b. The sample is drawn with replacement.

4.96 Use the results of Exercise 4.93 to find the following probabilities:
a. $P(x = 1)$ **b.** $P(x = 4)$
c. $P(x \leq 4)$ **d.** $P(x \geq 5)$
e. $P(x < 3)$ **f.** $P(x \geq 8)$

Applying the Concepts—Basic

4.97 On-site disposal of hazardous waste. The Resource Conservation and Recovery Act mandates the tracking and disposal of hazardous waste produced at U.S. facilities. *Professional Geographer* (Feb. 2000) reported the hazardous waste generation and disposal characteristics of 209 facilities. Only eight of these facilities treated hazardous waste on-site.
a. In a random sample of 10 of the 209 facilities, what is the expected number in the sample that treat hazardous waste on-site? Interpret this result.
b. Find the probability that four of the eight selected facilities treat hazardous waste on-site.

4.98 Male nannies. According to *USA Today* (Sept. 19, 2000), there are 650 members of the International Nanny Association (INA). Of these, only three are men. In Exercise 3.18 (p. 131), you found the probability that a randomly selected member of the INA is a man. Now find the probability that in a random sample of four INA members, at least one is a man.

4.99 Contaminated gun cartridges. Refer to the investigation of contaminated gun cartridges at a weapons manufacturer, Exercise 4.20 (p. 196). In a sample of 158 cartridges from a certain lot, 36 were found to be contaminated, and 122 were "clean." If you randomly select 5 of these 158 cartridges, what is the probability that all 5 will be "clean"?

4.100 Lot inspection sampling. Imagine you are purchasing small lots of a manufactured product. If it is very costly to test a single item, it may be desirable to test a sample of items from the lot instead of testing every item in the lot. Suppose each lot contains 10 items. You decide to sample four items per lot and reject the lot if you observe one or more defectives.
  a. If the lot contains one defective item, what is the probability that you will accept the lot?
  b. What is the probability that you will accept the lot if it contains two defective items?

Applying the Concepts—Intermediate

4.101 Extinct New Zealand birds. Refer to the *Evolutionary Ecology Research* (July 2003) study of the patterns of extinction in the New Zealand bird population, Exercise 3.79 (p. 157). Of the 132 bird species saved in the **NZBIRDS** file, 38 are extinct. Suppose you randomly select 10 of the 132 bird species (without replacement) and record the extinct status of each.
  a. What is the probability that exactly five of the 10 species you select are extinct?
  b. What is the probability that at most one species is extinct?

4.102 Birds in butterfly hotspots. "Hotspots" are species-rich geographical areas. A *Nature* (Sept. 1993) study estimated the probability of a bird species in Great Britain inhabiting a butterfly hotspot at .70. Consider a random sample of four British bird species selected from a total of 10 tagged species. Assume that seven of the 10 tagged species inhabit a butterfly hotspot.
  a. What is the probability that exactly half of the four bird species sampled inhabit a butterfly hotspot?
  b. What is the probability that at least one of the four bird species sampled inhabit a butterfly hotspot?

4.103 Testing for spoiled wine. Suppose you are purchasing cases of wine (twelve bottles per case) and that, periodically, you select a test case to determine the adequacy of the bottles' seals. To do this, you randomly select and test three bottles in the case. If a case contains one spoiled bottle of wine, what is the probability that this bottle will turn up in your sample?

Applying the Concepts—Advanced

4.104 Gender discrimination suit. The *Journal of Business & Economic Statistics* (July 2000) presented a case in which a charge of gender discrimination was filed against the U.S. Postal Service. At the time, there were 302 U.S. Postal Service employees (229 men and 73 women) who applied for promotion. Of the 72 employees who were awarded promotion, 5 were female. Make an inference about whether or not females at the U.S. Postal Service were promoted fairly.

4.105 Awarding of home improvement grants. A curious event was described in the *Minneapolis Star and Tribune*. The Minneapolis Community Development Agency (MCDA) makes home improvement grants each year to homeowners in depressed city neighborhoods. Of the $708,000 granted one year, $233,000 was awarded by the city council using a "random selection" of 140 homeowners' applications from among a total of 743 applications: 601 from the north side and 142 from the south side of Minneapolis. Oddly, all 140 grants awarded were from the north side—clearly a highly improbable outcome, if, in fact, the 140 winners were randomly selected from among the 743 applicants.
  a. Suppose the 140 winning applications were randomly selected from among the total of 743, and let x equal the number in the sample from the north side. Find the mean and standard deviation of x.
  b. Use the results of part **a** to support a contention that the grant winners were not randomly selected.

Quick Review

Key Terms

Note: Starred (*) terms are from the optional sections in this chapter.

Binomial distribution   208
Binomial experiment   204
Binomial random variable   205
Continuous random variable   191
Countable   191

Cumulative binomial probabilities   211
Discrete random variable   191
Expected value   198
*Hypergeometric probability distribution   225
*Hypergeometric random variable   225
Mean of a discrete random variable   198

*Poisson distribution   219
*Poisson random variable   218
Probability distribution   194
Random variable   189
Standard deviation of a discrete random variable   200
Variance of a discrete random variable   200

Key Formulas

Note: Starred (*) formulas are from the optional sections in this chapter.

Probability Distribution	Mean (μ)	Variance (σ^2)	
$p(x)$	$\sum_{\text{all } x} xp(x)$	$\sum_{\text{all } x}(x-\mu)^2 p(x)$	General discrete random variable 198, 200
$\binom{n}{x}p^x q^{n-x}$	np	npq	Binomial random variable 208, 210
$\dfrac{\lambda^x e^{-\lambda}}{x!}$	λ	λ	Poisson random variable* 219
$\dfrac{\binom{r}{x}\binom{N-r}{n-x}}{\binom{N}{n}}$	$\dfrac{nr}{N}$	$\dfrac{r(N-r)n(N-n)}{N^2(N-1)}$	Hypergeometric random variable* 225

Language Lab

Symbol	Pronunciation	Description
$p(x)$		Probability distribution of the random variable x
S		The outcome of a binomial trial denoted a "success"
F		The outcome of a binomial trial denoted a "failure"
p		The probability of success (S) in a binomial trial
q		The probability of failure (F) in a binomial trial, where $q = 1 - p$
λ	lambda	The mean (or expected) number of events for a Poisson random variable
e		A constant used in the Poisson probability distribution, where $e = 2.71828\ldots$

Chapter Summary Notes

- Two types of random variables: **discrete** and **continuous**
- Requirements for a discrete probability distribution: $p(x) \geq 0$ and $\Sigma p(x) = 1$
- Probability models discrete random variables: **binomial, Poisson,** and **hypergeometric**
- Characteristics of a **binomial random variable**: (1) n identical trials; (2) two possible outcomes, S and F, per trial; (3) $P(S)$ and $P(F)$ remain the same from trial to trial; (4) trials are independent; (5) x = number of S's in n trials

- Characteristics of a **Poisson random variable**: (1) x = number of times a rare event, S, occurs in a unit of time, area, or volume; (2) $P(S)$ remains the same for all units; (3) value of x in one unit is independent of value in another unit
- Characteristics of a **hypergeometric random variable**: (1) Draw n elements without replacement from a set of N elements, r of which have outcome S and $(N-r)$ of which have outcome F; (2) x = number of S's in n trials

Supplementary Exercises 4.106–4.133

Note: Starred (*) exercises refer to the optional sections in this chapter.

Understanding the Principles

4.106 Which of the following describe discrete random variables, and which describe continuous random variables?

a. The length of time that an exercise physiologist's program takes to elevate her client's heart rate to 140 beats per minute

b. The number of crimes committed on a college campus per year

c. The number of square feet of vacant office space in a large city

d. The number of voters who favor a new tax proposal

4.107 Identify the type of random variable—binomial, Poisson, or hypergeometric—described by each of the following probability distributions:

*a. $p(x) = \dfrac{.5^x e^{-.5}}{x!}$ $(x = 0, 1, 2, \dots)$

b. $p(x) = \dbinom{6}{x}(.2)^x (.8)^{6-x}$ $(x = 0, 1, 2, \dots, 6)$

c. $p(x) = \dfrac{10!}{x!(10-x)!}(.9)^x (.1)^{10-x}$
$(x = 0, 1, 2, \dots, 10)$

4.108 For each of the following examples, decide whether x is a binomial random variable and explain your decision:

a. A manufacturer of computer chips randomly selects 100 chips from each hour's production in order to estimate the proportion defectives. Let x represent the number of defectives in the 100 sampled chips.

b. Of five applicants for a job, two will be selected. Although all applicants appear to be equally qualified, only three have the ability to fulfill the expectations of the company. Suppose that the two selections are made at random from the five applicants, and let x be the number of qualified applicants selected.

c. A software developer establishes a support hotline for customers to call in with questions regarding use of the software. Let x represent the number of calls received on the support hotline during a specified workday.

d. Florida is one of a minority of states with no state income tax. A poll of 1,000 registered voters is conducted to determine how many would favor a state income tax in light of the state's current fiscal condition. Let x be the number in the sample who would favor the tax.

Learning the Mechanics

4.109 Suppose x is a binomial random variable with $n = 20$ and $p = .7$.
a. Find $P(x = 14)$.
b. Find $P(x \leq 12)$.
c. Find $P(x > 12)$.
d. Find $P(9 \leq x \leq 18)$.
e. Find $P(8 < x < 18)$.
f. Find μ, σ^2, and σ.
g. What is the probability that x is in the interval $\mu \pm 2\sigma$?

*4.110** Given that x is a hypergeometric random variable, compute $p(x)$ for each of the following cases:
a. $N = 8, n = 5, r = 3, x = 2$
b. $N = 6, n = 2, r = 2, x = 2$
c. $N = 5, n = 4, r = 4, x = 3$

4.111 Suppose x is a binomial random variable. Find $p(x)$ for each of the following combinations of x, n, and p.

a. $x = 1, n = 3, p = .1$
b. $x = 4, n = 20, p = .3$
c. $x = 0, n = 2, p = .4$
d. $x = 4, n = 5, p = .5$
e. $n = 15, x = 12, p = .9$
f. $n = 10, x = 8, p = .6$

4.112 Consider the discrete probability distribution shown here.

x	10	12	18	20
$p(x)$	.2	.3	.1	.4

a. Calculate μ, σ^2, and σ.
b. What is $P(x < 15)$?
c. Calculate $\mu \pm 2\sigma$.
d. What is the probability that x is in the interval $\mu \pm 2\sigma$?

*4.113** Suppose x is a Poisson random variable. Compute $p(x)$ for each of the following cases:
a. $\lambda = 2, x = 3$
b. $\lambda = 1, x = 4$
c. $\lambda = .5, x = 2$

Applying the Concepts—Basic

4.114 Use of laughing gas. According to the American Dental Association, 60% of all dentists use nitrous oxide ("laughing gas") in their practice. (*New York Times*, June 20, 1995.) If x equals the number of dentists in a random sample of five dentists who use laughing gas in practice, then the probability distribution of x is

x	0	1	2	3	4	5
$p(x)$	.0102	.0768	.2304	.3456	.2592	.0778

a. Find the probability that the number of dentists using laughing gas in the sample of five is less than 2.
b. Find $E(x)$ and interpret the result.
c. Show that the distribution of x is binomial with $n = 5$ and $p = .6$.

4.115 Accuracy of checkout scanners. A Federal Trade Commission (FTC) study of the pricing accuracy of electronic checkout scanners at stores found that one of every 30 items is priced incorrectly. (*Price Check II: A Follow-Up Report on the Accuracy of Checkout Scanner Prices*, Dec. 16, 1998.) Suppose the FTC randomly selects five items at a retail store and checks the accuracy of the scanner price of each. Let x represent the number of the five items that is priced incorrectly.
a. Show that x is (approximately) a binomial random variable.
b. Use the information in the FTC study to estimate p for the binomial experiment.
c. What is the probability that exactly one of the five items is priced incorrectly by the scanner?
d. What is the probability that at least one of the five items is priced incorrectly by the scanner?

4.116 Expected patient cost. A patient complaining of severe stomach pains checked into a local hospital. After a series of tests the doctors narrowed their diagnosis to four possible ailments. They believe there is a 40% chance that the patient has hepatitis; a 10% chance that she has cirrhosis; a 45% chance of gallstones; and a 5% chance of cancer of the pancreas. The doctors are certain that the patient has only one of the diseases, but will not know which disease until further tests are performed. The cost associated with treating each disease is given in the table:

Disease	Hepatitis	Cirrhosis	Gallstones	Pancreatic Cancer
Cost	$700	$1,100	$3,320	$16,450

a. Construct the probability distribution for the cost of treating the patient.

b. Calculate the mean of the probability distribution you constructed in part **a**. What does this number represent?

c. Further testing reveals that the patient has either hepatitis or cirrhosis. Given this information, construct the new probability distribution for the cost of treating the patient.

d. Calculate the mean of the probability distribution you constructed in part **c**. What does this number represent?

4.117 Married women study. According to *Ladies Home Journal* (June 1988), 80% of married women would marry their current husbands again, if given the chance. Consider the number x in a random sample of ten married women who would marry their husbands again. Identify the discrete probability distribution that best models the distribution of x. Explain.

*4.118 Emergency rescue vehicle use. An emergency rescue vehicle is used an average of 1.3 times daily. Use the Poisson distribution to find

a. The probability that the vehicle will be used exactly twice tomorrow

b. The probability that it will be used more than twice

c. The probability that it will be used exactly three times

4.119 New book reviews. In Exercise 2.171 (p. 108) you read about a study of book reviews in American history, geography, and area studies published in *Choice* magazine. (*Library Acquisitions: Practice and Theory*, Vol. 19, 1995.) The overall rating stated in each review was ascertained and recorded as follows: 1 = would not recommend, 2 = cautious or very little recommendation, 3 = little or no preference, 4 = favorable/recommended, 5 = outstanding/significant contribution. Based on a sample of 375 book reviews, the probability distribution of rating, x, follows.

a. Is this a valid probability distribution?

b. What is the probability that a book reviewed in *Choice* has a rating of 1?

c. What is the probability that a book reviewed in *Choice* has a rating of at least 4?

Book Rating x	$p(x)$
1	.051
2	.099
3	.093
4	.635
5	.122

d. What is the probability that a book reviewed in *Choice* has a rating of 2 or 3?

e. Find $E(x)$.

f. Interpret the result, part **e**.

*4.120 Dutch elm disease. A nursery advertises that it has 10 elm trees for sale. Unknown to the nursery, three of the trees have already been infected with Dutch elm disease and will die within a year.

a. If a buyer purchases two trees, what is the probability that both trees will be healthy?

b. Refer to part **a**. What is the probability that at least one of the trees is infected?

Applying the Concepts—Intermediate

4.121 Pesticides on food samples. The Food and Drug Administration (FDA) produces a quarterly report called *Total Diet Study*. The FDA's report covers more than 200 food items, each of which is analyzed for dangerous chemical compounds. One *Total Diet Study* reported that no pesticides at all were found on 65% of the domestically produced food samples. (*Consumer's Research*, June 1995.) Consider a random sample of 800 food items analyzed for the presence of pesticides.

a. Compute μ and σ for the random variable x, the number of food items found without any trace of pesticide.

b. Based on a sample of 800 food items, is it likely you would observe less than half without any traces of pesticide? Explain.

4.122 Factors identifying urban counties. Refer to the *Professional Geographer* (Feb. 2000) study of urban and rural counties, Exercise 3.157 (p. 181). Forty-five percent of county commissioners in Nevada feel that "population concentration" is the single most important factor in identifying urban counties. Suppose 10 county commissioners are selected at random to serve on a Nevada review board that will consider redefining urban and rural areas. What is the probability that more than half of the commissioners will specify "population concentration" as the single most important factor in identifying urban counties?

4.123 Parents behavior at a gym meet. *Pediatric Exercise Science* (Feb. 1995) published an article on the behavior of parents at competitive youth gymnastic meets. Based on a survey of the gymnasts, the researchers estimated the probability of a parent "yelling" at their child before, during, or after the meet as .05. In a random sample of 20 parents attending a gymnastic meet, find the probability that at least one parent yells at their child before, during, or after the meet.

*4.124 Accepting or rejecting a shipment of CDs. By mistake, a manufacturer of CD mini-rack systems includes three defective systems in a shipment of 10 going out to a small retailer. The retailer has decided to accept the shipment of CD systems only if none is found to be defective. Upon receipt of the shipment, the retailer examines only five of the CD systems.

   a. What is the probability that the shipment will be rejected?

   b. If the retailer inspects six of the CD systems, what is the probability the shipment will be accepted?

4.125 Smoking and nasal allergies. The *American Journal of Public Health* (July 1995) published a study of the relationship between passive smoking and nasal allergies in Japanese female students. The study revealed that 80% of students from heavy-smoking families showed signs of nasal allergies on physical examinations. Consider a sample of 25 Japanese female students exposed daily to heavy smoking.

   a. What is the probability that fewer than 20 of the students will have nasal allergies?

   b. What is the probability that more than 15 of the students will have nasal allergies?

   c. On average, how many of the 25 students would you expect to show signs of nasal allergies?

*4.126 Scottish cornrakes. The cornrake is a European species of bird in danger of worldwide extinction. A census revealed that 12 cornrakes inhabit mainland Scotland. (*Journal of Applied Ecology*, 1993.) Suppose that two of these Scottish cornrakes are captured for mating purposes. Let x be the number of these captured cornrakes that are capable of mating. If exactly four of the original 12 cornrakes inhabiting Scotland are infertile and hence unable to mate, find the probability distribution for x.

4.127 Efficacy of an insecticide. The efficacy of insecticides is often measured by the dose necessary to kill a certain percentage of insects. Suppose a certain dose of a new insecticide is supposed to kill 80% of the insects that receive it. To test the claim, 25 insects are exposed to the insecticide.

   a. If the insecticide really kills 80% of the exposed insects, what is the probability that fewer than 15 die?

   b. If you observed such a result, what would you conclude about the new insecticide? Explain your logic.

*4.128 Arrivals at a bank counter. The number x of people who arrive at a cashier's counter in a bank during a specified period of time often exhibits (approximately) a Poisson probability distribution. If we know the mean arrival rate λ, the Poisson probability distribution can be used to aid in the design of the customer service facility. Suppose you estimate that the mean number of arrivals per minute for cashier service at a bank is one person per minute.

   a. What is the probability that in a given minute the number of arrivals will equal three or more?

   b. Can you tell the bank manager that the number of arrivals will rarely exceed two per minute?

4.129 Construction company profit analysis. The owner of construction company A makes bids on jobs so that if awarded the job, company A will make a $10,000 profit. The owner of construction company B makes bids on jobs so that if awarded the job, company B will make a $15,000 profit. Each company describes the probability distribution of the number of jobs x the company is awarded per year as shown in the table.

Company A		Company B	
x	$P(x)$	x	$P(x)$
2	.05	2	.15
3	.15	3	.30
4	.20	4	.30
5	.35	5	.20
6	.25	6	.05

   a. Find the expected number of jobs each will be awarded in a year.

   b. What is the expected profit for each company?

   c. Find the variance and standard deviation of the distribution of number of jobs awarded per year for each company.

   d. Graph $p(x)$ for both companies A and B. For each company, what proportion of the time will x fall in the interval $\mu \pm 2\sigma$?

Applying the Concepts—Advanced

4.130 How many questionnaires to mail? The probability that a person responds to a mailed questionnaire is .4. How many questionnaires should be mailed if you want to be reasonably certain that at least 100 will be returned?

4.131 Reliability of a space vehicle. For a space vehicle to gain reentry into the earth's atmosphere, a particular system must work properly. One component of the system operates successfully only 85% of the time. To increase the reliability of the system, four of these components are installed in such a way that the system will operate successfully if at least one component is working. What is the probability that the system will fail? Assume the components operate independently.

*4.132 Emergency room bed availability. The mean number of patients admitted per day to the emergency room of a small hospital is 2.5. If, on a given day, there are only four beds available for new patients, what is the probability the hospital will not have enough beds to accommodate its newly admitted patients?

Critical Thinking Challenge

*4.133 **Space shuttle disaster.** On January 28, 1986, the space shuttle *Challenger* exploded, killing all seven astronauts aboard. An investigation concluded that the explosion was caused by the failure of the O-ring seal in the joint between the two lower segments of the right solid rocket booster. In a report made one year prior to the catastrophe, the National Aeronautics and Space Administration (NASA) claimed that the probability of such a failure was about $1/60,000$, or about once in every 60,000 flights. But a risk-assessment study conducted for the Air Force at about the same time assessed the probability to be $1/35$, or about once in every 35 missions. *Note*: The shuttle had flown 24 successful missions prior to the disaster. Given the events of January 28, 1986, which risk assessment—NASA's or the Air Force's—appears to be more appropriate?

Student Projects

Consider the following random variables:

1. The number x of people who recover from a certain disease out of a sample of five patients

2. The number x of voters in a sample of five who favor a method of tax reform

3. The number x of hits a baseball player gets in five official times at bat

In each case, x is a binomial random variable (or approximately so) with $n = 5$ trials. Assume that in each case the probability of Success is .3. (What is a Success in each of the examples?) If this were true, the probability distribution for x would be the same for each of the three examples. To obtain a relative frequency histogram for x, conduct the following experiment: Place 10 poker chips (pennies, marbles, or any 10 *identical* items) in a bowl and mark three of the 10 Success—the remaining seven will represent Failure. Randomly select a chip from the 10, observing whether it was a Success or Failure. Then return the chip and randomly select a second chip from the 10 available chips, and record this outcome. Repeat this process until a total of five trials has been conducted. Count the number x of Successes observed in the five trials. Repeat the entire process 100 times to obtain 100 observed values of x.

a. Use the 100 values of x obtained from the simulation to construct a relative frequency histogram for x. Note that this histogram is an approximation to $p(x)$.

b. Calculate the exact values of $p(x)$ for $n = 5$ and $p = .3$, and compare these values with the approximations found in part **a**.

c. If you were to repeat the simulation an extremely large number of times (say 100,000), how do you think the relative frequency histogram and true probability distribution would compare?

REFERENCES

Hogg, R. V., and Craig, A. *Introduction to Mathematical Statistics*, 5th ed. Upper Saddle River, N.J.: Prentice Hall, 1995.

Mendenhall, W. *Introduction to Mathematical Statistics*, 8th ed. Boston: Duxbury, 1991.

Parzen, E. *Modern Probability Theory and Its Applications*. New York: Wiley, 1960.

Wackerly, D., Mendenhall, W., and Scheaffer, R.L. *Mathematical Statistics with Applications*, 6th ed. North Scituate, Mass.: Duxbury, 2002.

Using Technology

Binomial, Poisson, and Hypergeometric Probabilities Using MINITAB

To obtain probabilities for the discrete random variables discussed in this chapter using MINITAB, first enter the values of x that you desire probabilities for in a column (e.g., C1) on the MINITAB worksheet. Now click on the "Calc" button on the MINITAB menu bar, next click on "Probability Distributions," then finally click on the distribution of your choice (e.g., "Binomial"), as shown in Figure 4.M.1. The resulting dialog box appears as shown in Figure 4.M.2. Select either "Probabilities" or "Cumulative probabilities," specify the parameters of the distribution (e.g., sample size n and probability of success p), and enter C1 in the "Input column." When you click "OK" the binomial probabilities for the values of x (saved in C1) will appear on the MINITAB worksheet.

[*Note*: For the MINITAB Poisson option, you will need to enter the value of the mean λ in the resulting dialog box. For the hypergeometric option, you will need to enter the values of N, r, and n, in that order, in the resulting dialog box.]

Figure 4.M.1
MINITAB Menu Options for Obtaining Probabilities

Figure 4.M.2
MINITAB Binomial
Distribution Dialog Box

5

Continuous Random Variables

Contents

5.1 Continuous Probability Distributions

5.2 The Uniform Distribution

5.3 The Normal Distribution

5.4 Descriptive Methods for Assessing Normality

5.5 Approximating a Binomial Distribution with a Normal Distribution (Optional)

5.6 The Exponential Distribution (Optional)

Statistics in Action

Super Weapons Development—
Optimizing the Hit Ratio

Using Technology

Cumulative Probabilities for
Continuous Random Variables
and Normal Probability Plots
Using MINITAB

Where We've Been

- Learned how to find probabilities of discrete events using the probability rules of Chapter 3

- Discussed probability models (distributions) for discrete random variables in Chapter 4

Where We're Going

- Develop the notion of a probability distribution for a continuous random variable.

- Study several important types of continuous random variables and their probability models.

- Introduce the normal probability distribution as one of the most useful distributions in statistics.

Statistics
in *ACTION*

Super Weapons Development—
Optimizing the Hit Ratio

The U.S. Army is working with a major defense contractor to develop a "super" weapon. The weapon is designed to fire a large number of sharp tungsten bullets—called flechettes—with a single shot that will destroy a large number of enemy soldiers. Flechettes are about the size of an average nail, with small fins at one end to stabilize them in flight. Since World War I, when France dropped them in large quantities from aircraft on masses of ground troops, munitions experts have experimented with using flechettes in a variety of guns. The problem with using flechettes as ammunition is accuracy—current weapons that fire large quantities of flechettes have unsatisfactory hit ratios when fired at long distances.

The defense contractor (not named here for both confidentiality and security reasons) has developed a prototype gun that fires 1,100 flechettes with a single round. In range tests, three 2-feet-wide targets were set up a distance of 500 meters (approximately 1,500 feet) from the weapon. Using a number line as a reference, the centers of the three targets were at 0, 5, and 10 feet, respectively, as shown in Figure SIA5.1. The prototype gun was aimed at the middle target

(center at 5 feet) and fired once. The point where each of the 1,100 flechettes landed at the 500-meter distance was measured using a horizontal and vertical grid. For the purposes of this application, only the horizontal measurements are considered. These 1,100 measurements are saved in the **MOAGUN** file. (The data are simulated for confidentiality reasons.) For example, a flechette with a value of $x = 5.5$ hit the middle target, but a flechette with a value of $x = 2.0$ did not hit any of the three targets (see Figure SIA5.1).

The defense contractor is interested in the likelihood of any one of the targets being hit by a flechette and, in particular, wants to set the gun specifications to maximize the number of target hits. The weapon is designed to have a mean horizontal value equal to the aim point (e.g., $\mu = 5$ feet when aimed at the center target). By changing specifications, the contractor can vary the standard deviation, σ. The **MOAGUN** file contains flechette measurements for three different range tests—one with a standard deviation of $\sigma = 1$ foot, one with $\sigma = 2$ feet, and one with $\sigma = 4$ feet.

In this chapter, two Statistics in Action Revisited examples demonstrate how we can use one of the probability models discussed in this chapter—the normal probability distribution—to aid the defense contractor in developing its "super" weapon.

Statistics in the Action Revisited

- Using the Normal Model to Maximize the Probability of a Hit with the Super Weapon (p. 256)
- Assessing whether the Normal Distribution is Appropriate for Modeling the Super Weapon Hit Data (p. 265)

Targets: 2 feet wide

Figure SIA5.1
Target placement on gun range

In this chapter we'll consider some continuous random variables that are commonly encountered. Recall that a continuous random variable is one that can assume any value within some interval or intervals. For example, the length of time between a person's visits to a doctor, the thickness of sheets of steel produced in a rolling mill, and the yield of wheat per acre of farmland are all continuous random variables. The methodology we employ to describe continuous random variables will necessarily be somewhat different from that used to describe discrete random variables. We first discuss the general form of **continuous probability distributions**, and then we explore three specific types that are used in making statistical decisions. The normal probability distribution, which plays a basic and important role in both the theory and application of statistics, is essential to the study of most of the subsequent chapters in this book. The other types have practical applications, but a study of these topics is optional.

5.1 Continuous Probability Distributions

The graphical form of the probability distribution for a continuous random variable x is a smooth curve that might appear as shown in Figure 5.1. This curve, a function of x, is denoted by the symbol $f(x)$ and is variously called a **probability density function**, a **frequency function**, or a **probability distribution**.

The areas under a probability distribution correspond to probabilities for x. For example, the area A beneath the curve between the two points a and b, as shown in Figure 5.1, is the probability that x assumes a value between a and $b (a < x < b)$. Because there is no area over a point, say $x = a$, it follows that (according to our model) the probability associated with a particular value of x is equal to 0; that is, $P(x = a) = 0$ and hence $P(a < x < b) = P(a \leq x \leq b)$. In other words, the probability is the same regardless of whether or not you include the endpoints of the interval. Also, because areas over intervals represent probabilities, it follows that the total area under a probability distribution, the probability assigned to all values of x, should equal 1. Note that probability distributions for continuous random variables possess different shapes depending on the relative frequency distributions of real data that the probability distributions are supposed to model.

Figure 5.1
A Probability Distribution $f(x)$ for a Continuous Random Variable x

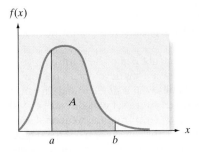

The areas under most probability distributions are obtained by using calculus or numerical methods.* Because these methods often involve difficult procedures, we will give the areas for some of the most common probability distributions in tabular form in Appendix A. Then, to find the area between two values of x, say $x = a$ and $x = b$, you simply have to consult the appropriate table.

For each of the continuous random variables presented in this chapter, we will give the formula for the probability distribution along with its mean μ and standard deviation σ. These two numbers will enable you to make some approximate probability statements about a random variable even when you do not have access to a table of areas under the probability distribution.

5.2 The Uniform Distribution

All the probability problems discussed in Chapter 3 had sample spaces that contained a finite number of sample points. In many of these problems, the sample points were assigned equal probabilities—for example, the die toss or the coin toss. For continuous random variables, there is an infinite number of values in the sample space, but in some cases the values may appear to be equally likely. For example, if a short exists in a 5-meter stretch of electrical wire, it may have an equal probability of being in any particular 1-centimeter segment along the line.

---

*Students with knowledge of calculus should note that the probability that x assumes a value in the interval $a < x < b$ is $P(a < x < b) = \int_a^b f(x)\, dx$, assuming the integral exists. Similar to the requirements for a discrete probability distribution, we require $f(x) \geq 0$ and $\int_{-\infty}^{\infty} f(x)\, dx = 1$.

Figure 5.2

The Uniform Probability Distribution

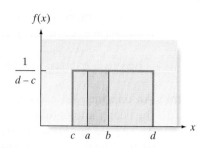

Or if a safety inspector plans to choose a time at random during the four afternoon work hours to pay a surprise visit to a certain area of a plant, then each 1-minute time interval in this 4-work-hour period will have an equally likely chance of being selected for the visit.

Continuous random variables that appear to have *equally likely outcomes over their range of possible values* possess a **uniform probability distribution**, perhaps the simplest of all continuous probability distributions. Suppose the random variable x can assume values only in an interval $c \leq x \leq d$. Then the uniform frequency function has a rectangular shape, as shown in Figure 5.2. Note that the possible values of x consist of all points in the interval between point c and point d. The height of $f(x)$ is constant in that interval and equals $1/(d - c)$. Therefore, the total area under $f(x)$ is given by

$$\text{Total area of rectangle} = (\text{Base})(\text{Height}) = (d - c)\left(\frac{1}{d - c}\right) = 1$$

The uniform probability distribution provides a model for continuous random variables that are *evenly distributed* over a certain interval. That is, a uniform random variable is one that is just as likely to assume a value in one interval as it is to assume a value in any other interval of equal size. There is no clustering of values around any value; instead, there is an even spread over the entire region of possible values.

The uniform distribution is sometimes referred to as the **randomness distribution**, since one way of generating a uniform random variable is to perform an experiment in which a point is *randomly selected* on the horizontal axis between the points c and d. If we were to repeat this experiment infinitely often, we would create a uniform probability distribution like that shown in Figure 5.2. The random selection of points in an interval can also be used to generate random numbers such as those in Table I of Appendix A. Recall that random numbers are selected in such a way that every number would have an equal probability of selection. Therefore, random numbers are realizations of a uniform random variable. (Random numbers were used to draw random samples in Section 3.7.) The formulas for the uniform probability distribution, its mean, and its standard deviation are shown in the box.

> ## Probability Distribution for a Uniform Random Variable x
>
> Probability density function: $f(x) = \dfrac{1}{d - c}$ $(c \leq x \leq d)$
>
> Mean: $\mu = \dfrac{c + d}{2}$ Standard deviation: $\sigma = \dfrac{d - c}{\sqrt{12}}$
>
> $P(a < x < b) = (b - a)/(d - c), c \leq a < b \leq d$

Suppose the interval $a < x < b$ lies within the domain of x; that is, it falls within the larger interval $c \leq x \leq d$. Then the probability that x assumes a value within the interval $a < x < b$ is equal to the area of the rectangle over the interval, namely, $(b - a)/(d - c)$.* (See the shaded area in Figure 5.2.)

EXAMPLE 5.1

APPLYING THE UNIFORM DISTRIBUTION

Problem   An unprincipled used car dealer sells a car to an unsuspecting buyer, even though the dealer knows that the car will have a major breakdown within the next 6 months. The dealer provides a warranty of 45 days on all cars sold. Let x represent the length of time until the breakdown occurs. Assume that x is a uniform random variable with values between 0 and 6 months.

a. Calculate and interpret the mean and standard deviation of x.

b. Graph the probability distribution of x, and show the mean on the horizontal axis. Also show 1- and 2-standard-deviation intervals around the mean.

c. Calculate the probability that the breakdown occurs while the car is still under warranty.

Solution   **a.** To calculate the mean and standard deviation for x, we substitute 0 and 6 months for c and d, respectively, in the formulas for uniform random variables. Thus,

$$\mu = \frac{c + d}{2} = \frac{0 + 6}{2} = 3 \text{ months}$$

$$\sigma = \frac{d - c}{\sqrt{12}} = \frac{6 - 0}{\sqrt{12}} = \frac{6}{3.464} = 1.73 \text{ months}$$

Our interpretations of μ and σ follow:

The average length of time until breakdown, x, for all similar used cars is $\mu = 3$ months. From Chebyshev's Theorem (Table 2.7, p. 74), we know that at least 75% of the values of x in the distribution will fall in the interval

$$\mu \pm 2\sigma = 3 \pm 2(1.73)$$
$$= 3 \pm 3.46$$

or, between $-.46$ and 6.46 months. Consequently, we expect the length of time until breakdown to be less than 6.46 months at least 75% of the time.

b. The uniform probability distribution is

$$f(x) = \frac{1}{d - c} = \frac{1}{6 - 0} = \frac{1}{6} \quad (0 \le x \le 6)$$

The graph of this function is shown in Figure 5.3. The mean and 1- and 2-standard-deviation intervals around the mean are shown on the horizontal

Figure 5.3
Distribution for x in
Example 5.1

*The student with knowledge of calculus should note that

$$P(a < x < b) = \int_a^b f(x)\, d(x) = \int_a^b [1/(d - c)]\, dx = (b - a)/(d - c)$$

Figure 5.4
Probability that Car
Breaks Down Within
1.5 Months of Purchase

axis. Note that the entire distribution of x lies within the $\mu \pm 2\sigma$ interval. (This demonstrates, once again, the conservativeness of Chebyshev's Theorem.)

c. To find the probability that the car is still under warranty when it breaks down, we must find the probability that x is less than 45 days, or (about) 1.5 months. As indicated in Figure 5.4, we need to calculate the area under the frequency function $f(x)$ between the points $x = 0$ and $x = 1.5$. Therefore, in this case $a = 0$ and $b = 1.5$. Applying the formula in the box, we have

$$P(x < 1.5) = (1.5 - 0)/(6 - 0) = 1.5/6 = .25$$

That is, there is a 25% chance that the car will break down while under warranty.

Look Back The calculated probability in part **c** is the area of a rectangle with base $1.5 - 0 = 1.5$ and height $= 1/6$. Alternatively, the probability that the unsuspecting car buyer will be able to have the car repaired at the dealer's expense is $P(0 < x < 1.5) = (\text{Base})(\text{Height}) = (1.5)(1/6) = .25$.

> Now Work *Exercise 5.6*

■ ■ ■

Exercises 5.1–5.16

Understanding the Principles

5.1 Give a characteristic of a uniform random variable.

5.2 The uniform distribution is sometimes referred to as the _____ distribution. (Fill in the blank.)

Learning the Mechanics

5.3 Suppose x is a random variable best described by a uniform probability distribution with $c = 10$ and $d = 30$.
  a. Find $f(x)$.
  b. Find the mean and standard deviation of x.
  c. Graph $f(x)$ and locate μ and the interval $\mu \pm 2\sigma$ on the graph. Note that the probability that x assumes a value within the interval $\mu \pm 2\sigma$ is equal to 1.

5.4 Refer to Exercise 5.3. Find the following probabilities:
  a. $P(10 \le x \le 25)$ **b.** $P(20 < x < 30)$
  c. $P(x \ge 25)$ **d.** $P(x \le 10)$
  e. $P(x \le 25)$ **f.** $P(20.5 \le x \le 25.5)$

5.5 Suppose x is a random variable best described by a uniform probability distribution with $c = 2$ and $d = 4$.
  a. Find $f(x)$.
  b. Find the mean and standard deviation of x.
  c. Find $P(\mu - \sigma \le x \le \mu + \sigma)$.
  d. Find $P(x > 2.78)$.

  e. Find $P(2.4 \le x \le 3.7)$.
  f. Find $P(x < 2)$.

5.6 Refer to Exercise 5.5. Find the value of a that makes
  NW each of the following probability statements true.
  a. $P(x \ge a) = .5$
  b. $P(x \le a) = .2$
  c. $P(x \le a) = 0$
  d. $P(2.5 \le x \le a) = .5$

5.7 The random variable x is best described by a uniform probability distribution with $c = 100$ and $d = 200$. Find the probability that x assumes a value
  a. More than 2 standard deviations from μ
  b. Less than 3 standard deviations from μ
  c. Within 2 standard deviations of μ

5.8 The random variable x is best described by a uniform probability distribution with mean 50 and standard deviation 5. Find c, d, and $f(x)$. Graph the probability distribution.

Applying the Concepts—Basic

5.9 **Maintaining pipe wall temperature.** Maintaining a constant pipe wall temperature in some hot process applications is critical. A new technique that utilizes bolt-on trace elements to maintain temperature was presented in the *Journal of Heat Transfer* (November

2000). Without bolt-on trace elements, the pipe wall temperature of a switch condenser used to produce plastic has a uniform distribution ranging from 260° to 290°F. When several bolt-on trace elements are attached to the piping, the wall temperature is uniform from 278° to 285°F.

a. Ideally, the pipe wall temperature should range between 280° and 284°F. What is the probability that the temperature will fall in this ideal range when no bolt-on trace elements are used? When bolt-on trace elements are attached to the pipe?

b. When the temperature is 268°F or lower, the hot liquid plastic hardens (or plates), causing a buildup in the piping. What is the probability of plastic plating when no bolt-on trace elements are used? When bolt-on trace elements are attached to the pipe?

5.10 Trajectory of an electrical circuit. Researchers at the University of California–Berkeley have designed, built, and tested a switched-capacitor circuit for generating random signals. (*International Journal of Circuit Theory and Applications*, May–June 1990.) The circuit's trajectory was shown to be uniformly distributed on the interval $(0, 1)$.

a. Give the mean and variance of the circuit's trajectory.

b. Compute the probability that the trajectory falls between .2 and .4.

c. Would you expect to observe a trajectory that exceeds .995? Explain.

5.11 Random numbers. The data set listed here was created using the MINITAB random number generator. Construct a relative frequency histogram for the data. Except for the expected variation in relative frequencies among the class intervals, does your histogram suggest that the data are observations on a uniform random variable with $c = 0$ and $d = 100$? Explain.

RANUNI

38.8759	98.0716	64.5788	60.8422	.8413
99.3734	31.8792	32.9847	.7434	93.3017
12.4337	11.7828	87.4506	94.1727	23.0892
47.0121	43.3629	50.7119	88.2612	69.2875
62.6626	55.6267	78.3936	28.6777	71.6829
44.0466	57.8870	71.8318	28.9622	23.0278
35.6438	38.6584	46.7404	11.2159	96.1009
95.3660	21.5478	87.7819	12.0605	75.1015

Applying the Concepts—Intermediate

5.12 Marine losses for an oil company. The frequency distribution shown in the table depicts the property and marine losses incurred by a large oil company over a 2-year period. In the insurance business, each "loss" interval is called a *layer*. *Research Review* (Summer 1998) demonstrated that analysts often treat the actual loss value within a layer as a uniform random variable.

Layer	Marine Losses ($ thousands)	Relative Frequency
1	0–10	.927
2	10–50	.053
3	50–100	.010
4	100–250	.006
5	250–500	.003
6	500–1,000	.001
7	1,000–2,500	.000

Source: Cozzolino, J. M., and Mikola, P. J. "Applications of the piecewise constant Pareto distribution." *Research Review,* Summer 1998.

a. Use the uniform distribution to find the mean loss amount in layer 2.

b. Use the uniform distribution to find the mean loss amount in layer 6.

c. If a loss occurs in layer 2, what is the probability that it exceeds $30,000?

d. If a loss occurs in layer 6, what is the probability that it is between $750,000 and $800,000?

5.13 Soft-drink dispenser. The manager of a local soft-drink bottling company believes that when a new beverage-dispensing machine is set to dispense 7 ounces, it in fact dispenses an amount x at random anywhere between 6.5 and 7.5 ounces inclusive. Suppose x has a uniform probability distribution.

a. Is the amount dispensed by the beverage machine a discrete or a continuous random variable? Explain.

b. Graph the frequency function for x, the amount of beverage the manager believes is dispensed by the new machine when it is set to dispense 7 ounces.

c. Find the mean and standard deviation for the distribution graphed in part **b**, and locate the mean and the interval $\mu \pm 2\sigma$ on the graph.

d. Find $P(x \geq 7)$.

e. Find $P(x < 6)$.

f. Find $P(6.5 \leq x \leq 7.25)$.

g. What is the probability that each of the next six bottles filled by the new machine will contain more than 7.25 ounces of beverage? Assume that the amount of beverage dispensed in one bottle is independent of the amount dispensed in another bottle.

5.14 Time delays at a bus stop. A bus is scheduled to stop at a certain bus stop every half hour on the hour and the half hour. At the end of the day, buses still stop after every 30 minutes, but because delays often occur earlier in the day, the bus is never early and likely to be late. The director of the bus line claims that the length of time a bus is late is uniformly distributed and the maximum time that a bus is late is 20 minutes.

a. If the director's claim is true, what is the expected number of minutes a bus will be late?

b. If the director's claim is true, what is the probability that the last bus on a given day will be more than 19 minutes late?

c. If you arrive at the bus stop at the end of a day at exactly half-past the hour and must wait more than 19 minutes for the bus, what would you conclude about the director's claim? Why?

Applying the Concepts—Advanced

5.15 Gouges on a spindle. A tool-and-die machine shop produces extremely high-tolerance spindles. The spindles are 18-inch slender rods used in a variety of military equipment. A piece of equipment used in the manufacture of the spindles malfunctions on occasion and places a single gouge somewhere on the spindle. However, if the spindle can be cut so that it has 14 consecutive inches without a gouge, then the spindle can be salvaged for other purposes. Assuming that the location of the gouge along the spindle is best described by a uniform distribution, what is the probability that a defective spindle can be salvaged?

5.16 Reliability of a robotic device. The *reliability* of a piece of equipment is frequently defined to be the probability, p, that the equipment performs its intended function successfully for a given period of time under specific conditions. (Render and Heizer, *Principles of Operations Management*, 1995.) Because p varies from one point in time to another, some reliability analysts treat p as if it were a random variable. Suppose an analyst characterizes the uncertainty about the reliability of a particular robotic device used in an automobile assembly line using the following distribution:

$$f(p) = \begin{cases} 1 & 0 \le p \le 1 \\ 0 & \text{otherwise} \end{cases}$$

a. Graph the analyst's probability distribution for p.
b. Find the mean and variance of p.
c. According to the analyst's probability distribution for p, what is the probability that p is greater than .95? Less than .95?
d. Suppose the analyst receives the additional information that p is definitely between .90 and .95, but that there is complete uncertainty about where it lies between these values. Describe the probability distribution the analyst should now use to describe p.

5.3 The Normal Distribution

One of the most commonly observed continuous random variables has a **bell-shaped** probability distribution (or **bell curve**) as shown in Figure 5.5. It is known as a **normal random variable** and its probability distribution is called a **normal distribution**.

The normal distribution plays a very important role in the science of statistical inference. Moreover, many phenomena generate random variables with probability distributions that are very well approximated by a normal distribution. For example, the error made in measuring a person's blood pressure may be a normal random variable, and the probability distribution for the yearly rainfall in a certain region might be approximated by a normal probability distribution. You can determine the adequacy of the normal approximation to an existing population of data by comparing the relative frequency distribution of a large sample of the data to the normal probability distribution. Methods to detect disagreement between a set of data and the assumption of normality are presented in Section 5.4.

Biography

CARL F. GAUSS (1777–1855)— The Gaussian Distribution

The normal distribution began in the eighteenth century as a theoretical distribution for errors in disciplines where fluctuations in nature were believed to behave randomly. Although he may not have been the first to discover the formula, the normal distribution was named the Gaussian distribution after Carl Friedrich Gauss.

A well-known and respected German mathematician, physicist, and astronomer, Gauss applied the normal distribution while studying the motion of planets and stars. Gauss's prowess as a mathematician was exemplified by one of his most important discoveries. At the young age of 22, Gauss constructed a regular 17-gon by ruler and compasses—a feat that was the most major advance in mathematics since the time of the ancient Greeks. In addition to publishing close to 200 scientific papers, Gauss invented the heliograph as well as a primitive telegraph device.

Figure 5.5

A Normal Probability
Distribution

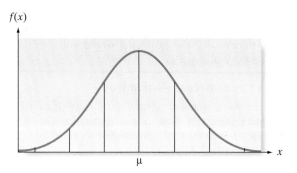

Figure 5.6

Several Normal
Distributions with
Different Means and
Standard Deviations

The normal distribution is perfectly symmetric about its mean μ, as can be seen in the examples in Figure 5.6. Its spread is determined by the value of its standard deviation σ.

The formula for the normal probability distribution is shown in the box. When plotted, this formula yields a curve like that shown in Figure 5.5.

Probability Distribution for a Normal Random Variable x

Probability density function: $f(x) = \dfrac{1}{\sigma\sqrt{2\pi}} e^{-(1/2)[(x-\mu)/\sigma]^2}$

where

μ = Mean of the normal random variable x
σ = Standard deviation
π = 3.1416...
e = 2.71828...

$P(x < a)$ is obtained from a table of normal probabilities.

Note that the mean μ and standard deviation σ appear in this formula, so that no separate formulas for μ and σ are necessary. To graph the normal curve we have to know the numerical values of μ and σ.

Computing the area over intervals under the normal probability distribution is a difficult task.* Consequently, we will use the computed areas listed in Table IV of Appendix A. Although there are an infinitely large number of normal curves—one for each pair of values for μ and σ—we have formed a single table that will apply to any normal curve.

Table IV is based on a normal distribution with mean $\mu = 0$ and standard deviation $\sigma = 1$, called a *standard normal distribution*. A random variable with a standard normal distribution is typically denoted by the symbol z. The formula for the probability distribution of z is given by

---

*The student with knowledge of calculus should note that there is not a closed-form expression for $P(a < x < b) = \int_a^b f(x)\,dx$ for the normal probability distribution. The value of this definite integral can be obtained to any desired degree of accuracy by numerical approximation procedures. For this reason, it is tabulated for the user.

$$f(z) = \frac{1}{\sqrt{2\pi}} e^{-(1/2)z^2}$$

Figure 5.7 shows the graph of a standard normal distribution.

Figure 5.7

Standard Normal
Distribution: $\mu = 0, \sigma = 1$

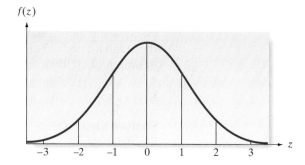

$f(z)$

DEFINITION 5.1

The **standard normal distribution** is a normal distribution with $\mu = 0$ and $\sigma = 1$. A random variable with a standard normal distribution, denoted by the symbol z, is called a **standard normal random variable**.

Since we will ultimately convert all normal random variables to standard normal in order to use Table IV to find probabilities, it is important that you learn to use Table IV well. A partial reproduction of Table IV is shown in Table 5.1. Note that the values of the standard normal random variable z are listed in the left-hand column. The entries in the body of the table give the area (probability) between 0 and z. Examples 5.2–5.5 illustrate the use of the table.

TABLE 5.1   Reproduction of Part of Table IV in Appendix A

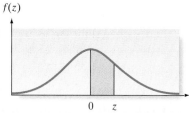

$f(z)$

z	.00	.01	.02	.03	.04	.05	.06	.07	.08	.09
.0	.0000	.0040	.0080	.0120	.0160	.0199	.0239	.0279	.0319	.0359
.1	.0398	.0438	.0478	.0517	.0557	.0596	.0636	.0675	.0714	.0753
.2	.0793	.0832	.0871	.0910	.0948	.0987	.1026	.1064	.1103	.1141
.3	.1179	.1217	.1255	.1293	.1331	.1368	.1406	.1443	.1480	.1517
.4	.1554	.1591	.1628	.1664	.1700	.1736	.1772	.1808	.1844	.1879
.5	.1915	.1950	.1985	.2019	.2054	.2088	.2123	.2157	.2190	.2224
.6	.2257	.2291	.2324	.2357	.2389	.2422	.2454	.2486	.2517	.2549
.7	.2580	.2611	.2642	.2673	.2704	.2734	.2764	.2794	.2823	.2852
.8	.2881	.2910	.2939	.2967	.2995	.3023	.3051	.3078	.3106	.3133
.9	.3159	.3186	.3212	.3238	.3264	.3289	.3315	.3340	.3365	.3389
1.0	.3413	.3438	.3461	.3485	.3508	.3531	.3554	.3577	.3599	.3621
1.1	.3643	.3665	.3686	.3708	.3729	.3749	.3770	.3790	.3810	.3830
1.2	.3849	.3869	.3888	.3907	.3925	.3944	.3962	.3980	.3997	.4015
1.3	.4032	.4049	.4066	.4082	.4099	.4115	.4131	.4147	.4162	.4177
1.4	.4192	.4207	.4222	.4236	.4251	.4265	.4279	.4292	.4306	.4319
1.5	.4332	.4345	.4357	.4370	.4382	.4394	.4406	.4418	.4429	.4441

EXAMPLE 5.2   USING THE STANDARD NORMAL TABLE

Problem   Find the probability that the standard normal random variable z falls between -1.33 and $+1.33$.

Solution   The standard normal distribution is shown again in Figure 5.8. Since all probabilities associated with standard normal random variables can be depicted as areas under the standard normal curve, you should always draw the curve and then equate the desired probability to an area.

Figure 5.8
Areas under the
Standard Normal Curve
for Example 5.2

In this example we want to find the probability that z falls between -1.33 and $+1.33$, which is equivalent to the area between -1.33 and $+1.33$, shown highlighted in Figure 5.8. Table IV provides the area between $z = 0$ and any value of z, so that if we look up $z = 1.33$ (the value in the 1.3 row and .03 column, as shown in Figure 5.9), we find that the area between $z = 0$ and $z = 1.33$ is .4082. This is the area labeled A_1 in Figure 5.8. To find the area A_2 located between $z = 0$ and $z = -1.33$, we note that the symmetry of the normal distribution implies that the area between $z = 0$ and any point to the left is equal to the area between $z = 0$ and the point equidistant to the right. Thus, in this example the area between $z = 0$ and $z = -1.33$ is equal to the area between $z = 0$ and $z = +1.33$. That is,

$$A_1 = A_2 = .4082$$

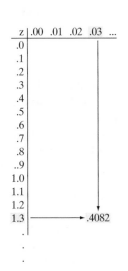

Figure 5.9
Finding $z = 1.33$ in the
Standard Normal Table,
Example 5.2

The probability that z falls between -1.33 and $+1.33$ is the sum of the areas of A_1 and A_2. We summarize in probabilistic notation:

$$P(-1.33 < z < +1.33) = P(-1.33 < z < 0) + P(0 < z \le 1.33)$$
$$= A_1 + A_2 = .4082 + .4082 = .8164$$

Look Back Remember that "$<$" and "$\le$" are equivalent in events involving z, because the inclusion (or exclusion) of a single point does not alter the probability of an event involving a continuous random variable.

| Now Work | *Exercise 5.23ef* |

■ ■ ■

EXAMPLE 5.3   USING THE STANDARD NORMAL TABLE

Problem   Find the probability that a standard normal random variable exceeds 1.64; that is, find $P(z > 1.64)$.

Solution   The area under the standard normal distribution to the right of 1.64 is the highlighted area labeled A_1 in Figure 5.10. This area represents the desired probability that z exceeds 1.64. However, when we look up $z = 1.64$ in Table IV, we must remember that the probability given in the table corresponds to the area between $z = 0$ and

Figure 5.10

Areas under the Standard Normal Curve for Example 5.3

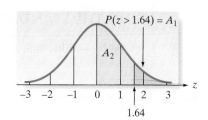

$P(z > 1.64) = A_1$

A_2

$-3 \quad -2 \quad -1 \quad 0 \quad 1 \quad 2 \quad 3$

1.64

$z = 1.64$ (the area labeled A_2 in Figure 5.10). From Table IV we find that $A_2 = .4495$. To find the area A_1 to the right of 1.64, we make use of two facts:

1. The standard normal distribution is symmetric about its mean $z = 0$.

2. The total area under the standard normal probability distribution equals 1.

Taken together, these two facts imply that the areas on either side of the mean $z = 0$ equal .5; thus, the area to the right of $z = 0$ in Figure 5.10 is $A_1 + A_2 = .5$. Then

$$P(z > 1.64) = A_1 = .5 - A_2 = .5 - .4495 = .0505$$

Look Back   To attach some practical significance to this probability, note that the implication is that the chance of a standard normal random variable exceeding 1.64 is only about .05.

Now Work   *Exercise 5.22a*

■ ■ ■

EXAMPLE 5.4

USING THE STANDARD NORMAL TABLE

Problem   Find the probability that a standard normal random variable lies to the left of .67.

Solution   The event is shown as the highlighted area in Figure 5.11. We want to find $P(z < .67)$. We divide the highlighted area into two parts: the area A_1 between $z = 0$ and $z = .67$, and the area A_2 to the left of $z = 0$. We must always make such a division when the desired area lies on both sides of the mean $(z = 0)$ because Table IV contains areas between $z = 0$ and the point you look up. We look up $z = .67$ in Table IV to find that $A_1 = .2486$. The symmetry of the standard normal distribution also implies that half the distribution lies on each side of the mean, so the area A_2 to the left of $z = 0$ is .5. Then

$$P(z < .67) = A_1 + A_2 = .2486 + .5 = .7486$$

Look Back   Note that this probability is approximately .75. Thus, about 75% of the time the standard normal random variable z will fall below .67. This implies that $z = .67$ represents the approximate 75th percentile for the distribution.

Figure 5.11

Areas under the Standard Normal Curve for Example 5.4

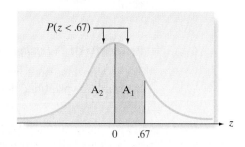

$P(z < .67)$

$A_2 \quad A_1$

$0 \quad .67$

Now Work   *Exercise 5.22h*

■ ■ ■

EXAMPLE 5.5   USING THE STANDARD NORMAL TABLE

Problem   Find the probability that a standard normal random variable exceeds 1.96 in absolute value.

Solution   The event is shown highlighted in Figure 5.12. We want to find

$$P(|z| > 1.96) = P(z < -1.96 \text{ or } z > 1.96)$$

Figure 5.12
Areas under the
Standard Normal Curve
for Example 5.5

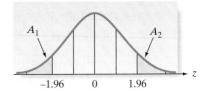

Note that the total highlighted area is the sum of two areas, A_1 and A_2—areas that are equal because of the symmetry of the normal distribution.

We look up $z = 1.96$ and find the area between $z = 0$ and $z = 1.96$ to be .4750. Then the area to the right of 1.96, A_2, is $.5 - .4750 = .0250$ so that

$$P(|z| > 1.96) = A_1 + A_2 = .0250 + .0250 = .05$$

Look Back   We emphasize, again, the importance of sketching the standard normal curve when finding normal probabilities.

■ ■ ■

To apply Table IV to a normal random variable x with any mean μ and any standard deviation σ, we must first convert the value of x to a z-score. The population z-score for a measurement was defined (in Section 2.6) as the *distance* between the measurement and the population mean, divided by the population standard deviation. Thus, the z-score gives the distance between a measurement and the mean in units equal to the standard deviation. In symbolic form, the z-score for the measurement x is

$$z = \frac{x - \mu}{\sigma}$$

Note that when $x = \mu$, we obtain $z = 0$.

An important property of the normal distribution is that if x is normally distributed with any mean and any standard deviation, z is *always* normally distributed with mean 0 and standard deviation 1. That is, z is a standard normal random variable.

Property of Normal Distributions

If x is a normal random variable with mean μ and standard deviation σ, then the random variable z defined by the formula

$$z = \frac{x - \mu}{\sigma}$$

has a standard normal distribution. The value z describes the number of standard deviations between x and μ.

Recall from Example 5.5 that $P(|z| > 1.96) = .05$. This probability coupled with our interpretation of z implies that any normal random variable lies more than 1.96 standard deviations from its mean only 5% of the time. Compare this to the Empirical Rule (Chapter 2), which tells us that about 5% of the measurements in mound-shaped distributions will lie beyond 2 standard deviations from the mean. The normal distribution actually provides the model on which the Empirical Rule is based, along with much "empirical" experience with real data that often approximately obey the rule, whether drawn from a normal distribution or not.

EXAMPLE 5.6

FINDING A NORMAL PROBABILITY

Problem   Assume that the length of time, x, between charges of a cellular phone is normally distributed with a mean of 10 hours and a standard deviation of 1.5 hours. Find the probability that the cell phone will last between 8 and 12 hours between charges.

Solution   The normal distribution with mean $\mu = 10$ and $\sigma = 1.5$ is shown in Figure 5.13. The desired probability that the cell phone lasts between 8 and 12 hours is highlighted. In order to find the probability, we must first convert the distribution to standard normal, which we do by calculating the z-score:

$$z = \frac{x - \mu}{\sigma}$$

The z-scores corresponding to the important values of x are shown beneath the x values on the horizontal axis in Figure 5.13. Note that $z = 0$ corresponds to the mean of $\mu = 10$ hours, whereas the x values 8 and 12 yield z-scores of -1.33 and $+1.33$, respectively. Thus, the event that the cell phone lasts between 8 and 12 hours is equivalent to the event that a standard normal random variable lies between -1.33 and $+1.33$. We found this probability in Example 5.2 (see Figure 5.8) by doubling the area corresponding to $z = 1.33$ in Table IV. That is,

$$P(8 \le x \le 12) = P(-1.33 \le z \le 1.33) = 2(.4082) = .8164$$

Figure 5.13
Areas under the Normal
Curve for Example 5.6

| Now Work | *Exercise 5.28a* |

The steps to follow when calculating a probability corresponding to a normal random variable are shown in the box.

Steps for Finding a Probability Corresponding to a Normal Random Variable

1. Sketch the normal distribution and indicate the mean of the random variable x. Then shade the area corresponding to the probability you want to find.

2. Convert the boundaries of the shaded area from x values to standard normal random variable z values using the formula

$$z = \frac{x - \mu}{\sigma}$$

Show the z values under the corresponding x values on your sketch.

3. Use Table IV in Appendix A to find the areas corresponding to the z values. If necessary, use the symmetry of the normal distribution to find areas corresponding to negative z values and the fact that the total area on each side of the mean equals .5 to convert the areas from Table IV to the probabilities of the event you have shaded.

Standard Normal Probabilities

Using the TI-83 Graphing Calculator

Graphing the Area under the Standard Normal Curve

Step 1 *Turn off all plots.*
Press **2nd PRGM** and select **1:ClrDraw**
Press **ENTER ENTER** and 'Done' will appear on the screen.
Press **2nd Y =** and select **4:PlotsOff**
Press **ENTER ENTER** and 'Done' will appear on the screen.

Step 2 *Set the viewing window. (Recall that almost all of the area under the standard normal curve falls between −5 and 5. A height of 0.5 is a good choice for Y max.)*
Set **Xmin = −5**
Xmax = 5
Xscl = 1
Ymin = 0
Ymax = .5
Yscl = 0
Xres = 1
Note: the negative sign is the gray key, not the blue key

Step 3 *View graph.*
Press **2nd VARS**
Arrow right to **DRAW**
Press **ENTER** to select **1:ShadeNorm(**
Enter your lower limit
Press **comma**
Enter your upper limit
Press) Press **ENTER**
The graph will be displayed along with the area, lower limit, and upper limit.

Example What is the probability that z is less than 1.5 under the Standard Normal curve? In this example, set the Window as shown in Step 2. For the limits in Step 3 use −5 for the lower limit and 1.5 for the upper limit.

The screens for this example are shown below.

Thus, $P(z < 1.5) = .9332$.

EXAMPLE 5.7   USING NORMAL PROBABILITIES TO MAKE AN INFERENCE

Problem   Suppose an automobile manufacturer introduces a new model that has an advertised mean in-city mileage of 27 miles per gallon. Although such advertisements seldom report any measure of variability, suppose you write the manufacturer for the details of the tests, and you find that the standard deviation is 3 miles per gallon. This information leads you to formulate a probability model for the random variable x, the in-city mileage for this car model. You believe that the probability distribution of x can be approximated by a normal distribution with a mean of 27 and a standard deviation of 3.

   a.   If you were to buy this model of automobile, what is the probability that you would purchase one that averages less than 20 miles per gallon for in-city driving? In other words, find $P(x < 20)$.

   b.   Suppose you purchase one of these new models and it does get less than 20 miles per gallon for in-city driving. Should you conclude that your probability model is incorrect?

Solution   **a.**   The probability model proposed for x, the in-city mileage, is shown in Figure 5.14. We are interested in finding the area A to the left of 20 since this area corresponds to the probability that a measurement chosen from this distribution falls below 20. In other words, if this model is correct, the area A represents the fraction of cars that can be expected to get less than 20 miles per gallon for in-city driving. To find A, we first calculate the z value corresponding to $x = 20$. That is,

$$z = \frac{x - \mu}{\sigma} = \frac{20 - 27}{3} = -\frac{7}{3} = -2.33$$

Then

$$P(x < 20) = P(z < -2.33)$$

as indicated by the highlighted area in Figure 5.14. Since Table IV gives only areas to the right of the mean (and because the normal distribution is symmetric about its mean), we look up 2.33 in Table IV and find that the corresponding area is .4901. This is equal to the area between $z = 0$ and $z = -2.33$, so we find

$$P(x < 20) = A = .5 - .4901 = .0099 \approx .01$$

According to this probability model, you should have only about a 1% chance of purchasing a car of this make with an in-city mileage under 20 miles per gallon.

Figure 5.14
Area under the Normal
Curve for Example 5.7

b. Now you are asked to make an inference based on a sample—the car you purchased. You are getting less than 20 miles per gallon for in-city driving. What do you infer? We think you will agree that one of two possibilities is true:

1. The probability model is correct. You simply were unfortunate to have purchased one of the cars in the 1% that get less than 20 miles per gallon in the city.

2. The probability model is incorrect. Perhaps the assumption of a normal distribution is unwarranted, or the mean of 27 is an overestimate, or the standard deviation of 3 is an underestimate, or some combination of these errors was made. At any rate, the form of the actual probability model certainly merits further investigation.

You have no way of knowing with certainty which possibility is correct, but the evidence points to the second one. We are again relying on the rare-event approach to statistical inference that we introduced earlier. The sample (one measurement in this case) was so unlikely to have been drawn from the proposed probability model that it casts serious doubt on the model. We would be inclined to believe that the model is somehow in error.

Look Back When applying the rare-event approach, the calculated probability must be small (say, less than or equal to .05) in order to infer that the observed event is, indeed, unlikely.

Now Work *Exercise 5.40*

■ ■ ■

Nonstandard Normal Probabilities

Using the T1-83 Graphing Calculator

Finding the Area under the Normal Curve

I. Finding the area without a graph

Step 1   *Find area.*
Press 2nd DISTR and select 2:Normalcdf(
Enter the lower limit
Press comma
Enter the upper limit
Press comma
Enter the mean
Press comma
Enter the standard deviation
Press)
Press ENTER
The area will be displayed on the screen.

Example   What is the P(x < 115) for a normal distribution with $\mu = 100$ and $\sigma = 10$?
In this example, the lower limit is $-\infty$, the upper limit is 115, the mean is 100, and the standard deviation is 10.

To represent $-\infty$ on the calculator, enter $(-)$ 1, press 2nd and press the comma key for EE, and then press 99. The screen is shown below.

II. Finding the area with a graph

Step 1   *Turn off all plots.*
Press **2nd PRGM** and select **1:ClrDraw**
Press **ENTER ENTER** and 'Done' will appear on the screen.
Press **2nd Y =** and select **4:PlotsOff**
Press **ENTER ENTER** and 'Done' will appear on the screen.

Step 2   Set the viewing window. (These values depend on the mean and standard deviation of the data.)
Press **WINDOW**
Set **Xmin** $= \mu - 5\sigma$
Xmax $= \mu + 5\sigma$
Xscl $= \sigma$
Ymin $= -.125/\sigma$
Ymax $= .5/\sigma$
Yscl $= 1$
Xres $= 1$
Note: the negative sign is the gray key, not the blue key

Step 3   *View graph.*
Press **2nd VARS**
Arrow right to **DRAW**
Press **ENTER** to select **1:ShadeNorm(**
Enter the lower limit
Press **comma**
Enter the upper limit
Press **comma**
Enter the mean
Press **comma**
Enter the standard deviation
Press **)**
Press **ENTER**
The graph will be displayed along with the area, lower limit, and upper limit.

Example   What is the P$(x < 115)$ for a normal distribution with $\mu = 100$ and $\sigma = 10$?
In this example, the lower limit is $-\infty$, the upper limit is 115, the mean is 100, and the standard deviation is 10.
To represent $-\infty$ on the calculator, enter $(-)$ 1, press 2nd and press the comma key for EE, and then press 99. The screens are shown below.

Thus, the P$(x < 115)$ is .9332.

Occasionally you will be given a probability and will want to find the values of the normal random variable that correspond to the probability. For example, suppose the scores on a college entrance examination are known to be normally distributed, and a certain prestigious university will consider for admission only those applicants whose scores exceed the 90th percentile of the test score distribution. To determine the minimum score for admission consideration, you will need to be able to use Table IV in reverse, as demonstrated in the following example.

EXAMPLE 5.8   USING THE NORMAL TABLE IN REVERSE

Problem Find the value of z, call it z_0, in the standard normal distribution that will be exceeded only 10% of the time. That is, find z_0 such that $P(z \geq z_0) = .10$.

Solution In this case we are given a probability, or an area, and asked to find the value of the standard normal random variable that corresponds to the area. Specifically, we want to find the value z_0 such that only 10% of the standard normal distribution exceeds z_0 (see Figure 5.15).

Figure 5.15
Areas under the Standard
Normal Curve for
Example 5.8

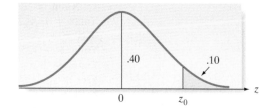

We know that the total area to the right of the mean $z = 0$ is .5, which implies that z_0 must lie to the right of (above) 0. To pinpoint the value, we use the fact that the area to the right of z_0 is .10, which implies that the area between $z = 0$ and z_0 is $.5 - .1 = .4$. But areas between $z = 0$ and some other z value are exactly the types given in Table IV. Therefore, we look up the area .4000 in the body of Table IV and find that the corresponding z value is (to the closest approximation) $z_0 = 1.28$. The implication is that the point 1.28 standard deviations above the mean is the 90th percentile of a normal distribution.

Look Back As with earlier problems, it is critical to correctly draw the normal probability of interest on the normal curve. Placement of z_0 to the left or right of 0 is the key. Be sure to shade the probability (area) involving z_0. If it does not agree with the probability of interest (i.e., the shaded area is greater than .5 and the probability of interest is smaller than .5), then you need to place z_0 on the opposite side of 0.

■ ■ ■

EXAMPLE 5.9   USING THE NORMAL TABLE IN REVERSE

Problem Find the value of z_0 such that 95% of the standard normal z values lie between $-z_0$ and $+z_0$—that is, $P(-z_0 \leq z \leq z_0) = .95$.

Solution Here we wish to move an equal distance z_0 in the positive and negative directions from the mean $z = 0$ until 95% of the standard normal distribution is enclosed. This means that the area on each side of the mean will be equal to $\frac{1}{2}(.95) = .475$, as shown in Figure 5.16. Since the area between $z = 0$ and z_0 is .475, we look up .475 in

Figure 5.16

Areas under the Standard
Normal Curve for
Example 5.9

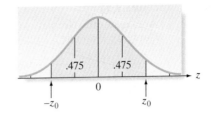

the body of Table IV to find the value $z_0 = 1.96$. Thus, as we found in the reverse
order in Example 5.5, 95% of a normal distribution lies between $+1.96$ and -1.96
standard deviations of the mean.

| Now Work | *Exercise 5.26a* |

■ ■ ■

Now that you have learned to use Table IV to find a standard normal z value
that corresponds to a specified probability, we demonstrate a practical application in
Example 5.10.

EXAMPLE 5.10

APPLICATION OF THE NORMAL TABLE IN REVERSE

Problem   Suppose the scores, x, on a college entrance examination are normally distributed
with a mean of 550 and a standard deviation of 100. A certain prestigious university
will consider for admission only those applicants whose scores exceed the 90th percentile of the distribution. Find the minimum score an applicant must achieve in
order to receive consideration for admission to the university.

Solution   In this example, we want to find a score, x_0, such that 90% of the scores (x values) in
the distribution fall below x_0 and only 10% fall above x_0. That is,

$$P(x \le x_0) = .90$$

Converting x to a standard normal random variable, where $\mu = 550$ and $\sigma = 100$,
we have

$$P(x \le x_0) = P\left(z \le \frac{x_0 - \mu}{\sigma}\right)$$
$$= P\left(z \le \frac{x_0 - 550}{100}\right) = .90$$

In Example 5.8 (see Figure 5.15) we found the 90th percentile of the standard normal
distribution to be $z_0 = 1.28$. That is, we found $P(z \le 1.28) = .90$. Consequently,
we know the minimum test score x_0 corresponds to a z-score of 1.28; that is,

$$\frac{x_0 - 550}{100} = 1.28$$

If we solve this equation for x_0, we find

$$x_0 = 550 + 1.28(100) = 550 + 128 = 678$$

This x-value is shown in Figure 5.17. Thus, the 90th percentile of the test score distribution is 678. An applicant must score at least 678 on the entrance exam to receive
consideration for admission by the university.

Figure 5.17
Area under the Normal
Curve for Example 5.10

550        $x_0 = 678$ x
0          $z_0 = 1.28$ z

Look Back As the example shows, in practical applications of the normal table in reverse, first find the value of z_0, then convert the value to the units of x using the z-score formula in reverse.

Now Work   *Exercise 5.39e*

■ ■ ■

Statistics in Action Revisited

Using the Normal Model to Maximize the Probability of a Hit with the Super Weapon

Recall that a defense contractor has developed a prototype gun for the U.S. Army that fires 1,100 flechettes with a single round. The specifications of the weapon are set so that when the gun is aimed at a target 500 meters away, the mean horizontal grid value of the flechettes is equal to the aim point. In the range test, the weapon was aimed at the center target in Figure SIA5.1; thus, $\mu = 5$ feet. For three different tests, the standard deviation was set at $\sigma = 1$ foot, $\sigma = 2$ feet, and $\sigma = 4$ feet. From past experience, the defense contractor has found that the distribution of the horizontal flechette measurements is closely approximated by a normal distribution. Therefore, we can use the normal distribution to find the probability that a single flechette shot from the weapon will hit any one of the three targets. Recall, from Figure SIA5.1, that the three targets range from -1 to 1, 4 to 6, and 9 to 11 feet on the horizontal grid.

Consider first the middle target. Letting x represent the horizontal measurement for a flechette shot from the gun, the flechette will hit the target if $4 \leq x \leq 6$. The probability that this flechette will hit the target when $\mu = 5$ and $\sigma = 1$ is, using the normal probability table (Table 4, Appendix I),

$$\text{Middle:}\quad P(4 \leq x \leq 6) = P\left(\frac{4-5}{1} < z < \frac{6-5}{1}\right)$$
$$\sigma = 1$$
$$= P(-1 < z < 1)$$
$$= 2(.3413) = .6826$$

Similarly, we find the probability that the flechette hits the left and right targets shown in Figure SIA5.1.

$$\text{Left:}\quad P(-1 \leq x \leq 1) = P\left(\frac{-1-5}{1} < z < \frac{1-5}{1}\right)$$
$$\sigma = 1$$
$$= P(-6 < z < -4) \approx 0$$

$$\text{Right:}\quad P(9 \leq x \leq 11) = P\left(\frac{9-5}{1} < z < \frac{11-5}{1}\right)$$
$$\sigma = 1$$
$$= P(4 < z < 6) \approx 0$$

You can see that there is about a 68% chance that a flechette will hit the middle target, but virtually no chance that one will hit the left and right targets when the standard deviation is set at 1 foot.

To find these three probabilities for $\sigma = 2$ and $\sigma = 4$, we use the normal probability function in MINITAB. Figure SIA5.2 is a MINITAB worksheet giving the cumulative probabilities of a normal random variable falling below the x-values in the first column. The cumulative probabilities for $\sigma = 2$ and $\sigma = 4$ are given in the columns named "sigma2" and "sigma4," respectively.

Using the cumulative probabilities in the figure to find the three probabilities when $\sigma = 2$, we have

$$\text{Middle:}\quad P(4 \leq x \leq 6) = P(x \leq 6) - P(x \leq 4)$$
$$\sigma = 2$$
$$= .6915 - .3085 = .3830$$

$$\text{Left:}\quad P(-1 \leq x \leq 1) = P(x \leq 1) - P(x \leq -1)$$
$$\sigma = 2$$
$$= .0227 - .0013 = .0214$$

Figure SIA5.2

MINITAB Worksheet with Cumulative Normal Probabilities

↓	C1	C2	C3	C4	C5
	x	sigma1	sigma2	sigma4	
1	-1	0.00000	0.001350	0.066807	
2	1	0.00003	0.022750	0.158655	
3	4	0.15866	0.308538	0.401294	
4	6	0.84134	0.691462	0.598706	
5	9	0.99997	0.977250	0.841345	
6	11	1.00000	0.998650	0.933193	
7					

Right: $P(9 \leq x \leq 11) = P(x \leq 11) - P(x \leq 9)$

$\sigma = 2$

$$= .9987 - .9773 = .0214$$

Thus, when $\sigma = 2$, there is about a 38% chance that a flechette will hit the middle target, a 2% chance that one will hit the left target, and a 2% chance that one will hit the right target. The probability that a flechette will hit either the middle or left or right target is simply the sum of these three probabilities (an application of the Additive Rule of Probability). This sum is .3830 + .0214 + .0214 = .4258; consequently, there is about a 42% chance of hitting any one of the three targets when specifications are set so that $\sigma = 2$.

Now, we use the cumulative probabilities in Figure SIA5.2 to find the three hit probabilities when $\sigma = 4$:

Middle: $P(4 \leq x \leq 6) = P(x \leq 6) - P(x \leq 4)$

$\sigma = 4$

$$= .5987 - .4013 = .1974$$

Left: $P(-1 \leq x \leq 1) = P(x \leq 1) - P(x \leq -1)$

$\sigma = 4$

$$= .1587 - .0668 = .0919$$

Right: $P(9 \leq x \leq 11) = P(x \leq 11) - P(x \leq 9)$

$\sigma = 4$

$$= .9332 - .8413 = .0919$$

Thus, when $\sigma = 4$, there is about a 20% chance that a flechette will hit the middle target, a 9% chance that one will hit the left target, and a 9% chance that one will hit the right target. The probability that a flechette will hit any one of the three targets is .1974 + .0919 + .0919 = .3712.

These probability calculations reveal a few patterns. First, the probability of hitting the middle target (the target where the gun is aimed) is reduced as the standard deviation is increased. Obviously, if the U.S. Army wants to maximize the chance of hitting the target that the prototype gun is aimed at, it will want specifications set with a small value of σ. But if the Army wants to hit multiple targets with a single shot of the weapon, σ should be increased. With a larger σ, not as many of the flechettes will hit the target aimed at, but more will hit peripheral targets. Whether σ should be set at 4 or 6 (or some other value) depends on how high of a hit rate is required for the peripheral targets.

Exercises 5.17–5.48

Understanding the Principles

5.17 Describe the shape of a normal probability distribution.

5.18 What is the name given to a normal distribution when $\mu = 0$ and $\sigma = 1$?

5.19 If x has a normal distribution with mean μ and standard deviation σ, describe the distribution of $z = (x - \mu)/\sigma$.

Learning the Mechanics

5.20 Find the area under the standard normal probability distribution between the following pairs of z-scores:
   a. $z = 0$ and $z = 2.00$
   b. $z = 0$ and $z = 1.00$
   c. $z = 0$ and $z = 3$
   d. $z = 0$ and $z = .58$

5.21 Find the area under the standard normal distribution between the following pairs of z-scores:
   a. $z = -2.00$ and $z = 0$
   b. $z = -1.00$ and $z = 0$
   c. $z = -1.69$ and $z = 0$
   d. $z = -.58$ and $z = 0$

5.22 Find the following probabilities for the standard normal random variable z:
   NW a. $P(z > 1.46)$
   b. $P(z < -1.56)$
   c. $P(.67 \leq z \leq 2.41)$
   d. $P(-1.96 \leq z < -.33)$
   e. $P(z \geq 0)$
   f. $P(-2.33 < z < 1.50)$
   g. $P(z \geq -2.33)$
   h. $P(z < 2.33)$

5.23 Find each of the following probabilities for a standard normal random variable z:
- **a.** $P(z = 1)$
- **b.** $P(z \leq 1)$
- **c.** $P(z < 1)$
- **d.** $P(z > 1)$
- NW **e.** $P(-1 \leq z \leq 1)$
- NW **f.** $P(-2 \leq z \leq 2)$
- **g.** $P(-2.16 \leq z \leq .55)$
- NW **h.** $P(-.42 < z < 1.96)$

5.24 Give the z-score for a measurement from a normal distribution for the following:
- **a.** 1 standard deviation above the mean
- **b.** 1 standard deviation below the mean
- **c.** Equal to the mean
- **d.** 2.5 standard deviations below the mean
- **e.** 3 standard deviations above the mean

5.25 Find a value of the standard normal random variable z, call it z_0, such that
- **a.** $P(z \geq z_0) = .05$
- **b.** $P(z \geq z_0) = .025$
- **c.** $P(z \leq z_0) = .025$
- **d.** $P(z \geq z_0) = .10$
- **e.** $P(z > z_0) = .10$

5.26 Find a value of the standard normal random variable z, call it z_0, such that
- NW **a.** $P(z \leq z_0) = .0401$
- **b.** $P(-z_0 \leq z \leq z_0) = .95$
- **c.** $P(-z_0 \leq z \leq z_0) = .90$
- **d.** $P(-z_0 \leq z \leq z_0) = .8740$
- **e.** $P(-z_0 \leq z \leq 0) = .2967$
- **f.** $P(-2 < z < z_0) = .9710$
- **g.** $P(z \geq z_0) = .5$
- **h.** $P(z \geq z_0) = .0057$

5.27 Suppose the random variable x is best described by a normal distribution with $\mu = 25$ and $\sigma = 5$. Find the z-score that corresponds to each of the following x values:
- **a.** $x = 25$ **b.** $x = 30$ **c.** $x = 37.5$
- **d.** $x = 10$ **e.** $x = 50$ **f.** $x = 32$

5.28 Suppose x is a normally distributed random variable with $\mu = 11$ and $\sigma = 2$. Find each of the following:
- NW **a.** $P(10 \leq x \leq 12)$
- **b.** $P(6 \leq x \leq 10)$
- **c.** $P(13 \leq x \leq 16)$
- **d.** $P(7.8 \leq x \leq 12.6)$
- **e.** $P(x \geq 13.24)$ **f.** $P(x \geq 7.62)$

5.29 The random variable x has a normal distribution with $\mu = 300$ and $\sigma = 30$.
- **a.** Find the probability that x assumes a value more than 2 standard deviations from its mean. More than 3 standard deviations from μ.
- **b.** Find the probability that x assumes a value within 1 standard deviation of its mean. Within 2 standard deviations of μ.
- **c.** Find the value of x that represents the 80th percentile of this distribution. The 10th percentile.

5.30 Suppose x is a normally distributed random variable with $\mu = 30$ and $\sigma = 8$. Find a value of the random variable, call it x_0, such that
- **a.** $P(x \geq x_0) = .5$
- **b.** $P(x < x_0) = .025$
- **c.** $P(x > x_0) = .10$
- **d.** $P(x > x_0) = .95$

5.31 Refer to Exercise 5.30. Find x_0 such that
- **a.** 10% of the values of x are less than x_0
- **b.** 80% of the values of x are less than x_0
- **c.** 1% of the values of x are greater than x_0

5.32 Suppose x is a normally distributed random variable with mean 100 and standard deviation 8. Draw a rough graph of the distribution of x. Locate μ and the interval $\mu \pm 2\sigma$ on the graph. Find the following probabilities:
- **a.** $P(\mu - 2\sigma \leq x \leq \mu + 2\sigma)$
- **b.** $P(x \geq \mu + 2\sigma)$
- **c.** $P(x \leq 92)$
- **d.** $P(92 \leq x \leq 116)$
- **e.** $P(92 \leq x \leq 96)$
- **f.** $P(76 \leq x \leq 124)$

5.33 The random variable x has a normal distribution with standard deviation 25. It is known that the probability that x exceeds 150 is .90. Find the mean μ of the probability distribution.

Applying the Concepts—Basic

5.34 **Dental anxiety study.** Psychology students at Wittenberg University completed the Dental Anxiety Scale questionnaire. (*Psychological Reports*, Aug. 1997.) Scores on the scale range from 0 (no anxiety) to 20 (extreme anxiety). The mean score was 11 and the standard deviation was 3.5. Assume that the distribution of all scores on the Dental Anxiety Scale is normal with $\mu = 11$ and $\sigma = 3.5$.
- **a.** Suppose you score a 16 on the Dental Anxiety Scale. Find the z value for this score.
- **b.** Find the probability that someone scores between a 10 and a 15 on the Dental Anxiety Scale.
- **c.** Find the probability that someone scores above a 17 on the Dental Anxiety Scale.

5.35 **Alkalinity of river water.** The alkalinity level of water specimens collected from the Han River in Seoul, Korea, has a mean of 50 milligrams per liter and a standard deviation of 3.2 milligrams per liter. (*Environmental Science & Engineering*, Sept. 1, 2000.) Assume the distribution of alkalinity levels is approximately normal and find the probability that a water specimen collected from the river has an alkalinity level
- **a.** exceeding 45 milligrams per liter.
- **b.** below 55 milligrams per liter.
- **c.** between 51 and 52 milligrams per liter.

5.36 **Improving SAT scores.** Refer to the *Chance* (Winter 2001) study of students who paid a private tutor to help them improve their Standardized Admission Test (SAT) scores, Exercise 2.101 (p. 81). The table summarizing the changes in both the SAT-Mathematics and

SAT-Verbal scores for these students is reproduced here. Assume that both distributions of SAT score changes are approximately normal.

	SAT-Math	SAT-Verbal
Mean change in score	19	7
Standard deviation of score changes	65	49

a. What is the probability that a student increases his or her score on the SAT-Math test by at least 50 points?

b. What is the probability that a student increases his or her score on the SAT-Verbal test by at least 50 points?

WPOWER50

5.37 Most powerful American women. Refer to the *Fortune* (Oct. 14, 2002) list of the 50 most powerful women in America, Exercise 2.58 (p. 64). Recall that the data on age (in years) of each woman is stored in the **WPOWER50** file. The ages in the data set can be shown to be approximately normally distributed with a mean of 50 years and a standard deviation of 6 years. A powerful woman is randomly selected from the data and her age is observed.

a. Find the probability that her age will fall between 55 and 60 years.

b. Find the probability that her age will fall between 48 and 52 years.

c. Find the probability that her age will be less than 35 years.

d. Find the probability that her age will exceed 40 years.

DDT

5.38 Weights of contaminated fish. Refer to the U.S. Army Corps of Engineers data on contaminated fish in the Tennessee River, saved in the **DDT** file. Recall that one of the variables measured for each captured fish is weight (in grams). The weights in the data set can be shown to be approximately normally distributed with a mean of 1,050 grams and a standard deviation of 375 grams. An observation is randomly selected from the data and the fish weight is observed.

a. Find the probability that the weight will fall between 1,000 and 1,400 grams.

b. Find the probability that the weight will fall between 800 and 1,000 grams.

c. Find the probability that the weight will be less than 1,750 grams.

d. Find the probability that the return will exceed 500 grams.

e. Ninety-five percent of the captured fish have a weight below what value?

CRASH

5.39 NHTSA crash safety tests. Refer to the National Highway Traffic Safety Administration (NHTSA) crash test data for new cars, introduced in Exercise 2.164 (p. 107) and saved in the **CRASH** file. One of the variables measured is the severity of a driver's head injury when the car is in a head-on collision with a fixed barrier while traveling at 35 miles per hour. The more points assigned to the head injury rating, the more severe the injury. The head injury ratings can be shown to be approximately normally distributed with a mean of 605 points and a standard deviation of 185 points. One of the crash-tested cars is randomly selected from the data and the driver's head injury rating is observed.

a. Find the probability that the rating will fall between 500 and 700 points.

b. Find the probability that the rating will fall between 400 and 500 points.

c. Find the probability that the rating will be less than 850 points.

d. Find the probability that the rating will exceed 1,000 points.

NW e. For what rating will only 10% of the crash-tested cars exceed?

Applying the Concepts—Intermediate

5.40 Fitness of cardiac patients. The physical fitness of a **NW** patient is often measured by the patient's maximum oxygen uptake (recorded in milliliters per kilogram, ml/kg). The mean maximum oxygen uptake for cardiac patients who regularly participate in sports or exercise programs was found to be 24.1 with a standard deviation of 6.30. (*Adapted Physical Activity Quarterly*, Oct. 1997.) Assume this distribution is approximately normal.

a. What is the probability that a cardiac patient who regularly participates in sports has a maximum oxygen uptake of at least 20 ml/kg?

b. What is the probability that a cardiac patient who regularly exercises has a maximum oxygen uptake of 10.5 ml/kg or lower?

c. Consider a cardiac patient with a maximum oxygen uptake of 10.5. Is it likely that this patient participates regularly in sports or exercise programs? Explain.

5.41 Visually impaired students. The *Journal of Visual Impairment & Blindness* (May–June 1997) published a study of the lifestyles of visually impaired students. Using diaries, the students kept track of several variables, including number of hours of sleep obtained in a typical day. These visually impaired students had a mean of 9.06 hours and a standard deviation of 2.11 hours. Assume that the distribution of the number of hours of sleep for this group of students is approximately normal.

a. Find the probability that a visually impaired student obtains less than 6 hours of sleep on a typical day.

b. Find the probability that a visually impaired student gets between 8 and 10 hours of sleep on a typical day.

c. Twenty percent of all visually impaired students obtain less than how many hours of sleep on a typical day?

5.42 Alcohol, threats, and electric shocks. A group of Florida State University psychologists examined the effects of alcohol on the reactions of people to a threat. (*Journal of Abnormal Psychology*, Vol. 107, 1998.) After obtaining a specified blood alcohol level, experimental subjects were placed in a room and threatened with electric shocks. Using sophisticated equipment to monitor the subjects' eye movements, the startle response (measured in milliseconds) was recorded for each subject. The mean and standard deviation of the startle responses were 37.9 and 12.4, respectively. Assume that the startle response x for a person with the specified blood alcohol level is approximately normally distributed.
  a. Find the probability that x is between 40 and 50 milliseconds.
  b. Find the probability that x is less than 30 milliseconds.
  c. Give an interval for x, centered around 37.9 milliseconds, so that the probability that x falls in the interval is .95.
  d. Ten percent of the experimental subjects have startle responses above what value?

5.43 Forest development following wildfires. *Ecological Applications* (May 1995) published a study on the development of forests following wildfires in the Pacific Northwest. One variable of interest to the researcher was tree diameter at breast height 110 years after the fire. The population of Douglas fir trees was shown to have an approximately normal diameter distribution, with $\mu = 50$ centimeters (cm) and $\sigma = 12$ cm. Find the diameter, d, such that 30% of the Douglas fir trees in the population have diameters that exceed d.

5.44 Gestation length of pregnant women. Based on data from the National Center for Health Statistics, N. Wetzel used the normal distribution to model the length of gestation for pregnant U.S. women (*Chance*, Spring 2001.) Gestation length has a mean of 280 days with a standard deviation of 20 days.
  a. Find the probability that gestation length is between 275.5 and 276.5 days. (This estimates the probability that a woman has her baby 4 days earlier than the "average" due date.)
  b. Find the probability that gestation length is between 258.5 and 259.5 days. (This estimates the probability that a woman has her baby 21 days earlier than the "average" due date.)
  c. Find the probability that gestation length is between 254.5 and 255.5 days. (This estimates the probability that a woman has her baby 25 days earlier than the "average" due date.)
  d. The *Chance* article referenced a newspaper story about three sisters who all gave birth on the same day (March 11, 1998). Karralee had her baby 4 days early; Marrianne had her baby 21 days early; and Jennifer had her baby 25 days early. Use the results, parts **a–c**, to estimate the probability that three women have their babies 4, 21, and 25 days early, respectively. Assume the births are independent events.

5.45 Cholesterol levels in psychiatric patients. A study of serum cholesterol levels in psychiatric patients of a maximum-security forensic hospital revealed that cholesterol level is approximately normally distributed with a mean of 208 milligrams per deciliter (mg/dL) and a standard deviation of 25 mg/dL. (*Journal of Behavioral Medicine*, Feb. 1995.) Prior research has shown that patients who exhibit violent behavior have cholesterol levels below 200 mg/dL.
  a. What is the probability of observing a psychiatric patient with a cholesterol level below 200 mg/dL?
  b. For three randomly selected patients, what is the probability that at least one will have a cholesterol level below 200 mg/dL?

Applying the Concepts—Advanced

5.46 Industrial filling process. The characteristics of an industrial filling process in which an expensive liquid is injected into a container were investigated in *Journal of Quality Technology* (July 1999). The quantity injected per container is approximately normally distributed with mean 10 units and standard deviation .2 units. Each unit of fill costs $20. If a container contains less than 10 units (i.e., is underfilled), it must be reprocessed at a cost of $10. A properly filled container sells for $230.
  a. Find the probability that a container is underfilled.
  b. A container is initially underfilled and must be reprocessed. Upon refilling it contains 10.6 units. How much profit will the company make on this container?
  c. The operations manager adjusts the mean of the filling process upward to 10.5 units in order to make the probability of underfilling approximately zero. Under these conditions, what is the expected profit per container?

5.47 Box plots and the standard normal distribution. What relationship exists between the standard normal distribution and the box-plot methodology (optional Section 2.8) for describing distributions of data using quartiles? The answer depends on the true underlying probability distribution of the data. Assume for the remainder of this exercise that the distribution is normal.
  a. Calculate the values of the standard normal random variable z, call them z_L and z_U, that correspond to the hinges of the box plot (i.e., the lower and upper quartiles, Q_L and Q_U) of the probability distribution.
  b. Calculate the z values that correspond to the inner fences of the box plot for a normal probability distribution.
  c. Calculate the z values that correspond to the outer fences of the box plot for a normal probability distribution.
  d. What is the probability that an observation lies beyond the inner fences of a normal probability distribution? The outer fences?
  e. Can you better understand why the inner and outer fences of a box plot are used to detect outliers in a distribution? Explain.

5.48 Dye discharged in paint. A machine used to regulate the amount of dye dispensed for mixing shades of paint can be set so that it discharges an average of μ milliliters (mL) of dye per can of paint. The amount of dye discharged is known to have a normal distribution with a standard deviation of .4 mL. If more than 6 mL of dye are discharged when making a certain shade of blue paint, the shade is unacceptable. Determine the setting for μ so that only 1% of the cans of paint will be unacceptable.

5.4 Descriptive Methods for Assessing Normality

In the chapters that follow, we learn how to make inferences about the population based on information in the sample. Several of these techniques are based on the assumption that the population is approximately normally distributed. Consequently, it will be important to determine whether the sample data come from a normal population before we can properly apply these techniques.

Several descriptive methods can be used to check for normality. In this section, we consider the three methods summarized in the box.

Determining Whether the Data Are from an Approximately Normal Distribution

1. Construct either a histogram or stem-and-leaf display for the data and note the shape of the graph. If the data are approximately normal, the shape of the histogram or stem-and-leaf display will be similar to the normal curve, Figure 5.5 (i.e., mound shaped and symmetric about the mean).

2. Compute the intervals $\bar{x} \pm s$, $\bar{x} \pm 2s$, and $\bar{x} \pm 3s$, and determine the percentage of measurements falling in each. If the data are approximately normal, the percentages will be approximately equal to 68%, 95%, and 100%, respectively.

3. Find the interquartile range, IQR, and standard deviation, s, for the sample, then calculate the ratio IQR/s. If the data are approximately normal, then IQR/$s \approx 1.3$.

4. Construct a normal probability plot for the data. If the data are approximately normal, the points will fall (approximately) on a straight line.

The first two methods come directly from the properties of a normal distribution established in Section 5.3. Method 3 is based on the fact that for normal distributions, the z values corresponding to the 25th and 75th percentiles are $-.67$ and $.67$, respectively (see Example 5.4). Since $\sigma = 1$ for a standard normal distribution,

$$\frac{\text{IQR}}{\sigma} = \frac{Q_U - Q_L}{\sigma} = \frac{.67 - (-.67)}{1} = 1.34$$

The final descriptive method for checking normality is based on a *normal probability plot*. In such a plot, the observations in a data set are ordered from smallest to largest and then plotted against the expected z-scores of observations calculated under the assumption that the data come from a normal distribution. When the data are, in fact, normally distributed, a linear (straight-line) trend will result. A nonlinear trend in the plot suggests that the data are non-normal.

DEFINITION 5.2

A **normal probability plot** for a data set is a scatterplot with the ranked data values on one axis and their corresponding expected z-scores from a standard normal distribution on the other axis. [*Note:* Computation of the expected standard normal z-scores are beyond the scope of this text. Therefore, we will rely on available statistical software packages to generate a normal probability plot.]

EXAMPLE 5.11   CHECKING FOR NORMAL DATA

Problem   The EPA mileage ratings on 100 cars, first presented in Chapter 2 (p. 41), are reproduced in Table 5.2. Numerical and graphical descriptive measures for the data are shown on the MINITAB and SPSS printouts, Figure 5.18a–c. Determine whether the EPA mileage ratings are from an approximate normal distribution.

Solution   As a first check, we examine the MINITAB histogram of the data shown in Figure 5.18a. Clearly, the mileages fall in an approximately mound-shaped, symmetric distribution centered around the mean of approximately 37 mpg. Note that a normal curve is superimposed on the figure. Therefore, using check #1 in the box, the data appear to be approximately normal.

To apply check #2, we obtain $\bar{x} = 37$ and $s = 2.4$ from the MINITAB printout, Figure 5.18b. The intervals $\bar{x} \pm s$, $\bar{x} \pm 2s$, and $\bar{x} \pm 3s$, are shown in Table 5.3, as well as the percentage of mileage ratings that fall in each interval. (We obtained these results in Section 2.6, p. 75) These percentages agree almost exactly with those from a normal distribution.

⊙ **EPAGAS**

TABLE 5.2   EPA Gas Mileage Ratings for 100 Cars (miles per gallon)

36.3	41.0	36.9	37.1	44.9	36.8	30.0	37.2	42.1	36.7
32.7	37.3	41.2	36.6	32.9	36.5	33.2	37.4	37.5	33.6
40.5	36.5	37.6	33.9	40.2	36.4	37.7	37.7	40.0	34.2
36.2	37.9	36.0	37.9	35.9	38.2	38.3	35.7	35.6	35.1
38.5	39.0	35.5	34.8	38.6	39.4	35.3	34.4	38.8	39.7
36.3	36.8	32.5	36.4	40.5	36.6	36.1	38.2	38.4	39.3
41.0	31.8	37.3	33.1	37.0	37.6	37.0	38.7	39.0	35.8
37.0	37.2	40.7	37.4	37.1	37.8	35.9	35.6	36.7	34.5
37.1	40.3	36.7	37.0	33.9	40.1	38.0	35.2	34.8	39.5
39.9	36.9	32.9	33.8	39.8	34.0	36.8	35.0	38.1	36.9

Figure 5.18a
MINITAB Histogram for Gas Mileage Data

Figure 5.18b
MINITAB Descriptive Statistics for Gas Mileage Data

Descriptive Statistics: MPG

Variable	N	Mean	StDev	Minimum	Q1	Median	Q3	Maximum
MPG	100	36.994	2.418	30.000	35.625	37.000	38.375	44.900

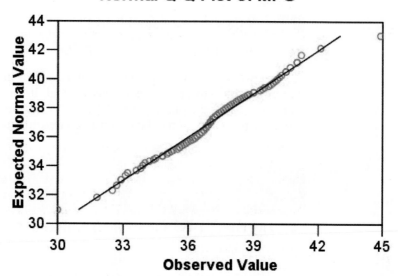

Normal Q-Q Plot of MPG

TABLE 5.3	Describing the 100 EPA Mileage Ratings
Interval	Percentage in Interval
$\bar{x} \pm s = (34.6, 39.4)$	68
$\bar{x} \pm 2s = (32.2, 41.8)$	96
$\bar{x} \pm 3s = (29.8, 44.2)$	99

Check #3 in the box requires that we find the ratio IQR/s. From Figure 5.18b, the 25th percentile (labeled Q_1 by MINITAB) is $Q_L = 35.625$ and the 75th percentile (labeled Q_3 by MINITAB) is $Q_U = 38.375$. Then IQR $= Q_U - Q_L = 2.75$ and the ratio is

$$\frac{\text{IRQ}}{s} = \frac{2.75}{2.4} = 1.15$$

Since this value is approximately equal to 1.3, we have further confirmation that the data are approximately normal.

A fourth descriptive method is to interpret a normal probability plot. An SPSS normal probability plot for the mileage data is shown in Figure 5.18c. Notice that the ordered mileage values (shown on the horizontal axis) fall reasonably close to a straight line when plotted against the expected values from a normal distribution. Thus, check #4 also suggests that the EPA mileage data are likely to be approximately normally distributed.

Look Back The checks for normality given in the box are simple, yet powerful, techniques to apply, but they are only descriptive in nature. It is possible (although unlikely) that the data are non-normal even when the checks are reasonably satisfied. Thus, we should be careful not to claim that the 100 EPA mileage ratings are, in fact, normally distributed. We can only state that it is reasonable to believe that the data are from a normal distribution.*

Now Work   *Exercise 5.56*

■ ■ ■

As we will learn in the next chapter, several inferential methods of analysis require the data to be approximately normal. If the data are clearly non-normal, inferences derived from the method may be invalid. Therefore, it is advisable to check the normality of the data prior to conducting the analysis.

Normal Probability Plot

Using the T1-83 Graphing Calculator

Step 1   *Enter the data*
press STAT and select 1:Edit
Note: If the list already contains data, clear the old data. Use the up arrow to highlight 'L1'. Press CLEAR ENTER.
Use the arrow and ENTER keys to enter the data set into L1.

Step 2   *Set up the Normal Probability Plot*
Press 2nd and press **Y =** for STAT PLOT
Press 1 for Plot 1
Set the cursor so that ON is flashing.
For Type, use the arrow and Enter keys to highlight and select the last graph in the bottom row.
For Data List, choose the column containing the data (in most cases, L1).
(Note: Press 2nd 1 for L1)
For Data Axis, choose X.

Step 3   *View Plot*
Press ZOOM 9
Your data will be displayed against their expected *z*-scores from a normal distribution. If you see a "generally" linear relationship, your data are near normal.

Example   Using a Normal Probability Plot, test whether or not the data are normally distributed.

| 9.7 | 93.1 | 33.0 | 21.2 | 81.4 | 51.1 |
| 43.5 | 10.6 | 12.8 | 7.8 | 18.1 | 12.7 |

*Statistical tests of normality that provide a measure of reliability for the inference are available. However, these tests tend to be very sensitive to slight departures from normality (i.e., they tend to reject the hypothesis of normality for any distribution that is not perfectly symmetrical and mound shaped). Consult the references (see Ramsey & Ramsey, 1990) if you want to learn more about these tests.

The screen below shows the normal probability plot. There is a noticeable curve to the plot, indicating that the data are not normally distributed.

Statistics in Action Revisited

Assessing Whether the Normal Distribution Is Appropriate for Modeling the Super Weapon Hit Data

In *Statistics in Action Revisited*, Section 5.3, we used the normal distribution to find the probability that a single flechette from a super weapon that shoots 1,100 flechettes at once hits one of three targets at 500 meters. Recall that for three range tests, the weapon was always aimed at the center target (i.e., the specification mean was set at $\mu = 5$ feet), but the specification standard deviation was varied at $\sigma = 1$ foot, $\sigma = 2$ feet, and $\sigma = 4$ feet. Table SIA5.1 shows the calculated normal probabilities of hitting the

TABLE SIA5.1 **Summary of Normal Probability Calculations and Actual Range Test Results**

Target	Specification	Normal Probability	Actual Number of Hits	Hit Ratio (Hits/1,100)
LEFT (−1 to 1)	$\sigma = 1$	.0000	0	.000
	$\sigma = 2$	.0214	30	.027
	$\sigma = 4$	.0919	73	.066
MIDDLE (4 to 6)	$\sigma = 1$	.6826	764	.695
	$\sigma = 2$	.3820	409	.372
	$\sigma = 4$	.1974	242	.220
RIGHT (9 to 11)	$\sigma = 1$	.0000	0	.000
	$\sigma = 2$	.0214	23	.021
	$\sigma = 4$	.0919	93	.085

Figure SIA5.3a

MINITAB Histogram for the Horizontal Hit Measurements when $\sigma = 1$

three targets for the different values of σ, as well as the actual results of the three range tests. (Recall that the actual data is saved in the **MOAGUN** file.) You can see that the proportion of the 1,100 flechettes that actually hit each target—called the hit ratio—agrees very well with the estimated probability of a hit using the normal distribution.

Consequently, it appears that our assumption that the horizontal hit measurements are approximately normally distributed is reasonably satisfied. Further evidence of this is provided by the MINITAB histograms of the horizontal hit measurements shown in Figures SIA5.3a–c. The normal curves superimposed on the histograms fit the data very well.

Figure SIA5.3b
MINITAB Histogram for the Horizontal Hit Measurements when $\sigma = 2$

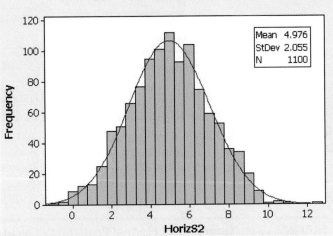

Figure SIA5.3c
MINITAB Histogram for the Horizontal Hit Measurements when $\sigma = 4$

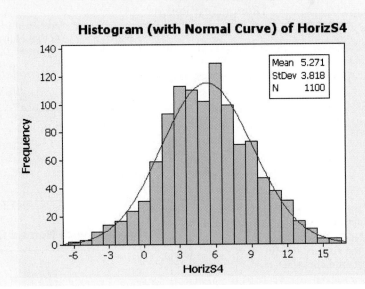

Exercises 5.49–5.65

Understanding the Principles

5.49 Why is it important to check whether the sample data come from a normal population?

5.50 Give four methods for determining whether the sample data come from a normal population.

5.51 If a population data set is normally distributed, what is the proportion of measurements you would expect to fall within the following intervals?
   a. $\mu \pm \sigma$ **b.** $\mu \pm 2\sigma$ **c.** $\mu \pm 3\sigma$

5.52 What is a normal probability plot and how is it used?

Learning the Mechanics

5.53 Normal probability plots for three data sets are shown at the top of p. 267. Which plot indicates that the data are approximately normally distributed?

5.54 Consider a sample data set with the following summary statistics: $s = 95, Q_L = 72, Q_U = 195$.

Plots for Exercise 5.53

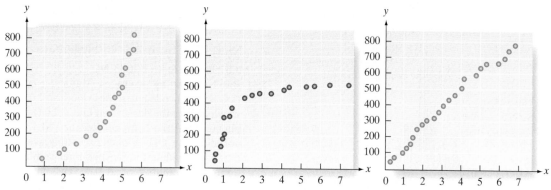

a. Calculate IQR.
b. Calculate IQR/s.
c. Is the value of IQR/s approximately equal to 1.3? What does this imply?

5.55 Examine the sample data in the table.

 LM5_55

32	48	25	135	53	37	5	39	213	165
109	40	1	146	39	25	21	66	64	57
197	60	112	10	155	134	301	304	107	82
35	81	60	95	401	308	180	3	200	59

a. Construct a stem-and-leaf plot to assess whether the data are from an approximately normal distribution.
b. Find the values of Q_L, Q_U, and s for the sample data.
c. Use the results, part **b**, to assess the normality of the data.
d. Generate a normal probability plot for the data and use it to assess whether the data are approximately normal.

5.56 Examine the sample data in the table.
NW

 LM5_56

5.9	5.3	1.6	7.4	8.6	3.2	2.1
4.0	7.3	8.4	5.9	6.7	4.5	6.3
6.0	9.7	3.5	3.1	4.3	3.3	8.4
4.6	8.2	6.5	1.1	5.0	9.4	6.4

a. Construct a stem-and-leaf plot to assess whether the data are from an approximately normal distribution.
b. Compute s for the sample data.
c. Find the values of Q_L and Q_U and the value of s from part **b** to assess whether the data come from an approximately normal distribution.
d. Generate a normal probability plot for the data and use it to assess whether the data are approximately normal.

Applying the Concepts—Basic

 WPOWER50

5.57 Most powerful American women. Refer to the *Fortune* (Oct. 14, 2002) list of the 50 most powerful women in America. In Exercise 5.37 (p. 259), you assumed that the ages (in years) of these women are approximately normally distributed. A MINITAB printout with summary statistics for the age distribution is reproduced below.
a. Use the relevant statistics on the printout to find the interquartile range, IQR.
b. Locate the value of the standard deviation, s, on the printout.
c. Use the results, parts **a** and **b**, to demonstrate that the age distribution is approximately normal.
d. Construct a relative frequency histogram for the age data. Use this graph to support your assumption of normality.

5.58 Galaxy velocity study. Refer to the *Astronomical Journal* (July 1995) study of galaxy velocities, Exercise 2.100 (p. 80). A histogram of the velocity for 103 galaxies located in a particular cluster named A2142 is reproduced at the top of p. 268. Comment on whether or not the galaxy velocities are approximately normally distributed.

 HABITAT

5.59 Habitats of endangered species. An evaluation of the habitats of endangered salmon species was performed in *Conservation Ecology* (December 2003). The researchers identified 734 sites (habitats) for Chinook, coho, or steelhead salmon species in Oregon, and assigned a habitat quality score to each. (Scores range from 0 to 36 points, with lower scores indicating poorly maintained or degraded habitats.) A MINITAB histogram for the data (saved in the **HABITAT** file) is displayed at the bottom of p. 268. Give your opinion on whether the data is normally distributed.

5.60 Dart throwing errors. How accurate are you at the game of darts? Researchers at Iowa State University

MINITAB Output for Exercise 5.57

Descriptive Statistics: AGE

Variable	N	Mean	StDev	Minimum	Q1	Median	Q3	Maximum
AGE	50	49.740	6.124	37.000	46.000	49.000	53.000	71.000

Figure for Exercise 5.58

A2142 Velocity Distribution

Observed velocity (/1000 km/sec)

Number of galaxies

Source: Oegerle, W. R., Hill, J. M., and Fitchett, M. J. "Observations of high dispersion clusters of galaxies: Constraints on cold dark matter." *The Astronomical Journal,* Vol. 110, No. 1, July 1995, p. 37 (Figure 1).

attempted to develop a probability model for dart throws (*Chance,* Summer 1997). For each of 590 throws made at certain targets on a dart board, the distance from the dart to the target point was measured (to the nearest millimeter). The error distribution for the dart throws is described by the frequency table shown on p. 269.

a. Construct a histogram for the data. Is the error distribution for the dart throws approximately normal?

b. Descriptive statistics for the distances from the target for the 590 throws are given below. Use this information to decide whether the error distribution is approximately normal.

$$\bar{x} = 24.4 \text{ mm}$$
$$s = 12.8 \text{ mm}$$
$$Q_L = 14 \text{ mm}$$
$$Q_U = 34 \text{ mm}$$

c. Construct a normal probability plot for the data and use it to assess whether the error distribution is approximately normal.

Applying the Concepts—Intermediate

MLB2003-AL & MLB2003-NL

5.61 Baseball batting averages. Major League Baseball (MLB) has two leagues: the American League (AL)—which utilizes the designated hitter (DH) to bat for the pitcher—and the National League (NL)—which does not allow the DH. A player's batting average is computed by dividing the player's total number of hits by his official number of at-bats. The batting averages for all AL and NL players with at least 100 official at-bats during the 2003 season are stored in the **MLB2003-AL** and **MLB2003-NL** files, respectively. Determine whether each batting average distribution is approximately normal.

DDT

5.62 Contaminated fish. Refer to the U.S. Army Corps of Engineers data on contaminated fish in the Tennessee River.

a. In Exercise 5.38 (p. 259), you assumed that the weight (in grams) of a captured fish is approximately normally distributed. Apply the methods of this chapter to the data saved in the **DDT** file to support this assumption.

b. Another variable saved in the **DDT** file is the amount of DDT (in parts per million) detected in each fish captured. Determine whether the DDT level is approximately normal.

CRASH

5.63 NHTSA crash tests. Refer to the National Highway Traffic Safety Administration (NHTSA) crash test data for new cars. In Exercise 5.39 (p. 259), you assumed that the driver's head injury rating is approximately normally

Source: Good, T. P., Harms, T. K., and Ruckelshaus, M. H. "Misuse of checklist assessments in endangered species recovery efforts," *Conservation Ecology,* Vol. 7, No. 2, Dec. 2003 (Figure 3).

MINITAB Output for Exercise 5.59

Histogram (with Normal Curve) of Score

Mean	12.21
StDev	6.311
N	734

Frequency

Score

Table for Exercise 5.60

DARTS

Distance from Target (mm)	Frequency	Distance from Target (mm)	Frequency	Distance from Target (mm)	Frequency
0	3	21	15	41	7
2	2	22	19	42	7
3	5	23	13	43	11
4	10	24	11	44	7
5	7	25	9	45	5
6	3	26	21	46	3
7	12	27	16	47	1
8	14	28	18	48	3
9	9	29	9	49	1
10	11	30	14	50	4
11	14	31	13	51	4
12	13	32	11	52	3
13	32	33	11	53	4
14	19	34	11	54	1
15	20	35	16	55	1
16	9	36	13	56	4
17	18	37	5	57	3
18	23	38	9	58	2
19	25	39	6	61	1
20	21	40	5	62	2
				66	1

Source: Stern, H. S., and Wilcox, W. "Shooting Darts." *Chance,* Vol. 10, No. 3, Summer 1997, p. 17 (adapted from Figure 2).

distributed. Apply the methods of this chapter to the data saved in the **CRASH** file to support this assumption.

SHIPSANIT

5.64 Cruise ship sanitation scores. Refer to the data on the May 2004, sanitation scores for 174 cruise ships, first presented in Exercise 2.93 (p. 79). The data are saved in the **SHIPSANIT** file. Assess whether the sanitation scores are approximately normally distributed.

5.65 Language skills study. Refer to the *Applied Psycholinguistics* (June 1998) study of language skills in young children, Exercise 2.98 (p. 80). Recall that the mean sentence complexity score (measured on a 0 to 48 point scale) of low income children was 7.62 with a standard deviation of 8.91. Demonstrate why the distribution of sentence complexity scores for low income children is unlikely to be normally distributed.

5.5   Approximating a Binomial Distribution with a Normal Distribution (Optional)

When the discrete binomial random variable (Section 4.4) can assume a large number of values, the calculation of its probabilities may become very tedious. To contend with this problem, we provide tables in Appendix A to give the probabilities for some values of n and p, but these tables are by necessity incomplete. Recall that the binomial probability table (Table II) can be used only for $n = 5, 6, 7, 8, 9, 10, 15, 20,$ or 25. To deal with this limitation, we seek approximation procedures for calculating the probabilities associated with a binomial probability distribution.

When n is large, a normal probability distribution may be used to provide a good approximation to the probability distribution of a binomial random variable. To show how this approximation works, we refer to Example 4.11, in which we used the binomial distribution to model the number x of 20 eligible voters who favor a candidate. We assumed that 60% of all the eligible voters favored the candidate. The mean and standard deviation of x were found to be $\mu = 12$ and $\sigma = 2.2$. The binomial distribution for $n = 20$ and $p = .6$ is shown in Figure 5.19, and the approximating normal distribution with mean $\mu = 12$ and standard deviation $\sigma = 2.2$ is superimposed.

Figure 5.19

Binomial Distribution for $n = 20$, $p = .6$ and Normal Distribution with $\mu = 12$, $\sigma = 2.2$

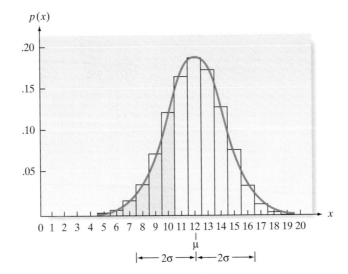

As part of Example 4.11, we used Table II to find the probability that $x \leq 10$. This probability, which is equal to the sum of the areas contained in the rectangles (shown in Figure 5.19) that correspond to $p(0)$, $p(1)$, $p(2)$, ..., $p(10)$, was found to equal .245. The portion of the approximating normal curve that would be used to approximate the area $p(0) + p(1) + p(2) + \cdots + p(10)$ is highlighted in Figure 5.19. Note that this highlighted area lies to the left of 10.5 (not 10), so we may include all of the probability in the rectangle corresponding to $p(10)$. Because we are approximating a discrete distribution (the binomial) with a continuous distribution (the normal), we call the use of 10.5 (instead of 10 or 11) a **correction for continuity**. That is, we are correcting the discrete distribution so that it can be approximated by the continuous one. The use of the correction for continuity leads to the calculation of the following standard normal z-value:

$$z = \frac{x - \mu}{\sigma} = \frac{10.5 - 12}{2.2} = -.68$$

Using Table IV, we find the area between $z = 0$ and $z = .68$ to be .2517. Then the probability that x is less than or equal to 10 is approximated by the area under the normal distribution to the left of 10.5, shown highlighted in Figure 5.19. That is,

$$P(x \leq 10) \approx P(z \leq -.68) = .5 - P(-.68 < z \leq 0) = .5 - .2517 = .2483$$

The approximation differs only slightly from the exact binomial probability, .245. Of course, when tables of exact binomial probabilities are available, we will use the exact value rather than a normal approximation.

Use of the normal distribution will not always provide a good approximation for binomial probabilities. The following is a useful rule of thumb to determine when n is large enough for the approximation to be effective: *The interval $\mu \pm 3\sigma$ should lie within the range of the binomial random variable x (i.e., 0 to n) in order for the normal approximation to be adequate.* The rule works well because almost all of the normal distribution falls within 3 standard deviations of the mean, so if this interval is contained within the range of x values, there is "room" for the normal approximation to work.

As shown in Figure 5.20a for the preceding example with $n = 20$ and $p = .6$, the interval $\mu \pm 3\sigma = 12 + 3(2.19) = (5.43, 18.57)$ lies within the range 0 to 20.

Figure 5.20

Rule of Thumb for Normal Approximation to Binomial Probabilities

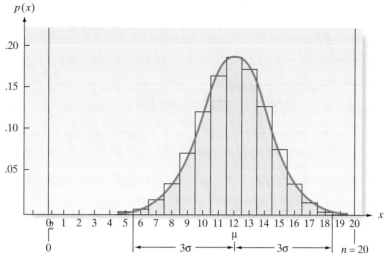

a. $n = 20$, $p = .6$: Normal approximation is good

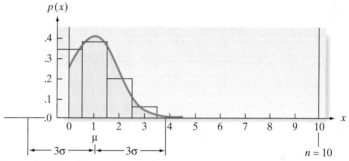

b. $n = 10$, $p = .1$: Normal approximation is poor

However, if we were to try to use the normal approximation with $n = 10$ and $p = .1$, the interval $\mu \pm 3\sigma$ is $1 \pm 3(.95)$, or $(-1.85, 3.85)$. As shown in Figure 5.20b, this interval is not contained within the range of x since $x = 0$ is the lower bound for a binomial random variable. Note in Figure 5.20b that the normal distribution will not "fit" in the range of x, and therefore it will not provide a good approximation to the binomial probabilities.

Biography

ABRAHAM DE MOIVRE (1667–1754)—Advisor to Gamblers

French-born mathematician Abraham de Moivre moved to London when he was 21 years old to escape religious persecution. In England, he earned a living first as a traveling teacher of mathematics and then as an advisor to gamblers, underwriters, and annuity brokers. De Moivre's major contributions to probability theory are contained in two of his books, *The Doctrine of Chances* (1718) and *Miscellanea Analytica* (1730). In these works he defines statistical independence, develops the formula for the normal probability distribution, and derives the normal curve as an approximation to the binomial distribution. Despite his eminence as a mathematician, de Moivre died in poverty. He is famous for predicting the day of his own death using an arithmetic progression.

EXAMPLE 5.12   APPROXIMATING A BINOMIAL PROBABILITY
WITH THE NORMAL DISTRIBUTION

Problem   One problem with any product that is mass-produced (e.g., a graphing calculator) is quality control. The process must be monitored or audited to be sure the output of the process conforms to requirements. One monitoring method is *lot acceptance sampling*, in which items being produced are sampled at various stages of the production process and are carefully inspected. The lot of items from which the sample is drawn is then accepted or rejected, based on the number of defectives in the sample. Lots that are accepted may be sent forward for further processing or may be shipped to customers; lots that are rejected may be reworked or scrapped. For example, suppose a manufacturer of calculators chooses 200 stamped circuits from the day's production and determines x, the number of defective circuits in the sample. Suppose that up to a 6% rate of defectives is considered acceptable for the process.

a. Find the mean and standard deviation of x, assuming the defective rate is 6%.

b. Use the normal approximation to determine the probability that 20 or more defectives are observed in the sample of 200 circuits (i.e., find the approximate probability that $x \geq 20$).

Solution   **a.** The random variable x is binomial with $n = 200$ and the fraction defective $p = .06$. Thus,

$$\mu = np = 200(.06) = 12$$
$$\sigma = \sqrt{npq} = \sqrt{200(.06)(.94)} = \sqrt{11.28} = 3.36$$

We first note that

$$\mu \pm 3\sigma = 12 \pm 3(3.36) = 12 \pm 10.08 = (1.92, 22.08)$$

lies completely within the range from 0 to 200. Therefore, a normal probability distribution should provide an adequate approximation to this binomial distribution.

b. Using the rule of complements, $P(x \geq 20) = 1 - P(x \leq 19)$. To find the approximating area corresponding to $x \leq 19$, refer to Figure 5.21. Note that we want to include all the binomial probability histograms from 0 to 19, inclusive. Since the event is of the form $x \leq a$, the proper correction for continuity is $a + .5 = 19 + .5 = 19.5$. Thus, the z value of interest is

$$z = \frac{(a + .5) - \mu}{\sigma} = \frac{19.5 - 12}{3.36} = 2.23$$

Figure 5.21
Normal Approximation to
the Binomial Distribution
with $n = 200$, $p = .06$

Figure 5.22
Standard Normal
Distribution

Referring to Table IV in Appendix A, we find that the area to the right of the mean 0 corresponding to $z = 2.23$ (see Figure 5.22) is .4871. So the area $A = P(z \leq 2.23)$ is

$$A = .5 + .4871 = .9871$$

Thus, the normal approximation to the binomial probability we seek is

$$P(x \geq 20) = 1 - P(x \leq 19) \approx 1 - .9871 = .0129$$

In other words, the probability is extremely small that 20 or more defectives will be observed in a sample of 200 circuits—*if in fact the true fraction of defectives is .06.*

Look Back If the manufacturer observes $x \geq 20$, the likely reason is that the process is producing more than the acceptable 6% defectives. The lot acceptance sampling procedure is another example of using the rare-event approach to make inferences.

Now Work *Exercise 5.69*

■ ■ ■

The steps for approximating a binomial probability by a normal probability are given in the accompanying box.

Using a Normal Distribution to Approximate Binomial Probabilities

1. After you have determined n and p for the binomial distribution, calculate the interval

$$\mu \pm 3\sigma = np \pm 3\sqrt{npq}$$

If the interval lies in the range 0 to n, the normal distribution will provide a reasonable approximation to the probabilities of most binomial events.

2. Express the binomial probability to be approximated in the form $P(x \leq a)$ or $P(x \leq b) - P(x \leq a)$. For example,

$$P(x < 3) = P(x \leq 2)$$
$$P(x \geq 5) = 1 - P(x \leq 4)$$
$$P(7 \leq x \leq 10) = P(x \leq 10) - P(x \leq 6)$$

3. For each value of interest a, the correction for continuity is $(a + .5)$, and the corresponding standard normal z value is

$$z = \frac{(a + .5) - \mu}{\sigma} \quad \text{(see Figure 5.23)}$$

4. Sketch the approximating normal distribution and shade the area corresponding to the probability of the event of interest, as in Figure 5.23. Verify that the rectangles you have included in the shaded area correspond to the event probability you wish to approximate. Using Table IV and the z value(s) you calculated in step 3, find the shaded area. This is the approximate probability of the binomial event.

Figure 5.23

Approximating Binomial Probabilities by Normal Probabilities

Exercises 5.66–5.84

Understanding the Principles

5.66 For large n (say, $n = 100$), why is it advantageous to use the normal distribution to approximate a binomial probability?

5.67 Why do we need a correction for continuity when approximating a binomial probability with the normal distribution?

Learning the Mechanics

5.68 Assume that x is a binomial random variable with n and p as specified in parts **a–f**. For which cases would it be appropriate to use a normal distribution to approximate the binomial distribution?
  a. $n = 100, p = .01$ **b.** $n = 20, p = .6$
  c. $n = 10, p = .4$ **d.** $n = 1,000, p = .05$
  e. $n = 100, p = .8$ **f.** $n = 35, p = .7$

5.69 Suppose x is a binomial random variable with $p = .4$
NW and $n = 25$.
  a. Would it be appropriate to approximate the probability distribution of x with a normal distribution? Explain.
  b. Assuming that a normal distribution provides an adequate approximation to the distribution of x, what are the mean and variance of the approximating normal distribution?
  c. Use Table II of Appendix A to find the exact value of $P(x \geq 9)$.
  d. Use the normal approximation to find $P(x \geq 9)$.

5.70 Assume that x is a binomial random variable with $n = 25$ and $p = .5$. Use Table II of Appendix A and the normal approximation to find the exact and approximate values, respectively, for the following probabilities:
  a. $P(x \leq 11)$
  b. $P(x \geq 16)$
  c. $P(8 \leq x \leq 16)$

5.71 Assume that x is a binomial random variable with $n = 100$ and $p = .40$. Use a normal approximation to find the following:
  a. $P(x \leq 35)$ **b.** $P(40 \leq x \leq 50)$
  c. $P(x \geq 38)$

5.72 Assume that x is a binomial random variable with $n = 1,000$ and $p = .50$. Find each of the following probabilities:
  a. $P(x > 500)$ **b.** $P(490 \leq x < 500)$
  c. $P(x > 550)$

Applying the Concepts—Basic

5.73 **Mobile phones with Internet access.** In Exercise 4.56 (p. 216), you learned that 20% of young adults who shop online own a mobile phone with Internet access. (*American Demographics*, May 2002.) In a random sample of 200 young adults who shop online, let x be the number who own a mobile phone with Internet access.
  a. Find the mean of x. (This value should agree with your answer to Exercise 4.56c.)
  b. Find the standard deviation of x.
  c. Find the z-score for the value $x = 50.5$.
  d. Find the approximate probability that the number of young adults who own a mobile phone with Internet access in a sample of 200 is less than or equal to 50.

5.74 **Melanoma deaths.** According to the *American Cancer Society*, melanoma, a form of skin cancer, kills 15% of Americans who suffer from the disease each year. Consider a sample of 10,000 melanoma patients.
  a. What are the expected value and variance of x, the number of the 10,000 melanoma patients who die of the affliction this year?
  b. Find the probability that x will exceed 1,600 patients per year.

c. Would you expect x, the number of patients dying of melanoma, to exceed 6,500 in any single year? Explain.

5.75 Quit smoking program. In Exercise 4.57 (p. 216), you learned that only 5% of the nation's cigarette smokers ever enter into a treatment program to help them quit smoking. (*USF Magazine*, Spring 2000.) In a random sample of 200 smokers, let x be the number who enter into a treatment program.

a. Find the mean of x. (This value should agree with your answer to Exercise 4.58)

b. Find the standard deviation of x.

c. Find the z-score for the value $x = 10.5$.

d. Find the approximate probability that the number of smokers in a sample of 200 who will enter into a treatment program is 11 or more.

5.76 Caesarian birth study. In Exercise 4.58 (p. 216), you learned that 22% of all births in the U.S. occur by Caesarian section each year. (*USA Today*, Sept. 19, 2000.) In a random sample of 1,000 births this year, let x be the number that occur by Caesarian section.

a. Find the mean of x. (This value should agree with your answer to Exercise 4.44**a**.)

b. Find the standard deviation of x. (This value should agree with your answer to Exercise 4.44**b**.)

c. Find the z-score for the value $x = 200.5$.

d. Find the approximate probability that the number of Caesarian sections in a sample of 1,000 births is less than or equal to 200.

Applying the Concepts—Intermediate

5.77 Defects in semiconductor wafers. The computer chips in notebook and laptop computers are produced from semiconductor wafers. Certain semiconductor wafers are exposed to an environment that generates up to 100 possible defects per wafer. The number of defects per wafer, x, was found to follow a binomial distribution if the manufacturing process is stable and generates defects that are randomly distributed on the wafers. (*IEEE Transactions on Semiconductor Manufacturing*, May 1995.) Let p represent the probability that a defect occurs at any one of the 100 points of the wafer. For each of the following cases, determine whether the normal approximation can be used to characterize x.

a. $p = .01$ **b.** $p = .50$ **c.** $p = .90$

5.78 Parents who condone spanking. In Exercise 4.60 (p. 217), you learned that 60% of parents with young children condone spanking their child as a regular form of punishment. (*Tampa Tribune*, Oct. 5, 2000.) A child psychologist with 150 parent clients claims that no more than 20 of the parents condone spanking. Do you believe this claim? Explain.

5.79 Fungi in beech forest trees. Refer to the *Applied Ecology and Environmental Research* (Vol. 1, 2003) study of beech trees damaged by fungi, Exercise 4.61 (p. 217). Recall that the researchers found that 25% of the beech trees in East Central Europe have been damaged by fungi. In an East Central European forest with 200 beech trees, how likely is it that more than half of the trees have fungi damage?

5.80 FTC price accuracy study. Refer to the FTC study of the pricing accuracy of supermarket electronic scanners, Exercise 4.115 (p. 230). Recall that the probability that a scanned item is priced incorrectly is $\frac{1}{30} = .033$.

a. Suppose 10,000 supermarket items are scanned. What is the approximate probability that you observe at least 100 items with incorrect prices?

b. Suppose 100 items are scanned and you are interested in the probability that fewer than five are incorrectly priced. Explain why the approximate method of part **a** may not yield an accurate estimate of the probability.

5.81 Victims of domestic abuse. In Exercise 4.63 (p. 217) you learned that some researchers believe that one in every three women are victims of domestic abuse. (*Annals of Internal Medicine*, Nov. 1995.)

a. For a random sample of 150 women, what is the approximate probability that more than half are victims of domestic abuse?

b. For a random sample of 150 women, what is the approximate probability that fewer than 50 are victims of domestic abuse?

c. Would you expect to observe fewer than 30 domestically abused women in a sample of 150? Explain.

Applying the Concepts—Advanced

5.82 Body fat in men. The percentage of fat in the bodies of American men is an approximately normal random variable with mean equal to 15% and standard deviation equal to 2%.

a. If these values were used to describe the body fat of men in the United States Army and if 20% or more body fat is characterized as obese, what is the approximate probability that a random sample of 10,000 soldiers will contain fewer than 50 who would actually be characterized as obese?

b. If the army actually were to check the percentage of body fat for a random sample of 10,000 men and if only 30 contained 20% (or higher) body fat, would you conclude that the army was successful in reducing the percentage of obese men below the percentage in the general population? Explain your reasoning.

5.83 Luggage inspection at Newark airport. According to *New Jersey Business* (Feb. 1996), Newark International Airport's new terminal handles an average of 3,000 international passengers an hour but is capable of handling twice that number. Also, 80% of arriving international passengers pass through without their luggage being inspected and the remainder are detained for inspection. The inspection facility can handle 600 passengers an hour without unreasonable delays for the travelers.

a. When international passengers arrive at the rate of 1,500 per hour, what is the expected number of passengers who will be detained for luggage inspection?

b. In the future, it is expected that as many as 4,000 international passengers will arrive per hour. When that occurs, what is the expected number of passengers who will be detained for luggage inspection?

c. Refer to part **b.** Find the approximate probability that more than 600 international passengers will be detained for luggage inspection. (This is also the probability that travelers will experience unreasonable luggage inspection delays.)

5.84 Waiting time at a doctor's office. The median time a patient waits to see a doctor in a large clinic is 20 minutes. On a day when 150 patients visit the clinic, what is the approximate probability that

a. More than half will wait more than 20 minutes?

b. More than 85 will wait more than 20 minutes?

c. More than 60 but fewer than 90 will wait more than 20 minutes?

5.6 The Exponential Distribution (Optional)

The length of time between emergency arrivals at a hospital, the length of time between breakdowns of manufacturing equipment, the length of time between catastrophic events (floods, earthquakes, etc.), and the distance traveled by a wildlife ecologist between sightings of an endangered species are all random phenomena that we might want to describe probabilistically. The amount of time or distance between occurrences of random events like these can often be described by the **exponential probability distribution**. For this reason, the exponential distribution is sometimes called the **waiting time distribution**. The formula for the exponential probability distribution is shown in the box along with its mean and standard deviation.

Probability Distribution for an Exponential Random Variable x

Probability density function: $f(x) = \dfrac{1}{\theta} e^{-x/\theta}$ $\quad (x > 0)$

Mean: $\mu = \theta$ $\quad$ Standard deviation: $\sigma = \theta$

Unlike the normal distribution, which has a shape and location determined by the values of the two quantities μ and σ, the shape of the exponential distribution is governed by a single quantity, θ. Further, it is a probability distribution with the property that its mean equals its standard deviation. Exponential distributions corresponding to $\theta = .5, 1,$ and 2 are shown in Figure 5.24.

To calculate probabilities for exponential random variables, we need to be able to find areas under the exponential probability distribution. Suppose we want to find the area A to the right of some number a, as shown in Figure 5.25.

This area can be calculated by using the formula shown in the box. Use Table V in Appendix A or a pocket calculator with an exponential function to find the value of $e^{-a/\theta}$ after substituting the appropriate numerical values for θ and a.

Figure 5.24
Exponential Distributions

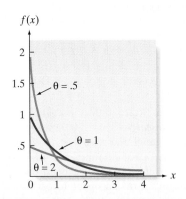

Finding the Area A to the Right of a Number a for an Exponential Distribution*

$$A = P(x \geq a) = e^{-a/\theta}$$

Figure 5.25

The Area A to the Right of a Number a for an Exponential Distribution

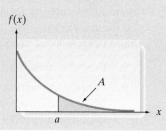

EXAMPLE 5.13

FINDING AN EXPONENTIAL PROBABILITY

Problem Suppose the length of time (in hours) between emergency arrivals at a certain hospital is modeled as an exponential distribution with $\theta = 2$. What is the probability that more than 5 hours pass without an emergency arrival?

Solution The probability we want is the area A to the right of $a = 5$ in Figure 5.26. To find this probability, use the formula given for area:

$$A = e^{-a/\theta} = e^{-(5/2)} = e^{-2.5}$$

Referring to Table V, we find

$$A = e^{-2.5} = .082085$$

Our exponential model indicates that the probability that more than 5 hours pass between emergency arrivals is about .08 for this hospital.

Look Back The value $e^{-2.5}$ can also be found using a standard hand calculator. Or, you can find the desired probability using a statistical software package.

Figure 5.26

Area to the Right of $a = 5$ for Example 5.13

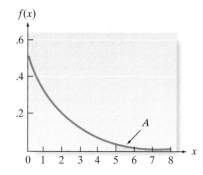

| Now Work | *Exercise 5.89* |

■ ■ ■

*For students with a knowledge of calculus, the highlighted area in Figure 5.25 corresponds to the integral

$$\int_a^\infty \frac{1}{\theta} e^{-x/\theta} \, dx = -e^{-x/\theta} \Big|_a^\infty = e^{-a/\theta}.$$

EXAMPLE 5.14   THE MEAN AND VARIANCE OF AN EXPONENTIAL
RANDOM VARIABLE

Problem   A microwave oven manufacturer is trying to determine the length of warranty period it should attach to its magnetron tube, the most critical component in the oven. Preliminary testing has shown that the length of life (in years), x, of a magnetron tube has an exponential probability distribution with $\theta = 6.25$.

    a. Find the mean and standard deviation of x.

    b. Suppose a warranty period of 5 years is attached to the magnetron tube. What fraction of tubes must the manufacturer plan to replace, assuming that the exponential model with $\theta = 6.25$ is correct?

    c. Find the probability that the length of life of a magnetron tube will fall within the interval $\mu - 2\sigma$ to $\mu + 2\sigma$.

Solution   **a.** Since $\theta = \mu = \sigma$, both μ and σ equal 6.25.

    b. To find the fraction of tubes that will have to be replaced before the 5-year warranty period expires, we need to find the area between 0 and 5 under the distribution. This area, A, is shown in Figure 5.27. To find the required probability, we recall the formula

$$P(x > a) = e^{-a/\theta}$$

Using this formula, we can find

$$P(x > 5) = e^{-a/\theta} = e^{-5/6.25} = e^{-.80} = .449329$$

(see Table V). To find the area A, we use the complementary relationship:

$$P(x \le 5) = 1 - P(x > 5) = 1 - .449329 = .550671$$

So approximately 55% of the magnetron tubes will have to be replaced during the 5-year warranty period.

    c. We would expect the probability that the life of a magnetron tube, x, falls within the interval $\mu - 2\sigma$ to $\mu + 2\sigma$ to be quite large. A graph of the exponential distribution showing the interval $\mu - 2\sigma$ to $\mu + 2\sigma$ is given in Figure 5.28. Since the point $\mu - 2\sigma$ lies below $x = 0$, we need to find only the area between $x = 0$ and $x = \mu + 2\sigma = 6.25 + 2(6.25) = 18.75$.

This area, P, which is highlighted in Figure 5.28, is

$$P = 1 - P(x > 18.75) = 1 - e^{-18.75/\theta} = 1 - e^{-18.75/6.25} = 1 - e^{-3}$$

Figure 5.27
Area to the Left of a = 5 for
Example 5.14

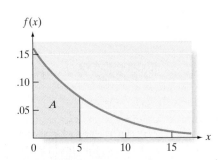

Figure 5.28
Area in the Interval $\mu \pm 2\sigma$
for Example 5.14

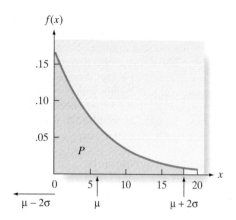

Using Table V or a calculator, we find $e^{-3} = .049787$. Therefore, the probability that the life x of a magnetron tube will fall within the interval $\mu - 2\sigma$ to $\mu + 2\sigma$ is

$$P = 1 - e^{-3} = 1 - .049787 = .950213$$

Look Back You can see that this probability agrees very well with the interpretation of a standard deviation given by the Empirical Rule (Table 2.7, p. 74) even though this probability distribution is not mound-shaped. (It is strongly skewed to the right.)

■ ■ ■

Exercises 5.85–5.101

Understanding the Principles

5.85 What are the characteristics of an exponential random variable?

5.86 The exponential distribution is often called the _____ distribution. (Fill in the blank.)

Learning the Mechanics

5.87 The random variables x and y have exponential distributions with $\theta = 3$ and $\theta = 1$, respectively. Using Table V in Appendix A, carefully plot both distributions on the same set of axes.

5.88 Use Table V in Appendix A to determine the value of $e^{-a/\theta}$ for each of the following cases.
  a. $\theta = 1, a = 1$ **b.** $\theta = 1, a = 2.5$
  c. $\theta = .4, a = 3$ **d.** $\theta = .2, a = .3$

5.89 Suppose x has an exponential distribution with $\theta = 1$.
NW Find the following probabilities:
  a. $P(x > 1)$ **b.** $P(x \leq 3)$
  c. $P(x > 1.5)$ **d.** $P(x \leq 5)$

5.90 Suppose x has an exponential distribution with $\theta = 2.5$. Find the following probabilities:
  a. $P(x \leq 4)$ **b.** $P(x > 5)$
  c. $P(x \leq 2)$ **d.** $P(x > 3)$

5.91 Suppose the random variable x has an exponential probability distribution with $\theta = 1$. Find the mean and standard deviation of x. Find the probability that x will assume a value within the interval $\mu \pm 2\sigma$.

5.92 The random variable x can be adequately approximated by an exponential probability distribution with $\theta = 2$. Find the probability that x assumes a value
  a. More than 3 standard deviations from μ.
  b. Less than 2 standard deviations from μ.
  c. Within .5 standard deviation of μ.

Applying the Concepts—Basic

5.93 Lead in metal shredder residue. Based on data collected from metal shredders across the nation, the amount x of extractable lead in metal shredder residue has an approximate exponential distribution with mean $\theta = 2.5$ milligrams per liter (Florida Shredder's Association).
  a. Find the probability that x is greater than 2 milligrams per liter.
  b. Find the probability that x is less than 5 milligrams per liter.

5.94 Life length of bacteria. After bacteria are subjected to a certain drug, the length of time until the bacteria die follows an exponential distribution with a mean of 30 minutes.
  a. How long will it take for half the bacteria to die after the drug is administered?
  b. What proportion of bacteria will die between 12 minutes and 60 minutes?

5.95 Forest development following wildfires. Refer to the *Ecological Applications* (May 1995) study of forest development 110 years following a wildfire, Exercise 5.43 (p. 260). Another species of tree, western hemlock, was found to have a breast height diameter distribution that resembled an exponential distribution with $\theta = 30$ centimeters. Find the probability that a western hemlock tree growing in the forest damaged by wildfire 110 years ago has a diameter that exceeds 25 centimeters.

Applying the Concepts—Intermediate

5.96 NHL overtime games. In the National Hockey League (NHL), games that are tied at the end of three periods are sent to "sudden-death" overtime. In overtime, the team to score the first goal wins. An analysis of NHL overtime games showed that the length of time elapsed before the winning goal is scored has an exponential distribution with mean 9.15 minutes (*Chance*, Winter 1995.)

   a. For a randomly selected overtime NHL game, find the probability that the winning goal is scored in 3 minutes or less.

   b. In the NHL, each period (including overtime) lasts 20 minutes. If neither team scores a goal in overtime, the game is considered a tie. What is the probability of an NHL game ending in a tie?

5.97 Machine repair times. An article in *IEEE Transactions* (Mar. 1990) gave an example of a flexible manufacturing system (FMS) with four machines operating independently. The repair rates for the machines (i.e., the time, in hours, it takes to repair a failed machine) are exponentially distributed with means $\mu_1 = 1$, $\mu_2 = 2$, $\mu_3 = .5$, and $\mu_4 = .5$, respectively.

   a. Find the probability that the repair time for machine 1 exceeds 1 hour.

   b. Repeat part **a** for machine 2.

   c. Repeat part **a** for machines 3 and 4.

   d. If all four machines fail simultaneously, find the probability that the repair time for the entire system exceeds 1 hour.

⚙ **FORFRAG**
5.98 Forest fragmentation study. Refer to the *Conservation Ecology* (December 2003) study on the causes of fragmentation for 54 South American forests, Exercise 2.148 (p. 100). Recall that the cause is classified as either anthropogenic or natural in origin. The anthropogenic fragmentation index (saved in the **FORFRAG** file) for the South American forests has an approximate exponential distribution with a mean of 23.

   a. Find the probability that a South American forest has an anthropogenic fragmentation index between 20 and 40.

   b. Find the probability that a South American forest has an anthropogenic fragmentation index below 50.

   c. The natural fragmentation index (also saved in the **FORGRAG** file) does not have an approximate exponential distribution. Why?

5.99 Ship-to-shore transfer times. Lack of port facilities or shallow water may require cargo on a large ship to be transferred to a pier using smaller craft. This process may require the smaller craft to cycle back and forth from ship to shore many times. Researchers G. Horne (Center for Naval Analysis) and T. Irony (George Washington University) developed models of this transfer process that provide estimates of ship-to-shore transfer times. (*Naval Research Logistics*, Vol. 41, 1994.) They modeled the time between arrivals of the smaller craft at the pier using an exponential distribution.

   a. Assume the mean time between arrivals at the pier is 17 minutes. Give the value of θ for this exponential distribution. Graph the distribution.

   b. Suppose there is only one unloading zone at the pier available for the small craft to use. If the first craft docks at 10:00 am and doesn't finish unloading until 10:15 am, what is the probability that the second craft will arrive at the unloading zone and have to wait before docking?

5.100 Modeling machine downtime. The importance of modeling machine downtime correctly in simulation studies was discussed in *Industrial Engineering* (Aug. 1990). The paper presented simulation results for a single-machine-tool system with the following properties:
   1. The interarrival times of jobs are exponentially distributed with a mean of 1.25 minutes
   2. The amount of time the machine operates before breaking down is exponentially distributed with a mean of 540 minutes

   a. Find the probability that two jobs arrive for processing at most 1 minute apart.

   b. Find the probability that the machine operates for at least 720 minutes (12 hours) before breaking down.

Applying the Concepts—Advanced

5.101 Life length of a halogen bulb. For a certain type of halogen light bulb, an old bulb that has been in use for a while tends to have a longer life length than a new bulb. Let x represent the life length (in hours) of a new halogen light bulb and assume that x has an exponential distribution with mean $\theta = 250$ hours. According to *Microelectronics and Reliability* (Jan. 1986), the "life" distribution of x is considered *new better than used* (NBU) if

$$P(x > a + b) \leq P(x > a)P(x > b)$$

Alternatively, a "life" distribution is considered *new worse than used* (NWU) if

$$P(x > a + b) \geq P(x > a)P(x > b)$$

   a. Show that when $a = 300$ and $b = 200$ the exponential distribution is both NBU and NWU.

   b. Choose any two positive numbers a and b, where $a > 0$ and $b > 0$, and repeat part **a**.

   c. Show that, in general, for any a and b ($a > 0$ and $b > 0$), the exponential distribution with mean θ is both NBU and NWU. Such a "life" distribution is said to be *new same as used* or *memoryless*. Explain why.

Quick Review

Key Terms

Note: Starred (*) terms are from the optional sections in this chapter.

Bell curve   243
Bell-shaped distribution   243
Continuous probability
  distribution   237
Continuous random variable   237

*Correction for continuity   270
*Exponential distribution   276
*Exponential random variable   276
  Frequency function   238
  Normal distribution   243
  Normal probability plot   261
  Normal random variable   244
  Probability density function   238
  Probability distribution   238

Randomness distribution   239
Standard normal distribution   245
Standard normal random
  variable   245
Uniform distribution   239
Uniform random variable   239
*Waiting time distribution   276

Key Formulas

Note: Starred (*) formulas are from the optional sections in this chapter.

Density Function	Mean	Standard Deviation	Random Variable
$f(x) = \dfrac{1}{d-c}(c \le x \le d)$	$\mu = \dfrac{c+d}{2}$	$\sigma = \dfrac{d-c}{\sqrt{12}}$	Uniform, x 239
$f(x) = \dfrac{1}{\sigma\sqrt{2\pi}}e^{-(1/2)[(x-\mu)/\sigma]^2}$	μ	σ	Normal, x 244
$f(z) = \dfrac{1}{\sqrt{2\pi}}e^{-(1/2)z^2}$	$\mu = 0$	$\sigma = 1$	Standard Normal, $z = \left(\dfrac{x-\mu}{\sigma}\right)$ 248
$f(x) = \dfrac{1}{\theta}e^{-x/\theta}(x > 0)$	$\mu = \theta$	$\sigma = \theta$	*Exponential, x 276

*Normal Approximation to Binomial: $P(x \le a) = P\left[z \le \dfrac{(a+.5)-\mu}{\sigma}\right]$ 273

Language Lab

Symbol	Pronunciation	Description
$f(x)$	f of x	Probability density function for a continuous random variable x
θ	theta	Mean of exponential random variable

Chapter Summary

- Three types of continuous random variables: **uniform**, **normal**, and **exponential**
- **Uniform probability distribution** is a model for continuous random variables that are evenly distributed over a certain interval
- **Normal probability distribution** is a model for continuous random variables that have a bell-shaped curve

- Methods for assessing normality: **histogram**, **stem-and-leaf display**, $\text{IQR}/s \approx 1.3$, and **normal probability plot**
- Normal distribution can be used to approximate a binomial probability when $\mu \pm 3\sigma$ falls within the interval $(0, n)$
- **Exponential probability distribution** is a model for continuous random variables that have a waiting time distribution

Supplementary Exercises 5.102–5.135

Note: Starred (*) exercises refer to the optional sections in this chapter.

Understanding the Principles

*5.102 Consider the following continuous random variables. Give the probability distribution (uniform, normal, or exponential) that is likely to best approximate the distribution of the random variable:

a. Score on an IQ test

b. Time (in minutes) waiting in line at a supermarket checkout counter

c. Amount of liquid (in ounces) dispensed into a can of soda

d. Difference between SAT scores for tests taken at two different times

*5.103 Identify the type of continuous random variable— uniform, normal, or exponential—described by each of the following probability density functions.

a. $f(x) = (e^{-x/7})/7, x > 0$

b. $f(x) = 1/20, 5 < x < 25$

c. $f(x) = \dfrac{e^{-.5[(x-10)/5]^2}}{5\sqrt{2\pi}}$

Learning the Mechanics

5.104 Assume that x is a random variable best described by a uniform distribution with $c = 40$ and $d = 70$.

a. Find $f(x)$.

b. Find the mean and standard deviation of x.

c. Graph the probability distribution for x and locate its mean and the interval $\mu \pm 2\sigma$ on the graph.

d. Find $P(x \leq 45)$.

e. Find $P(x \geq 58)$.

f. Find $P(x \leq 100)$.

g. Find $P(\mu - \sigma \leq x \leq \mu + \sigma)$.

h. Find $P(x > 60)$.

5.105 Find the following probabilities for the standard normal random variable z:

a. $P(z \leq 2.1)$

b. $P(z \geq 2.1)$

c. $P(z \geq -1.65)$

d. $P(-2.13 \leq z \leq -.41)$

e. $P(-1.45 \leq z \leq 2.15)$

f. $P(z \leq -1.43)$

5.106 Find a z-score, call it z_0, such that

a. $P(z \leq z_0) = .8708$

b. $P(z \geq z_0) = .0526$

c. $P(z \leq z_0) = .5$

d. $P(-z_0 \leq z \leq z_0) = .8164$

e. $P(z \geq z_0) = .8023$

f. $P(z \geq z_0) = .0041$

5.107 The random variable x has a normal distribution with $\mu = 70$ and $\sigma = 10$. Find the following probabilities:

a. $P(x \leq 75)$

b. $P(x \geq 90)$

c. $P(60 \leq x \leq 75)$

d. $P(x > 75)$

e. $P(x = 75)$

f. $P(x \leq 95)$

5.108 The random variable x has a normal distribution with $\mu = 40$ and $\sigma^2 = 36$. Find a value of x, call it x_0, such that

a. $P(x \geq x_0) = .5$

b. $P(x \leq x_0) = .9911$

c. $P(x \leq x_0) = .0028$

d. $P(x \geq x_0) = .0228$

e. $P(x \leq x_0) = .1003$

f. $P(x \geq x_0) = .7995$

*5.109 Assume that x is a binomial random variable with $n = 100$ and $p = .5$. Use the normal probability distribution to approximate the following probabilities:

a. $P(x \leq 48)$

b. $P(50 \leq x \leq 65)$

c. $P(x \geq 70)$

d. $P(55 \leq x \leq 58)$

e. $P(x = 62)$

f. $P(x \leq 49 \text{ or } x \geq 72)$

*5.110 Assume that x has an exponential distribution with $\theta = 3$. Find

a. $P(x \leq 1)$

b. $P(x > 1)$

c. $P(x = 1)$

d. $P(x \leq 6)$

e. $P(2 \leq x \leq 10)$

Applying the Concepts—Basic

5.111 Passing the FCAT math test. All Florida high schools require their students to demonstrate competence in mathematics by scoring 70% or above on the FCAT mathematics achievement test. The FCAT math scores of those students taking the test for the first time are normally distributed with a mean of 77% and a standard deviation of 7.3%. What percentage of students who take the test for the first time will pass the test?

5.112 No-hitters in baseball. In baseball, a "no-hitter" is a regulation 9-inning game in which the pitcher yields no hits to the opposing batters. *Chance* (Summer 1994) reported on a study of no-hitters in Major League Baseball (MLB). The initial analysis focused on the total number of hits yielded per game per team for all 9-inning MLB games played between 1989 and 1993. The distribution of hits/9-innings is approximately normal with mean 8.72 and standard deviation 1.10.

a. What percentage of 9-inning MLB games result in fewer than 6 hits?

b. Demonstrate, statistically, why a no-hitter is considered an extremely rare occurrence in MLB.

*5.113 Sickle-cell anemia. Eight percent of the African-American population is known to carry the trait for sickle-cell anemia. (Sickle Cell-Information Center, Atlanta, Ga.) If 1,000 African-Americans are sampled at random, what is the approximate probability that
a. More than 175 carry the trait?
b. Fewer than 140 carry the trait?

*5.114 Laser surgery complications. According to *Time* (Oct. 11, 1999), 1% of all patients who undergo laser surgery to correct their vision have serious postlaser vision problems. In a sample of 100,000 patients, what is the approximate probability that fewer than 950 will experience serious postlaser vision problems?

5.115 Lengths of sardines. *Fisheries Science* (Feb. 1995) published a study of the length distributions of sardines inhabiting Japanese waters. At two years of age, fish have a length distribution that is approximately normal with $\mu = 20.20$ centimeters (cm) and $\sigma = .65$ cm.
a. Find the probability that a two-year-old sardine inhabiting Japanese waters is between 20 and 21 cm long.
b. Find the probability that a two-year-old sardine in Japanese waters is less than 19.84 cm long.
c. Find the probability that a two-year-old sardine in Japanese waters is greater than 22.01 cm long.

5.116 Quality of river water. The Council on Environmental Quality (CEQ) considers a river with a dissolved oxygen content of less than 5 milligrams per liter (mg/L) of water to be undesirable because it is unlikely to support aquatic life. Suppose an industrial plant discharges its waste into a river and the downstream daily oxygen content measurements are normally distributed with a mean equal to 6.3 mg/L and a standard deviation of .6 mg/L.
a. What percentage of the days would the dissolved oxygen content in the river be considered undesirable by the CEQ?
b. Within what limits would we expect the dissolved oxygen content to fall?

5.117 Tropical island temperatures. Records indicate that the daily high January temperatures on a tropical island tend to have a uniform distribution over the interval from 75°F to 90°F. A tourist arrives on the island on a randomly selected day in January.
a. What is the probability that the temperature will be above 80°F?
b. What is the probability that the temperature will be between 80°F and 85°F?
c. What is the expected temperature?

*5.118 Hospital patient interarrival times. The length of time between arrivals at a hospital clinic has an approximately exponential probability distribution. Suppose the mean time between arrivals for patients at a clinic is 4 minutes.
a. What is the probability that a particular interarrival time (the time between the arrival of two patients) is less than 1 minute?

b. What is the probability that the next four interarrival times are all less than 1 minute?
c. What is the probability that an interarrival time will exceed 10 minutes?

Applying the Concepts—Intermediate

5.119 Waiting for an elevator. The manager of a large department store with three floors reports that the time a customer on the second floor must wait for an elevator has a uniform distribution ranging from 0 to 4 minutes. If it takes the elevator 15 seconds to go from floor to floor, find the probability that a hurried customer can reach the first floor in less than 1.5 minutes after pushing the second-floor elevator button.

5.120 Comparison of exam scores: red versus blue exam. Refer to the *Teaching Psychology* (May 1998) study of how external clues influence performance, Exercise 2.116 (p. 85). Recall that two different forms of a midterm psychology examination were given—one printed on blue paper and the other printed on red paper. Grading only the difficult questions, scores on the blue exam had a distribution with a mean of 53% and a standard deviation of 15%, while scores on the red exam had a distribution with a mean of 39% and a standard deviation of 12%. Assuming that both distributions are approximately normal, on which exam form is a student more likely to score below 20% on the difficult questions, the blue or the red exam? (Compare your answer to 2.116**c**.)

5.121 Galaxy velocity study. Recall *The Astronomical Journal* (July 1995) study of galaxy velocity, Exercise 5.58 (p. 267). The observed velocity of a galaxy located in galaxy cluster A2142 was found to have a normal distribution with mean 27,117 kilometers per second (km/s) and standard deviation 1,280 km/s. A galaxy with a velocity of 24,350 km/s is observed. Comment on the likelihood of this galaxy being located in cluster A2142.

5.122 Study of children with developmental delays. It is well known that children with developmental delays (i.e., mild mental retardation) are slower, cognitively, than normally developing children. Are their social skills also lacking? A study compared the social interactions of the two groups of children in a controlled playground environment. (*American Journal on Mental Retardation*, Jan. 1992.) One variable of interest was the number of intervals of "no play" by each child. Children with developmental delays had a mean of 2.73 intervals of "no play" and a standard deviation of 2.58 intervals. Based on this information, is it possible for the variable of interest to be normally distributed? Explain.

5.123 Chemical properties of a plant extract. The extract of a plant native to Taiwan (Republic of China) is being tested as a possible treatment for leukemia. The chemical properties of the extract were examined in *Planta Medica* (Apr. 1995). A particular compound produced from the plant extract was analyzed for the protein collagen. The collagen amount x for the compound was found to be normally distributed with $\mu = 76.8$ and $\sigma = 9.2$ grams per milliliter.

a. What percentage of compounds formed from the plant extract will have a collagen amount greater than 90 grams per milliliter?

b. Give an interval around the mean μ that contains the collagen amount for 80% of the compounds formed from the plant extract.

5.124 Mile run times. A physical-fitness association is including the mile run in its secondary-school fitness test for students. The time for this event for students in secondary school is approximately normally distributed with a mean of 450 seconds and a standard deviation of 40 seconds. If the association wants to designate the fastest 10% as "excellent," what time should the association set for this criterion?

5.125 Rubidium in metamorphic rock. A chemical analysis of metamorphic rock in western Turkey was reported in *Geological Magazine* (May 1995). The trace amount (in parts per million) of the element rubidium was measured for 20 rock specimens. The data are listed here. Assess whether the sample data come from a normal population.

RUBIDIUM

164	286	355	308	277	330	323	370	241	402
301	200	202	341	327	285	277	247	213	424

Source: Bozkurt, E. et al. "Geochemistry and the tectonic significance of augen gneisses from the southern Menderes Massif (West Turkey)." *Geological Magazine,* Vol. 132, No. 3, May 1995, p. 291 (Table 1).

5.126 Sedimentary deposits in reservoirs. Geologists have successfully used statistical models to evaluate the nature of sedimentary deposits (called *facies*) in reservoirs. One of the model's key parameters is the proportion P of facies bodies in a reservoir. An article in *Mathematical Geology* (Apr. 1995) demonstrated that the number of facies bodies that must be sampled to satisfactorily estimate P is approximately normally distributed with $\mu = 99$ and $\sigma = 4.3$. How many facies bodies are required to satisfactorily estimate P for 99% of the reservoirs evaluated?

5.127 Normal curve approximation. A. K. Shah published a simple approximation for areas under the normal curve in *The American Statistician* (Feb. 1985). Shah showed that the area A under the standard normal curve between 0 and z is

$$A \approx \begin{cases} z(4.4 - z)/10 & \text{for } 0 \leq z \leq 2.2 \\ .49 & \text{for } 2.2 < z < 2.6 \\ .50 & \text{for } z \geq 2.6 \end{cases}$$

a. Use the approximation to find
  i. $P(0 < z < 1.2)$
  ii. $P(0 < z < 2.5)$
  iii. $P(z > .8)$
  iv. $P(z < 1.0)$

b. Find the exact probabilities in part **a**.

c. Shah showed that the approximation has a maximum absolute error of .0052. Verify this for the approximations in part **a**.

*5.128 Spruce budworm infestation. An infestation of a certain species of caterpillar, the spruce budworm, can cause extensive damage to the timberlands of the northern United States. It is known that an outbreak of this type of infestation occurs, on the average, every 30 years. Assuming that this phenomenon obeys an exponential probability law, what is the probability that catastrophic outbreaks of spruce budworm infestation will occur within 6 years of each other?

5.129 Maximum time to take a test. A professor believes that if a class is allowed to work on an examination as long as desired, the times spent by the students would be approximately normal with mean 40 minutes and standard deviation 6 minutes. Approximately how long should be allotted for the examination if the professor wants almost all (say, 97.5%) of the class to finish?

*5.130 Modeling an airport taxi service. In an article published in the *European Journal of Operational Research* (Vol. 21, 1985), the vehicle-dispatching decisions of an airport-based taxi service were investigated. In modeling the system, the authors assumed travel times of successive taxi trips to and from the terminal to be independent exponential random variables. Assume $\theta = 20$ minutes.

a. What is the mean trip time for the taxi service?

b. What is the probability that a particular trip will take more than 30 minutes?

c. Two taxis have just been dispatched. What is the probability that both will be gone for more than 30 minutes? That at least one of the taxis will return within 30 minutes?

*5.131 Defective CD-ROMs. A manufacturer of CD-ROMs claims that 99.4% of its CDs are defect free. A large software company that buys and uses large numbers of the CDs wants to verify this claim, so it selects 1,600 CDs to be tested. The tests reveal 12 CDs to be defective. Assuming that the manufacturer's claim is correct, what is the probability of finding 12 or more defective CDs in a sample of 1,600? Does your answer cast doubt on the manufacturer's claim? Explain.

Applying the Concepts—Advanced

*5.132 Accidents at a plant. The number of serious accidents in a manufacturing plant has (approximately) a Poisson probability distribution with a mean of two serious accidents per month. If x, the number of events per unit time, has a Poisson distribution with mean λ, then it can be shown that the time between two successive events has an exponential probability distribution with mean $\theta = 1/\lambda$.

a. If an accident occurs today, what is the probability that the next serious accident will not occur within the next month?

b. What is the probability that more than one serious accident will occur within the next month?

5.133 Water retention of soil cores. A team of soil scientists investigated the water retention properties of soil cores sampled from an uncropped field consisting of silt loam (*Soil Science*, Jan. 1995). At a pressure of .1 megapascal (MPa), the water content of the soil (measured in cubic meters of water per cubic meter of soil) was determined to be approximately normally distributed with $\mu = .27$ and $\sigma = .04$. In addition to water content readings at a pressure of .1 MPa, measurements were obtained at pressures 0, .005, .01, .03, and 1.5 MPa. Consider a soil core with a water content reading of .14. Is it likely that this reading was obtained at a pressure of .1 MPa? Explain.

Critical Thinking Challenges

*5.134 Weights of corn chip bags. The net weight per bag of a certain brand of corn chips is listed as 10 ounces. The weight of chips actually dispensed in each bag by an automated machine, when operating to specifications, is a normal random variable with mean 10.5 ounces and standard deviation .25 ounce. A quality control inspector will randomly select 1,500 bags from the automated process and measure precisely the weight of each. Ideally, all of the bags should contain at least 10 ounces of corn chips. However, if at least 97% of the bags contain 10 ounces or more, the process is considered "under control" and no adjustments to the machine are deemed necessary. Assess the likelihood that the quality control inspector will find fewer than 97% of the bags with 10 ounces or more even if the process is "under control."

5.135 IQs and "The Bell Curve". In their controversial book *The Bell Curve* (Free Press, 1994), Professors Richard J. Herrnstein (a Harvard psychologist who died while the book was in production) and Charles Murray (a political scientist at MIT) explore, as the subtitle states, "intelligence and class structure in American life." *The Bell Curve* heavily employs statistical analyses in an attempt to support the authors' positions. Since the book's publication, many expert statisticians have raised doubts about the authors' statistical methods and the inferences drawn from them. (See, for example, "Wringing *The Bell Curve*: A cautionary tale about the relationships among race, genes, and IQ," *Chance*, Summer 1995.) One of the many controversies sparked by the book is the authors' tenet that level of intelligence (or lack thereof) is a cause of a wide range of intractable social problems, including constrained economic mobility. The measure of intelligence chosen by the authors is the well known Intelligent Quotient (IQ). Numerous tests have been developed to measure IQ; Herrnstein and Murray use the Armed Forces Qualification Test (AFQT), originally designed to measure the cognitive ability of military recruits. Psychologists traditionally treat IQ as a random variable having a normal distribution with mean $\mu = 100$ and standard deviation $\sigma = 15$.

In their book, Herrnstein and Murray refer to five cognitive classes of people defined by percentiles of the normal distribution. Class I ("very bright") consists of those with IQs above the 95th percentile; Class II ("bright") are those with IQs between the 75th and 95th percentiles; Class III ("normal") includes IQs between the 25th and 75th percentiles; Class IV ("dull") are those with IQs between the 5th and 25th percentiles; and Class V ("very dull") are IQs below the 5th percentile.

a. Assuming that the distribution of IQ is accurately represented by the normal curve, determine the proportion of people with IQs in each of the five cognitive classes defined by Herrnstein and Murray.

b. Although the cognitive classes above are defined in terms of percentiles, the authors stress that IQ scores should be compared with z-scores, not percentiles. In other words, it is more informative to give the difference in z-scores for two IQ scores than it is to give the difference in percentiles. Do you agree?

c. Researchers have found that scores on many intelligence tests are decidedly nonnormal. Some distributions are skewed toward higher scores, others toward lower scores. How would the proportions in the five cognitive classes (part **a**) differ for an IQ distribution that is skewed right? Skewed left?

Student Projects

For large values of n the computational effort involved in working with the binomial probability distribution is considerable. Fortunately, in many instances the normal distribution provides a good approximation to the binomial distribution. This project was designed to enable you to demonstrate to yourself how well the normal distribution approximates the binomial distribution.

a. Let the random variable x have a binomial probability with $n = 10$ and $p = .5$. Using the binomial distribution, find the probability that x takes on a value in each of the following intervals: $\mu \pm \sigma$, $\mu \pm 2\sigma$, and $\mu \pm 3\sigma$.

b. Find the probabilities requested in part **a** by using a normal approximation to the given binomial distribution.

c. Determine the magnitude of the difference between each of the three probabilities as determined by the binomial distribution and by the normal approximation.

d. Letting x have a binomial distribution with $n = 20$ and $p = .5$, repeat parts **a**, **b**, and **c**. Notice that the probability estimates provided by the normal distribution are more accurate for $n = 20$ than for $n = 10$.

e. Letting x have a binomial distribution with $n = 20$ and $p = .01$, repeat parts **a**, **b**, and **c**. Notice that the probability estimates provided by the normal distribution are very poor in this case. Explain why this occurs.

REFERENCES

Hogg, R. V., and Craig, A. T. *Introduction to Mathematical Statistics*, 5th ed. Upper Saddle River, N.J.: Prentice Hall, 1995.

Lindgren, B. W. *Statistical Theory*, 3rd ed. New York: Macmillan, 1976.

Mood, A. M., Graybill, F. A., and Boes, D. C. *Introduction to the Theory of Statistics*, 3rd ed. New York: McGraw-Hill, 1974.

Ramsey, P. P., and Ramsey, P. H. "Simple tests of normality in small samples." *Journal of Quality Technology*, Vol. 22, 1990.

Ross, S. M. *Stochastic Processes*, 2nd ed. New York: Wiley, 1996.

Wackerly, D., Mendenhall, W., and Scheaffer, R. L. *Mathematical Statistics with Applications*, 6th ed. North Scituate, Mass.: Duxbury, 2002.

Winkler, R. L., and Hays, W. *Statistics: Probability, Inference, and Decision*, 2nd ed. New York: Holt, Rinehart and Winston, 1975.

Using Technology

Cumulative Probabilities for Continuous Random Variables and Normal Probability Plots Using MINITAB

To obtain cumulative probabilities for the continuous random variables discussed in this chapter using MINITAB, click on the "Calc" button on the MINITAB menu bar, next click on "Probability Distributions," then finally click on the distribution of your choice (e.g., "Normal"), as shown in Figure 5.M.1. The resulting dialog box appears as shown in Figure 5.M.2. Select "Cumulative probability," specify the parameters of the distribution (e.g., the mean μ and standard deviation σ), and enter the value of x in the "Input constant" box. When you click "OK," the cumulative normal probability for the value of x will appear on the MINITAB session window.

Figure 5.M.1
MINITAB Menu Options
for Obtaining Probabilities

Figure 5.M.2
MINITAB Normal
Distribution Dialog Box

Figure 5.M.3

MINITAB Options for a
Normal Probability Plot

[*Note:* For the MINITAB exponential option, you will need to enter the value of the mean λ in the resulting dialog box. For the uniform option, you will need to enter the minimum and maximum values of the distribution.]

To obtain a normal probability plot using MINITAB, click on the "Graph" button on the MINITAB menu bar. Then click on "Probability Plot", as shown in Figure 5.M.3. Select "Single" (for one variable) on the next box, and the dialog box will appear as shown in Figure 5.M.4. Specify the variable of interest in the "Graph variables" box. Then click the "Distribution" button and select the "Normal" option. Click "OK" to return to the Probability Plot dialog box, and then click "OK" to generate the normal probability plot.

Figure 5.M.4
MINITAB Probability
Plot Dialog Box

6

Sampling Distributions

Contents

6.1 The Concept of a Sampling Distribution

6.2 Properties of Sampling Distributions: Unbiasedness and Minimum Variance

6.3 The Sampling Distribution of $\bar{x}$ and the Central Limit Theorem

Statistics in Action

The Insomnia Pill

Using Technology

Simulating a Sampling Distribution
Using MINITAB

Where We've Been

- Learned that the objective of most statistical investigations is inference—that is, making decisions about a population based on a sample

- Discovered that sample statistics such as the sample mean and sample variance can be used to make the decisions

- Found that probability distributions for random variables are used to construct theoretical models of populations

Where We're Going

- Establish that a sample statistic is a random variable with a probability distribution.

- Define a *sampling distribution* as the probability distribution of a sample statistic.

- Learn that the sampling distribution of the sample mean tends to be approximately normal.

Statistics in *ACTION*

The Insomnia Pill

A research report published in the *Proceedings of the National Academy of Sciences* (March 1994) brought encouraging news to insomniacs and international business travelers who suffer from jet lag. Neuroscientists at the Massachusetts Institute of Technology (MIT) have been experimenting with melatonin—a hormone secreted by the pineal gland in the brain—as a sleep-inducing hormone. Since the hormone is naturally produced, it is nonaddictive. The researchers believe melatonin may be effective in treating jet lag—the body's response to rapid travel across many time zones so that a daylight-darkness change disrupts sleep patterns.

In the MIT study, young male volunteers were given various doses of melatonin or a placebo (a dummy medication containing no melatonin). Then they were placed in a dark room at midday and told to close their eyes for 30 minutes. The variable of interest was the time (in minutes) elapsed before each volunteer fell asleep.

According to the lead investigator, Professor Richard Wurtman, "Our volunteers fall asleep in five or six minutes on melatonin, while those on placebo take about 15 minutes." Wurtman warns, however, that uncontrolled doses of melatonin could cause mood-altering side effects. (Melatonin is sold in some health food stores. However, sales are unregulated, and the purity and strength of the hormone are often uncertain.)

Now, consider a random sample of 40 young males, each of whom is given a dosage of the sleep-inducing hormone melatonin. The times (in minutes) to fall asleep for these 40 males are listed in Table SIA6.1 and saved in the **INSOMNIA** file. The researchers know that with the placebo (i.e., no hormone), the mean time to fall asleep is $\mu = 15$ minutes and the standard deviation is $\sigma = 10$ minutes. They want to use the data to make an inference about the true value of μ for those taking the melatonin. Specifically, the researchers want to know whether melatonin is an effective drug against insomnia.

In this chapter, a Statistics in Action Revisited example demonstrates how we can use one of the topics discussed in this chapter—the Central Limit Theorem—to make an inference about the effectiveness of melatonin as a sleep-inducing hormone.

Statistics in the Action Revisited

• Making an Inference about the Mean Sleep Time for Insomnia Pill Takers (p. 309)

⊙ INSOMNIA

TABLE SIA6.1   Times (in Minutes) for 40 Male Volunteers to Fall Asleep

7.6	2.1	1.4	1.5	3.6	17.0	14.9	4.4	4.7	20.1
7.7	2.4	8.1	1.5	10.3	1.3	3.7	2.5	3.4	10.7
2.9	1.5	15.9	3.0	1.9	8.5	6.1	4.5	2.2	2.6
7.0	6.4	2.8	2.8	22.8	1.5	4.6	2.0	6.3	3.2

[Note: These data are simulated sleep times based on summary information provided in the MIT study.]

In Chapters 4 and 5 we assumed that we knew the probability distribution of a random variable, and using this knowledge we were able to compute the mean, variance, and probabilities associated with the random variable. However, in most practical applications, this information is not available. To illustrate, in Example 4.12 (p. 212) we calculated the probability that the binomial random variable x, the number of 20 polled voters who favor a certain mayoral candidate, assumed specific values. To do this, it was necessary to assume some value for p, the proportion of all voters who favor the candidate. Thus, for the purposes of illustration, we assumed $p = .6$ when, in all likelihood, the exact value of p would be unknown. In fact, the probable purpose of taking the poll is to estimate p. Similarly, when we modeled the in-city gas mileage of a certain automobile model, we used the normal probability distribution with an *assumed* mean and standard deviation of 27 and 3 miles per gallon, respectively. In most situations, the true mean and standard deviation are unknown quantities that would have to be estimated. Numerical quantities that describe probability distributions are called *parameters*. Thus, p, the probability of a success in a binomial experiment, and μ and σ, the mean and standard deviation of a normal distribution, are examples of parameters.

DEFINITION 6.1

A **parameter** is a numerical descriptive measure of a population. Because it is based on the observations in the population, its value is almost always unknown.

We have also discussed the sample mean $\bar{x}$, sample variance s^2, sample standard deviation s, etc., which are numerical descriptive measures calculated from the sample. (See Table 6.1 for a list of the statistics covered so far in this text.) We will often use the information contained in these *sample statistics* to make inferences about the parameters of a population.

DEFINITION 6.2

A **sample statistic** is a numerical descriptive measure of a sample. It is calculated from the observations in the sample.

TABLE 6.1   List of Population Parameters and Corresponding Sample Statistics

	Population Parameter	Sample Statistic
Mean:	μ	$\bar{x}$
Variance:	σ^2	s^2
Standard deviation:	σ	s
Binomial proportion:	p	$\hat{p}$

Note that the term *statistic* refers to a *sample* quantity and the term *parameter* refers to a *population* quantity.

Before we can show you how to use sample statistics to make inferences about population parameters, we need to be able to evaluate their properties. Does one sample statistic contain more information than another about a population parameter? On what basis should we choose the "best" statistic for making inferences about a parameter? The purpose of this chapter is to answer these questions.

6.1 The Concept of a Sampling Distribution

If we want to estimate a parameter of a population—say, the population mean μ—we could use a number of sample statistics for our estimate. Two possibilities are the sample mean $\bar{x}$ and the sample median M. Which of these do you think will provide a better estimate of μ?

Before answering this question, consider the following example: Toss a fair die, and let x equal the number of dots showing on the up face. Suppose the die is tossed three times, producing the sample measurements 2, 2, 6. The sample mean is $\bar{x} = 3.33$ and the sample median is $M = 2$. Since the population mean of x is $\mu = 3.5$, you can see that for this sample of three measurements, the sample mean $\bar{x}$ provides an estimate that falls closer to μ than does the sample median (see Figure 6.1a). Now suppose we toss the die three more times and obtain the sample measurements 3, 4, 6.

Figure 6.1

Comparing the Sample Mean ($\bar{x}$) and Sample Median (M) as Estimators of the Population Mean (μ)

a. Sample 1: $\bar{x}$ is closer than M to μ b. Sample 2: M is closer than $\bar{x}$ to μ

The mean and median of this sample are $\bar{x} = 4.33$ and $M = 4$, respectively. This time M is closer to μ (see Figure 6.1b).

This simple example illustrates an important point: Neither the sample mean nor the sample median will *always* fall closer to the population mean. Consequently, we cannot compare these two sample statistics, or, in general, any two sample statistics, on the basis of their performance for a single sample. Instead, we need to recognize that sample statistics are themselves random variables, because different samples can lead to different values for the sample statistics. As random variables, sample statistics must be judged and compared on the basis of their probability distributions (i.e., the *collection* of values and associated probabilities of each statistic that would be obtained if the sampling experiment were repeated a *very large number of times*). We will illustrate this concept with another example.

Suppose it is known that in a certain part of Canada the daily high temperature recorded for all past months of January has a mean of $\mu = 10°F$ and a standard deviation of $\sigma = 5°F$. Consider an experiment consisting of randomly selecting 25 daily high temperatures from the records of past months of January and calculating the sample mean $\bar{x}$. If this experiment were repeated a very large number of times, the value of $\bar{x}$ would vary from sample to sample. For example, the first sample of 25 temperature measurements might have a mean $\bar{x} = 9.8$, the second sample a mean $\bar{x} = 11.4$, the third sample a mean $\bar{x} = 10.5$, etc. If the sampling experiment were repeated a very large number of times, the resulting histogram of sample means would be approximately the probability distribution of $\bar{x}$. If $\bar{x}$ is a good estimator of μ, we would expect the values of $\bar{x}$ to cluster around μ as shown in Figure 6.2. This probability distribution is called a *sampling distribution* because it is generated by repeating a sampling experiment a very large number of times.

DEFINITION 6.3

The **sampling distribution** of a sample statistic calculated from a sample of n measurements is the probability distribution of the statistic.

In actual practice, the sampling distribution of a statistic is obtained mathematically or (at least approximately) by simulating the sample on a computer using a procedure similar to that just described.

If $\bar{x}$ has been calculated from a sample of $n = 25$ measurements selected from a population with mean $\mu = 10$ and standard deviation $\sigma = 5$, the sampling distribution (Figure 6.2) provides information about the behavior of $\bar{x}$ in repeated sampling.

Figure 6.2

Sampling Distribution for $\bar{x}$ Based on a Sample of $n = 25$ Measurements

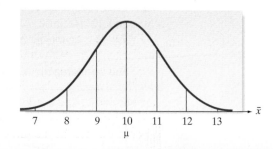

For example, the probability that you will draw a sample of 25 measurements and obtain a value of $\bar{x}$ in the interval $9 \leq \bar{x} \leq 10$ will be the area under the sampling distribution over that interval.

Since the properties of a statistic are typified by its sampling distribution, it follows that to compare two sample statistics you compare their sampling distributions. For example, if you have two statistics, A and B, for estimating the same parameter (for purposes of illustration, suppose the parameter is the population variance σ^2) and if their sampling distributions are as shown in Figure 6.3, you would choose statistic A in preference to statistic B. You would make this choice because the sampling distribution for statistic A centers over σ^2 and has less spread (variation) than the sampling distribution for statistic B. When you draw a single sample in a practical sampling situation, the probability is higher that statistic A will fall nearer σ^2.

Figure 6.3

Two Sampling Distributions for Estimating the Population Variance, σ^2

Remember that in practice we will not know the numerical value of the unknown parameter σ^2 so we will not know whether statistic A or statistic B is closer to σ^2 for a sample. We have to rely on our knowledge of the theoretical sampling distributions to choose the best sample statistic and then use it sample after sample. The procedure for finding the sampling distribution for a statistic is demonstrated in Example 6.1.

EXAMPLE 6.1   FINDING A SAMPLING DISTRIBUTION

Problem   Consider a game played with a standard 52-card bridge deck in which you can score 0, 3, or 12 points on any one hand. Suppose the population of points scored per hand is described by the probability distribution shown here. A random sample of $n = 3$ hands is selected from the population.

x	0	3	12
$p(x)$	$\frac{1}{3}$	$\frac{1}{3}$	$\frac{1}{3}$

a. Find the sampling distribution of the sample mean $\bar{x}$.

b. Find the sampling distribution of the sample median M.

Solution   Points for every possible sample of $n = 3$ hands is listed in Table 6.2 along with the sample mean and median. Also, because any one sample is as likely to be selected as any other (random sampling), the probability of observing any particular sample is $\frac{1}{27}$. The probability is also listed in Table 6.2.

a. From Table 6.2 you can see that $\bar{x}$ can assume the values 0, 1, 2, 3, 4, 5, 6, 8, 9, and 12. Because $\bar{x} = 0$ occurs in only one sample, $P(\bar{x} = 0) = \frac{1}{27}$. Similarly, $\bar{x} = 1$ occurs in three samples: $(0, 0, 3)$, $(0, 3, 0)$, and $(3, 0, 0)$. Therefore, $P(\bar{x} = 1) = \frac{3}{27} = \frac{1}{9}$. Calculating the probabilities of the remaining values of $\bar{x}$ and arranging them in a table, we obtain the probability distribution shown below.

$\bar{x}$	0	1	2	3	4	5	6	8	9	12
$p(\bar{x})$	$\frac{1}{27}$	$\frac{3}{27}$	$\frac{3}{27}$	$\frac{1}{27}$	$\frac{3}{27}$	$\frac{6}{27}$	$\frac{3}{27}$	$\frac{3}{27}$	$\frac{3}{27}$	$\frac{1}{27}$

TABLE 6.2   Outcomes for Three Hands of a Card Game

Possible Samples	$\bar{x}$	M	Probability
0, 0, 0	0	0	$1/27$
0, 0, 3	1	0	$1/27$
0, 0, 12	4	0	$1/27$
0, 3, 0	1	0	$1/27$
0, 3, 3	2	3	$1/27$
0, 3, 12	5	3	$1/27$
0, 12, 0	4	0	$1/27$
0, 12, 3	5	3	$1/27$
0, 12, 12	8	12	$1/27$
3, 0, 0	1	0	$1/27$
3, 0, 3	2	3	$1/27$
3, 0, 12	5	3	$1/27$
3, 3, 0	2	3	$1/27$
3, 3, 3	3	3	$1/27$
3, 3, 12	6	3	$1/27$
3, 12, 0	5	3	$1/27$
3, 12, 3	6	3	$1/27$
3, 12, 12	9	12	$1/27$
12, 0, 0	4	0	$1/27$
12, 0, 3	5	3	$1/27$
12, 0, 12	8	12	$1/27$
12, 3, 0	5	3	$1/27$
12, 3, 3	6	3	$1/27$
12, 3, 12	9	12	$1/27$
12, 12, 0	8	12	$1/27$
12, 12, 3	9	12	$1/27$
12, 12, 12	12	12	$1/27$

This is the sampling distribution for $\bar{x}$ because it specifies the probability associated with each possible value of $\bar{x}$.

b. In Table 6.2 you can see that the median M can assume one of the three values: 0, 3, or 12. The value $M = 0$ occurs in seven different samples. Therefore, $P(M = 0) = 7/27$. Similarly, $M = 3$ occurs in 13 samples and $M = 12$ occurs in seven samples. Therefore, the probability distribution (i.e., the sampling distribution) for the median M is as shown below.

M	0	3	12
$p(M)$	$7/27$	$13/27$	$7/27$

Look Back The sampling distributions of parts **a** and **b** are found by first listing all the distinct values of the statistic and then calculating the probability of each value.

Now Work *Exercise 6.3*

■ ■ ■

Example 6.1 demonstrates the procedure for finding the exact sampling distribution of a statistic when the number of different samples that could be selected from the population is relatively small. In the real world, populations often consist of a large number of different values, making samples difficult (or impossible) to enumerate. When this situation occurs, we may choose to obtain the approximate sampling distribution for a statistic by simulating the sampling over and over again and recording the proportion of times different values of the statistic occur. Example 6.2 illustrates this procedure.

EXAMPLE 6.2   SIMULATING A SAMPLING DISTRIBUTION

Problem   Suppose we perform the following experiment over and over again: Take a sample of 11 measurements from the uniform distribution shown in Figure 6.4. Calculate the two sample statistics

$$\bar{x} = \text{Sample mean} = \frac{\Sigma x}{11}$$

$M = \text{Median} = \text{Sixth sample measurement when the 11 measurements are arranged in ascending order}$

Obtain approximations to the sampling distributions of $\bar{x}$ and M.

Solution   We used MINITAB to generate 1,000 samples, each with $n = 11$ observations. Then we compute $\bar{x}$ and M for each sample. Our goal is to obtain approximations to the sampling distributions of $\bar{x}$ and M to find out which sample statistic ($\bar{x}$ or M) contains more information about μ. (Note that, in this particular example, we *know* the population mean for this uniform distribution is $\mu = .5$.) The first 10 of the 1,000 samples generated are presented in Table 6.3. For instance, the first computer-generated sample from the uniform distribution (arranged in ascending order) contained the following measurements: .045, .499, .860, .182, .644, .362, .502, .132, .691, .695, and .177. The sample mean $\bar{x}$ and median M computed for this sample are

$$\bar{x} = \frac{.045 + .499 + \cdots + .177}{11} = .435$$

$$M = \text{Sixth ordered measurement} = .499$$

The MINITAB relative frequency histograms for $\bar{x}$ and M for the 1,000 samples of size $n = 11$ are shown in Figure 6.5. These histograms represent approximations to the true sampling distributions of $\bar{x}$ and M.

Look Back You can see that the values of $\bar{x}$ tend to cluster around μ to a greater extent than do the values of M. Thus, on the basis of the observed sampling distributions, we conclude that $\bar{x}$ contains more information about μ than M does—at least for samples of $n = 11$ measurements from the uniform distribution.

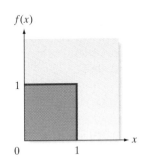

$f(x)$

1

0   1 x

Figure 6.4
Uniform Distribution from 0 to 1

TABLE 6.3   First 10 Samples of $n = 11$ Measurements from a Uniform Distribution

Sample	Measurements										
1	.045	.499	.860	.182	.644	.362	.502	.132	.691	.695	.177
2	.529	.918	.357	.156	.357	.965	.935	.515	.675	.662	.755
3	.247	.745	.085	.100	.034	.277	.002	.874	.788	.272	.156
4	.052	.454	.055	.877	.999	.467	.903	.683	.003	.845	.469
5	.082	.744	.614	.364	.882	.878	.527	.193	.186	.928	.175
6	.069	.331	.009	.083	.093	.329	.394	.732	.454	.220	.485
7	.056	.265	.367	.421	.679	.076	.548	.285	.912	.679	.862
8	.856	.528	.350	.340	.583	.785	.412	.581	.342	.022	.595
9	.689	.174	.432	.999	.186	.223	.950	.541	.053	.366	.702
10	.544	.074	.493	.326	.521	.258	.056	.087	.380	.931	.035

Figure 6.5
MINITAB Histograms for $\bar{x}$
and M, Example 6.2

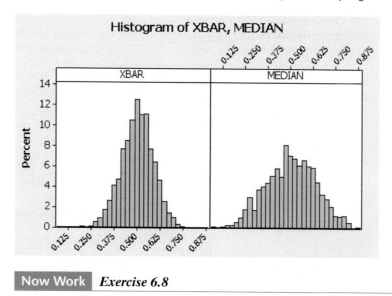

Now Work   *Exercise 6.8*

■ ■ ■

As noted earlier, many sampling distributions can be derived mathematically, but the theory necessary to do this is beyond the scope of this text. Consequently, when we need to know the properties of a statistic, we will present its sampling distribution and simply describe its properties. Several of the important properties we look for in sampling distributions are discussed in the next section.

Exercises 6.1–6.9

Understanding the Principles

6.1   What is the difference between a population parameter and a sample statistic?

6.2   What is a sampling distribution of a sample statistic?

Learning the Mechanics

6.3   The probability distribution shown here describes a **NW** population of measurements that can assume values of 0, 2, 4, and 6, each of which occurs with the same relative frequency:

x	0	2	4	6
$p(x)$	$\frac{1}{4}$	$\frac{1}{4}$	$\frac{1}{4}$	$\frac{1}{4}$

a. List all the different samples of $n = 2$ measurements that can be selected from this population.

b. Calculate the mean of each different sample listed in part **a**.

c. If a sample of $n = 2$ measurements is randomly selected from the population, what is the probability that a specific sample will be selected?

d. Assume that a random sample of $n = 2$ measurements is selected from the population. List the different values of $\bar{x}$ found in part **b**, and find the probability of each. Then give the sampling distribution of the sample mean $\bar{x}$ in tabular form.

e. Construct a probability histogram for the sampling distribution of $\bar{x}$.

6.4   Simulate sampling from the population described in Exercise 6.3 by marking the values of x, one on each of four identical coins (or poker chips, etc.). Place the coins (marked 0, 2, 4, and 6) into a bag, randomly select one, and observe its value. Replace this coin, draw a second coin, and observe its value. Finally, calculate the mean $\bar{x}$ for this sample of $n = 2$ observations randomly selected from the population (Exercise 6.3, part **b**). Replace the coins, mix, and using the same procedure, select a sample of $n = 2$ observations from the population. Record the numbers and calculate $\bar{x}$ for this sample. Repeat this sampling process until you acquire 100 values of $\bar{x}$. Construct a relative frequency distribution for these 100 sample means. Compare this distribution to the exact sampling distribution of $\bar{x}$ found in part **e** of Exercise 6.3. [*Note:* The distribution obtained in this exercise is an approximation to the exact sampling distribution. But, if you were to repeat the sampling procedure, drawing two coins not 100 times but 10,000 times, the relative frequency distribution for the 10,000 sample means would be almost identical to the sampling distribution of $\bar{x}$ found in Exercise 6.3, part **e**.]

6.5   Consider the population described by the probability distribution shown here.

x	1	2	3	4	5
$p(x)$	.2	.3	.2	.2	.1

The random variable x is observed twice. If these observations are independent, verify that the different samples of size 2 and their probabilities are as shown below.

Sample	Probability	Sample	Probability
1, 1	.04	3, 4	.04
1, 2	.06	3, 5	.02
1, 3	.04	4, 1	.04
1, 4	.04	4, 2	.06
1, 5	.02	4, 3	.04
2, 1	.06	4, 4	.04
2, 2	.09	4, 5	.02
2, 3	.06	5, 1	.02
2, 4	.06	5, 2	.03
2, 5	.03	5, 3	.02
3, 1	.04	5, 4	.02
3, 2	.06	5, 5	.01
3, 3	.04		

a. Find the sampling distribution of the sample mean $\bar{x}$.
b. Construct a probability histogram for the sampling distribution of $\bar{x}$.
c. What is the probability that $\bar{x}$ is 4.5 or larger?
d. Would you expect to observe a value of $\bar{x}$ equal to 4.5 or larger? Explain.

6.6   Refer to Exercise 6.5 and find $E(x) = \mu$. Then use the sampling distribution of $\bar{x}$ found in Exercise 6.5 to find the expected value of $\bar{x}$. Note that $E(\bar{x}) = \mu$.

6.7   Refer to Exercise 6.5. Assume that a random sample of $n = 2$ measurements is randomly selected from the population.

a. List the different values that the sample median M may assume and find the probability of each. Then give the sampling distribution of the sample median.
b. Construct a probability histogram for the sampling distribution of the sample median and compare it with the probability histogram for the sample mean (Exercise 6.5, part **b**).

6.8   In Example 6.2 we use the computer to generate 1,000 samples, each containing $n = 11$ observations, from a uniform distribution over the interval from 0 to 1. For this exercise, use the computer to generate 500 samples, each containing $n = 15$ observations, from this population.

a. Calculate the sample mean for each sample. To approximate the sampling distribution of $\bar{x}$, construct a relative frequency histogram for the 500 values of $\bar{x}$.
b. Repeat part **a** for the sample median. Compare this approximate sampling distribution with the approximate sampling distribution of $\bar{x}$ found in part **a**.

6.9   Consider a population that contains values of x equal
NW to 00, 01, 02, 03, . . . , 96, 97, 98, 99. Assume that these values of x occur with equal probability. Use the computer to generate 500 samples, each containing $n = 25$ measurements, from this population. Calculate the sample mean $\bar{x}$ and sample variance s^2 for each of the 500 samples.

a. To approximate the sampling distribution of $\bar{x}$, construct a relative frequency histogram for the 500 values of $\bar{x}$.
b. Repeat part **a** for the 500 values of s^2.

6.2   Properties of Sampling Distributions: Unbiasedness and Minimum Variance

The simplest type of statistic used to make inferences about a population parameter is a *point estimator*. A point estimator is a rule or formula that tells us how to use the sample data to calculate a single number that is intended to estimate the value of some population parameter. For example, the sample mean $\bar{x}$ is a point estimator of the population mean μ. Similarly, the sample variance s^2 is a point estimator of the population variance σ^2.

DEFINITION 6.4

A **point estimator** of a population parameter is a rule or formula that tells us how to use the sample data to calculate a single number that can be used as an *estimate* of the population parameter.

Often, many different point estimators can be found to estimate the same parameter. Each will have a sampling distribution that provides information about the point estimator. By examining the sampling distribution, we can determine how large the difference between an estimate and the true value of the parameter (called the **error of estimation**) is likely to be. We can also tell whether an estimator is more likely to overestimate or to underestimate a parameter.

EXAMPLE 6.3   COMPARING TWO STATISTICS

Problem   Suppose two statistics, A and B, exist to estimate the same population parameter, θ (theta). (Note that θ could be any parameter, μ, σ^2, σ, etc.) Suppose the two statistics have sampling distributions as shown in Figure 6.6. Based on these sampling distributions, which statistic is more attractive as an estimator of θ?

Figure 6.6

Sampling Distributions
of Unbiased and Biased
Estimators

Mean of sampling distribution

a. Unbiased sample statistic
   for the parameter θ

b. Biased sample statistic
   for the parameter θ

Solution   As a first consideration, we would like the sampling distribution to center over the value of the parameter we wish to estimate. One way to characterize this property is in terms of the mean of the sampling distribution. Consequently, we say that a statistic is *unbiased* if the mean of the sampling distribution is equal to the parameter it is intended to estimate. This situation is shown in Figure 6.6a, where the mean μ_A of statistic A is equal to θ. If the mean of a sampling distribution is not equal to the parameter it is intended to estimate, the statistic is said to be *biased*. The sampling distribution for a biased statistic is shown in Figure 6.6b. The mean μ_B of the sampling distribution for statistic B is not equal to θ; in fact, it is shifted to the right of θ.

Look Back You can see that biased statistics tend either to overestimate or to under-estimate a parameter. Consequently, when other properties of statistics tend to be equivalent, we will choose an unbiased statistic to estimate a parameter of interest.*

Now Work   *Exercise 6.14*

■ ■ ■

DEFINITION 6.5

If the sampling distribution of a sample statistic has a mean equal to the popu-lation parameter the statistic is intended to estimate, the statistic is said to be an **unbiased estimate** of the parameter.

If the mean of the sampling distribution is not equal to the parameter, the statistic is said to be a **biased estimate** of the parameter.

The standard deviation of a sampling distribution measures another important property of statistics—the spread of these estimates generated by repeated sam-pling. Suppose two statistics, A and B, are both unbiased estimators of the popula-tion parameter. Since the means of the two sampling distributions are the same, we turn to their standard deviations in order to decide which will provide estimates that fall closer to the unknown population parameter we are estimating. Naturally, we will choose the sample statistic that has the smaller standard deviation. Figure 6.7

*Unbiased statistics do not exist for all parameters of interest, but they do exist for the parameters considered in this text.

Figure 6.7

Sampling Distributions for
Two Unbiased Estimators

depicts sampling distributions for A and B. Note that the standard deviation of the distribution of A is smaller than the standard deviation for B, indicating that over a large number of samples, the values of A cluster more closely around the unknown population parameter than do the values of B. Stated differently, the probability that A is close to the parameter value is higher than the probability that B is close to the parameter value.

In summary, to make an inference about a population parameter, we use the sample statistic with a sampling distribution that is unbiased and has a small standard deviation (usually smaller than the standard deviation of other unbiased sample statistics). The derivation of this sample statistic will not concern us, because the "best" statistic for estimating specific parameters is a matter of record. We will simply present an unbiased estimator with its standard deviation for each population parameter we consider. [*Note:* The standard deviation of the sampling distribution of a statistic is also called the **standard error of the statistic**.]

EXAMPLE 6.4   BIASED AND UNBIASED ESTIMATORS

Problem   In Example 6.1, we found the sampling distributions of the sample mean $\bar{x}$ and the sample median M for random samples of $n = 3$ measurements from a population defined by the probability distribution shown below.

x	0	3	12
$p(x)$	$\frac{1}{3}$	$\frac{1}{3}$	$\frac{1}{3}$

The sampling distributions of $\bar{x}$ and M were found to be as shown here.

$\bar{x}$	0	1	2	3	4	5	6	8	9	12
$p(\bar{x})$	$\frac{1}{27}$	$\frac{3}{27}$	$\frac{3}{27}$	$\frac{1}{27}$	$\frac{3}{27}$	$\frac{6}{27}$	$\frac{3}{27}$	$\frac{3}{27}$	$\frac{3}{27}$	$\frac{1}{27}$

M	0	3	12
$p(M)$	$\frac{7}{27}$	$\frac{13}{27}$	$\frac{7}{27}$

a. Show that $\bar{x}$ is an unbiased estimator of μ in this situation.

b. Show that M is a biased estimator of μ in this situation.

Solution   **a.** The expected value of a discrete random variable x (see Section 4.3) is defined to be $E(x) = \Sigma x p(x)$, where the summation is over all values of x. Then

$$E(x) = \mu = \sum x p(x) = (0)(\tfrac{1}{3}) + (3)(\tfrac{1}{3}) + (12)(\tfrac{1}{3}) = 5$$

The expected value of the discrete random variable $\bar{x}$ is

$$E(\bar{x}) = \sum (\bar{x}) p(\bar{x})$$

summed over all values of $\bar{x}$. Or

$$E(\bar{x}) = (0)(\tfrac{1}{27}) + (1)(\tfrac{3}{27}) + 2(\tfrac{3}{27}) + \cdots + (12)(\tfrac{1}{27}) = 5$$

Since $E(\bar{x}) = \mu$, we see that $\bar{x}$ is an unbiased estimator of μ.

b. The expected value of the sample median M is

$$E(M) = \sum Mp(M) = (0)(\tfrac{7}{27}) + (3)(\tfrac{13}{27}) + (12)(\tfrac{7}{27}) = 4.56$$

Since the expected value of M is not equal to $\mu(\mu = 5)$, the sample median M is a biased estimator of μ.

Now Work   *Exercise 6.16*

■ ■ ■

EXAMPLE 6.5   VARIANCE OF ESTIMATORS

Problem   Refer to Example 6.4 and find the standard deviations of the sampling distributions of $\bar{x}$ and M. Which statistic would appear to be a better estimator of μ?

Solution   The variance of the sampling distribution of $\bar{x}$ (we denote it by the symbol $\sigma_{\bar{x}}^2$) is found to be

$$\sigma_{\bar{x}}^2 = E\{[\bar{x} - E(\bar{x})]^2\} = \sum (\bar{x} - \mu)^2 p(\bar{x})$$

where, from Example 6.4,

$$E(\bar{x}) = \mu = 5$$

Then

$$\sigma_{\bar{x}}^2 = (0 - 5)^2(\tfrac{1}{27}) + (1 - 5)^2(\tfrac{3}{27}) + (2 - 5)^2(\tfrac{3}{27})$$
$$+ \cdots + (12 - 5)^2(\tfrac{1}{27}) = 8.6667$$

and

$$\sigma_{\bar{x}} = \sqrt{8.6667} = 2.94$$

Similarly, the variance of the sampling distribution of M (we denote it by σ_M^2) is

$$\sigma_M^2 = E\{[M - E(M)]^2\}$$

where, from Example 6.4, the expected value of M is $E(M) = 4.56$. Then

$$\sigma_M^2 = E\{[M - E(M)]^2\} = \sum [M - E(M)]^2 p(M)$$
$$= (0 - 4.56)^2(\tfrac{7}{27}) + (3 - 4.56)^2(\tfrac{13}{27}) + (12 - 4.56)^2(\tfrac{7}{27}) = 20.9136$$

and

$$\sigma_M = \sqrt{20.9136} = 4.57$$

Which statistic appears to be the better estimator for the population mean μ: the sample mean $\bar{x}$ or the median M? To answer this question, we compare the sampling distributions of the two statistics. The sampling distribution of the sample median M is biased (i.e., it is located to the left of the mean μ) and its standard deviation $\sigma_M = 4.57$ is much larger than the standard deviation of the sampling distribution of $\bar{x}$, $\sigma_{\bar{x}} = 2.94$. Consequently, the sample mean $\bar{x}$ would be a better estimator of the population mean μ, for the population in question than would the sample median M.

Look Back Ideally, we desire an estimator that is unbiased *and* has the smallest variance among all unbiased estimators. We call this statistic the **minimum variance unbiased estimator** (**MVUE**).

Now Work *Exercise 6.16*

■ ■ ■

Exercises 6.10–6.20

Understanding the Principles

6.10 What is a point estimator of a population parameter?

6.11 What is the difference between a biased and unbiased estimator?

6.12 What is the MVUE for a parameter?

6.13 What are the properties of an ideal estimator?

Learning the Mechanics

6.14 Consider the probability distribution shown here.

NW

x	0	1	4
$p(x)$	$1/3$	$1/3$	$1/3$

a. Find μ and σ^2.

b. Find the sampling distribution of the sample mean $\bar{x}$ for a random sample of $n = 2$ measurements from this distribution.

c. Show that $\bar{x}$ is an unbiased estimator for μ. [*Hint:* Show that $E(\bar{x}) = \Sigma \bar{x} p(\bar{x}) = \mu$]

d. Find the sampling distribution of the sample variance s^2 for a random sample of $n = 2$ measurements from this distribution.

e. Show that s^2 is an unbiased estimator for σ^2.

6.15 Consider the probability distribution shown here.

x	2	4	9
$p(x)$	$1/3$	$1/3$	$1/3$

a. Calculate μ for this distribution.

b. Find the sampling distribution of the sample mean $\bar{x}$ for a random sample of $n = 3$ measurements from this distribution, and show that $\bar{x}$ is an unbiased estimator of μ.

c. Find the sampling distribution of the sample median M for a random sample of $n = 3$ measurements from this distribution, and show that the median is a biased estimator of μ.

d. If you wanted to estimate μ using a sample of three measurements from this population, which estimator would you use? Why?

6.16 Consider the probability distribution shown here.

NW

x	0	1	2
$p(x)$	$1/3$	$1/3$	$1/3$

a. Find μ.

b. For a random sample of $n = 3$ observations from this distribution, find the sampling distribution of the sample mean.

c. Find the sampling distribution of the median of a sample of $n = 3$ observations from this population.

d. Refer to parts **b** and **c** and show that both the mean and median are unbiased estimators of μ for this population.

e. Find the variances of the sampling distributions of the sample mean and the sample median.

f. Which estimator would you use to estimate μ? Why?

6.17 Use the computer to generate 500 samples, each containing $n = 25$ measurements, from a population that contains values of x equal to $1, 2, \ldots, 48, 49, 50$. Assume that these values of x are equally likely. Calculate the sample mean $\bar{x}$ and median M for each sample. Construct relative frequency histograms for the 500 values of $\bar{x}$ and the 500 values of M. Use these approximations to the sampling distributions of $\bar{x}$ and M to answer the following questions:

a. Does it appear that $\bar{x}$ and M are unbiased estimators of the population mean? [*Note:* $\mu = 25.5$.]

b. Which sampling distribution displays greater variation?

6.18 Refer to Exercise 6.5.

a. Show that $\bar{x}$ is an unbiased estimator of μ.

b. Find $\sigma_{\bar{x}}^2$

c. Find the probability that $\bar{x}$ will fall within $2\sigma_{\bar{x}}$ of μ.

6.19 Refer to Exercise 6.5.

a. Find the sampling distribution of s^2.

b. Find the population variance σ^2.

c. Show that s^2 is an unbiased estimator of σ^2.

d. Find the sampling distribution of the sample standard deviation s.

e. Show that s is a biased estimator of σ.

6.20 Refer to Exercise 6.7, where we found the sampling distribution of the sample median. Is the median an unbiased estimator of the population mean μ?

6.3 The Sampling Distribution of $\bar{x}$ and the Central Limit Theorem

Estimating the mean useful life of automobiles, the mean number of crimes per month in a large city, and the mean yield per acre of a new soybean hybrid are practical problems with something in common. In each case we are interested in making an inference about the mean μ of some population. As we mentioned in Chapter 2, the sample mean $\bar{x}$ is, in general, a good estimator of μ. We now develop pertinent information about the sampling distribution for this useful statistic. We will show that $\bar{x}$ is the minimum variance unbiased estimator (MVUE) for μ.

EXAMPLE 6.6   DESCRIBING THE SAMPLING DISTRIBUTION OF $\bar{X}$

Problem   Suppose a population has the uniform probability distribution given in Figure 6.8. The mean and standard deviation of this probability distribution are $\mu = .5$ and $\sigma = .29$. (See Section 5.2 for the formulas for μ and σ.) Now suppose a sample of 11 measurements is selected from this population. Describe the sampling distribution of the sample mean $\bar{x}$ based on the 1,000 sampling experiments discussed in Example 6.2.

Figure 6.8
Sampled Uniform
Population

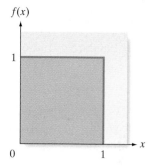

Solution   You will recall that in Example 6.2 we generated 1,000 samples of $n = 11$ measurements each. The MINITAB histogram for the 1,000 sample means is shown in Figure 6.9 with a normal probability distribution superimposed. You can see that this normal probability distribution approximates the computer-generated sampling distribution very well.

Figure 6.9
MINITAB Histogram
for $\bar{x}$ in 1,000 Samples

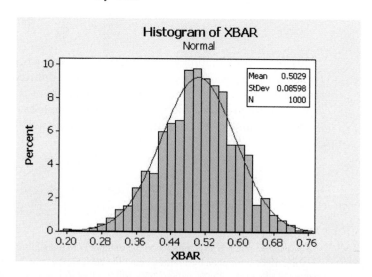

To fully describe a normal probability distribution, it is necessary to know its mean and standard deviation. MINITAB gives these statistics for the 1,000 $\bar{x}$'s in the upper right corner of the histogram, Figure 6.9. You can see that the mean is .503 and the standard deviation is .086.

To summarize our findings based on 1,000 samples, each consisting of 11 measurements from a uniform population, the sampling distribution of $\bar{x}$ appears to be approximately normal with a mean of about .5 and a standard deviation of about .09.

Look Back Note that the simulated value $\mu_{\bar{x}} = .503$ is very close to $\mu = .5$ for the uniform distribution. That is, the simulated sampling distribution of $\bar{x}$ appears to be unbiased for estimating μ.

--- ■ ■ ■ ---

The sampling distribution of $\bar{x}$ has the properties given in the next box, assuming only that a random sample of n observations has been selected from *any* population.

Properties of the Sampling Distribution of $\bar{x}$

1. Mean of sampling distribution equals mean of sampled population. That is, $\mu_{\bar{x}} = E(\bar{x}) = \mu$.

2. Standard deviation of sampling distribution equals

$$\frac{\text{Standard deviation of sampled population}}{\text{Square root of sample size}}$$

That is, $\sigma_{\bar{x}} = \sigma/\sqrt{n}$.*
The standard deviation $\sigma_{\bar{x}}$ is often referred to as the **standard error of the mean**.

You can see that our approximation to $\mu_{\bar{x}}$ in Example 6.6 was precise, since property 1 assures us that the mean is the same as that of the sampled population: .5. Property 2 tells us how to calculate the standard deviation of the sampling distribution of $\bar{x}$. Substituting $\sigma = .29$, the standard deviation of the sampled uniform distribution, and the sample size $n = 11$ into the formula for $\sigma_{\bar{x}}$, we find

$$\sigma_{\bar{x}} = \frac{\sigma}{\sqrt{n}} = \frac{.29}{\sqrt{11}} = .09$$

Thus, the approximation we obtained in Example 6.6, $\sigma_{\bar{x}} \approx .086$, is very close to the exact value, $\sigma_{\bar{x}} = .09$. It can be shown (proof omitted) that the value of $\sigma_{\bar{x}}^2$ is the smallest variance among all unbiased estimators of μ—thus, $\bar{x}$ is the MVUE for μ.

A third property, applicable when the sample size n is large, is contained in one of the most important theoretical results in statistics: the *Central Limit Theorem*.

Central Limit Theorem

Consider a random sample of n observations selected from a population (*any* population) with mean μ and standard deviation σ. Then, when n is sufficiently large,

---

*If the sample size n is large relative to the number N of elements in the population (e.g., 5% or more), $\sigma/\sqrt{n}$ must be multiplied by a finite population correction factor, $\sqrt{(N - n)/(N - 1)}$. For most sampling situations, this correction factor will be close to 1 and can be ignored.

the sampling distribution of $\bar{x}$ will be approximately a normal distribution with mean $\mu_{\bar{x}} = \mu$ and standard deviation $\sigma_{\bar{x}} = \sigma/\sqrt{n}$. The larger the sample size, the better will be the normal approximation to the sampling distribution of $\bar{x}$.*

Biography

PIERRE-SIMON LAPLACE (1749–1827)—The CLT Originator

As a boy growing up in Normandy, France, Pierre-Simon Laplace attended a Benedictine priory school. Upon graduation, he entered Caen University to study theology. During his two years there he discovered his mathematical talents and began his career as an eminent mathematician. In fact, he considered himself the best mathematician in France. Laplace's contributions to mathe- matics ranged from introducing new methods of solving differential equations to complex analyses of motions of astronomical bodies. While studying the angles of inclination of comet orbits in 1778, Laplace showed that the sum of the angles was normally distributed. Consequently, he is considered to be the originator of the Central Limit Theorem. (A rigorous proof of the theorem, however, was not provided until the early 1930s by another French mathematician, Paul Levy.) Laplace also discovered Bayes's theorem and established Bayesian statistical analysis as a valid approach to many practical problems of his time.

Thus, for sufficiently large samples the sampling distribution of $\bar{x}$ is approximately normal. How large must the sample size n be so that the normal distribution provides a good approximation for the sampling distribution of $\bar{x}$? The answer depends on the shape of the distribution of the sampled population, as shown by Figure 6.10. Generally speaking, the greater the skewness of the sampled population distribution, the larger the sample size must be before the normal distribution is an adequate approximation for the sampling distribution of $\bar{x}$. For most sampled populations, sample sizes of $n \geq 30$ will suffice for the normal approximation to be reasonable. We will use the normal approximation for the sampling distribution of $\bar{x}$ when the sample size is at least 30.

EXAMPLE 6.7   USING THE CENTRAL LIMIT THEOREM TO FIND A PROBABILITY

Problem   Suppose we have selected a random sample of $n = 36$ observations from a population with mean equal to 80 and standard deviation equal to 6. It is known that the population is not extremely skewed.

    a. Sketch the relative frequency distributions for the population and for the sampling distribution of the sample mean, $\bar{x}$.

    b. Find the probability that $\bar{x}$ will be larger than 82.

Solution   **a.** We do not know the exact shape of the population relative frequency distribution, but we do know that it should be centered about $\mu = 80$, its spread should be measured by $\sigma = 6$, and it is not highly skewed. One possibility is shown in Figure 6.11a. From the Central Limit Theorem, we know that the sampling distribution of $\bar{x}$ will be approximately normal since the sampled

---

*Moreover, because of the Central Limit Theorem, the sum of a random sample of n observations, Σx, will possess a sampling distribution that is approximately normal for large samples. This distribution will have a mean equal to $n\mu$ and a variance equal to $n\sigma^2$. Proof of the Central Limit Theorem is beyond the scope of this book, but it can be found in many mathematical statistics texts.

Figure 6.10

Sampling Distributions of $\bar{x}$ for Different Populations and Different Sample Sizes

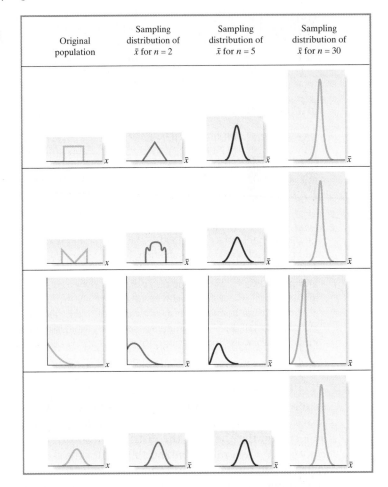

population distribution is not extremely skewed. We also know that the sampling distribution will have mean and standard deviation

$$\mu_{\bar{x}} = \mu = 80 \quad \text{and} \quad \sigma_{\bar{x}} = \frac{\sigma}{\sqrt{n}} = \frac{6}{\sqrt{36}} = 1$$

The sampling distribution of $\bar{x}$ is shown in Figure 6.11b.

b. The probability that $\bar{x}$ will exceed 82 is equal to the highlighted area in Figure 6.12. To find this area, we need to find the z value corresponding to $\bar{x} = 82$. Recall that the standard normal random variable z is the difference between any normally distributed random variable and its mean, expressed

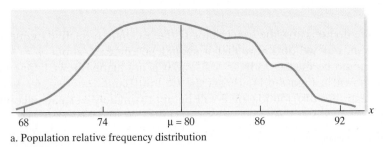

a. Population relative frequency distribution

b. Sampling distribution of $\bar{x}$

Figure 6.11

A Population Relative Frequency Distribution and the Sampling Distribution for $\bar{x}$

Figure 6.12
The Sampling Distribution
of $\bar{x}$

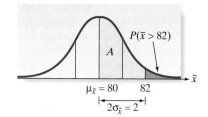

in units of its standard deviation. Since $\bar{x}$ is a normally distributed random variable with mean $\mu_{\bar{x}} = \mu$ and standard deviation $\sigma_{\bar{x}} = \sigma/\sqrt{n}$, it follows that the standard normal z value corresponding to the sample mean, $\bar{x}$, is

$$z = \frac{(\text{Normal random variable}) - (\text{Mean})}{\text{Standard Deviation}} = \frac{\bar{x} - \mu_{\bar{x}}}{\sigma_{\bar{x}}}$$

Therefore, for $\bar{x} = 82$, we have

$$z = \frac{\bar{x} - \mu_{\bar{x}}}{\sigma_{\bar{x}}} = \frac{82 - 80}{1} = 2$$

The area A in Figure 6.12 corresponding to $z = 2$ is given in the table of areas under the normal curve (see Table IV of Appendix A) as .4772. Therefore, the tail area corresponding to the probability that $\bar{x}$ exceeds 82 is

$$P(\bar{x} > 82) = P(z > 2) = .5 - .4772 = .0228$$

Look Back The key to finding the probability, part **b**, is to recognize that the distribution of $\bar{x}$ is normal with $\mu_{\bar{x}} = \mu$ and $\sigma_{\bar{x}} = \sigma/\sqrt{n}$.

Now Work   *Exercise 6.30*

■ ■ ■

EXAMPLE 6.8   A PRACTICAL APPLICATION OF THE CENTRAL LIMIT THEOREM

Problem   A manufacturer of automobile batteries claims that the distribution of the lengths of life of its best battery has a mean of 54 months and a standard deviation of 6 months. Suppose a consumer group decides to check the claim by purchasing a sample of 50 of these batteries and subjecting them to tests that determine battery life.

    a. Assuming that the manufacturer's claim is true, describe the sampling distribution of the mean lifetime of a sample of 50 batteries.

    b. Assuming that the manufacturer's claim is true, what is the probability the consumer group's sample has a mean life of 52 or fewer months?

Solution   **a.** Even though we have no information about the shape of the probability distribution of the lives of the batteries, we can use the Central Limit Theorem to deduce that the sampling distribution for a sample mean lifetime of 50 batteries is approximately normally distributed. Furthermore, the mean of this sampling distribution is the same as the mean of the sampled population, which is $\mu = 54$ months according to the manufacturer's claim. Finally, the standard deviation of the sampling distribution is given by

$$\sigma_{\bar{x}} = \frac{\sigma}{\sqrt{n}} = \frac{6}{\sqrt{50}} = .85 \text{ month}$$

Note that we used the claimed standard deviation of the sampled population, $\sigma = 6$ months. Thus, if we assume that the claim is true, the sampling distribution for the mean life of the 50 batteries sampled is as shown in Figure 6.13.

Figure 6.13

Sampling Distribution of $\bar{x}$ in Example 6.8 for $n = 50$

b. If the manufacturer's claim is true, the probability that the consumer group observes a mean battery life of 52 or fewer months for their sample of 50 batteries, $P(\bar{x} \leq 52)$, is equivalent to the highlighted area in Figure 6.13. Since the sampling distribution is approximately normal, we can find this area by computing the standard normal z value:

$$z = \frac{\bar{x} - \mu_{\bar{x}}}{\sigma_{\bar{x}}} = \frac{\bar{x} - \mu}{\sigma_{\bar{x}}} = \frac{52 - 54}{.85} = -2.35$$

where $\mu_{\bar{x}}$, the mean of the sampling distribution of $\bar{x}$, is equal to μ, the mean of the lifetimes of the sampled population, and $\sigma_{\bar{x}}$ is the standard deviation of the sampling distribution of $\bar{x}$. Note that z is the familiar standardized distance (z-score) of Section 2.6 and, since $\bar{x}$ is approximately normally distributed, it will possess the standard normal distribution of Section 5.3.

The area A shown in Figure 6.13 between $\bar{x} = 52$ and $\bar{x} = 54$ (corresponding to $z = -2.35$) is found in Table IV of Appendix A to be .4906. Therefore, the area to the left of $\bar{x} = 52$ is

$$P(\bar{x} \leq 52) = .5 - A = .5 - .4906 = .0094$$

Thus, the probability the consumer group will observe a sample mean of 52 or less is only .0094 if the manufacturer's claim is true.

Look Back If the 50 tested batteries do exhibit a mean of 52 or fewer months, the consumer group will have strong evidence that the manufacturer's claim is untrue, because such an event is very unlikely to occur if the claim is true. (This is still another application of the *rare-event approach* to statistical inference.)

Now Work *Exercise 6.34*

■ ■ ■

We conclude this section with two final comments on the sampling distribution of $\bar{x}$. First, from the formula $\sigma_{\bar{x}} = \sigma/\sqrt{n}$, we see that the standard deviation of the sampling distribution of $\bar{x}$ gets smaller as the sample size n gets larger. For example, we computed $\sigma_{\bar{x}} = .85$ when $n = 50$ in Example 6.8. However, for $n = 100$ we obtain $\sigma_{\bar{x}} = \sigma/\sqrt{n} = 6/\sqrt{100} = .60$. This relationship will hold true for most of the sample statistics encountered in this text. That is, *The standard deviation of the sampling distribution decreases as the sample size increases.* Consequently, the larger the sample size, the more accurate the sample statistic (e.g., $\bar{x}$) is in estimating a population parameter (e.g., μ). We will use this result in Chapter 7 to help us determine the sample size needed to obtain a specified accuracy of estimation.

Our second comment concerns the Central Limit Theorem. In addition to providing a very useful approximation for the sampling distribution of a sample mean, the Central Limit Theorem offers an explanation for the fact that many relative frequency distributions of data possess mound-shaped distributions. Many of the measurements we take in various areas of research are really means or sums of a large number of small phenomena. For example, a year's growth of a pine seedling is the total of the many individual components that affect the plant's growth. Similarly, we can view the length of time a construction company takes to build a house as the total of the times taken to complete a multitude of distinct jobs, and we can regard the monthly demand for blood at a hospital as the total of the many individual patients' needs. Whether or not the observations entering into these sums satisfy the assumptions basic to the Central Limit Theorem is open to question. However, it is a fact that many distributions of data in nature are mound shaped and possess the appearance of normal distributions.

Statistics in Action Revised

Making an Inference about the Mean Sleep Time for Insomnia Pill Takers

In a Massachusetts Institute of Technology (MIT) study, each in a sample of 40 young male volunteers was given a dosage of the sleep-inducing hormone, melatonin, placed in a dark room at midday, and told to close his eyes for 30 minutes. The researchers measured the time (in minutes) elapsed before each volunteer fell asleep. Recall that the data (shown in Table SIA6.1) are saved in the **INSOMNIA** file.

Previous research established that with the placebo (i.e., no hormone), the mean time to fall asleep is $\mu = 15$ minutes and the standard deviation is $\sigma = 10$ minutes. If the true value of μ for those taking the melatonin is $\mu < 15$ (i.e., if, on average, the volunteers fall asleep faster with the drug than with the placebo), then the researchers can infer that melatonin is an effective drug against insomnia.

Descriptive statistics for the 40 sleep times are displayed in the SPSS printout, Figure SIA6.1. You can see that the mean for the sample is $\bar{x} = 5.935$ minutes. If the drug is not effective in reducing sleep times, then the distribution of sleep times will be no different than the distribution with the placebo. That is, if the drug is not effective, the mean and standard deviation of the population of sleep times are $\mu = 15$ and $\sigma = 10$. If this is true, how likely is it to observe a sample mean that is below 6 minutes?

To answer this question, we desire the probability, $P(\bar{x} < 6)$. To find this probability, we invoke the Central

Limit Theorem (CLT). According to the theorem, the sampling distribution of $\bar{x}$ has the following mean and standard deviation:

$$\mu_{\bar{x}} = \mu = 15$$
$$\sigma_{\bar{x}} = \sigma/\sqrt{n} = 10/\sqrt{40} = 1.58$$

The CLT also states that the distribution of x is approximately normally distributed. Therefore, we find the desired probability (using the standard normal table) as follows:

$$P(\bar{x} < 6) = P\left(z < \frac{6 - \mu_{\bar{x}}}{\sigma_{\bar{x}}}\right)$$
$$= P\left(z < \frac{6 - 15}{1.58}\right) = P(z < -5.70) \approx 0$$

In other words, the probability that we observe a sample mean below $\bar{x} = 6$ minutes *if the mean and standard deviation of the sleep times are $\mu = 15$ and $\sigma = 10$ (i.e., if the drug is not effective)* is almost 0. Either the drug is not effective and the researchers have observed an extremely rare event (one with almost no chance of happening) or the true value of μ for those taking the melatonin pill is much less than 15 minutes. The rare-event approach to making statistical inferences, of course, would favor the second conclusion. Melatonin appears to be an effective insomnia pill, one that lowers the average time it takes the volunteers to fall asleep.

Figure SIA6.1

SPSS Descriptive Statistics for Sleep Time Data

Descriptive Statistics

	N	Minimum	Maximum	Mean	Std. Deviation
SLEEPTIM	40	1.3	22.8	5.935	5.3917
Valid N (listwise)	40				

Exercises 6.21–6.43

Understanding the Principles

6.21 What do the symbols $\mu_{\bar{x}}$ and $\sigma_{\bar{x}}$ represent?

6.22 How does the mean of the sampling distribution of $\bar{x}$ relate to the mean of the population from which the sample is selected?

6.23 How does the standard deviation of the sampling distribution of $\bar{x}$ relate to the standard deviation of the population from which the sample is selected?

6.24 Another name given to the standard deviation of $\bar{x}$ is the _____ . (Fill in the blank.)

6.25 State the Central Limit Theorem.

6.26 Will the sampling distribution of $\bar{x}$ always be approximately normally distributed? Explain.

Learning the Mechanics

6.27 Suppose a random sample of n measurements is selected from a population with mean $\mu = 100$ and variance $\sigma^2 = 100$. For each of the following values of n, give the mean and standard deviation of the sampling distribution of the sample mean $\bar{x}$.
  a. $n = 4$ **b.** $n = 25$
  c. $n = 100$ **d.** $n = 50$
  e. $n = 500$ **f.** $n = 1,000$

6.28 Suppose a random sample of $n = 25$ measurements is selected from a population with mean μ and standard deviation σ. For each of the following values of μ and σ, give the values of $\mu_{\bar{x}}$ and $\sigma_{\bar{x}}$.
  a. $\mu = 10, \sigma = 3$
  b. $\mu = 100, \sigma = 25$
  c. $\mu = 20, \sigma = 40$
  d. $\mu = 10, \sigma = 100$

6.29 Consider the probability distribution shown here.

x	1	2	3	8
$p(x)$	.1	.4	.4	.1

  a. Find μ, σ^2, and σ.
  b. Find the sampling distribution of $\bar{x}$ for random samples of $n = 2$ measurements from this distribution by listing all possible values of $\bar{x}$, and find the probability associated with each.
  c. Use the results of part **b** to calculate $\mu_{\bar{x}}$ and $\sigma_{\bar{x}}$. Confirm that $\mu_{\bar{x}} = \mu$ and that $\sigma_{\bar{x}} = \sigma/\sqrt{n} = \sigma/\sqrt{2}$.

6.30 A random sample of $n = 64$ observations is drawn from a population with a mean equal to 20 and standard deviation equal to 16.
  a. Give the mean and standard deviation of the (repeated) sampling distribution of $\bar{x}$.
  b. Describe the shape of the sampling distribution of $\bar{x}$. Does your answer depend on the sample size?
  c. Calculate the standard normal z-score corresponding to a value of $\bar{x} = 16$.

  d. Calculate the standard normal z-score corresponding to $\bar{x} = 23$.
  e. Find $P(\bar{x} < 16)$.
  f. Find $P(\bar{x} > 23)$.
  g. Find $P(16 < \bar{x} < 23)$.

6.31 A random sample of $n = 100$ observations is selected from a population with $\mu = 30$ and $\sigma = 16$.
  a. Find $\mu_{\bar{x}}$ and $\sigma_{\bar{x}}$.
  b. Describe the shape of the sampling distribution of $\bar{x}$.
  c. Find $P(\bar{x} \geq 28)$.
  d. Find $P(22.1 \leq \bar{x} \leq 26.8)$.
  e. Find $P(\bar{x} \leq 28.2)$.
  f. Find $P(\bar{x} \geq 27.0)$.

6.32 A random sample of $n = 900$ observations is selected from a population with $\mu = 100$ and $\sigma = 10$.
  a. What are the largest and smallest values of $\bar{x}$ that you would expect to see?
  b. How far, at the most, would you expect $\bar{x}$ to deviate from μ?
  c. Did you have to know μ to answer part **b**? Explain.

6.33 Consider a population that contains values of x equal to 0, 1, 2, ..., 97, 98, 99. Assume that the values of x are equally likely. For each of the following values of n, use the computer to generate 500 random samples and calculate $\bar{x}$ for each sample. For each sample size, construct a relative frequency histogram of the 500 values of $\bar{x}$. What changes occur in the histograms as the value of n increases? What similarities exist? Use $n = 2, n = 5, n = 10, n = 30$, and $n = 50$.

Applying the Concepts—Basic

6.34 **Children's attitude toward reading.** In the journal *Knowledge Quest* (January/February 2002), education professors at the University of Southern California investigated children's attitudes toward reading. One study measured third through sixth graders' attitudes toward recreational reading on a 140-point scale (where higher scores indicate a more positive attitude). The mean score for this population of children was 106 points with a standard deviation of 16.4 points. Consider a random sample of 36 children from this population and let $\bar{x}$ represent the mean recreational reading attitude score for the sample.
  a. What is $\mu_{\bar{x}}$?
  b. What is $\sigma_{\bar{x}}$?
  c. Describe the shape of the sampling distribution of $\bar{x}$.
  d. Find the z-score for the value $\bar{x} = 100$ points.
  e. Find $P(\bar{x} < 100)$.

6.35 **Dentists' use of anesthetics.** Refer to the *Current Allergy & Clinical Immunology* (March 2004) study of allergic reactions of dental patients to local anesthetics (LA), Exercise 2.95 (p. 79). The study reported that the mean number of units (ampoules) of LA used per week by dentists was 79 with a standard deviation of 23. Consider a random sample of 100 dentists and let $\bar{x}$ represent the mean number of units of LA used per week for the sample.

  a. What is $\mu_{\bar{x}}$?
  b. What is $\sigma_{\bar{x}}$?
  c. Describe the shape of the sampling distribution of $\bar{x}$.
  d. Find the z-score for the value $\bar{x} = 80$ ampoules.
  e. Find $P(\bar{x} > 80)$.

6.36 Research on eating disorders. Refer to *The American Statistician* (May 2001) study of female students who suffer from bulimia, Exercise 2.38 (p. 52). Recall that each student completed a questionnaire from which a "fear of negative evaluation" (FNE) score was produced. (The higher the score, the greater the fear of negative evaluation.) Suppose the FNE scores of bulimic students have a distribution with mean $\mu = 18$ and standard deviation $\sigma = 5$. Now consider a random sample of 45 female students with bulimia.

  a. What is the probability that the sample mean FNE score is greater than 17.5?
  b. What is the probability that the sample mean FNE score is between 18 and 18.5?
  c. What is the probability that the sample mean FNE score is less than 18.5?

6.37 Improving SAT scores. Refer to the *Chance* (Winter 2001) examination of Standardized Admission Test (SAT) scores of students who pay a private tutor to help them improve their results, Exercise 2.101 (p. 81). On the SAT-Mathematics test, these students had a mean score change of $+19$ points, with a standard deviation of 65 points. In a random sample of 100 students who pay a private tutor to help them improve their results, what is the likelihood that the sample mean score change is less than 10 points?

Applying the Concepts—Intermediate

6.38 Cost of unleaded fuel. According to the American Automobile Association (AAA), the average cost of a gallon unleaded fuel at gas stations in July 2004 was \$1.897 (*AAA Fuel Gauge Report*). Assume that the standard deviation of such costs is \$.15. Suppose that a random sample of $n = 100$ gas stations is selected from the population and the July 2004 cost per gallon of unleaded fuel is determined for each. Consider $\bar{x}$, the sample mean cost per gallon.

  a. Calculate $\mu_{\bar{x}}$ and $\sigma_{\bar{x}}$.
  b. What is the approximate probability that the sample has a mean fuel cost between \$1.90 and \$1.92?
  c. What is the approximate probability that the sample has a mean fuel cost that exceeds \$1.915?

  d. How would the sampling distribution of $\bar{x}$ change if the sample size n were doubled from 100 to 200? How do your answers to parts **b** and **c** change when the sample size is doubled?

6.39 Violence and stress. Interpersonal violence (e.g., rape) generally leads to psychological stress for the victim.

Clinical Psychology Review (Vol. 15, 1995) reported on the results of all recently published studies of the relationship between interpersonal violence and psychological stress. The distribution of the time elapsed between the violent incident and the initial sign of stress has a mean of 5.1 years and a standard deviation of 6.1 years. Consider a random sample of $n = 150$ victims of interpersonal violence. Let $\bar{x}$ represent the mean time elapsed between the violent act and the first sign of stress for the sampled victims.

  a. Give the mean and standard deviation of the sampling distribution of $\bar{x}$.
  b. Will the sampling distribution of $\bar{x}$ be approximately normal? Explain.
  c. Find $P(\bar{x} > 5.5)$.
  d. Find $P(4 < \bar{x} < 5)$.

6.40 Susceptibility to hypnosis. The Computer-Assisted Hypnosis Scale (CAHS) is designed to measure a person's susceptibility to hypnosis. In computer-assisted hypnosis, the computer serves as a facilitator of hypnosis by using digitized speech processing coupled with interactive involvement with the hypnotic subject. CAHS scores range from 0 (no susceptibility) to 12 (extremely high susceptibility). A study in *Psychological Assessment* (March 1995) reported a mean CAHS score of 4.59 and a standard deviation of 2.95 for University of Tennessee undergraduates. Assume that $\mu = 4.29$ and $\sigma = 2.95$ for this population. Suppose a psychologist uses CAHS to test a random sample of 50 subjects.

  a. Would you expect to observe a sample mean CAHS score of $\bar{x} = 6$ or higher? Explain.
  b. Suppose the psychologist actually observes $\bar{x} = 6.2$. Based on your answer to part **a**, make an inference about the population from which the sample was selected.

6.41 Use of sick days. Last year a company began a program to compensate its employees for unused sick days, paying each employee a bonus of one-half the usual wage earned for each unused sick day. The question that naturally arises is, "Did this policy motivate employees to use fewer sick days?" *Before* last year, the number of sick days used by employees had a distribution with a mean of 7 days and a standard deviation of 2 days.

  a. Assuming that these parameters did not change last year, find the approximate probability that the sample mean number of sick days used by 100 employees chosen at random was less than or equal to 6.4 last year.
  b. How would you interpret the result if the sample mean for the 100 employees was 6.4?

Applying the Concepts—Advanced

6.42 Test of Knowledge About Epilepsy. The Test of Knowledge About Epilepsy (KAE), which is designed to measure attitudes toward persons with epilepsy, uses 20 multiple-choice items where all of the choices are incorrect. For each person, two scores (ranging from 0 to 20) are obtained, an attitude score (KAE-A) and a general knowledge score (KAE-GK). Based on a large-scale study of college students, the distribution of KAE-A scores has a mean of $\mu = 11.92$ and a standard deviation of $\sigma = 2.95$ while the distribution of KAE-GK scores has a mean of $\mu = 6.35$ and a standard deviation of $\sigma = 2.12$ (*Rehabilitative Psychology*, Spring 1995.) Consider a random sample of 100 college students, and suppose you observe a sample mean KAE score of 6.5. Is this result more likely to be the mean of the attitude scores (KAE-A) or the general knowledge scores (KAE-GK)? Explain.

6.43 Handwashing versus handrubbing. Refer to the *British Medical Journal* (August 17, 2002) study to compare the effectiveness of handwashing with soap and handrubbing with alcohol, Exercise 2.97 (p. 80). Health care workers who used handrubbing had a mean bacterial count of 35 per hand with a standard deviation of 59. Health care workers who used handwashing had a mean bacterial count of 69 per hand with a standard deviation of 106. In a random sample of 50 health care workers, all using the same method of cleaning their hands, the mean bacterial count per hand ($\bar{x}$) is less than 30. Give your opinion on whether this sample of workers used handrubbing with alcohol or handwashing with soap.

Quick Review

Key Terms

Biased estimate   299
Central Limit Theorem   304
Error of estimation   298
Minimum variance unbiased
   estimator (MVUE)   302

Parameter   292
Point estimator   298
Sample statistic   292
Sampling distribution   293
Standard error of the mean   304

Standard error of the statistic   300
Unbiased estimate   299

Key Formulas

	Mean	Standard Deviation	z-score	
Sampling distribution of $\bar{x}$	$\mu_{\bar{x}} = \mu$	$\sigma_{\bar{x}} = \dfrac{\sigma}{\sqrt{n}}$	$z = \dfrac{\bar{x} - \mu_{\bar{x}}}{\sigma_{\bar{x}}} = \dfrac{\bar{x} - \mu}{\sigma/\sqrt{n}}$	304

Language Lab

Symbol	Pronunciation	Description
θ	theta	Population parameter (general)
$\mu_{\bar{x}}$	mu of x-bar	True mean of sampling distribution of $\bar{x}$
$\sigma_{\bar{x}}$	sigma of x-bar	True standard deviation of sampling distribution of $\bar{x}$

Chapter Summary

- **Sampling distribution of a statistic** is the theoretical probability distribution of the statistic in repeated sampling.
- **Unbiased estimator** is a statistic with a sampling distribution mean equal to the population parameter being estimated

- **Central Limit Theorem**—the sampling distribution of the sample mean, $\bar{x}$, is approximately normal for large n (e.g., $n \geq 30$).
- $\bar{x}$ is the **minimum variance unbiased estimator (MVUE)** of μ.

Supplementary Exercises 6.44–6.70

Understanding the Principles

6.44 Describe how you could obtain the simulated sampling distribution of a sample statistic.

6.45 True or False. The sample mean, $\bar{x}$, will always be equal to $\mu_{\bar{x}}$.

6.46 True or False. The sampling distribution of $\bar{x}$ is normally distributed regardless of the size of the sample n.

6.47 True or False. The standard error of $\bar{x}$ will always be smaller than σ.

Learning the Mechanics

6.48 The standard deviation (or, as it is usually called, the *standard error*) of the sampling distribution for the sample mean, $\bar{x}$, is equal to the standard deviation of the population from which the sample was selected divided by the square root of the sample size. That is,

$$\sigma_{\bar{x}} = \frac{\sigma}{\sqrt{n}}$$

a. As the sample size is increased, what happens to the standard error of $\bar{x}$? Why is this property considered important?

b. Suppose that a sample statistic has a standard error that is not a function of the sample size. In other words, the standard error remains constant as n changes. What would this imply about the statistic as an estimator of a population parameter?

c. Suppose another unbiased estimator (call it A) of the population mean is a sample statistic with a standard error equal to

$$\sigma_A = \frac{\sigma}{\sqrt[3]{n}}$$

Which of the sample statistics, $\bar{x}$ or A, is preferable as an estimator of the population mean? Why?

d. Suppose that the population standard deviation σ is equal to 10 and that the sample size is 64. Calculate the standard errors of $\bar{x}$ and A. Assuming that the sampling distribution of A is approximately normal, interpret the standard errors. Why is the assumption of (approximate) normality unnecessary for the sampling distribution of $\bar{x}$?

6.49 Consider a sample statistic A. As with all sample statistics, A is computed by utilizing a specified function (formula) of the sample measurements. (For example, if A were the sample mean, the specified formula would be to sum the measurements and divide by the number of measurements.)

a. Describe what we mean by the phrase "the sampling distribution of the sample statistic A."

*b. Suppose A is to be used to estimate a population parameter α. What is meant by the assertion that A is an unbiased estimator of α?

*c. Consider another sample statistic, B. Assume that B is also an unbiased estimator of the population parameter α. How can we use the sampling distributions of A and B to decide which is the better estimator of α?

d. If the sample sizes on which A and B are based are large, can we apply the Central Limit Theorem and assert that the sampling distributions of A and B are approximately normal? Why or why not?

6.50 A random sample of 40 observations is to be drawn from a large population of measurements. It is known that 30% of the measurements in the population are 1's, 20% are 2's, 20% are 3's, and 30% are 4's.

a. Give the mean and standard deviation of the (repeated) sampling distribution of $\bar{x}$, the sample mean of the 40 observations.

b. Describe the shape of the sampling distribution of $\bar{x}$. Does your answer depend on the sample size?

6.51 A random sample of $n = 68$ observations is selected from a population with $\mu = 19.6$ and $\sigma = 3.2$. Approximate each of the following probabilities.

a. $P(\bar{x} \le 19.6)$
b. $P(\bar{x} \le 19)$
c. $P(\bar{x} \ge 20.1)$
d. $P(19.2 \le \bar{x} \le 20.6)$

6.52 Use a statistical software package to generate 100 random samples of size $n = 2$ from a population characterized by a normal probability distribution with mean 100 and standard deviation 10. Compute $\bar{x}$ for each sample and plot a frequency distribution for the 100 values of $\bar{x}$. Repeat this process for $n = 5, 10, 30,$ and 50. How does the fact that the sampled population is normal affect the sampling distribution of $\bar{x}$?

6.53 Use a statistical software package to generate 100 random samples of size $n = 2$ from a population characterized by a uniform probability distribution with $c = 0$ and $d = 10$. Compute $\bar{x}$ for each sample, and plot a frequency distribution for the 100 $\bar{x}$ values. Repeat this process for $n = 5, 10, 30,$ and 50. Explain how your plots illustrate the Central Limit Theorem.

6.54 Suppose x equals the number of heads observed when a single coin is tossed; that is, $x = 0$ or $x = 1$. The population corresponding to x is the set of 0's and 1's generated when the coin is tossed repeatedly a large number of times. Suppose we select $n = 2$ observations from this population. (That is, we toss the coin twice and observe two values of x.)

a. List the three different samples (combinations of 0's and 1's) that could be obtained.

b. Calculate the value of $\bar{x}$ for each of the samples.

c. List the values that $\bar{x}$ can assume, and find the probabilities of observing these values.

d. Construct a graph of the sampling distribution of $\bar{x}$.

6.55 A random sample of size n is to be drawn from a large population with mean 100 and standard deviation 10, and the sample mean $\bar{x}$ is to be calculated. To see the effect of different sample sizes on the standard deviation of the sampling distribution of $\bar{x}$, plot $\sigma/\sqrt{n}$ against n for $n = 1, 5, 10, 20, 30, 40,$ and 50.

Applying the Concepts—Basic

⊘ **DDT**

6.56 Contaminated fish. Refer to Exercise 2.33 (p. 51) and the U.S. Army Corps of Engineers data on contaminated fish saved in the **DDT** file. Recall that the length (in centimeters), weight (in grams), and DDT level (in parts per million) was measured for each of 144 fish caught from the polluted Tennessee River in Alabama.

a. In Exercise 2.33a you found that the distribution of fish lengths was skewed to the left. Assume that this is true of the population of fish lengths and that the population has mean $\mu = 43$ centimeters and $\sigma = 7$ centimeters. Use this information to describe the sampling distribution of $\bar{x}$, the mean length of a sample of $n = 40$ fish caught from the Tennessee River.

b. In Exercise 2.33b you found that the distribution of fish weights was approximately normal. Assume that this is true of the population of fish weights and that the population has mean $\mu = 1,050$ grams and $\sigma = 376$ grams. Use this information to describe the sampling distribution of $\bar{x}$, the mean weight of a sample of $n = 40$ fish caught from the Tennessee River.

c. In Exercise 2.33c you found that the distribution of fish DDT levels was highly skewed to the right. Assume that this is true of the population of fish DDT levels and that the population has mean $\mu = 24$ ppm and $\sigma = 98$ ppm. Use this information to describe the sampling distribution of $\bar{x}$, the mean DDT level of a sample of $n = 40$ fish caught from the Tennessee River.

6.57 Clam harvesting. The ocean quahog is a type of clam found in the coastal waters of the mid-Atlantic states. A federal survey of offshore ocean quahog harvesting in New Jersey revealed an average catch per unit effort (CPUE) of 89.34 clams. The CPUE standard deviation was 7.74. (*Journal of Shellfish Research*, June 1995.) Let $\bar{x}$ represent the mean CPUE for a sample of 35 attempts to catch ocean quahogs off the New Jersey shore.

a. Compute $\mu_{\bar{x}}$ and $\sigma_{\bar{x}}$. Interpret their values.

b. Sketch the sampling distribution of $\bar{x}$.

c. Find $P(\bar{x} > 88)$.

d. Find $P(\bar{x} < 87)$.

6.58 Salaries of travel professionals. According to *Business Travel News* (July 15, 2002), the average salary of a travel management professional is $74,000. Assume that the standard deviation of such salaries is $30,000. Consider a random sample of 50 travel management professionals and let $\bar{x}$ represent the mean salary for the sample.

a. What is $\mu_{\bar{x}}$?

b. What is $\sigma_{\bar{x}}$?

c. Describe the shape of the sampling distribution of $\bar{x}$.

d. Find the z-score for the value $\bar{x} = \$65,000$.

e. Find $P(\bar{x} > 65,000)$.

6.59 Violent crimes. The distribution of violent crimes per day in a certain city possesses a mean equal to 1.3 and a standard deviation equal to 1.7. A random sample of 50 days is observed, and the daily mean number of crimes for this sample, $\bar{x}$, is calculated.

a. Give the mean and standard deviation of the sampling distribution of $\bar{x}$.

b. Will the sampling distribution of $\bar{x}$ be approximately normal? Explain.

c. Find an approximate value of $P(\bar{x} < 1)$.

d. Find an approximate value of $P(\bar{x} > 1.9)$.

Applying the Concepts—Intermediate

6.60 Producing machine bearings. To determine whether a metal lathe that produces machine bearings is properly adjusted, a random sample of 25 bearings is collected and the diameter of each is measured.

a. If the standard deviation of the diameters of the bearings measured over a long period of time is .001 inch, what is the approximate probability that the mean diameter $\bar{x}$ of the sample of 25 bearings will lie within .0001 inch of the population mean diameter of the bearings?

b. If the population of diameters has an extremely skewed distribution, how will your approximation in part **a** be affected?

6.61 Quality control. Refer to Exercise 6.60. The mean diameter of the bearings produced by the machine is supposed to be .5 inch. The company decides to use the sample mean (from Exercise 6.60) to decide whether the process is in control (i.e., whether it is producing bearings with a mean diameter of .5 inch). The machine will be considered out of control if the mean of the sample of $n = 25$ diameters is less than .4994 inch or larger than .5006 inch. If the true mean diameter of the bearings produced by the machine is .501 inch, what is the approximate probability that the test will imply that the process is out of control?

6.62 Length of job tenure. Researchers at the Terry College of Business at the University of Georgia sampled 344 business students and asked them this question: "Over the course of your lifetime, what is the maximum number of years you expect to work for any one employer?" The sample resulted in $\bar{x} = 19.1$ years. Assume the sample of students was randomly selected from the 6,000 undergraduate students at the Terry College and that $\sigma = 6$ years.

a. Describe the sampling distribution of $\bar{x}$.

b. If the mean for the 6,000 undergraduate students is $\mu = 18.5$ years, find $P(\bar{x} > 19.1)$.

c. If the mean for the 6,000 undergraduate students is $\mu = 19.5$ years, find $P(\bar{x} > 19.1)$.

d. If $P(\bar{x} > 19.1) = .5$, what is μ?

e. If $P(\bar{x} > 19.1) = .2$, is μ greater than or less than 19.1 years? Explain.

6.63 New method of teaching arithmetic. This past year, an elementary school began using a new method to teach arithmetic to first graders. A standardized test, administered at the end of the year, was used to measure the effectiveness of the new method. The distribution of past scores on the standardized test produced a mean of 75 and a standard deviation of 10.

a. If the new method is no different from the old method, what is the approximate probability that the mean score $\bar{x}$ of a random sample of 36 students will be greater than 79?

b. What assumptions must be satisfied to make your answer valid?

6.64 Supercooling temperature of frogs. Many species of terrestrial tree frogs that hibernate at or near the ground surface can survive prolonged exposure to low winter temperatures. In freezing conditions, the frog's body temperature, called its *supercooling temperature*, remains relatively higher because of an accumulation of glycerol in its body fluids. Recent studies have shown that the supercooling temperature of terrestrial frogs frozen at $-6°C$ has a relative frequency distribution with a mean of $-2°C$ and a standard deviation of $.3°C$ (The first of these studies was reported in *Science*, May 1983.) Consider the mean supercooling temperature, $\bar{x}$, of a random sample of $n = 42$ terrestrial frogs frozen at $-6°C$.

a. Find the probability that $\bar{x}$ exceeds $-2.05°C$.

b. Find the probability that $\bar{x}$ falls between $-2.20°C$ and $-2.10°C$.

6.65 Florida Employer Opinion Survey. The *Florida Employer Opinion Survey* gives the results of an extensive survey of employer opinions in Florida. Each employer was asked to rate his or her satisfaction with the preparation of employees by the public education system. Responses were 1, 1.5, or 2, representing very dissatisfied, neither satisfied nor dissatisfied, and very satisfied, respectively. A sample of 651 employers was selected. Assume that the mean for all employers in Florida is 1.50 (the "dividing line" between satisfied and dissatisfied) and the standard deviation is .45.

a. Which type of distribution describes the individual survey responses, continuous or discrete?

b. Describe the distribution that best approximates the sample mean response of 651 employers. What are the mean and standard deviation of this distribution? What assumptions, if any, are necessary to ensure the validity of your answers?

c. What is the approximate probability that the sample mean will be 1.45 or less?

d. The mean of the sample of 651 employers surveyed in a recent year was 1.36. Given this result, do you think it is likely that all Florida employers' opinions were evenly divided on the effectiveness of public education? That is, do you think the assumption that the population mean is 1.50 is correct? Why or why not?

6.66 Verbal ability of delinquents. Over the past 20 years, the *Journal of Abnormal Psychology* has published numerous studies on the relationship between juvenile delinquency and poor verbal abilities. Assume that scores on a verbal IQ test have a population mean $\mu = 107$ and a population standard deviation $\sigma = 15$.

a. What shape would you expect the sampling distribution of $\bar{x}$ for $n = 84$ juveniles to have? Does your answer depend on the shape of the distribution of verbal IQ scores for all juveniles?

b. Assuming that the population mean and standard deviation for juveniles with no record of delinquency are the same as those for all juveniles, approximate the probability that the sample mean verbal IQ for $n = 84$ juveniles will be 110 or more. State any assumptions you make.

c. In one cited study, the researchers found that a sample of $n = 84$ juveniles with no record of delinquency had a mean verbal IQ of $\bar{x} = 110$. Considering your answer to part **b**, do you think that the population mean and standard deviation for nondelinquent juveniles are the same as those for all juveniles? Explain.

Applying the Concepts—Advanced

6.67 Flaws in aluminum siding. [*Note:* This exercise refers to an optional section in Chapter 4.] A building contractor has decided to purchase a load of factory-reject aluminum siding as long as the average number of flaws per piece of siding in a sample of size 35 from the factory's reject pile is 2.1 or less. If it is known that the number of flaws per piece of siding in the factory's reject pile has a Poisson probability distribution with a mean of 2.5, find the approximate probability that the contractor will not purchase a load of siding. [*Hint:* If x is a Poisson random variable with mean λ, then $\sigma_{\bar{x}}^2$ also equals λ.]

6.68 Machine repair time. [*Note:* This exercise refers to an optional section in Chapter 5.] An article in *Industrial Engineering* (August 1990) discussed the importance of modeling machine downtime correctly in simulation studies. As an illustration, the researcher considered a single-machine-tool system with repair times (in minutes) that can be modeled by an exponential distribution with $\theta = 60$ (see optional Section 5.6). Of interest is the mean repair time, $\bar{x}$, of a sample of 100 machine breakdowns.

a. Find $E(\bar{x})$ and the variance of $\bar{x}$.

b. What probability distribution provides the best model of the sampling distribution of $\bar{x}$? Why?

c. Calculate the probability that the mean repair time, $\bar{x}$, is no longer than 30 minutes.

Critical Thinking Challenges

6.69 Soft drink bottles. A soft drink bottler purchases glass bottles from a vendor. The bottles are required to have an internal pressure of at least 150 pounds per square inch (psi). A prospective bottle vendor claims that its production process yields bottles with a mean internal pressure of 157 psi and a standard deviation of 3 psi. The bottler strikes an agreement with the vendor that permits the bottler to sample from the vendor's production process to verify the vendor's claim. The bottler randomly selects 40 bottles from the last 10,000 produced, measures the internal pressure of each, and finds the mean pressure for the sample to be 1.3 psi below the process mean cited by the vendor.

a. Assuming the vendor's claim to be true, what is the probability of obtaining a sample mean this far or farther below the process mean? What does your answer suggest about the validity of the vendor's claim?

b. If the process standard deviation were 3 psi as claimed by the vendor, but the mean were 156 psi, would the observed sample result be more or less likely than in part **a**? What if the mean were 158 psi?

c. If the process mean were 157 psi as claimed, but the process standard deviation were 2 psi, would the sample result be more or less likely than in part **a**? What if instead the standard deviation were 6 psi?

6.70 Fecal pollution at Huntington Beach. The state of California mandates fecal indicator bacteria monitoring at all public beaches. When the concentration of fecal bacteria in the water exceeds a certain limit (400 colony-forming units of fecal coliform per 100 milliliters), local health officials must post a sign (called surf zone posting) warning beachgoers of potential health risks with entering the water. For fecal bacteria, the state uses a single-sample standard; that is, if the fecal limit is exceeded in a single sample of water, surf zone posting is mandatory. This single-standard policy has led to a recent rash of beach closures in California.

Joon Ha Kim and Stanley B. Grant, engineers at the University of California, Irvine, conducted a study of the surf water quality at Huntington Beach in California and reported the results in *Environmental Science & Technology* (September 2004). The researchers found that beach closings were occurring despite low pollution levels in some instances and in others, signs were not posted when the fecal limit was exceeded. They attributed these "surf zone posting errors" to the variable nature of water quality in the surf zone (for example, fecal bacteria concentration tends to be higher during ebb tide and at night) and the inherent time delay between when a water sample is collected and when a sign is posted or removed. In order to prevent posting errors, the researchers recommend using an averaging method rather than a single sample to determine unsafe water quality. (For example, one simple averaging method is to take a random sample of multiple water specimens and compare the average fecal bacteria level of the sample to the limit of 400 cfu/100 mL in order to determine whether the water is safe.)

Discuss the pros and cons of using the single-sample standard versus the averaging method. Part of your discussion should address the probability of posting a sign when, in fact, the water is safe, and the probability of posting a sign when, in fact, the water is unsafe. (Assume that the fecal bacteria concentrations of water specimens at Huntington Beach follow an approximately normal distribution.)

Student Projects

To understand the Central Limit Theorem and sampling distribution, consider the following experiment: Toss four identical coins, and record the number of heads observed. Then repeat this experiment four more times, so that you end up with a total of five observations for the random variable x, the number of heads when four coins are tossed.

Now derive and graph the probability distribution for x, assuming the coins are balanced. Note that the mean of this distribution is $\mu = 2$ and the standard deviation is $\sigma = 1$. This probability distribution represents the one from which you are drawing a random sample of five measurements.

Next, calculate the mean $\bar{x}$ of the five measurements—that is, calculate the mean number of heads you observed in five repetitions of the experiment. Although you have repeated the basic experiment five times, you have only one observed value of $\bar{x}$. To derive the probability distribution or sampling distribution of $\bar{x}$ empirically, you have to repeat the entire process (of tossing four coins five times) many times. Do it 100 times.

The approximate sampling distribution of $\bar{x}$ can be derived theoretically by making use of the Central Limit Theorem. We expect at least an approximate normal probability distribution with a mean $\mu = 2$ and a standard deviation

$$\sigma_{\bar{x}} = \frac{\sigma}{\sqrt{n}} = \frac{1}{\sqrt{5}} = .45$$

Count the number of your 100 $\bar{x}$'s that fall in each of the intervals in the accompanying figure. Use the normal probability distribution with $\mu = 2$ and $\sigma_{\bar{x}} = .45$ to calculate the expected number of the 100 $\bar{x}$'s in each of the intervals. How closely does the theory describe your experimental results?

Interval ←—1—→	Interval ←—2—→	Interval ←—3—→	Interval ←—4—→	Interval ←—5—→	Interval ←—6—→
	1.10	1.55	2	2.45	2.90
	$\mu - 2\sigma_{\bar{x}}$	$\mu - \sigma_{\bar{x}}$	μ	$\mu + \sigma_{\bar{x}}$	$\mu + 2\sigma_{\bar{x}}$

REFERENCES

Hogg, R. V., and Craig, A. T. *Introduction to Mathematical Statistics*, 5th ed. Upper Saddle River, N.J.: Prentice Hall, 1995.

Larsen, R. J., and Marx, M. L. *An Introduction to Mathematical Statistics and Its Applications*, 3rd ed. Upper Saddle River, N.J.: Prentice Hall, 2001.

Lindgren, B. W. *Statistical Theory*, 3rd ed. New York: Macmillan, 1976.

Wackerly, D., Mendenhall, W., and Scheaffer, R. L. *Mathematical Statistics with Applications*, 6th ed. North Scituate, Mass.: Duxbury, 2002.

Using Technology

Simulating a Sampling Distribution Using MINITAB

To generate a sampling distribution for a sample statistic using MINITAB, click on the "Calc" button on the MINITAB menu bar, next click on "Random Data," then click on the distribution of your choice (e.g., "Uniform"). A dialog box similar to the one (the Uniform Distribution) shown in Figure 6.M.1 will appear. Specify the number of samples (e.g., 1,000) to generate in the "Generate ... rows of data" box and the columns where the data will be stored in the "Store in columns" box. (The number of columns will be equal to the sample size, e.g., 40.) Finally, specify the parameters of the distribution (e.g., the lower and upper range of the uniform distribution). When you click "OK," the simulated data will appear on the MINITAB worksheet.

Next, calculate the value of the sample statistic of interest for each sample. To do this, click on the "Calc" button on the MINITAB menu bar, then click on "Row Statistics," as shown in Figure 6.M.2. The resulting dialog box appears in Figure 6.M.3. Check the sample statistic (e.g., the mean) you want to calculate, and specify the "Input variables" (or columns) and the column where you want the value of the sample statistic to be saved. Click "OK" and the value of the statistic for each sample will appear on the MINITAB worksheet.

[*Note*: Use the MINITAB menu choices provided in the Chapter 2 Using Technology section to generate a histogram of the sampling distribution of the statistic or to find the mean and variance of the sampling distribution.]

Figure 6.M.1
MINITAB Dialog Box for
Simulating the Uniform
Distribution

Figure 6.M.2
MINITAB Selections for
Generating Sample Statistics
for the Simulated Data

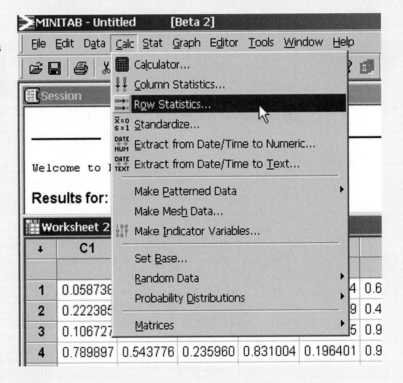

Figure 6.M.3
MINITAB Row Statistics
Dialog Box

7

Inferences Based on a Single Sample

Estimation with Confidence Intervals

Contents

7.1 Identifying the Target Parameter

7.2 Large-Sample Confidence Interval for a Population Mean

7.3 Small-Sample Confidence Interval for a Population Mean

7.4 Large-Sample Confidence Interval for a Population Proportion

7.5 Determining the Sample Size

Statistics in Action

Speed—Improving the Sprint Times of High School Football Players

Using Technology

Confidence Intervals Using MINITAB

Where We've Been

- Learned that populations are characterized by numerical descriptive measures—called *parameters*

- Found that decisions about population parameters are based on *statistics* computed from the sample

- Discovered that *inferences* about parameters are subject to uncertainty, and that this uncertainty is reflected in the *sampling distribution* of a statistic

Where We're Going

- Estimate a population parameter (means or proportion) based on a large sample selected from the population.

- Use the sampling distribution of a statistic to form a confidence interval for the population parameter.

- Show how to select the proper sample size for estimating a population parameter.

Statistics in ACTION

Speed—Improving the Sprint Times of High School Football Players

The game of football requires both skill and speed. Consider that one of the key "statistics" for National Football League (NFL) coaches in evaluating college players for the NFL draft is a player's 40-yard sprint time. There are a plethora of drills available to football coaches that have been successfully used to aid a player's skill development. However, many coaches are under the impression that "you can't teach speed." Michael Gray and Jessica Sauerbeck, researchers at Northern Kentucky University, designed and tested a speed training program for junior varsity and varsity high school football players (*The Sport Journal*, Winter 2004).

The training program was carried out over a five-week period and incorporated a number of speed improvement drills, including 50-yard sprints run at varying speeds, high knee running sprints, butt kick sprints, "crazy legs" straddle runs, quick feet drills, jumping, power skipping, and all-out sprinting. A sample of 38 high school athletes participated in the study. Each participant was timed in a 40-yard sprint prior to the start of the training program and timed again after completing the program. The decrease in times (mea-

sured in seconds) was recorded for each athlete. These data, saved in the **SPRINT** file, are shown in Table SIA 7.1. [*Note*: A negative decrease implies that the athlete's time after completion of the program was higher than his time prior to training.] The goal of the research is to demonstrate that the training program is effective in improving 40-yard sprint times.

In this chapter, several Statistics in Action Revisited examples demonstrate how confidence intervals can be used to evaluate the effectiveness of the speed training program.

Statistics in Action Revisited

- Estimating the Mean Decrease in Sprint Time (p. 328)
- Estimating the Proportion of Sprinters Who Improve after Training (p. 347)
- Determining the Number of Athletes to Participate in the Training Program (p. 355)

⬡ SPRINT

TABLE SIA7.1 Decrease in 40-Yard Sprint Times for 38 Football Players

−.01	.10	.10	.24	.25	.05	.28	.25	.20	.14
.32	.34	.30	.09	.05	0.00	.04	.17	0.00	.21
.15	.30	.02	.12	.14	.10	.08	.50	.36	.10
.01	.90	.34	.38	.44	.08	0.00	0.00		

Source: Gray, M., and Sauerbeck, J. A. "Speed training program for high school football players," *The Sport Journal,* Vol. 7, No. 1, Winter 2004 (Table 2).

7.1 Identifying the Target Parameter

In this chapter, our goal is to estimate the value of an unknown population parameter, such as a population mean or a proportion from a binomial population. For example, we might want to know the mean gas mileage for a new car model, or the average expected life of a flat screen computer monitor, or the proportion of Iraq War veterans with post-traumatic stress syndrome.

You'll see that different techniques are used for estimating a mean or proportion, depending on whether a sample contains a large or small number of measurements. Nevertheless, our objectives remain the same. We want to use the sample information to estimate the population parameter of interest (called the **target parameter**) and to assess the reliability of the estimate.

> **DEFINITION 7.1**
>
> The unknown population parameter (e.g., mean or proportion) that we are interested in estimating is called the **target parameter**.

Often, there are one or more key words in the statement of the problem that indicate the appropriate target parameter. Some key words associated with the two parameters covered in this section are listed in the accompanying box.

Determining the Target Parameter

Parameter	Key Words or Phrases	Type of Data
μ	Mean; average	Quantitative
p	Proportion; percentage; fraction; rate	Qualitative

For the examples given above, the words *mean* in "mean gas mileage" and *average* in "average life expectancy" imply that the target parameter is the population mean, μ. The word *proportion* in "proportion of Iraq War veterans with post-traumatic stress syndrome" indicated that the target parameter is the binomial proportion, p.

In addition to key words and phrases, the type of data (quantitative or qualitative) collected is indicative of the target parameter. With quantitative data, you are likely to be estimating the mean of the data. With qualitative data with two outcomes (success or failure), the binomial proportion of successes is likely to be the parameter of interest.

We consider a method of estimating a population mean using a large sample in Section 7.2 and a small sample in Section 7.3. Estimation of a population proportion is presented in Section 7.4. Finally, we show how to determine the sample sizes necessary for reliable estimates of the target parameters in Section 7.5.

7.2 Large-Sample Confidence Interval for a Population Mean

Suppose a large hospital wants to estimate the average length of time patients remain in the hospital. Hence, the hospital's target parameter is the population mean, μ. To accomplish this objective, the hospital administrators plan to randomly sample 100 of all previous patients' records and to use the sample mean, $\bar{x}$, of the lengths of stay to estimate μ, the mean of *all* patients' visits. The sample mean $\bar{x}$ represents a *point estimator* of the population mean μ (Definition 6.4). How can we assess the accuracy of this large-sample point estimator?

According to the Central Limit Theorem, the sampling distribution of the sample mean is approximately normal for large samples, as shown in Figure 7.1.

Let us calculate the interval

$$\bar{x} \pm 2\sigma_{\bar{x}} = \bar{x} \pm \frac{2\sigma}{\sqrt{n}}$$

That is, we form an interval 4 standard deviations wide—from 2 standard deviations below the sample mean to 2 standard deviations above the mean. Prior to drawing the sample, what are the chances that this interval will enclose μ, the population mean?

To answer this question, refer to Figure 7.1. If the 100 measurements yield a value of $\bar{x}$ that falls between the two lines on either side of μ (i.e., within 2 standard deviations of μ), then the interval $\bar{x} \pm 2\sigma_{\bar{x}}$ will contain μ; if $\bar{x}$ falls outside these boundaries, the interval $\bar{x} \pm 2\sigma_{\bar{x}}$ will not contain μ. Since the area under the normal curve (the sampling distribution of $\bar{x}$) between these boundaries is about .95 (more

Figure 7.1

Sampling Distribution of $\bar{x}$

precisely, from Table IV in Appendix A the area is .9544), we know that the interval $\bar{x} \pm 2\sigma_{\bar{x}}$ will contain μ with a probability approximately equal to .95.

For instance, consider the lengths of time spent in the hospital for 100 patients shown in Table 7.1. An SAS printout of summary statistics for the sample of 100 lengths of stay is shown in Figure 7.2.

From the top of the printout, we find $\bar{x} = 4.53$ days and $s = 3.68$ days. To achieve our objective, we must construct the interval

$$\bar{x} \pm 2\sigma_{\bar{x}} = 4.53 \pm 2\frac{\sigma}{\sqrt{100}}$$

But now we face a problem. You can see that without knowing the standard deviation σ of the original population—that is, the standard deviation of the lengths of

 HOSPLOS

TABLE 7.1   Lengths of Stay (in Days) for 100 Patients

2	3	8	6	4	4	6	4	2	5
8	10	4	4	4	2	1	3	2	10
1	3	2	3	4	3	5	2	4	1
2	9	1	7	17	9	9	9	4	4
1	1	1	3	1	6	3	3	2	5
1	3	3	14	2	3	9	6	6	3
5	1	4	6	11	22	1	9	6	5
2	2	5	4	3	6	1	5	1	6
17	1	2	4	5	4	4	3	2	3
3	5	2	3	3	2	10	2	4	2

Figure 7.2

SAS Printout with Summary Statistics and 95% Confidence Interval for Data on 100 Hospital Stays

```
Sample Statistics for LOS

     N            Mean          Std. Dev.          Std. Error
--------------------------------------------------------------
    100           4.53             3.68                0.37

Hypothesis Test

     Null hypothesis:      Mean of LOS  =  0
     Alternative:          Mean of LOS ^=  0

              t Statistic        Df         Prob > t
              ----------------------------------------
                12.318           99          <.0001


95 % Confidence Interval for the Mean

          Lower Limit:              3.80
          Upper Limit:              5.26
```

stay of *all* patients—we cannot calculate this interval. However, since we have a large sample ($n = 100$ measurements), we can approximate the interval by using the sample standard deviation s to approximate σ. Thus,

$$\bar{x} \pm 2\frac{\sigma}{\sqrt{100}} \approx \bar{x} \pm 2\frac{s}{\sqrt{100}} = 4.53 \pm 2\left(\frac{3.68}{10}\right) = 4.53 \pm .74$$

That is, we estimate the mean length of stay in the hospital for all patients to fall in the interval 3.79 to 5.27 days. (This interval is highlighted at the bottom of the SAS printout, Figure 7.2. Differences are due to rounding.)

Can we be sure that μ, the true mean, is in the interval 3.79 to 5.27? We cannot be certain, but we can be reasonably confident that it is. This confidence is derived from the knowledge that if we were to draw repeated random samples of 100 measurements from this population and form the interval $\bar{x} \pm 2\sigma_{\bar{x}}$ each time, approximately 95% of the intervals would contain μ. We have no way of knowing (without looking at all the patients' records) whether our sample interval is one of the 95% that contain μ or one of the 5% that do not, but the odds certainly favor its containing μ. Consequently, the interval 3.79 to 5.27 provides a reliable estimate of the mean length of patient stay in the hospital.

The formula that tells us how to calculate an interval estimate based on sample data is called an *interval estimator*, or *confidence interval*. The probability, .95, that measures the confidence we can place in the interval estimate is called a *confidence coefficient*. The percentage, 95%, is called the *confidence level* for the interval estimate. It is not usually possible to assess precisely the reliability of point estimators because they are single points rather than intervals. So, because we prefer to use estimators for which a measure of reliability can be calculated, we will generally use interval estimators.

DEFINITION 7.2

An **interval estimator** (or **confidence interval**) is a formula that tells us how to use sample data to calculate an interval that estimates a population parameter.

DEFINITION 7.3

The **confidence coefficient** is the probability that an interval estimator encloses the population parameter—that is, the relative frequency with which the interval estimator encloses the population parameter when the estimator is used repeatedly a very large number of times. The **confidence level** is the confidence coefficient expressed as a percentage.

Now we have seen how an interval can be used to estimate a population mean. When we use an interval estimator, we can usually calculate the probability that the estimation *process* will result in an interval that contains the true value of the population mean. That is, the probability that the interval contains the parameter in repeated usage is usually known. Figure 7.3 shows what happens when 10 different samples are drawn from a population, and a confidence interval for μ is calculated from each. The location of μ is indicated by the vertical line in the figure. Ten confidence intervals, each based on one of 10 samples, are shown as horizontal line segments. Note that the confidence intervals move from sample to sample—sometimes containing μ and other times missing μ. *If our confidence level is 95%, in the long run, 95% of our sample confidence intervals will contain μ.*

Suppose you wish to choose a confidence coefficient other than .95. Notice in Figure 7.1 that the confidence coefficient .95 is equal to the total area under the

Figure 7.3

Confidence Intervals for μ: 10 Samples

Biography

**JERZEY NEYMAN (1894–1981)—
Speaking Statistics
with a Polish Accent**

Polish-born Jerzey Neyman was educated at the University of Kharkov (Russia) in elementary mathematics but taught himself graduate mathematics by studying journal articles on the subject. After receiving his doctorate in 1924 from the University of Warsaw (Poland), Neyman accepted a position at University College (London). There, he developed a friendship with Egon Pearson; Neyman and Pearson together developed the theory of hypothesis testing (Chapter 8). In 1934, in a talk to the Royal Statistical Society, Neyman first proposed the idea of interval estimation, which he called "confidence intervals." (It is interesting that Neyman rarely receives credit in textbooks as the originator of the confidence interval procedure.) In 1938, he emigrated to the United States and the University of California at Berkeley. At Berkeley, he built one of the strongest statistics departments in the country. Jerzey Neyman is considered one of the great founders of modern statistics. He was a superb teacher and innovative researcher who loved his students, always sharing his ideas with them. Neyman's influence on those he met is best expressed by a quote from prominent statistician David Salsburg: "We have all learned to speak statistics with a Polish accent."

sampling distribution, less .05 of the area, which is divided equally between the two tails. Using this idea, we can construct a confidence interval with any desired confidence coefficient by increasing or decreasing the area (call it α) assigned to the tails of the sampling distribution (see Figure 7.4). For example, if we place area $\alpha/2$ in each tail and if $z_{\alpha/2}$ is the z value such that the area $\alpha/2$ will lie to its right, then the confidence interval with confidence coefficient $(1 - \alpha)$ is

$$\overline{x} \pm z_{\alpha/2}\sigma_{\overline{x}}$$

> **DEFINITION 7.4**
>
> The value z_α is defined as the value of the standard normal random variable z such that the area α will lie to its right. In other words, $P(z > z_\alpha) = \alpha$.

To illustrate, for a confidence coefficient of .90 we have $(1 - \alpha) = .90$, $\alpha = .10$, and $\alpha/2 = 0.5$; $z_{.05}$ is the z value that locates area .05 in the upper tail of the sampling distribution. Recall that Table IV in Appendix A gives the areas between the mean and a specified z-value. Since the total area to the right of the mean is .5, we find that $z_{.05}$ will be the z value corresponding to an area of $.5 - .05 = .45$ to the right of the mean (see Figure 7.5). This z value is $z_{.05} = 1.645$.

Confidence coefficients used in practice usually range from .90 to .99. The most commonly used confidence coefficients with corresponding values of α and $z_{\alpha/2}$ are shown in Table 7.2.

Figure 7.4

Locating $z_{\alpha/2}$ on the Standard Normal Curve

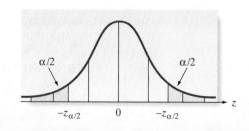

Figure 7.5
The z Value $(z_{.05})$ Corresponding to an Area Equal to .05 in the Upper Tail of the z-Distribution

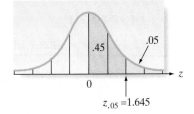

TABLE 7.2   Commonly Used Values of $z_{\alpha/2}$

Confidence Level 100$(1 - \alpha)$	α	$\alpha/2$	$z_{\alpha/2}$
90%	.10	.05	1.645
95%	.05	.025	1.96
99%	.01	.005	2.575

Now Work   *Exercise 7.7*

Large-Sample 100$(1 - \alpha)$% Confidence Interval for μ

$$\bar{x} \pm z_{\alpha/2}\sigma_{\bar{x}} = \bar{x} \pm z_{\alpha/2}\frac{\sigma}{\sqrt{n}}$$

where $z_{\alpha/2}$ is the z value with an area $\alpha/2$ to its right (see Figure 7.4) and $\sigma_{\bar{x}} = \sigma/\sqrt{n}$. The parameter σ is the standard deviation of the sampled population and n is the sample size.

Note: When σ is unknown (as is almost always the case) and n is large (say, $n \geq 30$), the confidence interval is approximately equal to

$$\bar{x} \pm z_{\alpha/2}\left(\frac{s}{\sqrt{n}}\right)$$

where s is the sample standard deviation.

Conditions Required for a Valid Large-Sample Confidence Interval for μ

1. A random sample is selected from the target population.
2. The sample size n is large (i.e., $n \geq 30$). (Due to the Central Limit Theorem, this condition guarantees that the sampling distribution of $\bar{x}$ is approximately normal.)

EXAMPLE 7.1   FINDING A LARGE-SAMPLE CONFIDENCE INTERVAL FOR μ

Problem   Unoccupied seats on flights cause airlines to lose revenue. Suppose a large airline wants to estimate its average number of unoccupied seats per flight over the past year. To accomplish this, the records of 225 flights are randomly selected, and the number of unoccupied seats is noted for each of the sampled flights. (The data are saved in the **AIRNOSHOWS** file.) Descriptive statistics for the data are displayed in the MINITAB printout, Figure 7.6.

AIRNOSHOWS

Estimate μ, the mean number of unoccupied seats per flight during the past year, using a 90% confidence interval.

Figure 7.6

Figure 7.6

MINITAB Printout with
Descriptive Statistics and
90% Confidence Interval
for Example 7.1

```
Variable    N     Mean   StDev  SE Mean        90% CI
NOSHOWS    225  11.5956  4.1026  0.2735  (11.1438, 12.0473)
```

Solution The general form of the 90% confidence interval for a population mean is

$$\bar{x} \pm z_{\alpha/2}\sigma_{\bar{x}} = \bar{x} \pm z_{.05}\sigma_{\bar{x}} = \bar{x} \pm 1.645\left(\frac{\sigma}{\sqrt{n}}\right)$$

From Figure 7.6, we find (after rounding) $\bar{x} = 11.6$. Since we do not know the value of σ (the standard deviation of the number of unoccupied seats per flight for all flights of the year), we use our best approximation—the sample standard deviation, $s = 4.1$, shown on the MINITAB printout. Then the 90% confidence interval is, approximately,

$$11.6 \pm 1.645\left(\frac{4.1}{\sqrt{225}}\right) = 11.6 \pm .45$$

or from 11.15 to 12.05. That is, at the 90% confidence level, we estimate the mean number of unoccupied seats per flight to be between 11.15 and 12.05 during the sampled year. This result is verified (except for rounding) on the right side of the MINITAB printout in Figure 7.6.

Look Back We stress that the confidence level for this example, 90%, refers to the procedure used. If we were to apply this procedure repeatedly to different samples, approximately 90% of the intervals would contain μ. Although we do not know for sure whether this particular interval (11.15, 12.05) is one of the 90% that contain μ or one of the 10% that do not, our knowledge of probability gives us "confidence" that the interval contains μ.

Now Work *Exercise 7.11*

■ ■ ■

The interpretation of confidence intervals for a population mean is summarized in the next box.

Sometimes, the estimation procedure yields a confidence interval that is too wide for our purposes. In this case, we will want to reduce the width of the interval to obtain a more precise estimate of μ. One way to accomplish this is to decrease the confidence coefficient, $1 - \alpha$. For example, consider the problem of estimating the mean length of stay, μ, for hospital patients. Recall that for a sample of 100 patients, $\bar{x} = 4.53$ days and $s = 3.68$ days. A 90% confidence interval for μ is

$$\bar{x} \pm 1.645(\sigma/\sqrt{n}) \approx 4.53 \pm (1.645)(3.68/\sqrt{100}) = 4.53 \pm .61$$

or (3.92, 5.14). You can see that this interval is narrower than the previously calculated 95% confidence interval, (3.79, 5.27). Unfortunately, we also have "less confidence" in the 90% confidence interval. An alternative method used to decrease the width of an interval without sacrificing "confidence" is to increase the sample size n. We demonstrate this method in Section 7.5.

Interpretation of a Confidence Interval for a Population Mean

When we form a $100(1 - \alpha)\%$ confidence interval for μ, we usually express our confidence in the interval with a statement such as, "We can be $100(1 - \alpha)\%$ confident that μ lies between the lower and upper bounds of the confidence interval," where for a particular application, we substitute the appropriate numerical values for the level of confidence and for the lower and upper bounds. *The statement reflects our confidence in the estimation process rather than in the particular interval that is calculated from the sample data.* We know that repeated application of the same procedure will result in different lower and upper bounds on the interval. Furthermore, we know that $100(1 - \alpha)\%$ of the resulting intervals will contain μ. There is (usually) no way to determine whether any particular interval is one of those that contain μ, or one that does not. However, unlike point estimators, confidence intervals have some measure of reliability, the confidence coefficient, associated with them. For that reason they are generally preferred to point estimators.

Statistics in Action Revisited

Estimating the Mean Decrease in Sprint Time

Refer to the speed training program for junior varsity and varsity high school football players described on p. 321. Recall that the 5-week training program incorporated a number of speed improvement drills for a sample of 38 high school athletes. The time in a 40-yard sprint run both before and after the training program was recorded for each athlete and the decrease in times (measured in seconds) was saved in the **SPRINT** file (Table SIA7.1). Is the training program really effective in improving 40-yard sprint times?

One way to answer this question is to form a confidence interval for the true mean decrease in sprint time for all athletes who participate in the speed training program. If the true decrease is positive (i.e., if the "before" mean time is greater than the "after" mean time), then we will conclude that the training program is effective. Since the sam-

ple size is large ($n = 38$), we can apply the large-sample methodology of this section.

The data is stored as a MINITAB worksheet and the software used to find a large-sample 95% confidence interval for the population mean decrease in sprint times. The MINITAB printout is displayed in Figure SIA7.1.

The interval, highlighted on the printout, is (.128, .247). Note that the entire interval falls above 0. Consequently, we are 95% confident that the true mean decrease in sprint times is positive. It appears that the speed training program is, in fact, effective in improving the average 40-yard sprint times of high school athletes. Note, however, that the mean decrease in time ranges from a minimum of .128 seconds to a maximum of .247 seconds. Although this decrease might be deemed critically important to world-class sprinters, it would probably be unnoticeable to high school football players.

Figure SIA7.1

MINITAB Confidence
Interval for Speed Training
Study

Variable	N	Mean	StDev	SE Mean	95% CI
DecrTime	38	0.187895	0.181423	0.029431	(0.128262, 0.247527)

Confidence Interval for a Population Mean (known σ or $n \geq 30$)

Using the TI-83 Graphing Calculator

Say we want to develop a **95%** confidence interval for the population mean from a sample size of **35** where we know the sample mean is **100** and the **population deviation** is **12**. For this problem we want **Z-Interval** because we are given sigma. On the calculator we will choose **"7:Zinterval"** from the **"TESTS"** menu.

Step 1   *Access the Statistical Tests Menu*
Press **STAT** (this screen will appear).
Arrow right to **"TEST"**
Arrow down to **"7:ZInterval"**
Press **ENTER**

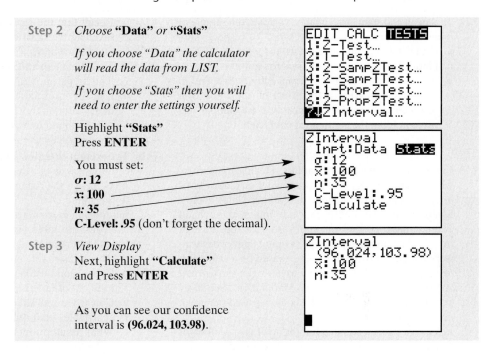

Step 2   *Choose* **"Data"** *or* **"Stats"**

If you choose "Data" the calculator will read the data from LIST.

If you choose "Stats" then you will need to enter the settings yourself.

Highlight **"Stats"**
Press **ENTER**

You must set:

σ: 12
$\bar{x}$: 100
n: 35
C-Level: .95 (don't forget the decimal).

Step 3   *View Display*
Next, highlight **"Calculate"**
and Press **ENTER**

As you can see our confidence interval is **(96.024, 103.98)**.

Exercises 7.1–7.24

Understanding the Principles

7.1   Define the target parameter.

7.2   What is the confidence coefficient in a 90% confidence interval for μ?

7.3   Explain the difference between an interval estimator and a point estimator for μ.

7.4   Explain what is meant by the statement, "We are 95% confident that an interval estimate contains μ."

7.5   Will a large-sample confidence interval be valid if the population from which the sample is taken is not normally distributed? Explain.

7.6   What conditions are required to form a valid large-sample confidence interval for μ?

Learning the Mechanics

7.7   Find $z_{\alpha/2}$ for each of the following:
NW   **a.** $\alpha = .10$ **b.** $\alpha = .01$
        c. $\alpha = .05$ **d.** $\alpha = .20$

7.8   What is the confidence level of each of the following confidence intervals for μ?

a. $\bar{x} \pm 1.96\left(\dfrac{\sigma}{\sqrt{n}}\right)$

b. $\bar{x} \pm 1.645\left(\dfrac{\sigma}{\sqrt{n}}\right)$

c. $\bar{x} \pm 2.575\left(\dfrac{\sigma}{\sqrt{n}}\right)$

d. $\bar{x} \pm 1.28\left(\dfrac{\sigma}{\sqrt{n}}\right)$

e. $\bar{x} \pm .99\left(\dfrac{\sigma}{\sqrt{n}}\right)$

7.9   A random sample of n measurements was selected from a population with unknown mean μ and standard deviation σ. Calculate a 95% confidence interval for μ for each of the following situations:
a. $n = 75$, $\bar{x} = 28$, $s^2 = 12$
b. $n = 200$, $\bar{x} = 102$, $s^2 = 22$
c. $n = 100$, $\bar{x} = 15$, $s = .3$
d. $n = 100$, $\bar{x} = 4.05$, $s = .83$
e. Is the assumption that the underlying population of measurements is normally distributed necessary to ensure the validity of the confidence intervals in parts **a–d**? Explain.

7.10   A random sample of 90 observations produced a mean $\bar{x} = 25.9$ and a standard deviation $s = 2.7$.
a. Find a 95% confidence interval for the population mean μ.
b. Find a 90% confidence interval for μ.
c. Find a 99% confidence interval for μ.

7.11   A random sample of 100 observations from a normally
NW   distributed population possesses a mean equal to 83.2 and a standard deviation equal to 6.4.
a. Find a 95% confidence interval for μ.
b. What do you mean when you say that a confidence coefficient is .95?
c. Find a 99% confidence interval for μ.
d. What happens to the width of a confidence interval as the value of the confidence coefficient is increased while the sample size is held fixed?
e. Would your confidence intervals of parts **a** and **c** be valid if the distribution of the original population was not normal? Explain.

7.12 The mean and standard deviation of a random sample of n measurements are equal to 33.9 and 3.3, respectively.
  a. Find a 95% confidence interval for μ if $n = 100$.
  b. Find a 95% confidence interval for μ if $n = 400$.
  c. Find the widths of the confidence intervals found in parts **a** and **b**. What is the effect on the width of a confidence interval of quadrupling the sample size while holding the confidence coefficient fixed?

Applying the Concepts—Basic

7.13 **Latex allergy in healthcare workers.** Healthcare workers who use latex gloves with glove powder on a daily basis are particularly susceptible to developing a latex allergy. Symptoms of a latex allergy include conjunctivitis, hand eczema, nasal congestion, skin rash, and shortness of breath. Each in a sample of 46 hospital employees who were diagnosed with latex allergy based on a skin-prick test reported on their exposure to latex gloves. (*Current Allergy & Clinical Immunology,* March 2004.) Summary statistics for the number of latex gloves used per week are $\bar{x} = 19.3$, $s = 11.9$.
  a. Give a point estimate for the average number of latex gloves used per week by all healthcare workers with a latex allergy.
  b. Form a 95% confidence interval for the average number of latex gloves used per week by all healthcare workers with a latex allergy.
  c. Give a practical interpretation of the interval, part **b**.
  d. Give the conditions required for the interval, part **b**, to be valid.

7.14 **Personal networks of older adults.** In sociology, a personal network is defined as the people who you make frequent contact with. The Living Arrangements and Social Networks of Older Adults (LSN) research program used a stratified random sample of men and women born between 1908 and 1937 to gauge the personal network size of older adults. Each adult in the sample was asked to "please name the people (e.g., in your neighborhood) you have frequent contact with and who are also important to you." Based on the number of people named, the personal network size for each adult was determined. The responses for 2,819 adults in the LSN sample yielded the following statistics on network size: $\bar{x} = 14.6$, $s = 9.8$. (*Sociological Methods & Research,* August 2001.)
  a. Give a point estimate for the mean personal network size of all older adults.
  b. Form a 95% confidence interval for the mean personal network size of all older adults.
  c. Give a practical interpretation of the interval, part **b**.
  d. Give the conditions required for the interval, part **b**, to be valid.

NZBIRDS

7.15 **Extinct New Zealand birds.** Refer to the *Evolutionary Ecology Research* (July 2003) study of the patterns of extinction in the New Zealand bird population, Exercise 2.96 (p. 80). Suppose you are interested in estimating the mean egg length (in millimeters) for the New Zealand bird population.
  a. What is the target parameter?

  b. Recall that the egg lengths for 132 bird species are saved in the **NZBIRDS** file. Obtain a random sample of 50 egg lengths from the data set.
  c. Find the mean and standard deviation of the 50 egg lengths, part **b**.
  d. Use the information, part **c**, to form a 99% confidence interval for the true mean egg length of a bird species found in New Zealand.
  e. Give a practical interpretation of the interval, part **d**.

7.16 **Tax-exempt charities.** Donations to tax-exempt organizations such as the Red Cross, the Salvation Army, the YMCA, and the American Cancer Society not only go to the stated charitable purpose, but are used to cover fundraising expenses and overhead. For a sample of 30 charities, the table lists their charitable commitment (i.e., the percentage of their expenses that go toward the stated charitable purpose).
  a. Give a point estimate for the mean charitable commitment of tax-exempt organizations.
  b. Construct a 98% confidence interval for the mean charitable commitment.
  c. What assumption(s) must hold for the method of estimation used in part **b** to be appropriate?
  d. Why is the confidence interval of part **b** a better estimator of the mean charitable commitment than the point estimator of part **a**?

CHARITY

Organization	Charitable Commitment
American Cancer Society	62%
American National Red Cross	91
Big Brothers Big Sisters of America	77
Boy Scouts of America National Council	81
Boys & Girls Clubs of America	81
CARE	91
Covenant House	15
Disabled American Veterans	65
Ducks Unlimited	78
Feed The Children	90
Girl Scouts of the USA	83
Goodwill Industries International	89
Habitat for Humanity International	81
Mayo Foundation	26
Mothers Against Drunk Drivers	71
Multiple Sclerosis Association of America	56
Museum of Modern Art	79
Nature Conservancy	77
Paralyzed Veterans of America	50
Planned Parenthood Federation	81
Salvation Army	84
Shriners Hospital for Children	95
Smithsonian Institution	87
Special Olympics	72
Trust for Public Land	88
United Jewish Appeal/Federation - NY	75
United States Olympic Committee	78
United Way of New York City	85
WGBH Educational Foundation	81
YMCA of the USA	80

Source: "Look Before You Give," *Forbes,* Dec. 27, 1999, pp. 206–216.

Applying the Concepts—Intermediate

7.17 Colored string preferred by chickens. Animal behaviorists have discovered that the more domestic chickens peck at objects placed in their environment, the healthier the chickens seem to be. White string has been found to be a particularly attractive pecking stimulus. In one experiment, 72 chickens were exposed to a string stimulus. Instead of white string, blue-colored string was used. The number of pecks each chicken took at the blue string over a specified time interval was recorded. Summary statistics for the 72 chickens were: $\bar{x} = 1.13$ pecks, $s = 2.21$ pecks. (*Applied Animal Behaviour Science*, October 2000.)

a. Estimate the population mean number of pecks made by chickens pecking at blue string using a 99% confidence interval. Interpret the result.

b. Previous research has shown that $\mu = 7.5$ pecks if chickens are exposed to white string. Based on the results, part **a**, is there evidence that chickens are more apt to peck at white string than blue string? Explain.

7.18 Sentence complexity study. Refer to the *Applied Psycholinguistics* (June 1998) study of language skills of low-income children, Exercise 2.98 (p. 80). Each in a sample of 65 low-income children was administered the Communicative Development Inventory (CDI) exam. The sentence complexity scores had a mean of 7.62 and a standard deviation of 8.91.

a. Construct a 90% confidence interval for the mean sentence complexity score of all low-income children.

b. Interpret the interval, part **a**, in the words of the problem.

c. Suppose we know that the true mean sentence complexity score of middle-income children is 15.55. Is there evidence that the true mean for low-income children differs from 15.55? Explain.

7.19 Improving SAT scores. Refer to the *Chance* (Winter 2001) and National Education Longitudinal Survey (NELS) study of 265 students who paid a private tutor to help them improve their SAT scores, Exercise 2.101 (p. 81). The changes in both the SAT-Mathematics and SAT-Verbal scores for these students are reproduced in the table.

	SAT-Math	SAT-Verbal
Mean change in score	19	7
Standard deviation of score changes	65	49

a. Construct and interpret a 95% confidence interval for the population mean change in SAT-Mathematics score for students who pay a private tutor.

b. Repeat part **a** for the population mean change in SAT-Verbal score.

c. Suppose the true population mean change in score on one of the SAT tests for all students who paid a private tutor is 15. Which of the two tests, SAT-Mathematics or SAT-Verbal, is most likely to have this mean change? Explain.

7.20 Velocity of light from galaxies. Refer to *The Astronomical Journal* (July 1995) study of the velocity of light emitted from a galaxy in the universe, Exercise 2.100 (p. 80). A sample of 103 galaxies located in the galaxy cluster A2142 had a mean velocity of $\bar{x} = 27{,}117$ kilometers per second (km/s) and a standard deviation of $s = 1{,}280$ km/s. Suppose your goal is to make an inference about the population mean light velocity of galaxies in cluster A2142.

a. In part **b** of Exercise 2.100, you constructed an interval that captured approximately 95% of the galaxy velocities in the cluster. Explain why this interval is inappropriate for this inference.

b. Construct a 95% confidence interval for the mean light velocity emitted from all galaxies in cluster A2142. Interpret the result.

7.21 Psychological study of participation and satisfaction. The relationship between an employee's participation in the performance appraisal process and subsequent subordinate reactions toward the appraisal was investigated in the *Journal of Applied Psychology* (August 1998). In Chapter 11 we will discuss a quantitative measure of the relationship between two variables, called the coefficient of correlation r. The researchers obtained r for a sample of 34 studies that examined the relationship between appraisal participation and a subordinate's satisfaction with the appraisal. These correlations are listed in the table. (Values of r near $+1$ reflect a strong positive relationship between the variables.) Find a 95% confidence interval for the mean of the data and interpret it in the words of the problem.

CORR34

.50	.58	.71	.46	.63	.66	.31	.35	.51	.06	.35	.19
.40	.63	.43	.16	−.08	.51	.59	.43	.30	.69	.25	.20
.39	.20	.51	.68	.74	.65	.34	.45	.31	.27		

Source: Cawley, B. D., Keeping, L. M., and Levy, P. E. "Participation in the performance appraisal process and employee reactions: A meta-analytic review of field investigations." *Journal of Applied Psychology,* Vol. 83, No. 4, Aug. 1998, pp. 632–633 (Appendix).

7.22 Attention time given to twins. Psychologists have found that twins, in their early years, tend to have lower IQs and pick up language more slowly than nontwins. The slower intellectual growth of most twins may be caused by benign parental neglect. Suppose it is desired to estimate the mean attention time given to twins per week by their parents. A sample of 50 sets of $2\frac{1}{2}$-year-old twin boys is taken, and at the end of 1 week the attention time given to each pair is recorded. The data (in hours) are listed in the accompanying table.

ATTIMES

20.7	16.7	22.5	12.1	2.9
23.5	6.4	1.3	39.6	35.6
10.9	7.1	46.0	23.4	29.4
44.1	13.8	24.3	9.3	3.4
15.7	46.6	10.6	6.7	5.4
14.0	20.7	48.2	7.7	22.2
20.3	34.0	44.5	23.8	20.0
43.1	14.3	21.9	17.5	9.6
36.4	0.8	1.1	19.3	14.6
32.5	19.1	36.9	27.9	14.0

Find a 90% confidence interval for the mean attention time given to all twin boys by their parents. Interpret the confidence interval.

Applying the Concepts—Advanced

7.23 Job satisfaction of workers. Research reported in the *Journal of Psychology and Aging* (May 1992) studied the role that the age of workers has in determining their level of job satisfaction. The researcher hypothesized that both younger and older workers would have a higher job satisfaction rating than middle-age workers. Each of a sample of 1,686 adults was given a job satisfaction score based on answers to a series of questions. Higher job satisfaction scores indicate higher levels of job satisfaction. The data, arranged by age group, are summarized below.

	Age Group		
	Younger 18–24	Middle Age 25–44	Older 45–64
$\bar{x}$	4.17	4.04	4.31
s	.75	.81	.82
n	241	768	677

a. Construct 95% confidence intervals for the mean job satisfaction scores of each age group. Carefully interpret each interval.

b. In the construction of three 95% confidence intervals, is it more or less likely that at least one of them will *not* contain the population mean it is intended to estimate than it is for a single confidence interval to miss the population mean? [*Hint:* Assume the three intervals are independent, and calculate the probability that at least one of them will not contain the population mean it estimates. Compare this probability to the probability that a single interval fails to enclose the mean.]

c. Based on these intervals, does it appear that the researcher's hypothesis is supported? [*Caution:* We'll learn how to use sample information to compare population means in Chapter 9, and we'll return to this exercise at that time. Here, simply base your opinion on the individual confidence intervals you constructed in part **a.**]

7.24 Study of cockroach growth. According to scientists, the cockroach has had 300 million years to develop a resistance to destruction. In a study conducted by researchers for S. C. Johnson & Son, Inc. (manufacturers of Raid and Off), 5,000 roaches (the expected number in a roach-infested house) were released in the Raid test kitchen. One week later the kitchen was fumigated and 16,298 dead roaches were counted, a gain of 11,298 roaches for the 1-week period. Assume that none of the original roaches died during the 1-week period and that the standard deviation of x, the number of roaches produced per roach in a 1-week period, is 1.5. Use the number of roaches produced by the sample of 5,000 roaches to find a 95% confidence interval for the mean number of roaches produced per week for each roach in a typical roach-infested house.

7.3 Small-Sample Confidence Interval for a Population Mean

Federal legislation requires pharmaceutical companies to perform extensive tests on new drugs before they can be marketed. Initially, a new drug is tested on animals. If the drug is deemed safe after this first phase of testing, the pharmaceutical company is then permitted to begin human testing on a limited basis. During this second phase, inferences must be made about the safety of the drug based on information in very small samples.

Suppose a pharmaceutical company must estimate the average increase in blood pressure of patients who take a certain new drug. Assume that only six patients (randomly selected from the population of all patients) can be used in the initial phase of human testing. The use of a *small sample* in making an inference about μ presents two immediate problems when we attempt to use the standard normal z as a test statistic.

Problem 1   The shape of the sampling distribution of the sample mean $\bar{x}$ (and the z-statistic) now depends on the shape of the population that is sampled. We can no longer assume that the sampling distribution of $\bar{x}$ is approximately normal, because the Central Limit Theorem ensures normality only for samples that are sufficiently large.

Solution to Problem 1   The sampling distribution of $\bar{x}$ (and z) is exactly normal even for relatively small samples if the sampled population is normal. It is approximately normal if the sampled population is approximately normal.

Problem 2   The population standard deviation σ is almost always unknown. Although it is still true that $\sigma_{\bar{x}} = \sigma/\sqrt{n}$, the sample standard deviation s may provide a poor approximation for σ when the sample size is small.

Solution to Problem 2   Instead of using the standard normal statistic

$$z = \frac{\bar{x} - \mu}{\sigma_{\bar{x}}} = \frac{\bar{x} - \mu}{\sigma/\sqrt{n}}$$

which requires knowledge of or a good approximation to σ, we define and use the statistic

$$t = \frac{\bar{x} - \mu}{s/\sqrt{n}}$$

in which the sample standard deviation, s, replaces the population standard deviation, σ.

Biography

WILLIAM S. GOSSET (1876–1937)— Student's *t*-Distribution

At the age of 23, William Gosset earned a degree in chemistry and mathematics at prestigious Oxford University. He was immediately hired by the Guinness Brewing Company in Dublin, Ireland, for his expertise in chemistry. However, Gosset's mathematical skills allowed him to solve numerous practical problems associated with brewing beer. For example, Gosset applied the Poisson distribution to model the number of yeast cells per unit volume in the fermentation process. His most important discovery was that of the *t*-distribution in 1908. Since most applied researchers worked with small samples, Gosset was interested in the behavior of the mean in the small sample case. He tediously took numerous small sets of numbers, calculated the mean and standard deviation, obtained their *t*-ratio, and plotted the results on graph paper. The shape of the distribution was always the same—the *t*-distribution. Under company policy, employees were forbidden to publish their research results; so Gosset used the penname *Student* to publish a paper on the subject. Hence, the distribution has been called Student's *t*-distribution.

If we are sampling from a normal distribution, the ***t*-statistic** has a sampling distribution very much like that of the z-statistic: mound shaped, symmetric, with mean 0. The primary difference between the sampling distributions of t and z is that the t-statistic is more variable than the z, which follows intuitively when you realize that t contains two random quantities ($\bar{x}$ and s), whereas z contains only one ($\bar{x}$).

The actual amount of variability in the sampling distribution of t depends on the sample size n. A convenient way of expressing this dependence is to say that the t statistic has $(n - 1)$ **degrees of freedom (df)**.* Recall that the quantity $(n - 1)$ is the divisor that appears in the formula for s^2. This number plays a key role in the sampling distribution of s^2 and appears in discussions of other statistics in later chapters. Particularly, the smaller the number of degrees of freedom associated with the t-statistic, the more variable will be its sampling distribution.

In Figure 7.7 we show both the sampling distribution of z and the sampling distribution of a t-statistic with 4 df. You can see that the increased variability of the t-statistic means that the t-value, t_α, that locates an area α in the upper tail of the t-distribution is larger than the corresponding value z_α. For any given value of α, the t-value, t_α, increases as the number of degrees of freedom (df) decreases. Values of t that will be used in forming small-sample confidence intervals of μ are

*Since degrees of freedom are related to the sample size, n, it is helpful to think of the number of degrees of freedom as the amount of information in the sample available for estimating the target parameter.

Figure 7.7
Standard Normal (z)
Distribution and
t-Distribution with 4 df

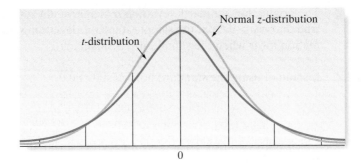

given in Table VI of Appendix A. A partial reproduction of this table is shown in Table 7.3.

Note that t_α values are listed for various degrees of freedom where α refers to the tail area under the t-distribution to the right of t_α. For example, if we want the t-value with an area of .025 to its right and 4 df, we look in the table under the column $t_{.025}$ for the entry in the row corresponding to 4 df. This entry is $t_{.025} = 2.776$, as shown in Figure 7.8. The corresponding standard normal z-score is $z_{.025} = 1.96$.

TABLE 7.3   Reproduction of Part of Table VI in Appendix A

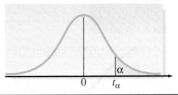

Degrees of Freedom	$t_{.100}$	$t_{.050}$	$t_{.025}$	$t_{.010}$	$t_{.005}$	$t_{.001}$	$t_{.0005}$
1	3.078	6.314	12.706	31.821	63.657	318.31	636.62
2	1.886	2.920	4.303	6.965	9.925	22.326	31.598
3	1.638	2.353	3.182	4.541	5.841	10.213	12.924
4	1.533	2.132	2.776	3.747	4.604	7.173	8.610
5	1.476	2.015	2.571	3.365	4.032	5.893	6.869
6	1.440	1.943	2.447	3.143	3.707	5.208	5.959
7	1.415	1.895	2.365	2.998	3.499	4.785	5.408
8	1.397	1.860	2.306	2.896	3.355	4.501	5.041
9	1.383	1.833	2.262	2.821	3.250	4.297	4.781
10	1.372	1.812	2.228	2.764	3.169	4.144	4.587
11	1.363	1.796	2.201	2.718	3.106	4.025	4.437
12	1.356	1.782	2.179	2.681	3.055	3.930	4.318
13	1.350	1.771	2.160	2.650	3.012	3.852	4.221
14	1.345	1.761	2.145	2.624	2.977	3.787	4.140
15	1.341	1.753	2.131	2.602	2.947	3.733	4.073
$\vdots$	$\vdots$	$\vdots$	$\vdots$	$\vdots$	$\vdots$	$\vdots$	$\vdots$
∞	1.282	1.645	1.960	2.326	2.576	3.090	3.291

Figure 7.8
The $t_{.025}$ Value in a
t-Distribution with 4 df
and the Corresponding
$z_{.025}$ Value

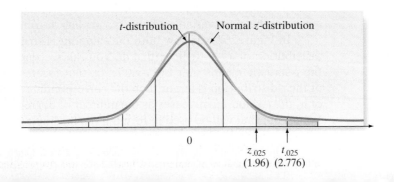

Note that the last row of Table VI, where df $= \infty$ (infinity), contains the standard normal z-values. This follows from the fact that as the sample size n grows very large, s becomes closer to σ and thus t becomes closer in distribution to z. In fact, when df $= 29$, there is little difference between corresponding tabulated values of z and t. Thus, we choose the arbitrary cutoff of $n = 30$ (df $= 29$) to distinguish between the large-sample and small-sample inferential techniques.

⊙ **BPINCR**

Returning to the example of testing a new drug, suppose that the six test patients have blood pressure increases of 1.7, 3.0, .8, 3.4, 2.7, and 2.1 points. How can we use this information to construct a 95% confidence interval for μ, the mean increase in blood pressure associated with the new drug for all patients in the population?

First, we know that we are dealing with a sample too small to assume that the sample mean $\bar{x}$ is approximately normally distributed by the Central Limit Theorem. That is, we do not get the normal distribution of $\bar{x}$ "automatically" from the Central Limit Theorem when the sample size is small. Instead, we must assume that the measured variable, in this case the increase in blood pressure, is normally distributed in order for the distribution of $\bar{x}$ to be normal.

Second, unless we are fortunate enough to know the population standard deviation σ, which in this case represents the standard deviation of *all* the patients' increases in blood pressure when they take the new drug, we cannot use the standard normal z-statistic to form our confidence interval for μ. Instead, we must use the t-distribution, with $(n - 1)$ degrees of freedom.

In this case, $n - 1 = 5$ df, and the t-value is found in Table 7.3 to be

$$t_{.025} = 2.571 \text{ with 5 df}$$

Recall that the large-sample confidence interval would have been of the form

$$\bar{x} \pm z_{\alpha/2}\sigma_{\bar{x}} = \bar{x} \pm z_{\alpha/2}\frac{\sigma}{\sqrt{n}} = \bar{x} \pm z_{.025}\frac{\sigma}{\sqrt{n}}$$

where 95% is the desired confidence level. To form the interval for a small sample from *a normal distribution, we simply substitute t for z and s for σ in the preceding formula:*

$$\bar{x} \pm t_{\alpha/2}\frac{s}{\sqrt{n}}$$

An SPSS printout showing descriptive statistics for the six blood pressure increases is displayed in Figure 7.9. Note that $\bar{x} = 2.283$ and $s = .950$. Substituting these numerical values into the confidence interval formula, we get

$$2.283 \pm (2.571)\left(\frac{.950}{\sqrt{6}}\right) = 2.283 \pm .997$$

or 1.286 to 3.280 points. Note that this interval agrees (except for rounding) with the confidence interval highlighted on the SPSS printout in Figure 7.9.

We interpret the interval as follows: We can be 95% confident that the mean increase in blood pressure associated with taking this new drug is between 1.286 and 3.28 points. As with our large-sample interval estimates, our confidence is in the process, not in this particular interval. We know that if we were to repeatedly use this estimation procedure, 95% of the confidence intervals produced would contain the true mean μ, *assuming that the probability distribution of changes in blood pressure from which our sample was selected is normal.* The latter assumption is necessary for the small-sample interval to be valid.

What price did we pay for having to utilize a small sample to make the inference? First, we had to assume the underlying population is normally distributed,

Figure 7.9

SPSS Confidence Interval for Mean Blood Pressure Increase

Descriptives

			Statistic	Std. Error
BPINCR	Mean		2.283	.3877
	95% Confidence Interval for Mean	Lower Bound	1.287	
		Upper Bound	3.280	
	5% Trimmed Mean		2.304	
	Median		2.400	
	Variance		.902	
	Std. Deviation		.9496	
	Minimum		.8	
	Maximum		3.4	
	Range		2.6	
	Interquartile Range		1.625	
	Skewness		-.573	.845
	Kurtosis		-.389	1.741

and if the assumption is invalid, our interval might also be invalid.* Second, we had to form the interval using a t value of 2.571 rather than a z-value of 1.96, resulting in a wider interval to achieve the same 95% level of confidence. If the interval from 1.286 to 3.28 is too wide to be of much use, we know how to remedy the situation: Increase the number of patients sampled in order to decrease the interval width (on average).

Now Work *Exercise 7.27*

The procedure for forming a small-sample confidence interval is summarized in the accompanying boxes.

Small-Sample Confidence Interval[†] for μ

$$\bar{x} \pm t_{\alpha/2}\left(\frac{s}{\sqrt{n}}\right)$$

where $t_{\alpha/2}$ is based on $(n - 1)$ degrees of freedom

---

Conditions Required for a Valid Small-Sample Confidence Interval for μ

1. A random sample is selected from the target population.

2. The population has a relative frequency distribution that is approximately normal.

---

*By *invalid*, we mean that the probability that the procedure will yield an interval that contains μ is not equal to $(1 - \alpha)$. Generally, if the underlying population is approximately normal, the confidence coefficient will approximate the probability that the interval contains μ.

[†]The procedure given in the box assumes that the population standard deviation σ is unknown, which is almost always the case. If σ is known, we can form the small-sample confidence interval just as we would a large-sample confidence interval using a standard normal z-value instead of t. However, we must still assume that the underlying population is approximately normal.

EXAMPLE 7.2   FINDING A SMALL-SAMPLE CONFIDENCE INTERVAL FOR μ

Problem   Some quality control experiments require *destructive sampling* (i.e., the test to
determine whether the item is defective destroys the item) in order to measure some
particular characteristic of the product. The cost of destructive sampling often dictates
small samples. Suppose a manufacturer of printers for personal computers wishes to
estimate the mean number of characters printed before the printhead fails. The printer
manufacturer tests $n = 15$ printheads and records the number of characters printed
until failure for each. These 15 measurements (in millions of characters) are listed in
Table 7.4, followed by a MINITAB summary statistics printout in Figure 7.10.

   a. Form a 99% confidence interval for the mean number of characters printed
before the printhead fails. Interpret the result.

   b. What assumption is required for the interval, part **a**, to be valid? Is it reasonably satisfied?

⊙ **PRINTHEAD**

TABLE 7.4   Number of Characters (in Millions) for $n = 15$ Printhead Tests

---

| 1.13 | 1.55 | 1.43 | .92 | 1.25 | 1.36 | 1.32 | .85 | 1.07 | 1.48 | 1.20 | 1.33 | 1.18 | 1.22 | 1.29 |

Figure 7.10

MINITAB Printout with
Descriptive Statistics and
90% Confidence Interval
for Example 7.2

```
Variable   N     Mean     StDev   SE Mean        99% CI
NUMCHAR    15   1.23867  0.19316  0.04987   (1.09020, 1.38714)
```

Solution   **a.** For this small sample ($n = 15$), we use the t-statistic to form the confidence
interval. We use a confidence coefficient of .99 and $n - 1 = 14$ degrees of
freedom to find $t_{\alpha/2}$ in Table VI:

$$t_{\alpha/2} = t_{.005} = 2.977$$

[*Note:* The small sample forces us to extend the interval almost 3 standard
deviations (of $\bar{x}$) on each side of the sample mean in order to form the 99%
confidence interval.] From the MINITAB printout, Figure 7.10, we find
$\bar{x} = 1.24$ and $s = .19$. Substituting these (rounded) values into the confidence
interval formula, we obtain

$$\bar{x} \pm t_{.005}\left(\frac{s}{\sqrt{n}}\right) = 1.24 \pm 2.977\left(\frac{.19}{\sqrt{15}}\right)$$
$$= 1.24 \pm .15 \quad \text{or} \quad (1.09, 1.39)$$

This interval is highlighted on Figure 7.10.

    Our interpretation is as follows: The manufacturer can be 99% confident
that the printhead has a mean life of between 1.09 and 1.39 million characters.
If the manufacturer were to advertise that the mean life of its printheads is
(at least) 1 million characters, the interval would support such a claim. Our confidence is derived from the fact that 99% of the intervals formed in repeated
applications of this procedure will contain μ.

   b. Since n is small, we must assume that the number of characters printed before
printhead failure is a random variable from a normal distribution. That is, we
assume that the population from which the sample of 15 measurements is
selected is distributed normally. One way to check this assumption is to graph
the distribution of data in Table 7.4. If the sample data is approximately
normal, then the population from which the sample is selected is very likely
to be normal. A MINITAB stem-and-leaf plot for the sample data is displayed

Figure 7.11
MINITAB Stem-and-Leaf
Display of Data in Table 7.4

Stem-and-Leaf Display: NUMBER

```
Stem-and-leaf of NUMBER   N  = 15
Leaf Unit = 0.010


  1     8    5
  2     9    2
  3    10    7
  5    11    38
 (4)   12    0259
  6    13    236
  3    14    38
  1    15    5
```

in Figure 7.11. The distribution is mound shaped and nearly symmetric. Therefore, the assumption of normality appears to be reasonably satisfied.

Look Back Other checks for normality, such as a normal probability plot and the ratio IQR/s, may also be used to verify the normality condition.

| Now Work | *Exercise 7.33* |

■ ■ ■

We have emphasized throughout this section that an assumption that the population is approximately normally distributed is necessary for making small-sample inferences about μ when using the t-statistic. Although many phenomena do have approximately normal distributions, it is also true that many random phenomena have distributions that are not normal or even mound shaped. Empirical evidence acquired over the years has shown that the t-distribution is rather insensitive to moderate departures from normality. That is, use of the t-statistic when sampling from slightly skewed mound-shaped populations generally produces credible results; however, for cases in which the distribution is distinctly non-normal, we must either take a large sample or use a *nonparametric method* (the topic of Chapter 14).

What Do You Do When the Population Relative Frequency Distribution Departs Greatly from Normality?

Answer: Use the nonparametric statistical methods of Chapter 14.

Confidence Interval for a Population Mean ($n < 30$)

Using the TI-83 Graphing Calculator

Step 1   *Enter the data*
Press **STAT** and select **1:Edit**
Note: If the list already contains data, clear the old data. Use the up arrow to highlight '**L1**'. Press **CLEAR ENTER**.
Use the arrow and **ENTER** keys to enter the data set into **L1**.

Step 2   *Access the Statistical Tests Menu*
Press **STAT**

Arrow right to **TESTS**
Arrow down to **8:TInterval**
Press **ENTER**

```
EDIT CALC TESTS
2↑T-Test…
3:2-SampZTest…
4:2-SampTTest…
5:1-PropZTest…
6:2-PropZTest…
7:ZInterval…
8↓TInterval…
```

Step 3   *Choose "**Data**" or "**Stats**". ("Data" is selected when you have entered the raw data into a List. "Stats" is selected when you are given only the mean, standard deviation, and sample size.)*
Press **ENTER**
If you selected "Data", set **List** to **L1**
Set **Freq** to **1**
Set **C-Level** to the confidence level
Arrow down to "**Calculate**"
Press ENTER

```
TInterval
Inpt:DATA Stats
List:L1
Freq:1
C-Level:.99
Calculate
```

If you selected "Stats", enter the mean, standard deviation, and sample size.
Set **C-Level** to the confidence level
Arrow down to **"Calculate"**
Press **ENTER**
(The screen below is set up for an example with a mean of 100 and a standard deviation of 10.)

```
TInterval
Inpt:Data Stats
x̄:100
Sx:10
n:19
C-Level:.95
Calculate
```

The confidence interval will be displayed with the mean, standard deviation, and the sample size.

Example   Compute a 99% confidence interval for the mean using the 15 pieces of data given in Example 7.2.

1.13	1.55	1.43	0.92	1.25
1.36	1.32	0.85	1.07	1.48
1.20	1.33	1.18	1.22	1.29

As you can see from the screen, our 99% confidence interval is $(1.0902, 1.3871)$. You will also notice it gives the mean, standard deviation, and the sample size.

```
TInterval
(1.0902,1.3871)
x̄=1.238666667
Sx=.1931641296
n=15

█
```

Exercises 7.25–7.41

Understanding the Principles

7.25 State the two problems (and corresponding solutions) with using a small sample to estimate μ.

7.26 Compare the shapes of the z- and t-distributions.

7.27 Explain the differences in the sampling distributions
NW of $\bar{x}$ for large and small samples under the following assumptions.
  a. The variable of interest, x, is normally distributed.
  b. Nothing is known about the distribution of the variable x.

Learning the Mechanics

7.28 Suppose you have selected a random sample of $n = 7$ measurements from a normal distribution. Compare the standard normal z-values with the corresponding t-values if you were forming the following confidence intervals.
  a. 80% confidence interval
  b. 90% confidence interval
  c. 95% confidence interval
  d. 98% confidence interval
  e. 99% confidence interval
  f. Use the table values you obtained in parts **a–e** to sketch the z- and t-distributions. What are the similarities and differences?

7.29 Let t_0 be a specific value of t. Use Table VI in Appendix A to find t_0 values such that the following statements are true.
  a. $P(t \geq t_0) = .025$ where df $= 10$
  b. $P(t \geq t_0) = .01$ where df $= 17$
  c. $P(t \leq t_0) = .005$ where df $= 6$
  d. $P(t \leq t_0) = .05$ where df $= 13$

7.30 Let t_0 be a particular value of t. Use Table VI of Appendix A to find t_0 values such that the following statements are true.
  a. $P(-t_0 < t < t_0) = .95$ where df $= 16$
  b. $P(t \leq -t_0 \text{ or } t \geq t_0) = .05$ where df $= 16$
  c. $P(t \leq t_0) = .05$ where df $= 16$
  d. $P(t \leq -t_0 \text{ or } t \geq t_0) = .10$ where df $= 12$
  e. $P(t \leq -t_0 \text{ or } t \geq t_0) = .01$ where df $= 8$

7.31 The following random sample was selected from a normal distribution: 4, 6, 3, 5, 9, 3.
  a. Construct a 90% confidence interval for the population mean μ.
  b. Construct a 95% confidence interval for the population mean μ.
  c. Construct a 99% confidence interval for the population mean μ.
  d. Assume that the sample mean $\bar{x}$ and sample standard deviation s remain exactly the same as those you just calculated but that they are based on a sample of $n = 25$ observations rather than $n = 6$ observations.

Repeat parts **a–c**. What is the effect of increasing the sample size on the width of the confidence intervals?

7.32 The following sample of 16 measurements was selected from a population that is approximately normally distributed:

  LM7_32

91	80	99	110	95	106	78	121	106	100
97	82	100	83	115	104				

  a. Construct an 80% confidence interval for the population mean.
  b. Construct a 95% confidence interval for the population mean and compare the width of this interval with that of part **a**.
  c. Carefully interpret each of the confidence intervals and explain why the 80% confidence interval is narrower.

Applying the Concepts—Basic

  LICHEN

7.33 Radioactive lichen. Refer to the Lichen Radionuclide
NW Baseline Research project at the University of Alaska, Exercise 2.34 (p. 51). Recall that the researchers collected 9 lichen specimens and measured the amount (in microcuries per milliliter) of the radioactive element, cesium-137, for each. (The natural logarithms of the data values are saved in the **LICHEN** file.) A MINITAB printout with summary statistics for the actual data is shown at the bottom of the page.
  a. Give a point estimate for the mean amount of cesium in lichen specimens collected in Alaska.
  b. Give the t-value used in a small-sample 95% confidence interval for the true mean amount of cesium in Alaskan lichen specimens.
  c. Use the result, part **b**, and the values of $\bar{x}$ and s shown on the MINITAB printout to form a 95% confidence interval for the true mean amount of cesium in Alaskan lichen specimens.
  d. Check your interval, part **c**, with the 95% confidence interval shown on the MINITAB printout.
  e. Give a practical interpretation for the interval, part **c**.

  GOBIANTS

7.34 Rainfall and desert ants. Refer to the *Journal of Biogeography* (December 2003) study of ants and their habitat in the desert of Central Asia, Exercise 2.66 (p. 66). Recall that botanists randomly selected five sites in the Dry Steppe region and six sites in the Gobi Desert where ants were observed. One of the variables of interest is the annual rainfall (in millimeters) at each site. (The data are saved in the **GOBIANTS** file.)

MINITAB Output for Exercise 7.33

Variable	N	Mean	StDev	SE Mean	95% CI
CESIUM	9	0.009027	0.004854	0.001618	(0.005296, 0.012759)

SAS Output for Exercise 7.34

The MEANS Procedure

Analysis Variable : RAIN

REGION	N Obs	Mean	Std Dev
DryStepp	5	183.4000000	20.6470337
Gobi	6	110.0000000	15.9749804

Summary statistics for the annual rainfall at each site are provided in the above SAS printout.

a. Give a point estimate for the average annual rainfall amount at ant sites in the Dry Steppe region of Central Asia.

b. Give the *t*-value used in a small-sample 90% confidence interval for the true average annual rainfall amount at ant sites in the Dry Steppe region.

c. Use the result, part **b**, and the values of $\bar{x}$ and s shown on the SAS printout to form a 90% confidence interval for the target parameter.

d. Give a practical interpretation for the interval, part **c**.

e. Use the data in the **GOBIANTS** file to check the validity of the confidence interval, part **c**.

f. Repeat parts **a–e** for the Gobi Desert region of Central Asia.

7.35 Lead and copper in drinking water. Periodically, the Hillsborough County (Florida) Water Department tests the drinking water of homeowners for contaminants such as lead and copper. The lead and copper levels in water specimens collected for a sample of 10 residents of the Crystal Lake Manors subdivision are shown below.

LEADCOPP

Lead (μg/L)	Copper (mg/L)
1.32	.508
0	.279
13.1	.320
.919	.904
.657	.221
3.0	.283
1.32	.475
4.09	.130
4.45	.220
0	.743

Source: Hillsborough County Water Department Environmental Laboratory, Tampa, Florida.

a. Construct a 99% confidence interval for the mean lead level in water specimens from Crystal Lake Manors.

b. Construct a 99% confidence interval for the mean copper level in water specimens from Crystal Lake Manors.

c. Interpret the intervals, parts **a** and **b**, in the words of the problem.

d. Discuss the meaning of the phrase, "99% confident."

7.36 Oven cooking study. A group of Harvard University School of Public Health researchers studied the impact of cooking on the size of indoor air particles. (*Environmental Science & Technology*, September 1, 2000.) The decay rate (measured as μm/hour) for fine particles produced from oven cooking or toasting was recorded on six randomly selected days. These six measurements are

DECAY

.95	.83	1.20	.89	1.45	1.12

Source: Abt, E., et al. "Relative contribution of outdoor and indoor particle sources to indoor concentrations." *Environmental Science & Technology,* Vol. 34, No. 17, Sept. 1, 2000 (Table 3).

a. Find and interpret a 95% confidence interval for the true average decay rate of fine particles produced from oven cooking or toasting.

b. Explain what the phrase "95% confident" implies in the interpretation of part **a**.

c. What must be true about the distribution of the population of decay rates for the inference to be valid?

Applying the Concepts—Intermediate

7.37 DOT traffic counts. It is customary practice in the United States to base roadway design on the 30th highest hourly volume in a year. Thus, all roadway facilities are expected to operate at acceptable levels of service for all but 29 hours of the year. The Florida Department of Transportation (DOT), however, has shifted from the 30th highest hour to the 100th highest hour as the basis for level-of-service determinators. Florida Atlantic University researcher Reid Ewing investigated whether this shift was warranted in the *Journal of STAR Research* (July 1994). The table on p. 342 gives the traffic counts at the 30th highest hour and the 100th highest hour of a recent year for 20 randomly selected DOT permanent count stations.

a. Describe the population from which the sample data is selected.

b. Does the sample appear to be representative of the population? Explain.

c. Compute and interpret the 95% confidence interval for the mean traffic count at the 30th highest hour.

TRAFFIC

Station	Type of Route	30th Highest Hour	100th Highest Hour
0117	small city	1,890	1,736
0087	recreational	2,217	2,069
0166	small city	1,444	1,345
0013	rural	2,105	2,049
0161	urban	4,905	4,815
0096	urban	2,022	1,958
0145	rural	594	548
0149	rural	252	229
0038	urban	2,162	2,048
0118	rural	1,938	1,748
0047	rural	879	811
0066	urban	1,913	1,772
0094	rural	3,494	3,403
0105	small city	1,424	1,309
0113	small city	4,571	4,425
0151	urban	3,494	3,359
0159	rural	2,222	2,137
0160	small city	1,076	989
0164	recreational	2,167	2,039
0165	recreational	3,350	3,123

Source: Ewing, R. "Roadway levels of service in an era of growth management." *Journal of STAR Research*, Vol. 3, July 1994, p. 103 (Table 2).

d. What assumption is necessary for the confidence interval to be valid? Does it appear to be satisfied? Explain.

e. Repeat parts **c** and **d** for the 100th highest hour.

7.38 **Hearing loss study.** Patients with normal hearing in one ear and unaided sensorineural hearing loss in the other are characterized as suffering from unilateral hearing loss. In a study reported in the *American Journal of Audiology* (March 1995), 8 patients with unilateral hearing loss were fitted with a special wireless hearing aid in the "bad" ear. The absolute sound pressure level (SPL) was then measured near the eardrum of the ear when noise was produced at a frequency of 500 hertz. The SPLs of the 8 patients, recorded in decibels, are listed below.

SOUND

73.0	80.1	82.8	76.8	73.5	74.3	76.0	68.1

Construct and interpret a 90% confidence interval for the true mean SPL of unilateral hearing loss patients when noise is produced at a frequency of 500 hertz.

7.39 **Research on brain specimens.** In Exercise 2.37 (p. 52) you learned that postmortem interval (PMI) is the elapsed time between death and the performance of an autopsy on the cadaver. *Brain and Language* (June 1995) reported on the PMIs of 22 randomly selected human brain specimens obtained at autopsy. The data are reproduced in the following table.

BRAINPMI

5.5	14.5	6.0	5.5	5.3	5.8	11.0	6.4
7.0	14.5	10.4	4.6	4.3	7.2	10.5	6.5
3.3	7.0	4.1	6.2	10.4	4.9		

Source: Hayes, T. L., and Lewis, D. A. "Anatomical specialization of the anterior motor speech area: Hemispheric differences in magnopyramidal neurons." *Brain and Language*, Vol. 49, No. 3, June 1995, p. 292 (Table 1).

a. Construct a 95% confidence interval for the true mean PMI of human brain specimens obtained at autopsy.

b. Interpret the interval, part **a**.

c. What assumption is required for the interval, part **a**, to be valid? Is this assumption satisfied? Explain.

d. What is meant by the phrase "95% confidence"?

7.40 **Eating disorders in females.** The "fear of negative evaluation" (FNE) scores for 11 bulimic female students and 14 normal female students, first presented in Exercise 2.38 (p. 52) are reproduced at the bottom of the page. (Recall that the higher the score, the greater the fear of negative evaluation.)

a. Construct a 95% confidence interval for the mean FNE score of the population of bulimic female students. Interpret the result.

b. Construct a 95% confidence interval for the mean FNE score of the population of normal female students. Interpret the result.

c. What assumptions are required for the intervals of parts **a** and **b** to be statistically valid? Are these assumptions reasonably satisfied? Explain.

Applying the Concepts—Advanced

7.41 **Study on waking sleepers early.** Scientists have discovered increased levels of the hormone adrenocorticotropin in people just before they awake from sleeping (*Nature*, January 7, 1999). In the study, 15 subjects were monitored during their sleep after being told they would be woken at a particular time. One hour prior to the designated wake-up time, the adrenocorticotropin level (pg/mL) was measured in each, with the following results:

$$\bar{x} = 37.3 \qquad s = 13.9$$

a. Estimate the true mean adrenocorticotropin level of sleepers one hour prior to waking using a 95% confidence interval.

b. Interpret the interval, part **a**, in the words of the problem.

BULIMIA

Bulimic students	21	13	10	20	25	19	16	21	24	13	14			
Normal students	13	6	16	13	8	19	23	18	11	19	7	10	15	20

Source: Randles, R. H. "On neutral responses (zeros) in the sign test and ties in the Wilcoxon-Mann-Whitney Test." *The American Statistician,* Vol. 55, No. 2, May 2001 (Figure 3).

c. The researchers also found that if the subjects were woken three hours earlier than they anticipated, the average adrenocorticotropin level was 25.5 pg/mL. Assume that $\mu = 25.5$ for all sleepers who are woken three hours earlier than expected. Use the interval, part **a**, to make an inference about the mean adrenocorticotropin level of sleepers under two conditions: one hour before anticipated wake-up time and three hours before anticipated wake-up time.

7.4　Large-Sample Confidence Interval for a Population Proportion

The number of public opinion polls has grown at an astounding rate in recent years. Almost daily, the news media report the results of some poll. Pollsters regularly determine the percentage of people in favor of the president's welfare-reform program, the fraction of voters in favor of a certain candidate, the fraction of customers who favor a particular brand of wine, and the proportion of people who smoke cigarettes. In each case, we are interested in estimating the percentage (or proportion) of some group with a certain characteristic. In this section we consider methods for making inferences about population proportions when the sample is large.

EXAMPLE 7.3　ESTIMATING A POPULATION PROPORTION

Problem　Public opinion polls are conducted regularly to estimate the fraction of U.S. citizens who trust the president. Suppose 1,000 people are randomly chosen and 637 answer that they trust the president. How would you estimate the true fraction of *all* U.S. citizens who trust the president?

Solution　What we have really asked is how you would estimate the probability p of success in a binomial experiment, where p is the probability that a person chosen trusts the president. One logical method of estimating p for the population is to use the proportion of successes in the sample. That is, we can estimate p by calculating

$$\hat{p} = \frac{\text{Number of people sampled who trust the president}}{\text{Number of people sampled}}$$

where $\hat{p}$ is read "p hat." Thus, in this case,

$$\hat{p} = \frac{637}{1,000} = .637$$

Look Back　To determine the reliability of the estimator $\hat{p}$, we need to know its sampling distribution. That is, if we were to draw samples of 1,000 people over and over again, each time calculating a new estimate $\hat{p}$, what would be the frequency distribution of all the $\hat{p}$-values? The answer lies in viewing $\hat{p}$ as the average, or mean, number of successes per trial over the n trials. If each success is assigned a value equal to 1 and a failure is assigned a value of 0, then the sum of all n sample observations is x, the total number of successes, and $\hat{p} = x/n$ is the average, or mean, number of successes per trial in the n trials. The Central Limit Theorem tells us that the relative frequency distribution of the sample mean for any population is approximately normal for sufficiently large samples.

Now Work　*Exercise 7.49a*

　■ ■ ■

The repeated sampling distribution of $\hat{p}$ has the characteristics listed in the next box and shown in Figure 7.12.

Figure 7.12
Sampling Distribution of $\hat{p}$

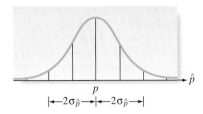

Sampling Distribution of $\hat{p}$

1. The mean of the sampling distribution of $\hat{p}$ is p; that is, $\hat{p}$ is an unbiased estimator of p.

2. The standard deviation of the sampling distribution of $\hat{p}$ is $\sqrt{pq/n}$; that is, $\sigma_p = \sqrt{pq/n}$, where $q = 1 - p$.

3. For large samples, the sampling distribution of $\hat{p}$ is approximately normal. A sample size is considered large if the interval $\hat{p} \pm 3\sigma_{\hat{p}}$ does not include 0 or 1. [*Note:* This requirement is almost equivalent to that given in Section 5.5 for approximating a binomial distribution with a normal one. The difference is that we assumed p to be known in Section 5.5; now we are trying to make inferences about an unknown p, so we use $\hat{p}$ to estimate p in checking the adequacy of the normal approximation.]

The fact that $\hat{p}$ is a "sample mean fraction of successes" allows us to form confidence intervals about p in a manner that is completely analogous to that used for large-sample estimation of μ.

Large-Sample Confidence Interval for p

$$\hat{p} \pm z_{\alpha/2}\sigma_{\hat{p}} = \hat{p} \pm z_{\alpha/2}\sqrt{\frac{pq}{n}} \approx \hat{p} \pm z_{\alpha/2}\sqrt{\frac{\hat{p}\hat{q}}{n}}$$

where $\hat{p} = \dfrac{x}{n}$ and $\hat{q} = 1 - \hat{p}$

Note: When n is large, $\hat{p}$ can approximate the value of p in the formula for $\sigma_{\hat{p}}$.

Conditions Required for a Valid Large-Sample Confidence Interval for p

1. A random sample is selected from the target population.

2. The sample size n is large. (This condition will be satisfied if $\hat{p} \pm 3\sigma_{\hat{p}}$ falls between 0 and 1.)

Thus, if 637 of 1,000 U.S. citizens say they trust the president, a 95% confidence interval for the proportion of *all* U.S. citizens who trust the president is

$$\hat{p} \pm z_{\alpha/2}\sigma_{\hat{p}} = .637 \pm 1.96\sqrt{\frac{pq}{1,000}}$$

where $q = 1 - p$. Just as we needed an approximation for σ in calculating a large-sample confidence interval for μ, we now need an approximation for p. As Table 7.5 shows, the approximation for p does not have to be especially accurate, because the value of $\sqrt{pq}$ needed for the confidence interval is relatively insensitive to changes in p. Therefore, we can use $\hat{p}$ to approximate p.

TABLE 7.5   Values of pq for Several Different Values of p

p	pq	$\sqrt{pq}$
.5	.25	.50
.6 or .4	.24	.49
.7 or .3	.21	.46
.8 or .2	.16	.40
.9 or .1	.09	.30

Keeping in mind that $\hat{q} = 1 - \hat{p}$, we substitute these values into the formula for the confidence interval:

$$\hat{p} \pm 1.96\sqrt{pq/1,000} \approx \hat{p} \pm 1.96\sqrt{\hat{p}\hat{q}/1,000}$$
$$= .637 \pm 1.96\sqrt{(.637)(.363)/1,000} = .637 \pm .030$$
$$= (.607, .667)$$

Then we can be 95% confident that the interval from 60.7% to 66.7% contains the true percentage of *all* U.S. citizens who trust the president. That is, in repeated construction of confidence intervals, approximately 95% of all samples would produce confidence intervals that enclose p. Note that the guidelines for interpreting a confidence interval about μ also apply to interpreting a confidence interval for p because p is the "population mean fraction of successes" in a binomial experiment.

EXAMPLE 7.4   FINDING A LARGE-SAMPLE CONFIDENCE INTERVAL FOR p

Problem   Many public polling agencies conduct surveys to determine the current consumer sentiment concerning the state of the economy. For example, the Bureau of Economic and Business Research (BEBR) at the University of Florida conducts quarterly surveys to gauge consumer sentiment in the Sunshine State. Suppose that BEBR randomly samples 484 consumers and finds that 257 are optimistic about the state of the economy. Use a 90% confidence interval to estimate the proportion of all consumers in Florida who are optimistic about the state of the economy. Based on the confidence interval, can BEBR infer that the majority of Florida consumers are optimistic about the economy?

Solution   The number, x, of the 484 sampled consumers who are optimistic about the Florida economy is a binomial random variable if we can assume that the sample was randomly selected from the population of Florida consumers and that the poll was conducted identically for each sampled consumer.

The point estimate of the proportion of Florida consumers who are optimistic about the economy is

$$\hat{p} = \frac{x}{n} = \frac{257}{484} = .531$$

We first check to be sure that the sample size is sufficiently large that the normal distribution provides a reasonable approximation for the sampling distribution of $\hat{p}$. We check the 3-standard-deviation interval around $\hat{p}$:

$$\hat{p} \pm 3\sigma_{\hat{p}} \approx \hat{p} \pm 3\sqrt{\frac{\hat{p}\hat{q}}{n}}$$
$$= .531 \pm 3\sqrt{\frac{(.531)(.469)}{484}} = .531 \pm .068 = (.463, .599)$$

Since this interval is wholly contained in the interval $(0, 1)$, we may conclude that the normal approximation is reasonable.

We now proceed to form the 90% confidence interval for p, the true proportion of Florida consumers who are optimistic about the state of the economy:

$$\hat{p} \pm z_{\alpha/2}\sigma_{\hat{p}} = \hat{p} \pm z_{\alpha/2}\sqrt{\frac{pq}{n}} \approx \hat{p} \pm z_{\alpha/2}\sqrt{\frac{\hat{p}\hat{q}}{n}}$$

$$= .531 \pm 1.645\sqrt{\frac{(.531)(.469)}{484}} = .531 \pm .037 = (.494, .568)$$

Thus, we can be 90% confident that the proportion of all Florida consumers who are confident about the economy is between .494 and .568. As always, our confidence stems from the fact that 90% of all similarly formed intervals will contain the true proportion p and not from any knowledge about whether this particular interval does.

Can we conclude that the majority of Florida consumers are optimistic about the economy based on this interval? If we wished to use this interval to infer that a majority is optimistic, the interval would have to support the inference that p exceeds .5—that is, that more than 50% of the Florida consumers are optimistic about the economy. Note that the interval contains some values below .5 (as low as .494) as well as some above .5 (as high as .568). Therefore, we cannot conclude that the true value of p exceeds .5 based on this 90% confidence interval.

Look Back If the entire confidence interval fell above .5 (e.g., an interval from .52 to .54), then we could conclude (with 90% confidence) that the true proportion of consumers who are optimistic exceeds .5.

Now Work *Exercise 7.49bc*

■ ■ ■

Caution

Unless n is extremely large, the large-sample procedure presented in this section performs poorly when p is near 0 or 1. For example, suppose you want to estimate the proportion of people who die from a bee sting. This proportion is likely to be near 0 (say, $p \approx .001$). Confidence intervals for p based on a sample of size $n = 50$ will probably be misleading.

To overcome this potential problem, an *extremely* large sample size is required. Since the value of n required to satisfy "extremely large" is difficult to determine, statisticians (see Agresti & Coull, 1998) have proposed an alternative method, based on the Wilson (1927) point estimator of p. The procedure is outlined in the box. Researchers have shown that this confidence interval works well for any p even when the sample size n is very small.

Adjusted $(1 - \alpha)$ 100% Confidence Interval for a Population Proportion, p

$$\tilde{p} \pm z_{\alpha/2}\sqrt{\frac{\tilde{p}(1 - \tilde{p})}{n + 4}}$$

where $\tilde{p} = \dfrac{x + 2}{n + 4}$ is the adjusted sample proportion of observations with the characteristic of interest, x is the number of successes in the sample, and n is the sample size.

EXAMPLE 7.5

APPLYING THE ADJUSTED CONFIDENCE INTERVAL PROCEDURE FOR p

Problem According to *True Odds: How Risk Affects Your Everyday Life* (Walsh, 1997), the probability of being the victim of a violent crime is less than .01. Suppose that in a random sample of 200 Americans, 3 were victims of a violent crime. Estimate the true proportion of Americans who were victims of a violent crime using a 95% confidence interval.

Solution Let p represent the true proportion of Americans who were victims of a violent crime. Since p is near 0, an "extremely large" sample is required to estimate its value using the usual large-sample method. Since we are unsure whether the sample size of 200 is large enough, we will apply Wilson's adjustment outlined in the box.

The number of "successes" (i.e., number of violent crime victims) in the sample is $x = 3$. Therefore, the adjusted sample proportion is

$$\widetilde{p} = \frac{x + 2}{n + 4} = \frac{3 + 2}{200 + 4} = \frac{5}{204} = .025$$

Note that this adjusted sample proportion is obtained by adding a total of four observations—two "successes" and two "failures"—to the sample data. Substituting $\widetilde{p} = .025$ into the equation for a 95% confidence interval, we obtain

$$\widetilde{p} \pm 1.96\sqrt{\frac{\widetilde{p}(1 - \widetilde{p})}{n + 4}} = .025 \pm 1.96\sqrt{\frac{(.025)(.975)}{204}}$$
$$= .025 \pm .021$$

or (.004, .046). Consequently, we are 95% confident that the true proportion of Americans who are victims of a violent crime falls between .004 and .046.

■ ■ ■

Statistics in Action Revisited

Estimating the Proportion of Sprinters Who Improve after Speed Training

In the previous Statistics in Action Revisited (p. 328), we discovered that a training program was effective in improving a high school athlete's speed in a 40-yard sprint. This inference was made by measuring the difference between an athlete's sprint time before and after the training program and then forming a confidence interval for the mean difference in times.

Another approach to the problem is to determine (based on the before and after sprint times) whether each athlete improved their speed and measure this qualitatively. Thus, each participating athlete's sprint performance will be classified as "Improved" (if the after time is less than the before time) or "Not Improved" (if the after time is greater than or the same as the before time). Now, the variable of interest is qualitative in nature with two possible outcomes and our goal is to estimate p, the true proportion of all high school athletes who attain improved sprint times after participating in the speed training program.

If you examine the data for the 38 sampled athletes (saved in the **SPRINT** file and listed in Table SIA7.1, p. 321), you will find that 33 of the high school athletes had an "Improved" time in the 40-yard sprint. Thus, our estimate of p is

$$\hat{p} = 33/38 = .868$$

A 95% confidence interval for p can be obtained using the confidence interval formula or with statistical software. A MINITAB printout of the analysis is displayed in Figure SIA7.2. The 95% confidence interval, highlighted on the printout, is (0.761, .976). Thus, we are 95% confident that anywhere from 76% to 97% of the athletes that participate in the speed training program will improve their 40-yard sprint time. These results present a strong case for claiming that the training program is effective in improving sprint speed. [*Note:* The MINITAB confidence interval in Figure SIA7.2 is based on a normal approximation which requires a "large" sample. A sample size of $n = 38$ athletes, although not small, may not be large

---

Test and CI for One Proportion: Status

```
Test of p = 0.5 vs p not = 0.5

Event = Improve


Variable   X   N   Sample p       95% CI          Z-Value  P-Value
Status    33  38   0.868421  (0.760944, 0.975898)    4.54    0.000


* NOTE * The normal approximation may be inaccurate for small samples.
```

Figure SIA7.2
MINITAB Confidence Interval for Proportion of Improved Sprint Times

---

enough for the sampling distribution of $\hat{p}$ to be normally distributed; thus, the interval may be inaccurate (as stated at the bottom of the MINITAB printout). To arrive at a more reliable estimate of the true proportion of improved sprint times, we may need a larger number of athletes to participate in the speed training program. In the next Statistics in Action Revisited (p. 00), we show how large of a sample needs to be selected.]

Confidence Interval for a Population Proportion

Using the TI-83 Graphing Calculator

Step 1 *Access the Statistical Tests Menu*
Press **STAT**
Arrow right to **TESTS**
Arrow down to **A:1-PropZInt**
Press **ENTER**

Step 2 *Enter the values for x, n and C-Level*
where **x** = number of successes
n = sample size
C-Level = level of confidence
Arrow down to "**Calculate**"
Press **ENTER**

Example Suppose that 1,100 U.S. citizens are randomly chosen and 532 answer that they favor a flat income tax rate. Use a 95% confidence interval to estimate the true proportion of citizens who favor a flat income tax rate.
In this example, x = 532, n = 1,100 and C-Level = .95.

The screens for this example are shown below.

Thus, we can be 95% confident that the interval from 45.4% to 51.3% contains the true percentage of all U.S. citizens who favor a flat income tax rate.

Exercises 7.42–7.59

Understanding the Principles

7.42 Describe the sampling distribution of $\hat{p}$ based on large samples of size n. That is, give the mean, the standard deviation, and the (approximate) shape of the distribution of $\hat{p}$ when large samples of size n are (repeatedly) selected from the binomial distribution with probability of success p.

7.43 Explain the meaning of the phrase "$\hat{p}$ is an unbiased estimator of p."

7.44 If p is near 0 or 1, how large a sample is needed to employ the large-sample confidence interval procedure?

Learning the Mechanics

7.45 A random sample of size $n = 196$ yielded $\hat{p} = .64$.
  a. Is the sample size large enough to use the methods of this section to construct a confidence interval for p? Explain.
  b. Construct a 95% confidence interval for p.
  c. Interpret the 95% confidence interval.
  d. Explain what is meant by the phrase "95% confidence interval."

7.46 A random sample of size $n = 144$ yielded $\hat{p} = .76$.
  a. Is the sample size large enough to use the methods of this section to construct a confidence interval for p? Explain.
  b. Construct a 90% confidence interval for p.
  c. What assumption is necessary to ensure the validity of this confidence interval?

7.47 For the binomial sample information summarized in each part, indicate whether the sample size is large enough to use the methods of this chapter to construct a confidence interval for p.
  a. $n = 500, \hat{p} = .05$ **b.** $n = 100, \hat{p} = .05$
  c. $n = 10, \hat{p} = .5$ **d.** $n = 10, \hat{p} = .3$

7.48 A random sample of 50 consumers taste-tested a new snack food. Their responses were coded (0: do not like; 1: like; 2: indifferent) and recorded as follows:

🍪 **SNACK**

1	0	0	1	2	0	1	1	0	0
0	1	0	2	0	2	2	0	0	1
1	0	0	0	0	1	0	2	0	0
0	1	0	0	1	0	0	1	0	1
0	2	0	0	1	1	0	0	0	1

  a. Use an 80% confidence interval to estimate the proportion of consumers who like the snack food.
  b. Provide a statistical interpretation for the confidence interval you constructed in part **a**.

Applying the Concepts—Basic

7.49 **Cell phone use by drivers.** In a July 2001 research note, NW the U.S. Department of Transportation reported the results of the *National Occupant Protection Use Survey*. One focus of the survey was to determine the level of cell phone use by drivers while they are in the act of driving a motor passenger vehicle. Data collected by observers at randomly selected intersections across the country revealed that in a sample of 1,165 drivers, 35 were using their cell phone.
  a. Give a point estimate of p, the true driver cell phone use rate (i.e., the true proportion of drivers who are using a cell phone while driving).
  b. Compute a 95% confidence interval for p.
  c. Give a practical interpretation of the interval, part **b**.

7.50 **Scary movie study.** According to a University of Michigan study, many adults have experienced lingering "fright" effects from a scary movie or TV show they saw as a teenager. (*Tampa Tribune*, March 10, 1999.) In a survey of 150 college students, 39 said they still experience "residual anxiety" from a scary TV show or movie.
  a. Give a point estimate, $\hat{p}$, for the true proportion of college students who experience "residual anxiety" from a scary TV show or movie.
  b. Find a 95% confidence interval for p.
  c. Interpret the interval, part **b**.

7.51 **Ancient Greek pottery.** Refer to the *Chance* (Fall 2000) study of 837 pottery pieces found at the ancient Greek settlement at Phylakopi, Exercise 2.12 (p. 38). Of these, 183 pieces were painted with either a curvilinear, geometric, or naturalistic decoration. Find a 90% confidence interval for the population proportion of all pottery artifacts at Phylakopi that are painted. Interpret the resulting interval.

7.52 **"Made in the USA" survey.** Refer to Exercise 2.13 (p. 38) and the *Journal of Global Business* (Spring 2002) survey to determine what "Made in the USA" means to consumers. Recall that 106 shoppers at a shopping mall in Muncie, Indiana, responded to the question, " 'Made in the USA' means what percentage of U.S. labor and materials?" Sixty-four shoppers answered "100%."
  a. Define the population of interest in the survey.
  b. What is the characteristic of interest in the population?
  c. Estimate the true proportion of consumers who believe "Made in the USA" means 100% U.S. labor and materials using a 90% confidence interval.
  d. Give a practical interpretation of the interval, part **c**.
  e. Explain what the phrase "90% confidence" means for this interval.

Applying the Concepts—Intermediate

7.53 **Exercise workout dropouts.** Researchers at the University of Florida's Department of Exercise and Sport Sciences conducted a study of variety in exercise workouts. (*Journal of Sport Behavior*, 2001.) A sample of 114 men and women were randomly divided into three groups, 38 people per group. Group 1 members varied their exercise routine in workouts, group 2 members performed the same exercise at each workout, and group 3 members had no set schedule or regulations for their workouts.

a. By the end of the study, 14 people had dropped out of the first exercise group. Estimate the dropout rate for exercisers who vary their routine in workouts. Use a 90% confidence interval and interpret the result.

b. By the end of the study, 23 people had dropped out of the third exercise group. Estimate the dropout rate for exercisers who have no set schedule for their workouts. Use a 90% confidence interval and interpret the result.

7.54 Using debit cards on the Internet. The Gallup Organization surveyed 1,252 debit cardholders in the U.S. and found that 180 had used the debit card to purchase a product or service on the Internet. (*Card Fax*, November 12, 1999.)

a. Describe the population of interest to the Gallup Organization.

b. Is the sample size large enough to construct a valid confidence interval for the proportion of debit cardholders who have used their card in making purchases over the Internet?

c. Estimate the proportion referred to in part **b** using a 99% confidence interval. Interpret your result in the context of the problem.

d. If you had constructed a 90% confidence interval instead, would it be wider or narrower?

7.55 Air bags pose danger for children. By law, all new cars must be equipped with both driver-side and passenger-side safety air bags. There is concern, however, over whether air bags pose a danger for children sitting on the passenger side. In a National Highway Traffic Safety Administration (NHTSA) study of 55 people killed by the explosive force of air bags, 35 were children seated on the front-passenger side. (*Wall Street Journal*, January 22, 1997.) This study led some car owners with children to disconnect the passenger-side air bag. Consider all fatal automobile accidents in which it is determined that air bags were the cause of death. Let p represent the true proportion of these accidents involving children seated on the front-passenger side.

a. Use the data from the NHTSA study to estimate p.

b. Construct a 99% confidence interval for p.

c. Interpret the interval, part **b**, in the words of the problem.

d. NHTSA investigators determined that 24 of 35 children killed by the air bags were not wearing seat belts or were improperly restrained. How does this information impact your assessment of the risk of an air bag fatality?

DDT

7.56 Contaminated fish in the Tennessee River. Refer to the U.S. Army Corps of Engineers data on a sample of 144 contaminated fish collected from the Tennessee River, adjacent to a chemical plant in Alabama. The data are saved in the **DDT** file. Estimate the proportion of contaminated fish that are of the channel catfish species. Use a 95% confidence interval and interpret the result.

7.57 Whistling dolphins. In Exercise 2.19 (p. 40) you learned about the signature whistles of bottlenose dolphins. Marine scientists categorize signature whistles by type—type a, type b, type c, etc. For one study of a sample of 185 whistles emitted from bottlenose dolphins in captivity, 97 were categorized as type a whistles (*Ethology*, July 1995).

a. Estimate the true proportion of bottlenose dolphin signature whistles that are type a whistles. Use a 99% confidence interval.

b. Interpret the interval, part **a**.

7.58 FTC checkout scanner study. Refer to the Federal Trade Commission (FTC) "Price Check" study of electronic checkout scanners, Exercise 4.115 (p. 230). The FTC inspected 1,669 scanners at retail stores and supermarkets by scanning a sample of items at each store and determining if the scanned price was accurate. The FTC gives a store a "passing" grade if 98% or more of the items are priced accurately. Of the 1,669 stores in the study, 1,185 passed inspection.

a. Find a 90% confidence interval for the true proportion of retail stores and supermarkets with electronic scanners that pass the FTC price-check test. Interpret the result.

b. Two years prior to the study, the FTC found that 45% of the stores passed inspection. Use the interval, part **a**, to determine whether the proportion of stores that now pass inspection exceeds .45.

Applying the Concepts—Advanced

7.59 Latex allergy in healthcare workers. Refer to the *Current Allergy & Clinical Immunology* (March 2004) study of healthcare workers who use latex gloves, Exercise 7.13 (p. 330). In addition to the 46 hospital employees who were diagnosed with a latex allergy based on a skin-prick test, another 37 healthcare workers were diagnosed with the allergy using a latex-specific serum test. Of these 83 workers with confirmed latex allergy, only 36 suspected that they had the allergy when asked on a questionnaire. Make a statement about the likelihood that a healthcare worker with latex allergy suspects he or she actually has the allergy. Attach a measure of reliability to your inference.

7.5 Determining the Sample Size

Recall (Section 1.5) that one way to collect the relevant data for a study used to make inferences about the population is to implement a designed (planned) experiment. Perhaps the most important design decision faced by the analyst is to determine the size of the sample. We show in this section that the appropriate sample size for making an inference about a population mean or proportion depends on the desired reliability.

Estimating a Population Mean

Consider the example from Section 7.2 in which we estimated the mean length of stay for patients in a large hospital. A sample of 100 patients' records produced the 95% confidence interval $\bar{x} \pm 2\sigma_{\bar{x}} \approx 4.53 \pm .74$. Consequently, our estimate $\bar{x}$ was within .74 day of the true mean length of stay μ for all the hospital's patients at the 95% confidence level. That is, the 95% confidence interval for μ was $2(.74) = 1.48$ days wide when 100 accounts were sampled. This is illustrated in Figure 7.13a.

Now suppose we want to estimate μ to within .25 day with 95% confidence. That is, we want to narrow the width of the confidence interval from 1.48 days to .50 day, as shown in Figure 7.13b. How much will the sample size have to be increased to accomplish this? If we want the estimator $\bar{x}$ to be within .25 day of μ, we must have

$$2\sigma_{\bar{x}} = .25 \qquad \text{or, equivalently,} \qquad 2\left(\frac{\sigma}{\sqrt{n}}\right) = .25$$

Note that we are using $\sigma_{\bar{x}} = \dfrac{\sigma}{\sqrt{n}}$ in the formula since we are dealing with the sampling distribution of $\bar{x}$ (the estimator of μ).

The necessary sample size is obtained by solving this equation for n. To do this we need an approximation for σ. We have an approximation from the initial sample of 100 patients' records—namely, the sample standard deviation, $s = 3.68$. Thus,

$$2\left(\frac{\sigma}{\sqrt{n}}\right) \approx 2\left(\frac{s}{\sqrt{n}}\right) = 2\left(\frac{3.68}{\sqrt{n}}\right) = .25$$

$$\sqrt{n} = \frac{2(3.68)}{.25} = 29.44$$

$$n = (29.44)^2 = 866.71 \approx 867$$

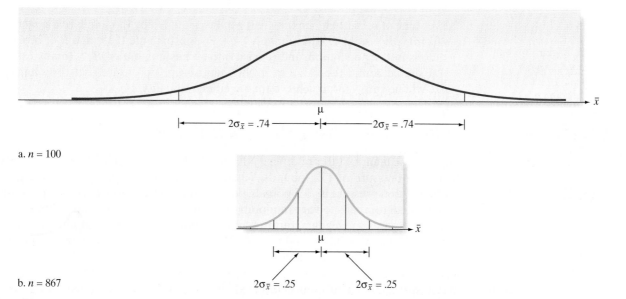

a. $n = 100$

b. $n = 867$

Figure 7.13

Relationship between Sample Size and Width of Confidence Interval: Hospital Stay Example

Approximately 867 patients' records will have to be sampled to estimate the mean length of stay μ to within .25 day with (approximately) 95% confidence. The confidence interval resulting from a sample of this size will be approximately .50 day wide (see Figure 7.13b).

In general, we express the reliability associated with a confidence interval for the population mean μ by specifying the **sampling error** within which we want to estimate μ with $100(1 - \alpha)\%$ confidence. The sampling error (denoted SE) then is equal to the half-width of the confidence interval, as shown in Figure 7.14.

Figure 7.14

Specifying the Sampling Error SE as the Half-Width of a Confidence Interval

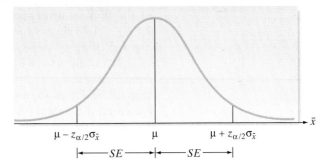

The procedure for finding the sample size necessary to estimate μ with a specific sampling error is given in the box.

> **Sample Size Determination for $100(1 - \alpha)\%$ Confidence Intervals for μ**
>
> In order to estimate μ with a sampling error SE and with $100(1 - \alpha)\%$ confidence, the required sample size is found as follows:
>
> $$z_{\alpha/2}\left(\frac{\sigma}{\sqrt{n}}\right) = SE$$
>
> The solution for n can be given by the equation
>
> $$n = \frac{(z_{\alpha/2})^2 \sigma^2}{(SE)^2}$$
>
> The value of σ is usually unknown. It can be estimated by the standard deviation s from a prior sample. Alternatively, we may approximate the range R of observations in the population, and (conservatively) estimate $\sigma \approx R/4$. In any case, you should round the value of n obtained *upward* to ensure that the sample size will be sufficient to achieve the specified reliability.

EXAMPLE 7.6   FINDING THE SAMPLE SIZE FOR ESTIMATING μ

Problem   Suppose the manufacturer of official NFL footballs uses a machine to inflate the new balls to a pressure of 13.5 pounds. When the machine is properly calibrated, the mean inflation pressure is 13.5 pounds, but uncontrollable factors cause the pressures of individual footballs to vary randomly from about 13.3 to 13.7 pounds. For quality control purposes, the manufacturer wishes to estimate the mean inflation pressure to within .025 pound of its true value with a 99% confidence interval. What sample size should be specified for the experiment?

Solution   We desire a 99% confidence interval that estimates μ with a sampling error of $SE = .025$ pound. For a 99% confidence interval, we have $z_{\alpha/2} = z_{.005} = 2.575$. To estimate σ, we note that the range of observations is $R = 13.7 - 13.3 = .4$

and use $\sigma \approx R/4 = .1$. Now we use the formula derived in the box to find the sample size n:

$$n = \frac{(z_{\alpha/2})^2 \sigma^2}{(SE)^2} \approx \frac{(2.575)^2(.1)^2}{(.025)^2} = 106.09$$

We round this up to $n = 107$. Realizing that σ was approximated by $R/4$, we might even advise that the sample size be specified as $n = 110$ to be more certain of attaining the objective of a 99% confidence interval with a sampling error of .025 pound or less.

Look Back To determine the value of the sampling error SE, look for the value that follows the key words "estimate μ to within . . .".

Now Work *Exercise 7.73*

■ ■ ■

Sometimes the formula will lead to a solution that indicates a small sample size is sufficient to achieve the confidence interval goal. Unfortunately, the procedures and assumptions for small samples differ from those for large samples, as we discovered in Section 7.3. Therefore, if the formulas yield a small sample size, one simple strategy is to select a sample size $n = 30$.

Estimating a Population Proportion

The method outlined above is easily applied to a population proportion p. For example, in Section 7.4 a pollster used a sample of 1,000 U.S. citizens to calculate a 95% confidence interval for the proportion who trust the president, obtaining the interval $.637 \pm .03$. Suppose the pollster wishes to estimate more precisely the proportion who trust the president, say, to within .015 with a 95% confidence interval.

The pollster wants a confidence interval for p with a sampling error of $SE = .015$. The sample size required to generate such an interval is found by solving the following equation for n:

$$z_{\alpha/2}\sigma_{\hat{p}} = SE \qquad \text{or} \qquad z_{\alpha/2}\sqrt{\frac{pq}{n}} = .015 \qquad \text{(see Figure 7.15)}$$

Since a 95% confidence interval is desired, the appropriate z-value is $z_{\alpha/2} = z_{.025} = 1.96$. We must approximate the value of the product pq before we can solve the equation for n. As shown in Table 7.5 (p. 345), the closer the values of p and q to .5, the larger the product pq. Thus, to find a conservatively large sample size that will generate a confidence interval with the specified reliability, we generally choose an approximation of p close to .5. In the case of the proportion of U.S. citizens who trust the president, however, we have an initial sample estimate of $\hat{p} = .637$.

Figure 7.15

Specifying the Sampling Error SE of a Confidence Interval for a Population Proportion p

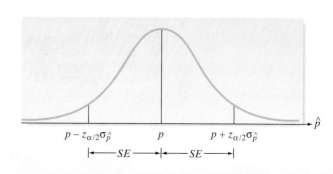

$p - z_{\alpha/2}\sigma_{\hat{p}}$ p $p + z_{\alpha/2}\sigma_{\hat{p}}$

$|\!\!\longleftarrow SE \longrightarrow\!\!|\!\!\longleftarrow SE \longrightarrow\!\!|$

A conservatively large estimate of pq can therefore be obtained by using, say, $p = .60$. We now substitute into the equation and solve for n:

$$1.96\sqrt{\frac{(.60)(.40)}{n}} = .015$$

$$n = \frac{(1.96)^2(.60)(.40)}{(.015)^2} = 4{,}097.7 \approx 4{,}098$$

The pollster must sample about 4,098 U.S. citizens to estimate the percentage who trust the president with a confidence interval of width .03.

The procedure for finding the sample size necessary to estimate a population proportion p with a specified sampling error SE is given in the box.

Sample Size Determination for $100(1 - \alpha)\%$ Confidence Interval for p

In order to estimate a binomial probability p with sampling error SE and with $100(1 - \alpha)\%$ confidence, the required sample size is found by solving the following equation for n:

$$z_{\alpha/2}\sqrt{\frac{pq}{n}} = SE$$

The solution for n can be written as follows:

$$n = \frac{(z_{\alpha/2})^2(pq)}{(SE)^2}$$

Since the value of the product pq is unknown, it can be estimated by using the sample fraction of successes, $\hat{p}$, from a prior sample. Remember (Table 7.5) that the value of pq is at its maximum when p equals .5, so that you can obtain conservatively large values of n by approximating p by .5 or values close to .5. In any case, you should round the value of n obtained *upward* to ensure that the sample size will be sufficient to achieve the specified reliability.

EXAMPLE 7.7   FINDING THE SAMPLE SIZE FOR ESTIMATING p

Problem   Suppose a large telephone manufacturer that entered the postregulation market quickly has an initial problem with excessive customer complaints and consequent returns of the phones for repair or replacement. The manufacturer wants to estimate the magnitude of the problem in order to design a quality control program. How many telephones should be sampled and checked in order to estimate the fraction defective, p, to within .01 with 90% confidence?

Solution   In order to estimate p to within .01 of its true value, we set the half-width of the confidence interval equal to $SE = .01$, as shown in Figure 7.16.

Figure 7.16
Specified Reliability for
Estimate of Fraction
Defective in Example 7.7

$$p - 1.645\sigma_{\hat{p}} \qquad p \qquad p + 1.645\sigma_{\hat{p}}$$
$$|\!\leftarrow\! SE = .01 \!\rightarrow\!|\!\leftarrow\! SE = .01 \!\rightarrow\!|$$

The equation for the sample size n requires an estimate of the product pq. We could most conservatively estimate $pq = .25$ (i.e., use $p = .5$), but this may be overly conservative when estimating a fraction defective. A value of .1, corresponding to 10% defective, will probably be conservatively large for this application. The solution is therefore

$$n = \frac{(z_{\alpha/2})^2(pq)}{(SE)^2} = \frac{(1.645)^2(.1)(.9)}{(.01)^2} = 2,435.4 \approx 2,436$$

Thus, the manufacturer should sample 2,436 telephones in order to estimate the fraction defective, p, to within .01 with 90% confidence.

Look Back Remember that this answer depends on our approximation for pq, where we used .09. If the fraction defective is closer to .05 than .10, we can use a sample of 1,286 telephones (check this) to estimate p to within .01 with 90% confidence.

Now Work   *Exercise 7.72*

━━━━━ ■ ■ ■ ━━━━━

The cost of sampling will also play an important role in the final determination of the sample size to be selected to estimate either μ or p. Although more complex formulas can be derived to balance the reliability and cost considerations, we will solve for the necessary sample size and note that the sampling budget may be a limiting factor. Consult the references for a more complete treatment of this problem.

Statistics in Action Revisited

Determining the Number of Athletes to Participate in the Training Program

In the previous Statistics in Action applications in this chapter, we used confidence intervals to (1) estimate μ, the population mean decrease in sprint time for athletes who participate in the speed training program (p. 328), and (2) estimate p, the population proportion of athletes who improve their sprint times after participating in the speed training program (p. 347). The confidence interval for p was fairly wide due to the relatively small number of athletes ($n = 38$) who participated in the program. In order to find a valid, narrower confidence interval for the true proportion, the researchers would need to include more athletes in the study.

How many high school athletes should be sampled to estimate p to within, say, .03 with 95% confidence? Here, we have the sampling error, $SE = .03$ and $z_{.025} = 1.96$ (since, for a 95% confidence interval, $\alpha = .05$ and $\alpha/2 = .025$). From our analysis on page 00, the estimated

proportion is $\hat{p} = .87$. Substituting these values into the formula given in the box (p. 354), we obtain

$$n = \frac{(z_{.025})^2(\hat{p})(1 - \hat{p})}{(SE)^2} = \frac{(1.96)^2(.87)(.13)}{(.03)^2} = 482.76$$

Consequently, the researchers would have to include 483 high school athletes in the training program in order to find a valid 95% confidence interval for p to within 3% of its true value.

Running the training program with this large number of athletes may be impractical. To reduce the size of the sample, the researchers could choose to increase the sampling error (i.e., the width) of the confidence interval for p or decrease the confidence level $(1 - \alpha)$. However, since both large- and small-sample confidence intervals are available for estimating μ, the researchers can rely on the inference made from the confidence interval for the mean decrease in sprint time (p. 328).

Exercises 7.60–7.80

Understanding the Principles

7.60 How does the sampling error SE compare to the width of a confidence interval?

7.61 **True or false.** For a specified sampling error SE, increasing the confidence level $(1 - \alpha)$ will lead to a larger n when determining sample size.

7.62 **True or false.** For a fixed confidence level $(1 - \alpha)$, increasing the sampling error SE will lead to a smaller n when determining sample size.

Learning the Mechanics

7.63 If you wish to estimate a population mean to within .2 using a 95% confidence interval and you know from prior sampling that σ^2 is approximately equal to 5.4, how many observations would you have to include in your sample?

7.64 If nothing is known about p, .5 can be substituted for p in the sample-size formula for a population proportion. But when this is done, the resulting sample size may be larger than needed. Under what circumstances will using $p = .5$ in the sample-size formula yield a sample size larger than needed to construct a confidence interval for p with a specified bound and a specified confidence level?

7.65 Suppose you wish to estimate a population mean correct to within .15 with a confidence level of .90. You do not know σ^2, but you know that the observations will range in value between 31 and 39.
  a. Find the approximate sample size that will produce the desired accuracy of the estimate. You wish to be conservative to ensure that the sample size will be ample to achieve the desired accuracy of the estimate. [*Hint:* Using your knowledge of data variation from Section 2.5, assume that the range of the observations will equal 4σ.]
  b. Calculate the approximate sample size making the less conservative assumption that the range of the observations is equal to 6σ.

7.66 In each case, find the approximate sample size required to construct a 95% confidence interval for p that has sampling error $SE = .06$.
  a. Assume p is near .3.
  b. Assume you have no prior knowledge about p, but you wish to be certain that your sample is large enough to achieve the specified accuracy for the estimate.

7.67 The following is a 90% confidence interval for p: $(.26, .54)$. How large was the sample used to construct this interval?

7.68 It costs you $10 to draw a sample of size $n = 1$ and measure the attribute of interest. You have a budget of $1,200.
  a. Do you have sufficient funds to estimate the population mean for the attribute of interest with a 95% confidence interval 4 units in width? Assume $\sigma = 12$.

  b. If a 90% confidence level were used, would your answer to part **a** change? Explain.

7.69 Suppose you wish to estimate the mean of a normal population using a 95% confidence interval, and you know from prior information that $\sigma^2 \approx 1$.
  a. To see the effect of the sample size on the width of the confidence interval, calculate the width of the confidence interval for $n = 16, 25, 49, 100,$ and 400.
  b. Plot the width as a function of sample size n on graph paper. Connect the points by a smooth curve and note how the width decreases as n increases.

Applying the Concepts—Basic

7.70 **Radioactive lichen.** Refer to the Alaskan Lichen Radionuclide Baseline Research study, Exercise 7.33 (p. 340). In a sample of $n = 9$ lichen specimens, the researchers found the mean and standard deviation of the amount of the radioactive element, cesium-137, present to be .009 and .005 microcuries per milliliter, respectively. Suppose the researchers want to increase the sample size in order to estimate the mean, μ, to within .001 microcuries per milliliter of its true value using a 95% confidence interval.
  a. What is the confidence level desired by the researchers?
  b. What is the sampling error desired by the researchers?
  c. Compute the sample size necessary to obtain the desired estimate.

7.71 **"Made in the USA" survey.** Refer to Exercise 7.52 (p. 349) and the *Journal of Global Business* (Spring 2002) survey to determine what "Made in the USA" means to consumers. Recall that 64 of 106 shoppers at a shopping mall in Muncie, Indiana, believe that "Made in the USA" implies all labor and materials are produced in the United States. Suppose the researchers want to increase the sample size in order to estimate the true proportion, p, to within .05 of its true value using a 90% confidence interval.
  a. What is the confidence level desired by the researchers?
  b. What is the sampling error desired by the researchers?
  c. Compute the sample size necessary to obtain the desired estimate.

7.72 **Aluminum cans contaminated by fire.** A gigantic warehouse located in Tampa, Florida, stores approximately 60 million empty aluminum beer and soda cans. Recently, a fire occurred at the warehouse. The smoke from the fire contaminated many of the cans with blackspot, rendering them unusable. A University of South Florida statistician was hired by the insurance company to estimate p, the true proportion of cans in the warehouse that were contaminated by the fire. How many aluminum cans should be randomly sampled to estimate the true proportion to within .02 with 90% confidence?

7.73 Water pollution testing. The EPA wants to test a ran-
NW domly selected sample of n water specimens and estimate μ, the mean daily rate of pollution produced by a
mining operation. If the EPA wants a 95% confidence
interval estimate with a sampling error of 1 milligram
per liter (mg/L), how many water specimens are required
in the sample? Assume that prior knowledge indicates
that pollution readings in water samples taken during a
day are approximately normally distributed with a standard deviation equal to 5 (mg/L).

Applying the Concepts—Intermediate

7.74 Training zoo animals. Refer to Exercise 2.63 (p. 65) and
the *Teaching of Psychology* (May 1998) study in which
students assisted in the training of zoo animals. A sample
of 15 psychology students rated "The Training Game" as a
"great" method of understanding the animal's perspective
during training on a 7–1 point scale (where 1 = strongly
disagree and 7 = strongly agree). The mean response was
5.87 with a standard deviation of 1.51.

   a. Construct a 95% confidence interval for the true
   mean response of the students.

   b. Suppose you want to reduce the width of the 95%
   confidence interval to half the size obtained in
   part **a**. How many students are required in the
   sample to obtain the desired confidence interval
   width?

7.75 Bacteria in bottled water. Is the bottled water you
drink safe? According to an article in *U.S. News &
World Report* (April 12, 1999), the Natural Resources
Defense Council warns that the bottled water you are
drinking may contain more bacteria and other poten-
tially carcinogenic chemicals than allowed by state and
federal regulations. Of the more than 1,000 bottles
studied, nearly one-third exceeded government levels.
Suppose that the Natural Resources Defense Council
wants an updated estimate of the population proportion of bottled water that violates at least one government standard. Determine the sample size (number of
bottles) needed to estimate this proportion to within
±0.01 with 99% confidence.

7.76 Asthma drug study. The chemical benzalkonium chloride (BAC) is an antibacterial agent that is added to
some asthma medications to prevent contamination.
Researchers at the University of Florida College of
Pharmacy have discovered that adding BAC to asthma
drugs can cause airway constriction in patients. In a
sample of 18 asthmatic patients, each of whom received
a heavy dose of BAC, 10 experienced a significant drop
in breathing capacity (*Journal of Allergy and Clinical
Immunology*, January 2001.) Based on this information,
a 95% confidence interval for the true percentage of
asthmatic patients who experience breathing difficulties
after taking BAC is (.326, .785).

   a. Why might the confidence interval lead to an erro-
   neous inference?

   b. How many asthma patients must be included in the
   study to estimate the true percentage who experience

a significant drop in breathing capacity to within 4%
using a 95% confidence interval?

7.77 Oven cooking study. Refer to Exercise 7.36 (p. 341).
Suppose that we want to estimate the average decay
rate of fine particles produced from oven cooking or
toasting to within .04 with 95% confidence. How large a
sample should be selected?

7.78 Caffeine content of coffee. According to a Food and
Drug Administration (FDA) study, a cup of coffee
contains an average of 115 milligrams (mg) of caffeine,
with the amount per cup ranging from 60 to 180 mg.
Suppose you want to repeat the FDA experiment to
obtain an estimate of the mean caffeine content in a
cup of coffee correct to within 5 mg with 95% confidence. How many cups of coffee would have to be
included in your sample?

7.79 USGA golf ball tests. The United States Golf Association (USGA) tests all new brands of golf balls to
ensure that they meet USGA specifications. One test
conducted is intended to measure the average distance traveled when the ball is hit by a machine
called "Iron Byron." Suppose the USGA wishes to
estimate the mean distance for a new brand to within
1 yard with 90% confidence. Assume that past tests
have indicated that the standard deviation of the distances Iron Byron hits golf balls is approximately 10
yards. How many golf balls should be hit by Iron
Byron to achieve the desired accuracy in estimating
the mean?

Applying the Concepts—Advanced

7.80 It costs more to produce defective items—since they
must be scrapped or reworked—than it does to produce
nondefective items. This simple fact suggests that manufacturers should ensure the quality of their products by
perfecting their production processes instead of
depending on inspection of finished products (Deming,
1986). In order to better understand a particular metal
stamping process, a manufacturer wishes to estimate the
mean length of items produced by the process during
the past 24 hours.

   a. How many parts should be sampled in order to estimate the population mean to within .1 millimeter
   (mm) with 90% confidence? Previous studies of this
   machine have indicated that the standard deviation
   of lengths produced by the stamping operation is
   about 2 mm.

   b. Time permits the use of a sample size no larger than
   100. If a 90% confidence interval for μ is constructed
   using $n = 100$, will it be wider or narrower than
   would have been obtained using the sample size
   determined in part **a**? Explain.

   c. If management requires that μ be estimated to
   within .1 mm and that a sample size of no more
   than 100 be used, what is (approximately) the
   maximum confidence level that could be attained
   for a confidence interval that meets management's
   specifications?

Quick Review

Key Terms

Confidence coefficient   324

Confidence interval   324

Confidence level   324

Degrees of freedom   333

Interval estimator   324

Sampling error   352

Target parameter   322

t-statistic   333

Wilson adjustment for estimating p 346

Key Formulas

$\hat{\theta} \pm (z_{\alpha/2})\sigma_{\hat{\theta}}$

Large-sample confidence interval for population parameter θ where $\hat{\theta}$ and $\sigma_{\hat{\theta}}$ are obtained from the table below.

Parameter θ	Estimator $\hat{\theta}$	Standard Error $\sigma_{\hat{\theta}}$	
Mean, μ	$\bar{x}$	$\sigma/\sqrt{n}$	326
Proportion, p	$\hat{p}$	$\sqrt{\dfrac{pq}{n}}$	344

$\bar{x} \pm t_{\alpha/2}\left(\dfrac{s}{\sqrt{n}}\right)$ Small-sample confidence interval for population mean μ 336

$\tilde{p} = \dfrac{x + 2}{n + 4}$ Adjusted estimator of p 346

$n = \dfrac{(z_{\alpha/2})^2\sigma^2}{(SE)^2}$ Determining the sample size n for estimating μ 352

$n = \dfrac{(z_{\alpha/2})^2(pq)}{(SE)^2}$ Determining the sample size n for estimating p 354

Language Lab

Symbol	Pronunciation	Description
θ	theta	General population parameter
μ	mu	Population mean
p		Population proportion
SE		Sampling error
α	alpha	$(1 - \alpha)$ represents the confidence coefficient
$z_{\alpha/2}$	z of alpha over 2	z value used in a $100(1 - \alpha)\%$ large-sample confidence interval
$t_{\alpha/2}$	t of alpha over 2	t value used in a $100(1 - \alpha)\%$ small-sample confidence interval
$\bar{x}$	x-bar	Sample mean; point estimate of μ
$\hat{p}$	p-hat	Sample proportion; point estimate of p
σ	sigma	Population standard deviation
s		Sample standard deviation; point estimate of σ
$\sigma_{\bar{x}}$	sigma of $\bar{x}$	Standard deviation of sampling distribution of $\bar{x}$
σ_p	sigma of $\hat{p}$	Standard deviation of sampling distribution of $\hat{p}$
$\tilde{p}$	p-curl	Wilson's adjusted estimate of p

Chapter Summary Notes

- **Confidence interval**—an interval which encloses an unknown population parameter with a certain level of confidence
- **Confidence coefficient**—the probability that a randomly selected confidence interval encloses the value of the population parameter
- Conditions required for a valid **large-sample confidence interval for μ**: (1) random sample, (2) large sample size ($n \geq 30$)

- Conditions required for a valid **small-sample confidence interval for μ**: (1) random sample, (2) population distribution is approximately normal
- Conditions required for a valid **large-sample confidence interval for p**: (1) random sample, (2) large sample size ($\hat{p} \pm 3\sigma_{\hat{p}}$ falls between 0 and 1)

Supplementary Exercises 7.81–7.109

Note: List the assumptions necessary for the valid implementation of the statistical procedures you use in solving all these exercises.

Understanding the Principles

7.81 For each of the following, identify the target parameter as μ or p.
  a. Average score on the SAT
  b. Mean time waiting at a supermarket checkout lane
  c. Proportion of voters in favor of legalizing marijuana
  d. Percentage of NFL players who have ever made the Pro Bowl
  e. Dropout rate of American college students

7.82 Interpret the phrase "95% confident" in the following statement: "We are 95% confident that the proportion of all PCs with a computer virus falls between .12 and .18."

7.83 In each of the following instances, determine whether you would use a z- or t-statistic (or neither) to form a 95% confidence interval; then look up the appropriate z- or t-value.
  a. Random sample of size $n = 21$ from a normal distribution with unknown mean μ and standard deviation σ
  b. Random sample of size $n = 175$ from a normal distribution with unknown mean μ and standard deviation σ
  c. Random sample of size $n = 12$ from a normal distribution with unknown mean μ and standard deviation $\sigma = 5$
  d. Random sample of size $n = 65$ from a distribution about which nothing is known
  e. Random sample of size $n = 8$ from a distribution about which nothing is known

Learning the Mechanics

7.84 Let t_0 represent a particular value of t from Table VI of Appendix A. Find the table values such that the following statements are true.

  a. $P(t \leq t_0) = .05$ where df $= 17$
  b. $P(t \geq t_0) = .005$ where df $= 14$
  c. $P(t \leq -t_0 \text{ or } t \geq t_0) = .10$ where df $= 6$
  d. $P(t \leq -t_0 \text{ or } t \geq t_0) = .01$ where df $= 22$

7.85 In a random sample of 400 measurements, 227 of the measurements possess the characteristic of interest, A.
  a. Use a 95% confidence interval to estimate the true proportion p of measurements in the population with characteristic A.
  b. How large a sample would be needed to estimate p to within .02 with 95% confidence?

7.86 A random sample of 225 measurements is selected from a population, and the sample mean and standard deviation are $\bar{x} = 32.5$ and $s = 30.0$, respectively.
  a. Use a 99% confidence interval to estimate the mean of the population, μ.
  b. How large a sample would be needed to estimate μ to within .5 with 99% confidence?
  c. What is meant by the phrase "99% confidence" as it is used in this exercise?

Applying the Concepts—Basic

7.87 **CDC health survey.** The Centers for Disease Control and Prevention (CDCP) in Atlanta, Georgia, conducts an annual survey of the general health of the U.S. population as part of its Behavioral Risk Factor Surveillance System. (*New York Times*, March 29, 1995.) Using random-digit dialing, the CDCP telephones U.S. citizens over 18 years of age and asks them the following four questions:
  (1) Is your health generally excellent, very good, good, fair, or poor?
  (2) How many days during the previous 30 days was your physical health not good because of injury or illness?
  (3) How many days during the previous 30 days was your mental health not good because of stress, depression, or emotional problems?

(4) How many days during the previous 30 days did your physical or mental health prevent you from performing your usual activities?

Identify the parameter of interest for each question.

7.88 CDC health survey. Refer to Exercise 7.87. According to the CDCP, 89,582 of 102,263 adults interviewed stated their health was good, very good, or excellent.

a. Use a 99% confidence interval to estimate the true proportion of U.S. adults who believe their health to be good to excellent. Interpret the interval.

b. Why might the estimate, part **a**, be overly optimistic (i.e., biased high)?

7.89 JAMA smoking study. The *Journal of the American Medical Association* (April 21, 1993) reported on the results of a National Health Interview Survey designed to determine the prevalence of smoking among U.S. adults. Current smokers (more than 11,000 adults in the survey) were asked, "On the average, how many cigarettes do you now smoke a day?" The results yielded a mean of 20.0 cigarettes per day with an associated 95% confidence interval of (19.7, 20.3).

a. Interpret the 95% confidence interval.

b. State any assumptions about the target population of current cigarette smokers that must be satisfied for inferences derived from the interval to be valid.

c. A tobacco industry researcher claims that the mean number of cigarettes smoked per day by regular cigarette smokers is less than 15. Comment on this claim.

7.90 JAMA smoking study. Refer to Exercise 7.89. Of the 43,732 survey respondents, 11,239 indicated that they were current smokers and 10,539 indicated they were former smokers.

a. Construct and interpret a 90% confidence interval for the percentage of U.S. adults who currently smoke cigarettes.

b. Construct and interpret a 90% confidence interval for the percentage of U.S. adults who are former cigarette smokers.

7.91 Crop weights of pigeons. The *Australian Journal of Zoology* (Vol. 43, 1995) reported on a study of the diets and water requirements of spinifex pigeons. Sixteen pigeons were captured in the desert and the crop (i.e., stomach) contents of each examined. The accompanying table reports the weight (in grams) of dry seed in the crop of each pigeon. Find a 99% confidence interval for the average weight of dry seeds in the crops of spinifex pigeons inhabiting the Western Australian desert. Interpret the result.

PIGEONS

.457	3.751	.238	2.967	2.509	1.384	1.454	.818
.335	1.436	1.603	1.309	.201	.530	2.144	.834

Source: Excerpted from Williams, J. B., Bradshaw, D., and Schmidt, L. "Field metabolism and water requirements of spinifex pigeons (*Geophaps plumifera*) in Western Australia." *Australian Journal of Zoology*, Vol. 43, No. 1, 1995, p. 7 (Table 2).

7.92 Ammonia in car exhaust. Refer to the *Environmental Science & Technology* (September 1, 2000) study on the ammonia levels near the exit ramp of a San Francisco highway tunnel, Exercise 2.59 (p. 64). The ammonia concentration (parts per million) data for eight randomly selected days during afternoon drive-time are reproduced in the table. Find a 99% confidence interval for the population mean daily ammonia level in air in the tunnel. Interpret your result.

AMMONIA

1.53	1.50	1.37	1.51	1.55	1.42	1.41	1.48

7.93 Homeless in the U.S. The *American Journal of Orthopsychiatry* (July 1995) published an article on the prevalence of homelessness in the United States. A sample of 487 U.S. adults were asked to respond to the question: "Was there ever a time in your life when you did not have a place to live?" A 95% confidence interval for the true proportion who were/are homeless, based on the survey data, was determined to be (.045, .091). Fully interpret the result.

Applying the Concepts—Intermediate

7.94 Pulse rates of joggers. Pulse rate is an important measure of the fitness of a person's cardiovascular system. The mean pulse rate for all U.S. adult males is approximately 72 heart beats per minute. A random sample of 21 U.S. adult males who jog at least 15 miles per week had a mean pulse rate of 52.6 beats per minute and a standard deviation of 3.22 beats per minute.

a. Find a 95% confidence interval for the mean pulse rate of all U.S. adult males who jog at least 15 miles per week.

b. Interpret the interval found in part **a**. Does it appear that jogging at least 15 miles per week reduces the mean pulse rate for adult males?

c. What assumptions are required for the validity of the confidence interval and the inference, part **b**?

7.95 Brown-bag lunches at work. In a study reported in *The Wall Street Journal* (April 4, 1999), the Tupperware Corporation surveyed 1,007 U.S. workers. Of the people surveyed, 665 indicated that they take their lunch to work with them. Of these 665 taking their lunch, 200 reported that they take it in brown bags.

a. Find a 95% confidence interval estimate of the population proportion of U.S. workers who take their lunch to work with them. Interpret the interval.

b. Consider the population of U.S. workers who take their lunch to work with them. Find a 95% confidence interval estimate of the population proportion who take brown-bag lunches. Interpret the interval.

7.96 Role importance for the elderly. Refer to the *Psychology and Aging* (December 2000) study of the roles that elderly people feel are the most important to them, Exercise 2.10 (p. 38). Recall that in a national sample of 1,102 adults, 65 years or older, 424 identified "spouse" as their most salient role. Use a 95% confidence interval to estimate the true percentage of adults, 65 years or older, who feel being a spouse is their most salient role. Give a practical interpretation of this interval.

7.97 Inbreeding of tropical wasps. Tropical swarm-founding wasps rely on female workers to raise their offspring. One possible explanation for this strange behavior is inbreeding, which increases relatedness among the wasps, presumably making it easier for the workers to pick out their closest relatives as propagators of their own genetic material. To test this theory, 197 swarm-founding wasps were captured in Venezuela, frozen at $-70°C$, and then subjected to a series of genetic tests (*Science*, November 1988). The data were used to generate an inbreeding coefficient, x, for each wasp specimen, with the following results: $\bar{x} = .044$ and $s = .884$.

  a. Construct a 99% confidence interval for the mean inbreeding coefficient of this species of wasp.
  b. A coefficient of 0 implies that the wasp has no tendency to inbreed. Use the confidence interval, part **a**, to make an inference about the tendency for this species of wasp to inbreed.

OILSPILL

7.98 Tanker oil spills. Refer to the *Marine Technology* (January 1995) study of the causes of fifty recent major oil spills from tankers and carriers, Exercise 2.182 (p. 112). The data are stored in the **OILSPILL** file.

  a. Give a point estimate for the proportion of major oil spills that are caused by hull failure.
  b. Form a 95% confidence interval for the estimate, part **a**. Interpret the result.

7.99 Time to solve a math programming problem. *IEEE Transactions* (June 1990) presented a hybrid algorithm for solving a polynomial zero-one mathematical programming problem. The algorithm incorporates a mixture of pseudo-Boolean concepts and time-proven implicit enumeration procedures. Fifty-two random problems were solved using the hybrid algorithm; the times to solution (CPU time in seconds) are listed in the table.

  a. Estimate, with 95% confidence, the mean solution time for the hybrid algorithm. Interpret the result.

  b. How many problems must be solved to estimate the mean, μ, to within .25 second with 95% confidence?

MATHCPU

.045	1.055	.136	1.894	.379	.136	.336	.258	1.070
.506	.088	.242	1.639	.912	.412	.361	8.788	.579
1.267	.567	.182	.036	.394	.209	.445	.179	.118
.333	.554	.258	.182	.070	3.985	.670	3.888	.136
.091	.600	.291	.327	.130	.145	4.170	.227	.064
.194	.209	.258	3.046	.045	.049	.079		

Source: Snyder, W. S., and Chrissis, J. W. "A hybrid algorithm for solving zero-one mathematical programming problems." *IEEE Transactions,* Vol. 22, No. 2, June 1990, p. 166 (Table 1). The Institute of Industrial Engineers, 25 Technology Park/Atlanta, Norcross, GA 30092. (770) 449-0461.

7.100 Weights of naphtha in drums. A company purchases large quantities of naphtha (a petroleum product) in 50-gallon drums. Because the purchases are ongoing, small shortages in the drums can represent a sizable loss to the company. The weights of the drums vary slightly from drum to drum, so the weight of the naphtha is determined by removing it from the drums and measuring it. Suppose the company samples the contents of 20 drums, measures the naphtha in each, and calculates $\bar{x} = 49.70$ gallons and $s = .32$ gallon. Find a 95% confidence interval for the mean number of gallons of naphtha per drum. What assumptions are necessary to assure the validity of the confidence interval?

SUICIDE

7.101 Jail suicide study. In Exercise 2.183 (p. 112) you considered data on suicides in correctional facilities, published in the *American Journal of Psychiatry* (July 1995). The researchers wanted to know what factors increase the risk of suicide by those incarcerated in urban jails. The data on 37 suicides that occurred in Wayne County Jail, Detroit, Michigan, are saved in the **SUICIDE** file. Answer each of the questions posed below, using a 95% confidence interval for the target parameter implied in the question. Fully interpret each confidence interval.

  a. What proportion of suicides at the jail are committed by inmates charged with murder/manslaughter?
  b. What proportion of suicides at the jail are committed at night?
  c. What is the average length of time an inmate is in jail before committing suicide?
  d. What percentage of suicides are committed by white inmates?

7.102 Recommendation letters for professors. Refer to the *American Psychologist* (July 1995) study of applications for university positions in experimental psychology, Exercise 2.62 (p. 65). One of the objectives of the analysis was to identify problems and errors (e.g., not submitting at least three letters of recommendation) in the application packages. In a sample of 148 applications for the positions, 30 applicants failed to provide *any* letters of recommendation. Estimate, with 90% confidence, the true fraction of applicants for a university position in experimental psychology that fail to provide letters of recommendation. Interpret the result.

7.103 Salmonella in ice cream bars. Recently, a case of salmonella (bacterial) poisoning was traced to a particular brand of ice cream bar, and the manufacturer removed the bars from the market. Despite this response, many consumers refused to purchase *any* brand of ice cream bars for some period of time after the event (McClave, personal consulting). One manufacturer conducted a survey of consumers 6 months after the poisoning. A sample of 244 ice cream bar consumers were contacted, and 23 of them indicated that they would not purchase ice cream bars because of the potential for food poisoning.

a. What is the point estimate of the true fraction of the entire market who refuse to purchase bars 6 months after the poisoning?

b. Is the sample size large enough to use the normal approximation for the sampling distribution of the estimator of the binomial probability? Justify your response.

c. Construct a 95% confidence interval for the true proportion of the market who still refuse to purchase ice cream bars 6 months after the event.

d. Interpret both the point estimate and confidence interval in terms of this application.

7.104 Salmonella in ice cream bars. Refer to Exercise 7.103. Suppose it is now 1 year after the poisoning was traced to ice cream bars. The manufacturer wishes to estimate the proportion who still will not purchase bars to within .02 using a 95% confidence interval. How many consumers should be sampled?

7.105 Removing a soil contaminate. A common hazardous compound found in contaminated soil is benzo(a)pyrene [B(a)p]. An experiment was conducted to determine the effectiveness of a method designed to remove B(a)p from soil. (*Journal of Hazardous Materials*, June 1995.) Three soil specimens contaminated with a known amount of B(a)p were treated with a toxin that inhibits microbial growth. After 95 days of incubation, the percentage of B(a)p removed from each soil specimen was measured. The experiment produced the following summary statistics: $\bar{x} = 49.3$ and $s = 1.5$.

a. Use a 99% confidence interval to estimate the mean percentage of B(a)p removed from a soil specimen in which the toxin was used.

b. Interpret the interval in terms of this application.

c. What assumption is necessary to ensure the validity of this confidence interval?

d. How many soil specimens must be sampled to estimate the mean percentage removed to within .5 using a 99% confidence interval?

7.106 Mail delivered on time. The accounting firm Price Waterhouse periodically monitors the U.S. Postal Service's performance. One parameter of interest is the percentage of mail delivered on time. In a sample of 332,000 mailed items, Price Waterhouse determined that 282,200 items were delivered on time. (*Tampa Tribune*, March 26, 1995.) Use this information to estimate with 99% confidence the true percentage of items delivered on time by the U.S. Postal Service. Interpret the result.

Applying the Concepts—Advanced

7.107 IMA salary survey. Each year *Management Accounting* reports the results of a salary survey of the members of the Institute of Management Accountants (IMA). One year, the 2,112 members responding had a salary distribution with a 20th percentile of $35,100; a median of $50,000; and an 80th percentile of $73,000.

a. Use this information to determine the minimum sample size that could be used in next year's survey to estimate the mean salary of IMA members to within $2,000 with 98% confidence. [*Hint*: To estimate s, first apply Chebyshev's Theorem to find k such that at least 60% of the data fall within k standard deviations of μ. Then find $s \approx$ (80th percentile $-$ 20th percentile)$/k$.]

b. Explain how you estimated the standard deviation required for the sample size calculation.

c. List any assumptions you make.

7.108 Cost of destructive sampling. Destructive sampling, in which the test to determine whether an item is defective destroys the item, is generally expensive, and the high costs involved often prohibit large sample sizes. For example, suppose the National Highway Traffic Safety Administration (NHTSA) wishes to determine the proportion of new tires that will fail when subjected to hard braking at a speed of 60 miles per hour. NHTSA can obtain the tires for $25 (wholesale price) each. Suppose the budget for the experiment is $10,000, and NHTSA wishes to estimate the percentage that will fail to within .02 with 95% confidence. Assuming that the entire $10,000 can be spent on tires (ignoring other costs) and that the true fraction that will fail is approximately .05, can NHTSA attain its goal while staying within the budget? Explain.

Critical Thinking Challenges

7.109 Scallops, sampling, and the law. MIT professor Arnold Bennett describes a recent legal case in which he served as a statistical "expert" in *Interfaces* (March–April 1995). The case involved a ship that fishes for scallops off the coast of New England. In order to protect baby scallops from being harvested, the U.S. Fisheries and Wildlife Service requires that "the average meat per scallop weigh at least $\frac{1}{36}$ of a pound." The ship was accused of violating this weight standard. Bennett lays out the scenario:

The vessel arrived at a Massachusetts port with 11,000 bags of scallops, from which the harbormaster randomly selected 18 bags for weighing. From each such bag, his agents took a large scoopful of scallops; then, to estimate the bag's average meat per scallop, they divided the total weight of meat in the scoopful by the number of scallops it contained. Based on the 18 [numbers] thus generated, the harbormaster estimated that each of the ship's scallops possessed an average $\frac{1}{39}$ of a pound of meat (that is, they were about seven percent lighter than the minimum requirement). Viewing this outcome as conclusive evidence that the weight standard had been violated, federal authorities at once confiscated 95 percent of the catch (which they then sold at auction). The fishing voyage was thus transformed into a financial catastrophe for its participants.

The actual scallop weight measurements for each of the 18 sampled bags are listed in the accompanying table. For ease of exposition, Bennett expressed each number as a multiple of $\frac{1}{36}$ of a pound, the minimum permissible average weight per scallop. Consequently, numbers below one indicate individual bags that do not meet the standard.

The ship's owner filed a lawsuit against the federal government, declaring that his vessel had fully complied with the weight standard. A Boston law firm was hired to represent the owner in legal proceedings and Bennett was retained by the firm to provide statistical litigation support and, if necessary, expert witness testimony.

a. Recall that the harbormaster sampled only 18 of the ship's 11,000 bags of scallops. One of the questions the lawyers asked Bennett was, "Can a reliable estimate of the mean weight of all the scallops be obtained from a sample of size 18?" Give your opinion on this issue.

b. As stated in the article, the government's decision rule is to confiscate a scallop catch if the sample mean weight of the scallops is less than $\frac{1}{36}$ of a pound. Do you see any flaws in this rule?

c. Develop your own procedure for determining whether a ship is in violation of the minimum weight restriction. Apply your rule to the data. Draw a conclusion about the ship in question.

SCALLOPS

.93	.88	.85	.91	.91	.84	.90	.98	.88
.89	.98	.87	.91	.92	.99	1.14	1.06	.93

Source: Bennett, A. "Misapplications review: Jail terms." *Interfaces,* Vol. 25, No. 2, Mar.–Apr. 1995, p. 20.

Student Projects

Choose a population pertinent to your major area of interest—a population that has an unknown mean or, if the population is binomial, that has an unknown probability of success. For example, a marketing major may be interested in the proportion of consumers who prefer a certain product. A sociology major may be interested in estimating the proportion of people in a certain socioeconomic group or the mean income of people living in a particular part of a city. A political science major may wish to estimate the proportion of an electorate in favor of a certain candidate, a certain amendment, or a certain presidential policy. A pre-med student might want to find the average length of time patients stay in the hospital or the average number of people treated daily in the emergency room. We could continue with examples, but the point should be clear—choose something of interest to you.

Define the parameter you want to estimate and conduct a *pilot study* to obtain an initial estimate of the parameter of interest and, more importantly, an estimate of the variability associated with the estimator. A pilot study is a small experiment (perhaps 20 to 30 observations) used to gain some information about the population of interest. The purpose of the study is to help plan more elaborate future experiments. Using the results of your pilot study, determine the sample size necessary to estimate the parameter to within a reasonable bound (of your choice) with a 95% confidence interval.

REFERENCES

Agresti, A., and Coull, B. A. "Approximate is better than 'exact' for interval estimation of binomial proportions." *The American Statistician,* Vol. 52, No. 2, May 1998, pp. 119–126.

Cochran, W. G. *Sampling Techniques,* 3rd ed. New York: Wiley, 1977.

Freedman, D., Pisani, R., and Purves, R. *Statistics.* New York: Norton, 1978.

Kish, L. *Survey Sampling.* New York: Wiley, 1965.

Mendenhall, W., Beaver, R. J., and Beaver, B. *Introduction to Probability and Statistics,* 11th ed. North Scituate, Mass.: Duxbury, 2002.

Wilson, E. G. "Probable inference, the law of succession, and statistical inference." *Journal of the American Statistical Association,* Vol. 22, 1927, pp. 209–212.

Using Technology

Confidence Intervals Using MINITAB

MINITAB can be used to obtain one-sample confidence intervals for both a population mean and a population proportion. To generate a confidence interval for the mean using a previously created sample data set, first access the MINITAB data worksheet. Next, click on the "Stat" button on the MINITAB menu bar, then click on "Basic Statistics" and "1-sample t," as shown in Figure 7.M.1. The resulting dialog box appears as shown in Figure 7.M.2. Click on "Samples in Columns," then specify the quantitative variable of interest in the open box. Now, click on the "Options" button at the bottom of the dialog box and specify the confidence level in the resulting dialog box as shown in Figure 7.M.3. Click "OK" to return to the "1-Sample t" dialog box, then click "OK" again to produce the confidence interval.

Figure 7.M.1

MINITAB Menu Options for a Confidence Interval for μ

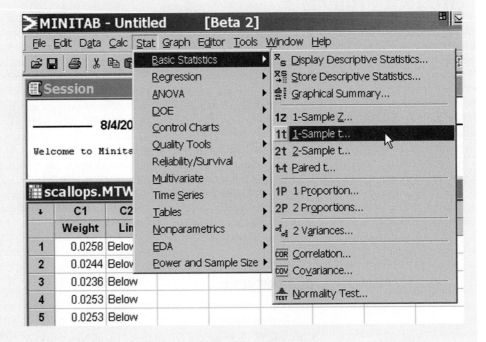

Figure 7.M.2
MINITAB 1-Sample t
Dialog Box

Figure 7.M.2
MINITAB 1-Sample t
Dialog Box

Figure 7.M.3
MINITAB 1-Sample t
Options Dialog Box

If you want to produce a confidence interval for the mean from summary information (e.g., the sample mean, sample standard deviation, and sample size), then click on "Summarized data" in the "1-Sample t" dialog box as shown in Figure 7.M.4. Enter the values of the summary statistics, then click "OK."

Figure 7.M.4
MINITAB 1-Sample t
Dialog Box with Summary
Statistics

[*Important Note*: The MINITAB 1-Sample t procedure uses the t-statistic to generate the confidence interval. When the sample size n is small, this is the appropriate method. When the sample size n is large, the t-value will be approximately equal to the large-sample z-value and the resulting interval will still be valid. If you have a large sample and you know the value of the population standard deviation σ (which is rarely the case), then select "1-Sample Z" from the "Basic Statistics" menu options (see Figure 7.M.1) and make the appropriate selections.]

To generate a confidence interval for a population proportion mean using a previously created sample data set, first access the MINITAB data worksheet. Next, click on the "Stat" button on the MINITAB menu bar, then click on "Basic Statistics" and "1 Proportion" (see Figure 7.M.1). The resulting dialog box appears as shown in Figure 7.M.5. Click on "Samples in Columns," then specify the qualitative variable of interest in the open box. Now, click on the "Options" button at the bottom of the dialog box and specify the confidence level in the resulting dialog box, as shown in Figure 7.M.6. Also, check the "Use test and interval based on normal distribution" box at the bottom. Click "OK" to return to the "1-Proportion" dialog box, then click "OK" again to produce the confidence interval.

Figure 7.M.5
MINITAB 1-Proportion
Dialog Box

Figure 7.M.6
MINITAB 1-Proportion
Dialog Box

If you want to produce a confidence interval for a proportion from summary information (e.g., the number of successes and the sample size), then click on "Summarized data" in the "1-Proportion" dialog box (see Figure 7.M.5). Enter the value for the number of trials (i.e., the sample size) and the number of events (i.e., the number of successes), then click "OK."

8

Inferences Based on a Single Sample

Tests of Hypothesis

Contents

8.1 The Elements of a Test of Hypothesis

8.2 Large-Sample Test of Hypothesis about a Population Mean

8.3 Observed Significance Levels: *p*-Values

8.4 Small-Sample Test of Hypothesis about a Population Mean

8.5 Large-Sample Test of Hypothesis about a Population Proportion

8.6 Calculating Type II Error Probabilities: More about β (Optional)

8.7 Test of Hypothesis about a Population Variance (Optional)

Statistics in Action

Diary of a Kleenex® User

Using Technology

Tests of Hypothesis Using MINITAB

Where We've Been

- Used sample information to provide a *point estimate* of a population parameter
- Used the sampling distribution of a statistic to assess the reliability of an estimate through a *confidence interval*

Where We're Going

- Test a specific value of a population parameter (mean or proportion)—called a *test of hypothesis*.
- Provide a measure of reliability for the hypothesis test—called the *significance level* of the test.

Statistics in *ACTION*

Diary of a KLEENEX® User

In 1924, Kimberly-Clark Corporation invented a facial tissue for removing cold cream and began marketing it as KLEENEX® brand tissues. Today, KLEENEX® is recognized as the top-selling brand of tissue in the world. A wide variety of KLEENEX® products is available, ranging from extra-large tissues to tissues with lotion. Over the past 80 years, Kimberly-Clark Corporation has packaged the tissues in boxes of different sizes and shapes and varied the number of tissues packaged in each box. For example, currently a family-size box contains 144 two-ply tissues, a cold-care box contains 70 tissues (coated with lotion), and a convenience pocket pack contains 15 miniature tissues.

How does Kimberly-Clark Corp. decide how many tissues to put in each box? According to the *Wall Street Journal*, marketing experts at the company use the results of à survey of KLEENEX® customers to help determine how many tissues are packed in a box. In the mid-1980s, when Kimberly-Clark Corp. developed the cold-care box designed especially for people who have a cold, the company conducted their initial survey of customers for this purpose. Hundreds of customers were asked to keep count of their KLEENEX® use in diaries. According to the *Wall Street Journal* report, the survey results left "little doubt

that the company should put 60 tissues in each box." The number 60 was "the average number of times people blow their nose during a cold." (*Note:* In 2000, the company increased the number of tissues packaged in a cold-care box to 70.)

From summary information provided in the *Wall Street Journal* (September 21, 1984) article, we constructed a data set that represents the results of a survey similar to the one just described. In the data file named **TISSUES**, we recorded the number of tissues used by each of 250 consumers during a period when they had a cold. We apply the hypothesis testing methodology presented in this chapter to this data set in several Statistics in Action Revisited examples.

Statistics in the Action Revisited

- Identifying the Key Elements of a Hypothesis Test Relevant to the KLEENEX® Survey (p. 375)
- Testing a Population Mean in the KLEENEX® Survey (p. 388)
- Testing a Population Proportion in the KLEENEX® Survey (p. 401)

Suppose you wanted to determine whether the mean level of a driver's blood alcohol exceeds the legal limit after two drinks, or whether the majority of registered voters approve of the president's performance. In both cases you are interested in making an inference about how the value of a parameter relates to a specific numerical value. Is it less than, equal to, or greater than the specified number? This type of inference, called a **test of hypothesis**, is the subject of this chapter.

We introduce the elements of a test of hypothesis in Section 8.1. We then show how to conduct a large-sample test of hypothesis about a population mean in Sections 8.2 and 8.3. In Section 8.4 we utilize small samples to conduct tests about means. Large-sample tests about binomial probabilities are the subject of Section 8.5, and some advanced methods for determining the reliability of a test are covered in optional Section 8.6. Finally, we show how to conduct a test about a population variance in optional Section 8.7.

8.1 The Elements of a Test of Hypothesis

Suppose building specifications in a certain city require that the average breaking strength of residential sewer pipe be more than 2,400 pounds per foot of length (i.e., per linear foot). Each manufacturer who wants to sell pipe in this city must demonstrate that its product meets the specification. Note that we are interested in making an inference about the mean μ of a population. However, in this example we are less interested in estimating the value of μ than we are in testing a *hypothesis* about its value. That is, *we want to decide whether the mean breaking strength of the pipe exceeds 2,400 pounds per linear foot.*

The method used to reach a decision is based on the rare-event concept explained in earlier chapters. We define two hypotheses: (1) The **null hypothesis** is that which represents the status quo to the party performing the sampling experiment—the hypothesis that will be supported unless the data provide convincing evidence that it is false. (2) The **alternative**, or **research**, **hypothesis** is that which will be accepted only if the data provide convincing evidence of its truth. From the point of view of the city conducting the tests, the null hypothesis is that the manufacturer's pipe does *not* meet specifications unless the tests provide convincing evidence otherwise. The null and alternative hypotheses are therefore

Null hypothesis (H_0): $\mu \leq 2{,}400$
    (i.e., the manufacturer's pipe does not meet specifications)
Alternative (research) hypothesis (H_a): $\mu > 2{,}400$
    (i.e., the manufacturer's pipe meets specifications)

> **Now Work** *Exercise 8.8*

How can the city decide when enough evidence exists to conclude that the manufacturer's pipe meets specifications? Since the hypotheses concern the value of the population mean μ, it is reasonable to use the sample mean $\bar{x}$ to make the inference, just as we did when forming confidence intervals for μ in Sections 7.1 and 7.2. The city will conclude that the pipe meets specifications only when the sample mean $\bar{x}$ convincingly indicates that the population mean exceeds 2,400 pounds per linear foot.

"Convincing" evidence in favor of the alternative hypothesis will exist when the value of $\bar{x}$ exceeds 2,400 by an amount that cannot be readily attributed to sampling variability. To decide, we compute a **test statistic**, which is the z-value that measures the distance between the value of $\bar{x}$ and the value of μ specified in the null hypothesis. When the null hypothesis contains more than one value of μ, as in this case (H_0: $\mu \leq 2{,}400$), we use the value of μ closest to the values specified in the alternative hypothesis. The idea is that if the hypothesis that μ *equals* 2,400 can be rejected in favor of $\mu > 2{,}400$, then μ *less than or equal to* 2,400 can certainly be rejected. Thus, the test statistic is

$$z = \frac{\bar{x} - 2{,}400}{\sigma_{\bar{x}}} = \frac{\bar{x} - 2{,}400}{\sigma/\sqrt{n}}$$

Note that a value of $z = 1$ means that $\bar{x}$ is 1 standard deviation above $\mu = 2{,}400$; a value of $z = 1.5$ means that $\bar{x}$ is 1.5 standard deviations above $\mu = 2{,}400$, etc. How large must z be before the city can be convinced that the null hypothesis can be rejected in favor of the alternative and conclude that the pipe meets specifications?

If you examine Figure 8.1, you will note that the chance of observing $\bar{x}$ more than 1.645 standard deviations above 2,400 is only .05—*if in fact the true mean μ is* 2,400. Thus, if the sample mean is more than 1.645 standard deviations above 2,400, either H_0 is true and a relatively rare event has occurred (.05 probability) or H_a is true and the population mean exceeds 2,400. Since we would most likely reject the notion that a rare event has occurred, we would reject the null hypothesis ($\mu \leq 2{,}400$) and conclude that the alternative hypothesis ($\mu > 2{,}400$) is true. What is the probability that this procedure will lead us to an incorrect decision?

Figure 8.1

The Sampling Distribution of $\bar{x}$, Assuming $\mu = 2{,}400$

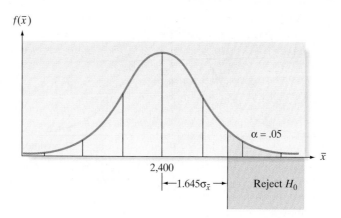

Such an incorrect decision—deciding that the null hypothesis is false when in fact it is true—is called a **Type I decision error**. As indicated in Figure 8.1, the risk of making a Type I error is denoted by the symbol α. That is,

$$\alpha = P \text{ (Type I error)}$$
$$= P \text{ (Rejecting the null hypothesis when in fact the null hypothesis is true)}$$

In our example

$$\alpha = P \text{ } (z > 1.645 \text{ when in fact } \mu = 2{,}400) = .05$$

We now summarize the elements of the test:

H_0: $\mu \leq 2{,}400$
H_a: $\mu > 2{,}400$

Test statistic: $z = \dfrac{\bar{x} - 2{,}400}{\sigma_{\bar{x}}}$

Rejection region: $z > 1.645$, which corresponds to $\alpha = .05$

Note that the **rejection region** refers to the values of the test statistic for which we will *reject the null hypothesis*.

To illustrate the use of the test, suppose we test 50 sections of sewer pipe and find the mean and standard deviation for these 50 measurements to be

$$\bar{x} = 2{,}460 \text{ pounds per linear foot} \qquad s = 200 \text{ pounds per linear foot}$$

As in the case of estimation, we can use s to approximate σ when s is calculated from a large set of sample measurements.

The test statistic is

$$z = \frac{\bar{x} - 2{,}400}{\sigma_{\bar{x}}} = \frac{\bar{x} - 2{,}400}{\sigma/\sqrt{n}} \approx \frac{\bar{x} - 2{,}400}{s/\sqrt{n}}$$

Substituting $\bar{x} = 2{,}460$, $n = 50$, and $s = 200$, we have

$$z \approx \frac{2{,}460 - 2{,}400}{200/\sqrt{50}} = \frac{60}{28.28} = 2.12$$

Therefore, the sample mean lies $2.12\sigma_{\bar{x}}$ above the hypothesized value of $\mu = 2{,}400$ as shown in Figure 8.2. Since this value of z exceeds 1.645, it falls in the rejection region. That is, we reject the null hypothesis that $\mu = 2{,}400$ and conclude that $\mu > 2{,}400$. Thus, it appears that the company's pipe has a mean strength that exceeds 2,400 pounds per linear foot.

How much faith can be placed in this conclusion? What is the probability that our statistical test could lead us to reject the null hypothesis (and conclude that the company's pipe meets the city's specifications) when in fact the null hypothesis is

Figure 8.2

Location of the Test Statistic for a Test of the Hypothesis $H_0: \mu = 2,400$

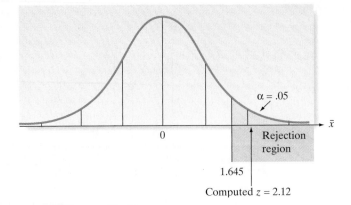

true? The answer is $\alpha = .05$. That is, we selected the level of risk, α, of making a Type I error when we constructed the test. Thus, the chance is only 1 in 20 that our test would lead us to conclude the manufacturer's pipe satisfies the city's specifications when in fact the pipe does *not* meet specifications.

Now, suppose the sample mean breaking strength for the 50 sections of sewer pipe turned out to be $\bar{x} = 2,430$ pounds per linear foot. Assuming that the sample standard deviation is still $s = 200$, the test statistic is

$$z = \frac{2,430 - 2,400}{2/\sqrt{50}} = \frac{30}{28.28} = 1.06$$

Therefore, the sample mean $\bar{x} = 2,430$ is only 1.06 standard deviations above the null hypothesized value of $\mu = 2,400$. As shown in Figure 8.3, this value does not fall into the rejection region $(z > 1.645)$. Therefore, we know that we cannot reject H_0 using $\alpha = .05$. Even though the sample mean exceeds the city's specification of 2,400 by 30 pounds per linear foot, it does not exceed the specification by enough to provide *convincing* evidence that the *population mean* exceeds 2,400.

Figure 8.3

Location of the Test Statistic When $\bar{x} = 2,430$

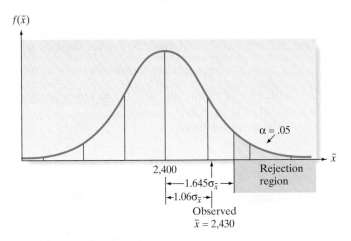

Should we accept the null hypothesis $H_0: \mu \leq 2,400$ and conclude that the manufacturer's pipe does not meet specifications? To do so would be to risk a **Type II error**—that of concluding that the null hypothesis is true (the pipe does not meet specifications) when in fact it is false (the pipe does meet specifications). We denote the probability of committing a Type II error by β, and we show in optional Section 8.6 that β is often difficult to determine precisely. Rather than make a decision (accept H_0) for which the probability of error (β) is unknown, we avoid the potential Type II error by avoiding the conclusion that the null hypothesis is true. Instead, we will simply state that *the sample evidence is insufficient to reject H_0 at $\alpha = .05$*. Since

Biography

EGON S. PEARSON (1895–1980)—The Neyman-Pearson Lemma

Egon Pearson was the only son of noteworthy British statistician Karl Pearson (see Biography, p. 786). As you might expect, Egon developed an interest in the statistical methods developed by his father and, upon completing graduate school, accepted a position to work for Karl in the Department of Applied Statistics at University College, Lon-

don. Egon is best known for his collaboration with Jerzey Neyman (see Biography, p. 325) on the development of the theory of hypothesis testing. One of the basic concepts in the Neyman-Pearson approach was that of the "null" and "alternative" hypotheses. Their famous "Neyman-Pearson" lemma was published in *Biometrika* in 1928. Egon Pearson had numerous other contributions to statistics and was known as an excellent teacher and lecturer. In his last major work, Egon fulfilled a promise made to his father by publishing an annotated version of Karl Pearson's lectures on the early history of statistics.

the null hypothesis is the "status-quo" hypothesis, the effect of not rejecting H_0 is to maintain the status quo. In our pipe-testing example, the effect of having insufficient evidence to reject the null hypothesis that the pipe does not meet specifications is probably to prohibit the utilization of the manufacturer's pipe unless and until there is sufficient evidence that the pipe does meet specifications. That is, until the data indicate convincingly that the null hypothesis is false, we usually maintain the status quo implied by its truth.

Table 8.1 summarizes the four possible outcomes of a test of hypothesis. The "true state of nature" columns in Table 8.1 refer to the fact that either the null hypothesis H_0 is true or the alternative hypothesis H_a is true. Note that the true state of nature is unknown to the researcher conducting the test. The "conclusion" rows in Table 8.1 refer to the action of the researcher, assuming that he or she will conclude either that H_0 is true or that H_a is true, based on the results of the sampling experiment. Note that a Type I error can be made *only* when the alternative hypothesis is accepted (equivalently, when the null hypothesis is rejected), and a Type II error can be made *only* when the null hypothesis is accepted. Our policy will be to make a decision only when we know the probability of making the error that corresponds to that decision. Since α is usually specified by the analyst (typically .05 in research), we will generally be able to reject H_0 (accept H_a) when the sample evidence supports that decision. However, since β is usually not specified, *we will generally avoid the decision to accept H_0, preferring instead to state that the sample evidence is insufficient to reject H_0 when the test statistic is not in the rejection region.*

Caution

Be careful not to "accept H_0" when conducting a test of hypothesis since the measure of reliability, $\beta = P(\text{Type II error})$, is almost always unknown. If the test statistic does not fall into the rejection region, it is better to state the conclusion as "insufficient evidence to reject H_0."

TABLE 8.1　Conclusions and Consequences for a Test of Hypothesis

	True State of Nature	
Conclusion	H_0 True	H_a True
Accept H_0 (Assume H_0 True)	Correct decision	Type II error (probability β)
Reject H_0 (Assume H_a True)	Type I error (probability α)	Correct decision

The elements of a test of hypothesis are summarized in the following box. Note that the first four elements are all specified *before* the sampling experiment is performed. In no case will the results of the sample be used to determine the hypotheses—the data are collected to test the predetermined hypotheses, not to formulate them.

Elements of a Test of Hypothesis

1. *Null hypothesis* (H_0): A theory about the values of one or more population parameters. The theory generally represents the status quo, which we adopt until it is proven false. By convention, the theory is stated as H_0: parameter = value.

2. *Alternative (research) hypothesis* (H_a): A theory that contradicts the null hypothesis. The theory generally represents that which we will accept only when sufficient evidence exists to establish its truth.

3. *Test statistic:* A sample statistic used to decide whether to reject the null hypothesis.

4. *Rejection region:* The numerical values of the test statistic for which the null hypothesis will be rejected. The rejection region is chosen so that the probability is α that it will contain the test statistic when the null hypothesis is true, thereby leading to a Type I error. The value of α is usually chosen to be small (e.g., .01, .05, or .10), and is referred to as the **level of significance** of the test.

5. *Assumptions:* Clear statement(s) of any assumptions made about the population(s) being sampled.

6. *Experiment and calculation of test statistic:* Performance of the sampling experiment and determination of the numerical value of the test statistic.

7. *Conclusion:*
   a. If the numerical value of the test statistic falls in the rejection region, we reject the null hypothesis and conclude that the alternative hypothesis is true. We know that the hypothesis-testing process will lead to this conclusion incorrectly (Type I error) only $100\alpha\%$ of the time when H_0 is true.
   b. If the test statistic does not fall in the rejection region, we do not reject H_0. Thus, we reserve judgment about which hypothesis is true. We do not conclude that the null hypothesis is true because we do not (in general) know the probability β that our test procedure will lead to an incorrect acceptance of H_0 (Type II error).

As with confidence intervals, the methodology for testing hypotheses varies depending on the target population parameter. In this chapter, we develop methods for testing a population mean, a population proportion, and a population variance. Some key words and the type of data associated with these target parameters are listed in the accompanying box.

Determining the Target Parameter

Parameter	Key Words or Phrases	Type of Data
μ	Mean; average	Quantitative
p	Proportion; percentage; fraction; rate	Qualitative
σ^2	Variance; variability; spread	Quantitative

Statistics in Action Revisited

Identifying the Key Elements of a Hypothesis Test Relevant to the KLEENEX® Survey

In Kimberly-Clark Corporation's survey of people with colds, each of 250 customers was asked to keep count of his or her use of KLEENEX® tissues in diaries. One goal of the company was to determine how many tissues to package in a cold-care box of KLEENEX®; consequently, the total number of tissues used was recorded for each person surveyed. Since number of tissues is a quantitative variable, the parameter of interest is either μ, the mean number of tissues used by all customers with colds, or σ^2, the variance of the number of tissues used.

Now, according to a *Wall Street Journal* report, there was "little doubt that the company should put 60 tissues" in a cold-care box of KLEENEX® tissues. This statement was based on a claim made by marketing experts that 60 is the average number of times a person will blow his/her nose during a cold. The key word *average* implies that the target parameter is μ, and the marketers are claiming that $\mu = 60$. Suppose we disbelieve the claim that $\mu = 60$, believing instead that the population mean is smaller than 60 tissues. In order to test the claim against our belief, we set up the following null and alternative hypothesis:

$$H_0: \mu = 60 \qquad H_a: \mu < 60$$

We'll conduct this test in the next Statistics in Action Revisited on p. 388.

Exercises 8.1–8.17

Understanding the Principles

8.1 Which hypothesis, the null or the alternative, is the status-quo hypothesis? Which is the research hypothesis?

8.2 Which element of a test of hypothesis is used to decide whether to reject the null hypothesis in favor of the alternative hypothesis?

8.3 What is the level of significance of a test of hypothesis?

8.4 What is the difference between Type I and Type II errors in hypothesis testing? How do α and β relate to Type I and Type II errors?

8.5 List the four possible results of the combinations of decisions and true states of nature for a test of hypothesis.

8.6 We (generally) reject the null hypothesis when the test statistic falls in the rejection region, but we do not accept the null hypothesis when the test statistic does not fall in the rejection region. Why?

8.7 If you test a hypothesis and reject the null hypothesis in favor of the alternative hypothesis, does your test prove that the alternative hypothesis is correct? Explain.

Applying the Concepts—Basic

8.8 **Calories in school lunches.** A University of Florida economist conducted a study of Virginia elementary school lunch menus. During the state-mandated testing period, school lunches averaged 863 calories. (*National Bureau of Economic Research*, November 2002.) The economist claims that after the testing period ends, the average caloric content of Virginia school lunches drops significantly. Set up the null and alternative hypothesis to test the economist's claim.

8.9 **A camera that detects liars.** According to *NewScientist* (January 2, 2002), a new thermal imaging camera that detects small temperature changes is now being used as a polygraph device. The United States Department of Defense Polygraph Institute (DDPI) claims the camera can correctly detect liars 75% of the time by monitoring the temperatures of their faces. Give the null hypothesis for testing the claim made by the DDPI.

8.10 **Work travel policy.** American Express Consulting reported in *USA Today* (June 15, 2001) that 80% of U.S. companies have formal, written travel and entertainment policies for their employees. Give the null hypothesis for testing the claim made by American Express Consulting.

8.11 **Use of herbal therapy.** According to the *Journal of Advanced Nursing* (January 2001), 45% of senior women (i.e., women over the age of 65) use herbal therapies to prevent or treat health problems. Also, of senior women who use herbal therapies, they use an average of 2.5 herbal products in a year.
  a. Give the null hypothesis for testing the first claim by the journal.
  b. Give the null hypothesis for testing the second claim by the journal.

8.12 **Infants listening time.** *Science* (January 1, 1999) reported that the mean listening time of 7-month-old infants exposed to a three-syllable sentence (e.g., "ga ti ti") is 9 seconds. Set up the null and alternative hypotheses for testing the claim.

8.13 **Cocaine-exposed babies.** Infants exposed to cocaine in their mother's womb are thought to be at a high risk for major birth defects. However, according to a University of Florida study, more than 75% of all cocaine-exposed babies suffer no major problems (*Explore*, Fall 1998). Set up the null and alternative hypotheses if you want to support the findings.

Applying the Concepts—Intermediate

8.14 Susceptibility to hypnosis. The Computer-Assisted Hypnosis Scale (CAHS) is designed to measure a person's susceptibility to hypnosis. CAHS scores range from 0 (no susceptibility to hypnosis) to 12 (extremely high susceptibility to hypnosis). *Psychological Assessment* (March 1995) reported that University of Tennessee undergraduates had a mean CAHS score of $\mu = 4.6$. Suppose you want to test whether undergraduates at your college or university are more susceptible to hypnosis than University of Tennessee undergraduates.

  a. Set up H_0 and H_a for the test.
  b. Describe a Type I error for this test.
  c. Describe a Type II error for this test.

8.15 Mercury levels in wading birds. According to a University of Florida wildlife ecology and conservation researcher, the average level of mercury uptake in wading birds in the Everglades has declined over the past several years. (*UF News*, December 15, 2000.) Five years ago, the average level was 15 parts per million.

  a. Give the null and alternative hypotheses for testing whether the average level today is less than 15 ppm.
  b. Describe a Type I error for this test.
  c. Describe a Type II error for this test.

Applying the Concepts—Advanced

8.16 Jury trial outcomes. Sometimes, the outcome of a jury trial defies the "commonsense" expectations of the general public (e.g., the O. J. Simpson verdict in the "Trial of the Century"). Such a verdict is more acceptable if we understand that the jury trial of an accused murderer is analogous to the statistical hypothesis-testing process. The null hypothesis in a jury trial is that the accused is innocent. (The status-quo hypothesis in the U.S. system of justice is innocence, which is assumed to be true until proven *beyond a reasonable doubt*.) The alternative hypothesis is guilt, which is accepted only when sufficient evidence exists to establish its truth. If the vote of the jury is unanimous in favor of guilt, the null hypothesis of innocence is rejected and the court concludes that the accused murderer is guilty. Any vote other than a unanimous one for guilt results in a "not guilty"

verdict. The court never accepts the null hypothesis; that is, the court never declares the accused "innocent." A "not guilty" verdict (as in the O. J. Simpson case) implies that the court could not find the defendant guilty *beyond a reasonable doubt*.

  a. Define Type I and Type II errors in a murder trial.
  b. Which of the two errors is the more serious? Explain.
  c. The court does not, in general, know the values of α and β; but ideally, both should be small. One of these probabilities is assumed to be smaller than the other in a jury trial. Which one, and why?
  d. The court system relies on the belief that the value of α is made very small by requiring a unanimous vote before guilt is concluded. Explain why this is so.
  e. For a jury prejudiced against a guilty verdict as the trial begins, will the value of α increase or decrease? Explain.
  f. For a jury prejudiced against a guilty verdict as the trial begins, will the value of β increase or decrease? Explain.

8.17 Intrusion detection systems. Refer to the *Journal of Research of the National Institute of Standards and Technology* (November–December, 2003) study of a computer intrusion detection system (IDS), Exercise 3.81 (p. 158). Recall that an IDS is designed to provide an alarm whenever unauthorized access (e.g., an intrusion) to a computer system occurs. The probability of the system giving a false alarm (i.e., providing a warning when, in fact, no intrusion occurs) is defined by the symbol α, while the probability of a missed detection (i.e., no warning given, when, in fact, an intrusion occurs) is defined by the symbol β. These symbols are used to represent Type I and Type II error rates, respectively, in a hypothesis testing scenario.

  a. What is the null hypothesis, H_0?
  b. What is the alternative hypothesis, H_a?
  c. According to actual data on the EMERALD system collected by the Massachusetts Institute of Technology Lincoln Laboratory, only 1 in 1,000 computer sessions with no intrusions resulted in a false alarm. For the same system, the laboratory found that only 500 of 1,000 intrusions were actually detected. Use this information to estimate the values of α and β.

8.2 Large-Sample Test of Hypothesis about a Population Mean

In Section 8.1 we learned that the null and alternative hypotheses form the basis for a test of hypothesis inference. The null and alternative hypotheses may take one of several forms. In the sewer pipe example we tested the null hypothesis that the population mean strength of the pipe is less than or equal to 2,400 pounds per linear foot against the alternative hypothesis that the mean strength exceeds 2,400. That is, we tested

$$H_0: \mu \leq 2,400$$
$$H_a: \mu > 2,400$$

This is a **one-tailed** (or **one-sided**) **statistical test** because the alternative hypothesis specifies that the population parameter (the population mean μ, in this example) is strictly greater than a specified value (2,400, in this example). If the null hypothesis had been $H_0: \mu \geq 2,400$ and the alternative hypothesis had been $H_a: \mu < 2,400$, the test would still be one-sided, because the parameter is still specified to be on "one side" of the null hypothesis value. Some statistical investigations seek to show that the population parameter is *either larger or smaller* than some specified value. Such an alternative hypothesis is called a **two-tailed** (or **two-sided**) **hypothesis**.

While alternative hypotheses are always specified as strict inequalities, such as $\mu < 2,400$, $\mu > 2,400$, or $\mu \neq 2,400$, null hypotheses are usually specified as equalities, such as $\mu = 2,400$. *Even when the null hypothesis is an inequality, such as $\mu \leq 2,400$, we specify $H_0: \mu = 2,400$, reasoning that if sufficient evidence exists to show that $H_a: \mu > 2,400$ is true when tested against $H_0: \mu = 2,400$, then surely sufficient evidence exists to reject $\mu < 2,400$ as well.* Therefore, the null hypothesis is specified as the value of μ closest to a one-sided alternative hypothesis and as the only value *not* specified in a two-tailed alternative hypothesis. The steps for selecting the null and alternative hypotheses are summarized in the box on p. 000.

The rejection region for a two-tailed test differs from that for a one-tailed test. When we are trying to detect departure from the null hypothesis in *either* direction, we must establish a rejection region in both tails of the sampling distribution of the test statistic. Figures 8.4a and 8.4b show the one-tailed rejection regions for lower- and upper-tailed tests, respectively. The two-tailed rejection region is illustrated in Figure 8.4c. Note that a rejection region is established in each tail of the sampling distribution for a two-tailed test.

The rejection regions corresponding to typical values selected for α are shown in Table 8.2 for one- and-two-tailed tests. Note that the smaller α you select, the more evidence (the larger z) you will need before you can reject H_0.

Steps for Selecting the Null and Alternative Hypotheses

1. Select the *alternative hypothesis* as that which the sampling experiment is intended to establish. The alternative hypothesis will assume one of three forms:

   a. One-tailed, upper-tailed   *Example: H_a:* $\mu > 2,400$
   b. One-tailed, lower-tailed   *Example: H_a:* $\mu < 2,400$
   c. Two-tailed   *Example: H_a:* $\mu \neq 2,400$

2. Select the *null hypothesis* as the status quo, that which will be presumed true unless the sampling experiment conclusively establishes the alternative hypothesis. The null hypothesis will be specified as that parameter value closest to the alternative in one-tailed tests, and as the complementary (or only unspecified) value in two-tailed tests.

   Example: $H_0: \mu = 2,400$

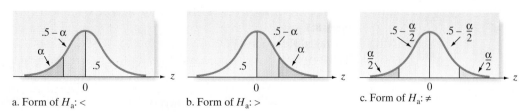

a. Form of H_a: <   b. Form of H_a: >   c. Form of H_a: ≠

Figure 8.4
Rejection Regions Corresponding to One- and Two-Tailed Tests

TABLE 8.2 Rejection Regions for Common Values of α

	Alternative Hypotheses		
	Lower-Tailed	Upper-Tailed	Two-Tailed
$\alpha = .10$	$z < -1.28$	$z > 1.28$	$z < -1.645$ or $z > 1.645$
$\alpha = .05$	$z < -1.645$	$z > 1.645$	$z < -1.96$ or $z > 1.96$
$\alpha = .01$	$z < -2.33$	$z > 2.33$	$z < -2.575$ or $z > 2.575$

EXAMPLE 8.1   SETTING UP A HYPOTHESIS TEST FOR μ

Problem   The effect of drugs and alcohol on the nervous system has been the subject of considerable research. Suppose a research neurologist is testing the effect of a drug on response time by injecting 100 rats with a unit dose of the drug, subjecting each to a neurological stimulus, and recording its response time. The neurologist knows that the mean response time for rats not injected with the drug (the "control" mean) is 1.2 seconds. She wishes to test whether the mean response time for drug-injected rats differs from 1.2 seconds. Set up the test of hypothesis for this experiment, using $\alpha = .01$.

Solution   Since the neurologist wishes to detect whether the mean response time, μ, for drug-injected rats differs from the control mean of 1.2 seconds in *either* direction—that is, $\mu < 1.2$ or $\mu > 1.2$—we conduct a two-tailed statistical test. Following the procedure for selecting the null and alternative hypotheses, we specify as the alternative hypothesis that the mean differs from 1.2 seconds, since determining whether the drug-injected mean differs from the control mean is the purpose of the experiment. The null hypothesis is the presumption that drug-injected rats have the same mean response time as control rats unless the research indicates otherwise. Thus,

$$H_0: \mu = 1.2$$
$$H_a: \mu \neq 1.2 \qquad \text{(i.e., } \mu < 1.2 \text{ or } \mu > 1.2\text{)}$$

The test statistic measures the number of standard deviations between the observed value of $\bar{x}$ and the null hypothesized value $\mu = 1.2$:

$$\textit{Test statistic:} \quad z = \frac{\bar{x} - 1.2}{\sigma_{\bar{x}}}$$

The rejection region must be designated to detect a departure from $\mu = 1.2$ in *either* direction, so we will reject H_0 for values of z that are either too small (negative) or too large (positive). To determine the precise values of z that comprise the rejection region, we first select α, the probability that the test will lead to incorrect rejection of the null hypothesis. Then we divide α equally between the lower and upper tail of the distribution of z, as shown in Figure 8.5. In this example, $\alpha = .01$, so

Figure 8.5
Two-Tailed Rejection
Region: $\alpha = .01$

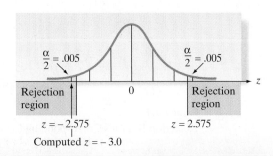

$\alpha/2 = .005$ is placed in each tail. The areas in the tails correspond to $z = -2.575$ and $z = 2.575$, respectively (from Table 8.2):

$$\textit{Rejection region}: z < -2.575 \text{ or } z > 2.575 \qquad \text{(see Figure 8.5)}$$

Assumptions: Since the sample size of the experiment is large enough ($n > 30$), the Central Limit Theorem will apply, and no assumptions need be made about the population of response time measurements. The sampling distribution of the sample mean response of 100 rats will be approximately normal regardless of the distribution of the individual rats' response times.

Look Back Note that the test is set up *before* the sampling experiment is conducted. The data are not used to develop the test. Evidently, the neurologist wants to conclude that the mean response time for the drug-injected rats differs from the control mean only when the evidence is very convincing, because the value of α has been set quite low at .01. If the experiment results in the rejection of H_0, she can be 99% confident that the mean response time of the drug-injected rats differs from the control mean.

Now Work   *Exercise 8.2*

■ ■ ■

Once the test is set up, she is ready to perform the sampling experiment and conduct the test. The test is performed in Example 8.2.

EXAMPLE 8.2   CARRYING OUT A HYPOTHESIS TEST FOR μ

Problem Refer to the neurological response-time test set up in Example 8.1. Suppose the sampling experiment is conducted with the following results:

$$n = 100 \text{ response times for drug-injected rats}$$
$$\bar{x} = 1.05 \text{ seconds} \qquad s = .5 \text{ second}$$

Use the results of the sampling experiment to conduct the test of hypothesis.

Solution Since the test is completely specified in Example 8.1, we simply substitute the sample statistics into the test statistic:

$$z = \frac{\bar{x} - 1.2}{\sigma_{\bar{x}}} = \frac{\bar{x} - 1.2}{\sigma/\sqrt{n}} = \frac{1.05 - 1.2}{\sigma/\sqrt{100}}$$
$$\approx \frac{1.05 - 1.2}{s/10} = \frac{-.15}{.5/10} = -3.0$$

The implication is that the sample mean, 1.05, is (approximately) 3 standard deviations below the null hypothesized value of 1.2 in the sampling distribution of $\bar{x}$. You can see in Figure 8.5 that this value of z is in the lower-tail rejection region, which consists of all values of $z < -2.575$. This sampling experiment provides sufficient evidence to reject H_0 and conclude, at the $\alpha = .01$ level of significance, that the mean response time for drug-injected rats differs from the control mean of 1.2 seconds. It appears that the rats receiving an injection of this drug have a mean response time that is less than 1.2 seconds.

Look Back Two points about the test of hypothesis in this example apply to all statistical tests:

1. Since z is less than -2.575, it is tempting to state our conclusion at a significance level lower than $\alpha = .01$. We resist the temptation because the level of α

is determined *before* the sampling experiment is performed. If we decide that we are willing to tolerate a 1% Type I error rate, the result of the sampling experiment should have no effect on that decision. *In general, the same data should not be used both to set up and to conduct the test.*

2. When we state our conclusion at the .01 level of significance, we are referring to the failure rate of the *procedure*, not the result of this particular test. We know that the test procedure will lead to the rejection of the null hypothesis only 1% of the time when in fact $\mu = 1.2$. *Therefore, when the test statistic falls in the rejection region, we infer that the alternative $\mu \neq 1.2$ is true and express our confidence in the procedure by quoting the α level of significance, or the $100(1 - \alpha)\%$ confidence level.*

> **Now Work**   *Exercise 8.26*

■ ■ ■

The setup of a large-sample test of hypothesis about a population mean is summarized in the following box. Both the one- and two-tailed tests are shown.

α is risk

Large-Sample Test of Hypothesis about μ

One-Tailed Test	**Two-Tailed Test**
$H_0: \mu = \mu_0$	$H_0: \mu = \mu_0$
⋆ $H_a: \mu < \mu_0$ (or $H_a: \mu > \mu_0$)	⋆ $H_a: \mu \neq \mu_0$
Test statistic: $z = \dfrac{\bar{x} - \mu_0}{\sigma_{\bar{x}}}$	Test statistics: $z = \dfrac{\bar{x} - \mu_0}{\sigma_{\bar{x}}}$ $\left(\dfrac{s}{\sqrt{n}}\right)$
Rejection region: $z < -z_{\alpha}$ (or $z > z_{\alpha}$ when $H_a: \mu > \mu_0$)	Rejection region: $z < -z_{\alpha/2}$ or $z > z_{\alpha/2}$
where z_{α} is chosen so that $P(z > z_{\alpha}) = \alpha$	where $z_{\alpha/2}$ is chosen so that $P(z > z_{\alpha/2}) = \alpha/2$

Note: μ_0 is the symbol for the numerical value assigned to μ under the null hypothesis.

Conditions Required for a Valid Large-Sample Hypothesis Test for μ

1. A random sample is selected from the target population.
2. The sample size n is large (i.e., $n \geq 30$). (Due to the Central Limit Theorem, this condition guarantees that the test statistic will be approximately normal regardless of the shape of the underlying probability distribution of the population.)

Once the test has been set up, the sampling experiment is performed and the test statistic is calculated. The next box contains possible conclusions for a test of hypothesis, depending on the result of the sampling experiment.

Possible Conclusions for a Test of Hypothesis

1. If the calculated test statistic falls in the rejection region, reject H_0 and conclude that the alternative hypothesis H_a is true. State that you are rejecting H_0 at the α level of significance. Remember that the confidence is in the testing *process*, not the particular result of a single test.

> **2.** If the test statistic does not fall in the rejection region, conclude that the sampling experiment does not provide sufficient evidence to reject H_0 at the α level of significance. [Generally, we will not "accept" the null hypothesis unless the probability β of a Type II error has been calculated (see optional Section 8.6).]

Exercises 8.18–8.35

Understanding the Principles

8.18 Explain the difference between a one-tailed and a two-tailed test.

8.19 What conditions are required for a valid large-sample test for μ?

8.20 For what values of the test statistic lead you to reject H_0? Fail to reject H_0?

Learning the Mechanics

8.21 For each of the following rejection regions, sketch the
NW sampling distribution for z and indicate the location of the rejection region.
  a. $z > 1.96$
  b. $z > 1.645$
  c. $z > 2.575$
  d. $z < -1.28$
  e. $z < -1.645$ or $z > 1.645$
  f. $z < -2.575$ or $z > 2.575$
  g. For each of the rejection regions specified in parts **a–f**, what is the probability that a Type I error will be made?

8.22 Suppose you are interested in conducting the statistical test of $H_0: \mu = 200$ against $H_a: \mu > 200$, and you have decided to use the following decision rule: Reject H_0 if the sample mean of a random sample of 100 items is more than 215. Assume that the standard deviation of the population is 80.
  a. Express the decision rule in terms of z.
  b. Find α, the probability of making a Type I error, by using this decision rule.

8.23 A random sample of 100 observations from a population with standard deviation 60 yielded a sample mean of 110.
  a. Test the null hypothesis that $\mu = 100$ against the alternative hypothesis that $\mu > 100$ using $\alpha = .05$. Interpret the results of the test.
  b. Test the null hypothesis that $\mu = 100$ against the alternative hypothesis that $\mu \neq 100$ using $\alpha = .05$. Interpret the results of the test.
  c. Compare the results of the two tests you conducted. Explain why the results differ.

8.24 A random sample of 64 observations produced the following summary statistics: $\bar{x} = .323$ and $s^2 = .034$.
  a. Test the null hypothesis that $\mu = .36$ against the alternative hypothesis that $\mu < .36$ using $\alpha = .10$.
  b. Test the null hypothesis that $\mu = .36$ against the alternative hypothesis that $\mu \neq .36$ using $\alpha = .10$. Interpret the result.

Applying the Concepts—Basic

8.25 **Teacher perceptions of child behavior.** *Development Psychology* (Mar. 2003) published a study on teacher perceptions of the behavior of elementary school children. Teachers rated the aggressive behavior of a sample of 11,160 New York City public school children by responding to the statement, "This child threatens or bullies others in order to get his/her own way." Responses were measured on a scale ranging from 1 (*never*) to 5 (*always*). Summary statistics for the sample of 11,160 children were reported as $\bar{x} = 2.15$ and $s = 1.05$. Let μ represent the mean response for the population of all New York City public school children. Suppose you want to test $H_0: \mu = 3$ against $H_a: \mu \neq 3$.
  a. In the words of the problem, define a Type I error and a Type II error.
  b. Use the sample information to conduct the test at a significance level of $\alpha = .05$.
  c. Conduct the test, part **b**, using $\alpha = .10$.

8.26 **Latex allergy in healthcare workers.** Refer to the
NW *Current Allergy & Clinical Immunology* (March 2004) study of $n = 46$ hospital employees who were diagnosed with a latex allergy from exposure to the powder on latex gloves, Exercise 7.13 (p. 00). The number of latex gloves used per week by the sampled workers is summarized as follows: $\bar{x} = 19.3$ and $s = 11.9$. Let μ represent the mean number of latex gloves used per week by all hospital employees. Consider testing $H_0: \mu = 20$ against $H_a: \mu < 20$.
  a. Give the rejection region for the test at a significance level of $\alpha = .01$.
  b. Calculate the value of the test statistic.
  c. Use the results, parts **a** and **b**, to make the appropriate conclusion.

8.27 **Alkalinity of river water.** In Exercise 5.35 (p. 258) you learned that the mean alkalinity level of water specimens collected from the Han River in Seoul, Korea, is 50 milligrams per liter. (*Environmental Science & Engineering*, September 1, 2000.) Consider a random sample of 100 water specimens collected from a tributary of the Han River. Suppose the mean and standard deviation of the alkalinity levels for the sample are $\bar{x} = 67.8$ mpl and $s = 14.4$ mpl. Is there sufficient evidence (at $\alpha = .01$) to indicate that the population mean alkalinity level of water in the tributary exceeds 50 mpl?

8.28 Visual imagery of athletes. A group of St. Louis University researchers administered the Vividness of Visual Imagery Questionnaire (VVIQ) to a sample of 51 college students on varsity sports teams. (*American Statistical Association Joint Meetings*, August 1996.) The mean and standard deviation of the VVIQ scores were 65.60 and 19.38, respectively. Scores range from 16 to 80, with a lower score representing greater vividness. In the general population, the mean VVIQ score is 67. Conduct a test to determine whether the mean VVIQ score of college athletes is less than 67. Test using $\alpha = .01$.

Applying the Concepts—Intermediate

8.29 Post-traumatic stress of POWs. *Psychological Assessment* (March 1995) published the results of a study of World War II aviators who were captured by German forces after they were shot down. Having located a total of 239 World War II aviator POW survivors, the researchers asked each veteran to participate in the study; 33 responded to the letter of invitation. Each of the 33 POW survivors were administered the Minnesota Multiphasic Personality Inventory, one component of which measures level of post-traumatic stress disorder (PTSD). [*Note:* The higher the score, the higher the level of PTSD.] The aviators produced a mean PTSD score of $\bar{x} = 9.00$ and a standard deviation of $s = 9.32$.

  a. Set up the null and alternative hypotheses for determining whether the true mean PTSD score of all World War II aviator POWs is less than 16. [*Note:* The value, 16, represents the mean PTSD score established for Vietnam POWs.]

  b. Conduct the test, part **a**, using $\alpha = .10$. What are the practical implications of the test?

  c. Discuss the representativeness of the sample used in the study and its ramifications.

8.30 Point spreads of NFL games. During the National Football League (NFL) season, Las Vegas oddsmakers establish a point spread on each game for betting purposes. For example, the New England Patriots were established as 3-point favorites over the Carolina Panthers in the 2004 Super Bowl. The final scores of NFL games were compared against the final point spreads established by the oddsmakers in *Chance* (Fall 1998). The difference between the game outcome and point spread (called a point-spread error) was calculated for 240 NFL games. The mean and standard deviation of the point-spread errors are $\bar{x} = -1.6$ and $s = 13.3$. Use this information to test the hypothesis that the true mean point-spread error for all NFL games is 0. Conduct the test at $\alpha = .01$ and interpret the result.

8.31 Bone fossil study. Humerus bones from the same species of animal tend to have approximately the same length-to-width ratios. When fossils of humerus bones are discovered, archeologists can often determine the species of animal by examining the length-to-width ratios of the bones. It is known that species A exhibits a

mean ratio of 8.5. Suppose 41 fossils of humerus bones were unearthed at an archeological site in East Africa, where species A is believed to have lived. (Assume that the unearthed bones were all from the same unknown species.) The length-to-width ratios of the bones were calculated and listed, as shown in the table.

BONES

10.73	8.89	9.07	9.20	10.33	9.98	9.84	9.59
8.48	8.71	9.57	9.29	9.94	8.07	8.37	6.85
8.52	8.87	6.23	9.41	6.66	9.35	8.86	9.93
8.91	11.77	10.48	10.39	9.39	9.17	9.89	8.17
8.93	8.80	10.02	8.38	11.67	8.30	9.17	12.00
9.38							

  a. Test whether the population mean ratio of all bones of this particular species differs from 8.5. Use $\alpha = .01$.

  b. What are the practical implications of the test, part **a**?

8.32 Solder joint inspections. Current technology uses X-rays and lasers for inspection of solder-joint defects on printed circuit boards (PCBs). (*Quality Congress Transactions*, 1986.) A particular manufacturer of laser-based inspection equipment claims that its product can inspect on average at least 10 solder joints per second when the joints are spaced .1 inch apart. The equipment was tested by a potential buyer on 48 different PCBs. In each case, the equipment was operated for exactly 1 second. The number of solder joints inspected on each run follows:

PCB

10	9	10	10	11	9	12	8	8	9	6	10
7	10	11	9	9	13	9	10	11	10	12	8
9	9	9	7	12	6	9	10	10	8	7	9
11	12	10	0	10	11	12	9	7	9	9	10

  a. The potential buyer wants to know whether the sample data refute the manufacturer's claim. Specify the null and alternative hypotheses that the buyer should test.

  b. In the context of this exercise, what is a Type I error? A Type II error?

  c. Conduct the hypothesis test you described in part **a**, and interpret the test's results in the context of this exercise. Use $\alpha = .05$.

8.33 Salaries of postgraduates. The *Economics of Education Review* (Vol. 21, 2002) published a paper on the relationship between education level and earnings. The data for the research were obtained from the National Adult Literacy Survey of over 25,000 respondents. The survey revealed that males with a postgraduate degree had a mean salary of $61,340 (with standard error $s_{\bar{x}} = \$2,185$), while females with a postgraduate degree had a mean of $32,227 (with standard error $s_{\bar{x}} = \$932$).

  a. The article reports that a 95% confidence interval for μ_M, the population mean salary of all males with postgraduate degrees, is ($57,050, $65,631). Based on this interval, is there evidence to say that μ_M differs from $60,000? Explain.

b. Use the summary information to test the hypothesis that the true mean salary of males with postgraduate degrees differs from $60,000. Use $\alpha = .05$. (*Note:* $s_{\bar{x}} = s/\sqrt{n}$.)

c. Explain why the inferences in parts **a** and **b** agree.

d. The article reports that a 95% confidence interval for μ_F, the population mean salary of all females with postgraduate degrees, is ($30,396, $34,058). Based on this interval, is there evidence to say that μ_F differs from $33,000? Explain.

e. Use the summary information to test the hypothesis that the true mean salary of females with postgraduate degrees differs from $33,000. Use $\alpha = .05$. (*Note:* $s_{\bar{x}} = s/\sqrt{n}$.)

f. Explain why the inferences in parts **d** and **e** agree.

8.34 Cyanide in soil. *Environmental Science & Technology* (October 1993) reported on a study of contaminated soil in The Netherlands. Seventy-two 400-gram soil specimens were sampled, dried, and analyzed for the contaminant cyanide. The cyanide concentration [in milligrams per kilogram (mg/kg) of soil] of each soil specimen was determined using an infrared microscopic method. The sample resulted in a mean cyanide level of $\bar{x} = 84$ mg/kg and a standard deviation of $s = 80$ mg/kg.

a. Test the hypothesis that the true mean cyanide level in soil in The Netherlands exceeds 100 mg/kg. Use $\alpha = .10$.

b. Would you reach the same conclusion as in part **a** using $\alpha = .05$? Using $\alpha = .01$? Why can the conclusion of a test change when the value of α is changed?

Applying the Concepts—Advanced

8.35 Social interaction of mental patients. The *Community Mental Health Journal* (Aug. 2000) presented the results of a survey of over 6,000 clients of the Department of Mental Health and Addiction Services (DMHAS) in Connecticut. One of the many variables measured for each mental health patient was frequency of social interaction (on a 5-point scale, where 1 = very infrequently, 3 = occasionally, and 5 = very frequently). The 6,681 clients who were evaluated had a mean social interaction score of 2.95 with a standard deviation of 1.10.

a. Conduct a hypothesis test (at $\alpha = .01$) to determine if the true mean social interaction score of all Connecticut mental health patients differs from 3.

b. Examine the results of the study from a practical view, then discuss why "statistical significance" does not always imply "practical significance."

c. Because the variable of interest is measured on a 5-point scale, it is unlikely that the population of ratings will be normally distributed. Consequently, some analysts may perceive the test, part **a**, to be invalid and search for alternative methods of analysis. Defend or refute this position.

8.3 Observed Significance Levels: *p*-Values

According to the statistical test procedure described in Section 8.2, the rejection region and, correspondingly, the value of α are selected prior to conducting the test, and the conclusions are stated in terms of rejecting or not rejecting the null hypothesis. A second method of presenting the results of a statistical test is one that reports the extent to which the test statistic disagrees with the null hypothesis and leaves to the reader the task of deciding whether to reject the null hypothesis. This measure of disagreement is called the *observed significance level* (or *p-value*) for the test.

> **DEFINITION 8.1**
>
> The **observed significance level**, or ***p*-value**, for a specific statistical test is the probability (assuming H_0 is true) of observing a value of the test statistic that is at least as contradictory to the null hypothesis, and supportive of the alternative hypothesis, as the actual one computed from the sample data.

For example, the value of the test statistic computed for the sample of $n = 50$ sections of sewer pipe was $z = 2.12$. Since the test is one-tailed (i.e., the alternative (research) hypothesis of interest is $H_a: \mu > 2,400$) values of the test statistic even more contradictory to H_0 than the one observed would be values larger than $z = 2.12$. Therefore, the observed significance level (*p*-value) for this test is

$$p\text{-value} = P(z \geq 2.12)$$

Figure 8.6
Finding the p-Value for an
Upper-Tailed Test When
$z = 2.12$

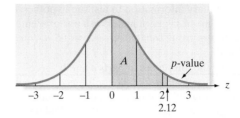

or, equivalently, the area under the standard normal curve to the right of $z = 2.12$ (see Figure 8.6).

The area A in Figure 8.6 is given in Table IV in Appendix A as .4830. Therefore, the upper-tail area corresponding to $z = 2.12$ is

$$p\text{-value} = .5 - .4830 = .0170$$

Consequently, we say that these test results are "statistically significant"; that is, they disagree (rather strongly) with the null hypothesis, $H_0: \mu = 2{,}400$, and favor $H_a: \mu > 2{,}400$. The probability of observing a z value as large as 2.12 is only .0170, if in fact the true value of μ is 2,400.

If you are inclined to select $\alpha = .05$ for this test, then you would reject the null hypothesis because the p-value for the test, .0170, is less than .05. In contrast, if you choose $\alpha = .01$, you would not reject the null hypothesis because the p-value for the test is larger than .01. Thus, the use of the observed significance level is identical to the test procedure described in the preceding sections except that the choice of α is left to you.

The steps for calculating the p-value corresponding to a test statistic for a population mean are given in the box.

Steps for Calculating the p-Value for a Test of Hypothesis

1. Determine the value of the test statistic z corresponding to the result of the sampling experiment.

2. **a.** If the test is one-tailed, the p-value is equal to the tail area beyond z in the same direction as the alternative hypothesis. Thus, if the alternative hypothesis is of the form $>$, the p-value is the area to the right of, or above, the observed z value. Conversely, if the alternative is of the form $<$, the p-value is the area to the left of, or below, the observed z value. (See Figure 8.7.)

   b. If the test is two-tailed, the p-value is equal to twice the tail area beyond the observed z value in the direction of the sign of z. That is, if z is positive, the p-value is twice the area to the right of, or above, the observed z value. Conversely, if z is negative, the p-value is twice the area to the left of, or below, the observed z value. (See Figure 8.8.)

Figure 8.7
Finding the p-Value for a
One-Tailed Test

a. Lower–tailed test, $H_a: \mu < \mu_0$ b. Upper–tailed test, $H_a: \mu > \mu_0$

Figure 8.8
Finding the *p*-Value
for a Two-Tailed Test:
p-Value = 2(*p*/2)

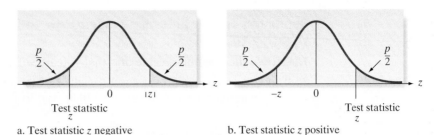

a. Test statistic *z* negative   b. Test statistic *z* positive

EXAMPLE 8.3

COMPUTING A *p*-VALUE

Problem   Find the observed significance level for the test of the mean response time for drug-injected rats in Examples 8.1 and 8.2.

Solution   Example 8.1 presented a two-tailed test of the hypothesis

$$H_0: \mu = 1.2 \text{ seconds}$$

against the alternative hypothesis

$$H_a: \mu \neq 1.2 \text{ seconds}$$

The observed value of the test statistic in Example 8.2 was $z = -3.0$, and any value of z less than -3.0 or greater than $+3.0$ (because this is a two-tailed test) would be even more contradictory to H_0. Therefore, the observed significance level for the test is

$$p\text{-value} = P(z < -3.0 \text{ or } z > +3.0)$$

Thus, we calculate the area below the observed z value, $z = -3.0$, and double it. Consulting Table IV in Appendix A, we find that $P(z < -3.0) = .5 - .4987 = .0013$. Therefore, the *p*-value for this two-tailed test is

$$2P(z < -3.0) = 2(.0013) = .0026$$

Look Back   We can interpret this *p*-value as a strong indication that the mean reaction time of drug-injected rats differs from the control mean ($\mu \neq 1.2$), since we would observe a test statistic this extreme or more extreme only 26 in 10,000 times if the drug-injected mean were equal to the control mean ($\mu = 1.2$). The extent to which the mean differs from 1.2 could be better determined by calculating a confidence interval for μ.

| Now Work | *Exercise 8.42*

■ ■ ■

When publishing the results of a statistical test of hypothesis in journals, case studies, reports, etc., many researchers make use of *p*-values. Instead of selecting a beforehand and then conducting a test, as outlined in this chapter, the researcher computes (usually with the aid of a statistical software package) and reports the value of the appropriate test statistic and its associated *p*-value. It is left to the reader of the report to judge the significance of the result (i.e., the reader must determine whether to reject the null hypothesis in favor of the alternative hypothesis, based on the reported *p*-value). Usually, the null hypothesis is rejected if the observed significance level is *less than* the fixed significance level, α, chosen by the reader. The inherent advantage of reporting test results in this manner is twofold: (1) Readers are permitted to select the maximum value of α that they would be willing to tolerate if they actually carried out a standard test of hypothesis in the manner outlined in this chapter, and (2) a measure of the degree of significance of the result (i.e., the *p*-value) is provided.

> ### Reporting Test Results as *p*-Values: How to Decide Whether to Reject H_0
>
> 1. Choose the maximum value of α that you are willing to tolerate.
> 2. If the observed significance level (*p*-value) of the test is less than the chosen value of α, reject the null hypothesis. Otherwise, do not reject the null hypothesis.

EXAMPLE 8.4   AN APPLICATION USING *p*-VALUES

Problem   The lengths of stay (in days) for 100 randomly selected hospital patients, first presented in Table 7.1, are reproduced in Table 8.3. Suppose we want to test the hypothesis that the true mean length of stay (LOS) at the hospital is less than 5 days, that is,

$$H_0: \mu = 5$$
$$H_a: \mu < 5$$

Assuming $\sigma = 3.68$, use the data in the table to conduct the test at $\alpha = .05$.

HOSPLOS

TABLE 8.3   Lengths of Stay for 100 Hospital Patients

2	3	8	6	4	4	6	4	2	5
8	10	4	4	4	2	1	3	2	10
1	3	2	3	4	3	5	2	4	1
2	9	1	7	17	9	9	9	4	4
1	1	1	3	1	6	3	3	2	5
1	3	3	14	2	3	9	6	6	3
5	1	4	6	11	22	1	9	6	5
2	2	5	4	3	6	1	5	1	6
17	1	2	4	5	4	4	3	2	3
3	5	2	3	3	2	10	2	4	2

Solution   The data were entered into a computer and MINITAB was used to conduct the analysis. The MINITAB printout for the lower-tailed test is displayed in Figure 8.9. Both the test statistic, $z = -1.28$, and *p*-value of the test, $p = .101$, are highlighted on the MINITAB printout. Since the *p*-value exceeds our selected α value, $\alpha = .05$, we cannot reject the null hypothesis. Hence, there is insufficient evidence (at $\alpha = .05$) to conclude that the true mean LOS at the hospital is less than 5 days.

Now Work   *Exercise 8.49*

■ ■ ■

Note: Some statistical software packages (e.g., SPSS) will conduct only two-tailed tests of hypothesis. For these packages, you obtain the *p*-value for a one-tailed test as shown in the box on p. 388.

Figure 8.9

MINITAB Printout for the Lower-Tailed Test in Example 8.4

```
Test of mu = 5 vs < 5
The assumed standard deviation = 3.68


                                          95%
                                        Upper
Variable    N      Mean     StDev   SE Mean    Bound      Z       P
LOS       100   4.53000   3.67755   0.36800  5.13531  -1.28   0.101
```

Hypothesis Testing

Using the TI-83 Graphing Calculator

Computing the *p*-value for a *z*-Test

Step 1   *Access the Statistical Tests Menu.*
Press **STAT**
Arrow right to **TESTS**
Press **ENTER** to select **Z-Test**

Step 2   *Choose "**Data**" or "**Stats**." ("Data" is selected when you have entered the raw data into a List. "Stats" is selected when you are given only the mean, standard deviation, and sample size.)*
Press **ENTER**

If you selected "Data," enter the values for the hypothesis test where μ_0 = the value for μ in the null hypothesis, σ = assumed value of the population standard deviation.
Set **List** to **L1**
Set **Freq** to **1**
Use the arrow to highlight the appropriate alternative hypothesis.
Press **ENTER**
Arrow down to "**Calculate**"
Press **ENTER**

If you selected "Stats," enter the values for the hypothesis test where μ_0 = the value for μ in the null hypothesis, σ = assumed value of the population standard deviation.
Enter the sample mean and sample size.
Arrow down to "**Calculate**"
Press **ENTER**

The chosen test will be displayed as well as the *z*-test statistic, the *p*-value, the sample mean, and the sample size.

Example   A manufacturer claims the average life expectancy of this particular model light bulb is at least 10,000 hours with σ = 1,000 hours. A simple random sample of 40 light bulbs shows a sample mean of 9755 hours. Using α = .05, test the manufacturer's claim.

For this problem the hypotheses will be:

$$H_0: \mu \geq 10{,}000$$
$$H_a: \mu < 10{,}000$$

The screens are shown below:

 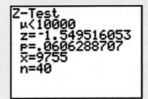

As you can see the *p*-value is 0.061. Since $p > .05$, ***do not*** reject H_0.

Converting a Two-Tailed p-Value from a Printout to a One-Tailed p-Value:

$$p = \frac{\text{Reported } p\text{-value}}{2} \quad \text{if} \begin{cases} H_a \text{ is of form} & > \quad \text{and } z \text{ is positive} \\ H_a \text{ is of form} & < \quad \text{and } z \text{ is negative} \end{cases}$$

$$p = 1 - \left(\frac{\text{Reported } p\text{-value}}{2} \right) \quad \text{if} \begin{cases} H_a \text{ is of form} & > \quad \text{and } z \text{ is negative} \\ H_a \text{ is of form} & < \quad \text{and } z \text{ is positive} \end{cases}$$

Statistics in Action Revisited

Testing a Population Mean in the KLEENEX® Survey

Refer to Kimberly-Clark Corporation's survey of 250 people who kept a count of their use of KLEENEX® tissues in diaries (p. 375). We want to test the claim made by marketing experts that $\mu = 60$ is the average number of tissues used by people with colds against our belief that the population mean is smaller than 60 tissues. That is, we want to test

$$H_0: \mu = 60 \qquad H_a: \mu < 60$$

We will select $\alpha = .05$ as the level of significance for the test.

The survey results for the 250 sampled KLEENEX® users are stored in the **TISSUES** data file. A MINITAB analysis of the data yielded the printout displayed in Figure SIA8.1.

The observed significance level of the test, highlighted on the printout, is p-value $= .018$. Since this p-value is less than $\alpha = .05$, we have sufficient evidence to reject H_0; therefore, we conclude that the mean number of tissues used by a person with a cold is less than 60 tissues. [*Note*: If we conduct the same test using $\alpha = .01$ as the level of significance, we would have insufficient evidence to reject H_0 since p-value $= .018$ is greater than $\alpha = .01$. Thus, at $\alpha = .01$, there is no evidence to support our alternative that the population mean is less than 60.]

```
Test of mu = 60 vs < 60


                                                95%
                                               Upper
Variable     N     Mean     StDev   SE Mean    Bound       T       P
NUMUSED    250   56.6760   25.0343   1.5833   59.2900   -2.10   0.018
```

Figure SIA8.1
MINITAB Test of $\mu = 60$ for KLEENEX® Survey

Exercises 8.36–8.52

Understanding the Principles

8.36 How does the observed significance level (p-value) of a test differ from the value of α?

8.37 In general, do large p-values or small p-values support the alternative hypothesis, H_a?

8.38 If a hypothesis test were conducted using $\alpha = .05$, for which of the following p-values would the null hypothesis be rejected?
a. .06   b. .10
c. .01   d. .001
e. .251   f. .042

8.39 For each α and observed significance level (p-value) pair, indicate whether the null hypothesis would be rejected.
a. $\alpha = .05$, p-value $= .10$
b. $\alpha = .10$, p-value $= .05$
c. $\alpha = .01$, p-value $= .001$
d. $\alpha = .025$, p-value $= .05$
e. $\alpha = .10$, p-value $= .45$

Learning the Mechanics

8.40 An analyst tested the null hypothesis $\mu \geq 20$ against the alternative hypothesis $\mu < 20$. The analyst reported a *p*-value of .06. What is the smallest value of α for which the null hypothesis would be rejected?

8.41 In a test of $H_0: \mu = 100$ against $H_a: \mu > 100$, the sample data yielded the test statistic $z = 2.17$. Find the *p*-value for the test.

8.42 In a test of $H_0: \mu = 100$ against $H_a: \mu \neq 100$, the sample
NW data yielded the test statistic $z = 2.17$. Find the *p*-value for the test.

8.43 In a test of the hypothesis $H_0: \mu = 50$ versus $H_a: \mu > 50$, a sample of $n = 100$ observations possessed mean $\bar{x} = 49.4$ and standard deviation $s = 4.1$. Find and interpret the *p*-value for this test.

8.44 In a test of the hypothesis $H_0: \mu = 10$ versus $H_a: \mu \neq 10$, a sample of $n = 50$ observations possessed mean $\bar{x} = 10.7$ and standard deviation $s = 3.1$. Find and interpret the *p*-value for this test.

8.45 Consider a test of $H_0: \mu = 75$ performed using the computer. SPSS reports a two-tailed *p*-value of .1032. Make the appropriate conclusion for each of the following situations:
  a. $H_a: \mu < 75, z = -1.63, \alpha = .05$
  b. $H_a: \mu < 75, z = 1.63, \alpha = .10$
  c. $H_a: \mu > 75, z = 1.63, \alpha = .10$
  d. $H_a: \mu \neq 75, z = -1.63, \alpha = .01$

Applying the Concepts—Basic

8.46 **Teacher perceptions of child behavior.** Refer to the *Development Psychology* (Mar. 2003) study on the aggressive behavior of elementary school children, Exercise 8.25 (p. 381). Recall that you tested $H_0: \mu = 3$ against $H_a: \mu \neq 3$, where μ is the mean level of aggressiveness for the population of all New York City public school children as perceived by their teachers, based on the summary statistics: $n = 11,160, \bar{x} = 2.15,$ and $s = 1.05$.
  a. Compute the *p*-value of the test.
  b. Compare the *p*-value to $\alpha = .10$ and make the appropriate conclusion.

8.47 **Latex allergy in healthcare workers.** Refer to the *Current Allergy & Clinical Immunology* (March 2004) study of latex allergy in healthcare workers, Exercise

8.26 (p. 381). Recall that you tested $H_0: \mu = 20$ against $H_a: \mu < 20$, where μ is the mean number of latex gloves used per week by all hospital employees, based on the summary statistics: $n = 46, \bar{x} = 19.3$ and $s = 11.9$.
  a. Compute the *p*-value of the test.
  b. Compare the *p*-value to $\alpha = .01$ and make the appropriate conclusion.

8.48 **Post-traumatic stress of POWs.** Refer to the *Psychological Assessment* study of World War II aviator POWs, Exercise 8.29 (p. 382). You tested whether the true mean post-traumatic stress disorder score of World War II aviator POWs is less than 16. Recall that $\bar{x} = 9.00$ and $s = 9.32$ for a sample of $n = 33$ POWs.
  a. Compute the *p*-value of the test.
  b. Refer to part **a**. Would the *p*-value have been larger or smaller if $\bar{x}$ had been larger? Explain.

8.49 **Bone fossil study.** In Exercise 8.31 (p. 382), you tested
NW $H_0: \mu = 8.5$ versus $H_a: \mu \neq 8.5$, where μ is the population mean length-to-width ratio of humerus bones of a particular species of animal. An SAS printout for the hypothesis test is provided below. Locate the *p*-value on the printout and interpret its value.

Applying the Concepts—Intermediate

8.50 **Colored string preferred by chickens.** Refer to the *Applied Animal Behaviour Science* (October 2000) study of domestic chickens exposed to a pecking stimulus, Exercise 7.17 (p. 331). Recall that the average number of pecks a chicken takes at a white string over a specified time interval is known to be $\mu = 7.5$ pecks. In an experiment where 72 chickens were exposed to blue string, the average number of pecks was $\bar{x} = 1.13$ pecks, with a standard deviation of $s = 2.21$ pecks.
  a. On average, are chickens more apt to peck at white string than at blue string? Conduct the appropriate test of hypothesis using $\alpha = .05$.
  b. Compare your answer to part **a** with your answer to Exercise 7.17**b**.
  c. Find the *p*-value for the test and interpret its value.

8.51 **Feminizing human faces.** Research published in *Nature* (August 27, 1998) revealed that people are more attracted

SAS Printout for Exercise 8.49

```
Sample Statistics for LWRATIO

     N          Mean        Std. Dev.      Std. Error
--------------------------------------------------------
     41         9.26          1.20            0.19

Hypothesis Test

    Null hypothesis:    Mean of LWRATIO =  8.5
    Alternative:        Mean of LWRATIO ^= 8.5

With a specified known standard deviation of 1.2

          Z Statistic        Prob > Z
          -----------        --------
            4.042             <.0001
```

to "feminized" faces, regardless of gender. In one experiment, 50 human subjects viewed both a Japanese female and Caucasian male face on a computer. Using special computer graphics, each subject could morph the faces (by making them more feminine or more masculine) until they attained the "most attractive" face. The level of feminization x (measured as a percentage) was measured.

a. For the Japanese female face, $\bar{x} = 10.2\%$ and $s = 31.3\%$. The researchers used this sample information to test the null hypothesis of a mean level of feminization equal to 0%. Verify that the test statistic is equal to 2.3.

b. Refer to part **a**. The researchers reported the p-value of the test as $p \approx .02$. Verify and interpret this result.

c. For the Caucasian male face, $\bar{x} = 15.0\%$ and $s = 25.1\%$. The researchers reported the test statistic (for the test of the null hypothesis stated in part **a**) as 4.23 with an associated p-value of approximately 0. Verify and interpret these results.

8.52 Ages of cable TV shoppers. In a paper presented at the 2000 Conference of the International Association for Time Use Research, professor Margaret Sanik of Ohio State University reported the results of her study on American cable TV viewers who purchase items from one of the home shopping channels. She found that the average age of these cable TV shoppers was 51 years. Suppose you want to test the null hypothesis, $H_0: \mu = 51$, using a sample of $n = 50$ cable TV shoppers.

a. Find the p-value of a two-tailed test if $\bar{x} = 52.3$ and $s = 7.1$.

b. Find the p-value of an upper-tailed test if $\bar{x} = 52.3$ and $s = 7.1$.

c. Find the p-value of a two-tailed test if $\bar{x} = 52.3$ and $s = 10.4$.

d. For each of the tests, parts **a–c**, give a value of α that will lead to a rejection of the null hypothesis.

e. If $\bar{x} = 52.3$, give a value of s that will yield a p-value of .01 or less.

8.4 Small-Sample Test of Hypothesis about a Population Mean

Most water-treatment facilities monitor the quality of their drinking water on an hourly basis. One variable monitored is pH, which measures the degree of alkalinity or acidity in the water. A pH below 7.0 is acidic, one above 7.0 is alkaline, and a pH of 7.0 is neutral. One water-treatment plant has a target pH of 8.5 (most try to maintain a slightly alkaline level). The mean and standard deviation of 1 hour's test results, based on 17 water samples at this plant, are

$$\bar{x} = 8.42 \qquad s = .16$$

Does this sample provide sufficient evidence that the mean pH level in the water differs from 8.5?

This inference can be placed in a test of hypothesis framework. We establish the target pH as the null hypothesized value and then utilize a two-tailed alternative that the true mean pH differs from the target:

$$H_0: \mu = 8.5$$
$$H_a: \mu \neq 8.5$$

Recall from Section 7.3 that when we are faced with making inferences about a population mean using the information in a small sample, two problems emerge:

1. The normality of the sampling distribution for $\bar{x}$ does not follow from the Central Limit Theorem when the sample size is small. We must assume that the distribution of measurements from which the sample was selected is approximately normally distributed in order to ensure the approximate normality of the sampling distribution of $\bar{x}$.

2. If the population standard deviation σ is unknown, as is usually the case, then we cannot assume that s will provide a good approximation for σ when the sample size is small. Instead, we must use the t-distribution rather than the standard normal z-distribution to make inferences about the population mean μ.

Therefore, as the test statistic of a small-sample test of a population mean, we use the t-statistic:

$$Test\ statistic: t = \frac{\bar{x} - \mu_0}{s/\sqrt{n}} = \frac{\bar{x} - 8.5}{s/\sqrt{n}}$$

Figure 8.10

Two-Tailed Rejection Region for Small-Sample t-Test

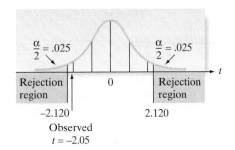

where μ_0 is the null hypothesized value of the population mean, μ. In our example, $\mu_0 = 8.5$.

To find the rejection region, we must specify the value of α, the probability that the test will lead to rejection of the null hypothesis when it is true, and then consult the t table (Table VI of Appendix A). Using $\alpha = .05$, the two-tailed rejection region is

$$Rejection\ region: t_{\alpha/2} = t_{.025} = 2.120 \text{ with } n - 1 = 16 \text{ degrees of freedom}$$

$$\text{Reject } H_0 \text{ if } t < -2.120 \text{ or } t > 2.120$$

The rejection region is shown in Figure 8.10.

We are now prepared to calculate the test statistic and reach a conclusion:

$$t = \frac{\bar{x} - \mu_0}{s/\sqrt{n}} = \frac{8.42 - 8.50}{.16/\sqrt{17}} = \frac{-.08}{.039} = -2.05$$

Since the calculated value of t does not fall in the rejection region (Figure 8.10), we cannot reject H_0 at the $\alpha = .05$ level of significance. Thus, the water-treatment plant should not conclude that the mean pH differs from the 8.5 target based on the sample evidence.

It is interesting to note that the calculated t value, -2.05, is *less than* the .05 level z value, -1.96. The implication is that if we had *incorrectly* used a z statistic for this test, we would have rejected the null hypothesis at the .05 level, concluding that the mean pH level differs from 8.5. The important point is that the statistical procedure to be used must always be closely scrutinized and all the assumptions understood. Many statistical lies are the result of misapplications of otherwise valid procedures.

The technique for conducting a small-sample test of hypothesis about a population mean is summarized in the following boxes.

Small-Sample Test of Hypothesis About μ

One-Tailed Test	**Two-Tailed Test**
H_0: $\mu = \mu_0$	H_0: $\mu = \mu_0$
H_a: $\mu < \mu_0$ (or H_a: $\mu > \mu_0$)	H_a: $\mu \neq \mu_0$
Test statistic: $t = \dfrac{\bar{x} - \mu_0}{s/\sqrt{n}}$	Test statistic: $t = \dfrac{\bar{x} - \mu_0}{s/\sqrt{n}}$
Rejection region: $t < -t_\alpha$ (or $t > t_\alpha$ when H_a: $\mu > \mu_0$)	Rejection region: $t < -t_{\alpha/2}$ or $t > t_{\alpha/2}$

where t_α and $t_{\alpha/2}$ are based on $(n - 1)$ degrees of freedom

---

Conditions Required for a Valid Small-Sample Hypothesis Test for μ

1. A random sample is selected from the target population.

2. The population from which the sample is selected has a distribution that is approximately normal.

EXAMPLE 8.5 CONDUCTING A SMALL-SAMPLE TEST FOR μ

Problem A major car manufacturer wants to test a new engine to determine whether it meets new air-pollution standards. The mean emission μ of all engines of this type must be less than 20 parts per million of carbon. Ten engines are manufactured for testing purposes, and the emission level of each is determined. The data (in parts per million) are listed in Table 8.4.

⊙ **EMISSIONS**

TABLE 8.4   Emission Levels for Ten Engines

15.6	16.2	22.5	20.5	16.4	19.4	19.6	17.9	12.7	14.9

Do the data supply sufficient evidence to allow the manufacturer to conclude that this type of engine meets the pollution standard? Assume that the manufacturer is willing to risk a Type I error with probability $\alpha = .01$.

Solution The manufacturer wants to support the research hypothesis that the mean emission level μ for all engines of this type is less than 20 parts per million. The elements of this small-sample one-tailed test are

$$H_0: \mu = 20$$
$$H_a: \mu < 20$$

$$\text{Test statistic: } t = \frac{\bar{x} - 20}{s/\sqrt{n}}$$

Rejection region: For $\alpha = .01$ and df $= n - 1 = 9$, the one-tailed rejection region (see Figure 8.11) is $t < -t_{.01} = -2.821$.

Assumption: The relative frequency distribution of the population of emission levels for all engines of this type is approximately normal. Based on the shape of the MINITAB stem-and-leaf display of the data shown in Figure 8.12, this assumption appears to be reasonably satisfied.

To calculate the test statistic, we analyzed the **EMISSIONS** data using MINITAB. The MINITAB printout is shown at the bottom of Figure 8.12. From the printout, we obtain $\bar{x} = 17.57$ and $s = 2.95$. Substituting these values into the test statistic formula, we get (rounding)

$$t = \frac{\bar{x} - 20}{s/\sqrt{n}} = \frac{17.57 - 20}{2.95/\sqrt{10}} = -2.60$$

Since the calculated t falls outside the rejection region (see Figure 8.11), the manufacturer cannot reject H_0. There is insufficient evidence to conclude that $\mu < 20$ parts per million and the new engine type meets the pollution standard.

Figure 8.11
A t-Distribution with 9 df and the Rejection Region for Example 8.5

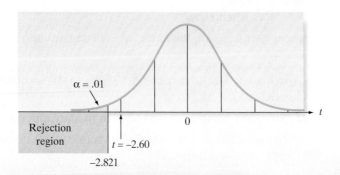

Figure 8.12
MINITAB Analysis of 10
Emission Levels, Example 8.5

Stem-and-Leaf Display: E-LEVEL

```
Stem-and-leaf of E-LEVEL  N  = 10
Leaf Unit = 1.0


   1    1   2
   3    1   45
  (3)   1   667
   4    1   99
   2    2   0
   1    2   2
```

One-Sample T: E-LEVEL

```
Test of mu = 20 vs < 20


                                             95%
                                           Upper
   Variable   N     Mean   StDev  SE Mean   Bound      T      P
   E-LEVEL   10  17.5700  2.9522   0.9336  19.2814  -2.60  0.014
```

Look Back Are you satisfied with the reliability associated with this inference? The probability is only $\alpha = .01$ that the test would support the research hypothesis if in fact it were false.

Now Work *Exercise 8.59a,b*

■ ■ ■

EXAMPLE 8.6

THE p-VALUE FOR A SMALL-SAMPLE TEST OF μ

Problem Find the observed significance level for the test described in Example 8.5. Interpret the result.

Solution The test of Example 8.5 was a lower-tailed test: H_0: $\mu = 20$ versus H_a: $\mu < 20$. Since the value of t computed from the sample data was $t = -2.60$, the observed significance level (or p-value) for the test is equal to the probability that t would assume a value less than or equal to -2.60 if in fact H_0 were true. This is equal to the area in the lower tail of the t-distribution (highlighted in Figure 8.13).

One way to find this area (i.e., the p-value for the test) is to consult the t-table (Table VI in Appendix A). Unlike the table of areas under the normal curve, Table VI gives only the t values corresponding to the areas .100, .050, .025, .010, .005, .001, and .0005. Therefore, we can only approximate the p-value for the test. Since the observed t value was based on 9 degrees of freedom, we use the df = 9 row in Table VI

Figure 8.13
The Observed Significance
Level for the Test of
Example 8.5

and move across the row until we reach the t values that are closest to the observed $t = -3.00$. [*Note:* We ignore the minus sign.] The t values corresponding to p-values of .010 and .005 are 2.821 and 3.250, respectively. Since the observed t value falls between $t_{.010}$ and $t_{.005}$, the p-value for the test lies between .005 and .010. In other words, $.005 < p\text{-value} < .01$. Thus, we would reject the null hypothesis, $H_0: \mu = 20$ parts per million, for any value of α larger than .01 (the upper bound of the p-value).

A second, more accurate, way to obtain the p-value is to use a statistical software package to conduct the test of hypothesis. Both the test statistic (-2.60) and p-value $(.014)$ are highlighted on the MINITAB printout, Figure. 8.12.

You can see that the actual p-value of the test falls within the bounds obtained from Table VI. Thus, the two methods agree; we will reject $H_0: \mu = 20$ in favor of $H_a: \mu < 20$ for any α level larger than .01.

Now Work   *Exercise 8.59c*

■ ■ ■

Small-sample inferences typically require more assumptions and provide less information about the population parameter than do large-sample inferences. Nevertheless, the t-test is a method of testing a hypothesis about a population mean of a normal distribution when only a small number of observations is available.

What Can Be Done If the Population Relative Frequency Distribution Departs Greatly from Normal?

Answer: Use one of the nonparametric statistical methods of Chapter 14.

Exercises 8.53–8.70

Understanding the Principles

8.53 Under what circumstances should you use the t-distribution in testing a hypothesis about a population mean?

8.54 In what ways are the distributions of the z-statistic and t-statistic alike? How do they differ?

Learning the Mechanics

8.55 For each of the following rejection regions, sketch the sampling distribution of t, and indicate the location of the rejection region on your sketch:
 a. $t > 1.440$ where df $= 6$
 b. $t < -1.782$ where df $= 12$
 c. $t < -2.060$ or $t > 2.060$ where df $= 25$

8.56 For each of the rejection regions defined in Exercise 8.55, what is the probability that a Type I error will be made?

8.57 A random sample of n observations is selected from a normal population to test the null hypothesis that $\mu = 10$. Specify the rejection region for each of the following combinations of H_a, α, and n:
 a. $H_a: \mu \neq 10; \alpha = .05; n = 14$
 b. $H_a: \mu > 10; \alpha = .01; n = 24$
 c. $H_a: \mu > 10; \alpha = .10; n = 9$
 d. $H_a: \mu < 10; \alpha = .01; n = 12$
 e. $H_a: \mu \neq 10; \alpha = .10; n = 20$
 f. $H_a: \mu < 10; \alpha = .05; n = 4$

8.58 The following sample of six measurements was randomly selected from a normally distributed population: $1, 3, -1, 5, 1, 2$.
 a. Test the null hypothesis that the mean of the population is 3 against the alternative hypothesis, $\mu < 3$. Use $\alpha = .05$.
 b. Test the null hypothesis that the mean of the population is 3 against the alternative hypothesis, $\mu \neq 3$. Use $\alpha = .05$.
 c. Find the observed significance level for each test.

8.59 A sample of five measurements, randomly selected from a normally distributed population, resulted in the following summary statistics: $\bar{x} = 4.8$, $s = 1.3$.
 a. Test the null hypothesis that the mean of the population is 6 against the alternative hypothesis, $\mu < 6$. Use $\alpha = .05$.
 b. Test the null hypothesis that the mean of the population is 6 against the alternative hypothesis, $\mu \neq 6$. Use $\alpha = .05$.
 c. Find the observed significance level for each test.

8.60 Suppose you conduct a t-test for the null hypothesis $H_0: \mu = 1{,}000$ versus the alternative hypothesis $H_a: \mu > 1{,}000$ based on a sample of 17 observations. The test results are $t = 1.89$, p-value $= .038$.
 a. What assumptions are necessary for the validity of this procedure?
 b. Interpret the results of the test.

Descriptive Statistics

	N	Minimum	Maximum	Mean	Std. Deviation
BOOKS	14	16	53	31.64	10.485
Valid N (listwise)	14				

c. Suppose the alternative hypothesis had been the two-tailed H_a: $\mu \neq 1,000$. If the t-statistic were unchanged, what would the p-value be for this test? Interpret the p-value for the two-tailed test.

Applying the Concepts—Basic

8.61 A new dental bonding agent. When bonding teeth, orthodontists must maintain a dry field. A new bonding adhesive (called "Smartbond") has been developed to eliminate the necessity of a dry field. However, there is concern that the new bonding adhesive is not as strong as the current standard, a composite adhesive. (*Trends in Biomaterials & Artificial Organs*, January 2003.) Tests on a sample of 10 extracted teeth bonded with the new adhesive resulted in a mean breaking strength (after 24 hours) of $\bar{x} = 5.07$ Mpa and a standard deviation of $s = .46$ Mpa. Where Mpa = Mega pascal, a measure of force per area. Orthodontists want to know if the true mean breaking strength of the new bonding adhesive is less than 5.70 Mpa, the mean breaking strength of the composite adhesive.

a. Set up the null and alternative hypothesis for the test.

b. Find the rejection region for the test using $\alpha = .01$.

c. Compute the test statistic.

d. Give the appropriate conclusion for the test.

e. What conditions are required for the test results to be valid?

🔘 JAPANESE

8.62 Reading Japanese books. Refer to the *Reading in a Foreign Language* (April 2004) experiment to improve the Japanese reading comprehension levels of University of Hawaii students, Exercise 2.31 (p. 51). Recall that 14 students participated in a 10-week extensive reading program in a second-semester Japanese course. The data on number of books read by each student are saved in the **JAPANESE** file. An SPSS printout giving descriptive statistics for the data is shown above.

a. Give the null and alternative hypothesis for determining whether the average number of books read by all students who participate in the extensive reading program exceeds 25.

b. Find the rejection region for the test using $\alpha = .05$.

c. Compute the test statistic.

d. Give the appropriate conclusion for the test.

e. What conditions are required for the test results to be valid?

8.63 Dental anxiety study. Refer to the *Psychological Reports* (August 1997) study of college students who completed the Dental Anxiety Scale, Exercise 5.34 (p. 258). Recall that scores range from 0 (no anxiety) to 20 (extreme anxiety). Summary statistics for the scores of the 27 students who completed the questionnaire follow: $\bar{x} = 10.7$, $s = 3.6$. Conduct a test of hypothesis to determine if the mean Dental Anxiety Scale score for the population of college students differs from $\mu = 11$. Use $\alpha = .05$.

8.64 Temperature of iron castings. The Cleveland Casting Plant produces iron automotive castings for Ford Motor Company. When the process is stable, the target pouring temperature of the molten iron is 2,550 degrees. (*Quality Engineering*, Vol. 7, 1995.) The pouring temperatures (in degrees Fahrenheit) for a random sample of 10 crankshafts produced at the plant are listed in the table. Use the SAS printout below to conduct a test to determine

```
Sample Statistics for IRONTEMP

     N           Mean        Std. Dev.      Std. Error
   ---------------------------------------------------
     10        2558.70         22.75           7.19

Hypothesis Test

     Null hypothesis:    Mean of IRONTEMP =  2550
     Alternative:        Mean of IRONTEMP ^= 2550

          t Statistic       Df        Prob > t
          ------------------------------------
             1.210           9          0.2573
```

whether the true mean pouring temperature differs from the target setting. Test using $\alpha = .01$.

IRONTEMP

2,543	2,541	2,544	2,620	2,560	2,559	2,562
2,553	2,552	2,553				

Source: Price, B., & Barth, B. "A structural model relating process inputs and final product characteristics." *Quality Engineering,* Vol. 7, No. 4, 1995, p. 696 (Table 2).

Applying the Concepts—Intermediate

LICHEN

8.65 Radioactive lichen. Refer to the 2003 Lichen Radionu-clide Baseline Research project to monitor the level of radioactivity in lichen, Exercise 7.33 (p. 340). Recall that University of Alaska researchers collected 9 lichen spec-imens and measured the amount of the radioactive ele-ment cesium-137 (in microcuries per milliliter) in each specimen. (The natural logarithms of the data values are saved in the **LICHEN** file.) Assume that in previous years the mean cesium amount in lichen was $\mu = .003$ microcuries per milliliter. Is there sufficient evidence to indicate that the mean amount of cesium in lichen specimens differs from this value? Use the MINITAB printout below to conduct a complete test of hypothesis at $\alpha = .10$.

8.66 Testing a mosquito repellent. A study was conducted to evaluate the effectiveness of a new mosquito repellent designed by the U.S. Army to be applied as camouflage face paint. (*Journal of the Mosquito Control Association,* June 1995.) The repellent was applied to the forearms of 5 volunteers and then they were exposed to 15 active mosquitos for a 10-hour period. The percentage of the forearm surface area protected from bites (called percent repellency) was calculated for each of the five

volunteers. For one color of paint (loam), the following summary statistics were obtained:

$$\bar{x} = 83\% \quad s = 15\%$$

a. The new repellent is considered effective if it pro-vides a percent repellency of at least 95. Conduct a test to determine whether the mean repellency per-centage of the new mosquito repellent is less than 95. Test using $\alpha = .10$.
b. What assumptions are required for the hypothesis test in part **a** to be valid?

8.67 Cracks in highway pavement. The Mississippi Depart-ment of Transportation collected data on the number of cracks (called *crack intensity*) in an undivided two-lane highway using van-mounted state-of-the-art video tech-nology. (*Journal of Infrastructure Systems,* March 1995.) The mean number of cracks found in a sample of eight 50-meter sections of the highway was $\bar{x} = .210$, with a variance of $s^2 = .011$. Suppose the American Associa-tion of State Highway and Transportation Officials (AASHTO) recommends a maximum mean crack in-tensity of .100 for safety purposes. Test the hypothesis that the true mean crack intensity of the Mississippi highway exceeds the AASHTO recommended maxi-mum. Use $\alpha = .01$.

8.68 Mongolian desert ants. Refer to the *Journal of Biogeog-raphy* (December 2003) study of ants in Mongolia (Cen-tral Asia), Exercise 2.66 (p. 66). Recall that botanists placed seed baits at 11 study sites and observed the num-ber of ant species attracted to each site. A portion of the data is provided in the table on p. 397. Do these data indicate that the average number of ant species at Mon-golian desert sites differs from 5 species? Conduct the appropriate test at $\alpha = .05$. Are the conditions required for a valid test satisfied?

MINITAB Printout for Exercise 8.65

Stem-and-Leaf Display: CESIUM

```
Stem-and-leaf of CESIUM   N  = 9
Leaf Unit = 0.0010

   1    0  2
   2    0  4
  (3)   0  667
   4    0
   4    1  01
   2    1
   2    1  5
   1    1  6
```

One-Sample T: CESIUM

```
Test of mu = 0.003 vs not = 0.003

Variable  N     Mean     StDev    SE Mean        95% CI          T      P
CESIUM    9   0.009027  0.004854  0.001618  (0.005296, 0.012759)  3.72  0.006
```

GOBIANTS

Site	Region	Number of Ant Species
1	Dry Steppe	3
2	Dry Steppe	3
3	Dry Steppe	52
4	Dry Steppe	7
5	Dry Steppe	5
6	Gobi Desert	49
7	Gobi Desert	5
8	Gobi Desert	4
9	Gobi Desert	4
10	Gobi Desert	5
11	Gobi Desert	4

Source: Pfeiffer, M., et al. "Community organization and species richness of ants in Mongolia along an ecological gradient from steppe to Gobi desert," *Journal of Biogeography,* Vol. 30, No. 12, Dec. 2003.

8.69 Head trauma study. The SCL-90-R is a 90-item symptom inventory checklist designed to reflect the psychological status of an individual. Each symptom (e.g., obsessive-compulsive behavior) is scored on a scale of 0 (none) to 4 (extreme). The total of these scores yields an individual's Positive Symptom Total (PST). "Normal" individuals are known to have a mean PST of about 40. The *Journal of Head Trauma Rehabilitation* (April 1995) reported that a sample of 23 patients diagnosed with mild to moderate traumatic brain injury had a mean PST score of $\bar{x} = 48.43$ and a standard deviation of $s = 20.76$. Is there sufficient evidence to claim that the true mean PST score of all patients with mild to moderate traumatic brain injury exceeds the "normal" value of 40? Test using $\alpha = .05$.

Applying the Concepts—Advanced

8.70 Lengths of great white sharks. One of the most feared predators in the ocean is the great white shark. It is known that the white shark grows to a mean length of 21 feet; however, one marine biologist believes that great white sharks off the Bermuda coast grow much longer owing to unusual feeding habits. To test this claim, some full-grown great white sharks were captured off the Bermuda coast, measured, and then set free. However, because the capture of sharks is difficult, costly, and very dangerous, only three specimens were sampled. Their lengths were 24, 20, and 22 feet. Do these data support the marine biologist's claim?

8.5 Large-Sample Test of Hypothesis about a Population Proportion

Inferences about population proportions (or percentages) are often made in the context of the probability, p, of "success" for a binomial distribution. We saw how to use large samples from binomial distributions to form confidence intervals for p in Section 7.4. We now consider tests of hypotheses about p.

Consider, for example, a method currently used by doctors to screen women for possible breast cancer. The method fails to detect cancer in 20% of the women who actually have the disease. Suppose a new method has been developed that researchers hope will detect cancer more accurately. This new method was used to screen a random sample of 140 women known to have breast cancer. Of these, the new method failed to detect cancer in 12 women. Does this sample provide evidence that the failure rate of the new method differs from the one currently in use?

We first view this as a binomial experiment with 140 screened women as the trials and failure to detect breast cancer as "Success" (in binomial terminology). Let p represent the probability that the new method fails to detect the breast cancer. If the new method is no better than the current one, then the failure rate is $p = .2$. On the other hand, if the new method is either better or worse than the current method, then the failure rate is either smaller or larger than 20%; that is, $p \neq .2$.

We can now place the problem in the context of a test of hypothesis:

$$H_0: p = .2$$
$$H_a: p \neq .2$$

Recall that the sample proportion, $\hat{p}$, is really just the sample mean of the outcomes of the individual binomial trials and, as such, is approximately normally distributed (for large samples) according to the Central Limit Theorem. Thus, for large samples we can use the standard normal z as the test statistic:

$$\text{Test statistic:} \quad z = \frac{\text{Sample proportion} - \text{Null hypothesized proportion}}{\text{Standard deviation of sample proportion}}$$
$$= \frac{\hat{p} - p_0}{\sigma_{\hat{p}}}$$

Figure 8.14

Rejection Region for Breast Cancer Example

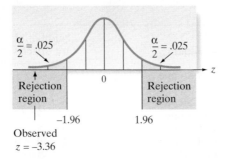

$\frac{\alpha}{2} = .025$

$\frac{\alpha}{2} = .025$

Rejection region

Rejection region

-1.96

1.96

Observed $z = -3.36$

where we use the symbol p_0 to represent the null hypothesized value of p.

Rejection region: We use the standard normal distribution to find the appropriate rejection region for the specified value of α. Using $\alpha = .05$, the two-tailed rejection region is

$$z < -z_{\alpha/2} = -z_{.025} = -1.96 \quad \text{or} \quad z > z_{\alpha/2} = z_{.025} = 1.96$$

See Figure 8.14.

We are now prepared to calculate the value of the test statistic. Before doing so, we want to be sure that the sample size is large enough to ensure that the normal approximation for the sampling distribution of $\hat{p}$ is reasonable. To check this, we calculate a 3-standard-deviation interval around the null hypothesized value, p_0, which is assumed to be the true value of p until our test procedure proves otherwise. Recall that $\sigma_{\hat{p}} = \sqrt{pq/n}$ and that we need an estimate of the product pq in order to calculate a numerical value of the test statistic z. Since the null hypothesized value is generally the accepted-until-proven-otherwise value, we use the value of $p_0 q_0$ (where $q_0 = 1 - p_0$) to estimate pq in the calculation of z. Thus,

$$\sigma_{\hat{p}} = \sqrt{\frac{pq}{n}} \approx \sqrt{\frac{p_0 q_0}{n}} = \sqrt{\frac{(.2)(.8)}{140}} = .034$$

and the 3-standard-deviation interval around p_0 is

$$p_0 \pm 3\sigma_{\hat{p}} \approx .2 \pm 3(.034) = (.098, .302)$$

As long as this interval does not contain 0 or 1 (i.e., is completely contained in the interval 0 to 1), as is the case here, the normal distribution will provide a reasonable approximation for the sampling distribution of $\hat{p}$.

Returning to the hypothesis test at hand, the proportion of the screenings that failed to detect breast cancer is

$$\hat{p} = \frac{12}{140} = .086$$

Finally, we calculate the number of standard deviations (the z value) between the sampled and hypothesized value of the binomial proportion:

$$z = \frac{\hat{p} - p_0}{\sigma_{\hat{p}}} = \frac{\hat{p} - p_0}{\sqrt{p_0 q_0/n}} = \frac{.086 - .2}{.034} = \frac{-.114}{.034} = -3.36$$

The implication is that the observed sample proportion is (approximately) 3.36 standard deviations below the null hypothesized proportion .2 (Figure 8.14). Therefore, we reject the null hypothesis, concluding at the .05 level of significance that the true failure rate of the new method for detecting breast cancer differs from .20. Since $\hat{p} = .086$, it appears that the new method is better (i.e., has a smaller failure rate) than the method currently in use. (To estimate the magnitude of the failure rate for the new method, a confidence interval can be constructed.)

The test of hypothesis about a population proportion p is summarized in the next box. Note that the procedure is entirely analogous to that used for conducting large-sample tests about a population mean.

Large-Sample Test of Hypothesis about p

One-Tailed Test

$H_0: p = p_0$

$H_a: p < p_0$ (or $H_a: p > p_0$)

Test statistic: $z = \dfrac{\hat{p} - p_0}{\sigma_{\hat{p}}}$

Two-Tailed Test

$H_0: p = p_0$

$H_a: p \neq p_0$

Test statistic: $z = \dfrac{\hat{p} - p_0}{\sigma_{\hat{p}}}$ $\leftarrow \sqrt{\dfrac{p_0 q_0}{n}}$

where, p_0 = hypothesized value of p, $\sigma_{\hat{p}} = \sqrt{p_0 q_0 / n}$ and $q_0 = 1 - p_0$

Rejection region: $z < -z_\alpha$
   (or $z > z_\alpha$ when $H_a: p > p_0$)

Rejection region: $z < -z_{\alpha/2}$ or $z > z_{\alpha/2}$

Conditions Required for a Valid Large-Sample Hypothesis Test for p

1. A random sample is selected from a binomial population.
2. The sample size n is large. (This condition will be satisfied if $p_0 \pm 3\sigma_{\hat{p}}$ falls between 0 and 1.)

EXAMPLE 8.7   CONDUCTING A HYPOTHESIS TEST FOR p

Problem   The reputations (and hence sales) of many businesses can be severely damaged by shipments of manufactured items that contain a large percentage of defectives. For example, a manufacturer of alkaline batteries may want to be reasonably certain that fewer than 5% of its batteries are defective. Suppose 300 batteries are randomly selected from a very large shipment; each is tested and 10 defective batteries are found. Does this provide sufficient evidence for the manufacturer to conclude that the fraction defective in the entire shipment is less than .05? Use $\alpha = .01$.

Solution   Before conducting the test of hypothesis, we check to determine whether the sample size is large enough to use the normal approximation for the sampling distribution of $\hat{p}$. The criterion is tested by the interval

$$p_0 \pm 3\sigma_{\hat{p}} = p_0 \pm 3\sqrt{\dfrac{p_0 q_0}{n}} = .05 \pm 3\sqrt{\dfrac{(.05)(.95)}{300}}$$

$$= .05 \pm .04 \quad \text{or} \quad (.01, .09)$$

Since the interval lies within the interval $(0, 1)$, the normal approximation will be adequate.

The objective of the sampling is to determine whether there is sufficient evidence to indicate that the fraction defective, p, is less than .05. Consequently, we will test the null hypothesis that $p = .05$ against the alternative hypothesis that $p < .05$. The elements of the test are

$H_0: p = .05$
$H_a: p < .05$

Test statistic: $z = \dfrac{\hat{p} - p_0}{\sigma_{\hat{p}}}$

Rejection region: $z < -z_{.01} = -2.33$ (see Figure 8.15)

Figure 8.15
Rejection Region
for Example 8.7

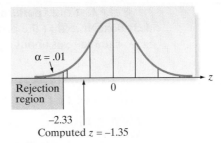

Rejection region

$\alpha = .01$

-2.33
Computed $z = -1.35$

We now calculate the test statistic:

$$z = \frac{\hat{p} - .05}{\sigma_{\hat{p}}} = \frac{(10/300) - .05}{\sqrt{p_0 q_0 / n}} = \frac{.033 - .05}{\sqrt{p_0 q_0 / 300}}$$

Notice that we use p_0 to calculate $\sigma_{\hat{p}}$ because, in contrast to calculating $\sigma_{\hat{p}}$ for a confidence interval, the test statistic is computed on the assumption that the null hypothesis is true—that is, $p = p_0$. Therefore, substituting the values for $\hat{p}$ and p_0 into the z statistic, we obtain

$$z \approx \frac{-.017}{\sqrt{(.05)(.95)/300}} = \frac{-.017}{.0126} = -1.35$$

As shown in Figure 8.15, the calculated z value does not fall in the rejection region. Therefore, there is insufficient evidence at the .01 level of significance to indicate that the shipment contains fewer than 5% defective batteries.

Now Work *Exercise 8.74ab*

■ ■ ■

EXAMPLE 8.8

FINDING THE *p*-VALUE FOR A TEST ABOUT *p*

Problem In Example 8.7 we found that we did not have sufficient evidence, at the $\alpha = .01$ level of significance, to indicate that the fraction defective p of alkaline batteries was less than $p = .05$. How strong was the weight of evidence favoring the alternative hypothesis $(H_a: p < .05)$? Find the observed significance level (*p*-value) for the test.

Solution The computed value of the test statistic z was $z = -1.35$. Therefore, for this lower-tailed test, the observed significance level is

$$p\text{-value} = P(z \le -1.35)$$

This lower-tail area is shown in Figure 8.16. The area between $z = 0$ and $z = 1.35$ is given in Table IV in Appendix A as .4115. Therefore, the observed significance level is $.5 - .4115 = .0885$.

Figure 8.16
The Observed Significance
Level for Example 8.8

$p\text{-value} = .0885$

$-1.35 \quad 0$

Look Back Note that this probability is quite small. Although we did not reject H_0: $p = .05$ at $\alpha = .01$, the probability of observing a z value as small as or smaller than -1.35 is only $.0885$ if in fact H_0 is true. Therefore, we would reject H_0 if we choose $\alpha = .10$ (since the observed significance level is less than .10), and we would not reject H_0 (the conclusion of Example 8.7) if we choose $\alpha = .05$ or $\alpha = .01$.

Now Work   *Exercise 8.74c*

■ ■ ■

Small-sample test procedures are also available for p, although most surveys use samples that are large enough to employ the large-sample tests presented in this section. A test of proportions that can be applied to small samples is discussed in Chapter 13.

Statistics in Action Revisited

Testing a Population Proportion in the KLEENEX® Survey

In the previous "Statistics in Action Revisited" (p. 388), we investigated Kimberly-Clark Corporation's assertion that the company should put 60 tissues in a cold-care box of KLEENEX® tissues. We did this by testing the claim that the mean number of tissues used by a person with a cold is $\mu = 60$ using data collected from a survey of 250 KLEENEX® users. Another approach to the problem is to consider proportion of KLEENEX® users who use fewer than 60 tissues when they have a cold. Now, the population parameter of interest is p, the proportion of all KLEENEX® users who use fewer than 60 tissues when they have a cold.

Kimberly-Clark Corporation's belief that the company should put 60 tissues in a cold-care box will be supported if half of the KLEENEX® users surveyed use less than 60 tissues and half use more than 60 tissues (i.e., if $p = .5$). Is there evidence to indicate that the population proportion differs from .5? To answer this question, we set up the following null and alternative hypothesis:

H_0: $p = .5$ H_a: $p \neq .5$

Recall that the survey results for the 250 sampled KLEENEX® users are stored in the **TISSUES** data file. In addition to the number of tissues used by each person, the file contains a qualitative variable—called USED60—representing whether the person used fewer or more than 60 tissues. (The values of USED60 in the data set are "BELOW" or "ABOVE.") A MINITAB analysis of this variable yielded the printout displayed in Figure SIA8.2.

On the MINITAB printout, x represents the number of the 250 people with colds that used less than 60 tissues. Note that $x = 143$. This value is used to compute the test statistic, $z = 2.28$, highlighted on the printout. The p-value of the test, also highlighted on the printout, is p-value = .023. Since this value is less than $\alpha = .05$, there is sufficient evidence (at $\alpha = .05$) to reject H_0; we conclude that the proportion of all KLEENEX® users who use fewer than 60 tissues when they have a cold differs from .5. However, if we test at $\alpha = .01$, there is insufficient evidence to reject H_0. Consequently, our choice of α (as in the previous "Statistics in the Action Revisited") is critical to our decision.

```
Test of p = 0.5 vs p not = 0.5

Event = BELOW


Variable    X    N  Sample p         95% CI        Z-Value  P-Value
USED60    143  250  0.572000  (0.510666, 0.633334)    2.28    0.023
```

Figure SIA8.2
MINITAB Test of $p = .5$ for KLEENEX® Survey

Exercises 8.71–8.89

Understanding the Principles

8.71 What type of data, quantitative or qualitative, is typically associated with making inferences about a population proportion, p?

8.72 What conditions are required for a valid large-sample test for p?

Learning the Mechanics

8.73 For the binomial sample sizes and null hypothesized values of p in each part, determine whether the sample size is large enough to use the normal approximation methodology presented in this section to conduct a test of the null hypothesis H_0: $p = p_0$.
 a. $n = 500$, $p_0 = .05$
 b. $n = 100$, $p_0 = .99$
 c. $n = 50$, $p_0 = .2$
 d. $n = 20$, $p_0 = .2$
 e. $n = 10$, $p_0 = .4$

8.74 Suppose a random sample of 100 observations from a
NW binomial population gives a value of $\hat{p} = .69$ and you wish to test the null hypothesis that the population parameter p is equal to .75 against the alternative hypothesis that p is less than .75.
 a. Noting that $\hat{p} = .69$, what does your intuition tell you? Does the value of $\hat{p}$ appear to contradict the null hypothesis?
 b. Use the large-sample z-test to test H_0: $p = .75$ against the alternative hypothesis H_a: $p < .75$. Use $\alpha = .05$. How do the test results compare with your intuitive decision from part **a**?
 c. Find and interpret the observed significance level of the test you conducted in part **b**.

8.75 Suppose the sample in Exercise 8.74 has produced $\hat{p} = .84$ and we wish to test H_0: $p = .9$ against the alternative H_a: $p < .9$.
 a. Calculate the value of the z statistic for this test.
 b. Note that the numerator of the z statistic $(\hat{p} - p_0 = .84 - .90 = -.06)$ is the same as for Exercise 8.74. Considering this, why is the absolute value of z for this exercise larger than that calculated in Exercise 8.74?
 c. Complete the test using $\alpha = .05$ and interpret the result.
 d. Find the observed significance level for the test and interpret its value.

8.76 A random sample of 100 observations is selected from a binomial population with unknown probability of success p. The computed value of $\hat{p}$ is equal to .74.
 a. Test H_0: $p = .65$ against H_a: $p > .65$. Use $\alpha = .01$.
 b. Test H_0: $p = .65$ against H_a: $p > .65$. Use $\alpha = .10$.
 c. Test H_0: $p = .90$ against H_a: $p \neq .90$. Use $\alpha = .05$.
 d. Form a 95% confidence interval for p.
 e. Form a 99% confidence interval for p.

SNACK

8.77 Refer to Exercise 7.48 (p. 349), in which 50 consumers taste-tested a new snack food.
 a. Test H_0: $p = .5$ against H_a: $p > .5$, where p is the proportion of customers who do not like the snack food. Use $\alpha = .10$.
 b. Report the observed significance level of your test.

Applying the Concepts—Basic

8.78 **"Made in the USA" survey.** Refer to the *Journal of Global Business* (Spring 2002) study of what "Made in the USA" means to consumers, Exercise 2.13 (p. 38). Recall that 64 of 106 randomly selected shoppers believed "Made in the USA" means 100% of labor and materials are from the United States. Let p represent the true proportion of consumers who believe "Made in the USA" means 100% of labor and materials are from the United States.
 a. Calculate a point estimate for p.
 b. A claim is made that $p = .70$. Set up the null and alternative hypothesis to test this claim.
 c. Calculate the test statistic for the test, part **b**.
 d. Find the rejection region for the test if $\alpha = .01$.
 e. Use the results, parts **c** and **d**, to make the appropriate conclusion.

8.79 **Unauthorized computer use.** Refer to the Computer Security Institute (CSI) survey of computer crime, Exercise 2.17 (p. 40). Recall that in 1999, 7% of reported unauthorized uses of business web sites came from inside the company. In a survey taken two years later, 7 of a sample of 163 reported unauthorized uses of business web sites came from inside the company. (*Computer Security Issues & Trends*, Vol. 7, Spring 2001.) Let p represent the true proportion of unauthorized uses of business websites in 2001 that came from inside the company.
 a. Calculate a point estimate for p.
 b. Set up the null and alternative hypothesis to test whether the value of p has changed since 1999.
 c. Calculate the test statistic for the test, part **b**.
 d. Find the rejection region for the test if $\alpha = .05$.
 e. Use the results, parts **c** and **d** to make the appropriate conclusion.
 f. Find the p-value of the test and confirm that the conclusion based on the p-value agrees with the conclusion in part **e**.

8.80 **Quality of cable-TV news.** In a survey of 500 television viewers with access to cable TV, each was asked whether they agreed with the statement, "Overall, I find the quality of news on cable networks (such as CNN, FOXNews, CNBC, and MSNBC) to be better than news on the

ABC, CBS, and NBC networks." A total of 248 viewers agreed with the statement. (*Cabletelevision Advertising Bureau*, May 2002.) *Note*: The survey respondents were contacted via e-mail on the Internet.

a. Identify the population parameter of interest in the survey.

b. Give a point estimate of the population parameter.

c. Set up H_0 and H_a for testing whether the true percentage of TV viewers who find cable news to be better quality than network news differs from 50%.

d. Conduct the test, part **c**, using $\alpha = .10$ Make the appropriate conclusion in the words of the problem.

e. What conditions are required for the inference, part **d**, to be valid? Do they appear to be satisfied?

8.81 Single-parent families. Examining data collected on 835 males from the National Youth Survey (a longitudinal survey of a random sample of U.S. households), researchers at Carnegie Mellon University found that 401 of the male youths were raised in a single-parent family. (*Sociological Methods & Research*, February 2001.) Does this information allow you to conclude that more than 45% of male youths are raised in a single-parent family? Test at $\alpha = .05$.

8.82 Cell phone use by drivers. Refer to the U.S. Department of Transportation (July 2001) study of the level of cell phone use by drivers while they are in the act of driving a motor passenger vehicle, Exercise 7.49 (p. 349). Recall that for a random sample of 1,165 drivers selected across the country, 35 were using their cell phone.

a. Conduct a test (at $\alpha = .05$) to determine if p, the true driver cell phone use rate, differs from .02.

b. Does your conclusion, part **a**, agree with the inference you derived from the 95% confidence interval for p in Exercise 7.49?

Applying the Concepts—Intermediate

8.83 Federal civil trial appeals. Refer to the *Journal of the American Law and Economics Association* (Vol. 3, 2001) study of appeals of federal civil trials, Exercise 3.51 (p. 144). A breakdown of 678 civil cases that were originally tried in front of a judge and appealed by either the plaintiff or defendant is reproduced in the table. Do the data provide sufficient evidence to indicate that the percentage of appealed civil cases that are actually reversed is less than 25%? Test using $\alpha = .01$.

Outcome of Appeal	Number of Cases
Plaintiff trial win—reversed	71
Plaintiff trial win—affirmed/dismissed	240
Defendant trial win—reversed	68
Defendant trial win—affirmed/dismissed	299
TOTAL	678

8.84 Verbs and double object datives. Any sentence that contains an animate noun as a direct object and another noun as a second object (e.g., "Sue offered Ann a cookie.") is termed a double object dative (DOD). The connection between certain verbs and a DOD was investigated in *Applied Psycholinguistics* (June 1998). The subjects were 35 native English speakers who were enrolled in an introductory English composition course at a Hawaiian community college. After viewing pictures of a family, each subject was asked to write a sentence about the family using a specified verb. Of the 35 sentences using the verb "buy," 10 had a DOD structure. Conduct a test to determine if the true fraction of sentences with the verb "buy" that are DODs is less than $1/3$. Use $\alpha = .05$.

8.85 Choosing portable grill displays. Refer to the *Journal of Consumer Research* (March 2003) experiment on influencing the choices of others by offering undesirable alternatives, Exercise 3.25 (p. 132). Recall that each of 124 college students selected three portable grills from five to display on the showroom floor. The students were instructed to include Grill #2 (a smaller-sized grill) and select the remaining two grills in the display to maximize purchases of Grill #2. If the six possible grill display combinations (1-2-3, 1-2-4, 1-2-5, 2-3-4, 2-3-5, and 2-4-5) are selected at random, then the proportion of students selecting any display will be $1/6 = .167$. One theory tested by the researcher is that the students will tend to choose the three-grill display so that Grill #2 is a compromise between a more desirable and a less desirable grill. Of the 124 students, 85 students selected a three-grill display that was consistent with this theory. Use this information to test the theory proposed by the researcher at $\alpha = .05$.

8.86 Study of lunar soil. *Meteoritics* (March 1995) reported the results of a study of lunar soil evolution. Data were obtained from the Apollo 16 mission to the moon, during which a 62-cm core was extracted from the soil near the landing site. Monomineralic grains of lunar soil were separated out and examined for coating with dust and glass fragments. Each grain was then classified as coated or uncoated. Of interest is the "coat index," that is, the proportion of grains that are coated. According to soil evolution theory, the coat index will exceed .5 at the top of the core, equal .5 in the middle of the core, and fall below .5 at the bottom of the core. Use the summary data in the accompanying table to test each part of the 3-part theory. Use $\alpha = .05$ for each test.

	Location (depth)		
	Top (4.25 cm)	Middle (28.1 cm)	Bottom (54.5 cm)
Number of grains sampled	84	73	81
Number coated	64	35	29

Source: Basu, A., and McKay, D. S. "Lunar soil evolution processes and Apollo 16 core 60013/60014." *Meteoritics*, Vol. 30, No. 2, Mar. 1995, p. 166 (Table 2).

8.87 Effectiveness of skin cream. Pond's Age-Defying Complex, a cream with alpha-hydroxy acid, advertises that it can reduce wrinkles and improve the skin. In a study published in *Archives of Dermatology* (June 1996), 33 middle-aged women used a cream with alpha-hydroxy acid for twenty-two weeks. At the end of the study period, a dermatologist judged whether each woman exhibited skin improvement. The results for the 33 women (where I = improved skin and N = no improvement) are listed in the accompanying table.

a. Do the data provide sufficient evidence to conclude that the cream will improve the skin of more than 60% of middle-aged women? Test using $\alpha = .05$.

b. Find and interpret the *p*-value of the test.

⊘ **SKINCREAM**

I	I	N	I	N	N	I	I	I	I	I	I
N	I	I	I	N	I	I	I	N	I	N	I
I	I	I	I	I	N	I	I	N			

Applying the Concepts—Advanced

8.88 Parents who condone spanking. In Exercise 4.60 (p. 217) you read about a nationwide survey that claimed that 60% of parents with young children condone spanking their child as a regular form of punishment. (*Tampa Tribune*, October 5, 2000.) In a random sample of 100 parents with young children, how many parents would need to say they condone spanking as a form of punishment in order to refute the claim?

8.89 Testing the placebo effect. The *placebo effect* describes the phenomenon of improvement in the condition of a patient taking a placebo—a pill that looks and tastes real but contains no medically active chemicals. Physicians at a clinic in La Jolla, California, gave what they thought were drugs to 7,000 asthma, ulcer, and herpes patients. Although the doctors later learned that the drugs were really placebos, 70% of the patients reported an improved condition. (*Forbes*, May 22, 1995.) Use this information to test (at $\alpha = .05$) the placebo effect at the clinic. Assume that if the placebo is ineffective, the probability of a patient's condition improving is .5.

8.6 Calculating Type II Error Probabilities: More about β (Optional)

In our introduction to hypothesis testing in Section 8.1, we showed that the probability of committing a Type I error, α, can be controlled by the selection of the rejection region for the test. Thus, when the test statistic falls in the rejection region and we make the decision to reject the null hypothesis, we do so knowing the error rate for incorrect rejections of H_0. The situation corresponding to accepting the null hypothesis, and thereby risking a Type II error, is not generally as controllable. For that reason, we adopted a policy of nonrejection of H_0 when the test statistic does not fall in the rejection region, rather than risking an error of unknown magnitude.

To see how β, the probability of a Type II error, can be calculated for a test of hypothesis, recall the example in Section 8.1 in which a city tests a manufacturer's pipe to see whether it meets the requirement that the mean strength exceed 2,400 pounds per linear foot. The setup for the test is as follows:

$$H_0: \mu = 2,400$$
$$H_a: \mu > 2,400$$

Test statistic: $z = \dfrac{\bar{x} - 2,400}{\sigma/\sqrt{n}}$

Rejection region: $z > 1.645$ for $\alpha = .05$

Figure 8.17a shows the rejection region for the **null distribution**—that is, the distribution of the test statistic assuming the null hypothesis is true. The area in the rejection region is .05, and this area represents α, the probability that the test statistic leads to rejection of H_0 when in fact H_0 is true.

The Type II error probability β is calculated assuming that the null hypothesis is false, because it is defined as the *probability of accepting H_0 when it is false*. Since H_0 is false for any value of μ exceeding 2,400, one value of β exists for each possible value of μ greater than 2,400 (an infinite number of possibilities). Figures 8.17b, 8.17c, and 8.17d show three of the possibilities, corresponding to alternative hypothesis values of μ equal to 2,425, 2,450, and 2,475, respectively. Note that β is the area in the *nonrejection* (or *acceptance*) *region* in each of these distributions and that β decreases as the true value of μ moves farther from the null hypothesized value of $\mu = 2,400$. This is sensible because

Figure 8.17

Values of α and β for Various Values of μ

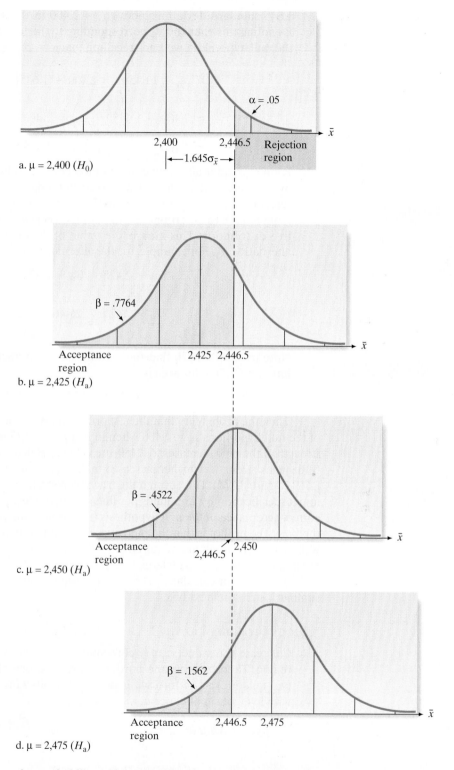

a. $\mu = 2,400$ (H_0)

b. $\mu = 2,425$ (H_a)

c. $\mu = 2,450$ (H_a)

d. $\mu = 2,475$ (H_a)

the probability of incorrectly accepting the null hypothesis should decrease as the distance between the null and alternative values of μ increases.

In order to calculate the value of β for a specific value of μ in H_a, we proceed as follows:

1. Calculate the value of $\bar{x}$ that corresponds to the border between the acceptance and rejection regions. For the sewer pipe example, this is the value of $\bar{x}$ that lies

1.645 standard deviations above $\mu = 2{,}400$ in the sampling distribution of $\bar{x}$. Denoting this value by $\bar{x}_0$, corresponding to the largest value of $\bar{x}$ that supports the null hypothesis, we find (recalling that $s = 200$ and $n = 50$)

$$\bar{x}_0 = \mu_0 + 1.645\sigma_{\bar{x}} = 2{,}400 + 1.645\left(\frac{\sigma}{\sqrt{n}}\right)$$

$$\approx 2{,}400 + 1.645\left(\frac{s}{\sqrt{n}}\right) = 2{,}400 + 1.645\left(\frac{200}{\sqrt{50}}\right)$$

$$= 2{,}400 + 1.645(28.28) = 2{,}446.5$$

2. For a particular alternative distribution corresponding to a value of μ denoted by μ_a, we calculate the z-value corresponding to $\bar{x}_0$, the border between the rejection and acceptance regions. We then use this z value and Table IV of Appendix A to determine the area in the *acceptance region* under the alternative distribution. This area is the value of β corresponding to the particular alternative μ_a. For example, for the alternative $\mu_a = 2{,}425$, we calculate

$$z = \frac{\bar{x}_0 - 2{,}425}{\sigma_{\bar{x}}} = \frac{\bar{x}_0 - 2{,}425}{\sigma/\sqrt{n}}$$

$$\approx \frac{\bar{x}_0 - 2{,}425}{s/\sqrt{n}} = \frac{2{,}446.5 - 2{,}425}{28.28} = .76$$

Note in Figure 8.17b that the area in the acceptance region is the area to the left of $z = .76$. This area is

$$\beta = .5 + .2764 = .7764$$

Thus, the probability that the test procedure will lead to an incorrect acceptance of the null hypothesis $\mu = 2{,}400$ when in fact $\mu = 2{,}425$ is about .78. As the average strength of the pipe increases to 2,450, the value of β decreases to .4522 (Figure 8.17c). If the mean strength is further increased to 2,475, the value of β is further decreased to .1562 (Figure 8.17d). Thus, even if the true mean strength of the pipe exceeds the minimum specification by 75 pounds per linear foot, the test procedure will lead to an incorrect acceptance of the null hypothesis (rejection of the pipe) approximately 16% of the time. The upshot is that the pipe must be manufactured so that the mean strength well exceeds the minimum requirement if the manufacturer wants the probability of its acceptance by the city to be large (i.e., β to be small).

The steps for calculating β for a large-sample test about a population mean are summarized in the next box.

Steps for Calculating β for a Large-Sample Test about μ

1. Calculate the value(s) of $\bar{x}$ corresponding to the border(s) of the rejection region. There will be one border value for a one-tailed test, and two for a two-tailed test. The formula is one of the following, corresponding to a test with level of significance α:

Upper-tailed test: $\bar{x}_0 = \mu_0 + z_\alpha\sigma_{\bar{x}} \approx \mu_0 + z_\alpha\left(\dfrac{s}{\sqrt{n}}\right)$

Lower-tailed test: $\bar{x}_0 = \mu_0 - z_\alpha\sigma_{\bar{x}} \approx \mu_0 - z_\alpha\left(\dfrac{s}{\sqrt{n}}\right)$

Two-tailed test: $\bar{x}_{0,\,L} = \mu_0 - z_{\alpha/2}\sigma_{\bar{x}} \approx \mu_0 - z_{\alpha/2}\left(\dfrac{s}{\sqrt{n}}\right)$

$\bar{x}_{0,\,U} = \mu_0 + z_{\alpha/2}\sigma_{\bar{x}} \approx \mu_0 + z_{\alpha/2}\left(\dfrac{s}{\sqrt{n}}\right)$

2. Specify the value of μ_a in the alternative hypothesis for which the value of β is to be calculated. Then convert the border value(s) of $\bar{x}_0$ to z value(s) using the alternative distribution with mean μ_a. The general formula for the z value is

$$z = \frac{\bar{x}_0 - \mu_a}{\sigma_{\bar{x}}}$$

Sketch the alternative distribution (centered at μ_a), and shade the area in the acceptance (nonrejection) region. Use the z-statistic(s) and Table IV of Appendix A to find the shaded area, which is β.

Following the calculation of β for a particular value of μ_a, you should interpret the value in the context of the hypothesis testing application. It is often useful to interpret the value of $1 - \beta$, which is known as the power of the test corresponding to a particular alternative, μ_a. Since β is the probability of accepting the null hypothesis when the alternative hypothesis is true with $\mu = \mu_a$, $1 - \beta$ is the probability of the complementary event, or the probability of rejecting the null hypothesis when the alternative $H_a\colon \mu = \mu_a$ is true. That is, the power $(1 - \beta)$ measures the likelihood that the test procedure will lead to the correct decision (reject H_0) for a particular value of the mean in the alternative hypothesis.

DEFINITION 8.2

The **power of a test** is the probability that the test will correctly lead to the rejection of the null hypothesis for a particular value of μ in the alternative hypothesis. The power is equal to $(1 - \beta)$ for the particular alternative considered.

For example, in the sewer pipe example we found that $\beta = .7764$ when $\mu = 2,425$. This is the probability that the test leads to the (incorrect) acceptance of the null hypothesis when $\mu = 2,425$. Or, equivalently, the power of the test is $1 - .7764 = .2236$, which means that the test will lead to the (correct) rejection of the null hypothesis only 22% of the time when the pipe exceeds specifications by 25 pounds per linear foot. When the manufacturer's pipe has a mean strength of 2,475 (that is, 75 pounds per linear foot in excess of specifications), the power of the test increases to $1 - .1562 = .8438$. That is, the test will lead to the acceptance of the manufacturer's pipe 84% of the time if $\mu = 2,475$.

EXAMPLE 8.9

FINDING THE POWER OF A TEST

Problem Recall the drug experiment in Examples 8.1 and 8.2, in which we tested to determine whether the mean response time for rats injected with a drug differs from the control mean response time of $\mu = 1.2$ seconds. The test setup is repeated here:

$H_0\colon \mu = 1.2$
$H_a\colon \mu \neq 1.2$ (i.e., $\mu < 1.2$ or $\mu > 1.2$)
Test statistic: $z = \dfrac{\bar{x} - 1.2}{\sigma_{\bar{x}}}$
Rejection region: $z < -1.96$ or $z > 1.96$ for $\alpha = .05$
$ z < -2.575$ or $z > 2.575$ for $\alpha = .01$

Note that two rejection regions have been specified corresponding to values of $\alpha = .05$ and $\alpha = .01$, respectively. Assume that $n = 100$ and $s = .5$.

a. Suppose drug-injected rats have a mean response time of 1.1 seconds, that is, $\mu = 1.1$. Calculate the values of β corresponding to the two rejection regions. Discuss the relationship between the values of α and β.

b. Calculate the power of the test for each of the rejection regions when $\mu = 1.1$.

Solution   **a.** We first consider the rejection region corresponding to $\alpha = .05$. The first step is to calculate the border values of $\bar{x}$ corresponding to the two-tailed rejection region, $z < -1.96$ or $z > 1.96$:

$$\bar{x}_{0,\,L} = \mu_0 - 1.96\sigma_{\bar{x}} \approx \mu_0 - 1.96\left(\frac{s}{\sqrt{n}}\right) = 1.2 - 1.96\left(\frac{.5}{10}\right) = 1.102$$

$$\bar{x}_{0,\,U} = \mu_0 + 1.96\sigma_{\bar{x}} \approx \mu_0 + 1.96\left(\frac{s}{\sqrt{n}}\right) = 1.2 + 1.96\left(\frac{.5}{10}\right) = 1.298$$

These border values are shown in Figure 8.18.

Figure 8.18

Calculation of β for Drug-Injected Rats (Example 8.9)

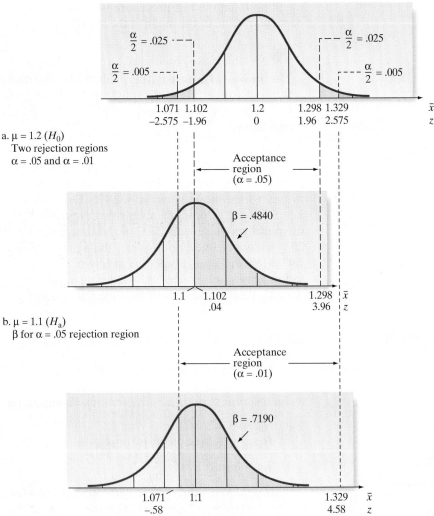

a. $\mu = 1.2$ (H_0)
  Two rejection regions
  $\alpha = .05$ and $\alpha = .01$

b. $\mu = 1.1$ (H_a)
  β for $\alpha = .05$ rejection region

c. $\mu = 1.1$ (H_a)
  β for $\alpha = .01$ rejection region

Next, we convert these values to z-values in the alternative distribution with $\mu_a = 1.1$:

$$z_L = \frac{\overline{x}_{0,L} - \mu_a}{\sigma_{\overline{x}}} \approx \frac{1.102 - 1.1}{.05} = .04$$

$$z_U = \frac{\overline{x}_{0,U} - \mu_a}{\sigma_{\overline{x}}} \approx \frac{1.298 - 1.1}{.05} = 3.96$$

These z-values are shown in Figure 8.18b. You can see that the acceptance (or nonrejection) region is the area between them. Using Table IV of Appendix A, we find that the area between $z = 0$ and $z = .04$ is .0160, and the area between $z = 0$ and $z = 3.96$ is (approximately) .5 (since $z = 3.96$ is off the scale of Table IV). Then the area between $z = .04$ and $z = 3.96$ is, approximately,

$$\beta = .5 - .0160 = .4840$$

Thus, the test with $\alpha = .05$ will lead to a Type II error about 48% of the time when the mean reaction time for drug-injected rats is .1 second less than the control mean response time.

For the rejection region corresponding to $\alpha = .01$, $z < -2.575$ or $z > 2.575$, we find

$$\overline{x}_{0,L} = 1.2 - 2.575\left(\frac{.5}{10}\right) = 1.0712$$

$$\overline{x}_{0,U} = 1.2 + 2.575\left(\frac{.5}{10}\right) = 1.3288$$

These border values of the rejection region are shown in Figure 8.18c.

Converting these to z-values in the alternative distribution with $\mu_a = 1.1$, we find $z_L = -.58$ and $z_U = 4.58$. The area between these values is, approximately,

$$\beta = .2190 + .5 = .7190$$

Thus, the chance that the test procedure with $\alpha = .01$ will lead to an incorrect acceptance of H_0 is about 72%.

Note that the value of β increases from .4840 to .7190 when we decrease the value of α from .05 to .01. This is a general property of the relationship between α and β: *as α is decreased (increased), β is increased (decreased).*

b. The power is defined to be the probability of (correctly) rejecting the null hypothesis when the alternative is true. When $\mu = 1.1$ and $\alpha = .05$, we find

$$\text{Power} = 1 - \beta = 1 - .4840 = .5160$$

When $\mu = 1.1$ and $\alpha = .01$, we find

$$\text{Power} = 1 - \beta = 1 - .7190 = .2810$$

You can see that the power of the test is decreased as the level of α is decreased. This means that as the probability of incorrectly rejecting the null hypothesis is decreased, the probability of correctly accepting the null hypothesis for a given alternative is also decreased.

Look Back A key point in this example is that the value of α must be selected carefully, with the realization that a test is made less capable of detecting departures from the null hypothesis when the value of α is decreased.

■ ■ ■

Power and Sample Size

```
1-Sample Z Test

Testing mean = null (versus not = null)
Calculating power for mean = null + difference
Alpha = 0.05  Assumed standard deviation = 0.5


              Sample
Difference     Size      Power
       0.1      100   0.516005
```

Note: Most statistical software packages now have options for computing the power of standard tests of hypothesis. Usually, you will need to specify the type of test (z-test or t-test), form of H_a ($<$, $>$, or $\neq$), standard deviation, sample size, and the value of the parameter in H_a (or the difference between the value in H_0 and the value in H_a). The MINITAB power analysis for Example 8.9 when $\alpha = .05$ is displayed in Figure 8.19. The power of the test (.516) is highlighted on the printout.

We have shown that the probability of committing a Type II error, β, is inversely related to α (Example 8.9), and that the value of β decreases as the value of μ_a moves farther from the null hypothesis value (sewer pipe example). The sample size n also affects β. Remember that the standard deviation of the sampling distribution of $\bar{x}$ is inversely proportional to the square root of the sample size ($\sigma_{\bar{x}} = \sigma/\sqrt{n}$). Thus, as illustrated in Figure 8.20, the variability of both the null and alternative sampling distributions is decreased as n is increased. If the value of α is specified and remains fixed, the value of β decreases as n increases, as illustrated in Figure 8.20. Conversely, the power of the test for a given alternative hypothesis is increased as the sample size is increased.

The properties of β and power are summarized in the following box.

Properties of β and Power

1. For fixed n and α, the value of β decreases and the power increases as the distance between the specified null value μ_0 and the specified alternative value μ_a increases (see Figure 8.17).

2. For fixed n and values of μ_0 and μ_a, the value of β increases and the power decreases as the value of α is decreased (see Figure 8.18).

3. For fixed α and values of μ_0 and μ_a, the value of β decreases and the power increases as the sample size n is increased (see Figure 8.20).

Figure 8.20
Relationship between
α, β, and n

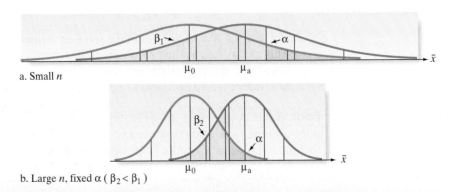

a. Small n

b. Large n, fixed α ($\beta_2 < \beta_1$)

Exercises 8.90–8.101

Understanding the Principles

8.90 Define the power of a test.

8.91 What is the relationship between β, the probability of committing a Type II error, and the power of the test?

8.92 List three factors that will increase the power of the test.

Learning the Mechanics

8.93 Suppose you want to test $H_0: \mu = 1,000$ against $H_a: \mu > 1,000$ using $\alpha = .05$. The population in question is normally distributed with standard deviation 120. A random sample of size $n = 36$ will be used.
 a. Sketch the sampling distribution of $\bar{x}$ assuming that H_0 is true.
 b. Find the value of $\bar{x}_0$, that value of $\bar{x}$ above which the null hypothesis will be rejected. Indicate the rejection region on your graph of part **a**. Shade the area above the rejection region and label it α.
 c. On your graph of part **a**, sketch the sampling distribution of $\bar{x}$ if $\mu = 1,020$. Shade the area under this distribution that corresponds to the probability that $\bar{x}$ falls in the nonrejection region when $\mu = 1,020$. Label this area β.
 d. Find β.
 e. Compute the power of this test for detecting the alternative $H_a: \mu = 1,020$.

8.94 Refer to Exercise 8.93.
 a. If $\mu = 1,040$ instead of 1,020, what is the probability that the hypothesis test will incorrectly fail to reject H_0? That is, what is β?
 b. If $\mu = 1,040$, what is the probability that the test will correctly reject the null hypothesis? That is, what is the power of the test?
 c. Compare β and the power of the test when $\mu = 1,040$ to the values you obtained in Exercise 8.93 for $\mu = 1,020$. Explain the differences.

8.95 It is desired to test $H_0: \mu = 50$ against $H_a: \mu < 50$ using $\alpha = .10$. The population in question is uniformly distributed with standard deviation 20. A random sample of size 64 will be drawn from the population.
 a. Describe the (approximate) sampling distribution of $\bar{x}$ under the assumption that H_0 is true.
 b. Describe the (approximate) sampling distribution of $\bar{x}$ under the assumption that the population mean is 45.
 c. If μ were really equal to 45, what is the probability that the hypothesis test would lead the investigator to commit a Type II error?
 d. What is the power of this test for detecting the alternative $H_a: \mu = 45$?

8.96 Refer to Exercise 8.95.
 a. Find β for each of the following values of the population mean: 49, 47, 45, 43, and 41.
 b. Plot each value of β you obtained in part **a** against its associated population mean. Show β on the vertical axis and μ on the horizontal axis. Draw a curve through the five points on your graph.
 c. Use your graph of part **b** to find the approximate probability that the hypothesis test will lead to a Type II error when $\mu = 48$.
 d. Convert each of the β values you calculated in part **a** to the power of the test at the specified value of μ. Plot the power on the vertical axis against μ on the horizontal axis. Compare the graph of part **b** to the *power curve* of this part.
 e. Examine the graphs of parts **b** and **d**. Explain what they reveal about the relationships among the distance between the true mean μ and the null hypothesized mean μ_0, the value of β, and the power.

8.97 Suppose you want to conduct the two-tailed test of $H_0: \mu = 10$ against $H_a: \mu \neq 10$ using $\alpha = .05$. A random sample of size 100 will be drawn from the population in question. Assume the population has a standard deviation equal to 1.0.
 a. Describe the sampling distribution of $\bar{x}$ under the assumption that H_0 is true.
 b. Describe the sampling distribution of $\bar{x}$ under the assumption that $\mu = 9.9$.
 c. If μ were really equal to 9.9, find the value of β associated with the test.
 d. Find the value of β for the alternative $H_a: \mu = 10.1$.

Applying the Concepts—Intermediate

8.98 **Post-traumatic stress of POWs.** Refer to Exercise 8.29 (p. 382), in which the null hypothesis that the mean PTSD score of World War II POWs is 16 is tested against the alternative hypothesis that the mean is less than 16. Recall that 33 POWs were included in the sample. Assume that the resulting standard deviation of $s = 9.32$ is a good estimate of the true standard deviation.
 a. Calculate the power of the test for the mean values of 15.5, 15.0, 14.5, 14.0, and 13.5.
 b. Plot the power of the test on the vertical axis against the mean on the horizontal axis. Draw a curve through the points.
 c. Use the power curve of part **b** to estimate the power for the mean value $\mu = 14.25$. Calculate the power for this value of μ, and compare it to your approximation.
 d. Use the power curve to approximate the power of the test when $\mu = 12.10$. If the true value of the mean PTSD score for WWII POWs is really 10, what (approximately) are the chances that the test will fail to reject the null hypothesis that the mean is 16?

8.99 **Increasing the sample size.** Refer to Exercise 8.98. Show what happens to the power curve when the sample size is increased from $n = 33$ to $n = 100$. Assume that the standard deviation is $\sigma = 9.32$.

8.100 **Gas mileage of the Honda Civic.** According to the Environmental Protection Agency (EPA) *Fuel Economy Guide*, the 2003 Honda Civic automobile obtains a mean of 38 miles per gallon (mpg) on the highway. Suppose Honda claims that the EPA has underestimated the Civic's mileage. To support its assertion, the company selects 36 model 2003 Civic cars and records the mileage obtained for each car over a driving course similar to the one used by the EPA. The following data resulted: $x = 40.3$ mpg, $s = 6.4$ mpg.

a. If Honda wishes to show that the mean mpg for 2003 Civic autos is greater than 38 mpg, what should the alternative hypothesis be? The null hypothesis?

b. Do the data provide sufficient evidence to support the auto manufacturer's claim? Test using $\alpha = .05$. List any assumptions you make in conducting the test.

c. Calculate the power of the test for the mean values of 38.5, 39.0, 39.5, 40.0, and 40.5, assuming $s = 6.4$ is a good estimate of σ.

d. Plot the power of the test on the vertical axis against the mean on the horizontal axis. Draw a curve through the points.

e. Use the power curve of part d to estimate the power for the mean value $\mu = 39.75$. Calculate the power for this value of μ, and compare it to your approximation.

f. Use the power curve to approximate the power of the test when $\mu = 43$. If the true value of the mean mpg for this model is really 43, what (approximately) are the chances that the test will fail to reject the null hypothesis that the mean is 38?

8.101 Solder joint inspections. Refer to Exercise 8.32 (p. 382), in which the performance of a particular type of laser-based inspection equipment was investigated. Assume that the standard deviation of the number of solder joints inspected on each run is 1.2. If $\alpha = .05$ is used in conducting the hypothesis test of interest using a sample of 48 circuit boards, and if the true mean number of solder joints that can be inspected is really equal to 9.5, what is the probability that the test will result in a Type II error?

8.7 Test of Hypothesis about a Population Variance (Optional)

Although many practical problems involve inferences about a population mean (or proportion), it is sometimes of interest to make an inference about a population variance, σ^2. To illustrate, a quality control supervisor in a cannery knows that the exact amount each can contains will vary since there are certain uncontrollable factors that affect the amount of fill. The mean fill per can is important, but equally important is the variation of fill. If σ^2, the variance of the fill, is large, some cans will contain too little and others too much. Suppose regulatory agencies specify that the standard deviation of the amount of fill in 16-ounce cans should be less than .1 ounce. To determine whether the process is meeting this specification, the supervisor randomly selects 10 cans and weighs the contents of each. The results are given in Table 8.5.

⊙ **FILLAMOUNTS**

TABLE 8.5   Fill Weights (ounces) of 10 Cans

16.00	15.95	16.10	16.02	15.99
16.06	16.04	16.05	16.03	16.02

Do these data provide sufficient evidence to indicate that the variability is as small as desired? To answer this question, we need a procedure for testing a hypothesis about σ^2.

Intuitively it seems that we should compare the sample variance σ^2 to the hypothesized value of σ^2 (or s to σ) in order to make a decision about the population's variability. The quantity

$$\frac{(n-1)s^2}{\sigma^2}$$

has been shown to have a sampling distribution called a **chi-square (χ^2) distribution** when the population from which the sample is taken is *normally distributed*. Several chi-square distributions are shown in Figure 8.21.

Figure 8.21
Several χ^2 Probability
Distributions

TABLE 8.6 Reproduction of Part of Table VII in Appendix A: Critical Values of Chi-Square

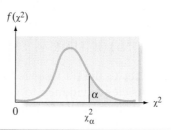

Degrees of Freedom	$\chi^2_{.100}$	$\chi^2_{.050}$	$\chi^2_{.025}$	$\chi^2_{.010}$	$\chi^2_{.005}$
1	2.70554	3.84146	5.02389	6.63490	7.87944
2	4.60517	5.99147	7.37776	9.21034	10.5966
3	6.25139	7.81473	9.34840	11.3449	12.8381
4	7.77944	9.48773	11.1433	13.2767	14.8602
5	9.23635	11.0705	12.8325	15.0863	16.7496
6	10.6446	12.5916	14.4494	16.8119	18.5476
7	12.0170	14.0671	16.0128	18.4753	20.2777
8	13.3616	15.5073	17.5346	20.0902	21.9550
9	14.6837	16.9190	19.0228	21.6660	23.5893
10	15.9871	18.3070	20.4831	23.2093	25.1882
11	17.2750	19.6751	21.9200	24.7250	26.7569
12	18.5494	21.0261	23.3367	26.2170	28.2995
13	19.8119	22.3621	24.7356	27.6883	29.8194
14	21.0642	23.6848	26.1190	29.1413	31.3193
15	22.3072	24.9958	27.4884	30.5779	32.8013
16	23.5418	26.2862	28.8454	31.9999	34.2672
17	24.7690	27.5871	30.1910	33.4087	35.7185
18	25.9894	28.8693	31.5264	34.8053	37.1564
19	27.2036	30.1435	32.8523	36.1908	38.5822

The upper-tail areas for this distribution have been tabulated and are given in Table VII of Appendix A, a portion of which is reproduced in Table 8.6. The table gives the values of χ^2, denoted as χ^2_α, that locate an area of α in the upper tail of the chi-square distribution; that is, $P(\chi^2 > \chi^2_\alpha) = \alpha$. In this case, as with the t-statistic, the shape of the chi-square distribution depends on the degrees of freedom associated with s^2, namely $(n - 1)$. Thus, for $n = 10$ and an upper-tail value $\alpha = .05$, you will have $n - 1 = 9$ df and $\chi^2_{.05} = 16.9190$ (highlighted area in Table 8.6). To further illustrate the use of Table VII, we return to the can-filling example.

Now Work *Exercise 8.106*

Biography

FRIEDRICH R. HELMERT (1843–1917)—Helmert Transformations

German Friedrich Helmert studied engineering sciences and mathematics at Dresden University, where he earned his Ph.D., then accepted a position as a professor of geodesy—the scientific study of the Earth's size and shape—at the technical school in Aachen. Helmert's mathematical solutions to geodesy problems led him to several statistics-related discoveries. His greatest statistical contribution occurred in 1876, when he was the first to prove that the sampling distribution of the sample variance, s^2, is a chi-square distribution. Helmert used a series of mathematical transformations to obtain the distribution of s^2—transformations that have since been named "Helmert transformations" in his honor. Later in life, Helmert was appointed professor of advanced geodesy at prestigious University of Berlin and director of the Prussian Geodetic Institute.

EXAMPLE 8.10   CONDUCTING A TEST FOR σ

Problem   Refer to the fill weights for the sample of ten 16 ounce cans in Table 8.5. Is there sufficient evidence to conclude that the true standard deviation σ of the fill measurements of 16-ounce cans is less than .1 ounce?

Solution   Here, we want to test whether $\sigma < .1$. Since the null and alternative hypotheses must be stated in terms of σ^2 (rather than σ), we want to test the null hypothesis that $\sigma^2 = (.1)^2 = .01$ against the alternative that $\sigma^2 < .01$. Therefore, the elements of the test are

$$H_0: \sigma^2 = .01$$
$$H_a: \sigma^2 < .01$$
$$\text{Test statistic: } \chi^2 = \frac{(n-1)s^2}{\sigma^2}$$

Assumption: The distribution of the amounts of fill is approximately normal.

Rejection region: The smaller the value of s^2 we observe, the stronger the evidence in favor of H_a. Thus, we reject H_0 for "small values" of the test statistic. With $\alpha = .05$ and 9 df, the χ^2 value for rejection is found in Table VII and pictured in Figure 8.22. We will reject H_0 if $\chi^2 < 3.32511$.

(Remember that the area given in Table VII is the area to the *right* of the numerical value in the table. Thus, to determine the lower-tail value, which has $\alpha = .05$ to its *left*, we used the $\chi^2_{.95}$ column in Table VII.)

Figure 8.22

Rejection Region for Example 8.10

Figure 8.23

SAS Test of Fill Amount Variance, Example 8.10

```
Sample Statistics for FILLAMT

     N       Mean        Std. Dev.       Variance
    ----------------------------------------------
    10      16.026         0.0412         0.0017


Hypothesis Test

    Null hypothesis:        Variance of FILLAMT => 0.01
    Alternative:            Variance of FILLAMT <  0.01

            Chi-square          Df          Prob
           --------------------------------------
              1.524             9          0.0030
```

A SAS printout of the analysis is displayed in Figure 8.23. The value of s (highlighted on the printout) is $s = .0412$. Substituting into the formula for the test statistic, we have

$$\chi^2 = \frac{(n-1)s^2}{\sigma^2} = \frac{9(.0412)^2}{.01} = 1.524$$

Since the value of the test statistic is less than 3.32511, the supervisor can conclude that the variance σ^2 of the population of all amounts of fill is less than .01 (i.e., $\sigma < .1$) with probability of a Type I error equal to $\alpha = .05$. If this procedure is repeatedly used, it will incorrectly reject H_0 only 5% of the time. Thus, the quality control supervisor is confident in the decision that the cannery is operating within the desired limits of variability.

Look Back Note that both the test statistic (1.524) and one-tailed p-value of the test (.0030) are shown on the SAS printout. Also note that the p-value is less than $\alpha = .05$, thus confirming our conclusion to reject H_0.

| Now Work | *Exercise 8.111* |

■ ■ ■

One-tailed and two-tailed tests of hypothesis for σ^2 are given in the following box.*

Test of Hypothesis about σ^2

One-Tailed Test	**Two-Tailed Test**
$H_0: \sigma^2 = \sigma_0^2$	$H_0: \sigma^2 = \sigma_0^2$
$H_a: \sigma^2 < \sigma_0^2$ (or $H_a: \sigma^2 > \sigma_0^2$)	$H_a: \sigma^2 \neq \sigma_0^2$
Test statistic: $\chi^2 = \dfrac{(n-1)s^2}{\sigma_0^2}$	Test statistic: $\chi^2 = \dfrac{(n-1)s^2}{\sigma_0^2}$
Rejection region: $\chi^2 < \chi^2_{(1-\alpha)}$ (or $\chi^2 > \chi^2_\alpha$ when $H_a: \sigma^2 > \sigma_0^2$)	Rejection region: $\chi^2 < \chi^2_{(1-\alpha/2)}$ or $\chi^2 > \chi^2_{(\alpha/2)}$

where σ_0^2 is the hypothesized variance and the distribution of χ^2 is based on $(n-1)$ degrees of freedom.

---

*A confidence interval for σ^2 can also be formed using the χ^2-distribution with $(n-1)$ degrees of freedom. A $(1-\alpha)$ 100% confidence interval is

$$\frac{(n-1)s^2}{\chi^2_{\alpha/2}} < \sigma^2 < \frac{(n-1)s^2}{\chi^2_{(1-\alpha/2)}}$$

> ### Conditions Required for a Valid Hypothesis Test for σ^2
>
> 1. A random sample is selected from the target population.
> 2. The population from which the sample is selected has a distribution that is approximately normal.

Caution

The procedure for conducting a hypothesis test for σ^2 in the preceding examples requires an assumption regardless of whether the sample size n is large or small. We must assume that the population from which the sample is selected has an approximate normal distribution. Unlike small sample tests for μ based on the t-statistic, *slight to moderate departures from normality will render the χ^2-test invalid.*

Exercises 8.102–8.118

Understanding the Principles

8.102 What is the sampling distribution used for making inferences about σ^2?

8.103 What conditions are required for a valid test for σ^2?

8.104 *True or False.* The null hypotheses, $H_0: \sigma^2 = .25$ and $H_0: \sigma = .5$, are equivalent.

8.105 *True or False.* When the sample size n is large, no assumptions about the population are necessary to test the population variance σ^2.

Learning the Mechanics

8.106 Let χ_0^2 be a particular value of χ^2. Find the value of χ_0^2 such that
   a. $P(\chi^2 > \chi_0^2) = .10$ for $n = 12$
   b. $P(\chi^2 > \chi_0^2) = .05$ for $n = 9$
   c. $P(\chi^2 > \chi_0^2) = .025$ for $n = 5$

8.107 A random sample of n observations is selected from a normal population to test the null hypothesis that $\sigma^2 = 25$. Specify the rejection region for each of the following combinations of H_a, α, and n:
   a. $H_a: \sigma^2 \neq 25; \alpha = .05; n = 16$
   b. $H_a: \sigma^2 > 25; \alpha = .01; n = 23$
   c. $H_a: \sigma^2 > 25; \alpha = .10; n = 15$
   d. $H_a: \sigma^2 < 25; \alpha = .01; n = 13$
   e. $H_a: \sigma^2 \neq 25; \alpha = .10; n = 7$
   f. $H_a: \sigma^2 < 25; \alpha = .05; n = 25$

8.108 A random sample of seven measurements gave $\bar{x} = 9.4$ and $s^2 = 1.84$.
   a. What assumptions must you make concerning the population in order to test a hypothesis about σ^2?
   b. Suppose the assumptions in part **a** are satisfied. Test the null hypothesis, $\sigma^2 = 1$, against the alternative hypothesis, $\sigma^2 > 1$. Use $\alpha = .05$.
   c. Test the null hypothesis that $\sigma^2 = 1$ against the alternative hypothesis that $\sigma^2 \neq 1$. Use $\alpha = .05$.

8.109 Refer to Exercise 8.108. Suppose we had $n = 100$, $\bar{x} = 9.4$, and $s^2 = 1.84$.
   a. Test the null hypothesis, $H_0: \sigma^2 = 1$, against the alternative hypothesis, $H_a: \sigma^2 > 1$.
   b. Compare your test result with that of Exercise 8.108.

8.110 A random sample of $n = 7$ observations from a normal population produced the following measurements: 4, 0, 6, 3, 3, 5, 9. Do the data provide sufficient evidence to indicate that $\sigma^2 < 2$? Test using $\alpha = .05$.

Applying the Concepts—Basic

8.111 **Point spreads for NFL games.** Refer to the *Chance* (Fall 1998) study of point-spread errors in NFL games, Exercise 8.30 (p. 382). Recall that the difference between the actual game outcome and the point spread established by oddsmakers—the point-spread error—was calculated for 240 NFL games. The results are summarized as follows: $\bar{x} = -1.6$, $s = 13.3$. Suppose the researcher wants to know whether the true standard deviation of the point-spread errors exceeds 15.
   a. Set up H_0 and H_a for the researcher.
   b. Compute the value of the test statistic.
   c. Conduct the test at $\alpha = .10$. Interpret the results in the words of the problem.

8.112 **A new dental bonding agent.** Refer to the *Trends in Biomaterials & Artificial Organs* (January 2003) study of a new bonding adhesive for teeth called "Smartbond," Exercise 8.61 (p. 395). Recall that tests on a sample of 10 extracted teeth bonded with the new adhesive resulted in a mean breaking strength (after 24 hours) of $\bar{x} = 5.07$ Mpa and a standard deviation of $s = .46$ Mpa. In addition to mean breaking strength, orthodontists are concerned about the variability in breaking strength of the new bonding adhesive.
   a. Set up the null and alternative hypothesis for a test to determine if the breaking strength variance differs from .5 Mpa.

b. Find the rejection region for the test using $\alpha = .01$.

c. Compute the test statistic.

d. Give the appropriate conclusion for the test.

e. What conditions are required for the test results to be valid?

8.113 Birthweights of cocaine babies. A group of researchers at the University of Texas-Houston conducted a comprehensive study of pregnant cocaine-dependent women. (*Journal of Drug Issues*, Summer 1997.) All the women in the study used cocaine on a regular basis (at least three times a week) for more than a year. One of the many variables measured was birthweight (in grams) of the baby delivered. For a sample of 16 cocaine-dependent women, the mean birthweight was 2,971 grams and the standard deviation was 410 grams. Test (at $\alpha = .01$) to determine whether the variance in birthweights of babies delivered by cocaine-dependent women is less than 200,000 grams^2.

Applying the Concepts—Intermediate

GOBIANTS

8.114 Mongolian desert ants. Refer to the *Journal of Biogeography* (December 2003) study of ants in Mongolia (Central Asia), Exercise 8.68 (p. 396). Data on the number of ant species attracted to 11 randomly selected desert sites are saved in the **GOBIANTS** file. Do these data indicate that the standard deviation of the number of ant species at all Mongolian desert sites exceeds 15 species? Conduct the appropriate test at $\alpha = .05$. Are the conditions required for a valid test satisfied?

8.115 Extracting toxic substances. A new technique for extracting toxic organic compounds was evaluated in *Chromatographia* (March 1995). Uncontaminated fish fillets were injected with a toxic substance and the method was used to extract the toxicant. To test the precision of the new method, 7 measurements were obtained on a single fish fillet injected with a toxin. Summary statistics on percent of the toxin recovered are given as follows: $\bar{x} = 99$, $s = 9$. Determine whether the standard deviation of the percent recovery using the new method differs from 15. (Use $\alpha = .10$.)

8.116 Ball-bearing diameters. It is essential in the manufacture of machinery to utilize parts that conform to specifications. In the past, diameters of the ball-bearings produced by a certain manufacturer had a variance of .00156. To cut costs, the manufacturer instituted a less expensive production method. The variance of the diameters of 100 randomly sampled bearings produced by the new process was .00211. Do the data provide sufficient evidence to indicate that diameters of ball-bearings produced by the new process are more variable than those produced by the old process?

8.117 Laser Spectroscopy of rocks. Geologists use laser Raman microprobe (LRM) spectroscopy to analyze *fluid inclusions* (pockets of gas or liquid) in rock. A chip of natural Brazilian quartz was artificially injected with several fluid inclusions of liquid carbon dioxide (CO_2) and then subjected to LRM spectroscopy. (*Applied Spectroscopy*, February 1986.) The amount of CO_2 present in the inclusion was recorded for the same inclusion on four different days. The data (in mole percent) follow:

CO2

86.6	84.6	85.5	85.9

a. Do the data indicate that the variation in the CO_2 concentration measurements using the LRM method differs from 1?

b. What assumption is required for the test to be valid?

Applying the Concepts—Advanced

8.118 Homogeneity of brain signals. To improve the signal-to-noise ratio (SNR) in the electrical activity of the brain, neurologists repeatedly stimulate subjects and average the responses—a procedure that assumes that signal responses are homogeneous. A study was conducted to test the homogeneous signal theory. (*IEEE Engineering in Medicine and Biology Magazine*, March 1990.) For this study, the variance of the SNR readings of subjects will equal .54 under the homogeneous signal theory. If the SNR variance exceeds .54, the researchers will conclude that the signals are nonhomogeneous. Signal-to-noise ratios recorded for a sample of 41 normal children ranged from .03 to 3.0. Use this information to test the theory at $\alpha = .10$.

Quick Review

Key Terms

Note: Starred (*) terms are from the optional sections in this chapter.

Alternative (research) hypothesis   370
Chi-square distribution*   412
Conclusion   380
Level of significance   374
Lower-tailed test   377

Null distribution*   404
Null hypothesis   370
Observed significance level
  (*p*-value)   383
One-tailed statistical test   376
Power of a test*   407
Rejection region   371

Test of hypothesis   369
Test statistic   370
Two-tailed hypothesis   377
Two-tailed test   377
Type I error   371
Type II error   372
Upper-tailed test   377

Key Formulas

Note: Starred (*) formulas are from the optional sections in this chapter.

For testing $H_0: \theta = \theta_0$, the **large-sample test statistic** is

$$z = \frac{\hat{\theta} - \theta_0}{\sigma_{\hat{\theta}}}$$

where $\hat{\theta}$, θ_0, and $\sigma_{\hat{\theta}}$ are obtained from the table below:

Parameter, θ	Hypothesized Parameter Value, θ_0	Estimator, $\hat{\theta}$	Standard Error of Estimator, $\sigma_{\hat{\theta}}$	
μ	μ_0	$\bar{x}$	$\dfrac{\sigma}{\sqrt{n}}$	380
p	p_0	$\hat{p}$	$\sqrt{\dfrac{p_0 q_0}{n}}$	399

For testing $H_0: \mu = \mu_0$, the **small-sample test statistic** is

$$t = \frac{\bar{x} - \mu_0}{s/\sqrt{n}} \quad 391$$

*$\beta = P(\hat{\theta}$ falls in acceptance region $|\theta = \theta_a)$ 406
*Power $= 1 - \beta$ 407
*For testing $H_0: \sigma^2 = \sigma_0^2$, the test statistic is

$$\chi^2 = \frac{(n-1)s^2}{\sigma_0^2} \quad 415$$

Language Lab

Symbol	Pronunciation	Description
H_0	*H*-oh	Null hypothesis
H_a	*H*-a	Alternative hypothesis
α	alpha	Probability of Type I error
β	beta	Probability of Type II error
χ^2	chi-square	Sampling distribution of s^2 when data are from a normal population

Chapter Summary Notes

- Elements of a **test of hypothesis**: **null hypothesis, alternative hypothesis, test statistic, significance level (α), rejection region, p-value,** and **conclusion**.
- Two types of errors in a hypothesis test: **Type I error** (reject H_0 when H_0 is true), **Type II error** (accept H_0 when H_0 is false).
- Probabilities of errors: $\alpha = $ **P(Type I error)** $= P$(Reject $H_0|H_0$ true), $\beta = $ **P(Type II error)** $= P$(Accept $H_0|H_0$ false).
- Three forms of the alternative hypothesis: **lower-tailed test ($<$), upper-tailed test ($>$), two-tailed test ($\neq$)**.
- **Observed significance level (p-value)** is the smallest value of α that can be used to reject the null hypothesis.

- Conditions required for a valid **large-sample test for μ**: (1) random sample, (2) large sample size ($n \geq 30$).
- Conditions required for a valid **small-sample test for μ**: (1) random sample, (2) population distribution is approximately normal.
- Conditions required for a valid **large-sample test for p**: (1) random sample, (2) large sample size ($p_0 \pm 3\sigma$ falls between 0 and 1).
- Conditions required for a valid **test for σ^2**: (1) random sample, (2) population distribution is approximately normal, regardless of sample size.
- **Power of the test** $= 1 - \beta = P$(Reject $H_0|H_0$ false).

Supplementary Exercises 8.119–8.151

Note: List the assumptions necessary for the valid implementation of the statistical procedures you use in solving all these exercises. Starred (*) exercises refer to the optional sections in this chapter.

Understanding the Principles

8.119 *Complete the following statement:* The smaller the p-value associated with a test of hypothesis, the stronger the support for the _____ hypothesis. Explain your answer.

8.120 Specify the differences between a large-sample and small-sample test of hypothesis about a population mean μ. Focus on the assumptions and test statistics.

8.121 Which of the elements of a test of hypothesis can and should be specified *prior* to analyzing the data that are to be utilized to conduct the test?

8.122 If the rejection of the null hypothesis of a particular test would cause your firm to go out of business, would you want α to be small or large? Explain.

8.123 *Complete the following statement:* The larger the p-value associated with a test of hypothesis, the stronger the support for the_____ hypothesis. Explain your answer.

Learning the Mechanics

8.124 A random sample of 20 observations selected from a normal population produced $\bar{x} = 72.6$ and $s^2 = 19.4$.
  a. Form a 90% confidence interval for the population mean.
  b. Test $H_0: \mu = 80$ against $H_a: \mu < 80$. Use $\alpha = .05$.
  c. Test $H_0: \mu = 80$ against $H_a: \mu \neq 80$. Use $\alpha = .01$.
  d. Form a 99% confidence interval for μ.
  e. How large a sample would be required to estimate μ to within 1 unit with 95% confidence?

8.125 A random sample of $n = 200$ observations from a binomial population yields $\hat{p} = .29$.
  a. Test $H_0: p = .35$ against $H_a: p < .35$. Use $\alpha = .05$.
  b. Test $H_0: p = .35$ against $H_a: p \neq .35$. Use $\alpha = .05$.
  c. Form a 95% confidence interval for p.
  d. Form a 99% confidence interval for p.
  e. How large a sample would be required to estimate p to within .05 with 99% confidence?

8.126 A random sample of 175 measurements possessed a mean $\bar{x} = 8.2$ and a standard deviation $s = .79$.
  a. Form a 95% confidence interval for μ.
  b. Test $H_0: \mu = 8.3$ against $H_a: \mu \neq 8.3$. Use $\alpha = .05$.
  c. Test $H_0: \mu = 8.4$ against $H_a: \mu \neq 8.4$. Use $\alpha = .05$.

8.127 A random sample of 41 observations from a normal population possessed a mean $\bar{x} = 88$ and a standard deviation $s = 6.9$.
  a. Test $H_0: \sigma^2 = 30$ against $H_a: \sigma^2 > 30$. Use $\alpha = .05$.
  b. Test $H_0: \sigma^2 = 30$ against $H_a: \sigma^2 \neq 30$. Use $\alpha = .05$.

8.128 A t-test is conducted for the null hypothesis $H_0: \mu = 10$ versus the alternative $H_a: \mu > 10$ for a random sample of $n = 17$ observations. The test results are $t = 1.174$, p-value $= .1288$.
  a. Interpret the p-value.
  b. What assumptions are necessary for the validity of this test?
  c. Calculate and interpret the p-value assuming the alternative hypothesis was instead $H_a: \mu \neq 10$.

Applying the Concepts—Basic

8.129 **FDA mandatory new drug testing.** When a new drug is formulated, the pharmaceutical company must subject it to lengthy and involved testing before receiving the necessary permission from the Food and Drug Administration (FDA) to market the drug. The FDA requires the pharmaceutical company to provide substantial evidence that the new drug is safe for potential consumers.
  a. If the new drug testing were to be placed in a test of hypothesis framework, would the null hypothesis be that the drug is safe or unsafe? The alternative hypothesis?
  b. Given the choice of null and alternative hypotheses in part **a**, describe Type I and Type II errors in terms of this application. Define α and β in terms of this application.
  c. If the FDA wants to be very confident that the drug is safe before permitting it to be marketed, is it more important that α or β be small? Explain.

8.130 **Online shopping.** According to *Forbes* (December 13, 1999), Creative Good, a New York consulting firm, claims that 40% of shoppers fail in their attempts to purchase merchandise online because web sites are too complex. Another consulting firm asked a random sample of 60 online shoppers to each test a different randomly selected e-commerce web site. Only 15 reported sufficient frustration with their sites to deter making a purchase.
  a. What are the appropriate null and alternative hypotheses to test the claim made by Creative Good?
  b. Do the data provide sufficient evidence to support the claim? Use $\alpha = .01$.
  c. Calculate and interpret the p-value for the test.

8.131 **Sleep deprivation study.** In a British study, 12 healthy college students, deprived of one night's sleep, received an array of tests intended to measure thinking time, fluency, flexibility, and originality of thought. The overall test scores of the sleep-deprived students were compared to the average score expected from students who received their accustomed sleep (*Sleep*, January 1989). Suppose the overall scores of the 12 sleep-deprived students had a mean of $\bar{x} = 63$ and a standard deviation of 17.

(Lower scores are associated with a decreased ability to think creatively.)

a. Test the hypothesis that the true mean score of sleep-deprived subjects is less than 80, the mean score of subjects who received sleep prior to taking the test. Use $\alpha = .05$.

b. What assumption is required for the hypothesis test of part a to be valid?

8.132 The "Pepsi challenge." "Take the Pepsi Challenge" was a marketing campaign used by the Pepsi-Cola Company. Coca-Cola drinkers participated in a blind taste test in which they tasted unmarked cups of Pepsi and Coke and were asked to select their favorite. Pepsi claimed that "in recent blind taste tests, more than half the Diet Coke drinkers surveyed said they preferred the taste of Diet Pepsi." (*Consumer's Research*, May 1993.) Suppose 100 Diet Coke drinkers took the Pepsi Challenge and 56 preferred the taste of Diet Pepsi. Test the hypothesis that more than half of all Diet Coke drinkers will select Diet Pepsi in a blind taste test. Use $\alpha = .05$.

8.133 Masculinizing human faces. Refer to the *Nature* (August 27, 1998) study of facial characteristics that are deemed attractive, Exercise 8.51 (p. 389). In another experiment, 67 human subjects viewed side-by-side an image of a Caucasian male face and the same image 50% masculinized. Each subject was asked to select the facial image that they deemed more attractive. Fifty-eight of the 67 subjects felt that masculinization of face shape decreased attractiveness of the male face. The researchers used this sample information to test whether the subjects showed preference for either the unaltered or morphed male face.

a. Set up the null and alternative hypotheses for this test.

b. Compute the test statistic.

c. The researchers reported *p*-value ≈ 0 for the test. Do you agree?

d. Make the appropriate conclusion in the words of the problem. Use $\alpha = .01$.

⚙ **MATHCPU**

*8.134 Refer to the *IEEE Transactions* (June 1990) study of a new hybrid algorithm for solving polynomial 0/1 mathematical programs, Exercise 7.99 (p. 361). An SAS printout giving descriptive statistics for the sample of 52 solution times is reproduced below. Use this information to determine whether the variance of the solution times differs from 2. Use $\alpha = .05$.

8.135 Mental health of the unemployed. A study reported in the *Journal of Occupational and Organizational Psychology* (December 1992) investigated the relationship of employment status to mental health. Each of a sample of 49 unemployed men was given a mental health examination using the General Health Questionnaire (GHQ). The GHQ is a widely recognized measure of present mental health, with lower values indicating better mental health. The mean and standard deviation of the GHQ scores were $\bar{x} = 10.94$ and $s = 5.10$, respectively.

a. Specify the appropriate null and alternative hypotheses if we wish to test the research hypothesis that the mean GHQ score for all unemployed men exceeds 10. Is the test one-tailed or two-tailed? Why?

b. If we specify $\alpha = .05$, what is the appropriate rejection region for this test?

c. Conduct the test and state your conclusion clearly in the language of this exercise.

Applying the Concepts—Intermediate

8.136 Errors in medical tests. Medical tests have been developed to detect many serious diseases. A medical test is designed to minimize the probability that it will produce a "false positive" or a "false negative." A false positive is a positive test result for an individual who does not have the disease, whereas a false negative is a negative test result for an individual who does have the disease.

a. If we treat a medical test for a disease as a statistical test of hypothesis, what are the null and alternative hypotheses for the medical test?

b. What are the Type I and Type II errors for the test? Relate each to false positives and false negatives.

c. Which of these errors has graver consequences? Considering this error, is it more important to minimize α or β? Explain.

8.137 Cropweights of pigeons. In Exercise 7.91 (p. 360), you analyzed data from a study of the diets of spinifex pigeons. The data, extracted from the *Australian Journal of Zoology*, are reproduced in the table. Each measurement in the data set represents the weight (in grams) of the crop content of a spinifex pigeon. Conduct a test at $\alpha = .05$ to determine whether the mean weight in the crops of all spinifex pigeons differs from 1 gram. Test the validity of any assumptions you make.

⚙ **PIGEONS**

.457	3.751	.238	2.967	2.509	1.384	1.454	.818
.335	1.436	1.603	1.309	.201	.530	2.144	.834

SAS Output for Exercie 8.134

The MEANS Procedure

Analysis Variable : CPU

Mean	Std Dev	Variance	N	Minimum	Maximum
0.8121923	1.5047603	2.2643035	52	0.0360000	8.7880000

8.138 Production of ketchup bottles. A consumer protection group is concerned that a ketchup manufacturer is filling its 20-ounce family-size containers with less than 20 ounces of ketchup. The group purchases 10 family-size bottles of this ketchup, weighs the contents of each, and finds that the mean weight is equal to 19.86 ounces, and the standard deviation is equal to .22 ounce.

a. Do the data provide sufficient evidence for the consumer group to conclude that the mean fill per family-size bottle is less than 20 ounces? Test using $\alpha = .05$.

b. If the test in part **a** were conducted on a periodic basis by the company's quality control department, is the consumer group more concerned about making a Type I error or a Type II error? (The probability of making this type of error is called the *consumer's risk*.)

c. The ketchup company is also interested in the mean amount of ketchup per bottle. It does not wish to overfill them. For the test conducted in part **a**, which type of error is more serious from the company's point of view—a Type I error or a Type II error? (The probability of making this type of error is called the *producer's risk*.)

8.139 Inbreeding of tropical wasps. Refer to the *Science* (November 1988) study of inbreeding in tropical swarm-founding wasps, Exercise 7.97 (p. 361). A sample of 197 wasps, captured, frozen, and subjected to a series of genetic tests, yielded a sample mean inbreeding coefficient of $\bar{x} = .044$ with a standard deviation of $s = .884$. Recall that if the wasp has no tendency to inbreed, the true mean inbreeding coefficient μ for the species will equal 0.

a. Test the hypothesis that the true mean inbreeding coefficient μ for this species of wasp exceeds 0. Use $\alpha = .05$.

b. Compare the inference, part **a**, to the inference obtained in Exercise 7.97 using a confidence interval. Do the inferences agree? Explain.

*8.140 Weights of parrotfish. A marine biologist wishes to use parrotfish for experimental purposes due to the belief that their weight is fairly stable (i.e., the variability in weights among parrotfish is small). The biologist randomly samples 10 parrotfish and finds that their mean weight is 4.3 pounds and the standard deviation is 1.4 pounds. The biologist will use the parrotfish only if there is evidence that the variance of their weights is less than 4.

a. Is there sufficient evidence for the biologist to claim that the variability in weights among parrotfish is small enough to justify their use in the experiment? Test at $\alpha = .05$.

b. State any assumptions that are needed for the test, part **a**, to be valid.

8.141 PCB in plant discharge. The EPA sets a limit of 5 parts per million (ppm) on PCB (a dangerous substance) in water. A major manufacturing firm producing PCB for electrical insulation discharges small amounts from the plant. The company management, attempting to control the PCB in its discharge, has given instructions to halt production if the mean amount of PCB in the effluent exceeds 3 ppm. A random sample of 50 water specimens produced the following statistics: $\bar{x} = 3.1$ ppm and $s = .5$ ppm.

a. Do these statistics provide sufficient evidence to halt the production process? Use $\alpha = .01$.

b. If you were the plant manager, would you want to use a large or a small value for α for the test in part **a**?

*8.142 PCB in plant discharge (cont'd). Refer to Exercise 8.141.

a. In the context of the problem, define a Type II error.

b. Calculate β for the test described in part **a** of Exercise 8.141 assuming that the true mean is $\mu = 3.1$ ppm.

c. What is the power of the test to detect the effluent's departure from the standard of 3.0 ppm when the mean is 3.1 ppm?

d. Repeat parts **b** and **c** assuming that the true mean is 3.2 ppm. What happens to the power of the test as the plant's mean PCB departs farther from the standard?

*8.143 PCB in plant discharge (cont'd). Refer to Exercises 8.141 and 8.142.

a. Suppose an α value of .05 is used to conduct the test. Does this change favor the manufacturer? Explain.

b. Determine the value of β and the power for the test when $\alpha = .05$ and $\mu = 3.1$.

c. What happens to the power of the test when α is increased?

8.144 Psychological study of obese adolescents. Research reported in the *Journal of Psychology* (March 1991) studied the personality characteristics of obese individuals. One variable, the locus of control (LOC), measures the individual's degree of belief that he or she has control over situations. High scores on the LOC scale indicate less perceived control. For one sample of 19 obese adolescents, the mean LOC score was 10.89 with a standard deviation of 2.48. Suppose we wish to test whether the mean LOC score for all obese adolescents exceeds 10, the average for "normal" individuals.

a. Specify the null and alternative hypotheses for this test.

b. Conduct the test, part **a**, and make the proper conclusion.

8.145 Ph.D.s awarded to foreign nationals. The National Science Foundation, in a survey of 2,237 engineering graduate students who earned their Ph.D. degrees, found that 607 were U.S. citizens; the majority (1,630) of the Ph.D. degrees were awarded to foreign nationals. (*Science*, September 24, 1993.) Conduct a test to determine whether the true percentage of engineering Ph.D. degrees awarded to foreign nationals exceeds 50%. Use $\alpha = .01$.

*8.146 **Interocular eye pressure.** Ophthalmologists require an instrument that can rapidly measure interocular pressure for glaucoma patients. The device now in general use is known to yield readings of this pressure with a variance of 10.3. The variance of five pressure readings on the same eye by a newly developed instrument is equal to 9.8. Does this sample variance provide sufficient evidence to indicate that the new instrument is more reliable than the instrument currently in use? (Use $\alpha = .05$.)

Applying the Concepts—Advanced

8.147 **Polygraph test error rates.** A group of physicians subjected the *polygraph* (or *lie detector*) to the same careful testing given to medical diagnostic tests. They found that if 1,000 people were subjected to the polygraph and 500 told the truth and 500 lied, the polygraph would indicate that approximately 185 of the truth-tellers were liars and that approximately 120 of the liars were truth-tellers (*Discover*, 1986).

   a. In the application of a polygraph test, an individual is presumed to be a truth-teller (H_0) until "proven" a liar (H_a). In this context, what is a Type I error? A Type II error?

   b. According to the study, what is the probability (approximately) that a polygraph test will result in a Type I error? A Type II error?

8.148 **NCAA March Madness.** For three weeks each March, the National Collegiate Athletic Association (NCAA) holds its annual men's basketball championship tournament. The 64 best college basketball teams in the nation play a single-elimination tournament—a total of 63 games—to determine the NCAA champion. Tournament followers, from hardcore gamblers to the casual fan who enters the office betting pool, have a strong interest in handicapping the games. To provide insight into this phenomenon, statisticians Hal Stern and Barbara Mock analyzed data from 13 previous NCAA tournaments and published their results in *Chance* (Winter 1998). The results of first-round games are summarized in the table at the bottom of the page.

   a. A common perception among fans, media, and gamblers is that the higher seeded team has a better than 50-50 chance of winning a first-round game. Is there evidence to support this perception? Conduct the appropriate test for each matchup. What trends do you observe?

   b. Is there evidence to support the claim that a 1-, 2-, 3-, or 4-seeded team will win by an average of more than 10 points in first-round games? Conduct the appropriate test for each matchup.

   c. Is there evidence to support the claim that a 5-, 6-, 7-, or 8-seeded team will win by an average of less than 5 points in first-round games? Conduct the appropriate test for each matchup.

*d. For each matchup, test the null hypothesis that the standard deviation of the victory margin is 11 points.

   e. The researchers also calculated the difference between the game outcome (victory margin, in points) and point spread established by Las Vegas oddsmakers for a sample of 360 recent NCAA tournament games. The mean difference is .7 and the standard deviation of the difference is 11.3. If the true mean difference is 0, then the point spread can be considered a good predictor of the game outcome. Use this sample information to test the hypothesis that the point spread, on average, is a good predictor of the victory margin in NCAA tournament games.

8.149 **Homes sold in California.** In 1999, the average size of single-family homes built in the U.S. was 2,230 square feet, an increase of over 200 square feet from a decade earlier. (*Wall Street Journal Interactive Edition*, January 7, 2000.) A random sample of 100 new homes sold in California in late 1999 yielded the following size information: $\bar{x} = 2{,}347$ square feet and $s = 257$ square feet.

   a. Assume the average size of U.S. homes is known with certainty. Do the sample data provide sufficient

Summary of First-Round NCAA Tournament Games, 1985–1997

Matchup (Seeds)	Number of Games	Number Won by Favorite (Higher Seed)	Margin of Victory (Points)	
			Mean	Standard Deviation
1 vs 16	52	52	22.9	12.4
2 vs 15	52	49	17.2	11.4
3 vs 14	52	41	10.6	12.0
4 vs 13	52	42	10.0	12.5
5 vs 12	52	37	5.3	10.4
6 vs 11	52	36	4.3	10.7
7 vs 10	52	35	3.2	10.5
8 vs 9	52	22	−2.1	11.0

Source: Stern, H. S., and Mock, B. "College basketball upsets: Will a 16-seed ever beat a 1-seed?" *Chance*, Vol. 11, No. 1, Winter 1998, p. 29 (Table 3).

evidence to conclude that the mean size of all California homes built in late 1999 exceeds the national average? Test using $\alpha = .01$.

b. What is the probability that the test will fail to reject the null hypothesis when in fact $\mu = 2,330$ square feet? What is the name given to this type of error?

c. What is the probability that the test will reject the null hypothesis when in fact $\mu = 2,330$ square feet? What is the name given to this type of error?

*__d.__ Suppose the actual mean size of new California homes was $\mu = 2,330$ square feet. What is the power of the test in part **a** to detect this 100-square-feet difference?

*__e.__ If the California mean were actually $\mu = 2,280$ square feet, what is the power of the test in part **a** to detect this 50-square-feet difference?

Critical Thinking Challenges

8.150 The Hot Tamale caper. "Hot Tamales" are chewy, cinnamon-flavored candies. A bulk vending machine is known to dispense, on average, 15 Hot Tamales per bag. *Chance* (Fall 2000) published an article on a classroom project in which students were required to purchase bags of Hot Tamales from the machine and count the number of candies per bag. One student group claimed they purchased five bags that had the following candy counts: 25, 23, 21, 21, and 20. There was some question as to whether the students had fabricated the data. Use a hypothesis test to gain insight into whether or not the data collected by the students are fabricated. Use a level of significance that gives the benefit of the doubt to the students.

8.151 Verifying voter petitions. To get their names on the ballot of a local election, political candidates often must obtain petitions bearing the signatures of a minimum number of registered voters. In Pinellas County, Florida, a certain political candidate obtained petitions with 18,200 signatures. (*St. Petersburg Times*, April 7, 1992.) To verify that the names on the petitions were signed by actual registered voters, election officials randomly sampled 100 of the names and checked each for authenticity. Only two were invalid signatures.

a. Is 98 out of 100 verified signatures sufficient to believe that more than 17,000 of the total 18,200 signatures are valid?

b. Repeat part **a** if only 16,000 valid signatures are required.

Student Projects

The "efficient market" theory postulates that the best predictor of a stock's price at some point in the future is the current price of the stock (with some adjustments for inflation and transaction costs, which we shall assume to be negligible for the purpose of this exercise). To test this theory, select a random sample of 25 stocks on the New York Stock Exchange and record the closing prices on the last days of two recent consecutive months. Calculate the increase or decrease in the stock price over the 1-month period.

a. Define μ as the mean change in price of all stocks over a 1-month period. Set up the appropriate null and alternative hypotheses in terms of μ.

b. Use the sample of the 25 stock price differences to conduct the test of hypothesis established in part **a**. Use $\alpha = .05$.

c. Tabulate the number of rejections and nonrejections of the null hypothesis in your class. If the null hypothesis were true, how many rejections of the null hypothesis would you expect among those in your class? How does this expectation compare with the actual number of nonrejections? What does the result of this exercise indicate about the efficient market theory?

REFERENCES

Snedecor, G. W., and Cochran, W. G. *Statistical Methods*, 7th ed. Ames: Iowa State University Press, 1980.

Wackerly, D., Mendenhall, W., and Scheaffer, R. *Mathematical Statistics with Applications*, 6th ed. North Scituate, Mass.: Duxbury, 2002.

Using Technology

Tests of Hypothesis Using MINITAB

MINITAB can be used to obtain one-sample tests for both a population mean and a population proportion but cannot currently produce a test for a population variance. To generate a hypothesis test for the mean using a previously created sample data set, first access the MINITAB data worksheet. Next, click on the "Stat" button on the MINITAB menu bar, then click on "Basic Statistics" and "1-Sample t," as shown in Figure 8.M.1. The resulting dialog box appears as shown in Figure 8.M.2. Click on "Samples in Columns," then specify the quantitative variable of interest in the open box. Specify the value of μ_0 for the null hypothesis in the "Test mean" box. Now, click on the "Options" button at the bottom of the dialog box and specify the form of the alternative hypothesis as shown in Figure 8.M.3. Click "OK" to return to the "1-Sample t" dialog box, then click "OK" again to produce the hypothesis test.

Figure 8.M.1
MINITAB Menu Options for a Test about μ

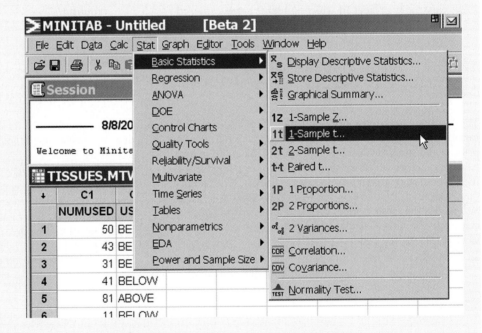

If you want to produce a test for the mean from summary information (e.g., the sample mean, sample standard deviation, and sample size), then click on "Summarized data" in the "1-Sample t" dialog box, enter the values of the summary statistics and μ_0, then click "OK."

[*Important Note*: The MINITAB one-sample *t*-procedure uses the *t*-statistic to generate the hypothesis test. When the sample size *n* is small, this is the appropriate method. When the sample size *n* is large, the *t*-value will be approximately equal to the large-sample *z*-value and the resulting test will still be valid. If you have a large sample and you know the value of the population standard deviation σ (which is rarely the case), then select "1-sample Z" from the "Basic Statistics" menu options (see Figure 8.M.1) and make the appropriate selections.]

To generate a test for a population proportion using a previously created sample data set, first access the MINITAB data worksheet. Next, click on the "Stat" button on the MINITAB menu bar, then click on "Basic Statistics" and "1 Proportion" (see Figure 8.M.1). The resulting dialog box appears as shown in Figure 8.M.4. Click on "Samples in Columns," then specify the qualitative variable of interest in the open box. Now, click on the "Options" button at the bottom of the dialog box and specify the null hypothesis value p_0 and the form of the alternative hypothesis in the resulting dialog box, as shown in Figure 8.M.5. Also, check the "Use test and interval based on normal distribution" box at the bottom. Click "OK" to return to the "1-Proportion" dialog box, then click "OK" again to produce the test results.

Figure 8.M.4
MINITAB 1-Proportion
Dialog Box

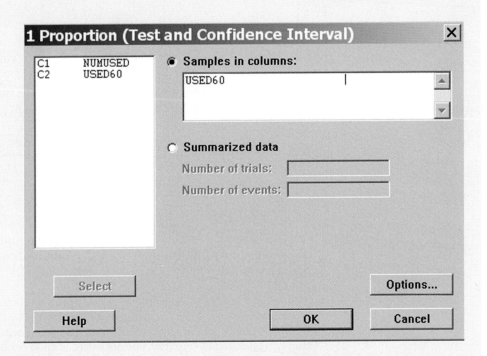

Figure 8.M.5
MINITAB 1-Proportion
Options

If you want to produce a confidence interval for a proportion from summary information (e.g., the number of successes and the sample size), then click on "Summarized data" in the "1-Proportion" dialog box (see Figure 8.M.4). Enter the value for the number of trials (i.e., the sample size) and the number of events (i.e., the number of successes), then click "OK."

9

Inferences Based on Two Samples

Confidence Intervals and Tests of Hypotheses

Contents

9.1 Identifying the Target Parameter

9.2 Comparing Two Population Means: Independent Sampling

9.3 Comparing Two Population Means: Paired Difference Experiments

9.4 Comparing Two Population Proportions: Independent Sampling

9.5 Determining the Sample Size

9.6 Comparing Two Population Variances: Independent Sampling (Optional)

Statistics in Action

Detection of Rigged Milk Prices

Using Technology

Two-Sample Inferences Using MINITAB

Where We've Been

- Explored two methods for making statistical inferences: *confidence intervals* and *tests of hypotheses*

- Studied confidence intervals and tests for a single population mean μ, a single population proportion p, and a single population variance σ^2

- Learned how to select the sample size necessary to estimate a population parameter with a specified margin of error

Where We're Going

- Learn how to compare two populations using confidence intervals and tests of hypotheses.

- Apply these inferential methods to problems where we want to compare two population means, two population proportions, or two population variances.

- Determine the sizes of the samples necessary to estimate the difference between two population parameters with a specified margin of error.

Statistics
in *ACTION*

Detection of Rigged Milk Prices

Many products and services are purchased by governments, cities, states, and businesses on the basis of sealed bids, and contracts are awarded to the lowest bidders. This process works extremely well in competitive markets, but it has the potential to increase the cost of purchasing if the markets are noncompetitive or if bidders are engaged in collusive practices. An investigation that began with a statistical analysis of bids in the Florida school milk market in the mid-1980s led to the recovery of more than $33 million from dairies who had conspired to rig the bids there. The investigation spread quickly to other states, and settlements and fines from dairies exceed $100 million for school milk bid-rigging in twenty other states. This case concerns a school milk bid-rigging investigation in Kentucky.

Each year, the state of Kentucky invites bids from dairies to supply half-pint containers of fluid milk products for its school districts. The products include whole white milk, low-fat white milk, and low-fat chocolate milk. In several school districts in northern Kentucky, the suppliers (dairies) were accused of "price fixing"—that is, conspiring to allocate the districts so that the "winner" was predetermined and the price per pint was set above the fair, or competitive, price. A market analysis disclosed that two dairies—Meyer Dairy and Trauth Dairy—were the only two bidders on the milk contracts in the school districts in the tricounty market of Boone, Campbell, and Kenton counties between 1983 and 1991. Consequently, these two companies

were awarded all the milk contracts in the market. (In contrast, a large number of different dairies won the milk contracts for school districts in the remainder of the northern Kentucky market—called the surrounding market.) Speculation is that Meyer and Trauth conspired to rig their bids in the tricounty market.

The Commonwealth of Kentucky maintains a database on all bids received from the dairies competing for the milk contracts. With permission, some of these data have been made available for analysis to determine whether there is empirical evidence of bid collusion in the tricounty market. The data, saved in the **MILK** file, are described in detail in Table SIA9.1.

In this chapter, several Statistics in Action Revisited examples demonstrate how we can use the methodology of this chapter to investigate the possibility of bid-rigging in the northern Kentucky milk market.

Statistics in the Action Revisited

- Comparing the Mean Winning Bid Prices of Two Kentucky Milk Markets (p. 446)
- Comparing the Incumbency Rates of Two Kentucky Milk Markets (p. 476)
- Comparing the Dispersion of Bid Prices in Two Kentucky Milk Markets (p. 490)

⊚ **MILK**

TABLE SIA9.1   Description of Data Saved in the MILK file

Number of observations: 392

Variable	Type	Description
YEAR	QN	Year in which milk contract awarded
MARKET	QL	Northern Kentucky market (TRI-COUNTY or SURROUND)
WINNER	QL	Name of winning dairy
WWBID	QN	Winning bid price of whole white milk (dollars per half-pint)
LFWBID	QN	Winning bid price of low-fat white milk (dollars per half-pint)
LFCBID	QN	Winning bid price of low-fat chocolate milk (dollars per half-pint)
DISTRICT	QL	School district number

9.1 Identifying the Target Parameter

Many experiments involve a comparison of two populations. For instance, a sociologist may want to estimate the difference in mean life expectancy between innercity and suburban residents. A consumer group may want to test whether two major brands of food freezers differ in the average amount of electricity they use. A political candidate might want to estimate the difference in the proportions of voters in two districts who favor his or her candidacy. A professional golfer might be interested in comparing the variability in the distance that two competing brands of golf balls travel when struck with the same club. In this chapter, we consider techniques for using two samples to compare the populations from which they were selected.

The same procedures that are used to estimate and test hypotheses about a single population can be modified to make inferences about two populations. As in Chapters 7 and 8, the methodology used will depend on the sizes of the samples and the parameter of interest (i.e., the *target parameter*). Some key words and the type of data associated with the parameters covered in this chapter are listed in the box.

Determining the Target Parameter

Parameter	Key Words or Phrases	Type of Data
$\mu_1 - \mu_2$	Mean difference; difference in averages	Quantitative
$p_1 - p_2$	Difference between proportions, percentages, fractions, or rates; compare proportions	Qualitative
$(\sigma_1)^2/(\sigma_2)^2$	Ratio of variances; difference in variability or spread; compare variation	Quantitative

You can see that the key words *difference* and *compare* help identify the fact that two populations are to be compared. For the examples given above, the words *mean* in *mean life expectancy* and *average* in *average amount of electricity* imply that the target parameter is the difference in population means, $\mu_1 - \mu_2$. The word *proportions* in *proportions of voters in two districts* indicates that the target parameter is the difference in proportions, $p_1 - p_2$. Finally, the key word *variability* in *variability in the distance* identifies the ratio of population variances, $(\sigma_1)^2/(\sigma_2)^2$, as the target parameter.

As with inferences about a single population, the type of data (quantitative or qualitative) collected on the two samples is also indicative of the target parameter. With quantitative data, you are likely to be interested in comparing the means or variances of the data. With qualitative data with two outcomes (success or failure), a comparison of the proportions of successes is likely to be of interest.

We consider methods for comparing two population means in Sections 9.2 and 9.3. A comparison of population proportions is presented in Section 9.4 and population variances in optional Section 9.6. We show how to determine the sample sizes necessary for reliable estimates of the target parameters in Section 9.5.

9.2 Comparing Two Population Means: Independent Sampling

In this section we develop both large-sample and small-sample methodologies for comparing two population means. In the large-sample case we use the z-statistic, while in the small-sample case we use the t-statistic.

Large Samples

EXAMPLE 9.1   A LARGE-SAMPLE CONFIDENCE INTERVAL FOR $\mu_1 - \mu_2$

Problem   A dietitian has developed a diet that is low in fats, carbohydrates, and cholesterol. Although the diet was initially intended to be used by people with heart disease, the dietitian wishes to examine the effect this diet has on the weights of obese people. Two random samples of 100 obese people each are selected, and one group of 100 is placed on the low-fat diet. The other 100 are placed on a diet that contains approximately the same quantity of food but is not as low in fats, carbohydrates, and cholesterol. For each person, the amount of weight lost (or gained) in a 3-week period is recorded. The data, saved in the **DIETSTUDY** file, are listed in Table 9.1. Form a 95% confidence interval for the difference between the population mean weight losses for the two diets. Interpret the result.

Solution   Recall that the general form of a large-sample confidence interval for a single mean μ is $\bar{x} \pm z_{\alpha/2}\sigma_{\bar{x}}$. That is, we add and subtract $z_{\alpha/2}$ standard deviations of the sample estimate, $\bar{x}$, to the value of the estimate. We employ a similar procedure to form the confidence interval for the difference between two population means.

Let μ_1 represent the mean of the conceptual population of weight losses for all obese people who could be placed on the low-fat diet. Let μ_2 be similarly defined for the other diet. We wish to form a confidence interval for $(\mu_1 - \mu_2)$. An intuitively appealing estimator for $(\mu_1 - \mu_2)$ is the difference between the sample means, $(\bar{x}_1 - \bar{x}_2)$. Thus, we will form the confidence interval of interest by

$$(\bar{x}_1 - \bar{x}_2) \pm z_{\alpha/2}\sigma_{(\bar{x}_1 - \bar{x}_2)}$$

⊙ **DIETSTUDY**

TABLE 9.1   Diet Study Data, Example 9.1

Weight Losses for Lowfat Diet									
8	10	10	12	9	3	11	7	9	2
21	8	9	2	2	20	14	11	15	6
13	8	10	12	1	7	10	13	14	4
8	12	8	10	11	19	0	9	10	4
11	7	14	12	11	12	4	12	9	2
4	3	3	5	9	9	4	3	5	12
3	12	7	13	11	11	13	12	18	9
6	14	14	18	10	11	7	9	7	2
16	16	11	11	3	15	9	5	2	6
5	11	14	11	6	9	4	17	20	10

Weight Losses for Regular Diet									
6	6	5	5	2	6	10	3	9	11
14	4	10	13	3	8	8	13	9	3
4	12	6	11	12	9	8	5	8	7
6	2	6	8	5	7	16	18	6	8
13	1	9	8	12	10	6	1	0	13
11	2	8	16	14	4	6	5	12	9
11	6	3	9	9	14	2	10	4	13
8	1	1	4	9	4	1	1	5	6
14	0	7	12	9	5	9	12	7	9
8	9	8	10	5	8	0	3	4	8

Figure 9.1

SPSS Analysis of Diet
Study Data

Group Statistics

	DIET	N	Mean	Std. Deviation	Std. Error Mean
WTLOSS	LOWFAT	100	9.31	4.668	.467
	REGULAR	100	7.40	4.035	.404

Independent Samples Test

		Levene's Test for Equality of Variances		t-test for Equality of Means					95% Confidence Interval of the Difference	
		F	Sig.	t	df	Sig. (2-tailed)	Mean Difference	Std. Error Difference	Lower	Upper
WTLOSS	Equal variances assumed	1.367	.244	3.095	198	.002	1.910	.617	.693	3.127
	Equal variances not assumed			3.095	193.940	.002	1.910	.617	.693	3.127

Assuming the two samples are independent, the standard deviation of the difference between the sample means is

$$\sigma_{(\bar{x}_1 - \bar{x}_2)} = \sqrt{\frac{\sigma_1^2}{n_1} + \frac{\sigma_2^2}{n_2}} \approx \sqrt{\frac{s_1^2}{n_1} + \frac{s_2^2}{n_2}}.$$

Summary statistics for the diet data are displayed at the top of the SPSS printout, Figure 9.1. Note that $\bar{x}_1 = 9.31$, $\bar{x}_2 = 7.40$, $s_1 = 4.67$, and $s_2 = 4.04$. Using these values and noting that $\alpha = .05$ and $z_{.025} = 1.96$, we find that the 95% confidence interval is, approximately,

$$(9.31 - 7.40) \pm 1.96\sqrt{\frac{(4.67)^2}{100} + \frac{(4.04)^2}{100}} = 1.91 \pm (1.96)(.62) = 1.91 \pm 1.22$$

or $(.69, 3.13)$. This interval (rounded) is also given at the bottom of Figure 9.1.

Using this estimation procedure over and over again for different samples, we know that approximately 95% of the confidence intervals formed in this manner will enclose the difference in population means ($\mu_1 - \mu_2$). Therefore, we are highly confident that the mean weight loss for the low-fat diet is between .69 and 3.13 pounds more than the mean weight loss for the other diet. With this information, the dietitian better understands the potential of the low-fat diet as a weight-reducing diet.

Look Back If the confidence interval for ($\mu_1 - \mu_2$) contains 0 [e.g., $(-2.5, 1.3)$], then it is possible for the difference between the population means to be 0 (i.e., $\mu_1 - \mu_2 = 0$). In this case we could not conclude that a significant difference exits between the mean weight losses for the two diets.

Now Work   *Exercise 9.6a*

■ ■ ■

Figure 9.2

Sampling Distribution
of $(\bar{x}_1 - \bar{x}_2)$

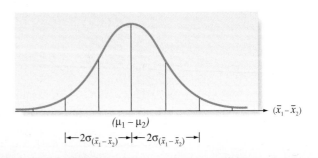

   The justification for the procedure used in Example 9.1 to estimate $(\mu_1 - \mu_2)$ relies on the properties of the sampling distribution of $(\bar{x}_1 - \bar{x}_2)$. The performance of the estimator in repeated sampling is pictured in Figure 9.2, and its properties are summarized in the next box.

Properties of the Sampling Distribution of $(\bar{x}_1 - \bar{x}_2)$

1. The mean of the sampling distribution of $(\bar{x}_1 - \bar{x}_2)$ is $(\mu_1 - \mu_2)$.

2. If the two samples are independent, the standard deviation of the sampling distribution is

$$\sigma_{(\bar{x}_1 - \bar{x}_2)} = \sqrt{\frac{\sigma_1^2}{n_1} + \frac{\sigma_2^2}{n_2}}$$

where σ_1^2 and σ_2^2 are the variances of the two populations being sampled and n_1 and n_2 are the respective sample sizes. We also refer to $\sigma_{(\bar{x}_1 - \bar{x}_2)}$ as the **standard error** of the statistic $(\bar{x}_1 - \bar{x}_2)$.

3. The sampling distribution of $(\bar{x}_1 - \bar{x}_2)$ is approximately normal for *large samples* by the Central Limit Theorem.

   In Example 9.1, we noted the similarity in the procedures for forming a large-sample confidence interval for one population mean and a large-sample confidence interval for the difference between two population means. When we are testing hypotheses, the procedures are again very similar. The general large-sample procedures for forming confidence intervals and testing hypotheses about $(\mu_1 - \mu_2)$ are summarized in the following boxes.

Large Sample Confidence Interval for $(\mu_1 - \mu_2)$

$$(\bar{x}_1 - \bar{x}_2) \pm z_{\alpha/2}\sigma_{(\bar{x}_1 - \bar{x}_2)} = (\bar{x}_1 - \bar{x}_2) \pm z_{\alpha/2}\sqrt{\frac{\sigma_1^2}{n_1} + \frac{\sigma_2^2}{n_2}}$$

$$\approx (\bar{x}_1 - \bar{x}_2) \pm z_{\alpha/2}\sqrt{\frac{s_1^2}{n_1} + \frac{s_2^2}{n_2}}$$

Large-Sample Test of Hypothesis for $(\mu_1 - \mu_2)$

One-Tailed Test	**Two-Tailed Test**
$H_0: (\mu_1 - \mu_2) = D_0$	$H_0: (\mu_1 - \mu_2) = D_0$
$H_a: (\mu_1 - \mu_2) < D_0$	$H_a: (\mu_1 - \mu_2) \neq D_0$
[or $H_a: (\mu_1 - \mu_2) > D_0$]	

where $D_0 =$ Hypothesized difference between the means (this difference is often hypothesized to be equal to 0)

Test statistic:

$$z = \frac{(\bar{x}_1 - \bar{x}_2) - D_0}{\sigma_{(\bar{x}_1 - \bar{x}_2)}} \quad \text{where} \quad \sigma_{(\bar{x}_1 - \bar{x}_2)} = \sqrt{\frac{\sigma_1^2}{n_1} + \frac{\sigma_2^2}{n_2}} \approx \sqrt{\frac{s_1^2}{n_1} + \frac{s_2^2}{n_2}}$$

Rejection region: $z < -z_\alpha$	*Rejection region:* $|z| > z_{\alpha/2}$
[or $z > z_\alpha$ when	
$H_a: (\mu_1 - \mu_2) > D_0$]	

> **Conditions Required for Valid Large-Sample Inferences about $\mu_1 - \mu_2$**
>
> **1.** The two samples are randomly selected in an independent manner from the two target populations.
>
> **2.** The sample sizes, n_1 and n_2, are both large (i.e., $n_1 \geq 30$ and $n_2 \geq 30$). (Due to the Central Limit Theorem, this condition guarantees that the sampling distribution of $(\bar{x}_1 - \bar{x}_2)$ will be approximately normal regardless of the shapes of the underlying probability distributions of the populations. Also, s_1^2 and s_2^2 will provide good approximations to σ_1^2 and σ_2^2 when both the samples are large.)

EXAMPLE 9.2   A LARGE SAMPLE TEST FOR $\mu_1 - \mu_2$

Problem   Refer to the study of obese people on a low-fat diet and a regular diet, Example 9.1. Another way to compare the mean weight losses for the two different diets is to conduct a test of hypothesis. Use the information on the SPSS printout, Figure 9.1, to conduct the test. Use $\alpha = .05$.

Solution   Again, we let μ_1 and μ_2 represent the population mean weight losses of obese people on the low-fat diet and regular diet, respectively. If one diet is more effective in reducing the weights of obese people, then either $\mu_1 < \mu_2$ or $\mu_2 < \mu_1$; that is, $\mu_1 \neq \mu_2$.

Thus, the elements of the test are as follows:

$H_0: (\mu_1 - \mu_2) = 0$ (i.e., $\mu_1 = \mu_2$; note that $D_0 = 0$ for this hypothesis test)

$H_a: (\mu_1 - \mu_2) \neq 0$ (i.e., $\mu_1 \neq \mu_2$)

Test statistic: $z = \dfrac{(\bar{x}_1 - \bar{x}_2) - D_0}{\sigma_{(\bar{x}_1 - \bar{x}_2)}} = \dfrac{\bar{x}_1 - \bar{x}_2 - 0}{\sigma_{(\bar{x}_1 - \bar{x}_2)}}$

Rejection region: $z < -z_{\alpha/2} = -1.96$ or $z > z_{\alpha/2} = 1.96$ (see Figure 9.3)

Substituting the summary statistics given in Figure 9.1 into the test statistic, we obtain

$$z = \frac{(\bar{x}_1 - \bar{x}_2) - 0}{\sigma_{(\bar{x}_1 - \bar{x}_2)}} = \frac{9.31 - 7.40}{\sqrt{\dfrac{\sigma_1^2}{n_1} + \dfrac{\sigma_2^2}{n_2}}}$$

$$\approx \frac{1.91}{\sqrt{\dfrac{s_1^2}{n_1} + \dfrac{s_2^2}{n_2}}} = \frac{1.91}{\sqrt{\dfrac{(4.67)^2}{100} + \dfrac{(4.04)^2}{100}}} = \frac{1.91}{.617} = 3.09$$

[*Note:* The value of the test statistic is also shown (highlighted) at the bottom of the SPSS printout, Figure 9.1.]

As you can see in Figure 9.3, the calculated z-value clearly falls in the rejection region. Therefore, the samples provide sufficient evidence, at $\alpha = .05$, for the dietitian to conclude that the mean weight losses for the two diets differ.

Figure 9.3
Rejection Region
for Example 9.2

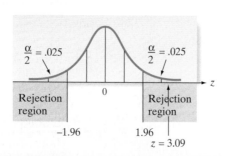

Look Back This conclusion agrees with the inference drawn from the 95% confidence interval in Example 9.1. However, the confidence interval provides more information on the mean weight losses. From the hypothesis test, we know only that the two means differ; that is, $\mu_1 \neq \mu_2$. From the confidence interval in Example 9.1, we found that the mean weight loss μ_1 of the low-fat diet was between .69 and 3.13 pounds more than the mean weight loss μ_2 of the regular diet. In other words, the test tells us that the means differ, but the confidence interval tells us how large the difference is. Both inferences are made with the same degree of reliability—namely, with 95% confidence (or, at $\alpha = .05$).

■ ■ ■

EXAMPLE 9.3

THE p-VALUE FOR A TEST OF $\mu_1 - \mu_2$

Problem Find the observed significance level for the test in Example 9.2. Interpret the result.

Solution The alternative hypothesis in Example 9.2, $H_a\colon \mu_1 - \mu_2 \neq 0$, required a two-tailed test using

$$z = \frac{\bar{x}_1 - \bar{x}_2}{\sigma_{(\bar{x}_1 - \bar{x}_2)}}$$

as a test statistic. Since the z-value calculated from the sample data was 3.09, the observed significance level (p-value) for the two-tailed test is the probability of observing a value of z at least as contradictory to the null hypothesis as $z = 3.09$; that is,

$$p\text{-value} = 2 \cdot P(z \geq 3.09)$$

This probability is computed assuming H_0 is true and is equal to the highlighted area shown in Figure 9.4.

The tabulated area corresponding to $z = 3.09$ in Table IV of Appendix A is .4990. Therefore,

$$P(z \geq 3.09) = .5 - .4990 = .0010$$

and the observed significance level for the test is

$$p\text{-value} = 2(.001) = .002$$

Since our selected α value, .05, exceeds this p-value, we have sufficient evidence to reject $H_0\colon \mu_1 - \mu_2 = 0$.

Figure 9.4
The Observed Significance
Level for Example 9.2

Look Back The p-value of the test is more easily obtained from a statistical software package. The p-value is highlighted at the bottom of the SPSS printout, Figure 9.1. This value agrees with our calculated p-value.

■ ■ ■

Now Work   *Exercise 9.6b*

■ ■ ■

Small Samples

When comparing two population means with small samples (say, $n_1 < 30$ and $n_2 < 30$), the methodology of the previous three examples is invalid. The reason? When the sample sizes are small, estimates of σ_1^2 and σ_2^2 are unreliable and the Central Limit Theorem (which guarantees that the z statistic is normal) can no longer be applied. But as in the case of a single mean (Section 8.4), we use the familiar Student's t-distribution described in Chapter 7.

To use the t-distribution, both sampled populations must be approximately normally distributed with equal population variances, and the random samples must be selected independently of each other. The normality and equal variances assumptions imply relative frequency distributions for the populations that would appear as shown in Figure 9.5.

Since we assume the two populations have equal variances ($\sigma_1^2 = \sigma_2^2 = \sigma^2$), it is reasonable to use the information contained in both samples to construct a **pooled sample estimator σ^2** for use in confidence intervals and test statistics. Thus, if s_1^2 and s_2^2 are the two sample variances (both estimating the variance σ^2 common to both populations), the pooled estimator of σ^2, denoted as s_p^2, is

$$s_p^2 = \frac{(n_1 - 1)s_1^2 + (n_2 - 1)s_2^2}{(n_1 - 1) + (n_2 - 1)} = \frac{(n_1 - 1)s_1^2 + (n_2 - 1)s_2^2}{n_1 + n_2 - 2}$$

or

$$s_p^2 = \frac{\overbrace{\sum(x_1 - \bar{x}_1)^2}^{\text{From sample 1}} + \overbrace{\sum(x_2 - \bar{x}_2)^2}^{\text{From sample 2}}}{n_1 + n_2 - 2}$$

where x_1 represents a measurement from sample 1 and x_2 represents a measurement from sample 2. Recall that the term *degrees of freedom* was defined in Section 7.2 as 1 less than the sample size. Thus, in this case, we have $(n_1 - 1)$ degrees of freedom for sample 1 and $(n_2 - 1)$ degrees of freedom for sample 2. Since we are pooling the information on σ^2 obtained from both samples, the degrees of freedom associated with the pooled variance s_p^2 is equal to the sum of the degrees of freedom for the two samples, namely, the denominator of s_p^2; that is, $(n_1 - 1) + (n_2 - 1) = n_1 + n_2 - 2$.

Note that the second formula given for s_p^2 shows that the pooled variance is simply a *weighted average* of the two sample variances s_1^2 and s_2^2. The weight given each variance is proportional to its degrees of freedom. If the two variances have the same number of degrees of freedom (i.e., *if the sample sizes are equal*), *then the pooled variance is a simple average of the two sample variances*. The result is an average or "pooled" variance that is a better estimate of σ^2 than either s_1^2 or s_2^2 alone.

Figure 9.5

Assumptions for the Two-Sample t: (1) Normal Populations, (2) Equal Variances

Biography

Bradley Efron (1938–present)—The Bootstrap Method

Bradley Efron was raised in St. Paul, Minnesota, the son of a truck driver who was the amateur statistician for his bowling and baseball leagues. Efron received a B.S. in mathematics from California Institute of Technology in 1960, but, by his own admission, had no talent for modern abstract math. His interest in the science of statistics developed after reading a book, cover-to-cover, by Harold Cramer. Efron went to the University of Stanford to study statistics and earned his Ph.D there in 1964. He has been a faculty member in Stanford's Department of Statistics since 1966. Over his career, Efron has received numerous awards and prizes for his contributions to modern statistics, including the MacArthur Prize Fellow (1983), the American Statistical Association Wilks Medal (1990), and the Parzen Prize for Statistical Innovation (1998). In 1979, Efron invented a method—called the *bootstrap*—of estimating and testing population parameters in situations where either the sampling distribution is unknown or the assumptions are violated. The method involves repeatedly taking samples of size n (with replacement) from the original sample and calculating the value of the point estimate. Efron showed that the sampling distribution of the estimator is simply the frequency distribution of the bootstrap estimates.

Both the confidence interval and the test of hypothesis procedures for comparing two population means with small samples are summarized in the accompanying boxes.

Small-Sample Confidence Interval for $(\mu_1 - \mu_2)$: Independent Samples

$$(\bar{x}_1 - \bar{x}_2) \pm t_{\alpha/2}\sqrt{s_p^2\left(\frac{1}{n_1} + \frac{1}{n_2}\right)}$$

where $s_p^2 = \dfrac{(n_1 - 1)s_1^2 + (n_2 - 1)s_2^2}{n_1 + n_2 - 2}$

and $t_{\alpha/2}$ is based on $(n_1 + n_2 - 2)$ degrees of freedom.

Small-Sample Test of Hypothesis for $(\mu_1 - \mu_2)$: Independent Samples

One-Tailed Test

$H_0: (\mu_1 - \mu_2) = D_0$

$H_a: (\mu_1 - \mu_2) < D_0$
  [or $H_a: (\mu_1 - \mu_2) > D_0$]

Two-Tailed Test

$H_0: (\mu_1 - \mu_2) = D_0$

$H_a: (\mu_1 - \mu_2) \neq D_0$

Test statistic:

$$t = \frac{(\bar{x}_1 - \bar{x}_2) - D_0}{\sqrt{s_p^2\left(\dfrac{1}{n_1} + \dfrac{1}{n_2}\right)}}$$

Rejection region: $t < -t_\alpha$
  [or $t > t_\alpha$ when
  $H_a: (\mu_1 - \mu_2) > D_0$]

Rejection region: $|t| > t_{\alpha/2}$

where t_α and $t_{\alpha/2}$ are based on $(n_1 + n_2 - 2)$ degrees of freedom.

> **Conditions Required for Valid Small-Sample Inferences about $(\mu_1 - \mu_2)$**
>
> 1. The two samples are randomly selected in an independent manner from the two target populations.
> 2. Both sampled populations have distributions that are approximately normal.
> 3. The population variances are equal (i.e., $\sigma_1^2 = \sigma_2^2$).

EXAMPLE 9.4   A SMALL-SAMPLE CONFIDENCE INTERVAL FOR $\mu_1 - \mu_2$

Problem   Suppose you wish to compare a new method of teaching reading to "slow learners" to the current standard method. You decide to base this comparison on the results of a reading test given at the end of a learning period of 6 months. Of a random sample of 22 slow learners, 10 are taught by the new method and 12 are taught by the standard method. All 22 children are taught by qualified instructors under similar conditions for a 6-month period. The results of the reading test at the end of this period are given in Table 9.2.

⊚ **READING**

TABLE 9.2   Reading Test Scores for Slow Learners

New Method				Standard Method			
80	80	79	81	79	62	70	68
76	66	71	76	73	76	86	73
70	85			72	68	75	66

a. Use the data in the table to estimate the true mean difference between the test scores for the new method and the standard method. Use a 95% confidence interval.

b. Interpret the interval, part **a**.

c. What assumptions must be made in order that the estimate be valid? Are they reasonably satisfied?

Solution   **a.** For this experiment, let μ_1 and μ_2 represent the mean reading test scores of slow learners taught with the new and standard methods, respectively. Then the objective is to obtain a 95% confidence interval for $(\mu_1 - \mu_2)$.

The first step in constructing the confidence interval is to obtain summary statistics (e.g., $\bar{x}$ and s) on reading test scores for each method. The data of Table 9.2 were entered into a computer, and SAS was used to obtain these descriptive statistics. The SAS printout appears in Figure 9.6. Note that $\bar{x}_1 = 76.4$, $s_1 = 5.8348$, $\bar{x}_2 = 72.333$, and $s_2 = 6.3437$

Next, we calculate the pooled estimate of variance:

$$s_p^2 = \frac{(n_1 - 1)s_1^2 + (n_2 - 1)s_2^2}{n_1 + n_2 - 2}$$

$$= \frac{(10 - 1)(5.8348)^2 + (12 - 1)(6.3437)^2}{10 + 12 - 2} = 37.45$$

where s_p^2 is based on $(n_1 + n_2 - 2) = (10 + 12 - 2) = 20$ degrees of freedom. Also, we find $t_{\alpha/2} = t_{.025} = 2.086$ (based on 20 degrees of freedom) from Table VI of Appendix A.

Figure 9.6
SAS Printout for Example 9.4

```
                          Two Sample t-test for the Means of SCORE within METHOD

Sample Statistics

        Group           N       Mean      Std. Dev.    Std. Error
        --------------------------------------------------------------
        NEW             10      76.4        5.8348        1.8451
        STD             12   72.33333       6.3437        1.8313

Hypothesis Test

        Null hypothesis:      Mean 1 - Mean 2 =  0
        Alternative:          Mean 1 - Mean 2 ^= 0

        If Variances Are      t statistic        Df        Pr > t
        --------------------------------------------------------------
        Equal                   1.552            20        0.1364
        Not Equal               1.564          19.77       0.1336

95% Confidence Interval for the Difference between Two Means

                  Lower Limit      Upper Limit
                  -----------      -----------
                     -1.40            9.53
```

Finally, the 95% confidence interval for $(\mu_1 - \mu_2)$, the difference between mean test scores for the two methods, is

$$(\bar{x}_1 - \bar{x}_2) \pm t_{\alpha/2}\sqrt{s_{\mathrm{p}}^2\left(\frac{1}{n_1} + \frac{1}{n_2}\right)} = (76.4 - 72.33) \pm t_{.025}\sqrt{37.45\left(\frac{1}{10} + \frac{1}{12}\right)}$$

$$= 4.07 \pm (2.086)(2.62)$$
$$= 4.07 \pm 5.47$$

or $(-1.4, 9.54)$. This interval agrees (except for rounding) with the one shown at the bottom of the SAS printout, Figure 9.6.

b. The interval can be interpreted as follows. With a confidence coefficient equal to .95, we estimate the difference in mean test scores between using the new method of teaching and using the standard method to fall in the interval -1.4 to 9.54. In other words, we estimate (with 95% confidence) the mean test score for the new method to be anywhere from 1.4 points less than to 9.54 points more than the mean test score for the standard method. Although the sample means seem to suggest that the new method is associated with a higher mean test score, there is insufficient evidence to indicate that $(\mu_1 - \mu_2)$ differs from 0 because the interval includes 0 as a possible value for $(\mu_1 - \mu_2)$. To show a difference in mean test scores (if it exists), you could increase the sample size and thereby narrow the width of the confidence interval for $(\mu_1 - \mu_2)$. An alternative is to design the experiment differently. This possibility is discussed in the next section.

c. To properly use the small-sample confidence interval, the following assumptions must be satisfied:
  (1) The samples are randomly and independently selected from the populations of slow learners taught by the new method and the standard method.
  (2) The test scores are normally distributed for both teaching methods.
  (3) The variance of the test scores are the same for the two populations, that is, $\sigma_1^2 = \sigma_2^2$.

Figure 9.7
MINITAB Normal
Probability Plots for
Example 9.4

The first assumption is satisfied, based on the information provided about the sampling procedure in the problem description. To check the plausibility of the remaining two assumptions, we resort to graphical methods. Figure 9.7 is a MINITAB printout that gives normal probability plots for the test scores of the two samples of slow learners. The near straight-line trends on both plots indicate that the score distributions are approximately mound-shaped and symmetric. Consequently, each sample data set appears to come from a population that is approximately normal.

One way to check assumption #3 is to test the null hypothesis $H_0: \sigma_1^2 = \sigma_2^2$. This test is covered in Section 9.6. Another approach is to examine box plots for the sample data. Figure 9.8 is a MINITAB printout

Figure 9.8
MINITAB Box Plots
for Example 9.4

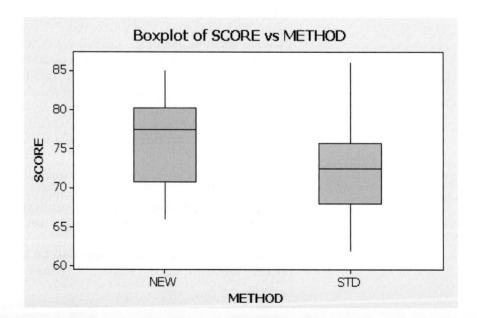

that shows side-by-side vertical box plots for the test scores in the two samples. Recall, from Section 2.9, that the box plot represents the "spread" of a data set. The two box plots appear to have about the same spread; thus, the samples appear to come from populations with approximately the same variance.

Look Back All three assumptions, then, appear to be reasonably satisfied for this application of the small-sample confidence interval.

| Now Work | *Exercise 9.9* |

■ ■ ■

The two-sample *t*-statistic is a powerful tool for comparing population means when the assumptions are satisfied. It has also been shown to retain its usefulness when the sampled populations are only approximately normally distributed. And when the sample sizes are equal, the assumption of equal population variances can be relaxed. That is, if $n_1 = n_2$, then σ_1^2 and σ_2^2 can be quite different and the test statistic will still possess, approximately, a Student's *t*-distribution. In the case where $\sigma_1^2 \neq \sigma_2^2$ and $n_1 \neq n_2$, an approximate small-sample confidence interval or test can be obtained by modifying the degrees of freedom associated with the *t*-distribution.

Confidence Interval for $\mu_1 - \mu_2$

Using The TI-83 Graphing Calculator

For this calculation, you have the option of entering the raw data or using the summary statistics

Step 1   *If you are using the raw data, enter the data into L1 and L2.*

Press **STAT** and select **1:Edit**
Note: If a list already contains data, clear the old data. Use the up arrow to highlight the name at the top of the list. Press **CLEAR ENTER**.
Use the **Down Arrow** or **ENTER** key to enter the data sets into **L1** and **L2**.

Step 2   *Access the Statistical Tests Menu*

Press **STAT**
Arrow right to **TESTS**
Arrow down to **0: 2-Samp TInt**
Press **ENTER**

Step 3   *Choose "**Data**" or "**Stats**". ("Data" is selected when you have entered the raw data into L1 and L2. "Stats" is selected when you are using the summary statistics.)*

Press **ENTER**

If you selected "Data":
Set **List1** to **L1.** Note: If List1 is not already set to L1, arrow down to List1: and hit **2nd** and '**1**'.
Set **List2** to **L2.** Note: If List2 is not already set to L2, arrow down to List2: and hit **2nd** and '**2**'.
Set **Freq1** to **1.** Note: If Freq1 is not already set to 1, arrow down to Freq1 and hit **Alpha** and '**1**'.

Set **Freq2** to **1.** Note: If Freq2 is not already set to 1, arrow down to Freq2 and hit **Alpha** and **'1'**.
Arrow down to **C-Level** and enter the confidence level.
Arrow down to **Pooled**: highlight **No** or **Yes** and Press **Enter**. Note: Select **Yes** if you have made the assumption of equal population variances, otherwise select **No.**
Arrow down to **"Calculate"**
Press **ENTER**

If you selected "Stats", enter the mean, standard deviation and sample size for each of the two datasets.
Arrow down to **C-Level** and enter the confidence level.
Arrow down to **Pooled**: highlight **No** or **Yes** and Press **Enter**. Note: Select **Yes** if you have made the assumption of equal population variances, otherwise select **No**.
Arrow down to **"Calculate"**
Press **ENTER**

Step 4   *View the Output*

The confidence interval will be displayed along with the calculated degrees of freedom, the means, the standard deviations, the pooled standard deviation (if **Yes** was highlighting for **Pooled**) and the sample sizes.

Example   *Consider Example 9.4 with data in Table 9.2 on pg. 438. For this example, the raw data will be used, so begin with Step 1 of the instructions.*

Step 1   *Enter the data into L1 and L2.*

Press **STAT** and select **1:Edit**
Note: If a list already contains data, clear the old data. Use the up arrow to highlight the name at the top of the list. Press **CLEAR ENTER**.
Use the **Down Arrow** or **ENTER** key to enter the data sets into **L1 and L2.**

Step 2   *Access the Statistical Tests Menu*

Press **STAT**
Arrow right to **TESTS**
Arrow down to **0: 2-Samp TInt**
Press **ENTER**

Step 3   *Choose "Data"*

Set **List1** to **L1.**
Set **List2** to **L2.**

Set **Freq1** to **1.**
Set **Freq2** to **1.**
Arrow down to **C-Level** and enter .95 for the confidence level.
Arrow down to **Pooled**: highlight **Yes** and Press **Enter**. Note: You have made
the assumption of equal population variances.

Arrow down to **"Calculate"**
Press **ENTER**

Step 4   *View the Output*

The confidence interval will be displayed with the sample information.

Hypothesis Test for $\mu_1 - \mu_2$

Using the TI-83 Graphing Calculator

For this calculation, you have the option of entering the raw data or using the summary statistics

Step 1   *If you are using the raw data, enter the data into L1 and L2.*

Press **STAT** and select **1:Edit**
Note: If a list already contains data, clear the old data. Use the up arrow to
highlight the name at the top of the list. Press **CLEAR ENTER**.
Use the **Down Arrow** or **ENTER** key to enter the data sets into **L1** and **L2**.

Step 2   *Access the Statistical Tests Menu*

Press **STAT**
Arrow right to **TESTS**
Arrow down to **4 : 2-Samp TTest**
Press **ENTER**

Step 3   *Choose "**Data**" or "**Stats**". ("Data" is selected when you have entered
the raw data into L1 and L2. "Stats" is selected when you are using the
summary statistics.)*

Press **ENTER**

If you selected "Data":

Set **List1** to **L1**. Note: If List1 is not already set to L1, arrow down to List1: and hit **2nd** and '**1**'.

Set **List2** to **L2**. Note: If List2 is not already set to L2, arrow down to List2: and hit **2nd** and '**2**'.

Set **Freq1** to **1**. Note: If Freq1 is not already set to 1, arrow down to Freq1 and hit **Alpha** and '**1**'.

Set **Freq2** to **1**. Note: If Freq2 is not already set to 1, arrow down to Freq2 and hit **Alpha** and '**1**'.

Arrow down to the next line and select the appropriate alternative hypothesis by using the right arrow to highlight $\neq u2$, $<u2$, or $>u2$ and press **ENTER**.

Arrow down to **Pooled**: highlight **No** or **Yes** and Press **Enter**. Note: Select **Yes** if you have made the assumption of equal population variances, otherwise select **No**.

Arrow down to **Calculate Draw**. You may choose either one of these for your output.

Press **ENTER**

If you selected "Stats", enter the mean, standard deviation and sample size for each of the two datasets. Arrow down to the next line and select the appropriate alternative hypothesis by using the right arrow to highlight $\neq u2$, $<u2$, or $>u2$ and press **ENTER**.

Arrow down to **Pooled**: highlight **No** or **Yes** and Press **Enter**. Note: Select **Yes** if you have made the assumption of equal population variances, otherwise select **No**.

Arrow down to **Calculate Draw**. You may choose either one of these for your output.

Press **ENTER**

Step 4 *View the Output*

If you chose **Calculate**, the output will display the alternative hypothesis, the t-value, the p-value, the calculated degrees of freedom, the means, the standard deviations, the pooled standard deviation (if **Yes** was highlighting for **Pooled**) and the sample sizes.

If you chose **Draw**, a graph of the normal curve will be displayed along with the t-value and the p-value. The area under the curve that represents the p-value is shaded. Note: In order to use the **Draw** feature, you must first clear all equations from the **Y-registers**. Hit '**Y =**' and delete all equations.

Example *Consider Exercise 9.12 part a on pg. 449. For this example, the summary statistics will be used so begin with Step2 of the instructions.*

Step 2 *Access the Statistical Tests Menu*

Press **STAT**
Arrow right to **TESTS**
Arrow down to **4:2-SampTTest**
Press **ENTER**

Step 3   *Choose "**Stats**"*

Enter the standard deviations, means, and sample sizes.

Arrow down to the next line and select ≠**u2** and press **ENTER**
Arrow down to **Pooled**: highlight **No** and Press **Enter**. Note: You are not
making the assumption of equal population variances
Arrow down to **Calculate Draw**. You may choose either one of these for your
output.

Press **ENTER**

Step 4   *View the Output*

If you chose **Calculate**, the output will display the alternative hypothesis, the
t-value, the p-value, the calculated degrees of freedom, the means, the standard
deviations, and the sample sizes.

If you chose **Draw**, a graph of the normal curve will be displayed along with
the t-value and the p-value. The area under the curve that represents the
p-value is shaded. Note: In order to use the **Draw** feature, you must first clear
all equations from the **Y-registers**. Hit 'Y=' and delete all equations.

The next box gives the approximate small-sample procedures to use when the
assumption of equal variances is violated. The test for the "unequal sample sizes"
case is based on Satterthwaite's (1946) approximation.

Approximate Small-Sample Procedures when $\sigma_1^2 \neq \sigma_2^2$

Equal Sample Sizes ($n_1 = n_2 = n$)

Confidence interval: $(\bar{x}_1 - \bar{x}_2) \pm t_{\alpha/2}\sqrt{(s_1^2 + s_2^2)/n}$

Test statistic for H_0: $(\mu_1 - \mu_2) = 0$: $t = (\bar{x}_1 - \bar{x}_2)/\sqrt{(s_1^2 + s_2^2)/n}$
where t is based on $\nu = n_1 + n_2 - 2 = 2(n - 1)$ degrees of freedom.

Unequal Sample Sizes ($n_1 \neq n_2$)

Confidence interval: $\qquad\qquad (\bar{x}_1 - \bar{x}_2) \pm t_{\alpha/2}\sqrt{(s_1^2/n_1) + (s_2^2/n_2)}$

Test statistic for H_0: $(\mu_1 - \mu_2) = 0$: $\qquad t = (\bar{x}_1 - \bar{x}_2)/\sqrt{(s_1^2/n_1) + (s_2^2/n_2)}$
where t is based on degrees of freedom equal to

$$\nu = \frac{(s_1^2/n_1 + s_2^2/n_2)^2}{\dfrac{(s_1^2/n_1)^2}{n_1 - 1} + \dfrac{(s_2^2/n_2)^2}{n_2 - 1}}$$

Note: The value of ν will generally not be an integer. Round ν down to the nearest integer to use the t-table.

When the assumptions are not clearly satisfied, you can select larger samples from the populations or you can use other available statistical tests (**nonparametric statistical tests**, which are described in Chapter 14).

What Should You Do If the Assumptions Are Not Satisfied?

Answer: If you are concerned that the assumptions are not satisfied, use the Wilcoxon rank sum test for independent samples to test for a shift in population distributions. See Chapter 14.

Statistics in Action Revisited

Comparing the Mean Winning Bid Prices of Two Kentucky Milk Markets

In the Statistics in Action study for this chapter (see p. 00), we want to determine whether there is evidence of collusive bidding in the northern Kentucky school milk market. Numerous economic and statistical methods exist for detecting the possibility of collusive practices among bidders. These typically involve (1) market-shares analyses, (2) an analysis of incumbency rates (i.e., the percentage of markets that are won by the same vendor who won the previous year), (3) an examination of bid levels and their dispersion, (4) price-distance analyses, (5) bid-sequence analyses, (6) comparison of mean winning prices, and (7) econometric modeling of the winning price. Here, we focus on a comparison of the mean winning bid prices.

Consider two similar markets, one in which the bids are rigged and the other in which bids are made competitively. In theory, the mean winning price in the "rigged" market will be higher than the mean winning price in the competitive market. Recall that in this case, the speculation is that from 1983 to 1991 the tricounty milk market (where Meyer and Trauth dairies supplied almost all of the milk) was rigged while the school districts in the surrounding market were competitive. Consequently, we want to compare the mean winning price in the tricounty market with that of the surrounding market

for each milk product sold (whole white, low-fat white, and low-fat chocolate).

If we let μ_1 represent the population mean winning price in the surrounding market and μ_2 represent the population mean winning price in the tricounty market, then the speculation is that $\mu_1 < \mu_2$ (i.e., the mean winning price in the "competitive" market is less than the mean winning price in the "rigged" market). Of interest, then, is the one-tailed test, H_0: $(\mu_1 - \mu_2) = 0$ versus H_a: $(\mu_1 - \mu_2) < 0$, for each of the three milk price variables. An examination of the data saved in the **MILK** file reveals that both samples are large ($n_1 \geq 200$ and $n_2 \geq 70$); thus, the large-sample z-test is appropriate and no assumptions about the price distributions are required. We conducted these tests using MINITAB. The output is shown in Figure SIA9.1.

The one-tailed p-values of the three tests are highlighted on Figure SIA9.1. All three milk price variables (WWBID, LFWBID, and LFCBID) show a significant difference at $\alpha = .05$ (p-values all $= .0000$). Therefore, there is sufficient evidence to conclude that the mean winning bid price for the surrounding ("competitive") market is significantly less than the mean winning bid price for the tricounty ("rigged") market. Consequently, there is support for the claim that the dairies in the tricounty market participated in collusive practices.

Two-Sample T-Test and CI: WWBID, Market

```
Two-sample T for WWBID

Market       N    Mean    StDev   SE Mean
SURROUND    254  0.1331  0.0158   0.00099
TRI-COUNTY  100  0.1431  0.0133   0.0013


Difference = mu (SURROUND) - mu (TRI-COUNTY)
Estimate for difference:  -0.009970
95% upper bound for difference:  -0.007232
T-Test of difference = 0 (vs <): T-Value = -6.02  P-Value = 0.000  DF = 213
```

Two-Sample T-Test and CI: LFWBID, Market

```
Two-sample T for LFWBID

Market       N    Mean    StDev   SE Mean
SURROUND    258  0.1242  0.0166   0.0010
TRI-COUNTY  114  0.1366  0.0136   0.0013


Difference = mu (SURROUND) - mu (TRI-COUNTY)
Estimate for difference:  -0.012445
95% upper bound for difference:  -0.009744
T-Test of difference = 0 (vs <): T-Value = -7.61  P-Value = 0.000  DF = 261
```

Two-Sample T-Test and CI: LFCBID, Market

```
Two-sample T for LFCBID

Market       N    Mean    StDev   SE Mean
SURROUND    259  0.1251  0.0172   0.0011
TRI-COUNTY   70  0.1401  0.0149   0.0018


Difference = mu (SURROUND) - mu (TRI-COUNTY)
Estimate for difference:  -0.015091
95% upper bound for difference:  -0.011642
T-Test of difference = 0 (vs <): T-Value = -7.25  P-Value = 0.000  DF = 122
```

Figure SIA9.1
MINITAB Comparison of Means for Two Kentucky Milk Markets

Exercises 9.1–9.29

Understanding the Principles

9.1 Describe the sampling distribution of $(\bar{x}_1 - \bar{x}_2)$ when the samples are large.

9.2 To use the t-statistic to test for a difference between the means of two populations, what assumptions must be made about the two populations? About the two samples?

9.3 Two populations are described in each of the following cases. In which cases would it be appropriate to apply the small-sample t-test to investigate the difference between the population means?

a. Population 1: Normal distribution with variance σ_1^2
Population 2: Skewed to the right with variance $\sigma_2^2 = \sigma_1^2$

b. Population 1: Normal distribution with variance σ_1^2
Population 2: Normal distribution with variance $\sigma_2^2 \neq \sigma_1^2$

c. Population 1: Skewed to the left with variance σ_1^2 Population 2: Skewed to the left with variance $\sigma_2^2 = \sigma_1^2$

d. Population 1: Normal distribution with variance σ_1^2
Population 2: Normal distribution with variance $\sigma_2^2 = \sigma_1^2$

e. Population 1: Uniform distribution with variance σ_1^2
Population 2: Uniform distribution with variance $\sigma_2^2 = \sigma_1^2$

9.4 A confidence interval for $(\mu_1 - \mu_2)$ is $(-10, 4)$. Which of the following inferences is correct?

   a. $\mu_1 > \mu_2$
   b. $\mu_1 < \mu_2$
   c. $\mu_1 = \mu_2$
   d. no significant difference between means

9.5 A confidence interval for $(\mu_1 - \mu_2)$ is $(-10, -4)$. Which of the following inferences is correct?

   a. $\mu_1 > \mu_2$
   b. $\mu_1 < \mu_2$
   c. $\mu_1 = \mu_2$
   d. no significant difference between means

Learning the Mechanics

9.6 In order to compare the means of two populations, independent random samples of 400 observations are selected from each population, with the following results:

Sample 1	Sample 2
$\bar{x}_1 = 5{,}275$	$\bar{x}_2 = 5{,}240$
$s_1 = 150$	$s_2 = 200$

   a. Use a 95% confidence interval to estimate the difference between the population means $(\mu_1 - \mu_2)$. Interpret the confidence interval.
   b. Test the null hypothesis $H_0: (\mu_1 - \mu_2) = 0$ versus the alternative hypothesis $H_a: (\mu_1 - \mu_2) \neq 0$. Give the significance level of the test, and interpret the result.
   c. Suppose the test in part **b** was conducted with the alternative hypothesis $H_a: (\mu_1 - \mu_2) > 0$. How would your answer to part **b** change?
   d. Test the null hypothesis $H_0: (\mu_1 - \mu_2) = 25$ versus the alternative $H_a: (\mu_1 - \mu_2) \neq 25$. Give the significance level, and interpret the result. Compare your answer to the test conducted in part **b**.
   e. What assumptions are necessary to ensure the validity of the inferential procedures applied in parts **a–d**?

9.7 Independent random samples of 100 observations each are chosen from two normal populations with the following means and standard deviations:

Population 1	Population 2
$\mu_1 = 14$	$\mu_2 = 10$
$\sigma_1 = 4$	$\sigma_2 = 3$

Let $\bar{x}_1$ and $\bar{x}_2$ denote the two sample means.
   a. Give the mean and standard deviation of the sampling distribution of $\bar{x}_1$.
   b. Give the mean and standard deviation of the sampling distribution of $\bar{x}_2$.
   c. Suppose you were to calculate the difference $(\bar{x}_1 - \bar{x}_2)$ between the sample means. Find the mean and standard deviation of the sampling distribution of $(\bar{x}_1 - \bar{x}_2)$.

   d. Will the statistic $(\bar{x}_1 - \bar{x}_2)$ be normally distributed? Explain.

9.8 Assume that $\sigma_1^2 = \sigma_2^2 = \sigma^2$. Calculate the pooled estimator of σ^2 for each of the following cases:
   a. $s_1^2 = 200$, $s_2^2 = 180$, $n_1 = n_2 = 25$
   b. $s_1^2 = 25$, $s_2^2 = 40$, $n_1 = 20$, $n_2 = 10$
   c. $s_1^2 = .20$, $s_2^2 = .30$, $n_1 = 8$, $n_2 = 12$
   d. $s_1^2 = 2{,}500$, $s_2^2 = 1{,}800$, $n_1 = 16$, $n_2 = 17$

   e. Note that the pooled estimate is a weighted average of the sample variances. To which of the variances does the pooled estimate fall nearer in each of the above cases?

9.9 Independent random samples from normal populations produced the results shown below:

LM9_9

Sample 1	Sample 2
1.2	4.2
3.1	2.7
1.7	3.6
2.8	3.9
3.0	

   a. Calculate the pooled estimate of σ^2.
   b. Do the data provide sufficient evidence to indicate that $\mu_2 > \mu_1$? Test using $\alpha = .10$.
   c. Find a 90% confidence interval for $(\mu_1 - \mu_2)$.
   d. Which of the two inferential procedures, the test of hypothesis in part **b** or the confidence interval in part **c**, provides more information about $(\mu_1 - \mu_2)$?

9.10 Two independent random samples have been selected, 100 observations from population 1 and 100 from population 2. Sample means $\bar{x}_1 = 70$ and $\bar{x}_2 = 50$ were obtained. From previous experience with these populations, it is known that the variances are $\sigma_1^2 = 100$ and $\sigma_2^2 = 64$.
   a. Find $\sigma_{(\bar{x}_1 - \bar{x}_2)}$.
   b. Sketch the approximate sampling distribution $(\bar{x}_1 - \bar{x}_2)$ assuming $(\mu_1 - \mu_2) = 5$.
   c. Locate the observed value of $(\bar{x}_1 - \bar{x}_2)$ on the graph you drew in part **b**. Does it appear that this value contradicts the null hypothesis $H_0: (\mu_1 - \mu_2) = 5$?
   d. Use the z-table to determine the rejection region for the test of $H_0: (\mu_1 - \mu_2) = 5$ against $H_a: (\mu_1 - \mu_2) \neq 5$. Use $\alpha = .05$.

   e. Conduct the hypothesis test of part **d** and interpret your result.
   f. Construct a 95% confidence interval for $(\mu_1 - \mu_2)$. Interpret the interval.
   g. Which inference provides more information about the value of $(\mu_1 - \mu_2)$—the test of hypothesis in part **e** or the confidence interval in part **f**?

9.11 Independent random samples are selected from two populations and used to test the hypothesis $H_0: (\mu_1 - \mu_2) = 0$ against the alternative $H_a: (\mu_1 - \mu_2) \neq 0$. An analysis of 233 observations from population 1 and 312 from population 2 yielded a p-value of .115.

a. Interpret the results of the computer analysis.

b. If the alternative hypothesis had been H_a: $(\mu_1 - \mu_2) < 0$, how would the p-value change? Interpret the p-value for this one-tailed test.

9.12 Independent random samples selected from two normal populations produced the sample means and standard deviations shown below:

Sample 1	Sample 2
$n_1 = 17$	$n_2 = 12$
$\bar{x}_1 = 5.4$	$\bar{x}_2 = 7.9$
$s_1 = 3.4$	$s_2 = 4.8$

a. Conduct the test $H_0: (\mu_1 - \mu_2) = 0$ against H_a: $(\mu_1 - \mu_2) \neq 0$.

b. Find and interpret the 95% confidence interval for $(\mu_1 - \mu_2)$.

Applying the Concepts—Basic

9.13 **Reading Japanese books.** Refer to the *Reading in a Foreign Language* (Apr. 2004) experiment to improve the Japanese reading comprehension levels of University of Hawaii students, Exercise 2.31 (p. 51). Recall that 14 students participated in a ten-week extensive reading program in a second semester Japanese course. The numbers of books read by each student and the student's course grade are repeated in the table.

JAPANESE

Number of Books	Course Grade	Number of Books	Course Grade
53	A	30	A
42	A	28	B
40	A	24	A
40	B	22	C
39	A	21	B
34	A	20	B
34	A	16	B

Source: Hitosugi, C. I., and Day, R. R. "Extensive Reading in Japanese," *Reading in a Foreign Language,* Vol. 16, No. 1, Apr. 2004 (Table 4).

a. Consider two populations of students who participate in the reading program prior to taking a second semester Japanese course—those who earn an A grade and those who earn a B or "C" grade. Of interest is the difference in the mean number of books read by the two populations of students. Identify the parameter of interest in words and symbols.

b. Form a 95% confidence interval for the target parameter identified in part **a**.

c. Give a practical interpretation of the confidence interval, part **b**.

d. Compare the inference in part **c** with the inference you derived from stem-and-leaf plots in Exercise 2.31b.

9.14 **Rating service at five-star hotels.** A study published in *The Journal of American Academy of Business, Cambridge* (March 2002) examined whether the perception of service quality at five-star hotels in Jamaica differed by gender. Hotel guests were randomly selected from the lobby and restaurant areas and asked to rate ten service-related items (e.g., "The personal attention you received from our employees"). Each item was rated on a 5-point scale (1 = "much worse than I expected," 5 = "much better than I expected") and the sum of the items for each guest was determined. A summary of the guest scores are provided in the table.

Gender	Sample Size	Mean Score	Standard Deviation
Males	127	39.08	6.73
Females	114	38.79	6.94

a. Construct a 90% confidence interval for the difference between the population mean service-rating scores given by male and female guests at Jamaican 5-star hotels.

b. Use the interval, part **a**, to make an inference about whether the perception of service quality at five-star hotels in Jamaica differs by gender.

9.15 **Heights of grade school repeaters.** Are children who repeat a grade in elementary school shorter on average, than their peers? To answer this question, researchers compared the heights of Australian school children who repeated a grade to those who did not. (*The Archives of Disease in Childhood,* Apr. 2000.) All height measurements were standardized using z-scores. A summary of the results, by gender, is shown in the table.

	Never Repeated	Repeated a Grade
Boys	$n = 1{,}349$ $\bar{x} = .30$ $s = .97$	$n = 86$ $\bar{x} = -.04$ $s = 1.17$
Girls	$n = 1{,}366$ $\bar{x} = .22$ $s = 1.04$	$n = 43$ $\bar{x} = .26$ $s = .94$

Source: Wake, M., Coghlan, D., and Hesketh, K. "Does height influence progression through primary school grades?" *The Archives of Disease in Childhood,* Vol. 82, Apr. 2000 (Table 3).

a. Set up the null and alternative hypothesis for determining whether the average height of Australian boys who repeated a grade is less than the average height of boys who never repeated.

b. Conduct the test, part **a**, using $\alpha = .05$.

c. Repeat parts **a** and **b** for Australian girls.

9.16 **Short-term memory study.** A group of University of Florida psychologists investigated the effects of age and gender on the short-term memory of adults. (*Cognitive Aging Conference,* Apr. 1996.) Each in a sample of 152 adults was asked to place 20 common household items (e.g., eyeglasses, keys, hat, hammer) into the rooms of

BULIMIA

Bulimic students	21	13	10	20	25	19	16	21	24	13	14		
Normal students	13	6	16	13	8	19	23	18	11	19	7	10	15	20

Source: Randles, R. H. "On neutral responses (zeros) in the sign test and ties in the Wilcoxon-Mann-Whitney test." *The American Statistician,* Vol. 55, No. 2, May 2001 (Figure 3).

a computer-image house. After performing some unrelated activities, each subject was asked to recall the locations of the objects they had placed. The number of correct responses (out of 20) was recorded.

a. The researchers theorized that women will have a higher mean recall score than men. Set up the null and alternative hypotheses to test this theory.

b. Refer to part **a.** The 43 men in the study had a mean recall score of 13.5, while the 109 women had a mean recall score of 14.4. The observed significance level for comparing these two means was found to be $p = .0001$. Interpret this value.

c. The researchers also hypothesized that younger adults would have a higher mean recall score than older adults. Set up H_0 and H_a to test this theory.

d. The observed significance level for the test of part **c** was reported as $p = .0001$. Interpret this result.

9.17 Watching cable TV shopping networks. Refer to the International Association for Time Use Research study on cable TV viewers who purchase items from one of the home shopping channels, Exercise 8.52 (p. 390). The 1,600 sampled viewers described their motivation for watching cable TV shopping networks by giving their level of agreement (on a 5-point scale, where 1 = strongly disagree and 5 = strongly agree) with the statement "I have nothing else to do." The researcher wanted to compare the mean responses of viewers who watch the shopping network at noon with those viewers who do not watch at noon.

a. Give the null and alternative hypotheses for determining whether the mean response of noontime watchers differs from the mean response of non-noontime watchers.

b. The researcher found the p-value for the test, part **a,** to be .02. Interpret this result, assuming $\alpha = .05$.

c. Interpret the result, part **b**, assuming $\alpha = .01$.

d. The sample means for noontime watchers and non-watchers were found to be 3.3 and 3.4, respectively. Comment on the practical significance of this result.

9.18 Impact of exam question order. Do the early questions in an exam affect your performance on later questions? Research reported in the *Journal of Psychology* (Jan. 1991) investigated this relationship by conducting the following experiment: 140 college students were randomly assigned to two groups. Group A took an exam that contained 15 difficult questions followed by five moderate questions. Group B took an exam that contained 15 easy questions followed by the same five moderate questions. One of the goals of the study was to compare the average score on the moderate questions for the two groups.

a. The researchers hypothesized that the students who had the easy questions would score better than the students who had the difficult questions. Set up the appropriate null and alternative hypotheses to test their research hypothesis, defining any symbols you use.

b. Suppose the p-value for this test was reported as .3248. What conclusion would you reach based on this p-value?

c. What assumptions are necessary to ensure the validity of this conclusion?

9.19 Bulimia study. The "fear of negative evaluation" (FNE) scores for 11 female students known to suffer from the eating disorder bulimia and 14 female students with normal eating habits, first presented in Exercise 2.38 (p. 52), are reproduced above. (Recall that the higher the score, the greater the fear of negative evaluation.)

a. Find a 95% confidence interval for the difference between the population means of the FNE scores for bulimic and normal female students. Interpret the result.

b. What assumptions are required for the interval of part **a** to be statistically valid? Are these assumptions reasonably satisfied? Explain.

Applying the Concepts—Intermediate

9.20 Patent infringement case. *Chance* (Fall 2002) described a lawsuit where Intel Corp. was charged with infringing on a patent for an invention used in the automatic manufacture of computer chips. In response, Intel accused the inventor of adding material to his patent notebook after the patent was witnessed and granted. The case rested on whether a patent witness' signature was written on top of key text in the notebook, or under the key text. Intel hired a physicist who used an X-ray beam to measure the relative concentration of certain elements (e.g., nickel, zinc, potassium) at several spots on the notebook page. The zinc measurements for three notebook locations—on a text line, on a witness line, and on the intersection of the witness and text line—are provided in the table.

PATENT

Text line:	.335	.374	.440			
Witness line:	.210	.262	.188	.329	.439	.397
Intersection:	.393	.353	.285	.295	.319	

a. Use a test or a confidence interval (at $\alpha = .05$) to compare the mean zinc measurement for the text line with the mean for the intersection.

b. Use a test or a confidence interval (at $\alpha = .05$) to compare the mean zinc measurement for the witness line with the mean for the intersection.

c. From the results, parts **a** and **b**, what can you infer about the mean zinc measurements at the three notebook locations?

d. What assumptions are required for the inferences to be valid? Are they reasonably satisfied?

9.21 Family involvement in homework. Teachers Involve Parents in Schoolwork (TIPS) is an interactive homework process designed to improve the quality of homework assignments for elementary, middle, and high school students. TIPS homework assignments require students to conduct interactions with family partners (parents, guardians, etc.) while completing the homework. Frances Van Voorhis (Johns Hopkins University) conducted a study to investigate the effects of TIPS in science, mathematics, and language arts homework assignments (April 2001). Each in a sample of 128 middle school students was assigned to complete TIPS homework assignments, while 98 students in a second sample were assigned traditional, noninteractive, homework assignments (called ATIPS). At the end of the study, all students reported on the level of family involvement in their homework on a 4-point scale (0 = never, 1 = rarely, 2 = sometimes, 3 = frequently, 4 = always). Three scores were recorded for each student: one for science homework, one for math homework, and one for language arts homework. The data for the study are saved in the **HWSTUDY** file. (The first 5 and last 5 observations in the data set are listed in the table.)

HWSTUDY (First and last 5 observations)

Homework Condition	Science	Math	Language
ATIPS	1	0	0
ATIPS	0	1	1
ATIPS	0	1	0
ATIPS	1	2	0
ATIPS	1	1	2
TIPS	2	3	2
TIPS	1	4	2
TIPS	2	4	2
TIPS	4	0	3
TIPS	2	0	1

Source: Van Voorhis, F. L., "Teachers' use of interactive homework and its effects on family involvement and science achievement of middle grade students." Paper presented at the annual meeting of the American Educational Research Association, Seattle, April 2001.

a. Conduct an analysis to compare the mean level of family involvement in science homework assignments of TIPS and ATIPS students. Use $\alpha = .05$. Make a practical conclusion.

b. Repeat part **a** for mathematics homework assignments.

c. Repeat part **a** for language arts homework assignments.

d. What assumptions are necessary for the inferences of parts **a–c** to be valid? Are they reasonably satisfied?

9.22 Pig castration study. Two methods of castrating male piglets were investigated in *Applied Animal Behaviour Science* (Nov. 1, 2000). Method 1 involved an incision of the spermatic cords while Method 2 involved pulling and severing the cords. Forty-nine male piglets were randomly allocated to one of the two methods. During castration, the researchers measured the number of high frequency vocal responses (squeals) per second over a 5-second period. The data are summarized in the table. Conduct a test of hypothesis to determine whether the population mean number of high frequency vocal responses differs for piglets castrated by the two methods. Use $\alpha = .05$.

	Method 1	Method 2
Sample size	24	25
Mean number of squeals	.74	.70
Standard deviation	.09	.09

Source: Taylor, A. A., and Weary, D. M. "Vocal responses of piglets to castration: Identifying procedural sources of pain." *Applied Animal Behaviour Science,* Vol. 70, No. 1, November 1, 2000.

9.23 Mongolian desert ants. Refer to the *Journal of Biogeography* (Dec. 2003) study of ants in Mongolia (Central Asia), Exercise 2.66 (p. 66). Recall that botanists placed seed baits at 5 sites in the Dry Steppe region and 6 sites in the Gobi Desert and observed the number of ant species attracted to each site. These data are listed in the accompanying table. Is there evidence to conclude that a difference exists between the average number of ant species found at sites in the two regions of Mongolia? Draw the appropriate conclusion using $\alpha = .05$.

GOBIANTS

Site	Region	Number of Ant Species
1	Dry Steppe	3
2	Dry Steppe	3
3	Dry Steppe	52
4	Dry Steppe	7
5	Dry Steppe	5
6	Gobi Desert	49
7	Gobi Desert	5
8	Gobi Desert	4
9	Gobi Desert	4
10	Gobi Desert	5
11	Gobi Desert	4

Source: Pfeiffer, M., et al. "Community organization and species richness of ants in Mongolia along an ecological gradient from steppe to Gobi desert," *Journal of Biogeography,* Vol. 30, No. 12, Dec. 2003.

9.24 Accuracy of mental maps. To help students organize global information about people, places, and environments, geographers encourage them to develop "mental maps" of the world. A series of lessons was designed to aid students in the development of mental maps. (*Journal of Geography,* May/June 1997.) In one experiment, a class of 24 seventh-grade geography students was given mental map lessons while a second class of 20 students received traditional instruction. All students were asked to sketch a map of the world, and each portion of the map was evaluated for accuracy using a 5-point scale (1 = low accuracy, 5 = high accuracy).

a. The mean accuracy scores of the two groups of seventh-graders were compared using a test of hypothesis. State H_0 and H_a for a test to determine whether the mental map lessons improve a student's ability to sketch a world map.

b. What assumptions (if any) are required for the test to be statistically valid?

c. The observed significance level of the test for comparing the mean accuracy scores for continents drawn is .0507. Interpret this result.

d. The observed significance level of the test for comparing the mean accuracy scores for labeling oceans is .7371. Interpret the result.

e. The observed significance level of the test for comparing the mean accuracy scores for the entire map is .0024. Interpret the result.

9.25 Masculinity and crime. The *Journal of Sociology* (July 2003) published a study on the link between the level of masculinity and criminal behavior in men. Using a sample of newly incarcerated men in Nebraska, the researcher identified 1,171 violent events and 532 avoided-violent events that the men were involved in. (A violent event involved use of a weapon, throwing of objects, punching, choking, or kicking. An avoided-violent event included pushing, shoving, grabbing, or threats of violence that did not escalate into a violent event.) Each of the sampled men took the Masculinity-Femininity Scale (MFS) test to determine his level of masculinity based on common male stereotyped traits. MFS scores ranged from 0 to 56 points, with lower scores indicating a more masculine orientation. One goal of the research was to compare the mean MFS scores for two groups of men—those involved in violent events and those involved in avoided-violent events.

a. Identify the target parameter for this study.

b. The sample mean MFS score for the violent event group was 44.50 while the sample mean MFS score for the avoided-violent event group was 45.06. Is this sufficient information to make the comparison desired by the researcher? Explain.

c. In a large-sample test of hypothesis to compare the two means, the test statistic was computed to be $z = 1.21$. Compute the two-tailed p-value of the test.

d. Make the appropriate conclusion using $\alpha = .10$.

9.26 Mating habits of snails. Hermaphrodites are animals that possess the reproductive organs of both sexes. *Genetical Research* (June 1995) published a study of the mating systems of hermaphroditic snail species. The mating habits of the snails were classified into two groups: (1) self-fertilizing (selfing) snails that mate with snails of the same sex and (2) cross-fertilizing (outcrossing) snails that mate with snails of the opposite sex. One variable of interest in the study was the effective population size of the snail species. The means and standard deviations of the effective population size for independent random samples of 17 outcrossing snail species and 5 selfing snail species are given

in the table. Compare the mean effective population sizes of the two types of snail species with a 90% confidence interval. Interpret the result.

Snail Mating System	Sample Size	Effective Population Size	
		Mean	Standard Deviation
Outcrossing	17	4,894	1,932
Selfing	5	4,133	1,890

Source: Jarne, P. "Mating system, bottlenecks, and genetic polymorphism in hermaphroditic animals." *Genetical Research,* Vol. 65, No. 3, June 1995, p. 197 (Table 4).

9.27 Children's use of pronouns. Refer to the *Journal of Communication Disorders* (Mar. 1995) study of specifically language-impaired (SLI) children, Exercise 2.65 (p. 65). The data on deviation intelligence quotient (DIQ) for 10 SLI children and 10 younger, normally developing (YND) children are reproduced in the table. Use the methodology of this section to compare the mean DIQ of the two groups of children. (Use $\alpha = .10$.) What do you conclude?

SLI

SLI Children			YND Children		
86	87	84	110	90	105
94	86	107	92	92	96
89	98	95	86	100	92
110			90		

9.28 Personalities of cocaine users. Do cocaine abusers have radically different personalities than nonabusing college students? This was one of the questions researched in *Psychological Assessment* (June 1995). A personality questionnaire (ZKPQ) was administered to a sample of 450 cocaine abusers and a sample of 589 college students. The ZKPQ yields scores (measured on a 20-point scale) on each of five dimensions: impulsive–sensation seeking, sociability, neuroticism–anxiety, aggression–hostility, and activity. The results are summarized in the table. Compare the mean ZKPQ scores of the two groups on each dimension using a statistical test of hypothesis. Interpret the results at $\alpha = .01$.

ZKPQ Dimension	Cocaine Abusers ($n = 450$)		College Students ($n = 589$)	
	Mean	Std. Dev.	Mean	Std. Dev.
Impulsive–sensation seeking	9.4	4.4	9.5	4.4
Sociability	10.4	4.3	12.5	4.0
Neuroticism–anxiety	8.6	5.1	9.1	4.6
Aggression–hostility	8.6	3.9	7.3	4.1
Activity	11.1	3.4	8.0	4.1

Source: Ball, S. A. "The validity of an alternative five-factor measure of personality in cocaine abusers." *Psychological Assessment,* Vol. 7, No. 2, June 1995, p. 150 (Table 1).

9.29 Ethnicity and pain perception. An investigation of ethnic differences in reports of pain perception was presented at the annual meeting of the American Psychosomatic Society (March 2001). A sample of 55 blacks and 159 whites participated in the study. Subjects rated (on a 13-point scale) the intensity and unpleasantness of pain felt when a bag of ice was placed on their foreheads for two minutes. (Higher ratings correspond to higher pain intensity.) A summary of the results is provided in the accompanying table.

	Blacks	Whites
Sample size	55	159
Mean pain intensity	8.2	6.9

a. Why is it dangerous to draw a statistical inference from the summarized data? Explain.

b. Give values of the missing sample standard deviations that would lead you to conclude (at $\alpha = .05$) that blacks, on average, have a higher pain intensity rating than whites.

c. Give values of the missing sample standard deviations that would lead you to an inconclusive decision (at $\alpha = .05$) regarding whether blacks or whites have a higher mean intensity rating.

9.3 Comparing Two Population Means: Paired Difference Experiments

In Example 9.4, we compared two methods of teaching reading to slow learners by means of a 95% confidence interval. Suppose it is possible to measure the slow learners' "reading IQs" *before* they are subjected to a teaching method. Eight pairs of slow learners with similar reading IQs are found, and one member of each pair is randomly assigned to the standard teaching method while the other is assigned to the new method. The data are given in Table 9.3. Do the data support the hypothesis that the population mean reading test score for slow learners taught by the new method is greater than the mean reading test score for those taught by the standard method?

We want to test

$$H_0: (\mu_1 - \mu_2) = 0$$
$$H_a: (\mu_1 - \mu_2) > 0$$

One way to conduct this test is to use the t statistic for two independent samples (Section 9.2). The analysis is shown on the MINITAB printout, Figure 9.9. The test statistic, $t = 1.26$, is highlighted on the printout as well as the p-value of the test, $p = .115$. At $\alpha = .10$, the p-value exceeds α. Thus, from *this* analysis we might conclude that we do not have sufficient evidence to infer a difference in the mean test scores for the two methods.

If you carefully examine the data in Table 9.3, however, you will find this result difficult to accept. The test score of the new method is larger than the corresponding test score for the standard method *for every one of the eight pairs of slow learners.* This, in itself, seems to provide strong evidence to indicate that μ_1 exceeds μ_2. Why,

⦿ **PAIREDSCORES**

TABLE 9.3   Reading Test Scores for Eight Pairs of Slow Learners

Pair	New Method (1)	Standard Method (2)
1	77	72
2	74	68
3	82	76
4	73	68
5	87	84
6	69	68
7	66	61
8	80	76

Figure 9.9
MINITAB Analysis
of Reading Test Scores
in Table 9.3

```
Two-sample T for NEW vs STANDARD

           N    Mean  StDev  SE Mean
NEW        8   76.00   6.93      2.4
STANDARD   8   71.63   7.01      2.5


Difference = mu (NEW) - mu (STANDARD)
Estimate for difference:   4.37500
95% lower bound for difference:   -1.76200
T-Test of difference = 0 (vs >):  T-Value = 1.26   P-Value = 0.115   DF = 14
Both use Pooled StDev = 6.9687
```

then, did the t-test fail to detect this difference? The answer is; *The independent samples t-test is not a valid procedure to use with this set of data.*

The t-test is inappropriate because the assumption of independent samples is invalid. We have randomly chosen *pairs of test scores,* and thus, once we have chosen the sample for the new method, we have *not* independently chosen the sample for the standard method. The dependence between observations within pairs can be seen by examining the pairs of test scores, which tend to rise and fall together as we go from pair to pair. This pattern provides strong visual evidence of a violation of the assumption of independence required for the two-sample t-test of Section 9.2. Note, also, that

$$s_p^2 = \frac{(n_1 - 1)s_1^2 + (n_2 - 1)s_2^2}{n_1 + n_2 - 2} = \frac{(8 - 1)(6.93)^2 + (8 - 1)(7.01)^2}{8 + 8 - 2} = 48.55$$

Thus, there is a *large variation within samples* (reflected by the large value of s_p^2) in comparison to the relatively *small difference between the sample means.* Because s_p^2 is so large, the t-test of Section 9.2 is unable to detect a difference between μ_1 and μ_2.

We now consider a valid method of analyzing the data of Table 9.3. In Table 9.4 we add the column of differences between the test scores of the pairs of slow learners. We can regard these differences in test scores as a random sample of differences for all pairs (matched on reading IQ) of slow learners, past and present. Then we can use this sample to make inferences about the mean of the population of differences, μ_D, which is equal to the difference $(\mu_1 - \mu_2)$. That is, the mean of the population (and sample) of differences equals the difference between the population (and sample) means. Thus, our test becomes

$$H_0: \mu_D = 0 \quad (\mu_1 - \mu_2 = 0)$$
$$H_a: \mu_D > 0 \quad (\mu_1 - \mu_2 > 0)$$

TABLE 9.4   Differences in Reading Test Scores

Pair	New Method	Standard Method	Difference (New Method − Standard Method)
1	77	72	5
2	74	68	6
3	82	76	6
4	73	68	5
5	87	84	3
6	69	68	1
7	66	61	5
8	80	76	4

The test statistic is a one-sample t (Section 8.4), since we are now analyzing a single sample of differences for small n:

$$\text{Test statistic:} \quad t = \frac{\bar{x}_D - 0}{s_D / \sqrt{n_D}}$$

where

$$\bar{x}_D = \text{Sample mean difference}$$
$$s_D = \text{Sample standard deviation of differences}$$
$$n_D = \text{Number of differences} = \text{Number of pairs}$$

Assumptions: The population of differences in test scores is approximately normally distributed. The sample differences are randomly selected from the population differences. [*Note:* We do not need to make the assumption that $\sigma_1^2 = \sigma_2^2$.]

Rejection region: At significance level $\alpha = .05$, we will reject H_0: if $t > t_{.05}$, where $t_{.05}$ is based on $(n_D - 1)$ degrees of freedom.

Referring to Table VI in Appendix A, we find the t-value corresponding to $\alpha = .05$ and $n_D - 1 = 8 - 1 = 7$ df to be $t_{.05} = 1.895$. Then we will reject the null hypothesis if $t > 1.895$ (see Figure 9.10). Note that the number of degrees of freedom decreases from $n_1 + n_2 - 2 = 14$ to 7 when we use the paired difference experiment rather than the two independent random samples design.

Figure 9.10

Rejection Region for Example 9.4

t-distribution with 7 df

$\alpha = .05$

0

Rejection region

$t = 1.895$

Summary statistics for the $n = 8$ differences are shown in the MINITAB printout, Figure 9.11. Note that $\bar{x}_D = 4.375$ and $s_D = 1.685$. Substituting these values into the formula for the test statistic, we have

$$t = \frac{\bar{x}_D - 0}{s_D / \sqrt{n_D}} = \frac{4.375}{1.685 / \sqrt{8}} = 7.34$$

Because this value of t falls in the rejection region, we conclude (at $\alpha = .05$) that the population mean test score for slow learners taught by the new method exceeds the population mean score for those taught by the standard method. We can reach the same conclusion by noting that the p-value of the test, highlighted in Figure 9.11, is much smaller than $\alpha = .05$.

Figure 9.11

MINITAB Paired Difference Analysis of Reading Test Scores

```
Paired T for NEW - STANDARD

               N     Mean     StDev   SE Mean
NEW            8   76.0000   6.9282    2.4495
STANDARD       8   71.6250   7.0089    2.4780
Difference     8    4.37500  1.68502   0.59574


95% lower bound for mean difference: 3.24632
T-Test of mean difference = 0 (vs > 0): T-Value = 7.34  P-Value = 0.000
```

Now Work *Exercise 9.35ab*

This kind of experiment, in which observations are paired and the differences are analyzed, is called a **paired difference experiment**. In many cases, a paired difference experiment can provide more information about the difference between population means than an independent samples experiment. The idea is to compare population means by comparing the differences between pairs of experimental units (objects, people, etc.) that were very similar prior to the experiment. The differencing removes sources of variation that tend to inflate σ^2. For example, when two children are taught to read by two different methods, the observed difference in achievement may be due to a difference in the effectiveness of the two teaching methods *or* it may be due to differences in the initial reading levels and IQs of the two children (random error). To reduce the effect of differences in the children on the observed differences in reading achievement, the two methods of reading are imposed on two children who are more likely to possess similar intellectual capacity, namely children with nearly equal IQs. The effect of this pairing is to remove the larger source of variation that would be present if children with different abilities were randomly assigned to the two samples. Making comparisons within groups of similar experimental units is called **blocking**, and the paired difference experiment is a simple example of a **randomized block experiment**. In our example, pairs of children with matching IQ scores represent the blocks.

Some other examples for which the paired difference experiment might be appropriate are the following:

1. Suppose you want to estimate the difference $(\mu_1 - \mu_2)$ in mean price per gallon between two major brands of premium gasoline. If you choose two independent random samples of stations for each brand, the variability in price due to geographic location may be large. To eliminate this source of variability you could choose pairs of stations of similar size, one station for each brand, in close geographic proximity and use the sample of differences between the prices of the brands to make an inference about $(\mu_1 - \mu_2)$.

2. Suppose a college placement center wants to estimate the difference $(\mu_1 - \mu_2)$ in mean starting salaries for men and women graduates who seek jobs through the center. If it independently samples men and women, the starting salaries may vary because of their different college majors and differences in grade point averages. To eliminate these sources of variability, the placement center could match male and female job-seekers according to their majors and grade point averages. Then the differences between the starting salaries of each pair in the sample could be used to make an inference about $(\mu_1 - \mu_2)$.

3. Suppose you wish to estimate the difference $(\mu_1 - \mu_2)$ in mean absorption rate into the bloodstream for two drugs that relieve pain. If you independently sample people, the absorption rates might vary because of age, weight, sex, blood pressure, etc. In fact, there are many possible sources of nuisance variability, and pairing individuals who are similar in all the possible sources would be quite difficult. However, it may be possible to obtain two measurements *on the same person*. First, we administer one of the two drugs and record the time until absorption. After a sufficient amount of time, the other drug is administered and a second measurement on absorption time is obtained. The differences between the measurements for each person in the sample could then be used to estimate $(\mu_1 - \mu_2)$. This procedure would be advisable only if the amount of time allotted between drugs is sufficient to guarantee little or no carryover effect. Otherwise, it would be better to use different people matched as closely as possible on the factors thought to be most important.

Now Work   *Exercise 9.33*

The hypothesis-testing procedures and the method of forming confidence intervals for the difference between two means using a paired difference experiment are summarized in the following boxes for both large and small n.

Paired Difference Confidence Interval for $\mu_D = \mu_1 - \mu_2$

Large Sample

$$\bar{x}_D \pm z_{\alpha/2}\frac{\sigma_D}{\sqrt{n_D}} \approx \bar{x}_D \pm z_{\alpha/2}\frac{s_D}{\sqrt{n_D}}$$

Small Sample

$$\bar{x}_D \pm t_{\alpha/2}\frac{s_D}{\sqrt{n_D}}$$

where $t_{\alpha/2}$ is based on $(n_D - 1)$ degrees of freedom

---

Paired Difference Test of Hypothesis for $\mu_D = \mu_1 - \mu_2$

One-Tailed Test

$H_0: \mu_D = D_0$
$H_a: \mu_D < D_0$
   [or $H_a: \mu_D > D_0$]

Two-Tailed Test

$H_0: \mu_D = D_0$
$H_a: \mu_D \neq D_0$

Large Sample

Test statistic: $z = \dfrac{\bar{x}_D - D_0}{\sigma_D/\sqrt{n_D}} \approx \dfrac{\bar{x}_D - D_0}{s_D/\sqrt{n_D}}$

Rejection region: $z < -z_\alpha$
   [or $z > z_\alpha$ when $H_a: \mu_D > D_0$]

Rejection region: $|z| > z_{\alpha/2}$

Small Sample

Test statistic: $t = \dfrac{\bar{x}_D - D_0}{s_D/\sqrt{n_D}}$

Rejection region: $t < -t_\alpha$
   [or $t > t_\alpha$ when $H_a: \mu_D > D_0$]

Rejection region: $|t| > t_{\alpha/2}$

where t_α and $t_{\alpha/2}$ are based on $(n_D - 1)$ degrees of freedom

---

Conditions Required for Valid Large-Sample Inferences about μ_D

1. A random sample of differences is selected from the target population of differences.
2. The sample size n_D is large (i.e., $n_D \geq 30$). (Due to the Central Limit Theorem, this condition guarantees that the test statistic will be approximately normal regardless of the shape of the underlying probability distribution of the population.)

Conditions Required for Valid Small-Sample Inferences about μ_D

1. A random sample of differences is selected from the target population of differences.
2. The population of differences has a distribution that is approximately normal.

EXAMPLE 9.5

A CONFIDENCE INTERVAL FOR μ_D

Problem   An experiment is conducted to compare the starting salaries of male and female college graduates who find jobs. Pairs are formed by choosing a male and a female with the same major and similar grade point averages (GPA). Suppose a random sample of 10 pairs is formed in this manner and the starting annual salary of each person is recorded. The results are shown in Table 9.5. Compare the mean starting salary, μ_1, for males to the mean starting salary, μ_2, for females using a 95% confidence interval. Interpret the results.

⊙ GRADPAIRS

TABLE 9.5   Data on Annual Salaries for Matched Pairs of College Graduates

Pair	Male	Female	Difference Male − Female	Pair	Male	Female	Difference Male − Female
1	$29,300	$28,800	$ 500	6	$37,800	$38,000	$−200
2	41,500	41,600	−100	7	69,500	69,200	300
3	40,400	39,800	600	8	41,200	40,100	1,100
4	38,500	38,500	0	9	38,400	38,200	200
5	43,500	42,600	900	10	59,200	58,500	700

Solution   Since the data on annual salary are collected in pairs of males and females matched on GPA and major, a paired difference experiment is performed. To conduct the analysis, we first compute the differences between the salaries, as shown in Table 9.5. Summary statistics for these $n = 10$ differences are displayed at the top of the SAS printout, Figure 9.12.

Figure 9.12
SAS Analysis of Salary
Differences

```
                         The MEANS Procedure

                     Analysis Variable : DIFF

        Mean          Std Dev       N        Minimum        Maximum

   400.0000000     434.6134937     10     -200.0000000     1100.00
```

```
        Two Sample Paired t-test for the Means of MALE and FEMALE

     Sample Statistics

        Group       N      Mean     Std. Dev.   Std. Error
        -------------------------------------------------------
        MALE        10     43930       11665       3688.8
        FEMALE      10     43530       11617       3673.6


     Hypothesis Test

        Null hypothesis:      Mean of (MALE - FEMALE) =  0
        Alternative:          Mean of (MALE - FEMALE) ^= 0

            t Statistic       Df       Prob > t
            ------------------------------------
               2.910           9        0.0173


     95% Confidence Interval for the Difference between Two Paired Means

                Lower Limit       Upper Limit
                -----------       -----------
                   89.10            710.90
```

The 95% confidence interval for $\mu_D = (\mu_1 - \mu_2)$ for this small sample is

$$\bar{x}_D \pm t_{\alpha/2} \frac{s_D}{\sqrt{n_D}}$$

where $t_{\alpha/2} = t_{.025} = 2.262$ (obtained from Table VI, Appendix A) is based on $n - 1 = 9$ degrees of freedom. Substituting the values of $\bar{x}_D$ and s_D shown on the printout, we obtain

$$
\begin{aligned}
\bar{x}_D \pm 2.262 \frac{s_D}{\sqrt{n_D}} &= 400 \pm 2.262\left(\frac{434.613}{\sqrt{10}}\right) \\
&= 400 \pm 310.88 \approx 400 \pm 311 = (\$89, \$711)
\end{aligned}
$$

[*Note:* This interval is also shown highlighted at the bottom of the SAS printout, Figure 9.12.] Our interpretation is that the true mean difference between the starting salaries of males and females falls between $89 and $711, with 95% confidence. Since the interval falls above 0, we infer that $\mu_1 - \mu_2 > 0$; that is, the mean salary for males exceeds the mean salary for females.

Look Back Remember that $\mu_D = \mu_1 - \mu_2$. So if $\mu_D > 0$, then $\mu_1 > \mu_2$. Alternatively, if $\mu_D < 0$, then $\mu_1 < \mu_2$.

Now Work *Exercise 9.40*

■ ■ ■

To measure the amount of information about $(\mu_1 - \mu_2)$ gained by using a paired difference experiment in Example 9.5 rather than an independent samples experiment, we can compare the relative widths of the confidence intervals obtained by the two methods. A 95% confidence interval for $(\mu_1 - \mu_2)$ using the paired difference experiment is, from Example 9.5, ($89, $711). If we analyzed the same data as though this were an independent samples experiment,* we would first obtain the descriptive statistics shown in the SAS printout, Figure 9.13. Then we substitute the sample means and standard deviations shown on the printout into the formula for a 95% confidence interval for $(\mu_1 - \mu_2)$ using independent samples:

$$(\bar{x}_1 - \bar{x}_2) \pm t_{.025}\sqrt{s_p^2\left(\frac{1}{n_1} + \frac{1}{n_2}\right)}$$

Figure 9.13

SPSS Analysis of Salaries, assuming Independent Samples

Group Statistics

	GENDER	N	Mean	Std. Deviation	Std. Error Mean
SALARY	M	10	43930.00	11665.148	3688.844
	F	10	43530.00	11616.946	3673.601

Independent Samples Test

		Levene's Test for Equality of Variances		t-test for Equality of Means						
									95% Confidence Interval of the Difference	
		F	Sig.	t	df	Sig. (2-tailed)	Mean Difference	Std. Error Difference	Lower	Upper
SALARY	Equal variances assumed	.000	.991	.077	18	.940	400.00	5206.046	-10537.5	11337.50
	Equal variances not assumed			.077	18.000	.940	400.00	5206.046	-10537.5	11337.51

*This is done only to provide a measure of the increase in the amount of information obtained by a paired design in comparison to an unpaired design. Actually, if an experiment is designed using pairing, an unpaired analysis would be invalid because the assumption of independent samples would not be satisfied.

where

$$s_p^2 = \frac{(n_1 - 1)s_1^2 + (n_2 - 1)s_2^2}{n_1 + n_2 - 2}$$

SPSS performed these calculations and obtained the interval ($-10,537.50$, $11,337.50$). This interval is highlighted on Figure 9.13.

Notice that the independent samples interval includes 0. Consequently, if we were to use this interval to make an inference about $(\mu_1 - \mu_2)$, we would incorrectly conclude that the mean starting salaries of males and females do not differ! You can see that the confidence interval for the independent sampling experiment is about five times wider than for the corresponding paired difference confidence interval. Blocking out the variability due to differences in majors and grade point averages significantly increases the information about the difference in male and female mean starting salaries by providing a much more accurate (smaller confidence interval for the same confidence coefficient) estimate of $(\mu_1 - \mu_2)$.

You may wonder whether conducting a paired difference experiment is always superior to an independent samples experiment. The answer is, Most of the time, but not always. We sacrifice half the degrees of freedom in the t-statistic when a paired difference design is used instead of an independent samples design. This is a loss of information, and unless this loss is more than compensated for by the reduction in variability obtained by blocking (pairing), the paired difference experiment will result in a net loss of information about $(\mu_1 - \mu_2)$. Thus, we should be convinced that the pairing will significantly reduce variability before performing the paired difference experiment. Most of the time this will happen.

One final note: The pairing of the observations is determined *before* the experiment is performed (that is, by the *design* of the experiment). A paired difference experiment is *never* obtained by pairing the sample observations after the measurements have been acquired.

What Do You Do when the Assumption of a Normal Distribution for the Population of Differences Is Not Satisfied?

Answer: Use the Wilcoxon signed rank test for the paired difference design (Chapter 14).

Confidence Interval for a Paired Difference

Using The TI-83 Graphing Calculator

For this calculation, you have the option of entering the raw data or using the summary statistics

Step 1   *If you are using the raw data, enter the data into L1 and L2 and create a column of differences in L3.*

Press **STAT** and select **1:Edit**
Note: If a list already contains data, clear the old data. Use the up arrow to highlight the name at the top of the list. Press **CLEAR ENTER**.
Use the **Down Arrow** or **ENTER** key to enter the data sets into **L1** and **L2**. Move the cursor so that it is flashing on '**L3**' at the top of the third column and press **ENTER**.
The cursor will be positioned at the bottom of the screen to the right of '**L3** = .' Type in 'L1-L2' by hitting **2nd** and '**1**' - **2nd** and '**2.**' Press **ENTER**.

Step 2   *Access the Statistical Tests Menu*

Press **STAT**
Arrow right to **TESTS**
Arrow down to **8: TInterval**
Press **ENTER**

Step 3   *Choose "**Data**" or "**Stats**". ("Data" is selected when you have entered the raw data into L1 and L2. "Stats" is selected when you are using the summary statistics.)*

Press **ENTER**

If you selected "Data":
Set **List** to **L3**. Note: Arrow down to List: and hit **2nd** and '**3**'.
Set **Freq** to **1**. Note: If Freq is not already set to 1, arrow down to Freq and hit **Alpha** and '**1**'.
Arrow down to **C-Level** and enter the confidence level.
Arrow down to **"Calculate"**
Press **ENTER**

If you selected "Stats", enter the mean of the paired differences, the standard deviation of the paired differences and sample size of the paired differences.
Arrow down to **C-Level** and enter the confidence level.
Arrow down to **"Calculate"**
Press **ENTER**

Step 4   *View the Output*

The confidence interval will be displayed with the mean and standard deviation of the paired differences and the sample size.

Example   *Consider Example 9.5 with data in Table 9.5 on pg. 458. For this example, the raw data will be used, so begin with Step1 of the instructions.*

Step 1   *Enter the salaries for the Males into L1 and the salaries for the Females into L2 and create a column of differences in L3.*

Press **STAT** and select **1:Edit**
Note: If a list already contains data, clear the old data. Use the up arrow to highlight the name at the top of the list. Press **CLEAR ENTER**.
Use the **Down Arrow** or **Enter** key to enter the data sets into **L1** and **L2**.
Move the cursor so that it is flashing on '**L3**' at the top of the third column and press **ENTER**.
The cursor will be positioned at the bottom of the screen to the right of '**L3 = .**' Type in 'L1-L2' by hitting **2nd** and '**1**' - **2nd** and '**2**.' Press **ENTER**.

L1	L2	L3	3
29300	28800	500	
41500	41600	-100	
40400	39800	600	
38500	38500	0	
43500	42600	900	
37800	38000	-200	
69500	69200	300	

L3(1)=500

Step 2   *Access the Statistical Tests Menu*

Press **STAT**
Arrow right to **TESTS**
Arrow down to **8: TInterval**
Press **ENTER**

Step 3   *Choose "**Data**"*

Press **ENTER**

Set **List** to **L3**. Note: Arrow down to List: and hit **2nd** and '**3**'.
Set **Freq** to **1**. Note: If Freq is not already set to 1, arrow down to Freq and hit **Alpha** and '**1**'.

Arrow down to **C-Level** and enter the confidence level.
Arrow down to **"Calculate"**
Press **ENTER**

```
TInterval
 Inpt:DATA Stats
 List:L₃
 Freq:1
 C-Level:.95
 Calculate
```

Step 4   *View the Output*

The confidence interval will be displayed with the mean and standard
deviation of the paired differences and the sample size.

```
TInterval
 (89.096,710.9)
 x̄=400
 Sx=434.6134937
 n=10
```

Hypothesis Test for
a Paired Difference

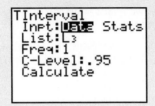

Using The TI-83 Graphing Calculator

**For this calculation, you have the option of
entering the raw data or using the summary statistics**

Step 1   *If you are using the raw data, enter the data into L1 and L2 and create a column
of differences in L3.*

Press **STAT** and select **1:Edit**
Note: If a list already contains data, clear the old data. Use the up arrow to
highlight the name at the top of the list. Press **CLEAR ENTER**.
Use the **Down Arrow** or **ENTER** key to enter the data sets into **L1** and **L2**.
Move the cursor so that it is flashing on **'L3'** at the top of the third column and
press **ENTER**.
The cursor will be positioned at the bottom of the screen to the right of
'L3 = .' Type in 'L1-L2' by hitting **2nd** and **'1' - 2nd** and **'2.'** Press **ENTER**.

Step 2   *Access the Statistical Tests Menu*

Press **STAT**
Arrow right to **TESTS**
Arrow down to **2 : TTest**
Press **ENTER**

Step 3   *Choose "**Data**" or "**Stats**". ("Data" is selected when you have entered the raw data
into L1 and L2. "Stats" is selected when you are using the summary statistics.)*

Press **ENTER**

If you selected "Data":
Arrow down to μ_0 and enter the value for D_0 from the null hypothesis.
Note: In most cases, the value for D_0 is 0.
Set **List** to **L3**. Note: Arrow down to List: and hit **2nd** and **'3'**.
Set **Freq** to **1**. Note: If Freq is not already set to 1, arrow down to Freq and hit
Alpha and **'1'**.

Arrow down to the next line and select the appropriate alternative hypothesis by using the right arrow to highlight $\neq u_0$, $< u_0$, or $> u_0$ and press **ENTER**. Arrow down to **Calculate Draw**. You may choose either one of these for your output.
Press **ENTER**

If you selected "Stats":
Arrow down to μ_0 and enter the value for D_0 from the null hypothesis.
Note: In most cases, the value for D_0 is 0.
Enter the mean of the paired differences, the standard deviation of the paired differences and sample size of the paired differences.
Arrow down to the next line and select the appropriate alternative hypothesis by using the right arrow to highlight $\neq u_0$, $< u_0$, or $> u_0$ and press **ENTER**.
Arrow down to **Calculate Draw**. You may choose either one of these for your output.
Press **ENTER**

Step 4 *View the Output*

If you chose **Calculate,** the output will display the alternative hypothesis, the t-value, the p-value, the mean and standard deviation of the paired differences and the sample size.
If you chose **Draw,** a graph of the normal curve will be displayed along with the t-value and the p-value.
The area under the curve that represents the p-value is shaded. Note: In order to use the **Draw** feature, you must first clear all equations from the **Y-registers**.
Hit '**Y =** ' and delete all equations.

Example *Consider Exercise 9.42 on pg. 466. For this example, the raw data will be used, so begin with Step 1 of the instructions.*

Step 1 *Enter the 'Attitude toward Father' into L1 and the 'Attitude toward Mother' into L2 and create a column of differences in L3.*

Press **STAT** and select **1:Edit**
Note: If a list already contains data, clear the old data. Use the up arrow to highlight the name at the top of the list. Press **CLEAR ENTER**.
Use the **Down Arrow** or **ENTER** key to enter the data sets into **L1** and **L2**.
Move the cursor so that it is flashing on '**L3**' at the top of the third column and press **ENTER**.
The cursor will be positioned at the bottom of the screen to the right of '**L3 =** .' Type in 'L1-L2' by hitting **2nd** and '**1**' - **2nd** and '**2.**' Press **ENTER**.

L1	L2	L3	3
2	3	▓	
5	5	0	
4	3	1	
4	5	-1	
3	4	-1	
5	4	1	
4	5	-1	
L3(1)= -1				

Step 2 *Access the Statistical Tests Menu*

Press **STAT**
Arrow right to **TESTS**
Arrow down to **2 : TTest**
Press **ENTER**

Step 3 *Choose "Data"*

Press **ENTER**
Arrow down to μ_0 and enter 0, the value for D_0 from the null hypothesis.
Set **List** to **L3**. Note: Arrow down to List: and hit **2nd** and '**3**'.
Set **Freq** to **1**. Note: If Freq is not already set to 1, arrow down to Freq and hit **Alpha** and '**1**'.

Arrow down to the next line and select $\neq u_0$ and press **ENTER**.
Arrow down to **Calculate Draw**. You may choose either one of these for your output.
Press **ENTER**

Step 4   *View the Output*

If you chose **Calculate,** the output will display the alternative hypothesis, the t-value, the p-value, the mean and standard deviation of the paired differences and the sample size.

If you chose **Draw,** a graph of the normal curve will be displayed along with the t-value and the p-value. The area under the curve that represents the p-value is shaded. Note: In order to use the **Draw** feature, you must first clear all equations from the **Y-registers**. Hit 'Y = ' and delete all equations.

Exercises 9.30–9.48

Understanding the Principles

9.30 What are the advantages of using a paired difference experiment over an independent samples design?

9.31 In a paired difference experiment, when should the observations be paired—before or after collecting the data?

9.32 What conditions are required for valid large-sample inferences about μ_D? Small-sample inferences?

Learning the Mechanics

9.33 A paired difference experiment yielded n_D pairs of
NW observations. In each case, what is the rejection region for testing $H_0: \mu_D = 2$ against $H_a: \mu_D > 2$?
  a. $n_D = 10, \alpha = .05$
  b. $n_D = 20, \alpha = .10$
  c. $n_D = 5, \alpha = .025$
  d. $n_D = 9, \alpha = .01$

9.34 A paired difference experiment produced the following data:

$$n_D = 16 \quad \bar{x}_1 = 143 \quad \bar{x}_2 = 150 \quad \bar{x}_D = -7 \quad s_D^2 = 64$$

  a. Determine the values of t for which the null hypothesis, $\mu_1 - \mu_2 = 0$, would be rejected in favor of the alternative hypothesis, $\mu_1 - \mu_2 < 0$. Use $\alpha = .10$.
  b. Conduct the paired difference test described in part **a**. Draw the appropriate conclusions.
  c. What assumptions are necessary so that the paired difference test will be valid?
  d. Find a 90% confidence interval for the mean difference μ_D.
  e. Which of the two inferential procedures, the confidence interval of part **d** or the test of hypothesis of part **b**, provides more information about the difference between the population means?

9.35 The data for a random sample of six paired observa-
[NW] tions are shown in the table.

⊚ **LM9_35**

Pair	Sample from Population 1	Sample from Population 2
1	7	4
2	3	1
3	9	7
4	6	2
5	4	4
6	8	7

a. Calculate the difference between each pair of observations by subtracting observation 2 from observation 1. Use the differences to calculate $\bar{x}_D$ and s_D^2.
b. If μ_1 and μ_2 are the means of populations 1 and 2,
respectively, express μ_D in terms of μ_1 and μ_2.
c. Form a 95% confidence interval for μ_D.
d. Test the null hypothesis $H_0: \mu_D = 0$ against the alternative hypothesis $H_a: \mu_D \neq 0$. Use $\alpha = .05$.

9.36 The data for a random sample of 10 paired observations are shown in the next table.

⊚ **LM9_36**

Pair	Population 1	Population 2
1	19	24
2	25	27
3	31	36
4	52	53
5	49	55
6	34	34
7	59	66
8	47	51
9	17	20
10	51	55

a. If you wish to test whether these data are sufficient
to indicate that the mean for population 2 is larger
than that for population 1, what are the appropriate
null and alternative hypotheses? Define any symbols
you use.
b. Conduct the test, part **a**, using $\alpha = .10$. What is your
decision?
c. Find a 90% confidence interval for μ_D. Interpret this
interval.
d. What assumptions are necessary to ensure the validity of this analysis?

9.37 A paired difference experiment yielded the following
results:

$$n_D = 40$$
$$\bar{x}_D = 11.7$$
$$s_D = 6.$$

a. Test $H_0: \mu_D = 10$ against $H_a: \mu_D \neq 10$, where $\mu_D = (\mu_1 - \mu_2)$. Use $\alpha = .05$.
b. Report the p-value for the test you conducted in part **a**.
Interpret the p-value.

Applying the Concepts—Basic

9.38 Life expectantcy of oscar winners. Does winning an
Academy of Motion Picture Arts and Sciences award
lead to long-term mortality for movie actors? In an
article in the *Annals of Internal Medicine* (May 15,
2001), researchers sampled 762 Academy Award winners and matched each one with another actor of the
same sex who was in the same winning film and was
born in the same era. The life expectancy (age) of each
pair of actors was compared.
a. Explain why the data should be analyzed as a paired
difference experiment.
b. Set up the null hypothesis for a test to compare the
mean life expectancies of Academy Award winners
and nonwinners.
c. The sample mean life expectancies of Academy
Award winners and nonwinners were reported as
79.7 years and 75.8 years, respectively. The p-value
for comparing the two population means was
reported as $p = .003$. Interpret this value in the context of the problem.

9.39 The placebo effect and pain. According to research
published in *Science* (Feb. 20, 2004), the mere belief
that you are receiving an effective, treatment for pain
can reduce the pain you actually feel. Researchers
from the University of Michigan and Princeton
University tested this placebo effect on 24 volunteers
as follows. Each volunteer was put inside a magnetic
resonance imaging machine (MRI) for two consecutive sessions. During the first session, electric shocks
were applied to their arms and the blood oxygen level-
dependent (BOLD) signal (a measure related to
neural activity in the brain) was recorded during pain.
The second session was identical to the first, except
that prior to applying the electric shocks the
researchers smeared a cream on the volunteer's arms.
The volunteers were informed that the cream would
block the pain, when, in fact, it was just a regular skin
lotion (i.e., a placebo). If the placebo is effective in
reducing the pain experience, the BOLD measurements should be higher, on average, in the first MRI
session than in the second MRI session.
a. Identify the target parameter for this study.
b. What type of design was used to collect the data?

c. Give the null and alternative hypothesis for testing
the placebo effect theory.
d. The differences between the BOLD measurements
in the first and second sessions were computed and
summarized in the study as follows: $n_D = 24$,
$\bar{x}_D = .21$, $s_D = .47$. Use this information to calculate
the test statistic.
e. The p-value of the test was reported as p-value $= .02$.
Make the appropriate conclusion at $\alpha = .05$.

⊚ **CRASH**
9.40 NHTSA new car crash tests. Refer to the National
[NW] Highway Traffic Safety, Administration (NHTSA)
crash test data for new cars saved in the **CRASH** file.

Crash test dummies were placed in the driver's seat and front passenger's seat of a new car model, and the car was steered by remote control into a head-on collision with a fixed barrier while traveling at 35 miles per hour. Two of the variables measured for each of the 98 new cars in the data set are (1) the severity of the driver's chest injury and (2) the severity of the passenger's chest injury. (The more points assigned to the chest injury rating, the more severe the injury.) Suppose the NHTSA wants to determine whether the true mean driver chest injury rating exceeds the true mean passenger chest injury rating, and if so, by how much.

a. State the parameter of interest to the NHTSA.

b. Explain why the data should be analyzed as matched pairs.

c. Find a 99% confidence interval for the true difference between the mean chest injury ratings of drivers and front-seat passengers.

d. Interpret the interval, part **c.** Does the true mean driver chest injury rating exceed the true mean passenger chest injury rating? If so, by how much?

e. What conditions are required for the analysis to be valid? Do these conditions hold for these data?

9.41 Depo-Provera drug study. Hypersexual behavior caused by traumatic brain injury (TBI) is often treated with the drug Depo-Provera. In one clinical study, eight young male TBI patients who exhibited hypersexual behavior were treated weekly with 400 milligrams of Depo-Provera for six months. (*Journal of Head Trauma Rehabilitation,* June 1995.) The testosterone levels (in nanograms per deciliter) of the patients both prior to treatment and at the end of the 6-month treatment period are given in the table below.

DEPOPROV

Patient	Pretreatment	After 6 months on Depo-Provera
1	849	96
2	903	41
3	890	31
4	1,092	124
5	362	46
6	900	53
7	1,006	113
8	672	174

Source: Emory, L. E., Cole, C. M., and Meyer, W. J. "Use of Depo-Provera to control sexual aggression in persons with traumatic brain injury." *Journal of Head Trauma Rehabilitation,* Vol. 10, No. 3, June 1995, p. 52 (Table 2).

a. Construct a 99% confidence interval for the true mean difference between the pretreatment and after-treatment testosterone levels of young male TBI patients.

b. Use the interval, part **a,** to make an inference about the effectiveness of Depo-Provera in reducing testosterone levels of young male TBI patients.

9.42 Students attitudes toward parents. Researchers at the University of South Alabama compared the attitudes of male college students toward their fathers with their attitudes toward their mothers. (*Journal of Genetic Psychology,* March 1998.) Each of a sample of 13 males was asked to complete the following statement about each of their parents: My relationship with my father (mother) can best be described as (1) Awful, (2) Poor, (3) Average, (4) Good, or (5) Great. The following data were obtained:

FMATTITUDES

Student	Attitude toward Father	Attitude toward Mother
1	2	3
2	5	5
3	4	3
4	4	5
5	3	4
6	5	4
7	4	5
8	2	4
9	4	5
10	5	4
11	4	5
12	5	4
13	3	3

Source: Adapted from Vitulli, W. F., and Richardson, D. K. "College student's attitudes toward relationships with parents: A five-year comparative analysis." *Journal of Genetic Psychology,* Vol. 159, No. 1, (March 1998), pp. 45–52.

a. Specify the appropriate hypotheses for testing whether male students' attitudes toward their fathers differ from their attitudes toward their mothers, on average.

b. Conduct the test of part **a** at $\alpha = .05$. Interpret the results in the context of the problem.

Applying the Concepts—Intermediate

9.43 Reading tongue-twisters. According to *Webster's New World Dictionary,* a tongue-twister is "a phrase that is hard to speak rapidly." Do tongue-twisters have an effect on the length of time it takes to read silently? To answer this question, 42 undergraduate psychology students participated in a reading experiment. (*Memory & Cognition,* Sept. 1997.) Two lists, each comprised of 600 words, were constructed. One list contained a series of tongue-twisters and the other list (called the *control*) did not contain any tongue-twisters. Each student read both lists and the length of time (in minutes) required to complete the lists was recorded. The researchers used a test of hypothesis to compare the mean reading response times for the tongue-twister and control lists.

a. Set up the null hypothesis for the test.

b. Use the information in the table at the top of p. 467 to find the test statistic and *p*-value of the test.

c. Give the appropriate conclusion. Use $\alpha = .05$.

List Type	Response Time (minutes)	
	Mean	Standard Deviation
Tongue-twister	6.59	1.94
Control	6.34	1.92
Difference	.25	.78

Source: Robinson, D. H., and Katayama, A. D. "At-lexical, articulatory interference in silent reading: The 'upstream' tongue-twister effect." *Memory & Cognition,* Vol. 25, No. 5, Sept. 1997, p. 663.

9.44 Visual search and memory study. When searching for an item (e.g., a roadside traffic sign, a lost earring, or a tumor in a mammogram), common sense dictates that you will not re-examine items previously rejected. However, researchers at Harvard Medical School found that a visual search has no memory. (*Nature,* Aug. 6, 1998.) In their experiment, nine subjects searched for the letter "T" mixed among several letters "L." Each subject conducted the search under two conditions: random and static. In the random condition, the location of the letters were changed every 111 milliseconds; in the static condition, the location of the letters remained unchanged. In each trial, the reaction time (i.e., the amount of time it took the subject to locate the target letter) was recorded in milliseconds.

a. One goal of the research is to compare the mean reaction times of subjects in the two experimental conditions. Explain why the data should be analyzed as a paired-difference experiment.

b. If a visual search has no memory, then the main reaction times in the two conditions will not differ. Specify H_0 and H_a for testing the "no memory" theory.

c. The test statistic was calculated as $t = 1.52$ with p-value $= .15$. Make the appropriate conclusion.

9.45 Linking dementia and leisure activities. Does participation in leisure activities in your youth reduce the risk of Alzheimer's disease and other forms of dementia? To answer this question, a group of university researchers studied a sample of 107 same-sex Swedish twin pairs. (*Journal of Gerontology: Psychological Sciences and Social Sciences,* Sept. 2003.) Each twin pair was discordant for dementia—that is, one member of each pair was diagnosed with Alzheimer's disease while the other member (the control) was nondemented for at least five years after the sibling's onset of dementia. The level of overall leisure activity (measured on an 80-point scale, where higher values indicate higher levels of leisure activity) of each twin pair member 20 years prior to onset of dementia was obtained from the Swedish Twin Registry database. The leisure activity scores (simulated, based on summary information presented in the journal article) are saved in the **DEMENTIA** file. The first five and last five observations are shown in the table.

DEMENTIA (first and last 5 observations)

Pair	Control	Demented
1	27	13
2	57	57
3	23	31
4	39	46
5	37	37
·	·	·
·	·	·
103	22	14
104	32	23
105	33	29
106	36	37
107	24	1

a. Explain why the data should be analyzed as a paired difference experiment.

b. Conduct the appropriate analysis using $\alpha = .05$. Make an inference about which group, the demented or control (nondemented) twin members, had the largest average level of leisure activity.

9.46 Swim maze study. Merck Research Labs conducted an experiment to evaluate the effect of a new drug using the single-T swim maze. Nineteen impregnated dam rats were allocated a dosage of 12.5 milligrams of the drug. One male and one female rat pup were randomly selected from each resulting litter to perform in the swim maze. Each pup was placed in the water at one end of the maze and allowed to swim until it escaped at the opposite end. If the pup failed to escape after a certain period of time, it was placed at the beginning of the maze and given another chance. The experiment was repeated until each pup accomplished three successful escapes. The accompanying table reports the number of swims required by each pup to perform three successful escapes. Is there sufficient evidence of a difference between the mean number of swims required by male and female pups? Conduct the test (at $\alpha = .10$). Comment on the assumptions required for the test to be valid.

RATPUPS

Litter	Male	Female	Litter	Male	Female
1	8	5	11	6	5
2	8	4	12	6	3
3	6	7	13	12	5
4	6	3	14	3	8
5	6	5	15	3	4
6	6	3	16	8	12
7	3	8	17	3	6
8	5	10	18	6	4
9	4	4	19	9	5
10	4	4			

Source: Thomas E. Bradstreet, Merck Research Labs, BL 3–2, West Point, PA 19486.

Applying the Concepts—Advanced

9.47 Homophone confusion in Alzheimer's patients. A *homophone* is a word whose pronunciation is the same as that of another word having a different meaning and spelling (e.g., *nun* and *none, doe* and *dough,* etc.). *Brain and Language* (Apr. 1995) reported on a study of homophone spelling in patients with Alzheimer's disease. Twenty Alzheimer's patients were asked to spell 24 homophone pairs given in random order, then the number of homophone confusions (e.g., spelling *doe* given the context, *bake bread dough*) was recorded for each patient. One year later, the same test was given to the same patients. The data for the study are provided in the table. The researchers posed the following question: "Do Alzheimer's patients show a significant increase in mean homophone confusion errors over time?" Perform an analysis of the data to answer the researchers' question. What assumptions are necessary for the procedure used to be valid? Are they satisfied?

HOMOPHONE

Patient	Time 1	Time 2
1	5	5
2	1	3
3	0	0
4	1	1
5	0	1
6	2	1
7	5	6
8	1	2
9	0	9
10	5	8
11	7	10
12	0	3
13	3	9
14	5	8
15	7	12
16	10	16
17	5	5
18	6	3
19	9	6
20	11	8

Source: Neils, J., Roeltgen, D. P., and Constantinidou, F. "Decline in homophone spelling associated with loss of semantic influence on spelling in Alzheimer's disease." *Brain and Language,* Vol. 49, No. 1, Apr. 1995, p. 36 (Table 3).

9.48 Alcoholic fermentation in wines. Determining alcoholic fermentation in wine is critical to the winemaking process. Must/wine density is a good indicator of the fermentation point since the density value decreases as sugars are converted into alcohol. For decades, winemakers have measured must/wine density with a hydrometer. Although accurate, the hydrometer employs a manual process that is very time consuming. Consequently, large wineries are searching for more rapid measures of density measurement. An alternative method utilizes the hydrostatic balance instrument (similar to the hydrometer, but digital). A winery in Portugal collected the must/wine density measurements for white wine samples randomly selected from the fermentation process for a recent harvest. For each sample, the density of the wine at 20°C was measured with both the hydrometer and the hydrostat balance. The densities for 40 wine samples are saved in the **WINE40** file. The first five and last five observations are shown in the table. The winery will use the alternative method of measuring wine density only if it can be demonstrated that the mean difference between the density measurements of the two methods does not exceed .002. Perform the analysis for the winery. Provide the winery with a written report of your conclusions.

WINE40 (first and last 5 observations)

Sample	Hydrometer	Hydrostatic
1	1.08655	1.09103
2	1.00270	1.00272
3	1.01393	1.01274
4	1.09467	1.09634
5	1.10263	1.10518
.	.	.
.	.	.
36	1.08084	1.08097
37	1.09452	1.09431
38	0.99479	0.99498
39	1.00968	1.01063
40	1.00684	1.00526

Source: Cooperative Cellar of Borba *(Adega Cooperative de Borba),* Portugal.

9.4 Comparing Two Population Proportions: Independent Sampling

Suppose a presidential candidate wants to compare the preference of registered voters in the northeastern United States (NE) to those in the southeastern United States (SE). Such a comparison would help determine where to concentrate campaign efforts. The candidate hires a professional pollster to randomly choose 1,000 registered voters in the northeast and 1,000 in the southeast and interview each to learn her or his voting preference. The objective is to use this sample information to make an inference about the difference $(p_1 - p_2)$ between the proportion p_1 of *all*

TABLE 9.6 Results of Poll

NE	SE
$n_1 = 1,000$	$n_2 = 1,000$
$x_1 = 546$	$x_2 = 475$

registered voters in the northeast and the proportion p_2 of *all* registered voters in the southeast who plan to vote for the presidential candidate.

The two samples represent independent binomial experiments. (See Section 4.4 for the characteristics of binomial experiments.) The binomial random variables are the numbers x_1 and x_2 of the 1,000 sampled voters in each area who indicate they will vote for the candidate. The results are summarized in Table 9.6

We can now calculate the sample proportions $\hat{p}_1$ and $\hat{p}_2$ of the voters in favor of the candidate in the northeast and southeast, respectively:

$$\hat{p} = \frac{x_1}{n_1} = \frac{546}{1,000} = .546 \quad \hat{p}_2 = \frac{x_2}{n_2} = \frac{475}{1,000} = .475$$

The difference between the sample proportions $(\hat{p}_1 - \hat{p}_2)$ makes an intuitively appealing point estimator of the difference between the population $(p_1 - p_2)$. For our example, the estimate is

$$(\hat{p}_1 - \hat{p}_2) = .546 - .475 = .071$$

To judge the reliability of the estimator $(\hat{p}_1 - \hat{p}_2)$, we must observe its performance in repeated sampling from the two populations. That is, we need to know the sampling distribution of $(\hat{p}_1 - \hat{p}_2)$. The properties of the sampling distribution are given in the following box. Remember that $\hat{p}_1$ and $\hat{p}_2$ can be viewed as means of the number of successes per trial in the respective samples, so the Central Limit Theorem applies when the sample sizes are large.

> **Properties of the Sampling Distribution of $(\hat{p}_1 - \hat{p}_2)$**
>
> **1.** The mean of the sampling distribution of $(\hat{p}_1 - \hat{p}_2)$ is $(p_1 - p_2)$ that is,
>
> $$E(\hat{p}_1 - \hat{p}_2) = p_1 - p_2$$
>
> Thus, $(\hat{p}_1 - \hat{p}_2)$ is an unbiased estimator of $(p_1 - p_2)$.
>
> **2.** The standard deviation of the sampling distribution of $(\hat{p}_1 - \hat{p}_2)$ is
>
> $$\sigma_{(\hat{p}_1 - \hat{p}_2)} = \sqrt{\frac{p_1 q_1}{n_1} + \frac{p_2 q_2}{n_2}}$$
>
> **3.** If the sample sizes n_1 and n_2 are large (see Section 7.3 for a guideline), the sampling distribution of $(\hat{p}_1 - \hat{p}_2)$ is approximately normal.

Since the distribution of $(\hat{p}_1 - \hat{p}_2)$ in repeated sampling is approximately normal, we can use the z statistic to derive confidence intervals for $(p_1 - p_2)$ or to test a hypothesis about $(p_1 - p_2)$.

For the voter example, a 95% confidence interval for the difference $(p_1 - p_2)$ is

$$(\hat{p}_1 - \hat{p}_2) \pm 1.96\sigma_{(\hat{p}_1 - \hat{p}_2)} \text{ or } (\hat{p}_1 - \hat{p}_2) \pm 1.96\sqrt{\frac{p_1 q_1}{n_1} + \frac{p_2 q_2}{n_2}}$$

The quantities $p_1 q_1$ and $p_2 q_2$ must be estimated in order to complete the calculation of the standard deviation, $\sigma_{(\hat{p}_1 - \hat{p}_2)}$, and hence the calculation of the confidence interval. In Section 7.3 we showed that the value of pq is relatively insensitive to the value chosen to approximate p. Therefore, $\hat{p}_1 \hat{q}_1$ and $\hat{p}_2 \hat{q}_2$ will provide satisfactory estimates to approximate $p_1 q_1$ and $p_2 q_2$, respectively. Then

$$\sqrt{\frac{p_1 q_1}{n_1} + \frac{p_2 q_2}{n_2}} \approx \sqrt{\frac{\hat{p}_1 \hat{q}_1}{n_1} + \frac{\hat{p}_2 \hat{q}_2}{n_2}}$$

and we will approximate the 95% confidence interval by

$$(\hat{p}_1 - \hat{p}_2) \pm 1.96\sqrt{\frac{\hat{p}_1\hat{q}_1}{n_1} + \frac{\hat{p}_2\hat{q}_2}{n_2}}$$

Substituting the sample quantities yields

$$(.546 - .475) \pm 1.96\sqrt{\frac{(.546)(.454)}{1,000} + \frac{(.475)(.525)}{1,000}}$$

or $.071 \pm .044$. Thus, we are 95% confident that the interval from .027 to .115 contains $(p_1 - p_2)$.

We infer that there are between 2.7% and 11.5% more registered voters in the northeast than in the southeast who plan to vote for the presidential candidate. It seems that the candidate should direct a greater campaign effort in the southeast compared to the northeast.

Now Work *Exercise 9.59*

The general form of a confidence interval for the difference $(p_1 - p_2)$ between population proportions is given in the following box.

Large-Sample $100(1 - \alpha)\%$ Confidence Interval for $(p_1 - p_2)$

$$(\hat{p}_1 - \hat{p}_2) \pm z_{\alpha/2}\sigma_{(\hat{p}_1 - \hat{p}_2)} = (\hat{p}_1 - \hat{p}_2) \pm z_{\alpha/2}\sqrt{\frac{p_1 q_1}{n_1} + \frac{p_2 q_2}{n_2}}$$

$$\approx (\hat{p}_1 - \hat{p}_2) \pm z_{\alpha/2}\sqrt{\frac{\hat{p}_1\hat{q}_1}{n_1} + \frac{\hat{p}_2\hat{q}_2}{n_2}}$$

The z-statistic,

$$z = \frac{(\hat{p}_1 - \hat{p}_2) - (p_1 - p_2)}{\sigma_{(\hat{p}_1 - \hat{p}_2)}}$$

is used to test the null hypothesis that $(p_1 - p_2)$ equals some specified difference, say D_0. For the special case where $D_0 = 0$, that is, where we want to test the null hypothesis $H_0: (p_1 - p_2) = 0$ (or, equivalently, $H_0: p_1 = p_2$), the best estimate of $p_1 = p_2 = p$ is obtained by dividing the total number of successes $(x_1 + x_2)$ for the two samples by the total number of observations $(n_1 + n_2)$; that is,

$$\hat{p} = \frac{x_1 + x_2}{n_1 + n_2} \quad \text{or} \quad \hat{p} = \frac{n_1\hat{p}_1 + n_2\hat{p}_2}{n_1 + n_2}$$

The second equation shows that $\hat{p}$ is a weighted average of $\hat{p}_1$ and $\hat{p}_2$, with the larger sample receiving more weight. If the sample sizes are equal, then $\hat{p}$ is a simple average of the two sample proportions of successes.

We now substitute the weighted average $\hat{p}$ for both p_1 and p_2 in the formula for the standard deviation of $(\hat{p}_1 - \hat{p}_2)$:

$$\sigma_{(\hat{p}_1 - \hat{p}_2)} = \sqrt{\frac{p_1 q_1}{n_1} + \frac{p_2 q_2}{n_2}} \approx \sqrt{\frac{\hat{p}\hat{q}}{n_1} + \frac{\hat{p}\hat{q}}{n_2}} = \sqrt{\hat{p}\hat{q}\left(\frac{1}{n_1} + \frac{1}{n_2}\right)}$$

The test is summarized in the next box.

Large-Sample Test of Hypothesis About $(p_1 - p_2)$

One-Tailed Test	**Two-Tailed Test**

One-Tailed Test

$H_0: (p_1 - p_2) = 0*$
$H_a: (p_1 - p_2) < 0$
  [or $H_a: (p_1 - p_2) > 0$]

Test statistic:

Rejection region: $z < -z_\alpha$
  [or $z > z_\alpha$ when $H_a: (p_1 - p_2) > 0$]

Two-Tailed Test

$H_0: (p_1 - p_2) = 0$
$H_a: (p_1 - p_2) \neq 0$

$$z = \frac{(\hat{p}_1 - \hat{p}_2)}{\sigma_{(\hat{p}_1 - \hat{p}_2)}}$$

Rejection region: $|z| > z_{\alpha/2}$

Note: $\sigma_{(\hat{p}_1 - \hat{p}_2)} = \sqrt{\dfrac{p_1 q_1}{n_1} + \dfrac{p_2 q_2}{n_2}} \approx \sqrt{\hat{p}\hat{q}\left(\dfrac{1}{n_1} + \dfrac{1}{n_2}\right)}$ where $\hat{p} = \dfrac{x_1 + x_2}{n_1 + n_2}$

Conditions Required for Valid Large-Sample Inferences about $(p_1 - p_2)$

1. The two samples are randomly selected in an independent manner from the two target populations.

2. The sample sizes, n_1 and n_2, are both large so that the sampling distribution of $(\hat{p}_1 - \hat{p}_2)$ will be approximately normal. (This condition will be satisfied if both intervals, $\hat{p}_1 \pm 3\sigma_{\hat{p}_1}$ and $\hat{p}_2 \pm 3\sigma_{\hat{p}_2}$, fall between 0 and 1.)

EXAMPLE 9.6

LARGE-SAMPLE TEST ABOUT $p_1 - p_2$

Problem In the past decade intensive antismoking campaigns have been sponsored by both federal and private agencies. Suppose the American Cancer Society randomly sampled 1,500 adults in 1995 and then sampled 1,750 adults in 2005 to determine whether there was evidence that the percentage of smokers had decreased. The results of the two sample surveys are shown in Table 9.7, where x_1 and x_2 represent the numbers of smokers in the 1995 and 2005 samples, respectively. Do these data indicate that the fraction of smokers decreased over this 10-year period? Use $\alpha = .05$.

Solution If we define p_1 and p_2 as the true proportions of adult smokers in 1995 and 2005, the elements of our test are

$$H_0: (p_1 - p_2) = 0$$
$$H_a: (p_1 - p_2) > 0$$

TABLE 9.7 Results of Smoking Survey

1995	2005
$n_1 = 1{,}500$	$n_2 = 1{,}750$
$x_1 = 555$	$x_2 = 578$

(The test is one-tailed since we are interested only in determining whether the proportion of smokers *decreased*.)

$$Test\ statistic: z = \frac{(\hat{p}_1 - \hat{p}_2) - 0}{\sigma_{(\hat{p}_1 - \hat{p}_2)}}$$

Rejection region using $\alpha = .05$:
$$z > z_\alpha = z_{.05} = 1.645 \qquad \text{(see Figure 9.14)}$$

---

*The test can be adapted to test for a difference $D_0 \neq 0$. Because most applications call for a comparison of p_1 and p_2, implying $D_0 = 0$. we will confine our attention to this case.

Figure 9.14
Rejection Region
for Example 9.6

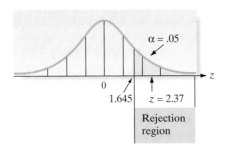

We now calculate the sample proportions of smokers

$$\hat{p}_1 = \frac{555}{1,500} = .37 \qquad \hat{p}_2 = \frac{578}{1,750} = .33$$

Then

$$z = \frac{(\hat{p}_1 - \hat{p}_2) - 0}{\sigma_{(\hat{p}_1 - \hat{p}_2)}} \approx \frac{(\hat{p}_1 - \hat{p}_2)}{\sqrt{\hat{p}\hat{q}\left(\dfrac{1}{n_1} + \dfrac{1}{n_2}\right)}}$$

where

$$\hat{p} = \frac{x_1 + x_2}{n_1 + n_2} = \frac{555 + 578}{1,500 + 1,750} = .349$$

Note that $\hat{p}$ is a weighted average of $\hat{p}_1$ and $\hat{p}_2$, with more weight given to the larger (2005) sample.

Thus, the computed value of the test statistic is

$$z = \frac{.37 - .33}{\sqrt{(.349)(.651)\left(\dfrac{1}{1,500} + \dfrac{1}{1,750}\right)}} = \frac{.040}{.0168} = 2.37$$

There is sufficient evidence at the $\alpha = .05$ level to conclude that the proportion of adults who smoke has decreased over the 1995–2005 period.

Look Back We could place a confidence interval on $(p_1 - p_2)$ if we were interested in estimating the extent of the decrease.

Now Work   *Exercise 9.60*

■ ■ ■

EXAMPLE 9.7

FINDING THE OBSERVED SIGNIFICANCE LEVEL OF A TEST FOR $p_1 - p_2$

Problem   Use a statistical software package to conduct the test in Example 9.6. Find and interpret the *p*-value of the test.

Solution   We entered the sample sizes (n_1 and n_2) and numbers of successes (x_1 and x_2) into MINITAB and obtained the printout shown in Figure 9.15. The test statistic for this one-tailed test, $z = 2.37$, is shaded on the printout, as well as the *p*-value of the test. Note that *p*-value = .009 is smaller than $\alpha = .05$. Consequently, we have strong evidence to reject H_0 and conclude that p_1 exceeds p_2.

Figure 9.15
MINITAB Output for Test
of Two Proportions

Test and CI for Two Proportions

```
Sample    X     N    Sample p
1        555  1500   0.370000
2        578  1750   0.330286


Difference = p (1) - p (2)
Estimate for difference:  0.0397143
95% lower bound for difference:  0.0121024
Test for difference = 0 (vs > 0):  Z = 2.37  P-Value = 0.009
```

■ ■ ■

Confidence Interval for $p_1 - p_2$

Using the TI-83 Graphing Calculator

Step 1 *Access the Statistical Tests Menu*

Press **STAT**
Arrow right to **TESTS**
Arrow down to **B: 2-PropZint**
Press **ENTER**

Step 2 *Enter the summary statistics.*

For x_1, enter the number of successes in the first data set.
For n_1, enter the sample size for the first data set.
For x_2, enter the number of successes in the second data set.
For n_2, enter the sample size for the second data set.
For **C-Level**, enter the confidence level.
Arrow down to "**Calculate**"
Press **ENTER**

Step 3 *View the Output*

The confidence interval will be displayed along with the two sample proportions ($\hat{p}_1$ and $\hat{p}_2$) and the sample sizes.

Example *Consider the data in Table 9.6 on pg. ###*

Step 1 *Access the Statistical Tests Menu*

Press **STAT**
Arrow right to **TESTS**
Arrow down to **B: 2-PropZint**
Press **ENTER**

```
EDIT CALC TESTS
6↑2-PropZTest…
7:ZInterval…
8:TInterval…
9:2-SampZInt…
0:2-SampTInt…
A:1-PropZInt…
B∎2-PropZInt…
```

Step 2 *Enter the summary statistics.*

For x_1, enter the number of successes in the first data set.
For n_1, enter the sample size for the first data set.

For $\mathbf{x_2}$, enter the number of successes in the second data set.
For $\mathbf{n_2}$, enter the sample size for the second data set.
For **C-Level**, enter the confidence level.
Arrow down to "**Calculate**"
Press **ENTER**

```
2-PropZInt
 x1:546
 n1:1000
 x2:475
 n2:1000
 C-Level:.95
 Calculate
```

Step 3 *View the Output*

The confidence interval will be displayed along with the two sample
proportions ($\hat{p}_1$ and $\hat{p}_2$) and the sample sizes.

```
2-PropZInt
 (.02729,.11471)
 p1=.546
 p2=.475
 n1=1000
 n2=1000

 ■
```

Hypothesis Test for
$p_1 - p_2$

Using the TI-83 Graphing Calculator

Step 1 *Access the Statistical Tests Menu*

Press **STAT**
Arrow right to **TESTS**
Arrow down to **6: 2-PropZTest**
Press **ENTER**

Step 2 *Enter the summary statistics.*

For $\mathbf{x_1}$, enter the number of successes in the first data set.
For $\mathbf{n_1}$, enter the sample size for the first data set.
For $\mathbf{x_2}$, enter the number of successes in the second data set.
For $\mathbf{n_2}$, enter the sample size for the second data set.
Arrow down to the next line and select the appropriate alternative hypothesis
by using the right arrow to highlight $\neq$**p2, <p2, or >p2** and press **ENTER**
Arrow down to **Calculate Draw**. You may choose either one of these for your
output.
Press **ENTER**

Step 3 *View the Output*

If you chose **Calculate**, the output will display the alternative hypothesis, the
z-value and the p-value, along with the two sample proportions ($\hat{p}_1$ and $\hat{p}_2$), and
$\hat{p}$, the weighted average of the two sample proportions and the sample sizes.

If you chose **Draw**, a graph of the normal curve will be displayed along
with the z-value and the p-value. The area under the curve that represents

the p-value is shaded. Note: In order to use the **Draw** feature, you must first clear all equations from the **Y - registers**. Hit "**Y =** " and delete all equations.

Example *Consider Example 9.6 with data in Table 9.7 on pg. 471*

Step 1 *Access the Statistical Tests Menu*

Press **STAT**
Arrow right to **TESTS**
Arrow down to **6: 2-PropZTest**
Press **ENTER**

Step 2 *Enter the summary statistics.*

For x_1, enter the number of successes in the first data set.
For n_1, enter the sample size for the first data set.
For x_2, enter the number of successes in the second data set.
For n_2, enter the sample size for the second data set.
Arrow down to the next line and select **>p2** and press **ENTER**.
Arrow down to **Calculate Draw**. You may choose either one of these for your output.
Press **ENTER**

```
2-PropZTest
 x1:555
 n1:1500
 x2:578
 n2:1750
 p1:≠p2 <p2 >p2
 Calculate Draw
```

Step 3 *View the Output*

If you chose **Calculate**, the output will display the alternative hypothesis, the z-value and the p-value, along with the two sample proportions ($\hat{p}_1$ and $\hat{p}_2$), and $\hat{p}$, the weighted average of the two sample proportions and the sample sizes.

```
2-PropZTest
 p1 >p2
 z=2.368523545
 p=.0089296078
 p̂1=.37
 p̂2=.3302857143
↓p̂=.3486153846
■
```

If you chose **Draw**, a graph of the normal curve will be displayed along with the z-value and the p-value. The are under the curve that represents the p-value is shaded. Note: In order to use the **Draw** feature, you must first clear all equations from the **Y-registers**. Hit 'Y = ' and delete all equations.

Statistics in Action Revisited

Comparing the Incumbency Rates of Two Kentucky Milk Markets

We now return to the Statistics in Action investigation of collusive bidding in the northern Kentucky school milk market (p. 429). Market allocation is a common form of collusive behavior in bid-rigging conspiracies. Under collusion, the same dairy usually controls the same school districts year after year. The *incumbency rate* for a market is defined as the proportion of school districts that are won by the same vendor who won the previous year. Past experience with milk bids in a competitive environment reveals that a typical incumbency rate is .7. That is, 70% of the school districts are expected to purchase their milk from the same dairy who won the previous year. Incumbency rates of .9 or higher are strong indicators of collusive bidding.

Another method of detecting bid collusion is to compare the incumbency rates in the two milk markets— the tricounty ("rigged") and the surrounding ("competitive") markets. Since an incumbency rate is a population proportion, the target parameter is $(p_1 - p_2)$, where p_1 is the incumbency rate for the surrounding market and p_2 is the incumbency rate for the tricounty market. If, in fact, the two dairies bidding in the tricounty market were rigging the bids, then $p_1 < p_2$. Thus, we are interested in the one-tailed test, $H_0: (p_1 - p_2) = 0$ versus $H_a: (p_1 - p_2) < 0$.

Over the years 1985–1988, when bid collusion was alleged to have occurred in northern Kentucky, there were 51 potential vendor transitions (i.e., changes in milk supplier from one year to the next in a district) in the tricounty market and 134 potential vendor transitions in the surrounding market. These values represent the sample sizes ($n_1 = 134$ and $n_2 = 51$) for calculating incumbency rates. Examining the data saved in the **MILK** file, we find that in 50 of the 51 potential vendor transitions for the tricounty market, the winning dairy from the previous year won the bid the next year; similarly, we find 91 of the 134 potential vendor transitions for the surrounding area had the same dairy winning the bid the next year. Consequently, the estimated incumbency rates are

$$p_1 = 91/134 = .679 \quad \text{and} \quad p_2 = 50/51 = .980$$

The MINITAB large-sample z-test for comparing the two proportions is shown in Figure SIA9.2. The one-tailed p-value of the test (highlighted at the bottom of the printout) is .000. Therefore, there is sufficient evidence to conclude (at $\alpha = .01$) that the true incumbency rate for the surrounding ("competitive") market is significantly less than the true incumbency rate for the tricounty ("rigged") market. This result, as well as the fact that the sample incumbency rate for the tricounty market ($\hat{p}_2 = .980$) is much higher than the typical rate of about .7, lends further support for the bid collusion theory.

Figure SIA9.2

MINITAB Comparison of Incumbency Rate for Two Kentucky Milk Markets

Test and CI for Two Proportions

```
Sample    X    N   Sample p
1        91   134  0.679104
2        50    51  0.980392


Difference = p (1) - p (2)
Estimate for difference:  -0.301288
95% upper bound for difference:  -0.227669
Test for difference = 0 (vs < 0):   Z = -4.30   P-Value = 0.000
```

Exercises 9.49–9.69

Understanding the Principles

9.49 Consider making an inference about $p_1 - p_2$, where there are x_1 successes in n_1 binomial trials and x_2 successes in n_2 binomial trials.
  a. Describe the distributions of x_1 and x_2.
  b. For large samples, describe the sampling distribution of $(\hat{p}_1 - \hat{p}_2)$.

9.50 What is the problem with using the z-statistic to make inferences about $p_1 - p_2$ when the sample sizes are both small?

9.51 What conditions are required for valid large-sample inferences about $p_1 - p_2$?

Learning the Mechanics

9.52 In each case, determine whether the sample sizes are large enough to conclude that the sampling distribution of $(\hat{p}_1 - \hat{p}_2)$ is approximately normal.
  a. $n_1 = 10, n_2 = 12, \hat{p}_1 = .50, \hat{p}_2 = .50$
  b. $n_1 = 10, n_2 = 12, \hat{p}_1 = .10, \hat{p}_2 = .08$
  c. $n_1 = n_2 = 30, \hat{p}_1 = .20, \hat{p}_2 = .30$

d. $n_1 = 100, n_2 = 200, \hat{p}_1 = .05, \hat{p}_2 = .09$
e. $n_1 = 100, n_2 = 200, \hat{p}_1 = .95, \hat{p}_2 = .91$

9.53 For each of the following values of α, find the values of z for which $H_0: (p_1 - p_2) = 0$ would be rejected in favor of $H_a: (p_1 - p_2) < 0$.
a. $\alpha = .01$ **b.** $\alpha = .025$
c. $\alpha = .05$ **d.** $\alpha = .10$

9.54 Independent random samples, each containing 800 observations, were selected from two binomial populations. The samples from populations 1 and 2 produced 320 and 400 successes, respectively.
a. Test $H_0: (p_1 - p_2) = 0$ against $H_a: (p_1 - p_2) \neq 0$. Use $\alpha = .05$.
b. Test $H_0: (p_1 - p_2) = 0$ against $H_a: (p_1 - p_2) \neq 0$. Use $\alpha = .01$.
c. Test $H_0: (p_1 - p_2) = 0$ against $H_a: (p_1 - p_2) < 0$. Use $\alpha = .01$.
d. Form a 90% confidence interval for $(p_1 - p_2)$.

9.55 Construct a 95% confidence interval for $(p_1 - p_2)$ in each of the following situations:
a. $n_1 = 400, \hat{p}_1 = .65; n_2 = 400, \hat{p}_2 = .58$
b. $n_1 = 180, \hat{p}_1 = .31; n_2 = 250, \hat{p}_2 = .25$
c. $n_1 = 100, \hat{p}_1 = .46; n_2 = 120, \hat{p}_2 = .61$

9.56 Sketch the sampling distribution of $(\hat{p}_1 - \hat{p}_2)$ based on independent random samples of $n_1 = 100$ and $n_2 = 200$ observations from two binomial populations with success probabilities $p_1 = .1$ and $p_2 = .5$, respectively.

9.57 Random samples of size $n_1 = 50$ and $n_2 = 60$ were drawn from populations 1 and 2, respectively. The samples yielded $\hat{p}_1 = .4$ and $\hat{p}_2 = .2$. Test $H_0: (p_1 - p_2) = .1$ against $H_a: (p_1 - p_2) > .1$ using $\alpha = .05$.

Applying the Concepts—Basic

9.58 Executive workout dropouts. Refer to the *Journal of Sport Behavior* (2001) study of variety in exercise workouts, Exercise 7.53 (p. 349). One group of 38 people varied their exercise routine in workouts while a second group of 38 exercisers had no set schedule or regulations for their workouts. By the end of the study, 14 people had dropped out of the first exercise group and 23 had dropped out of the second group.
a. Find the dropout rates (i.e., the percentage of exercisers who had dropped out of the exercise group) for each of the two groups of exercisers.
b. Find a 90% confidence interval for the difference between the dropout rates of the two groups of exercisers.
c. Give a practical interpretation of the confidence interval, part **c**.

9.59 The "winner's curse" in auction bidding. In auction bidding, the "winner's curse" is the phenomenon of the winning (or highest) bid price being above the expected value of the item being auctioned. *The Review of Economics and Statistics* (Aug. 2001) published a study on whether bid experience impacts the likelihood of the winner's curse occurring. Two groups of bidders in a sealed-bid auction were compared: (1) super-experienced bidders

and (2) less-experienced bidders. In the super-experienced group, 29 of 189 winning bids were above the item's expected value; in the less-experienced group, 32 of 149 winning bids were above the item's expected value.
a. Find an estimate of p_1, the true proportion of super-experienced bidders who fall prey to the winner's curse.
b. Find an estimate of p_2, the true proportion of less-experienced bidders who fall prey to the winner's curse.
c. Construct a 90% confidence interval for $p_1 - p_2$.
d. Give a practical interpretation of the confidence interval, part **c**. Make a statement about whether bid experience impacts the likelihood of the winner's curse occurring.

9.60 Planning habits survey. *American Demographics* (Jan. 2002) reported the results of a survey on the planning habits of men and women. In response to the question, "What is your preferred method of planning and keeping track of meetings, appointments and deadlines?", 56% of the men and 46% of the women answered "keep them in my head." A nationally representative sample of 1,000 adults participated in the survey; therefore, assume that 500 were men and 500 were women.
a. Set up the null and alternative hypotheses for testing whether the percentage of men who prefer keeping track of appointments in their head is larger than the corresponding percentage of women.
b. Compute the test statistic for the test.
c. Give the rejection region for the test using $\alpha = .01$.
d. Find the p-value for the test.
e. Make the appropriate conclusion.

9.61 Treating depression with St. John's wort. The *Journal of the American Medical Association* (April 18, 2001) published a study of the effectiveness of using extracts of the herbal medicine, St. John's wort, in treating major depression. In an 8-week randomized, controlled trial, 200 patients diagnosed with major depression were divided into two groups: one group ($n_1 = 98$) received St. John's wort extract while the other group ($n_2 = 102$) received a placebo (no drug). At the end of the study period, 14 of the St. John's wort patients were in remission compared to 5 of the placebo patients.
a. Compute the proportion of the St. John's wort patients who were in remission.
b. Compute the proportion of the placebo patients who were in remission.
c. If St. John's wort is effective in treating major depression, then the proportion of St. John's wort patients in remission will exceed the proportion of placebo patients in remission. At $\alpha = .01$, is St. John's wort effective in treating major depression?
d. Repeat part **c**, but use $\alpha = .10$.
e. Explain why the choice of α is critical for this study.

Applying the Concepts—Intermediate

9.62 Effectiveness of drug tests of Olympic athletes. Erythropoietin (EPO) is a banned drug used by athletes to increase the oxygen carrying capacity of their blood. New tests for EPO were first introduced prior to the 2000 Olympic Games held in Sydney, Australia. *Chance* (Spring 2004) reported that of a sample of 830 world-class athletes, 159 did not compete in the 1999 World Championships (a year prior to the new EPO test). Similarly, 133 of 825 potential athletes did not compete in the 2000 Olympic games. Was the new test effective in deterring an athlete's participation in the 2000 Olympics? If so, then the proportion of non-participating athletes in 2000 will be more than the proportion of nonparticipating athletes in 1999. Conduct the analysis (at $\alpha = .10$) and make the proper conclusion.

9.63 Killing moths with carbon dioxide. A University of South Florida biologist conducted an experiment to determine whether increased levels of carbon dioxide kill leaf-eating moths. (*USF Magazine,* Winter 1999.) Moth larvae were placed in open containers filled with oak leaves. Half the containers had normal carbon dioxide levels while the other half had double the normal level of carbon dioxide. Ten percent of the larvae in the containers with high carbon dioxide levels died, compared to 5 percent in the containers with normal levels. Assume that 80 moth larvae were placed, at random, in each of the two types of containers. Do the experimental results demonstrate that an increased level of carbon dioxide is effective in killing a higher percentage of leaf-eating moth larvae? Test using $\alpha = .01$.

9.64 Switching majors in college. When female undergraduates switch from science, mathematics, and engineering (SME) majors into disciplines that are not science-based, are their reasons different from those of their male counterparts? This question was investigated in *Science Education* (July 1995). A sample of 335 junior/senior undergraduates—172 females and 163 males—at two large research universities were identified as "switchers," that is, they left a declared SME major for a non-SME major. Each student listed one or more factors that contributed to the switching decision.

a. Of the 172 females in the sample, 74 listed lack or loss of interest in SME (i.e., "turned off" by science) as a major factor, compared to 72 of the 163 males. Conduct a test (at $\alpha = .10$) to determine whether the proportion of female switchers who give "lack of interest in SME" as a major reason for switching differs from the corresponding proportion of males.

b. Thirty-three of the 172 females in the sample indicated that they were discouraged or lost confidence because of low grades in SME during their early years, compared to 44 of 163 males. Construct a 90% confidence interval for the difference between the proportions of female and male switchers who lost confidence due to low grades in SME. Interpret the result.

9.65 "Tip-of-the-tongue" study. Trying to think of a word you know, but can't instantly retrieve, is called the "tip of the tongue" phenomenon. *Psychology and Aging* (Sept. 2001) published a study of this phenomenon in senior citizens. The researchers compared 40 people between 60 and 72 years of age with 40 between 73 and 83 years of age. When primed with the initial syllable of a missing word (e.g., seeing the word *include* to help recall the word *incisor*), the younger seniors had a higher recall rate. Suppose 31 of the 40 seniors in the younger group could recall the word when primed with the initial syllable, while only 22 of the 40 seniors could recall the word. Compare the recall rates of the two groups using $\alpha = .05$. Does one group of elderly people have a significantly higher recall rate than the other?

9.66 Gambling in public high schools. With the rapid growth in legalized gambling in the United States, there is concern that the involvement of youth in gambling activities is also increasing. University of Minnesota professor Randy Stinchfield compared the rates of gambling among Minnesota public school students between 1992 and 1998. (*Journal of Gambling Studies*, Winter 2001.) Based on survey data, the table shows the percentages of ninth-grade boys who gambled weekly or daily on any game (e.g., cards, sports betting, lotteries) for the two years.

	1992	1998
Number of ninth-grade boys in survey	21,484	23,199
Number who gambled weekly/daily	4,684	5,313

a. Are the percentages of ninth-grade boys who gambled weekly or daily on any game in 1992 and 1998 significantly different? (Use $\alpha = .01$.)

b. Professor Stinchfield states that "because of the large sample sizes, even small differences may achieve statistical significance, so interpretations of the differences should include a judgement regarding the magnitude of the difference and its public health significance." Do you agree with this statement? If not, why not? If so, obtain a measure of the magnitude of the difference between 1992 and 1998 and attach a measure of reliability to the difference.

NZBIRDS

9.67 Extinct New Zealand birds. Refer to the *Evolutionary Ecology Research* (July 2003) study of the patterns of extinction in the New Zealand bird population, Exercise 2.18 (p. 40). Recall that the **NZBIRDS** file contains data on flight capability and extinct status for 132 bird species at the time of the Maori colonization of New Zealand. Ecologists want to compare the proportions of flightless birds for two New Zealand bird populations—those that are extinct and those that are not extinct. The sample information shown on p. 479 is obtained from the **NZBIRDS** file. The ecologists are investigating the theory that the proportion of flightless birds will be greater for extinct species than for nonextinct species. Test the theory using $\alpha = .01$.

Bird Population	Number of Species Sampled	Number of Flightless Species
Extinct	38	21
Nonextinct	78	7

9.68 Reducing the risk of heart attacks. Can stress management help heart patients reduce their risk of heart attacks or heart surgery? In a study published in the *Archives of Internal Medicine* (Oct. 27, 1997), 107 heart patients were randomly divided into three groups. One group participated in a stress management program, the second group underwent an exercise program, and the third group received usual heart care from their doctors. After three years, the number in each group suffering "cardiac events" (e.g., heart attack, bypass surgery, or angioplasty) was recorded. The results are shown in the table.

	Management	Exercise	Usual Care
Number of heart patients	33	34	40
Number who suffer a "cardiac event"	3	7	12

a. Use a 99% confidence interval to compare the proportion of stress management patients who suffer a cardiac event to the proportion of exercise patients who suffer a cardiac event. What inference can you make?

b. Repeat part **a,** but compare the stress management group to the usual care group.

c. Repeat part **a,** but compare the exercise group to the usual care group.

Applying the Concepts—Advanced

9.69 Food craving study. Do you have an insatiable craving for chocolate or some other food? Since many people apparently do, psychologists are designing scientific studies to examine the phenomenon. According to the *New York Times* (Feb. 22, 1995), one of the largest studies of food cravings involved a survey of 1,000 McMaster University (Canada) students. The survey revealed that 97% of the women in the study acknowledged specific food cravings while only 67% of the men did.

a. How large do n_1 and n_2 have to be to conclude that the true proportion of women who acknowledge having food cravings exceeds the corresponding proportion of men? Assume $\alpha = .01$.

b. Why is it dangerous to conclude from the study that women have a higher incidence of food cravings than men?

9.5 Determining the Sample Size

You can find the appropriate sample size to estimate the difference between a pair of parameters with a specified sampling error (SE) and degree of reliability by using the method described in Section 7.4. That is, to estimate the difference between a pair of parameters correct to within *SE* units with confidence level $(1 - \alpha)$, let $z_{\alpha/2}$ standard deviations of the sampling distribution of the estimator equal *SE*. Then solve for the sample size. To do this, you have to solve the problem for a specific ratio between n_1 and n_2. Most often, you will want to have equal sample sizes, that is, $n_1 = n_2 = n$. We will illustrate the procedure with two examples.

EXAMPLE 9.8

FINDING THE SAMPLE SIZES FOR ESTIMATING $\mu_1 - \mu_2$

Problem New fertilizer compounds are often advertised with the promise of increased crop yields. Suppose we want to compare the mean yield μ_1 of wheat when a new fertilizer is used to the mean yield μ_2 with a fertilizer in common use. The estimate of the difference in mean yield per acre is to be correct to within .25 bushel with a confidence coefficient of .95. If the sample sizes are to be equal, find $n_1 = n_2 = n$, the number of 1-acre plots of wheat assigned to each fertilizer.

Solution To solve the problem, you need to know something about the variation in the bushels of yield per acre. Suppose from past records you know the yields of wheat possess a range of approximately 10 bushels per acre. You could then approximate $\sigma_1 = \sigma_2 = \sigma$ by letting the range equal 4σ. Thus,

$$4\sigma \approx 10 \text{ bushels}$$
$$\sigma \approx 2.5 \text{ bushels}$$

The next step is to solve the equation

$$z_{\alpha/2}\sigma_{(\bar{x}_1-\bar{x}_2)} = SE \quad \text{or} \quad z_{\alpha/2}\sqrt{\frac{\sigma_1^2}{n_1} + \frac{\sigma_2^2}{n_2}} = SE$$

for n, where $n = n_1 = n_2$. Since we want the estimate to lie within $SE = .25$ of $(\mu_1 - \mu_2)$ with confidence coefficient equal to .95, we have $z_{\alpha/2} = z_{.025} = 1.96$. Then, letting $\sigma_1 = \sigma_2 = 2.5$ and solving for n, we have

$$1.96\sqrt{\frac{(2.5)^2}{n} + \frac{(2.5)^2}{n}} = .25$$

$$1.96\sqrt{\frac{2(2.5)^2}{n}} = .25$$

$$n = 768.32 \approx 769 \text{ (rounding up)}$$

Consequently, you will have to sample 769 acres of wheat for each fertilizer to estimate the difference in mean yield per acre to within .25 bushel.

Look Back Since $n = 769$ would necessitate extensive and costly experimentation, you might decide to allow a larger sampling error (say, $SE = .50$ or $SE = 1$) in order to reduce the sample size, or you might decrease the confidence coefficient. The point is that we can obtain an idea of the experimental effort necessary to achieve a specified precision in our final estimate by determining the approximate sample size *before* the experiment is begun.

Now Work   *Exercise 9.74*

■ ■ ■

EXAMPLE 9.9   FINDING THE SAMPLE SIZES FOR ESTIMATING $p_1 - p_2$

Problem A production supervisor suspects that a difference exists between the proportions p_1 and p_2 of defective items produced by two different machines. Experience has shown that the proportion defective for each of the two machines is in the neighborhood of .03. If the supervisor wants to estimate the difference in the proportions to within .005 using a 95% confidence interval, how many items must be randomly sampled from the production of each machine? (Assume that the supervisor wants $n_1 = n_2 = n$.)

Solution In this sampling problem, the sampling error $SE = .005$, and for the specified level of reliability, $z_{\alpha/2} = z_{.025} = 1.96$. Then, letting $p_1 = p_2 = .03$ and $n_1 = n_2 = n$, we find the required sample size per machine by solving the following equation for n:

$$z_{\alpha/2}\sigma_{(\hat{p}_1-\hat{p}_2)} = SE$$

or

$$z_{\alpha/2}\sqrt{\frac{p_1 q_1}{n_1} + \frac{p_2 q_2}{n_2}} = SE$$

$$1.96\sqrt{\frac{(.03)(.97)}{n} + \frac{(.03)(.97)}{n}} = .005$$

$$1.96\sqrt{\frac{2(.03)(.97)}{n}} = .005$$

$$n = 8,943.2$$

Look Back This large n will likely result in a tedious sampling procedure. If the supervisor insists on estimating $(p_1 - p_2)$ correct to within .005 with 95% confidence, approximately 9,000 items will have to be inspected for each machine.

Now Work   *Exercise 9.75a*

■ ■ ■

You can see from the calculations in Example 9.9 that $\sigma_{(\hat{p}_1 - \hat{p}_2)}$ (and hence the solution, $n_1 = n_2 = n$) depends on the actual (but unknown) values of p_1 and p_2. In fact, the required sample size $n_1 = n_2 = n$ is largest when $p_1 = p_2 = .5$. Therefore, if you have no prior information on the approximate values of p_1 and p_2, use $p_1 = p_2 = .5$ in the formula for $\sigma_{(\hat{p}_1 - \hat{p}_2)}$. If p_1 and p_2 are in fact close to .5, then the values of n_1 and n_2 that you have calculated will be correct. If p_1 and p_2 differ substantially from .5, then your solutions for n_1 and n_2 will be larger than needed. Consequently, using $p_1 = p_2 = .5$ when solving for n_1 and n_2 is a conservative procedure because the sample sizes n_1 and n_2 will be at least as large as (and probably larger than) needed.

The procedures for determining sample sizes necessary for estimating $(\mu_1 - \mu_2)$ or $(p_1 - p_2)$ for the case $n_1 = n_2$ are given in the following boxes.

Determination of Sample Size for Estimating $\mu_1 - \mu_2$

To estimate $(\mu_1 - \mu_2)$ to within a given sampling error SE and with confidence level $(1 - \alpha)$, use the following formula to solve for equal sample sizes that will achieve the desired reliability:

$$n_1 = n_2 = \frac{(z_{\alpha/2})^2(\sigma_1^2 + \sigma_2^2)}{(SE)^2}$$

You will need to substitute estimates for the values of σ_1^2 and σ_2^2 before solving for the sample size. These estimates might be sample variances s_1^2 and s_2^2 from prior sampling (e.g., a pilot study), or from an educated (and conservatively large) guess based on the range—that is, $s \approx R/4$.

Determination of Sample Size for Estimating $p_1 - p_2$

To estimate $(p_1 - p_2)$ to within a given sampling error SE and with confidence level $(1 - \alpha)$, use the following formula to solve for equal sample sizes that will achieve the desired reliability:

$$n_1 = n_2 = \frac{(z_{\alpha/2})^2(p_1 q_1 + p_2 q_2)}{(SE)^2}$$

You will need to substitute estimates for the values of p_1 and p_2 before solving for the sample size. These estimates might be based on prior samples, obtained from educated guesses or, most conservatively, specified as $p_1 = p_2 = .5$.

Exercises 9.70–9.83

Understanding the Principles

9.70 When determining the sample sizes for estimating $\mu_1 - \mu_2$, how do you obtain estimates of the population variances $(\sigma_1)^2$ and $(\sigma_2)^2$ used in the calculations?

9.71 When determining the sample sizes for estimating $p_1 - p_2$, how do you obtain estimates of the binomial proportions p_1 and p_2 used in the calculations?

9.72 If the sample size calculation yields a value of n that is too large to be practical, how should you proceed?

Learning the Mechanics

9.73 Suppose you want to estimate the difference between two population means correct to within 2.2 with probability .95. If prior information suggests that the population variances are approximately equal to $\sigma_1^2 = \sigma_2^2 = 15$ and you want to select independent random samples of equal size from the populations, how large should the sample sizes, n_1 and n_2, be?

9.74 Find the appropriate values of n_1 and n_2 (assume **NW** $n_1 = n_2$) needed to estimate $(\mu_1 - \mu_2)$ with
   a. A sampling error equal to 3.2 with 95% confidence. From prior experience it is known that $\sigma_1 \approx 15$ and $\sigma_2 \approx 17$.
   b. A sampling error equal to 8 with 99% confidence. The range of each population is 60.
   c. A 90% confidence interval of width 1.0. Assume that $\sigma_1^2 \approx 5.8$ and $\sigma_2^2 \approx 7.5$.

9.75 Assuming that $n_1 = n_2$, find the sample sizes needed to **NW** estimate $(p_1 - p_2)$ for each of the following situations:
   a. $SE = .01$ with 99% confidence. Assume that $p_1 \approx .4$ and $p_2 \approx .7$.
   b. A 90% confidence interval of width .05. Assume there is no prior information available to obtain approximate values of p_1 and p_2.
   c. $SE = .03$ with 90% confidence. Assume that $p_1 \approx .2$ and $p_2 \approx .3$.

9.76 Enough money has been budgeted to collect independent random samples of size $n_1 = n_2 = 100$ from populations 1 and 2 in order to estimate $(p_1 - p_2)$. Prior information indicates that $p_1 = p_2 \approx .6$. Have sufficient funds been allocated to construct a 90% confidence interval for $(p_1 - p_2)$ of width .1 or less? Justify your answer.

Applying the Concepts—Basic

9.77 Bulimia study. Refer to *The American Statistician* (May 2001) study comparing the "fear of negative evaluation" (FNE) scores for bulimic and normal female students, Exercise 9.19 (p. 450). Suppose you want to estimate $(\mu_B - \mu_N)$, the difference between the population means of the FNE scores for bulimic and normal female students, using a 95% confidence interval with a sampling error of two points. Find the sample sizes required to obtain such an estimate. Assume equal sample sizes of $\sigma_B^2 = \sigma_N^2 = 25$.

9.78 Students attitudes towards parents. Refer to the *Journal of Genetic Psychology* (Mar. 1998) study comparing male students' attitudes toward their fathers and mothers, Exercise 9.42 (p. 466). Suppose you want to estimate $\mu_D = (\mu_F - \mu_M)$, the difference between the population mean attitudes toward fathers and mothers, using a 90% confidence interval with a sampling error of .3. Find the number of male students required to obtain such an estimate. Assume the variance of the paired differences is $\sigma_D^2 = 1$.

9.79 Executive workout dropouts. Refer to the *Journal of Sport Behavior* (2001) study comparing the dropout rates of two groups of exercisers, Exercise 9.58 (p. 477). Suppose you want to reduce the sampling error for estimating $(p_1 - p_2)$ with a 90% confidence interval to .1.

Determine the number of exercisers to be sampled from each group in order to obtain such an estimate. Assume equal sample sizes, $p_1 \approx .4$, and $p_2 \approx .6$.

Applying the Concepts—Intermediate

9.80 Cable-TV home shoppers. All cable television companies carry at least one home shopping channel. Who uses these home shopping services? Are the shoppers primarily men or women? Suppose you want to estimate the difference in the proportions of men and women who say they have used or expect to use televised home shopping using an 80% confidence interval of width .06 or less.
   a. Approximately how many people should be included in your samples?
   b. Suppose you want to obtain individual estimates for the two proportions of interest. Will the sample size found in part **a** be large enough to provide estimates of each proportion correct to within .02 with probability equal to .90? Justify your response.

9.81 Health hazards of housework. Is housework hazardous to your health? A study in the *Public Health Reports* (July–Aug. 1992) compares the life expectancies of 25-year-old white women in the labor force to those who are housewives. How large a sample would have to be taken from each group in order to be 95% confident that the estimate of difference in mean life expectancies for the two groups is within 1 year of the true difference? Assume that equal sample sizes will be selected from the two groups, and that the standard deviation for both groups is approximately 15 years.

9.82 Rat damage in sugarcane. Poisons are used to prevent rat damage in sugarcane fields. The U.S. Department of Agriculture is investigating whether the rat poison should be located in the middle of the field or on the outer perimeter. One way to answer this question is to determine where the greater amount of damage occurs. If damage is measured by the proportion of cane stalks that have been damaged by rats, how many stalks from each section of the field should be sampled in order to estimate the true difference between proportions of stalks damaged in the two sections to within .02 with 95% confidence?

9.83 Scouting an NFL free agent. In seeking a free agent NFL running back, a general manager is looking for a player with high mean yards gained per carry and a small standard deviation. Suppose the GM wishes to compare the mean yards gained per carry for two free agents based on independent random samples of their yards gained per carry. Data from last year's pro football season indicate that $\sigma_1 = \sigma_2 \approx 5$ yards. If the GM wants to estimate the difference in means correct to within 1 yard with a confidence level of .90, how many runs would have to be observed for each player? (Assume equal sample sizes.)

9.6 Comparing Two Population Variances: Independent Sampling (Optional)

Many times it is of practical interest to use the techniques developed in this chapter to compare the means or proportions of two populations. However, there are also important instances when we wish to compare two population variances. For example, when two devices are available for producing precision measurements (scales, calipers, thermometers, etc.), we might want to compare the variability of the measurements of the devices before deciding which one to purchase. Or when two standardized tests can be used to rate job applicants, the variability of the scores for both tests should be taken into consideration before deciding which test to use.

For problems like these we need to develop a statistical procedure to compare population variances. The common statistical procedure for comparing population variances, σ_1^2 and σ_2^2, makes an inference about the ratio σ_1^2/σ_2^2. In this section, we will show how to test the null hypothesis that the ratio σ_1^2/σ_2^2 equals 1 (the variances are equal) against the alternative hypothesis that the ratio differs from 1 (the variances differ):

$$H_0: \frac{\sigma_1^2}{\sigma_2^2} = 1 \quad (\sigma_1^2 = \sigma_2^2)$$

$$H_a: \frac{\sigma_1^2}{\sigma_2^2} \neq 1 \quad (\sigma_1^2 \neq \sigma_2^2)$$

To make an inference about the ratio σ_1^2/σ_2^2, it seems reasonable to collect sample data and use the ratio of the sample variances, s_1^2/s_2^2. We will use the test statistic

$$F = \frac{s_1^2}{s_2^2}$$

To establish a rejection region for the test statistic, we need to know the sampling distribution of s_1^2/s_2^2. As you will subsequently see, the sampling distribution of s_1^2/s_2^2 is based on two of the assumptions already required for the t-test:

1. The two sampled populations are normally distributed.

2. The samples are randomly and independently selected from their respective populations.

When these assumptions are satisfied and when the null hypothesis is true (that is, $\sigma_1^2 = \sigma_2^2$), the sampling distribution of $F = s_1^2/s_2^2$ is the **F-distribution** with $(n_1 - 1)$ numerator degrees of freedom and $(n_2 - 1)$ denominator degrees of freedom, respectively. The shape of the F-distribution depends on the degrees of freedom associated with s_1^2 and s_2^2—that is, on $(n_1 - 1)$ and $(n_2 - 1)$. An F-distribution with 7 and 9 df is shown in Figure 9.16. As you can see, the distribution is skewed to the right, since s_1^2/s_2^2 cannot be less than 0 but can increase without bound.

Figure 9.16
An F-Distribution with
7 Numerator and
9 Denominator Degrees
of Freedom

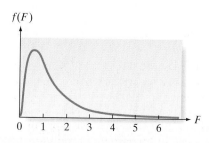

Biography

**GEORGE W. SNEDECOR
(1882–1974)—
Snedecor's F-test**

George W. Snedecor's education began at the University of Alabama, where he obtained his bachelor's degree in mathematics and physics. He went on to the University of Michigan for his master's degree in physics and finally earned his Ph.D in mathematics at the University of Kentucky. Snedecor learned of an opening for an assistant professor of mathematics at the University of Iowa, packed his belongings in his car, and began driving to apply for the position. By mistake, he ended up in Ames, Iowa, home of Iowa State University—then an agricultural school that had no need for a mathematics teacher. Nevertheless, Snedecor stayed and founded a

statistics laboratory, eventually teaching the first course in statistics at Iowa State in 1915. In 1933, Snedecor turned the statistics laboratory into the first ever Department of Statistics in the United States. During his tenure as chair of the department, Snedecor published his landmark textbook, *Statistical Methods* (1937). The text contained the first published reference for a test of hypothesis to compare two variances. Although Snedecor named it the *F*-test in honor of statistician R. A. Fisher (who had developed the *F*-distribution a few years earlier—see Biography, p. 516), many researchers still refer to it as Snedecor's *F*-test. Now in its ninth edition, *Statistical Methods* (with William Cochran as a coauthor) continues to be one of the most frequently cited texts in the statistics field.

We need to be able to find *F*-values corresponding to the tail areas of this distribution in order to establish the rejection region for our test of hypothesis because we expect the ratio *F* of the sample variances to be either very large or very small when the population variances are unequal. The upper-tail *F* values for $\alpha = .10, .05, .025,$ and $.01$ can be found in Tables VIII, IX, X, and XI of Appendix A. Table IX is partially reproduced in Table 9.8. It gives *F* values that correspond to $\alpha = .05$ upper-tail areas for

TABLE 9.8 **Reproduction of Part of Table IX in Appendix A: Percentage Points of the *F*-distribution, $\alpha = .05$**

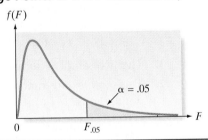

ν_1	Numerator Degrees of Freedom								
ν_2	1	2	3	4	5	6	7	8	9
1	161.4	199.5	215.7	224.6	230.2	234.0	236.8	238.9	240.5
2	18.51	19.00	19.16	19.25	19.30	19.33	19.35	19.37	19.38
3	10.13	9.55	9.28	9.12	9.01	8.94	8.89	8.85	8.81
4	7.71	6.94	6.59	6.39	6.26	6.16	6.09	6.04	6.00
5	6.61	5.79	5.41	5.19	5.05	4.95	4.88	4.82	4.77
6	5.99	5.14	4.76	4.53	4.39	4.28	4.21	4.15	4.10
7	5.59	4.74	4.35	4.12	3.97	3.87	3.79	3.73	3.68
8	5.32	4.46	4.07	3.84	3.69	3.58	3.50	3.44	3.39
9	5.12	4.26	3.86	3.63	3.48	3.37	3.29	3.23	3.18
10	4.96	4.10	3.71	3.48	3.33	3.22	3.14	3.07	3.02
11	4.84	3.98	3.59	3.36	3.20	3.09	3.01	2.95	2.90
12	4.75	3.89	3.49	3.25	3.11	3.00	2.91	2.85	2.80
13	4.67	3.81	3.41	3.18	3.03	2.92	2.83	2.77	2.71
14	4.60	3.74	3.34	3.11	2.96	2.85	2.76	2.70	2.65

Denominator Degrees of Freedom

Figure 9.17
An F-Distribution for $\nu_1 = 7$
and $\nu_2 = 9$ df; $\alpha = .05$

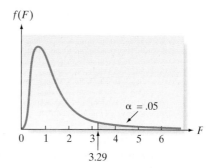

different degrees of freedom; the columns correspond to the degrees of freedom ν_1 for the numerator sample variance, s_1^2, whereas the rows correspond to the degrees of freedom ν_2 for the denominator sample variance, s_2^2. Thus, if the numerator degrees of freedom is $\nu_1 = 7$ and the denominator degrees of freedom is $\nu_2 = 9$, we look in the seventh column and ninth row to find $F_{.05} = 3.29$. As shown in Figure 9.17, $\alpha = .05$ is the tail area to the right of 3.29 in the F-distribution with 7 and 9 df. That is, if $\sigma_1^2 = \sigma_2^2$, then the probability that the F-statistic will exceed 3.29 is $\alpha = .05$.

Now Work   *Exercise 9.88*

EXAMPLE 9.10   CONDUCTING AN F-TEST

Problem   An experimenter wants to compare the metabolic rates of white mice subjected to different drugs. The weights of the mice may affect their metabolic rates, and thus the experimenter wishes to obtain mice that are relatively homogeneous with respect to weight. Five hundred mice will be needed to complete the study. Currently, 13 mice from supplier 1 and another 18 mice from supplier 2 are available for comparison. The experimenter weighs these mice and obtains the data shown in Table 9.9. Do these data provide sufficient evidence to indicate a difference in the variability of weights of mice obtained from the two suppliers? (Use $\alpha = .10$.) Using the results of this analysis, what would you suggest to the experimenter?

 MICEWTS

TABLE 9.9   Weights (in ounces) of Experimental Mice

Supplier 1					
4.23	4.35	4.05	3.75	4.41	4.37
4.01	4.06	4.15	4.19	4.52	4.21
4.29					

Supplier 2					
4.14	4.26	4.05	4.11	4.31	4.12
4.17	4.35	4.25	4.21	4.05	4.28
4.15	4.20	4.32	4.25	4.02	4.14

Solution   Let

$\sigma_1^2 = $ Population variance of weights of white mice from supplier 1
$\sigma_2^2 = $ Population variance of weights of white mice from supplier 2

The hypotheses of interest are then

$$H_0: \frac{\sigma_1^2}{\sigma_2^2} = 1 \quad (\sigma_1^2 = \sigma_2^2)$$

$$H_a: \frac{\sigma_1^2}{\sigma_2^2} \neq 1 \quad (\sigma_1^2 \neq \sigma_2^2)$$

The nature of the F-tables given in Appendix A affects the form of the test statistic. To form the rejection region for a two-tailed F-test, we want to make certain that the upper tail is used, because only the upper-tail values of F are shown in Tables VIII, IX, X, and XI. To accomplish this, *we will always place the larger sample variance in the numerator of the F-test statistic.* This has the effect of doubling the tabulated value for α, since we double the probability that the F-ratio will fall in the upper tail by always placing the larger sample variance in the numerator. That is, we establish a one-tailed rejection region by putting the larger variance in the numerator rather than establishing rejection regions in both tails.

To calculate the value of the test statistic, we require the sample variances. These are shown on the MINITAB printout, Figure 9.19. The sample variances are $s_1^2 = .0409$ and $s_2^2 = .00964$. Therefore,

$$F = \frac{\text{Larger sample variance}}{\text{Smaller sample variance}} = \frac{s_1^2}{s_2^2} = \frac{(.0409)}{(.00964)} = 4.24$$

For our example, we have a numerator s_1^2 with df $= \nu_1 = n_1 - 1 = 12$ and a denominator s_2^2 with df $= \nu_2 = n_2 - 1 = 17$. Therefore, we will reject $H_0: \sigma_1^2 = \sigma_2^2$ for $\alpha = .10$ when the calculated value of F exceeds the tabulated value:

$$F_{\alpha/2} = F_{.05} = 2.38 \quad \text{(see Figure 9.18)}$$

Note that $F = 4.24$ falls in the rejection region. Therefore, the data provide sufficient evidence to indicate that the population variances differ. It appears that the weights of mice obtained from supplier 2 tend to be more homogeneous (less variable) than the weights of mice obtained from supplier 1. On the basis of this evidence, we would advise the experimenter to purchase the mice from supplier 2.

Look Back What would you have concluded if the value of F calculated from the samples had not fallen in the rejection region? Would you conclude that the null hypothesis of equal variances is true? No, because then you risk the possibility of a Type II error (accepting H_0 if H_a is true) without knowing the value of β, the

Figure 9.18
Rejection Region for Example 9.10

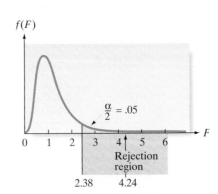

Figure 9.19
MINITAB Summary
Statistics and F-Test
for Mice Weights

Descriptive Statistics: WEIGHT

Variable	SUPPLIER	N	Mean	StDev	Variance	Minimum	Maximum
WEIGHT	1	13	4.1992	0.2021	0.0409	3.7500	4.5200
	2	18	4.1878	0.0982	0.00964	4.0200	4.3500

Test for Equal Variances: WEIGHT versus SUPPLIER

95% Bonferroni confidence intervals for standard deviations

SUPPLIER	N	Lower	StDev	Upper
1	13	0.138579	0.202133	0.361467
2	18	0.070860	0.098193	0.156836

```
F-Test (normal distribution)
Test statistic = 4.24, p-value = 0.007


Levene's Test (any continuous distribution)
Test statistic = 4.31, p-value = 0.047
```

probability of accepting H_0: $\sigma_1^2 = \sigma_2^2$ if in fact it is false. Since we will not consider the calculation of β for specific alternatives in this text, when the F-statistic does not fall in the rejection region we simply conclude that insufficient sample evidence exists to refute the null hypothesis that $\sigma_1^2 = \sigma_2^2$.

Now Work   *Exercise 9.93a*

■ ■ ■

EXAMPLE 9.11   THE p-VALUE OF AN F-TEST

Problem   Find the p-value for the test in Example 9.10 using the F-tables in Appendix A. Compare this to the exact p-value obtained from a computer printout.

Solution   Since the observed value of the F-statistic in Example 9.10 was 4.24, the observed significance level of the test would equal the probability of observing a value of F at least as contradictory to H_0: $\sigma_1^2 = \sigma_2^2$ as $F = 4.24$, if in fact H_0 is true. Since we give the F-tables in Appendix A only for values of α equal to .10, .05, .025, and .01, we can only approximate the observed significance level. Checking Table XI, we find $F_{.01} = 3.46$. Since the observed value of F is greater than $F_{.01}$, the observed significance level for the test is less than $2(.01) = .02$. (Note that we double the α value shown in Table XI because this is a two-tailed test.) The exact p-value, $p = .007$, is highlighted at the bottom of the MINITAB printout, Figure 9.19.

Look Back   We double the α value in Table XI because this is a two-tailed test.

Now Work   *Exercise 9.93b*

■ ■ ■

In addition to a hypothesis test for σ_1^2/σ_2^2, we can use the F-statistic to estimate the ratio with a confidence interval. The following boxes summarize the confidence interval and testing procedures.

A $(1 - \alpha) \times 100\%$ Confidence Interval for $(\sigma_1)^2/(\sigma_2)^2$

$$\left(\frac{s_1^2}{s_2^2}\right)\left(\frac{1}{F_{L,\alpha/2}}\right) < \left(\frac{\sigma_1^2}{\sigma_2^2}\right) < \left(\frac{s_1^2}{s_2^2}\right)F_{U,\alpha/2}$$

where $F_{L,\alpha/2}$ is the value of F that places an area $\alpha/2$ in the upper tail of an F-distribution with $v_1 = (n_1 - 1)$ numerator and $v_2 = (n_2 - 1)$ denominator degrees of freedom, and $F_{U,\alpha/2}$ is the value of F that places an area $\alpha/2$ in the upper tail of an F-distribution with $v_1 = (n_2 - 1)$ numerator and $v_2 = (n_1 - 1)$ denominator degrees of freedom.

F-Test for Equal Population Variances*

One-Tailed Test

$H_0: \sigma_1^2 = \sigma_2^2$
$H_a: \sigma_1^2 < \sigma_2^2$ (or $H_a: \sigma_1^2 > \sigma_2^2$)

Test statistic:

$$F = \frac{s_2^2}{s_1^2}$$

$$\left(\text{or } F = \frac{s_1^2}{s_2^2} \text{ when } H_a: \sigma_1^2 > \sigma_2^2\right)$$

Rejection region:
$F > F_\alpha$

Two-Tailed Test

$H_0: \sigma_1^2 = \sigma_2^2$
$H_a: \sigma_1^2 \neq \sigma_2^2$

Test statistic:

$$F = \frac{\text{Larger sample variance}}{\text{Smaller sample variance}}$$

$$= \frac{s_1^2}{s_2^2} \text{ when } s_1^2 > s_2^2$$

$$\left(\text{or } \frac{s_2^2}{s_1^2} \text{ when } s_2^2 > s_1^2\right)$$

Rejection region:
$F > F_{\alpha/2}$

where F_α and $F_{\alpha/2}$ are based on $v_1 =$ numerator degrees of freedom and $v_2 =$ denominator degrees of freedom; v_1 and v_2 are the degrees of freedom for the numerator and denominator sample variances, respectively.

Conditions Required for Valid Inferences about $(\sigma_1)^2/(\sigma_2)^2$

1. The samples are random and independent.
2. Both populations are normally distributed.

To conclude this section, we consider the comparison of population variances as a check of the assumption $\sigma_1^2 = \sigma_2^2$ needed for the two-sample t-test. Rejection of the null hypothesis $\sigma_1^2 = \sigma_2^2$ would indicate that the assumption is invalid. [*Note:* Nonrejection of the null hypothesis does *not* imply that the assumption is valid.]

*Although a test of a hypothesis of equality of variances is the most common application of the F-test, it can also be used to test a hypothesis that the ratio between the population variances is equal to some specified value, $H_0: \sigma_1^2/\sigma_2^2 = k$. The test is conducted in exactly the same way as specified in the box, except that we use the test statistic

$$F = \left(\frac{s_1^2}{s_2^2}\right)\left(\frac{1}{k}\right)$$

EXAMPLE 9.12

CHECKING THE ASSUMPTION OF EQUAL VARIANCES

Problem   In Example 9.4 (Section 9.2) we used the two-sample t-statistic to compare the mean reading scores of two groups of slow learners who had been taught to read using two different methods. The data are repeated in Table 9.10 for convenience. The use of the t-statistic was based on the assumption that the population variances of the test scores were equal for the two methods. Conduct a test of hypothesis to check this assumption at $\alpha = .10$.

🔵 READING

TABLE 9.10   Reading Test Scores for Slow Learners

New Method				Standard Method			
80	80	79	81	79	62	70	68
76	66	71	76	73	76	86	73
70	85			72	68	75	66

Solution   We want to test

$$H_0: \sigma_1^2/\sigma_2^2 = 1 \quad (\text{i.e., } \sigma_1^2 = \sigma_2^2)$$
$$H_a: \sigma_1^2/\sigma_2^2 \neq 1 \quad (\text{i.e., } \sigma_1^2 \neq \sigma_2^2)$$

The data were entered into SAS, and the SAS printout shown in Figure 9.20 was obtained. Both the test statistic, $F = .85$, and two-tailed p-value, .8148, are highlighted on the printout. Since $\alpha = .10$ is less than the p-value, we do not reject the null hypothesis that the population variances of the reading test scores are equal. It is here that the temptation to misuse the F-test is strongest. *We cannot conclude that the data justify the use of the t-statistic.* This is equivalent to accepting H_0, and we have repeatedly warned against this conclusion because the probability of a Type II error, β, is unknown. The α level of .10 protects us only against rejecting H_0 if it is true. This use of the F-test may prevent us from abusing the t procedure when we obtain a value of F that leads to a rejection of

Figure 9.20
SAS F-Test for Testing
Assumption of Equal
Variances

```
                    Two Sample Test for Variances of SCORE within METHOD

        Sample Statistics

            METHOD
            Group       N       Mean      Std. Dev.     Variance
            ------------------------------------------------------
            NEW         10      76.4        5.8348       34.04444
            STD         12      72.33333    6.3437       40.24242


        Hypothesis Test

            Null hypothesis:       Variance 1 / Variance 2 =  1
            Alternative:           Variance 1 / Variance 2 ^= 1

                           - Degrees of Freedom -
                F          Numer.      Denom.            Pr > F
            ------------------------------------------------------
               0.85          9           11             0.8148


        95% Confidence Interval of the Ratio of Two Variances

                    Lower Limit      Upper Limit
                    -----------      -----------
                       0.2358           3.3096
```

the assumption that $\sigma_1^2 = \sigma_2^2$. But when the F-statistic does not fall in the rejection region, we know little more about the validity of the assumption than before we conducted the test.

Look Back A 95% confidence interval for the ratio $(\sigma_1)^2/(\sigma_2)^2$ is shown at the bottom of the SAS printout, Figure 9.20. Note that the interval, (.2358, 3.3096), includes 1; hence, we cannot conclude that the ratio differs significantly from 1. Thus the confidence interval leads to the same conclusion as the two-tailed test—there is insufficient evidence of a difference between the population variances.

> **Now Work** *Exercise 9.97*

■ ■ ■

What Do You Do If the Assumption of Normal Population Distributions Is Not Satisfied?

Answer: The F-test is much less robust (i.e., much more sensitive) to departures from normality than the t-test for comparing the population means (Section 9.2). If you have doubts about the normality of the population frequency distributions, use a *nonparametric method* for comparing the two population variances. A method can be found in the nonparametric statistics texts listed in the references.

Statistics in Action Revisited

Comparing the Dispersion of Bid Prices in Two Kentucky Milk Markets

We return, once more, to the Statistics in Action investigation of collusive bidding in the northern Kentucky school milk market (p. 429). In competitive sealed bid markets, vendors do not share information about their bids. Consequently, more dispersion or variability among the bids is typically observed than in collusive markets, where vendors communicate about their bids and have a tendency to submit bids in close proximity to one another in an attempt to make the bidding appear competitive.

If collusion exists in the tricounty milk market, the variation in winning bid prices in the surrounding ("competitive") market will be significantly larger than the corresponding variation in the tricounty ("rigged") market. Let $(\sigma_1)^2$ and $(\sigma_2)^2$ represent the population milk price variances for the surrounding market and the tricounty market, respectively. To test this theory, we test the null hypothesis, $H_0: (\sigma_1)^2 = (\sigma_2)^2$, against the one-sided alternative hypothesis, $H_a: (\sigma_1)^2 > (\sigma_2)^2$, for each of the three milk products (whole white, low-fat white, and low-fat chocolate).

A MINITAB analysis of the the data in the **MILK** file yielded the printouts in Figure SIA9.3. The two-tailed p-values of the F-tests are highlighted on the figure. To

Figure SIA9.3

MINITAB Comparison of Bid Price Variances for Two Kentucky Milk Markets

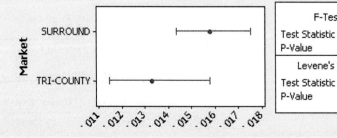

Test for Equal Variances for WWBID

	F-Test	
Test Statistic	1.41
P-Value	0.048

	Levene's Test	
Test Statistic	1.25
P-Value	0.264

Figure SIA9.3
Continued

obtain the one-tailed *p*-values, we divide these values in half. Therefore, the one-tailed *p*-values are .048/2 = .024 (for whole white milk), .016/2 = .008 (for low-fat white milk), and .172/2 = .086 (for low-fat chocolate milk). At $\alpha = .05$, the tests provide evidence that the bid price variance for the surrounding market exceeds the bid price variance for the tricounty market for two of the three milk products—whole milk and low-fat white milk. Only for

low-fat chocolate is there insufficient evidence to support the bid collusion theory.

[*Note:* For the inferences derived from these *F*-tests to be statistically valid, however, we require the bid price distributions for each market to be approximately normal. (Remember, the normality assumption is required regardless of the sizes of the samples.) The MINITAB printouts in Figure SIA9.4 show histograms (with the

Figure SIA9.4
MINITAB Histograms of
Bid Prices for Two Kentucky
Milk Markets

Figure SIA9.4
Continued

Panel variable: Market

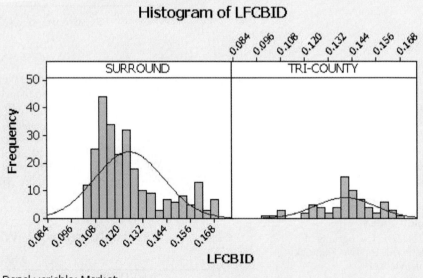

Panel variable: Market

normal distribution superimposed) of the milk prices for each of the two markets. The data for the tricounty market appear to be approximately normal; but the data for the surrounding market have a tendency to be rightward skewed. Since the F-test is not robust for nonnormal data, the test results may not be valid. A more robust test for comparing variances is the Levene test. (See box, p. 00) The p-values for the Levene tests are shown below the F-tests on the MINITAB printout, Figure SIA9.3. When converted to one-tailed p-values, these values all exceed $\alpha = .10$. Thus, the more conservative Levene test does not find significant differences between the bid price variances for any of the three milk products. Consequently, the state of Kentucky may choose to omit the bid dispersion theory in its argument that bid collusion existed in the tricounty market.]

Hypothesis Test for Two Population Variances

Using the TI-83 Graphing Calculator

For this calculation, you have the option of entering the raw data or using the summary statistics

Step 1   *If you are using the raw data, enter the data into L1 and L2.*

Press **STAT** and select **1:Edit**
Note: If a list already contains data, clear the old data. Use the up arrow to highlight the name at the top of the list. Press **CLEAR ENTER**.
Use the **Down Arrow** or **ENTER** key to enter the data sets into **L1** and **L2**.

Step 2   *Access the Statistical Tests Menu*

Press **STAT**
Arrow right to **TESTS**
Arrow down to **D : 2-SampFTest**
Press **ENTER**

Step 3   *Choose **"Data"** or **"Stats"**. ("Data" is selected when you have entered the raw data into L1 and L2. "Stats" is selected when you are using the summary statistics.)*

Press **ENTER**

If you selected "Data":
Set **List1** to **L1**. Note: If List1 is not already set to L1, arrow down to List1: and hit **2nd** and '**1**'.
Set **List2** to **L2**. Note: If List2 is not already set to L2, arrow down to List2: and hit **2nd** and '**2**'.
Set **Freq1** to **1**. Note: If Freq1 is not already set to 1, arrow down to Freq1 and hit **Alpha** and '**1**'.
Set **Freq2** to **1**. Note: If Freq2 is not already set to 1, arrow down to Freq2 and hit **Alpha** and '**1**'.
Arrow down to the next line and select the appropriate alternative hypothesis by using the right arrow to highlight $\neq \sigma2, <\sigma2,$ or $>\sigma2$ and press **ENTER**.
Arrow down to **Calculate Draw**. You may choose either one of these for your output.
Press **ENTER**

If you selected "Stats", enter the sample standard deviations and sample sizes.
Arrow down to the next line and select the appropriate alternative hypothesis by using the right arrow to highlight $\neq \sigma2, <\sigma2,$ or $>\sigma2$ and press **ENTER**.
Arrow down to **Calculate Draw**. You may choose either one of these for your output.
Press **ENTER**.

Step 4   *View the Output*

If you chose **Calculate**, the output will display the alternative hypothesis, the F-value, the p-value and the summary statistics (sample standard deviations and sample sizes.)

If you chose **Draw**, a graph of the F-distribution will be displayed along with the F-value and the p-value. The area under the curve that represents the p-value is shaded. Note: In order to use the **Draw** feature, you must first clear all equations from the **Y-registers**. Hit '**Y =** ' and delete all equations.

Example *Consider Example 9.10 with data in Table 9.9 on pg. 485. For this example, the raw data will be used, so begin with Step1 of the instructions.*

Step 1 *Enter the data for Supplier 1 into L1 and the data for Supplier 2 into L2.*

Press **STAT** and select **1:Edit**
Note: If a list already contains data, clear the old data. Use the up arrow to highlight the name at the top of the list. Press **CLEAR ENTER**.
Use the **Down Arrow** or **ENTER** key to enter the data sets into **L1 and L2.**

L1	L2	L3	2
4.23	4.14	------	
4.35	4.26		
4.05	4.05		
3.75	4.11		
4.41	4.31		
4.37	4.13		
4.01	4.17		

L2(1)=4.14

Step 2 *Access the Statistical Tests Menu*

Press **STAT**
Arrow right to **TESTS**
Arrow down to **D : 2-SampFTest**
Press **ENTER**

```
EDIT CALC TESTS
8↑TInterval…
9:2-SampZInt…
0:2-SampTInt…
A:1-PropZInt…
B:2-PropZInt…
C:X²-Test…
D:2-SampFTest…
```

Step 3 *Choose "Data"*

Set **List1** to **L1**. Note: If List1 is not already set to L1, arrow down to List1: and hit **2nd** and **'1'**.
Set **List2** to **L2**. Note: If List2 is not already set to L2, arrow down to List2: and hit **2nd** and **'2'**.
Set **Freq1** to **1.** Note: If Freq1 is not already set to 1, arrow down to Freq1 and hit **Alpha** and **'1'**.
Set **Freq2** to **1.** Note: If Freq2 is not already set to 1, arrow down to Freq2 and hit **Alpha** and **'1'**.
Arrow down to the next line and select $\neq \sigma 2$, and press **ENTER**
Arrow down to **Calculate Draw.** You may choose either one of these for your output.
Press **ENTER**

```
2-SampFTest
 Inpt:Data Stats
 List1:L1
 List2:L2
 Freq1:1
 Freq2:1
 σ1:≠σ2 <σ2 >σ2
 Calculate Draw
```

Step 4 *View the Output*

If you chose **Calculate**, the output will display the alternative hypothesis, the F-value, the p-value and the summary statistics (sample standard deviations and sample sizes.)

If you chose **Draw**, a graph of the F-distribution will be displayed along with the F-value and the p-value. The area under the curve that represents the p-value is shaded. Note: In order to use the **Draw** feature, you must first clear all equations from the **Y-registers**. Hit '**Y =**' and delete all equations.

Note: The shaded area under the curve is not noticeable because the p-value is so small.

Exercises 9.84–9.102

Understanding the Principles

9.84 Describe the sampling distribution of $(s_1)^2/(s_2)^2$ for normal data.

9.85 What conditions are required for valid inferences about $(\sigma_1)^2/(\sigma_2)^2$?

9.86 *True or false.* The *F*-statistic used for testing $H_0: \sigma_1^2 = \sigma_2^2$ against $H_a: \sigma_1^2 < \sigma_2^2$ is $F = (s_1)^2/(s_2)^2$.

9.87 *True or false.* $H_0: \sigma_1^2 = \sigma_2^2$ is equivalent to $H_0: \sigma_1^2/\sigma_2^2 = 0$.

Learning the Mechanics

9.88 Use Tables VIII, IX, X, and XI of Appendix A to find
NW each of the following *F*-values:
   a. $F_{.05}$ where $\nu_1 = 8$ and $\nu_2 = 5$
   b. $F_{.01}$ where $\nu_1 = 20$ and $\nu_2 = 14$
   c. $F_{.025}$ where $\nu_1 = 10$ and $\nu_2 = 5$
   d. $F_{.10}$ where $\nu_1 = 20$ and $\nu_2 = 5$

9.89 Given ν_1 and ν_2, find the following probabilities:
   a. $\nu_1 = 2, \nu_2 = 30, P(F \geq 4.18)$
   b. $\nu_1 = 24, \nu_2 = 14, P(F < 1.94)$
   c. $\nu_1 = 9, \nu_2 = 1, P(F \leq 6,022.0)$
   d. $\nu_1 = 30, \nu_2 = 30, P(F > 1.84)$

9.90 For each of the following cases, identify the rejection region that should be used to test $H_0: \sigma_1^2 = \sigma_2^2$ against $H_a: \sigma_1^2 > \sigma_2^2$. Assume $\nu_1 = 20$ and $\nu_2 = 30$.
   a. $\alpha = .10$ **b.** $\alpha = .05$
   c. $\alpha = .025$ **d.** $\alpha = .01$

9.91 For each of the following cases, identify the rejection region that should be used to test $H_0: \sigma_1^2 = \sigma_2^2$ against $H_a: \sigma_1^2 \neq \sigma_2^2$. Assume $\nu_1 = 8$ and $\nu_2 = 40$.
   a. $\alpha = .20$

   b. $\alpha = .10$
   c. $\alpha = .05$
   d. $\alpha = .02$

9.92 Specify the appropriate rejection region for testing against $H_0: \sigma_1^2 = \sigma_2^2$ in each of the following situations:
   a. $H_a: \sigma_1^2 > \sigma_2^2; \alpha = .05, n_1 = 25, n_2 = 20$

   b. $H_a: \sigma_1^2 < \sigma_2^2; \alpha = .05, n_1 = 10, n_2 = 15$

   c. $H_a: \sigma_1^2 \neq \sigma_2^2; \alpha = .10, n_1 = 21, n_2 = 31$

   d. $H_a: \sigma_1^2 < \sigma_2^2; \alpha = .01, n_1 = 31, n_2 = 41$

   e. $H_a: \sigma_1^2 \neq \sigma_2^2; \alpha = .05, n_1 = 7, n_2 = 16$

9.93 Independent random samples were selected from each
NW of two normally distributed populations, $n_1 = 16$ from population 1 and $n_2 = 25$ from population 2. The means and variances for the two samples are shown in the table.

Sample 1	Sample 2
$n_1 = 16$	$n_2 = 25$
$\bar{x}_1 = 22.5$	$\bar{x}_2 = 28.2$
$s_1^2 = 2.87$	$s_2^2 = 9.85$

   a. Test the null hypothesis $H_0: \sigma_1^2 = \sigma_2^2$ against the alternative hypothesis $H_a: \sigma_1^2 \neq \sigma_2^2$. Use $\alpha = .05$.
   b. Find and interpret the *p*-value of the test.

9.94 Independent random samples were selected from each of two normally distributed populations, $n_1 = 6$ from population 1 and $n_2 = 4$ from population 2. The data are shown in the table.

⊙ **LM9_94**

Sample 1	Sample 2
3.1	2.3
4.3	1.4
1.2	3.7
1.7	8.9
.6	
3.4	

a. Test $H_0: \sigma_1^2 = \sigma_2^2$ against $H_a: \sigma_1^2 < \sigma_2^2$. Use $\alpha = .01$.
b. Test $H_0: \sigma_1^2 = \sigma_2^2$ against $H_a: \sigma_1^2 \neq \sigma_2^2$. Use $\alpha = .10$.

Applying the Concepts—Basic

9.95 Rating service at five-star hotels. Refer to *The Journal of American Academy of Business, Cambridge* (March 2002) study of how guests perceive the service quality at five-star hotels in Jamaica, Exercise 9.14 (p. 449). A summary of the guest perception scores, by gender, are reproduced in the table. Let σ_M^2 and σ_F^2 represent the true variances in scores for male and female guests, respectively.

Gender	Sample size	Mean score	Standard deviation
Males	127	39.08	6.73
Females	114	38.79	6.94

a. Set up H_0 and H_a for determining whether σ_M^2 is less than σ_F^2.
b. Find the test statistic for the test.
c. Give the rejection region for the test if $\alpha = .10$.

d. Find the approximate p-value of the test.
e. Make the appropriate conclusion in the words of the problem.
f. What conditions are required for the test results to be valid?

⊙ **GOBIANTS**

9.96 Mongolian desert ants. Refer to the *Journal of Biogeography* (Dec. 2003) study of ants in Mongolia (Central Asia), Exercise 9.23 (p. 451), where you compared the mean number of ants at two desert sites. Since the sample sizes were small, the variances of the populations at the two sites must be equal in order for the inference to be valid.
a. Set up H_0 and H_a for determining whether the variances are the same.
b. Use the data in the **GOBIANTS** file to find the test statistic for the test.

c. Give the rejection region for the test if $\alpha = .05$.

d. Find the approximate p-value of the test.
e. Make the appropriate conclusion in the words of the problem.
f. What conditions are required for the test results to be valid?

9.97 Bulimia study. Refer to Exercise 9.19 (p. 450). The "fear of negative evaluation" (FNE) scores for the 11 bulimic females and 14 females with normal eating habits are reproduced in the table at the bottom of the page. The confidence interval you constructed in Exercise 9.19 requires that the variance of the FNE scores of bulimic females is equal to the variance of the FNE scores of normal females. Conduct a test (at $\alpha = .05$) to determine the validity of this assumption.

9.98 Gender differences in math test scores. The *American Educational Research Journal* (Fall 1998) published a study to compare the mathematics achievement test scores of male and female students. The researchers hypothesized that the distribution of test scores for males is more variable than the corresponding distribution for females. Use the summary information reproduced in the table to test this claim at $\alpha = .01$.

	Males	Females
Sample size	1,764	1,739
Mean	48.9	48.4
Standard deviation	12.96	11.85

Source: Bielinski, J., and Davison, M. L. "Gender differences by item difficulty interactions in multiple-choice mathematics items." *American Educational Research Journal,* Vol. 35, No. 3, Fall 1998, p. 464 (Table 1).

Applying the Concepts—Intermediate

9.99 Patent infringement case. Refer to the *Chance* (Fall 2002) description of a patent infringement case against Intel Corp., Exercise 9.20 (p. 450). The zinc measurements for three locations on the original inventor's notebook—on a text line, on a witness line, and on the intersection of the witness and text line—are reproduced in the table.

⊙ **PATENT**

Text line:	.335	.374	.440			
Witness line:	.210	.262	.188	.329	.439	.397
Intersection:	.393	.353	.285	.295	.319	

a. Use a test (at $\alpha = .05$) to compare the variation in zinc measurements for the text line with the corresponding variation for the intersection.

BULIMIA

Bulimic students	21	13	10	20	25	19	16	21	24	13	14		
Normal students	13	6	16	13	8	19	23	18	11	19	7	10	15	20

Source: Randles, R. H. "On neutral responses (zeros) in the sign test and ties in the Wilcoxon-Mann-Whitney test." *The American Statistician. Vol. 55, No. 2, May 2001 (Figure 3).*

b. Use a test (at $\alpha = .05$) to compare the variation in zinc measurements for the witness line with the corresponding variation for the intersection.

c. From the results, parts **a** and **b**, what can you infer about the variation in zinc measurements at the three notebook locations?

d. What assumptions are required for the inferences to be valid? Are they reasonably satisfied? (You checked these assumptions when answering Exercise 9.20d.)

9.100 Human inspection errors. Tests of product quality using human inspectors can lead to serious inspection error problems (*Journal of Quality Technology*, Apr. 1986.) To evaluate the performance of inspectors in a new company, a quality manager had a sample of 12 novice inspectors evaluate 200 finished products. The same 200 items were evaluated by 12 experienced inspectors. The quality of each item—whether defective or nondefective—was known to the manager. The following table lists the number of inspection errors (classifying a defective item as nondefective or vice versa) made by each inspector.

INSPECT

Novice Inspectors				Experienced Inspectors			
30	35	26	40	31	15	25	19
36	20	45	31	28	17	19	18
33	29	21	48	24	10	20	21

a. Prior to conducting this experiment, the manager believed the variance in inspection errors was lower for experienced inspectors than for novice inspectors. Do the sample data support her belief? Test using $\alpha = .05$.

b. What is the appropriate p-value of the test you conducted in part **a**?

9.101 Mating habits of snails. Refer to the *Genetical Research* (June 1995) study of the mating habits of hermaphroditic snails, Exercise 9.26 (p. 452). Recall that the snails were identified as either selfers or outcrossers and that the mean effective population sizes of the two groups were compared. The data for the study are reproduced in the table. Geneticists are often more interested in comparing the variation in population size of the two types of mating systems.

Conduct this analysis for the researcher. Interpret the result.

Snail Mating System	Sample Size	Effective Population Size	
		Mean	Standard Deviation
Outcrossing	17	4,894	1,932
Selfing	5	4,133	1,890

Source: Jarne, P. "Mating system, bottlenecks, and genetic polymorphism in hermaphroditic animals." *Genetical Research,* Vol. 65, No. 3, June 1995, p. 197 (Table 4).

9.102 Following the initial Persian Gulf War, the Pentagon changed its logistics processes to be more corporate-like. The extravagant "just-in-case" mentality was replaced with "just-in-time" systems. Emulating Federal Express and United Parcel Service, deliveries from factories to foxholes are now expedited using bar codes, laser cards, radio tags, and databases to track supplies. The table contains order-to-delivery times (in days) for a sample of shipments from the U.S. to the Persian Gulf in 1991 and a sample of shipments to Bosnia in 1995.

ORDTIMES

Persian Gulf	Bosnia
28.0	15.1
20.0	6.4
26.5	5.0
10.6	11.4
9.1	6.5
35.2	6.5
29.1	3.0
41.2	7.0
27.5	5.5

Source: Adapted from Crock, S. "The Pentagon goes to B-school." *Business Week,* Dec. 11, 1995, p. 98.

a. Determine whether the variances in order-to-delivery times for Persian Gulf and Bosnia shipments are equal. Use $\alpha = .05$.

b. Given your answer to part **a**, is it appropriate to construct a confidence interval for the difference between the mean order-to-delivery times? Explain.

Quick Review

Key Terms

Note: Starred (*) terms are from the optional section in this chapter.

Blocking 456
F-distribution* 483
Nonparametric method 446

Paired difference experiment 456
Pooled sample estimator σ^2 436

Randomized block experiment 456
Standard error 433

Key Formulas

Note: Starred (*) formulas are from the optional section in this chapter.

$(1 - \alpha)100\%$ confidence interval for θ: (see table)

$$\text{Large samples:} \quad \hat{\theta} \pm z_{\alpha/2}\sigma_{\hat{\theta}}$$

$$\text{Small samples:} \quad \hat{\theta} \pm t_{\alpha/2}\sigma_{\hat{\theta}}$$

For testing H_0: $\theta = D_0$: (see table)

$$\text{Large samples:} \quad z = \frac{\hat{\theta} - D_0}{\sigma_{\hat{\theta}}}$$

$$\text{Small samples:} \quad t = \frac{\hat{\theta} - D_0}{\sigma_{\hat{\theta}}}$$

Parameter, θ	Estimator, $\hat{\theta}$	Standard Error of Estimator, $\sigma_{\hat{\theta}}$	Estimated Standard Error	
$\mu_1 - \mu_2$ (independent samples)	$\bar{x}_1 - \bar{x}_2$	$\sqrt{\dfrac{\sigma_1^2}{n_1} + \dfrac{\sigma_2^2}{n_2}}$	Large n: $\sqrt{\dfrac{s_1^2}{n_1} + \dfrac{s_2^2}{n_2}}$	433
			Small n: $\sqrt{s_p^2\left(\dfrac{1}{n_1} + \dfrac{1}{n_2}\right)}$	437
μ_D (paired sample)	$\bar{x}_D$	$\dfrac{\sigma_D}{\sqrt{n_D}}$	$\dfrac{s_D}{\sqrt{n_D}}$	457
$p_1 - p_2$ (large, independent samples)	$\hat{p}_1 - \hat{p}_2$	$\sqrt{\dfrac{p_1q_1}{n_1} + \dfrac{p_2q_2}{n_2}}$	Confidence intervals: $\sqrt{\dfrac{\hat{p}_1\hat{q}_1}{n_1} + \dfrac{\hat{p}_2\hat{q}_2}{n_2}}$	469, 470
			Hypothesis tests: $\sqrt{\hat{p}\hat{q}\left(\dfrac{1}{n_1} + \dfrac{1}{n_2}\right)}$	471

Pooled sample variance:	$s_p^2 = \dfrac{(n_1 - 1)s_1^2 + (n_2 - 1)s_2^2}{n_1 + n_2 - 2}$	437
Pooled sample proportion:	$\hat{p} = \dfrac{x_1 + x_2}{n_1 + n_2}, \quad \hat{q} = 1 - \hat{p}$	471
Determining the sample size for estimating $\mu_1 - \mu_2$:	$n_1 = n_2 = \dfrac{(z_{\alpha/2})^2(\sigma_1^2 + \sigma_2^2)}{(\text{SE})^2}$	481
Determining the sample size for estimating $p_1 - p_2$:	$n_1 = n_2 = \dfrac{(z_{\alpha/2})^2(p_1q_1 + p_2q_2)}{(\text{SE})^2}$	481
*Test statistic for testing H_0: $\dfrac{\sigma_1^2}{\sigma_2^2}$	$F = \dfrac{\text{larger } s^2}{\text{smaller } s^2}$ if H_a: $\dfrac{\sigma_1^2}{\sigma_2^2} \neq 1$	488
	$F = \dfrac{s_1^2}{s_2^2}$ if H_a: $\dfrac{\sigma_1^2}{\sigma_2^2} > 1$	

Language Lab

Symbol	Pronunciation	Description
$\mu_1 - \mu_2$	mu-1 minus mu-2	Difference between population means
$\bar{x}_1 - \bar{x}_2$	x-bar-1 minus x-bar-2	Difference between sample means
$\sigma_{(\bar{x}_1 - \bar{x}_2)}$	sigma of x-bar-1 minus x-bar-2	Standard deviation of the sampling distribution of $(\bar{x}_1 - \bar{x}_2)$
s_p^2	s-p squared	Pooled sample variance
D_0	D naught	Hypothesized value of difference

μ_D	mu D	Difference between population means, paired data
$\bar{x}_D$	x-bar D	Mean of sample differences
s_D	s-D	Standard deviation of sample differences
n_D	n-D	Number of differences in sample
$p_1 - p_2$	p-1 minus p-2	Difference between population proportions
$\hat{p}_1 - \hat{p}_2$	p-1 hat minus p-2 hat	Difference between sample proportions
$\sigma_{(\hat{p}_1 - \hat{p}_2)}$	sigma of p-1 hat minus p-2 hat	Standard deviation of the sampling distribution of $(\hat{p}_1 - \hat{p}_2)$
F_α	F-alpha	Critical value of F associated with tail area α
ν_1	nu-1	Numerator degrees of freedom for F statistic
ν_2	nu-2	Denominator degrees of freedom for F statistic
$\dfrac{\sigma_1^2}{\sigma_2^2}$	sigma-1 squared over sigma-2 squared	Ratio of two population variances

Chapter Summary Notes

- Key words/phrases for identifying $\mu_1 - \mu_2$ as the parameter of interest: *difference between means or averages, compare two means using independent samples*
- Key words/phrases for identifying μ_D as the parameter of interest: *mean or average of paired differences, compare two means using matched pairs*
- Key words/phrases for identifying $p_1 - p_2$ as the parameter of interest: *difference between proportions or percentages, compare two proportions using independent samples*
- Key words/phrases for identifying σ_1^2/σ_2^2 as the parameter of interest: *difference between variances, compare variation in two populations using independent samples*
- Conditions required for a valid **large-sample inferences for $\mu_1 - \mu_2$**: (1) independent random samples, (2) large sample sizes ($n_1 \geq 30$ and $n_2 \geq 30$)

- Conditions required for a valid **small-sample inferences for $\mu_1 - \mu_2$**: (1) independent random samples, (2) both populations are approximately normal, (3) $\sigma_1^2 = \sigma_2^2$
- Conditions required for a valid **large-sample inferences for μ_D** (1) random sample of paired differences, (2) large sample size ($n_d \geq 30$)
- Conditions required for a valid **small-sample inferences for μ_D** (1) random sample of paired differences, (2) population of differences are approximately normal
- Conditions required for a valid **large-sample inferences for $p_1 - p_2$**: (1) independent random samples, (2) large sample sizes (both $p_1 \pm 3\sigma$ and $p_2 \pm 3\sigma$ fall between 0 and 1)
- Conditions required for a valid **inferences for σ_1^2/σ_2^2**: (1) independent random samples, (2) both populations are approximately normal

Supplementary Exercises 9.103–9.136

Note: Starred (*) exercises refer to the optional section in this chapter.

Understanding the Principles

9.103 For each of the following, identify the target parameter as $\mu_1 - \mu_2$, $p_1 - p_2$, or σ_1^2/σ_2^2.
  a. Compare average SAT scores of males and females.
  b. Difference between mean waiting times at two supermarket checkout lanes
  c. Compare proportions of Democrats and Republicans who favor legalization of marijuana.
  *d. Compare variation in salaries of NBA players picked in the first round and the second round.
  e. Difference in dropout rates of college student athletes and regular students

9.104 List the assumptions necessary for each of the following inferential techniques:
  a. Large-sample inferences about the difference $(\mu_1 - \mu_2)$ between population means using a two-sample z-statistic
  b. Small-sample inferences about $(\mu_1 - \mu_2)$ using an independent samples design and a two-sample t-statistic
  c. Small-sample inferences about $(\mu_1 - \mu_2)$ using a paired difference design and a single-sample t-statistic to analyze the differences
  d. Large-sample inferences about the differences $(p_1 - p_2)$ between binomial proportions using a two-sample z-statistic
  *e. Inferences about the ratio σ_1^2/σ_2^2 of two population variances using an F-test

Learning the Mechanics

9.105 Independent random samples were selected from two normally distributed populations with means μ_1 and μ_2, respectively. The sample sizes, means, and variances are shown in the following table.

Sample 1	Sample 2
$n_1 = 12$	$n_2 = 14$
$\bar{x}_1 = 17.8$	$\bar{x}_2 = 15.3$
$s_1^2 = 74.2$	$s_2^2 = 60.5$

a. Test $H_0: (\mu_1 - \mu_2) = 0$ against $H_a: (\mu_1 - \mu_2) > 0$. Use $\alpha = .05$.

b. Form a 99% confidence interval for $(\mu_1 - \mu_2)$.

c. How large must n_1 and n_2 be if you wish to estimate $(\mu_1 - \mu_2)$ to within 2 units with 99% confidence? Assume that $n_1 = n_2$.

9.106 Two independent random samples were selected from normally distributed populations with means and variances (μ_1, σ_1^2) and (μ_2, σ_2^2), respectively. The sample sizes, means, and variances are shown in the table.

Sample 1	Sample 2
$n_1 = 20$	$n_2 = 15$
$\bar{x}_1 = 123$	$\bar{x}_2 = 116$
$s_1^2 = 31.3$	$s_2^2 = 120.1$

*a. Test $H_0: \sigma_1^2 = \sigma_2^2$ against $H_a: \sigma_1^2 \neq \sigma_2^2$. Use $\alpha = .05$.

b. Would you be willing to use a t-test to test the null hypothesis $H_0: (\mu_1 - \mu_2) = 0$ against the alternative hypothesis $H_a: (\mu_1 - \mu_2) \neq 0$? Why?

9.107 Two independent random samples are taken from two populations. The results of these samples are summarized in the following table.

Sample 1	Sample 2
$n_1 = 135$	$n_2 = 148$
$\bar{x}_1 = 12.2$	$\bar{x}_2 = 8.3$
$s_1^2 = 2.1$	$s_2^2 = 3.0$

a. Form a 90% confidence interval for $(\mu_1 - \mu_2)$.

b. Test $H_0: (\mu_1 - \mu_2) = 0$ against $H_a: (\mu_1 - \mu_2) \neq 0$. Use $\alpha = .01$.

c. What sample size would be required if you wish to estimate $(\mu_1 - \mu_2)$ to within .2 with 90% confidence? Assume that $n_1 = n_2$.

9.108 Independent random samples were selected from two binomial populations. The size and number of observed successes for each sample are shown in the table.

Sample 1	Sample 2
$n_1 = 200$	$n_2 = 200$
$x_1 = 110$	$x_2 = 130$

a. Test $H_0: (p_1 - p_2) = 0$ against $H_a: (p_1 - p_2) < 0$. Use $\alpha = .10$.

b. Form a 95% confidence interval for $(p_1 - p_2)$.

c. What sample sizes would be required if we wish to use a 95% confidence interval of width .01 to estimate $(p_1 - p_2)$?

9.109 A random sample of five pairs of observations were selected, one observation from a population with mean μ_1, the other from a population with mean μ_2. The data are shown in the accompanying table.

⊙ **LM9_109**

Pair	Value from Population 1	Value from Population 2
1	28	22
2	31	27
3	24	20
4	30	27
5	22	20

a. Test the null hypothesis $H_0: \mu_D = 0$ against $H_a: \mu_D \neq 0$, where $\mu_D = \mu_1 - \mu_2$. Use $\alpha = .05$.

b. Form a 95% confidence interval for μ_D.

c. When are the procedures you used in parts **a** and **b** valid?

Applying the Concepts—Basic

⊙ **OILSPILL**

9.110 Hull failure of oil tankers. Refer to the *Marine Technology* (Jan. 1995) study of major oil spills from tankers and carriers, Exercise 2.182 (p. 112). The data for the 50 spills are saved in the **OILSPILL** file.

a. Construct a 90% confidence interval for the difference between the mean spillage amount of accidents caused by collision and the mean spillage amount of accidents caused by fire/explosion. Interpret the result.

b. Conduct a test of hypothesis to compare the mean spillage amount of accidents caused by grounding to the corresponding mean of accidents caused by hull failure. Use $\alpha = .05$.

c. Refer to parts **a** and **b**. State any assumptions required for the inferences derived from the analyses to be valid. Are these assumptions reasonably satisfied?

*d. Conduct a test of hypothesis to compare the variation in spillage amounts for accidents caused by collision and accidents caused by grounding. Use $\alpha = .02$.

⊙ **EVOS**

9.111 Oil spill impact on seabirds. Refer to the *Journal of Agricultural, Biological, and Environmental Statistics* (Sept. 2000) impact study of a tanker oil spill on the seabird population in Alaska, Exercise 2.179 (p. 111). Recall that for each of 96 shoreline locations (called transects), the number of seabirds found, the length (in kilometers) of the transect, and whether or not the transect was in an oiled area were recorded. (The data are saved in the **EVOS** file.) Observed seabird density is defined as the observed count divided by the length of

MINITAB Output for Exercise 9.111

Two-Sample T-Test and CI: Density, Oil

```
Two-sample T for Density

Oil   N   Mean   StDev   SE Mean
no    36  3.27   6.70      1.1
yes   60  3.50   5.97      0.77


Difference = mu (no ) - mu (yes)
Estimate for difference:  -0.221165
95% CI for difference:  (-2.927767, 2.485436)
T-Test of difference = 0 (vs not =): T-Value = -0.16  P-Value = 0.871  DF = 67
```

the transect. A comparison of the mean densities of oiled and unoiled transects is displayed in the MINITAB printout above. Use this information to make an inference about the difference in the population mean seabird densities of oiled and unoiled transects.

9.112 Tapeworms in brill fish. The *Journal of Fish Biology* (Aug. 1990) reported on a study to compare the incidence of parasites (tapeworms) in species of Mediterranean and Atlantic fish. In the Mediterranean Sea, 588 brill were captured and dissected, and 211 were found to be infected by the parasite. In the Atlantic Ocean, 123 brill were captured and dissected, and 26 were found to be infected. Compare the proportions of infected brill at the two capture sites using a 90% confidence interval. Interpret the interval.

9.113 Effect of altitude on climbers. Dr. Philip Lieberman, a neuroscientist at Brown University, recently conducted a field experiment to gauge the effect of high altitude on a person's ability to think critically. (*New York Times*, Aug. 23, 1995.) The subjects of the experiment were five male members of an American expedition climbing Mount Everest. At the base camp, Lieberman read sentences to the climbers while they looked at simple pictures in a book. The length of time (in seconds) it took for each climber to match the picture with a sentence was recorded. Using a radio, Lieberman repeated the task when the climbers reached a camp 5 miles above sea level. At this altitude, he noted that the climbers took 50% longer to complete the task.
a. What is the variable measured for this experiment?
b. What are the experimental units?
c. Discuss how the data should be analyzed.

***9.114 Bear vs. pig bile study.** Bear gallbladder is used in Chinese medicine to treat inflamation. A study in the *Journal of Ethnopharmacology* (June 1995) examined the easier to obtain pig gallbladder as an effective substitute for bear gallbladder. Twenty male mice were divided randomly into two groups: 10 were given a dosage of bear bile and 10 were given a dosage of pig bile. All the mice then received an injection of croton oil in the left ear lobe to induce inflammation. Four hours later, both the left and right ear lobes were weighed, with the difference (in milligrams) representing the degree of swelling. Summary statistics on the degree of swelling are provided in the following table.

Bear Bile	Pig Bile
$n_1 = 10$	$n_2 = 10$
$\bar{x}_1 = 9.19$	$\bar{x}_2 = 9.71$
$s_1 = 4.17$	$s_2 = 3.33$

a. Use a hypothesis test (at $\alpha = .05$) to compare the variation in degree of swelling for mice treated with bear and pig bile.
b. What assumptions are necessary for the inference, part **a**, to be valid?

9.115 Self-concepts of female students. A study reported in the *Journal of Psychology* (Mar. 1991) measures the change in female students' self-concepts as they move from high school to college. A sample of 133 Boston College female students were selected for the study. Each was asked to evaluate several aspects of her life at two points in time: at the end of her senior year of high school, and during her sophomore year of college. Each student was asked to evaluate where she believed she stood on a scale that ranged from top 10% of class (1) to lowest 10% of class (5). The results for three of the traits evaluated are reported in the table below.

Trait	n	Senior Year of High School $\bar{x}$	Sophomore Year of College $\bar{x}$
Leadership	133	2.09	2.33
Popularity	133	2.48	2.69
Intellectual self-confidence	133	2.29	2.55

a. What null and alternative hypotheses would you test to determine whether the mean self-concept of females decreases between the senior year of high school and the sophomore year of college as measured by each of these three traits?
b. Are these traits more appropriately analyzed using an independent samples test or a paired difference test? Explain.
c. Noting the size of the sample, what assumptions are necessary to ensure the validity of the tests?
d. The article reports that the leadership test results in a *p*-value greater than .05, while the tests for popularity and intellectual self-confidence result in *p*-values less than .05. Interpret these results.

9.116 Environmental impact study. Some power plants are located near rivers or oceans so that the available water can be used for cooling the condensers. Suppose that, as part of an environmental impact study, a power company wants to estimate the difference in mean water temperature between the discharge of its plant and the offshore waters. How many sample measurements must be taken at each site in order to estimate the true difference between means to within .2°C with 95% confidence? Assume that the range in readings will be about 4°C at each site and the same number of readings will be taken at each site.

9.117 Hatching tree frog eggs. Scientists have linked a catastrophic decline in the number of frogs inhabiting the world to ultraviolet radiation. (*Tampa Tribune*, Mar. 1, 1994.) The Pacific tree frog, however, is not believed to be in decline, possibly because it manufactures an enzyme that protects its eggs from ultraviolet radiation. Researchers at Oregon State University compared the hatching rates of two groups of Pacific tree frog eggs. One group of eggs was shielded with ultraviolet-blocking sun shades, while the second group was not. The number of eggs successfully hatched in each group is provided in the following table.

	Sun-Shaded Eggs	Unshaded Eggs
Total number	70	80
Number hatched	34	31

a. Set up H_0 and H_a for testing whether the hatching rates of the two groups of Pacific tree frog eggs differ.
b. Conduct the test at $\alpha = .01$. What do you conclude?

9.118 Pulling strength of firefighters. Consider a study conducted to compare the abilities of men and women to perform the strenuous tasks required of a shipboard firefighter. (*Human Factors*, Vol. 24, 1982.) The researchers measured the pulling force (in newtons) that a firefighter was able to exert in pulling the starter cord of a P-250 water pump. Firefighters were matched in pairs according to weight, thus producing data for a matched pairs (or paired difference) experiment, as shown below.

PULLFORCE

Pair	Female	Male
1	40.03	84.51
2	75.62	80.06
3	53.38	102.30
4	62.27	88.96

Source: Phillips, M. D., and Pepper, R. L., "Shipboard firefighting performance of females and males." *Human Factors*, Vol. 24, No. 3, 1982.

a. Do the data provide sufficient evidence to indicate a difference in mean pulling force between female and male firefighters? Test using $\alpha = .05$.
b. Find a 95% confidence interval for the difference in mean pulling force between female and male firefighters. Interpret the interval.

9.119 Job satisfaction study. Does the time of day during which one works affect job satisfaction? A study in *The Journal of Occupational Psychology* (Sept. 1991) examined differences in job satisfaction between day-shift and night-shift nurses. Nurses' satisfaction with their hours of work, free time away from work, and breaks during work were measured. The table shows the mean scores for each measure of job satisfaction (higher scores indicate greater satisfaction), along with the observed significance level comparing the means for the day-shift and night-shift samples:

	Day Shift	Night Shift	p-Value
Mean satisfaction with:			
Hours of work	3.91	3.56	.813
Free time	2.55	1.72	.047
Breaks	2.53	3.75	.0073

a. Specify the null and alternative hypotheses if we wish to test whether a difference in job satisfaction exists between day-shift and night-shift nurses on each of the three measures. Define any symbols you use.
b. Interpret the p-value for each of the tests. (Each of the p-values in the table is two-tailed.)
c. Assume that each of the tests is based on small samples of nurses from each group. What assumptions are necessary for the tests to be valid?

Applying the Concepts—Intermediate

9.120 Consumer reaction to silverware patterns. A pupillometer is a device used to observe changes in an individual's pupil dilations as he or she is exposed to different visual stimuli. The Design and Market Research Laboratories of the Container Corporation of America used a pupillometer to evaluate consumer reaction to different silverware patterns for one of its clients. Suppose 15 consumers were chosen at random, and each was shown two different silverware patterns. The pupillometer readings (in millimeters) for each consumer are shown below.

PUPILL

Consumer	Pattern 1	Pattern 2
1	1.00	.80
2	.97	.66
3	1.45	1.22
4	1.21	1.00
5	.77	.81
6	1.32	1.11
7	1.81	1.30
8	.91	.32
9	.98	.91
10	1.46	1.10
11	1.85	1.60
12	.33	.21
13	1.77	1.50
14	.85	.65
15	.15	.05

a. Which type of experiment does this represent—independent samples or paired difference? Explain.

b. Use a 90% confidence interval to estimate the difference in mean pupil dilation per consumer for silverware patterns 1 and 2. Interpret the confidence interval, assuming that the pupillometer indeed measures consumer interest.

c. Test the hypothesis that the mean dilation differs for the two patterns. Use $\alpha = .10$. Does the test conclusion support your interpretation of the confidence interval in part **b**?

d. What assumptions are necessary to ensure the validity of the inferences in parts **b** and **c**?

9.121 Teaching nursing skills. A traditional approach to teaching basic nursing skills was compared with an innovative approach in the *Journal of Nursing Education* (Jan. 1992). The innovative approach utilizes Vee heuristics and concept maps to link theoretical concepts with practical skills. Forty-two students enrolled in an upper-division nursing course participated in the study. Half (21) were randomly assigned to labs that utilized the innovative approach. After completing the course, all students were given short-answer questions about scientific principles underlying each of 10 nursing skills. The objective of the research is to compare the mean scores of the two groups of students.

a. What is the appropriate test to use to compare the two groups?

b. Are any assumptions required for the test?

c. One question dealt with the use of clean/sterile gloves. The mean scores for this question were 3.28 (traditional) and 3.40 (innovative). Is there sufficient information to perform the test?

d. Refer to part **c**. The *p*-value for the test was reported as $p = .79$. Interpret this result.

e. Another question concerned the choice of a stethoscope. The mean scores of the two groups were 2.55 (traditional) and 3.60 (innovative) with an associated *p*-value of .02. Interpret these results.

9.122 Identical twins reared apart. Twins, because they share an identical genotype, make ideal subjects for investigating the degree to which various environmental conditions impact personality. The classical method of studying this phenomenon and the subject of an interesting book by Susan Farber (*Identical Twins Reared Apart*, New York: Basic Books, 1981) is the study of identical twins separated early in life and reared apart. Much of Farber's discussion focuses on a comparison of IQ scores. The data for this analysis appear in the table. One member (A) of each of the $n = 32$ pairs of twins was reared by a natural parent; the other member (B) was reared by a relative or some other person. Is there a significant difference between the average IQ scores of identical twins, where one member of the pair is reared by the natural parents and the other member of the pair is not? Use $\alpha = .05$ to make your conclusion.

TWINSIQ

Pair ID	Twin A	Twin B	Pair ID	Twin A	Twin B
112	113	109	228	100	88
114	94	100	232	100	104
126	99	86	236	93	84
132	77	80	306	99	95
136	81	95	308	109	98
148	91	106	312	95	100
170	111	117	314	75	86
172	104	107	324	104	103
174	85	85	328	73	78
180	66	84	330	88	99
184	111	125	338	92	111
186	51	66	342	108	110
202	109	108	344	88	83
216	122	121	350	90	82
218	97	98	352	79	76
220	82	94	416	97	98

Source: Adapted from *Identical Twins Reared Apart*, by Susan L. Farber 1981 by Basic Books, Inc.

9.123 Treatments for panic disorder. Inositol is a complex cyclic alcohol found to be effective against clinical depression. Medical researchers believe inositol may also be used to treat panic disorder. To test this theory, a double-blind, placebo-controlled study of 21 patients diagnosed with panic disorder was conducted. (*American Journal of Psychiatry*, July 1995.) Patients completed daily panic diaries recording the occurrence of their panic attacks. The data for a week in which patients received a glucose placebo and for a week when they were treated with inositol are provided in the table. [*Note:* Neither the patients nor the treating physicians knew which week the placebo was given.] Analyze the data and interpret the results. Comment on the validity of the assumptions.

INOSITOL

Patient	Placebo	Inositol	Patient	Placebo	Inositol
1	0	0	12	0	2
2	2	1	13	3	1
3	0	3	14	3	1
4	1	2	15	3	4
5	0	0	16	4	2
6	10	5	17	6	4
7	2	0	18	15	21
8	6	4	19	28	8
9	1	1	20	30	0
10	1	0	21	13	0
11	1	3			

Source: Benjamin, J., et al. "Double-blind, placebo-controlled, crossover trial of inositol treatment for panic disorder." *American Journal of Psychiatry,* Vol. 152, No. 7, July 1995, p. 1085 (Table 1).

9.124 Aerobic exercise study. Excess postexercise oxygen consumption (EPOC) describes energy expended during the body's recovery period immediately following aerobic exercise. *The Journal of Sports Medicine and Physical Fitness* (Dec. 1994) published a study designed to investigate the effect of fitness level on the magnitude and duration of EPOC. Ten healthy young adult males volunteered for the study. Five of these were endurance-trained and comprised the fit group; the other five were not engaged in any systematic training and comprised the sedentary group. Each volunteer engaged in a weight-supported exercise on a cycle ergometer until 300 kilocalories were expended. The magnitude (in kilocalories) and duration (in minutes) of the EPOC of each exerciser were measured. The study results are summarized in the table below.

Variable		Fit ($n = 5$)	Sedentary ($n = 5$)	p-value
Magnitude	Mean	12.2	12.2	.998
(kcal)	Std. dev.	3.1	4.3	
Duration	Mean	16.6	20.4	.344
(min)	Std. dev.	3.1	7.8	

Source: Sedlock, D. A. "Fitness levels and postexercise energy expenditure." *The Journal of Sports Medicine and Physical Fitness,* Vol. 34, No. 4, Dec. 1994, p. 339 (Table III).

a. Conduct a test of hypothesis to determine whether the true mean magnitude of EPOC differs for fit and sedentary young adult males. Use $\alpha = .10$.

b. The p-value for the test, part **a**, is given in the table. Interpret this value.

c. Conduct a test of hypothesis to determine whether the true mean duration of EPOC differs for fit and sedentary young adult males. Use $\alpha = .10$.

d. The p-value for the test, part **c**, is given in the table. Interpret this value.

9.125 Inositol-fed infants. Inositol—a complex alcohol nutrient found in breast milk—has been found to reduce the risk of lung and eye damage in premature infants. The study, published in the *New England Journal of Medicine* (May 7, 1992), involved 220 premature infants. The infants were randomly divided into two groups; half (110) of the infants received an intravenous feeding of inositol, while the other half received a standard diet. The researchers found that 14 of the inositol-fed infants suffered retinopathy of prematurity, an eye injury that results from the high oxygen levels needed to compensate for poorly developed lungs. In contrast, 29 of the infants on the standard diet developed this disease. Analyze the results with a test of hypothesis. Use $\alpha = .01$.

9.126 Radiation exposure of sailors. Operation Crossroads was a 1946 military exercise in which atomic bombs were detonated over empty target ships in the Pacific Ocean. The Navy assigned sailors to wash down the test ships immediately after the atomic blasts. The National Academy of Science reported "that the overall death rate among Operation Crossroads sailors was 4.6% higher than among a comparable group of sailors.... However, this increase was not statistically significant." (*Tampa Tribune,* Oct. 30, 1996.)

a. Describe the parameter of interest in the National Academy of Science study.

b. Interpret the statement: "This increase was not statistically significant."

9.127 Rating music teachers. Students enrolled in music classes at the University of Texas (Austin) participated in a study to compare the observations and teacher evaluations of music education majors and nonmusic majors. (*Journal of Research in Music Education,* Winter 1991.) Independent random samples of 100 music majors and 100 nonmajors rated the overall performance of their teacher using a 6-point scale, where 1 = lowest rating and 6 = highest rating. Use the information in the table to compare the mean teacher ratings of the two groups of music students with a 95% confidence interval. Interpret the result.

	Music Majors	Nonmusic Majors
Sample size	100	100
Mean "overall" rating	4.26	4.59
Standard deviation	.81	.78

Source: Duke, R. A., and Blackman, M. D. "The relationship between observers' recorded teacher behavior and evaluation of music instruction." *Journal of Research in Music Education,* Vol. 39, No. 4, Winter 1991 (Table 2).

9.128 Identifying the target parameter. For each of the following studies, give the parameter of interest and state any assumptions that are necessary for the inferences to be invalid.

a. To investigate a possible link between jet lag and memory impairment, a University of Bristol (England) neurologist recruited 20 female flight attendants who worked flights across several time zones. Half of the attendants had only a short recovery time between flights and half had a long recovery time between flights. The average size of the right temporal lobe of the brain for the short-recovery group was significantly smaller than the average size of the right temporal lobe of the brain for the long-recovery group. (*Tampa Tribune,* May 23, 2001.)

b. In a study presented at the March, 2001, meeting of the Association for the Advancement of Applied Sport Psychology, researchers revealed that the proportion of athletes who have a good self-image of their body is 20% higher than the corresponding proportion of nonathletes.

c. A University of Florida animal sciences professor has discovered that feeding chickens corn oil causes them to produce larger eggs. (*UF News,* April 11, 2001.) The weight of eggs produced by each of a sample of chickens on a regular feed diet was recorded. Then, the same chickens were fed a diet supplemented by corn oil, and the weight of eggs produced by each was recorded. The mean weight of the eggs produced with corn oil was 3 grams heavier than the mean weight produced with the regular diet.

*9.129 **Instrument precision.** The quality control department of a paper company measures the brightness (a measure of reflectance) of finished paper on a periodic basis throughout the day. Two instruments that are available to measure the paper specimens are subject to error, but they can be adjusted so that the mean readings for a control paper specimen are the same for both instruments. Suppose you are concerned about the precision of the two instruments and want to compare the variability in the readings of instrument 1 to those of instrument 2. Five brightness measurements were made on a single paper specimen using each of the two instruments. The data are shown in the table.

⊚ **BRIGHT**

Instrument 1	Instrument 2
29	26
28	34
30	30
28	32
30	28

a. Is the variance of the measurements obtained by instrument 1 significantly different from the variance of the measurements obtained using instrument 2?

b. What assumptions must be satisfied for the test in part **a** to be valid?

9.130 **Genetic Study of cell growth.** Geneticists at Duke University Medical Center have identified the E2F1 transcription factor as an important component of cell proliferation control. (*Nature*, Sept. 23, 1993.) The researchers induced DNA synthesis in two batches of serum-starved cells. Each cell in one batch was microinjected with the E2F1 gene, while the cells in the second batch (the controls) were not exposed to E2F1. After 30 hours, the number of cells in each batch that exhibited altered growth was determined. The results of the experiment are summarized in the table.

	Control	E2F1-Treated Cells
Total number of cells	158	92
Number of growth-altered cells	15	41

Source: Johnson, D. G., et al. "Expression of transcription factor E2F1 induces quiescent cells to enter S phase." *Nature,* Vol. 365, No. 6444, Sept, 23, 1993, p. 351 (Table 1).

a. Compare the percentages of cells exhibiting altered growth in the two batches with a 90% confidence interval.

b. Use the interval, part **a**, to make an inference about the ability of the E2F1 transcription factor to induce cell growth.

9.131 **Kicking the cigarette habit.** Can taking an antidepressant drug help cigarette smokers kick their habit? The *New England Journal of Medicine* (Oct. 23, 1997) published a study in which 615 smokers (all who wanted to give up smoking) were randomly assigned to receive either Zyban (an antidepressant) or a placebo (a dummy pill) for six weeks. Of the 309 patients who received Zyban, 71 were not smoking one year later. Of the 306 patients who received a placebo, 37 were not smoking one year later. Conduct a test of hypothesis (at $\alpha = .05$) to answer the research question posed above.

9.132 **Muscle properties of crayfish.** Marine biochemists at the University of Tokyo studied the properties of crustacean striated muscles. (*The Journal of Experimental Zoology*, Sept. 1993.) The main purpose of the experiment was to compare the biochemical properties of fast and slow muscles of crayfish. Using crayfish obtained from a local supplier, the researchers excised twelve fast-muscle fiber bundles and tested each fiber bundle for uptake of calcium. Twelve slow-muscle fiber bundles were excised from a second sample of crayfish, and calcium uptake was measured. The results of the experiment are summarized here. (All calcium measurements are in moles per milligram.) Analyze the data using a 95% confidence interval. Make an inference about the difference between the calcium uptake means of fast and slow muscles.

Fast Muscle	Slow Muscle
$n_1 = 12$	$n_2 = 12$
$\bar{x}_1 = .57$	$\bar{x}_2 = .37$
$s_1 = .104$	$s_2 = .035$

Source: Ushio, H., and Watabe, S. "Ultrastructural and biochemical analysis of the sarcoplasmic reticulum from crayfish fast and slow striated muscles." *The Journal of Experimental Zoology,* Vol. 267, Sept. 1993, p. 16 (Table 1). Copyright © 1993 John Wiley & Sons, Inc. Reprinted with permission.

Applying the Concepts—Advanced

9.133 **Isolation timeouts for students.** Researchers at Rochester Institute of Technology investigated the use of isolation timeout as a behavioral management technique (*Exceptional Children*, Feb. 1995.) Subjects for the study were 155 emotionally disturbed students enrolled in a special education facility. The students were randomly assigned to one of two types of classrooms—Option II classrooms (one teacher, one paraprofessional, and a maximum of 12 students) and Option III classrooms (one teacher, one paraprofessional, and a maximum of 6 students). Over the academic year the number of behavioral incidents resulting in an isolation timeout was recorded for each student. Summary statistics for the two groups of students are shown in the following table.

	Option II	Option III
Number of students	100	55
Mean number of timeout incidents	78.67	102.87
Standard deviation	59.08	69.33

Source: Costenbader, V., and Reading-Brown, M. "Isolation timeout used with students with emotional disturbance." *Exceptional Children,* Vol. 61, No. 4, Feb. 1995, p. 359 (Table 3).

Do you agree with the following statement: "On average, students in Option III classrooms had significantly more timeout incidents than students in Option II classrooms?"

9.134 Feeding habits of sea urchins. The *Florida Scientist* (Summer/Autumn 1991) reported on a study of the feeding habits of sea urchins. A sample of 20 urchins were captured from Biscayne Bay (Miami), placed in marine aquaria, then starved for 48 hours. Each sea urchin was then fed a 5-cm blade of turtle grass. Ten of the urchins received only green blades, while the other half received only decayed blades. (Assume that the two samples of sea urchins—10 urchins per sample—were randomly and independently selected.) The ingestion time, measured from the time the blade first made contact with the urchin's mouth to the time the urchin had finished ingesting the blade, was recorded. A summary of the results is provided in the next table.

	Green Blades	Decayed Blades
Number of sea urchins	10	10
Mean ingestion time (hours)	3.35	2.36
Standard deviation (hours)	.79	.47

Source: Montague, J. R., et al. "Laboratory measurement of ingestion rate for the sea urchin *Lytechinus variegatus.*" *Florida Scientist,* Vol. 54, Nos. 3/4, Summer/Autumn, 1991 (Table 1).

According to the researchers, "the difference in rates at which the urchins ingested the blades suggest that green, unblemished turtle grass may not be a particularly palatable food compared with decayed turtle grass. If so, urchins in the field may find it more profitable to selectively graze on decayed portions of the leaves." Do the results support this conclusion?

Critical Thinking Challenges

9.135 Self-managed work teams and family life. To improve quality, productivity, and timeliness, more and more American industries are utilizing self-managed work teams (SMWTs). A team typically consists of 5 to 15 workers who are collectively responsible for making decisions and performing all tasks related to a particular project. Researchers L. Stanley-Stevens (Tarleton State University), D. E. Yeatts, and R. R. Seward (both University of North Texas) investigated the connection between SMWT, work characteristics and workers' perceptions of positive spillover into family life (*Quality Management Journal*, Summer 1995.) Survey data were collected from 114 AT&T employees who work in one of fifteen SMWTs at an AT&T technical division. The workers were divided into two groups: (1) those who reported positive spillover of work skills to family life and (2) those who did not report positive work spillover. The two groups were compared on a variety of job and demographic characteristics, several of which are shown below. All but the demographic characteristics were measured on a 7-point scale, ranging from 1 = "strongly disagree" to 7 = "strongly agree"; thus, the larger the number, the more of the characteristic indicated.

SPILLOVER

Variables Measured in the SMWT Survey

Characteristic	Variable
Information Flow	Use of creative ideas (7-point scale)
Information Flow	Utilization of information (7-point scale)
Decision-Making	Participation in decisions regarding personnel matters (7-pt. scale)
Job	Good use of skills (7-point scale)
Job	Task identity (7-point scale)
Demographic	Age (years)
Demographic	Education (years)
Demographic	Gender (male or female)
Comparison	Group (positive spillover or no spillover)

The file named **SPILLOVER** includes the values of the variables listed above for each of the 114 survey participants. The researchers' objectives were to compare the two groups of workers on each characteristic. In particular, they want to know which job-related characteristics are most highly associated with positive work spillover. Conduct a complete analysis of the data for the researchers.

9.136 MS and exercise study. A study published in *Clinical Kinesiology* (Spring 1995) was designed to examine the metabolic and cardiopulmonary responses during exercise of persons diagnosed with multiple sclerosis (MS). Leg cycling and arm cranking exercises were performed by 10 MS patients and 10 healthy (non-MS) control subjects. Each member of the control group was selected based on gender, age, height, and weight to match (as closely as possible) with one member of the MS group. Consequently, the researchers compared the MS and non-MS groups by matched-pairs *t*-tests on such outcome variables as oxygen uptake, carbon dioxide output, and peak aerobic power. The data on the matching variables used in the experiment are shown in the table on p. 507. Have the researchers successfully matched the MS and non-MS subjects?

MSSTUDY

	MS Subjects				Non-MS Subjects			
Matched Pair	Gender	Age (years)	Height (cm)	Weight (kg)	Gender	Age (years)	Height (cm)	Weight (kg)
1	M	48	171.0	80.8	M	45	173.0	76.3
2	F	34	158.5	75.0	F	34	158.0	75.6
3	F	34	167.6	55.5	F	34	164.5	57.7
4	M	38	167.0	71.3	M	34	161.3	70.0
5	M	45	182.5	90.9	M	39	179.0	96.0
6	F	42	166.0	72.4	F	42	167.0	77.8
7	M	32	172.0	70.5	M	34	165.8	74.7
8	F	35	166.5	55.3	F	43	165.1	71.4
9	F	33	166.5	57.9	F	31	170.1	60.4
10	F	46	175.0	79.9	F	43	175.0	77.9

Source: Ponichtera-Mulcare, J. A., et al. "Maximal aerobic exercise of individuals with multiple sclerosis using three modes of ergometry." *Clinical Kinesiology,* Vol. 49, No. 1, Spring 1995, p. 7 (Table 1).

Student Projects

We have now discussed two methods of collecting data to compare two population means. In many experimental situations a decision must be made either to collect two independent samples or to conduct a paired difference experiment. The importance of this decision cannot be overemphasized, since the amount of information obtained and the cost of the experiment are both directly related to the method of experimentation that is chosen.

Choose two populations (pertinent to your major area) that have unknown means and for which you could both collect two independent samples and collect paired observations. Before conducting the experiment, state which method of sampling you think will provide more information (and why). Compare the two methods, first performing the independent sampling procedure by collecting 10 observations from each population (a total of 20 measurements), then performing the paired difference experiment by collecting 10 pairs of observations.

Construct two 95% confidence intervals, one for each experiment you conduct. Which method provides the narrower confidence interval and hence more information on this performance of the experiment? Does this result agree with your preliminary expectations?

REFERENCES

Freedman, D., Pisani, R., and Purves, R. *Statistics.* New York: W. W. Norton and Co., 1978.

Gibbons, J. D. *Nonparametric Statistical Inference,* 2nd ed. New York: McGraw-Hill, 1985.

Hollander, M., and Wolfe, D. A. *Nonparametric Statistical Methods.* New York: Wiley, 1973.

Mendenhall, W., Beaver, R. J., and Beaver, B. *Introduction to Probability and Statistics,* 11th ed. North Scituate, Mass.: Duxbury, 2002.

Satterthwaite, F. W. "An approximate distribution of estimates of variance components." *Biometrics Bulletin,* Vol. 2, 1946, pp. 110–114.

Snedecor, G. W., and Cochran, W. *Statistical Methods,* 7th ed. Ames: Iowa State University Press, 1980.

Steel, R. G. D., and Torrie, J. H. *Principles and Procedures of Statistics,* 2nd ed. New York: McGraw-Hill, 1980.

Using Technology

Two Sample Inferences Using MINITAB

MINITAB can be used to make two-sample inferences about $\mu_1 - \mu_2$ for independent samples, μ_D for paired samples, $p_1 - p_2$ and σ_1^2/σ_2^2.

To carry out an analysis for $\mu_1 - \mu_2$, first access the MINITAB worksheet that contains the sample data. Next, click on the "Basic Statistics" button on the MINITAB menu bar, then click on "2-Sample t", as shown in Figure 9.M.1. The resulting dialog box appears as shown in Figure 9.M.2.

If the worksheet contains data for one quantitative variable (which the means will be computed on) and one qualitative variable (which represents the two groups or populations), select "Samples in one column", then specify the quantitative variable in the "Samples" area and the qualitative variable in the "Subscripts" area. (See Figure 9.M.2.)

If the worksheet contains the data for the first sample in one column and the data for the second sample in another column, select "Samples in different columns", then specify the "First" and "Second" variables. Alternatively, if you have only summarized data (i.e., sample sizes, sample means, and sample standard deviations), select "Summarized data" and enter these summarized values in the appropriate boxes.

Once you have made the appropriate menu selection, click the "Options" button on the MINITAB "2-Sample T" dialog box. Specify the confidence level for a confidence interval, the null hypothesized value of the difference, $\mu_1 - \mu_2$, and the form of the alternative hypothesis (lower tailed, two tailed, or upper tailed) in the resulting dialog box, as shown in Figure 9.M.3. Click "OK" to return to the "2-Sample T" dialog box, then click "OK" again to generate the MINITAB printout.

Figure 9.M.1

MINITAB Menu Options for Inferences about $\mu_1 - \mu_2$

Figure 9.M.2
MINITAB 2-Sample
T Dialog Box

Figure 9.M.3
MINITAB Options
Dialog Box

[*Important Note:* The MINITAB two-sample *t*-procedure uses the *t*-statistic to conduct the test of hypothesis. When the sample sizes are small, this is the appropriate method. When the sample sizes are large, the *t*-value will be approximately equal to the large-sample *z*-value and the resulting test will still be valid.]

To carry out an analysis of μ_d for matched pairs, first access the MINITAB worksheet that contains the sample data. The data file should contain two quantitative variables—one with the data values for the first group (or, population) and one with the data values for the second group. (*Note:* The sample size should be the same for each group.) Next, click on the "Basic Statistics" button on the MINITAB menu bar, then click on "Paired t" (see Figure 9.M.1). The resulting dialog box appears as shown in Figure 9.M.4.

Select the "Samples in columns" option and specify the two quantitative variables of interest in the "First sample" and "Second sample" boxes, as shown in Figure 9.M.4. [Alternatively, if you have only summarized data of the paired differences, select the "Summarized data (differences)" option and enter the sample size, sample mean, and sample standard deviation in the appropriate boxes.]

Figure 9.M.4
MINITAB Paired-Samples
Dialog Box

Next, click the "Options" button and specify the confidence level for a confidence interval, the null hypothesized value of the difference, μ_D, and the form of the alternative hypothesis (lower tailed, two tailed, or upper tailed) in the resulting dialog box. (See Figure 9.M.3.) Click "OK" to return to the "Paired t" dialog box, then click "OK" again to generate the MINITAB printout.

To analyze the difference between two proportions, $p_1 - p_2$, first access the MINITAB worksheet that contains the sample data. Next, click on the "Basic Statistics" button on the MINITAB menu bar, then click on "2 Proportions", as shown in Figure 9.M.1. The resulting dialog box appears as shown in Figure 9.M.5.

Figure 9.M.5
MINITAB 2 Proportions
Dialog Box

Figure 9.M.6
MINITAB 2 Proportions
Options Box

Select the data option ("Samples in one column" or "Samples in different columns" or "Summarized data") and make the appropriate menu choices. (Figure 9.M.5 shows the menu options when you select "Summarized data".)

Next, click the "Options" button and specify the confidence level for a confidence interval, the null hypothesized value of the difference, and the form of the alternative hypothesis (lower tailed, two tailed, or upper tailed) in the resulting dialog box, as shown in Figure 9.M.6. (If you desire a pooled estimate of p for the test, be sure to check the appropriate box.) Click "OK" to return to the "2 Proportions" dialog box, then click "OK" again to generate the MINITAB printout.

To carry out an analysis for the ratio of two variances, σ_1^2/σ_2^2, first access the MINITAB worksheet that contains the sample data. Next, click on the "Basic Statistics" button on the MINITAB menu bar, then click on "2 Variances", as shown in Figure 9.M.1. The resulting dialog box appears as shown in Figure 9.M.7. The menu selections and options are similar to those for the two-sample t-test. Once the selections are made, click "OK" to produce the MINITAB F-test printout.

Figure 9.M.7
MINITAB 2 Variances
Dialog Box

Appendix A
Tables

TABLE I   Random Numbers   882

TABLE II   Binomial Probabilities   885

TABLE III   Poisson Probabilities   889

TABLE IV   Normal Curve Areas   894

TABLE V   Exponentials   895

TABLE VI   Critical Values of t 896

TABLE VII   Critical Values of χ^2 897

TABLE VIII   Percentage Points of the F-Distribution, $\alpha = .10$ 899

TABLE IX   Percentage Points of the F-Distribution, $\alpha = .05$ 901

TABLE X   Percentage Points of the F-Distribution, $\alpha = .025$ 903

TABLE XI   Percentage Points of the F-Distribution, $\alpha = .01$ 905

TABLE XII   Critical Values of T_L and T_U for the Wilcoxon Rank Sum Test: Independent Samples   907

TABLE XIII   Critical Values of T_0 in the Wilcoxon Paired Difference Signed Ranks Test   908

TABLE XIV   Critical Values of Spearman's Rank Correlation Coefficient   909

TABLE XV   Critical Values of the Studentized Range, $\alpha = .05$ 910

TABLE XVI   Critical Values of the Studentized Range, $\alpha = .01$ 912

TABLE I Random Numbers

Row	1	2	3	4	5	6	7	8	9	10	11	12	13	14
1	10480	15011	01536	02011	81647	91646	69179	14194	62590	36207	20969	99570	91291	90700
2	22368	46573	25595	85393	30995	89198	27982	53402	93965	34095	52666	19174	39615	99505
3	24130	48360	22527	97265	76393	64809	15179	24830	49340	32081	30680	19655	63348	58629
4	42167	93093	06243	61680	07856	16376	39440	53537	71341	57004	00849	74917	97758	16379
5	37570	39975	81837	16656	06121	91782	60468	81305	49684	60672	14110	06927	01263	54613
6	77921	06907	11008	42751	27756	53498	18602	70659	90655	15053	21916	81825	44394	42880
7	99562	72905	56420	69994	98872	31016	71194	18738	44013	48840	63213	21069	10634	12952
8	96301	91977	05463	07972	18876	20922	94595	56869	69014	60045	18425	84903	42508	32307
9	89579	14342	63661	10281	17453	18103	57740	84378	25331	12566	58678	44947	05585	56941
10	85475	36857	53342	53988	53060	59533	38867	62300	08158	17983	16439	11458	18593	64952
11	28918	69578	88231	33276	70997	79936	56865	05859	90106	31595	01547	85590	91610	78188
12	63553	40961	48235	03427	49626	69445	18663	72695	52180	20847	12234	90511	33703	90322
13	09429	93969	52636	92737	88974	33488	36320	17617	30015	08272	84115	27156	30613	74952
14	10365	61129	87529	85689	48237	52267	67689	93394	01511	26358	85104	20285	29975	89868
15	07119	97336	71048	08178	77233	13916	47564	81056	97735	85977	29372	74461	28551	90707
16	51085	12765	51821	51259	77452	16308	60756	92144	49442	53900	70960	63990	75601	40719
17	02368	21382	52404	60268	89368	19885	55322	44819	01188	65255	64835	44919	05944	55157
18	01011	54092	33362	94904	31273	04146	18594	29852	71585	85030	51132	01915	92747	64951
19	52162	53916	46369	58586	23216	14513	83149	98736	23495	64350	94738	17752	35156	35749
20	07056	97628	33787	09998	42698	06691	76988	13602	51851	46104	88916	19509	25625	58104
21	48663	91245	85828	14346	09172	30168	90229	04734	59193	22178	30421	61666	99904	32812
22	54164	58492	22421	74103	47070	25306	76468	26384	58151	06646	21524	15227	96909	44592
23	32639	32363	05597	24200	13363	38005	94342	28728	35806	06912	17012	64161	18296	22851
24	29334	27001	87637	87308	58731	00256	45834	15398	46557	41135	10367	07684	36188	18510
25	02488	33062	28834	07351	19731	92420	60952	61280	50001	67658	32586	86679	50720	94953
26	81525	72295	04839	96423	24878	82651	66566	14778	76797	14780	13300	87074	79666	95725
27	29676	20591	68086	26432	46901	20849	89768	81536	86645	12659	92259	57102	80428	25280
28	00742	57392	39064	66432	84673	40027	32832	61362	98947	96067	64760	64584	96096	98253
29	05366	04213	25669	26422	44407	44048	37937	63904	45766	66134	75470	66520	34693	90449
30	91921	26418	64117	94305	26766	25940	39972	22209	71500	64568	91402	42416	07844	69618
31	00582	04711	87917	77341	42206	35126	74087	99547	81817	42607	43808	76655	62028	76630
32	00725	69884	62797	56170	86324	88072	76222	36086	84637	93161	76038	65855	77919	88006
33	69011	65795	95876	55293	18988	27354	26575	08625	40801	59920	29841	80150	12777	48501
34	25976	57948	29888	88604	67917	48708	18912	82271	65424	69774	33611	54262	85963	03547
35	09763	83473	73577	12908	30883	18317	28290	35797	05998	41688	34952	37888	38917	88050

(continued)

TABLE I Continued

Row	1	2	3	4	5	6	7	8	9	10	11	12	13	14
36	91576	42595	27958	30134	04024	86385	29880	99730	55536	84855	29080	09250	79656	73211
37	17955	56349	90999	49127	20044	59931	06115	20542	18059	02008	73708	83517	36103	42791
38	46503	18584	18845	49618	02304	51038	20655	58727	28168	15475	56942	53389	20562	87338
39	92157	89634	94824	78171	84610	82834	09922	25417	44137	48413	25555	21246	35509	20468
40	14577	62765	35605	81263	39667	47358	56873	56307	61607	49518	89656	20103	77490	18062
41	98427	07523	33362	64270	01638	92477	66969	98420	04880	45585	46565	04102	46880	45709
42	34914	63976	88720	82765	34476	17032	87589	40836	32427	70002	70663	88863	77775	69348
43	70060	28277	39475	46473	23219	53416	94970	25832	69975	94884	19661	72828	00102	66794
44	53976	54914	06990	67245	68350	82948	11398	42878	80287	88267	47363	46634	06541	97809
45	76072	29515	40980	07391	58745	25774	22987	80059	39911	96189	41151	14222	60697	59583
46	90725	52210	83974	29992	65831	38857	50490	83765	55657	14361	31720	57375	56228	41546
47	64364	67412	33339	31926	14883	24413	59744	92351	97473	89286	35931	04110	23726	51900
48	08962	00358	31662	25388	61642	34072	81249	35648	56891	69352	48373	45578	78547	81788
49	95012	68379	93526	70765	10592	04542	76463	54328	02349	17247	28865	14777	62730	92277
50	15664	10493	20492	38391	91132	21999	59516	81652	27195	48223	46751	22923	32261	85653
51	16408	81899	04153	53381	79401	21438	83035	92350	36693	31238	59649	91754	72772	02338
52	18629	81953	05520	91962	04739	13092	97662	24822	94730	06496	35090	04822	86774	98289
53	73115	35101	47498	87637	99016	71060	88824	71013	18735	20286	23153	72924	35165	43040
54	57491	16703	23167	49323	45021	33132	12544	41035	80780	45393	44812	12512	98931	91202
55	30405	83946	23792	14422	15059	45799	22716	19792	09983	74353	68668	30429	70735	25499
56	16631	35006	85900	98275	32388	52390	16815	69290	82732	38480	73817	32523	41961	44437
57	96773	20206	42559	78985	05300	22164	24369	54224	35083	19687	11052	91491	60383	19746
58	38935	64202	14349	82674	66523	44133	00697	35552	35970	19124	63318	29686	03387	59846
59	31624	76384	17403	53363	44167	64486	64758	75366	76554	31601	12614	33072	60332	92325
60	78919	19474	23632	27889	47914	02584	37680	20801	72152	39339	34806	08930	85001	87820
61	03931	33309	57047	74211	63445	17361	62825	39908	05607	91284	68833	25570	38818	46920
62	74426	33278	43972	10110	89917	15665	52872	73823	73144	88662	88970	74492	51805	99378
63	09066	00903	20795	95452	92648	45454	09552	88815	16553	51125	79375	97596	16296	66092
64	42238	12426	87025	14267	20979	04508	64535	31355	86064	29472	47689	05974	52468	16834
65	16153	08002	26504	41744	81959	65642	74240	56302	00033	67107	77510	70625	28725	34191
66	21457	40742	29820	96783	29400	21840	15035	34537	33310	06116	95240	15957	16572	06004
67	21581	57802	02050	89728	17937	37621	47075	42080	97403	48626	68995	43805	33386	21597
68	55612	78095	83197	33732	05810	24813	86902	60397	16489	03264	88525	42786	05269	92532
69	44657	66999	99324	51281	84463	60563	79312	93454	68876	25471	93911	25650	12682	73572
70	91340	84979	46949	81973	37949	61023	43997	15263	80644	43942	89203	71795	99533	50501

(continued)

TABLE I Continued

Row \ Column	1	2	3	4	5	6	7	8	9	10	11	12	13	14
71	91227	21199	31935	27022	84067	05462	35216	14486	29891	68607	41867	14951	91696	85065
72	50001	38140	66321	19924	72163	09538	12151	06878	91903	18749	34405	56087	82790	70925
73	65390	05224	72958	28609	81406	39147	25549	48542	42627	45233	57202	94617	23772	07896
74	27504	96131	83944	41575	10573	08619	64482	73923	36152	05184	94142	25299	84387	34925
75	37169	94851	39117	89632	00959	16487	65536	49071	39782	17095	02330	74301	00275	48280
76	11508	70225	51111	38351	19444	66499	71945	05422	13442	78675	84081	66938	93654	59894
77	37449	30362	06694	54690	04052	53115	62757	95348	78662	11163	81651	50245	34971	52924
78	46515	70331	85922	38329	57015	15765	97161	17869	45349	61796	66345	81073	49106	79860
79	30986	81223	42416	58353	21532	30502	32305	86482	05174	07901	54339	58861	74818	46942
80	63798	64995	46583	09785	44160	78128	83991	42865	92520	83531	80377	35909	81250	54238
81	82486	84846	99254	67632	43218	50076	21361	64816	51202	88124	41870	52689	51275	83556
82	21885	32906	92431	09060	64297	51674	64126	62570	26123	05155	59194	52799	28225	85762
83	60336	98782	07408	53458	13564	59089	26445	29789	85205	41001	12535	12133	14645	23541
84	43937	46891	24010	25560	86355	33941	25786	54990	71899	15475	95434	98227	21824	19585
85	97656	63175	89303	16275	07100	92063	21942	18611	47348	20203	18534	03862	78095	50136
86	03299	01221	05418	38982	55758	92237	26759	86367	21216	98442	08303	56613	91511	75928
87	79626	06486	03574	17668	07785	76020	79924	25651	83325	88428	85076	72811	22717	50585
88	85636	68335	47539	03129	65651	11977	02510	26113	99447	68645	34327	15152	55230	93448
89	18039	14367	64337	06177	12143	46609	32989	74014	64708	00533	35398	58408	13261	47908
90	08362	15656	60627	36478	65648	16764	53412	09013	07832	41574	17639	82163	60859	75567
91	79556	29068	04142	16268	15387	12856	66227	38358	22478	73373	88732	09443	82558	05250
92	92608	82674	27072	32534	17075	27698	98204	63863	11951	34648	88022	56148	34925	57031
93	23982	25835	40055	67006	12293	02753	14827	23235	35071	99704	37543	11601	35503	85171
94	09915	96306	05908	97901	28395	14186	00821	80703	70426	75647	76310	88717	37890	40129
95	59037	33300	26695	62247	69927	76123	50842	43834	86654	70959	79725	93872	28117	19233
96	42488	78077	69882	61657	34136	79180	97526	43092	04098	73571	80799	76536	71255	64239
97	46764	86273	63003	93017	31204	36692	40202	35275	57306	55543	53203	18098	47625	88684
98	03237	45430	55417	63282	90816	17349	88298	90183	36600	78406	06216	95787	42579	90730
99	86591	81482	52667	61582	14972	90053	89534	76036	49199	43716	97548	04379	46370	28672
100	38534	01715	94964	87288	65680	43772	39560	12918	86537	62738	19636	51132	25739	56947

Source: Abridged from W. H. Beyer (ed.). CRC Standard Mathematical Tables, 24th edition. (Cleveland: The Chemical Rubber Company), 1976. Reproduced by permission of the publisher.

TABLE II   Binomial Probabilities

Tabulated values are $\sum_{x=0}^{k} p(x)$. *(Computations are rounded at the third decimal place.)*

a. $n = 5$

k \ p	.01	.05	.10	.20	.30	.40	.50	.60	.70	.80	.90	.95	.99
0	.951	.774	.590	.328	.168	.078	.031	.010	.002	.000	.000	.000	.000
1	.999	.977	.919	.737	.528	.337	.188	.087	.031	.007	.000	.000	.000
2	1.000	.999	.991	.942	.837	.683	.500	.317	.163	.058	.009	.001	.000
3	1.000	1.000	1.000	.993	.969	.913	.812	.663	.472	.263	.081	.023	.001
4	1.000	1.000	1.000	1.000	.998	.990	.969	.922	.832	.672	.410	.226	.049

b. $n = 6$

k \ p	.01	.05	.10	.20	.30	.40	.50	.60	.70	.80	.90	.95	.99
0	.941	.735	.531	.262	.118	.047	.016	.004	.001	.000	.000	.000	.000
1	.999	.967	.886	.655	.420	.233	.109	.041	.011	.002	.000	.000	.000
2	1.000	.998	.984	.901	.744	.544	.344	.179	.070	.017	.001	.000	.000
3	1.000	1.000	.999	.983	.930	.821	.656	.456	.256	.099	.016	.002	.000
4	1.000	1.000	1.000	.998	.989	.959	.891	.767	.580	.345	.114	.033	.001
5	1.000	1.000	1.000	1.000	.999	.996	.984	.953	.882	.738	.469	.265	.059

c. $n = 7$

k \ p	.01	.05	.10	.20	.30	.40	.50	.60	.70	.80	.90	.95	.99
0	.932	.698	.478	.210	.082	.028	.008	.002	.000	.000	.000	.000	.000
1	.998	.956	.850	.577	.329	.159	.063	.019	.004	.000	.000	.000	.000
2	1.000	.996	.974	.852	.647	.420	.227	.096	.029	.005	.000	.000	.000
3	1.000	1.000	.997	.967	.874	.710	.500	.290	.126	.033	.003	.000	.000
4	1.000	1.000	1.000	.995	.971	.904	.773	.580	.353	.148	.026	.004	.000
5	1.000	1.000	1.000	1.000	.996	.981	.937	.841	.671	.423	.150	.044	.002
6	1.000	1.000	1.000	1.000	1.000	.998	.992	.972	.918	.790	.522	.302	.068

(continued)

TABLE II Continued

d. n = 8

k \ p	.01	.05	.10	.20	.30	.40	.50	.60	.70	.80	.90	.95	.99
0	.923	.663	.430	.168	.058	.017	.004	.001	.000	.000	.000	.000	.000
1	.997	.943	.813	.503	.255	.106	.035	.009	.001	.000	.000	.000	.000
2	1.000	.994	.962	.797	.552	.315	.145	.050	.011	.001	.000	.000	.000
3	1.000	1.000	.995	.944	.806	.594	.363	.174	.058	.010	.000	.000	.000
4	1.000	1.000	1.000	.990	.942	.826	.637	.406	.194	.056	.005	.000	.000
5	1.000	1.000	1.000	.999	.989	.950	.855	.685	.448	.203	.038	.006	.000
6	1.000	1.000	1.000	1.000	.999	.991	.965	.894	.745	.497	.187	.057	.003
7	1.000	1.000	1.000	1.000	1.000	.999	.996	.983	.942	.832	.570	.337	.077

e. n = 9

k \ p	.01	.05	.10	.20	.30	.40	.50	.60	.70	.80	.90	.95	.99
0	.914	.630	.387	.134	.040	.010	.002	.000	.000	.000	.000	.000	.000
1	.997	.929	.775	.436	.196	.071	.020	.004	.000	.000	.000	.000	.000
2	1.000	.992	.947	.738	.463	.232	.090	.025	.004	.000	.000	.000	.000
3	1.000	.999	.992	.914	.730	.483	.254	.099	.025	.003	.000	.000	.000
4	1.000	1.000	.999	.980	.901	.733	.500	.267	.099	.020	.001	.000	.000
5	1.000	1.000	1.000	.997	.975	.901	.746	.517	.270	.086	.008	.001	.000
6	1.000	1.000	1.000	1.000	.996	.975	.910	.768	.537	.262	.053	.008	.000
7	1.000	1.000	1.000	1.000	1.000	.996	.980	.929	.804	.564	.225	.071	.003
8	1.000	1.000	1.000	1.000	1.000	1.000	.998	.990	.960	.866	.613	.370	.086

f. n = 10

k \ p	.01	.05	.10	.20	.30	.40	.50	.60	.70	.80	.90	.95	.99
0	.904	.599	.349	.107	.028	.006	.001	.000	.000	.000	.000	.000	.000
1	.996	.914	.736	.736	.149	.046	.011	.002	.000	.000	.000	.000	.000
2	1.000	.988	.930	.678	.383	.167	.055	.012	.002	.000	.000	.000	.000
3	1.000	.999	.987	.879	.650	.382	.172	.055	.011	.001	.000	.000	.000
4	1.000	1.000	.998	.967	.850	.633	.377	.166	.047	.006	.000	.000	.000
5	1.000	1.000	1.000	.999	.953	.834	.623	.367	.150	.033	.002	.000	.000
6	1.000	1.000	1.000	.999	.989	.945	.828	.618	.350	.121	.013	.001	.000
7	1.000	1.000	1.000	1.000	.998	.988	.945	.833	.617	.322	.070	.012	.000
8	1.000	1.000	1.000	1.000	1.000	.998	.989	.954	.851	.624	.264	.086	.004
9	1.000	1.000	1.000	1.000	1.000	1.000	.999	.994	.972	.893	.651	.401	.096

(continued)

TABLE II   Continued

g. $n = 15$

k \ p	.01	.05	.10	.20	.30	.40	.50	.60	.70	.80	.90	.95	.99
0	.860	.463	.206	.035	.005	.000	.000	.000	.000	.000	.000	.000	.000
1	.990	.829	.549	.167	.035	.005	.000	.000	.000	.000	.000	.000	.000
2	1.000	.964	.816	.398	.127	.027	.004	.000	.000	.000	.000	.000	.000
3	1.000	.995	.944	.648	.297	.091	.018	.002	.000	.000	.000	.000	.000
4	1.000	.999	.987	.838	.515	.217	.059	.009	.001	.000	.000	.000	.000
5	1.000	1.000	.998	.939	.722	.403	.151	.034	.004	.000	.000	.000	.000
6	1.000	1.000	1.000	.982	.869	.610	.304	.095	.015	.001	.000	.000	.000
7	1.000	1.000	1.000	.996	.950	.787	.500	.213	.050	.004	.000	.000	.000
8	1.000	1.000	1.000	.999	.985	.905	.696	.390	.131	.018	.000	.000	.000
9	1.000	1.000	1.000	1.000	.996	.966	.849	.597	.278	.061	.002	.000	.000
10	1.000	1.000	1.000	1.000	.999	.991	.941	.783	.485	.164	.013	.001	.000
11	1.000	1.000	1.000	1.000	1.000	.998	.982	.909	.703	.352	.056	.005	.000
12	1.000	1.000	1.000	1.000	1.000	1.000	.996	.973	.873	.602	.184	.036	.000
13	1.000	1.000	1.000	1.000	1.000	1.000	1.000	.995	.965	.833	.451	.171	.010
14	1.000	1.000	1.000	1.000	1.000	1.000	1.000	1.000	.995	.965	.794	.537	.140

h. $n = 20$

k \ p	.01	.05	.10	.20	.30	.40	.50	.60	.70	.80	.90	.95	.99
0	.818	.358	.122	.012	.001	.000	.000	.000	.000	.000	.000	.000	.000
1	.983	.736	.392	.069	.008	.001	.000	.000	.000	.000	.000	.000	.000
2	.999	.925	.677	.206	.035	.004	.000	.000	.000	.000	.000	.000	.000
3	1.000	.984	.867	.411	.107	.016	.001	.000	.000	.000	.000	.000	.000
4	1.000	.997	.957	.630	.238	.051	.006	.000	.000	.000	.000	.000	.000
5	1.000	1.000	.989	.804	.416	.126	.021	.002	.000	.000	.000	.000	.000
6	1.000	1.000	.998	.913	.608	.250	.058	.006	.000	.000	.000	.000	.000
7	1.000	1.000	1.000	.968	.772	.416	.132	.021	.001	.000	.000	.000	.000
8	1.000	1.000	1.000	.990	.887	.596	.252	.057	.005	.000	.000	.000	.000
9	1.000	1.000	1.000	.997	.952	.755	.412	.128	.017	.001	.000	.000	.000
10	1.000	1.000	1.000	.999	.983	.872	.588	.245	.048	.003	.000	.000	.000
11	1.000	1.000	1.000	1.000	.995	.943	.748	.404	.113	.010	.000	.000	.000
12	1.000	1.000	1.000	1.000	.999	.979	.868	.584	.228	.032	.000	.000	.000
13	1.000	1.000	1.000	1.000	1.000	.994	.942	.750	.392	.087	.002	.000	.000
14	1.000	1.000	1.000	1.000	1.000	.998	.979	.874	.584	.196	.011	.000	.000
15	1.000	1.000	1.000	1.000	1.000	1.000	.994	.949	.762	.370	.043	.003	.000
16	1.000	1.000	1.000	1.000	1.000	1.000	.999	.984	.893	.589	.133	.016	.000
17	1.000	1.000	1.000	1.000	1.000	1.000	1.000	.996	.965	.794	.323	.075	.001
18	1.000	1.000	1.000	1.000	1.000	1.000	1.000	.999	.992	.931	.608	.264	.017
19	1.000	1.000	1.000	1.000	1.000	1.000	1.000	1.000	.999	.988	.878	.642	.182

(continued)

TABLE II   Continued

i. $n = 25$

k \ p	.01	.05	.10	.20	.30	.40	.50	.60	.70	.80	.90	.95	.99
0	.778	.277	.072	.004	.000	.000	.000	.000	.000	.000	.000	.000	.000
1	.974	.642	.271	.027	.002	.000	.000	.000	.000	.000	.000	.000	.000
2	.998	.873	.537	.098	.009	.000	.000	.000	.000	.000	.000	.000	.000
3	1.000	.966	.764	.234	.033	.002	.000	.000	.000	.000	.000	.000	.000
4	1.000	.993	.902	.421	.090	.009	.000	.000	.000	.000	.000	.000	.000
5	1.000	.999	.967	.617	.193	.029	.002	.000	.000	.000	.000	.000	.000
6	1.000	1.000	.991	.780	.341	.074	.007	.000	.000	.000	.000	.000	.000
7	1.000	1.000	.998	.891	.512	.154	.022	.001	.000	.000	.000	.000	.000
8	1.000	1.000	1.000	.953	.677	.274	.054	.004	.000	.000	.000	.000	.000
9	1.000	1.000	1.000	.983	.811	.425	.115	.013	.000	.000	.000	.000	.000
10	1.000	1.000	1.000	.994	.902	.586	.212	.034	.002	.000	.000	.000	.000
11	1.000	1.000	1.000	.998	.956	.732	.345	.078	.006	.000	.000	.000	.000
12	1.000	1.000	1.000	1.000	.983	.846	.500	.154	.017	.000	.000	.000	.000
13	1.000	1.000	1.000	1.000	.994	.922	.655	.268	.044	.002	.000	.000	.000
14	1.000	1.000	1.000	1.000	.998	.966	.788	.414	.098	.006	.000	.000	.000
15	1.000	1.000	1.000	1.000	1.000	.987	.885	.575	.189	.017	.000	.000	.000
16	1.000	1.000	1.000	1.000	1.000	.996	.946	.726	.323	.047	.000	.000	.000
17	1.000	1.000	1.000	1.000	1.000	.999	.978	.846	.488	.109	.002	.000	.000
18	1.000	1.000	1.000	1.000	1.000	1.000	.993	.926	.659	.220	.009	.000	.000
19	1.000	1.000	1.000	1.000	1.000	1.000	.998	.971	.807	.383	.033	.001	.000
20	1.000	1.000	1.000	1.000	1.000	1.000	1.000	.991	.910	.579	.098	.007	.000
21	1.000	1.000	1.000	1.000	1.000	1.000	1.000	.998	.967	.766	.236	.034	.000
22	1.000	1.000	1.000	1.000	1.000	1.000	1.000	1.000	.991	.902	.463	.127	.002
23	1.000	1.000	1.000	1.000	1.000	1.000	1.000	1.000	.998	.973	.729	.358	.026
24	1.000	1.000	1.000	1.000	1.000	1.000	1.000	1.000	1.000	.996	.928	.723	.222

TABLE III Poisson Probabilities

Tabulated values are $\sum_{x=0}^{k} p(x)$. (Computations are rounded at the third decimal place.)

λ \ k	0	1	2	3	4	5	6	7	8	9
.02	.980	1.000								
.04	.961	.999	1.000							
.06	.942	.998	1.000							
.08	.923	.997	1.000							
.10	.905	.995	1.000							
.15	.861	.990	.999	1.000						
.20	.819	.982	.999	1.000						
.25	.779	.974	.998	1.000						
.30	.741	.963	.996	1.000						
.35	.705	.951	.994	1.000						
.40	.670	.938	.992	.999	1.000					
.45	.638	.925	.989	.999	1.000					
.50	.607	.910	.986	.998	1.000					
.55	.577	.894	.982	.998	1.000					
.60	.549	.878	.977	.997	1.000					
.65	.522	.861	.972	.996	.999	1.000				
.70	.497	.844	.966	.994	.999	1.000				
.75	.472	.827	.959	.993	.999	1.000				
.80	.449	.809	.953	.991	.999	1.000				
.85	.427	.791	.945	.989	.998	1.000				
.90	.407	.772	.937	.987	.998	1.000				
.95	.387	.754	.929	.981	.997	1.000				
1.00	.368	.736	.920	.981	.996	.999	1.000			
1.1	.333	.699	.900	.974	.995	.999	1.000			
1.2	.301	.663	.879	.966	.992	.998	1.000			
1.3	.273	.627	.857	.957	.989	.998	1.000			
1.4	.247	.592	.833	.946	.986	.997	.999	1.000		
1.5	.223	.558	.809	.934	.981	.996	.999	1.000		

(continued)

TABLE III   Continued

λ \ k	0	1	2	3	4	5	6	7	8	9
1.6	.202	.525	.783	.921	.976	.994	.999	1.000		
1.7	.183	.493	.757	.907	.970	.992	.998	1.000		
1.8	.165	.463	.731	.891	.964	.990	.997	.999	1.000	
1.9	.150	.434	.704	.875	.956	.987	.997	.999	1.000	
2.0	.135	.406	.677	.857	.947	.983	.995	.999	1.000	
2.2	.111	.355	.623	.819	.928	.975	.993	.998	1.000	
2.4	.091	.308	.570	.779	.904	.964	.988	.997	.999	1.000
2.6	.074	.267	.518	.736	.877	.951	.983	.995	.999	1.000
2.8	.061	.231	.469	.692	.848	.935	.976	.992	.998	.999
3.0	.050	.199	.423	.647	.815	.916	.966	.988	.996	.999
3.2	.041	.171	.380	.603	.781	.895	.955	.983	.994	.998
3.4	.033	.147	.340	.558	.744	.871	.942	.977	.992	.997
3.6	.027	.126	.303	.515	.706	.844	.927	.969	.988	.996
3.8	.022	.107	.269	.473	.668	.816	.909	.960	.984	.994
4.0	.018	.092	.238	.433	.629	.785	.889	.949	.979	.992
4.2	.015	.078	.210	.395	.590	.753	.867	.936	.972	.989
4.4	.012	.066	.185	.359	.551	.720	.844	.921	.964	.985
4.6	.010	.056	.163	.326	.513	.686	.818	.905	.955	.980
4.8	.008	.048	.143	.294	.476	.651	.791	.887	.944	.975
5.0	.007	.040	.125	.265	.440	.616	.762	.867	.932	.968
5.2	.006	.034	.109	.238	.406	.581	.732	.845	.918	.960
5.4	.005	.029	.095	.213	.373	.546	.702	.822	.903	.951
5.6	.004	.024	.082	.191	.342	.512	.670	.797	.886	.941
5.8	.003	.021	.072	.170	.313	.478	.638	.771	.867	.929
6.0	.002	.017	.062	.151	.285	.446	.606	.744	.847	.916

λ	10	11	12	13	14	15	16
2.8	1.000						
3.0	1.000						
3.2	1.000						
3.4	.999	1.000					
3.6	.999	1.000					
3.8	.998	.999	1.000				
4.0	.997	.999	1.000				
4.2	.996	.999	1.000				
4.4	.994	.998	.999	1.000			
4.6	.992	.997	.999	1.000			
4.8	.990	.996	.999	1.000			
5.0	.986	.995	.998	.999	1.000		
5.2	.982	.993	.997	.999	1.000		
5.4	.977	.990	.996	.999	1.000		
5.6	.972	.988	.995	.998	.999	1.000	
5.8	.965	.984	.993	.997	.999	1.000	
6.0	.957	.980	.991	.996	.999	.999	1.000

(continued)

TABLE III   Continued

λ \ k	0	1	2	3	4	5	6	7	8	9
6.2	.002	.015	.054	.134	.259	.414	.574	.716	.826	.902
6.4	.002	.012	.046	.119	.235	.384	.542	.687	.803	.886
6.6	.001	.010	.040	.105	.213	.355	.511	.658	.780	.869
6.8	.001	.009	.034	.093	.192	.327	.480	.628	.755	.850
7.0	.001	.007	.030	.082	.173	.301	.450	.599	.729	.830
7.2	.001	.006	.025	.072	.156	.276	.420	.569	.703	.810
7.4	.001	.005	.022	.063	.140	.253	.392	.539	.676	.788
7.6	.001	.004	.019	.055	.125	.231	.365	.510	.648	.765
7.8	.000	.004	.016	.048	.112	.210	.338	.481	.620	.741
8.0	.000	.003	.014	.042	.100	.191	.313	.453	.593	.717
8.5	.000	.002	.009	.030	.074	.150	.256	.386	.523	.653
9.0	.000	.001	.006	.021	.055	.116	.207	.324	.456	.587
9.5	.000	.001	.004	.015	.040	.089	.165	.269	.392	.522
10.0	.000	.000	.003	.010	.029	.067	.130	.220	.333	.458

λ \ k	10	11	12	13	14	15	16	17	18	19
6.2	.949	.975	.989	.995	.998	.999	1.000			
6.4	.939	.969	.986	.994	.997	.999	1.000			
6.6	.927	.963	.982	.992	.997	.999	.999	1.000		
6.8	.915	.955	.978	.990	.996	.998	.999	1.000		
7.0	.901	.947	.973	.987	.994	.998	.999	1.000		
7.2	.887	.937	.967	.984	.993	.997	.999	.999	1.000	
7.4	.871	.926	.961	.980	.991	.996	.998	.999	1.000	
7.6	.854	.915	.954	.976	.989	.995	.998	.999	1.000	
7.8	.835	.902	.945	.971	.986	.993	.997	.999	1.000	
8.0	.816	.888	.936	.966	.983	.992	.996	.998	.999	1.000
8.5	.763	.849	.909	.949	.973	.986	.993	.997	.999	.999
9.0	.706	.803	.876	.926	.959	.978	.989	.995	.998	.999
9.5	.645	.752	.836	.898	.940	.967	.982	.991	.996	.998
10.0	.583	.697	.792	.864	.917	.951	.973	.986	.993	.997

λ \ k	20	21	22
8.5	1.000		
9.0	1.000		
9.5	.999	1.000	
10.0	.998	.999	1.000

(continued)

TABLE III   Continued

λ \ k	0	1	2	3	4	5	6	7	8	9
10.5	.000	.000	.002	.007	.021	.050	.102	.179	.279	.397
11.0	.000	.000	.001	.005	.015	.038	.079	.143	.232	.341
11.5	.000	.000	.001	.003	.011	.028	.060	.114	.191	.289
12.0	.000	.000	.001	.002	.008	.020	.046	.090	.155	.242
12.5	.000	.000	.000	.002	.005	.015	.035	.070	.125	.201
13.0	.000	.000	.000	.001	.004	.011	.026	.054	.100	.166
13.5	.000	.000	.000	.001	.003	.008	.019	.041	.079	.135
14.0	.000	.000	.000	.000	.002	.006	.014	.032	.062	.109
14.5	.000	.000	.000	.000	.001	.004	.010	.024	.048	.088
15.0	.000	.000	.000	.000	.001	.003	.008	.018	.037	.070

λ \ k	10	11	12	13	14	15	16	17	18	19
10.5	.521	.639	.742	.825	.888	.932	.960	.978	.988	.994
11.0	.460	.579	.689	.781	.854	.907	.944	.968	.982	.991
11.5	.402	.520	.633	.733	.815	.878	.924	.954	.974	.986
12.0	.347	.462	.576	.682	.772	.844	.899	.937	.963	.979
12.5	.297	.406	.519	.628	.725	.806	.869	.916	.948	.969
13.0	.252	.353	.463	.573	.675	.764	.835	.890	.930	.957
13.5	.211	.304	.409	.518	.623	.718	.798	.861	.908	.942
14.0	.176	.260	.358	.464	.570	.669	.756	.827	.883	.923
14.5	.145	.220	.311	.413	.518	.619	.711	.790	.853	.901
15.0	.118	.185	.268	.363	.466	.568	.664	.749	.819	.875

λ \ k	20	21	22	23	24	25	26	27	28	29
10.5	.997	.999	.999	1.000						
11.0	.995	.998	.999	1.000						
11.5	.992	.996	.998	.999	1.000					
12.0	.988	.994	.987	.999	.999	1.000				
12.5	.983	.991	.995	.998	.999	.999	1.000			
13.0	.975	.986	.992	.996	.998	.999	1.000			
13.5	.965	.980	.989	.994	.997	.998	.999	1.000		
14.0	.952	.971	.983	.991	.995	.997	.999	.999	1.000	
14.5	.936	.960	.976	.986	.992	.996	.998	.999	.999	1.000
15.0	.917	.947	.967	.981	.989	.994	.997	.998	.999	1.000

(continued)

TABLE III   Continued

λ \ k	0	1	2	3	4	5	6	7	8	9
16	.000	.001	.004	.010	.022	.043	.077	.127	.193	.275
17	.000	.001	.002	.005	.013	.026	.049	.085	.135	.201
18	.000	.000	.001	.003	.007	.015	.030	.055	.092	.143
19	.000	.000	.001	.002	.004	.009	.018	.035	.061	.098
20	.000	.000	.000	.001	.002	.005	.011	.021	.039	.066
21	.000	.000	.000	.000	.001	.003	.006	.013	.025	.043
22	.000	.000	.000	.000	.001	.002	.004	.008	.015	.028
23	.000	.000	.000	.000	.000	.001	.002	.004	.009	.017
24	.000	.000	.000	.000	.000	.000	.001	.003	.005	.011
25	.000	.000	.000	.000	.000	.000	.001	.001	.003	.006

λ \ k	14	15	16	17	18	19	20	21	22	23
16	.368	.467	.566	.659	.742	.812	.868	.911	.942	.963
17	.281	.371	.468	.564	.655	.736	.805	.861	.905	.937
18	.208	.287	.375	.469	.562	.651	.731	.799	.855	.899
19	.150	.215	.292	.378	.469	.561	.647	.725	.793	.849
20	.105	.157	.221	.297	.381	.470	.559	.644	.721	.787
21	.072	.111	.163	.227	.302	.384	.471	.558	.640	.716
22	.048	.077	.117	.169	.232	.306	.387	.472	.556	.637
23	.031	.052	.082	.123	.175	.238	.310	.389	.472	.555
24	.020	.034	.056	.087	.128	.180	.243	.314	.392	.473
25	.012	.022	.038	.060	.092	.134	.185	.247	.318	.394

λ \ k	24	25	26	27	28	29	30	31	32	33
16	.978	.987	.993	.996	.998	.999	.999	1.000		
17	.959	.975	.985	.991	.995	.997	.999	.999	1.000	
18	.932	.955	.972	.983	.990	.994	.997	.998	.999	1.000
19	.893	.927	.951	.969	.980	.988	.993	.996	.998	.999
20	.843	.888	.922	.948	.966	.978	.987	.992	.995	.997
21	.782	.838	.883	.917	.944	.963	.976	.985	.991	.994
22	.712	.777	.832	.877	.913	.940	.959	.973	.983	.989
23	.635	.708	.772	.827	.873	.908	.936	.956	.971	.981
24	.554	.632	.704	.768	.823	.868	.904	.932	.953	.969
25	.473	.553	.629	.700	.763	.818	.863	.900	.929	.950

λ \ k	34	35	36	37	38	39	40	41	42	43
19	.999	1.000								
20	.999	.999	1.000							
21	.997	.998	.999	.999	1.000					
22	.994	.996	.998	.999	.999	1.000				
23	.988	.993	.996	.997	.999	.999	1.000			
24	.979	.987	.992	.995	.997	.998	.999	.999	1.000	
25	.966	.978	.985	.991	.991	.997	.998	.999	.999	1.000

TABLE IV   Normal Curve Areas

$Z = .56$

$= .2123$

z	.00	.01	.02	.03	.04	.05	.06	.07	.08	.09
.0	.0000	.0040	.0080	.0120	.0160	.0199	.0239	.0279	.0319	.0359
.1	.0398	.0438	.0478	.0517	.0557	.0596	.0636	.0675	.0714	.0753
.2	.0793	.0832	.0871	.0910	.0948	.0987	.1026	.1064	.1103	.1141
.3	.1179	.1217	.1255	.1293	.1331	.1368	.1406	.1443	.1480	.1517
.4	.1554	.1591	.1628	.1664	.1700	.1736	.1772	.1808	.1844	.1879
.5	.1915	.1950	.1985	.2019	.2054	.2088	.2123	.2157	.2190	.2224
.6	.2257	.2291	.2324	.2357	.2389	.2422	.2454	.2486	.2517	.2549
.7	.2580	.2611	.2642	.2673	.2704	.2734	.2764	.2794	.2823	.2852
.8	.2881	.2910	.2939	.2967	.2995	.3023	.3051	.3078	.3106	.3133
.9	.3159	.3186	.3212	.3238	.3264	.3289	.3315	.3340	.3365	.3389
1.0	.3413	.3438	.3461	.3485	.3508	.3531	.3554	.3577	.3599	.3621
1.1	.3643	.3665	.3686	.3708	.3729	.3749	.3770	.3790	.3810	.3830
1.2	.3849	.3869	.3888	.3907	.3925	.3944	.3962	.3980	.3997	.4015
1.3	.4032	.4049	.4066	.4082	.4099	.4115	.4131	.4147	.4162	.4177
1.4	.4192	.4207	.4222	.4236	.4251	.4265	.4279	.4292	.4306	.4319
1.5	.4332	.4345	.4357	.4370	.4382	.4394	.4406	.4418	.4429	.4441
1.6	.4452	.4463	.4474	.4484	.4495	.4505	.4515	.4525	.4535	.4545
1.7	.4554	.4564	.4573	.4582	.4591	.4599	.4608	.4616	.4625	.4633
1.8	.4641	.4649	.4656	.4664	.4671	.4678	.4686	.4693	.4699	.4706
1.9	.4713	.4719	.4726	.4732	.4738	.4744	.4750	.4756	.4761	.4767
2.0	.4772	.4778	.4783	.4788	.4793	.4798	.4803	.4808	.4812	.4817
2.1	.4821	.4826	.4830	.4834	.4838	.4842	.4846	.4850	.4854	.4857
2.2	.4861	.4864	.4868	.4871	.4875	.4878	.4881	.4884	.4887	.4890
2.3	.4893	.4896	.4898	.4901	.4904	.4906	.4909	.4911	.4913	.4916
2.4	.4918	.4920	.4922	.4925	.4927	.4929	.4931	.4932	.4934	.4936
2.5	.4938	.4940	.4941	.4943	.4945	.4946	.4948	.4949	.4951	.4952
2.6	.4953	.4955	.4956	.4957	.4959	.4960	.4961	.4962	.4963	.4964
2.7	.4965	.4966	.4967	.4968	.4969	.4970	.4971	.4972	.4973	.4974
2.8	.4974	.4975	.4976	.4977	.4977	.4978	.4979	.4979	.4980	.4981
2.9	.4981	.4982	.4982	.4983	.4984	.4984	.4985	.4985	.4986	.4986
3.0	.4987	.4987	.4987	.4988	.4988	.4989	.4989	.4989	.4990	.4990

Source: Abridged from Table I of A. Hald, *Statistical Tables and Formulas* (New York: Wiley), 1952. Reproduced by permission of A. Hald.

TABLE V   Exponentials

λ	$e^{-\lambda}$	λ	$e^{-\lambda}$	λ	$e^{-\lambda}$	λ	$e^{-\lambda}$	λ	$e^{-\lambda}$
.00	1.000000	2.05	.128735	4.05	.017422	6.05	.002358	8.05	.000319
.05	.951229	2.10	.122456	4.10	.016573	6.10	.002243	8.10	.000304
.10	.904837	2.15	.116484	4.15	.015764	6.15	.002133	8.15	.000289
.15	.860708	2.20	.110803	4.20	.014996	6.20	.002029	8.20	.000275
.20	.818731	2.25	.105399	4.25	.014264	6.25	.001930	8.25	.000261
.25	.778801	2.30	.100259	4.30	.013569	6.30	.001836	8.30	.000249
.30	.740818	2.35	.095369	4.35	.012907	6.35	.001747	8.35	.000236
.35	.704688	2.40	.090718	4.40	.012277	6.40	.001661	8.40	.000225
.40	.670320	2.45	.086294	4.45	.011679	6.45	.001581	8.45	.000214
.45	.637628	2.50	.082085	4.50	.011109	6.50	.001503	8.50	.000204
.50	.606531	2.55	.078082	4.55	.010567	6.55	.001430	8.55	.000194
.55	.576950	2.60	.074274	4.60	.010052	6.60	.001360	8.60	.000184
.60	.548812	2.65	.070651	4.65	.009562	6.65	.001294	8.65	.000175
.65	.522046	2.70	.067206	4.70	.009095	6.70	.001231	8.70	.000167
.70	.496585	2.75	.063928	4.75	.008652	6.75	.001171	8.75	.000158
.75	.472367	2.80	.060810	4.80	.008230	6.80	.001114	8.80	.000151
.80	.449329	2.85	.057844	4.85	.007828	6.85	.001059	8.85	.000143
.85	.427415	2.90	.055023	4.90	.007447	6.90	.001008	8.90	.000136
.90	.406570	2.95	.052340	4.95	.007083	6.95	.000959	8.95	.000130
.95	.386741	3.00	.049787	5.00	.006738	7.00	.000912	9.00	.000123
1.00	.367879	3.05	.047359	5.05	.006409	7.05	.000867	9.05	.000117
1.05	.349938	3.10	.045049	5.10	.006097	7.10	.000825	9.10	.000112
1.10	.332871	3.15	.042852	5.15	.005799	7.15	.000785	9.15	.000106
1.15	.316637	3.20	.040762	5.20	.005517	7.20	.000747	9.20	.000101
1.20	.301194	3.25	.038774	5.25	.005248	7.25	.000710	9.25	.000096
1.25	.286505	3.30	.036883	5.30	.004992	7.30	.000676	9.30	.000091
1.30	.272532	3.35	.035084	5.35	.004748	7.35	.000643	9.35	.000087
1.35	.259240	3.40	.033373	5.40	.004517	7.40	.000611	9.40	.000083
1.40	.246597	3.45	.031746	5.45	.004296	7.45	.000581	9.45	.000079
1.45	.234570	3.50	.030197	5.50	.004087	7.50	.000553	9.50	.000075
1.50	.223130	3.55	.028725	5.55	.003887	7.55	.000526	9.55	.000071
1.55	.212248	3.60	.027324	5.60	.003698	7.60	.000501	9.60	.000068
1.60	.201897	3.65	.025991	5.65	.003518	7.65	.000476	9.65	.000064
1.65	.192050	3.70	.024724	5.70	.003346	7.70	.000453	9.70	.000061
1.70	.182684	3.75	.023518	5.75	.003183	7.75	.000431	9.75	.000058
1.75	.173774	3.80	.022371	5.80	.003028	7.80	.000410	9.80	.000056
1.80	.165299	3.85	.021280	5.85	.002880	7.85	.000390	9.85	.000053
1.85	.157237	3.90	.020242	5.90	.002739	7.90	.000371	9.90	.000050
1.90	.149569	3.95	.019255	5.95	.002606	7.95	.000353	9.95	.000048
1.95	.142274	4.00	.018316	6.00	.002479	8.00	.000336	10.00	.000045
2.00	.135335								

TABLE VI   Critical Values of t

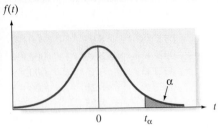

$f(t)$

0 t_α t

α

Degrees of Freedom	80% $t_{.100}$	90% $t_{.050}$	95% $t_{.025}$	98% $t_{.010}$	99% $t_{.005}$	$t_{.001}$	$t_{.0005}$
1	3.078	6.314	12.706	31.821	63.657	318.31	636.62
2	1.886	2.920	4.303	6.965	9.925	22.326	31.598
3	1.638	2.353	3.182	4.541	5.841	10.213	12.924
4	1.533	2.132	2.776	3.747	4.604	7.173	8.610
5	1.476	2.015	2.571	3.365	4.032	5.893	6.869
6	1.440	1.943	2.447	3.143	3.707	5.208	5.959
7	1.415	1.895	2.365	2.998	3.499	4.785	5.408
8	1.397	1.860	2.306	2.896	3.355	4.501	5.041
9	1.383	1.833	2.262	2.821	3.250	4.297	4.781
10	1.372	1.812	2.228	2.764	3.169	4.144	4.587
11	1.363	1.796	2.201	2.718	3.106	4.025	4.437
12	1.356	1.782	2.179	2.681	3.055	3.930	4.318
13	1.350	1.771	2.160	2.650	3.012	3.852	4.221
14	1.345	1.761	2.145	2.624	2.977	3.787	4.140
15	1.341	1.753	2.131	2.602	2.947	3.733	4.073
16	1.337	1.746	2.120	2.583	2.921	3.686	4.015
17	1.333	1.740	2.110	2.567	2.898	3.646	3.965
18	1.330	1.734	2.101	2.552	2.878	3.610	3.922
19	1.328	1.729	2.093	2.539	2.861	3.579	3.883
20	1.325	1.725	2.086	2.528	2.845	3.552	3.850
21	1.323	1.721	2.080	2.518	2.831	3.527	3.819
22	1.321	1.717	2.074	2.508	2.819	3.505	3.792
23	1.319	1.714	2.069	2.500	2.807	3.485	3.767
24	1.318	1.711	2.064	2.492	2.797	3.467	3.745
25	1.316	1.708	2.060	2.485	2.787	3.450	3.725
26	1.315	1.706	2.056	2.479	2.779	3.435	3.707
27	1.314	1.703	2.052	2.473	2.771	3.421	3.690
28	1.313	1.701	2.048	2.467	2.763	3.408	3.674
29	1.311	1.699	2.045	2.462	2.756	3.396	3.659
30	1.310	1.697	2.042	2.457	2.750	3.385	3.646
40	1.303	1.684	2.021	2.423	2.704	3.307	3.551
60	1.296	1.671	2.000	2.390	2.660	3.232	3.460
120	1.289	1.658	1.980	2.358	2.617	3.160	3.373
∞	1.282	1.645	1.960	2.326	2.576	3.090	3.291

TABLE VII   Critical Values of χ^2

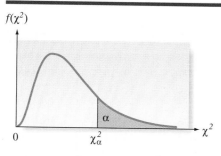

Degrees of Freedom	$\chi^2_{.995}$	$\chi^2_{.990}$	$\chi^2_{.975}$	$\chi^2_{.950}$	$\chi^2_{.900}$
1	.0000393	.0001571	.0009821	.0039321	.0157908
2	.0100251	.0201007	.0506356	.102587	.210720
3	.0717212	.114832	.215795	.351846	.584375
4	.206990	.297110	.484419	.710721	1.063623
5	.411740	.554300	.831211	1.145476	1.61031
6	.675727	.872085	1.237347	1.63539	2.20413
7	.989265	1.239043	1.68987	2.16735	2.83311
8	1.344419	1.646482	2.17973	2.73264	3.48954
9	1.734926	2.087912	2.70039	3.32511	4.16816
10	2.15585	2.55821	3.24697	3.94030	4.86518
11	2.60321	3.05347	3.81575	4.57481	5.57779
12	3.07382	3.57056	4.40379	5.22603	6.30380
13	3.56503	4.10691	5.00874	5.89186	7.04150
14	4.07468	4.66043	5.62872	6.57063	7.78953
15	4.60094	5.22935	6.26214	7.26094	8.54675
16	5.14224	5.81221	6.90766	7.96164	9.31223
17	5.69724	6.40776	7.56418	8.67176	10.0852
18	6.26481	7.01491	8.23075	9.39046	10.8649
19	6.84398	7.63273	8.90655	10.1170	11.6509
20	7.43386	8.26040	9.59083	10.8508	12.4426
21	8.03366	8.89720	10.28293	11.5913	13.2396
22	8.64272	9.54249	10.9823	12.3380	14.0415
23	9.26042	10.19567	11.6885	13.0905	14.8479
24	9.88623	10.8564	12.4011	13.8484	15.6587
25	10.5197	11.5240	13.1197	14.6114	16.4734
26	11.1603	12.1981	13.8439	15.3791	17.2919
27	11.8076	12.8786	14.5733	16.1513	18.1138
28	12.4613	13.5648	15.3079	16.9279	18.9392
29	13.1211	14.2565	16.0471	17.7083	19.7677
30	13.7867	14.9535	16.7908	18.4926	20.5992
40	20.7065	22.1643	24.4331	26.5093	29.0505
50	27.9907	29.7067	32.3574	34.7642	37.6886
60	35.5346	37.4848	40.4817	43.1879	46.4589
70	43.2752	45.4418	48.7576	51.7393	55.3290
80	51.1720	53.5400	57.1532	60.3915	64.2778
90	59.1963	61.7541	65.6466	69.1260	73.2912
100	67.3276	70.0648	74.2219	77.9295	82.3581

Source: From C. M. Thompson, "Tables of the Percentage Points of the χ^2-Distribution," *Biometrika,* 1941, 32, 188–189. Reproduced by permission of the *Biometrika* Trustees.

(continued)

TABLE VII   Continued

Degrees of Freedom	$\chi^2_{.100}$	$\chi^2_{.050}$	$\chi^2_{.025}$	$\chi^2_{.010}$	$\chi^2_{.005}$
1	2.70554	3.84146	5.02389	6.63490	7.87944
2	4.60517	5.99147	7.37776	9.21034	10.5966
3	6.25139	7.81473	9.34840	11.3449	12.8381
4	7.77944	9.48773	11.1433	13.2767	14.8602
5	9.23635	11.0705	12.8325	15.0863	16.7496
6	10.6446	12.5916	14.4494	16.8119	18.5476
7	12.0170	14.0671	16.0128	18.4753	20.2777
8	13.3616	15.5073	17.5346	20.0902	21.9550
9	14.6837	16.9190	19.0228	21.6660	23.5893
10	15.9871	18.3070	20.4831	23.2093	25.1882
11	17.2750	19.6751	21.9200	24.7250	26.7569
12	18.5494	21.0261	23.3367	26.2170	28.2995
13	19.8119	22.3621	24.7356	27.6883	29.8194
14	21.0642	23.6848	26.1190	29.1413	31.3193
15	22.3072	24.9958	27.4884	30.5779	32.8013
16	23.5418	26.2962	28.8454	31.9999	34.2672
17	24.7690	27.5871	30.1910	33.4087	35.7185
18	25.9894	28.8693	31.5264	34.8053	37.1564
19	27.2036	30.1435	32.8523	36.1908	38.5822
20	28.4120	31.4104	34.1696	37.5662	39.9968
21	29.6151	32.6705	35.4789	38.9321	41.4010
22	30.8133	33.9244	36.7807	40.2894	42.7956
23	32.0069	35.1725	38.0757	41.6384	44.1813
24	33.1963	36.4151	39.3641	42.9798	45.5585
25	34.3816	37.6525	40.6465	44.3141	46.9278
26	35.5631	38.8852	41.9232	45.6417	48.2899
27	36.7412	40.1133	43.1944	46.9630	49.6449
28	37.9159	41.3372	44.4607	48.2782	50.9933
29	39.0875	42.5569	45.7222	49.5879	52.3356
30	40.2560	43.7729	46.9792	50.8922	53.6720
40	51.8050	55.7585	59.3417	63.6907	66.7659
50	63.1671	67.5048	71.4202	76.1539	79.4900
60	74.3970	79.0819	83.2976	88.3794	91.9517
70	85.5271	90.5312	95.0231	100.425	104.215
80	96.5782	101.879	106.629	112.329	116.321
90	107.565	113.145	118.136	124.116	128.299
100	118.498	124.342	129.561	135.807	140.169

TABLE VIII **Percentage Points of the _F_-distribution, $\alpha = .10$**

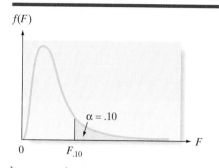

		NUMERATOR DEGREES OF FREEDOM							
v_2	1	2	3	4	5	6	7	8	9
1	39.86	49.50	53.59	55.83	57.24	58.20	58.91	59.44	59.86
2	8.53	9.00	9.16	9.24	9.29	9.33	9.35	9.37	9.38
3	5.54	5.46	5.39	5.34	5.31	5.28	5.27	5.25	5.24
4	4.54	4.32	4.19	4.11	4.05	4.01	3.98	3.95	3.94
5	4.06	3.78	3.62	3.52	3.45	3.40	3.37	3.34	3.32
6	3.78	3.46	3.29	3.18	3.11	3.05	3.01	2.98	2.96
7	3.59	3.26	3.07	2.96	2.88	2.83	2.78	2.75	2.72
8	3.46	3.11	2.92	2.81	2.73	2.67	2.62	2.59	2.56
9	3.36	3.01	2.81	2.69	2.61	2.55	2.51	2.47	2.44
10	3.29	2.92	2.73	2.61	2.52	2.46	2.41	2.38	2.35
11	3.23	2.86	2.66	2.54	2.45	2.39	2.34	2.30	2.27
12	3.18	2.81	2.61	2.48	2.39	2.33	2.28	2.24	2.21
13	3.14	2.76	2.56	2.43	2.35	2.28	2.23	2.20	2.16
14	3.10	2.73	2.52	2.39	2.31	2.24	2.19	2.15	2.12
15	3.07	2.70	2.49	2.36	2.27	2.21	2.16	2.12	2.09
16	3.05	2.67	2.46	2.33	2.24	2.18	2.13	2.09	2.06
17	3.03	2.64	2.44	2.31	2.22	2.15	2.10	2.06	2.03
18	3.01	2.62	2.42	2.29	2.20	2.13	2.08	2.04	2.00
19	2.99	2.61	2.40	2.27	2.18	2.11	2.06	2.02	1.98
20	2.97	2.59	2.38	2.25	2.16	2.09	2.04	2.00	1.96
21	2.96	2.57	2.36	2.23	2.14	2.08	2.02	1.98	1.95
22	2.95	2.56	2.35	2.22	2.13	2.06	2.01	1.97	1.93
23	2.94	2.55	2.34	2.21	2.11	2.05	1.99	1.95	1.92
24	2.93	2.54	2.33	2.19	2.10	2.04	1.98	1.94	1.91
25	2.92	2.53	2.32	2.18	2.09	2.02	1.97	1.93	1.89
26	2.91	2.52	2.31	2.17	2.08	2.01	1.96	1.92	1.88
27	2.90	2.51	2.30	2.17	2.07	2.00	1.95	1.91	1.87
28	2.89	2.50	2.29	2.16	2.06	2.00	1.94	1.90	1.87
29	2.89	2.50	2.28	2.15	2.06	1.99	1.93	1.89	1.86
30	2.88	2.49	2.28	2.14	2.05	1.98	1.93	1.88	1.85
40	2.84	2.44	2.23	2.09	2.00	1.93	1.87	1.83	1.79
60	2.79	2.39	2.18	2.04	1.95	1.87	1.82	1.77	1.74
120	2.75	2.35	2.13	1.99	1.90	1.82	1.77	1.72	1.68
∞	2.71	2.30	2.08	1.94	1.85	1.77	1.72	1.67	1.63

Source: From M. Merrington and C. M. Thompson, "Tables of Percentage Points of the Inverted Beta (_F_)-Distribution," _Biometrika,_ 1943, 33, 73–88.

(continued)

TABLE VIII   Continued

ν_2 \ ν_1	NUMERATOR DEGREES OF FREEDOM									
	10	12	15	20	24	30	40	60	120	∞
1	60.19	60.71	61.22	61.74	62.00	62.26	62.53	62.79	63.06	63.33
2	9.39	9.41	9.42	9.44	9.45	9.46	9.47	9.47	9.48	9.49
3	5.23	5.22	5.20	5.18	5.18	5.17	5.16	5.15	5.14	5.13
4	3.92	3.90	3.87	3.84	3.83	3.82	3.80	3.79	3.78	3.76
5	3.30	3.27	3.24	3.21	3.19	3.17	3.16	3.14	3.12	3.10
6	2.94	2.90	2.87	2.84	2.82	2.80	2.78	2.76	2.74	2.72
7	2.70	2.67	2.63	2.59	2.58	2.56	2.54	2.51	2.49	2.47
8	2.54	2.50	2.46	2.42	2.40	2.38	2.36	2.34	2.32	2.29
9	2.42	2.38	2.34	2.30	2.28	2.25	2.23	2.21	2.18	2.16
10	2.32	2.28	2.24	2.20	2.18	2.16	2.13	2.11	2.08	2.06
11	2.25	2.21	2.17	2.12	2.10	2.08	2.05	2.03	2.00	1.97
12	2.19	2.15	2.10	2.06	2.04	2.01	1.99	1.96	1.93	1.90
13	2.14	2.10	2.05	2.01	1.98	1.96	1.93	1.90	1.88	1.85
14	2.10	2.05	2.01	1.96	1.94	1.91	1.89	1.86	1.83	1.80
15	2.06	2.02	1.97	1.92	1.90	1.87	1.85	1.82	1.79	1.76
16	2.03	1.99	1.94	1.89	1.87	1.84	1.81	1.78	1.75	1.72
17	2.00	1.96	1.91	1.86	1.84	1.81	1.78	1.75	1.72	1.69
18	1.98	1.93	1.89	1.84	1.81	1.78	1.75	1.72	1.69	1.66
19	1.96	1.91	1.86	1.81	1.79	1.76	1.73	1.70	1.67	1.63
20	1.94	1.89	1.84	1.79	1.77	1.74	1.71	1.68	1.64	1.61
21	1.92	1.87	1.83	1.78	1.75	1.72	1.69	1.66	1.62	1.59
22	1.90	1.86	1.81	1.76	1.73	1.70	1.67	1.64	1.60	1.57
23	1.89	1.84	1.80	1.74	1.72	1.69	1.66	1.62	1.59	1.55
24	1.88	1.83	1.78	1.73	1.70	1.67	1.64	1.61	1.57	1.53
25	1.87	1.82	1.77	1.72	1.69	1.66	1.63	1.59	1.56	1.52
26	1.86	1.81	1.76	1.71	1.68	1.65	1.61	1.58	1.54	1.50
27	1.85	1.80	1.75	1.70	1.67	1.64	1.60	1.57	1.53	1.49
28	1.84	1.79	1.74	1.69	1.66	1.63	1.59	1.56	1.52	1.48
29	1.83	1.78	1.73	1.68	1.65	1.62	1.58	1.55	1.51	1.47
30	1.82	1.77	1.72	1.67	1.64	1.61	1.57	1.54	1.50	1.46
40	1.76	1.71	1.66	1.61	1.57	1.54	1.51	1.47	1.42	1.38
60	1.71	1.66	1.60	1.54	1.51	1.48	1.44	1.40	1.35	1.29
120	1.65	1.60	1.55	1.48	1.45	1.41	1.37	1.32	1.26	1.19
∞	1.60	1.55	1.49	1.42	1.38	1.34	1.30	1.24	1.17	1.00

DENOMINATOR DEGREES OF FREEDOM

TABLE IX   Percentage Points of the *F*-distribution, $\alpha = .05$

$f(F)$

$\alpha = .05$

0 $F_{.05}$ F

ν_1				NUMERATOR DEGREES OF FREEDOM					
ν_2	1	2	3	4	5	6	7	8	9
1	161.4	199.5	215.7	224.6	230.2	234.0	236.8	238.9	240.5
2	18.51	19.00	19.16	19.25	19.30	19.33	19.35	19.37	19.38
3	10.13	9.55	9.28	9.12	9.01	8.94	8.89	8.85	8.81
4	7.71	6.94	6.59	6.39	6.26	6.16	6.09	6.04	6.00
5	6.61	5.79	5.41	5.19	5.05	4.95	4.88	4.82	4.77
6	5.99	5.14	4.76	4.53	4.39	4.28	4.21	4.15	4.10
7	5.59	4.74	4.35	4.12	3.97	3.87	3.79	3.73	3.68
8	5.32	4.46	4.07	3.84	3.69	3.58	3.50	3.44	3.39
9	5.12	4.26	3.86	3.63	3.48	3.37	3.29	3.23	3.18
10	4.96	4.10	3.71	3.48	3.33	3.22	3.14	3.07	3.02
11	4.84	3.98	3.59	3.36	3.20	3.09	3.01	2.95	2.90
12	4.75	3.89	3.49	3.26	3.11	3.00	2.91	2.85	2.80
13	4.67	3.81	3.41	3.18	3.03	2.92	2.83	2.77	2.71
14	4.60	3.74	3.34	3.11	2.96	2.85	2.76	2.70	2.65
15	4.54	3.68	3.29	3.06	2.90	2.79	2.71	2.64	2.59
16	4.49	3.63	3.24	3.01	2.85	2.74	2.66	2.59	2.54
17	4.45	3.59	3.20	2.96	2.81	2.70	2.61	2.55	2.49
18	4.41	3.55	3.16	2.93	2.77	2.66	2.58	2.51	2.46
19	4.38	3.52	3.13	2.90	2.74	2.63	2.54	2.48	2.42
20	4.35	3.49	3.10	2.87	2.71	2.60	2.51	2.45	2.39
21	4.32	3.47	3.07	2.84	2.68	2.57	2.49	2.42	2.37
22	4.30	3.44	3.05	2.82	2.66	2.55	2.46	2.40	2.34
23	4.28	3.42	3.03	2.80	2.64	2.53	2.44	2.37	2.32
24	4.26	3.40	3.01	2.78	2.62	2.51	2.42	2.36	2.30
25	4.24	3.39	2.99	2.76	2.60	2.49	2.40	2.34	2.28
26	4.23	3.37	2.98	2.74	2.59	2.47	2.39	2.32	2.77
27	4.21	3.35	2.96	2.73	2.57	2.46	2.37	2.31	2.25
28	4.20	3.34	2.95	2.71	2.56	2.45	2.36	2.29	2.24
29	4.18	3.33	2.93	2.70	2.55	2.43	2.35	2.28	2.22
30	4.17	3.32	2.92	2.69	2.53	2.42	2.33	2.27	2.21
40	4.08	3.23	2.84	2.61	2.45	2.34	2.25	2.18	2.12
60	4.00	3.15	2.76	2.53	2.37	2.25	2.17	2.10	2.04
120	3.92	3.07	2.68	2.45	2.29	2.17	2.09	2.02	1.96
∞	3.84	3.00	2.60	2.37	2.21	2.10	2.01	1.94	1.88

DENOMINATOR DEGREES OF FREEDOM

Source: From M. Merrington and C. M. Thompson, "Tables of Percentage Points of the Inverted Beta (*F*)-Distribution," *Biometrika*, 1943, 33, 73–88.

(continued)

TABLE IX   Continued

ν_2 \ ν_1	NUMERATOR DEGREES OF FREEDOM									
	10	12	15	20	24	30	40	60	120	∞
1	241.9	243.9	245.9	248.0	249.1	250.1	251.1	252.2	253.3	254.3
2	19.40	19.41	19.43	19.45	19.45	19.46	19.47	19.48	19.49	19.50
3	8.79	8.74	8.70	8.66	8.64	8.62	8.59	8.57	8.55	8.53
4	5.96	5.91	5.86	5.80	5.77	5.75	5.72	5.69	5.66	5.63
5	4.74	4.68	4.62	4.56	4.53	4.50	4.46	4.43	4.40	4.36
6	4.06	4.00	3.94	3.87	3.84	3.81	3.77	3.74	3.70	3.67
7	3.64	3.57	3.51	3.44	3.41	3.38	3.34	3.30	3.27	3.23
8	3.35	3.28	3.22	3.15	3.12	3.08	3.04	3.01	2.97	2.93
9	3.14	3.07	3.01	2.94	2.90	2.86	2.83	2.79	2.75	2.71
10	2.98	2.91	2.85	2.77	2.74	2.70	2.66	2.62	2.58	2.54
11	2.85	2.79	2.72	2.65	2.61	2.57	2.53	2.49	2.45	2.40
12	2.75	2.69	2.62	2.54	2.51	2.47	2.43	2.38	2.34	2.30
13	2.67	2.60	2.53	2.46	2.42	2.38	2.34	2.30	2.25	2.21
14	2.60	2.53	2.46	2.39	2.35	2.31	2.27	2.22	2.18	2.13
15	2.54	2.48	2.40	2.33	2.29	2.25	2.20	2.16	2.11	2.07
16	2.49	2.42	2.35	2.28	2.24	2.19	2.15	2.11	2.06	2.01
17	2.45	2.38	2.31	2.23	2.19	2.15	2.10	2.06	2.01	1.96
18	2.41	2.34	2.27	2.19	2.15	2.11	2.06	2.02	1.97	1.92
19	2.38	2.31	2.23	2.16	2.11	2.07	2.03	1.98	1.93	1.88
20	2.35	2.28	2.20	2.12	2.08	2.04	1.99	1.95	1.90	1.84
21	2.32	2.25	2.18	2.10	2.05	2.01	1.96	1.92	1.87	1.81
22	2.30	2.23	2.15	2.07	2.03	1.98	1.94	1.89	1.84	1.78
23	2.27	2.20	2.13	2.05	2.01	1.96	1.91	1.86	1.81	1.76
24	2.25	2.18	2.11	2.03	1.98	1.94	1.89	1.84	1.79	1.73
25	2.24	2.16	2.09	2.01	1.96	1.92	1.87	1.82	1.77	1.71
26	2.22	2.15	2.07	1.99	1.95	1.90	1.85	1.80	1.75	1.69
27	2.20	2.13	2.06	1.97	1.93	1.88	1.84	1.79	1.73	1.67
28	2.19	2.12	2.04	1.96	1.91	1.87	1.82	1.77	1.71	1.65
29	2.18	2.10	2.03	1.94	1.90	1.85	1.81	1.75	1.70	1.64
30	2.16	2.09	2.01	1.93	1.89	1.84	1.79	1.74	1.68	1.62
40	2.08	2.00	1.92	1.84	1.79	1.74	1.69	1.64	1.58	1.51
60	1.99	1.92	1.84	1.75	1.70	1.65	1.59	1.53	1.47	1.39
120	1.91	1.83	1.75	1.66	1.61	1.55	1.50	1.43	1.35	1.25
∞	1.83	1.75	1.67	1.57	1.52	1.46	1.39	1.32	1.22	1.00

DENOMINATOR DEGREES OF FREEDOM

TABLE X   Percentage Points of the F-distribution, $\alpha = .025$

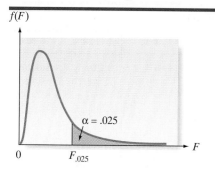

v_1	NUMERATOR DEGREES OF FREEDOM								
v_2	**1**	**2**	**3**	**4**	**5**	**6**	**7**	**8**	**9**
1	647.8	799.5	864.2	899.6	921.8	937.1	948.2	956.7	963.3
2	38.51	39.00	39.17	39.25	39.30	39.33	39.36	39.37	39.39
3	17.44	16.04	15.44	15.10	14.88	14.73	14.62	14.54	14.47
4	12.22	10.65	9.98	9.60	9.36	9.20	9.07	8.98	8.90
5	10.01	8.43	7.76	7.39	7.15	6.98	6.85	6.76	6.68
6	8.81	7.26	6.60	6.23	5.99	5.82	5.70	5.60	5.52
7	8.07	6.54	5.89	5.52	5.29	5.12	4.99	4.90	4.82
8	7.57	6.06	5.42	5.05	4.82	4.65	4.53	4.43	4.36
9	7.21	5.71	5.08	4.72	4.48	4.32	4.20	4.10	4.03
10	6.94	5.46	4.83	4.47	4.24	4.07	3.95	3.85	3.78
11	6.72	5.26	4.63	4.28	4.04	3.88	3.76	3.66	3.59
12	6.55	5.10	4.47	4.12	3.89	3.73	3.61	3.51	3.44
13	6.41	4.97	4.35	4.00	3.77	3.60	3.48	3.39	3.31
14	6.30	4.86	4.24	3.89	3.66	3.50	3.38	3.29	3.21
15	6.20	4.77	4.15	3.80	3.58	3.41	3.29	3.20	3.12
16	6.12	4.69	4.08	3.73	3.50	3.34	3.22	3.12	3.05
17	6.04	4.62	4.01	3.66	3.44	3.28	3.16	3.06	2.98
18	5.98	4.56	3.95	3.61	3.38	3.22	3.10	3.01	2.93
19	5.92	4.51	3.90	3.56	3.33	3.17	3.05	2.96	2.88
20	5.87	4.46	3.86	3.51	3.29	3.13	3.01	2.91	2.84
21	5.83	4.42	3.82	3.48	3.25	3.09	2.97	2.87	2.80
22	5.79	4.38	3.78	3.44	3.22	3.05	2.93	2.84	2.76
23	5.75	4.35	3.75	3.41	3.18	3.02	2.90	2.81	2.73
24	5.72	4.32	3.72	3.38	3.15	2.99	2.87	2.78	2.70
25	5.69	4.29	3.69	3.35	3.13	2.97	2.85	2.75	2.68
26	5.66	4.27	3.67	3.33	3.10	2.94	2.82	2.73	2.65
27	5.63	4.24	3.65	3.31	3.08	2.92	2.80	2.71	2.63
28	5.61	4.22	3.63	3.29	3.06	2.90	2.78	2.69	2.61
29	5.59	4.20	3.61	3.27	3.04	2.88	2.76	2.67	2.59
30	5.57	4.18	3.59	3.25	3.03	2.87	2.75	2.65	2.57
40	5.42	4.05	3.46	3.13	2.90	2.74	2.62	2.53	2.45
60	5.29	3.93	3.34	3.01	2.79	2.63	2.51	2.41	2.33
120	5.15	3.80	3.23	2.89	2.67	2.52	2.39	2.30	2.22
∞	5.02	3.69	3.12	2.79	2.57	2.41	2.29	2.19	2.11

The left axis is labelled **DENOMINATOR DEGREES OF FREEDOM**.

Source: From M. Merrington and C. M. Thompson, "Tables of Percentage Points of the Inverted Beta (*F*)-Distribution," *Biometrika*, 1943, 33, 73–88.

(continued)

TABLE X Continued

v_2 \ v_1	NUMERATOR DEGREES OF FREEDOM									
	10	12	15	20	24	30	40	60	120	∞
1	968.6	976.7	984.9	993.1	997.2	1,001	1,006	1,010	1,014	1,018
2	39.40	39.41	39.43	39.45	39.46	39.46	39.47	39.48	39.49	39.50
3	14.42	14.34	14.25	14.17	14.12	14.08	14.04	13.99	13.95	13.90
4	8.84	8.75	8.66	8.56	8.51	8.46	8.41	8.36	8.31	8.26
5	6.62	6.52	6.43	6.33	6.28	6.23	6.18	6.12	6.07	6.02
6	5.46	5.37	5.27	5.17	5.12	5.07	5.01	4.96	4.90	4.85
7	4.76	4.67	4.57	4.47	4.42	4.36	4.31	4.25	4.20	4.14
8	4.30	4.20	4.10	4.00	3.95	3.89	3.84	3.78	3.73	3.67
9	3.96	3.87	3.77	3.67	3.61	3.56	3.51	3.45	3.39	3.33
10	3.72	3.62	3.52	3.42	3.37	3.31	3.26	3.20	3.14	3.08
11	3.53	3.43	3.33	3.23	3.17	3.12	3.06	3.00	2.94	2.88
12	3.37	3.28	3.18	3.07	3.02	2.96	2.91	2.85	2.79	2.72
13	3.25	3.15	3.05	2.95	2.89	2.84	2.78	2.72	2.66	2.60
14	3.15	3.05	2.95	2.84	2.79	2.73	2.67	2.61	2.55	2.49
15	3.06	2.96	2.86	2.76	2.70	2.64	2.59	2.52	2.46	2.40
16	2.99	2.89	2.79	2.68	2.63	2.57	2.51	2.45	2.38	2.32
17	2.92	2.82	2.72	2.62	2.56	2.50	2.44	2.38	2.32	2.25
18	2.87	2.77	2.67	2.56	2.50	2.44	2.38	2.32	2.26	2.19
19	2.82	2.72	2.62	2.51	2.45	2.39	2.33	2.27	2.20	2.13
20	2.77	2.68	2.57	2.46	2.41	2.35	2.29	2.22	2.16	2.09
21	2.73	2.64	2.53	2.42	2.37	2.31	2.25	2.18	2.11	2.04
22	2.70	2.60	2.50	2.39	2.33	2.27	2.21	2.14	2.08	2.00
23	2.67	2.57	2.47	2.36	2.30	2.24	2.18	2.11	2.04	1.97
24	2.64	2.54	2.44	2.33	2.27	2.21	2.15	2.08	2.01	1.94
25	2.61	2.51	2.41	2.30	2.24	2.18	2.12	2.05	1.98	1.91
26	2.59	2.49	2.39	2.28	2.22	2.16	2.09	2.03	1.95	1.88
27	2.57	2.47	2.36	2.25	2.19	2.13	2.07	2.00	1.93	1.85
28	2.55	2.45	2.34	2.23	2.17	2.11	2.05	1.98	1.91	1.83
29	2.53	2.43	2.32	2.21	2.15	2.09	2.03	1.96	1.89	1.81
30	2.51	2.41	2.31	2.20	2.14	2.07	2.01	1.94	1.87	1.79
40	2.39	2.29	2.18	2.07	2.01	1.94	1.88	1.80	1.72	1.64
60	2.27	2.17	2.06	1.94	1.88	1.82	1.74	1.67	1.58	1.48
120	2.16	2.05	1.94	1.82	1.76	1.69	1.61	1.53	1.43	1.31
∞	2.05	1.94	1.83	1.71	1.64	1.57	1.48	1.39	1.27	1.00

DENOMINATOR DEGREES OF FREEDOM

TABLE XI   Percentage Points of the *F*-distribution, $\alpha = .01$

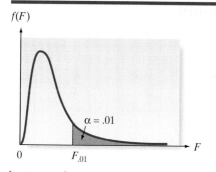

ν_2 \ ν_1	1	2	3	4	5	6	7	8	9
1	4,052	4,999.5	5,403	5,625	5,764	5,859	5,928	5,982	6,022
2	98.50	99.00	99.17	99.25	99.30	99.33	99.36	99.37	99.39
3	34.12	30.82	29.46	28.71	28.24	27.91	27.67	27.49	27.35
4	21.20	18.00	16.69	15.98	15.52	15.21	14.98	14.80	14.66
5	16.26	13.27	12.06	11.39	10.97	10.67	10.46	10.29	10.16
6	13.75	10.92	9.78	9.15	8.75	8.47	8.26	8.10	7.98
7	12.25	9.55	8.45	7.85	7.46	7.19	6.99	6.84	6.72
8	11.26	8.65	7.59	7.01	6.63	6.37	6.18	6.03	5.91
9	10.56	8.02	6.99	6.42	6.06	5.80	5.61	5.47	5.35
10	10.04	7.56	6.55	5.99	5.64	5.39	5.20	5.06	4.94
11	9.65	7.21	6.22	5.67	5.32	5.07	4.89	4.74	4.63
12	9.33	6.93	5.95	5.41	5.06	4.82	4.64	4.50	4.39
13	9.07	6.70	5.74	5.21	4.86	4.62	4.44	4.30	4.19
14	8.86	6.51	5.56	5.04	4.69	4.46	4.28	4.14	4.03
15	8.68	6.36	5.42	4.89	4.56	4.32	4.14	4.00	3.89
16	8.53	6.23	5.29	4.77	4.44	4.20	4.03	3.89	3.78
17	8.40	6.11	5.18	4.67	4.34	4.10	3.93	3.79	3.68
18	8.29	6.01	5.09	4.58	4.25	4.01	3.84	3.71	3.60
19	8.18	5.93	5.01	4.50	4.17	3.94	3.77	3.63	3.52
20	8.10	5.85	4.94	4.43	4.10	3.87	3.70	3.56	3.46
21	8.02	5.78	4.87	4.37	4.04	3.81	3.64	3.51	3.40
22	7.95	5.72	4.82	4.31	3.99	3.76	3.59	3.45	3.35
23	7.88	5.66	4.76	4.26	3.94	3.71	3.54	3.41	3.30
24	7.82	5.61	4.72	4.22	3.90	3.67	3.50	3.36	3.26
25	7.77	5.57	4.68	4.18	3.85	3.63	3.46	3.32	3.22
26	7.72	5.53	4.64	4.14	3.82	3.59	3.42	3.29	3.18
27	7.68	5.49	4.60	4.11	3.78	3.56	3.39	3.26	3.15
28	7.64	5.45	4.57	4.07	3.75	3.53	3.36	3.23	3.12
29	7.60	5.42	4.54	4.04	3.73	3.50	3.33	3.20	3.09
30	7.56	5.39	4.51	4.02	3.70	3.47	3.30	3.17	3.07
40	7.31	5.18	4.31	3.83	3.51	3.29	3.12	2.99	2.89
60	7.08	4.98	4.13	3.65	3.34	3.12	2.95	2.82	2.72
120	6.85	4.79	3.95	3.48	3.17	2.96	2.79	2.66	2.56
∞	6.63	4.61	3.78	3.32	3.02	2.80	2.64	2.51	2.41

The numerator degrees of freedom span the columns (**NUMERATOR DEGREES OF FREEDOM**, ν_1) and the denominator degrees of freedom span the rows (**DENOMINATOR DEGREES OF FREEDOM**, ν_2).

Source: From M. Merrington and C. M. Thompson, "Tables of Percentage Points of the Inverted Beta (*F*)-Distribution," *Biometrika,* 1943, 33, 73–88.

(continued)

TABLE XI   Continued

v_2 \ v_1	NUMERATOR DEGREES OF FREEDOM									
	10	**12**	**15**	**20**	**24**	**30**	**40**	**60**	**120**	**∞**
1	6,056	6,106	6,157	6,209	6,235	6,261	6,287	6,313	6,339	6,366
2	99.40	99.42	99.43	99.45	99.46	99.47	99.47	99.48	99.49	99.50
3	27.23	27.05	26.87	26.69	26.60	26.50	26.41	26.32	26.22	26.13
4	14.55	14.37	14.20	14.02	13.93	13.84	13.75	13.65	13.56	13.46
5	10.05	9.89	9.72	9.55	9.47	9.38	9.29	9.20	9.11	9.02
6	7.87	7.72	7.56	7.40	7.31	7.23	7.14	7.06	6.97	6.88
7	6.62	6.47	6.31	6.16	6.07	5.99	5.91	5.82	5.74	5.65
8	5.81	5.67	5.52	5.36	5.28	5.20	5.12	5.03	4.95	4.86
9	5.26	5.11	4.96	4.81	4.73	4.65	4.57	4.48	4.40	4.31
10	4.85	4.71	4.56	4.41	4.33	4.25	4.17	4.08	4.00	3.91
11	4.54	4.40	4.25	4.10	4.02	3.94	3.86	3.78	3.69	3.60
12	4.30	4.16	4.01	3.86	3.78	3.70	3.62	3.54	3.45	3.36
13	4.10	3.96	3.82	3.66	3.59	3.51	3.43	3.34	3.25	3.17
14	3.94	3.80	3.66	3.51	3.43	3.35	3.27	3.18	3.09	3.00
15	3.80	3.67	3.52	3.37	3.29	3.21	3.13	3.05	2.96	2.87
16	3.69	3.55	3.41	3.26	3.18	3.10	3.02	2.93	2.84	2.75
17	3.59	3.46	3.31	3.16	3.08	3.00	2.92	2.83	2.75	2.65
18	3.51	3.37	3.23	3.08	3.00	2.92	2.84	2.75	2.66	2.57
19	3.43	3.30	3.15	3.00	2.92	2.84	2.76	2.67	2.58	2.49
20	3.37	3.23	3.09	2.94	2.86	2.78	2.69	2.61	2.52	2.42
21	3.31	3.17	3.03	2.88	2.80	2.72	2.64	2.55	2.46	2.36
22	3.26	3.12	2.98	2.83	2.75	2.67	2.58	2.50	2.40	2.31
23	3.21	3.07	2.93	2.78	2.70	2.62	2.54	2.45	2.35	2.26
24	3.17	3.03	2.89	2.74	2.66	2.58	2.49	2.40	2.31	2.21
25	3.13	2.99	2.85	2.70	2.62	2.54	2.45	2.36	2.27	2.17
26	3.09	2.96	2.81	2.66	2.58	2.50	2.42	2.33	2.23	2.13
27	3.06	2.93	2.78	2.63	2.55	2.47	2.38	2.29	2.20	2.10
28	3.03	2.90	2.75	2.60	2.52	2.44	2.35	2.26	2.17	2.06
29	3.00	2.87	2.73	2.57	2.49	2.41	2.33	2.23	2.14	2.03
30	2.98	2.84	2.70	2.55	2.47	2.39	2.30	2.21	2.11	2.01
40	2.80	2.66	2.52	2.37	2.29	2.20	2.11	2.02	1.92	1.80
60	2.63	2.50	2.35	2.20	2.12	2.03	1.94	1.84	1.73	1.60
120	2.47	2.34	2.19	2.03	1.95	1.86	1.76	1.66	1.53	1.38
∞	2.32	2.18	2.04	1.88	1.79	1.70	1.59	1.47	1.32	1.00

DENOMINATOR DEGREES OF FREEDOM

TABLE XII Critical Values of T_L and T_U for the Wilcoxon Rank Sum Test: Independent Samples

Test statistic is the rank sum associated with the smaller sample (if equal sample sizes, either rank sum can be used).

a. $\alpha = .025$ one-tailed; $\alpha = .05$ two-tailed

n_2 \ n_1	3		4		5		6		7		8		9		10	
	T_L	T_U	T_L	T_U	T_L	T_U	T_L	T_U	T_L	T_U	T_L	T_U	T_L	T_U	T_L	T_U
3	5	16	6	18	6	21	7	23	7	26	8	28	8	31	9	33
4	6	18	11	25	12	28	12	32	13	35	14	38	15	41	16	44
5	6	21	12	28	18	37	19	41	20	45	21	49	22	53	24	56
6	7	23	12	32	19	41	26	52	28	56	29	61	31	65	32	70
7	7	26	13	35	20	45	28	56	37	68	39	73	41	78	43	83
8	8	28	14	38	21	49	29	61	39	73	49	87	51	93	54	98
9	8	31	15	41	22	53	31	65	41	78	51	93	63	108	66	114
10	9	33	16	44	24	56	32	70	43	83	54	98	66	114	79	131

b. $\alpha = .05$ one-tailed; $\alpha = .10$ two-tailed

n_2 \ n_1	3		4		5		6		7		8		9		10	
	T_L	T_U	T_L	T_U	T_L	T_U	T_L	T_U	T_L	T_U	T_L	T_U	T_L	T_U	T_L	T_U
3	6	15	7	17	7	20	8	22	9	24	9	27	10	29	11	31
4	7	17	12	24	13	27	14	30	15	33	16	36	17	39	18	42
5	7	20	13	27	19	36	20	40	22	43	24	46	25	50	26	54
6	8	22	14	30	20	40	28	50	30	54	32	58	33	63	35	67
7	9	24	15	33	22	43	30	54	39	66	41	71	43	76	46	80
8	9	27	16	36	24	46	32	58	41	71	52	84	54	90	57	95
9	10	29	17	39	25	50	33	63	43	76	54	90	66	105	69	111
10	11	31	18	42	26	54	35	67	46	80	57	95	69	111	83	127

Source: From F. Wilcoxon and R. A. Wilcox, "Some Rapid Approximate Statistical Procedures," 1964, 20–23.

TABLE XIII   Critical Values of T_0 in the Wilcoxon Paired Difference Signed Rank Test

One-Tailed	Two-Tailed	$n = 5$	$n = 6$	$n = 7$	$n = 8$	$n = 9$	$n = 10$
$\alpha = .05$	$\alpha = .10$	1	2	4	6	8	11
$\alpha = .025$	$\alpha = .05$		1	2	4	6	8
$\alpha = .01$	$\alpha = .02$			0	2	3	5
$\alpha = .005$	$\alpha = .01$				0	2	3
		$n = 11$	$n = 12$	$n = 13$	$n = 14$	$n = 15$	$n = 16$
$\alpha = .05$	$\alpha = .10$	14	17	21	26	30	36
$\alpha = .025$	$\alpha = .05$	11	14	17	21	25	30
$\alpha = .01$	$\alpha = .02$	7	10	13	16	20	24
$\alpha = .005$	$\alpha = .01$	5	7	10	13	16	19
		$n = 17$	$n = 18$	$n = 19$	$n = 20$	$n = 21$	$n = 22$
$\alpha = .05$	$\alpha = .10$	41	47	54	60	68	75
$\alpha = .025$	$\alpha = .05$	35	40	46	52	59	66
$\alpha = .01$	$\alpha = .02$	28	33	38	43	49	56
$\alpha = .005$	$\alpha = .01$	23	28	32	37	43	49
		$n = 23$	$n = 24$	$n = 25$	$n = 26$	$n = 27$	$n = 28$
$\alpha = .05$	$\alpha = .10$	83	92	101	110	120	130
$\alpha = .025$	$\alpha = .05$	73	81	90	98	107	117
$\alpha = .01$	$\alpha = .02$	62	69	77	85	93	102
$\alpha = .005$	$\alpha = .01$	55	61	68	76	84	92
		$n = 29$	$n = 30$	$n = 31$	$n = 32$	$n = 33$	$n = 34$
$\alpha = .05$	$\alpha = .10$	141	152	163	175	188	201
$\alpha = .025$	$\alpha = .05$	127	137	148	159	171	183
$\alpha = .01$	$\alpha = .02$	111	120	130	141	151	162
$\alpha = .005$	$\alpha = .01$	100	109	118	128	138	149
		$n = 35$	$n = 36$	$n = 37$	$n = 38$	$n = 39$	
$\alpha = .05$	$\alpha = .10$	214	228	242	256	271	
$\alpha = .025$	$\alpha = .05$	195	208	222	235	250	
$\alpha = .01$	$\alpha = .02$	174	186	198	211	224	
$\alpha = .005$	$\alpha = .01$	160	171	183	195	208	
		$n = 40$	$n = 41$	$n = 42$	$n = 43$	$n = 44$	$n = 45$
$\alpha = .05$	$\alpha = .10$	287	303	319	336	353	371
$\alpha = .025$	$\alpha = .05$	264	279	295	311	327	344
$\alpha = .01$	$\alpha = .02$	238	252	267	281	297	313
$\alpha = .005$	$\alpha = .01$	221	234	248	262	277	292
		$n = 46$	$n = 47$	$n = 48$	$n = 49$	$n = 50$	
$\alpha = .05$	$\alpha = .10$	389	408	427	446	466	
$\alpha = .025$	$\alpha = .05$	361	379	397	415	434	
$\alpha = .01$	$\alpha = .02$	329	345	362	380	398	
$\alpha = .005$	$\alpha = .01$	307	323	339	356	373	

Source: From F. Wilcoxon and R. A. Wilcox, "Some Rapid Approximate Statistical Procedures," 1964, p. 28.

TABLE XIV   Critical Values of Spearman's Rank Correlation Coefficient

The α values correspond to a one-tailed test of H_0: $\rho = 0$. The value should be doubled for two-tailed tests.

n	$\alpha = .05$	$\alpha = .025$	$\alpha = .01$	$\alpha = .005$	n	$\alpha = .05$	$\alpha = .025$	$\alpha = .01$	$\alpha = .005$
5	.900	—	—	—	18	.399	.476	.564	.625
6	.829	.886	.943	—	19	.388	.462	.549	.608
7	.714	.786	.893	—	20	.377	.450	.534	.591
8	.643	.738	.833	.881	21	.368	.438	.521	.576
9	.600	.683	.783	.833	22	.359	.428	.508	.562
10	.564	.648	.745	.794	23	.351	.418	.496	.549
11	.523	.623	.736	.818	24	.343	.409	.485	.537
12	.497	.591	.703	.780	25	.336	.400	.475	.526
13	.475	.566	.673	.745	26	.329	.392	.465	.515
14	.457	.545	.646	.716	27	.323	.385	.456	.505
15	.441	.525	.623	.689	28	.317	.377	.448	.496
16	.425	.507	.601	.666	29	.311	.370	.440	.487
17	.412	.490	.582	.645	30	.305	.364	.432	.478

Source: From E. G. Olds, "Distribution of Sums of Squares of Rank Differences for Small Samples," *Annals of Mathematical Statistics,* 1938, 9.

TABLE XV   Critical Values of the Studentized Range, $\alpha = .05$

ν \ k	2	3	4	5	6	7	8	9	10	11
1	17.97	26.98	32.82	37.08	40.41	43.12	45.40	47.36	49.07	50.59
2	6.08	8.33	9.80	10.88	11.74	12.44	13.03	13.54	13.99	14.39
3	4.50	5.91	6.82	7.50	8.04	8.48	8.85	9.18	9.46	9.72
4	3.93	5.04	5.76	6.29	6.71	7.05	7.35	7.60	7.83	8.03
5	3.64	4.60	5.22	5.67	6.03	6.33	6.58	6.80	6.99	7.17
6	3.46	4.34	4.90	5.30	5.63	5.90	6.12	6.32	6.49	6.65
7	3.34	4.16	4.68	5.06	5.36	5.61	5.82	6.00	6.16	6.30
8	3.26	4.04	4.53	4.89	5.17	5.40	5.60	5.77	5.92	6.05
9	3.20	3.95	4.41	4.76	5.02	5.24	5.43	5.59	5.74	5.87
10	3.15	3.88	4.33	4.65	4.91	5.12	5.30	5.46	5.60	5.72
11	3.11	3.82	4.26	4.57	4.82	5.03	5.20	5.35	5.49	5.61
12	3.08	3.77	4.20	4.51	4.75	4.95	5.12	5.27	5.39	5.51
13	3.06	3.73	4.15	4.45	4.69	4.88	5.05	5.19	5.32	5.43
14	3.03	3.70	4.11	4.41	4.64	4.83	4.99	5.13	5.25	5.36
15	3.01	3.67	4.08	4.37	4.60	4.78	4.94	5.08	5.20	5.31
16	3.00	3.65	4.05	4.33	4.56	4.74	4.90	5.03	5.15	5.26
17	2.98	3.63	4.02	4.30	4.52	4.70	4.86	4.99	5.11	5.21
18	2.97	3.61	4.00	4.28	4.49	4.67	4.82	4.96	5.07	5.17
19	2.96	3.59	3.98	4.25	4.47	4.65	4.79	4.92	5.04	5.14
20	2.95	3.58	3.96	4.23	4.45	4.62	4.77	4.90	5.01	5.11
24	2.92	3.53	3.90	4.17	4.37	4.54	4.68	4.81	4.92	5.01
30	2.89	3.49	3.85	4.10	4.30	4.46	4.60	4.72	4.82	4.92
40	2.86	3.44	3.79	4.04	4.23	4.39	4.52	4.63	4.73	4.82
60	2.83	3.40	3.74	3.98	4.16	4.31	4.44	4.55	4.65	4.73
120	2.80	3.36	3.68	3.92	4.10	4.24	4.36	4.47	4.56	4.64
∞	2.77	3.31	3.63	3.86	4.03	4.17	4.29	4.39	4.47	4.55

(continued)

TABLE XV   Continued

ν \ k	12	13	14	15	16	17	18	19	20
1	51.96	53.20	54.33	55.36	56.32	57.22	58.04	58.83	59.56
2	14.75	15.08	15.38	15.65	15.91	16.14	16.37	16.57	16.77
3	9.95	10.15	10.35	10.52	10.69	10.84	10.98	11.11	11.24
4	8.21	8.37	8.52	8.66	8.79	8.91	9.03	9.13	9.23
5	7.32	7.47	7.60	7.72	7.83	7.93	8.03	8.12	8.21
6	6.79	6.92	7.03	7.14	7.24	7.34	7.43	7.51	7.59
7	6.43	6.55	6.66	6.76	6.85	6.94	7.02	7.10	7.17
8	6.18	6.29	6.39	6.48	6.57	6.65	6.73	6.80	6.87
9	5.98	6.09	6.19	6.28	6.36	6.44	6.51	6.58	6.64
10	5.83	5.93	6.03	6.11	6.19	6.27	6.34	6.40	6.47
11	5.71	5.81	5.90	5.98	6.06	6.13	6.20	6.27	6.33
12	5.61	5.71	5.80	5.88	5.95	6.02	6.09	6.15	6.21
13	5.53	5.63	5.71	5.79	5.86	5.93	5.99	6.05	6.11
14	5.46	5.55	5.64	5.71	5.79	5.85	5.91	5.97	6.03
15	5.40	5.49	5.57	5.65	5.72	5.78	5.85	5.90	5.96
16	5.35	5.44	5.52	5.59	5.66	5.73	5.79	5.84	5.90
17	5.31	5.39	5.47	5.54	5.61	5.67	5.73	5.79	5.84
18	5.27	5.35	5.43	5.50	5.57	5.63	5.69	5.74	5.79
19	5.23	5.31	5.39	5.46	5.53	5.59	5.65	5.70	5.75
20	5.20	5.28	5.36	5.43	5.49	5.55	5.61	5.66	5.71
24	5.10	5.18	5.25	5.32	5.38	5.44	5.49	5.55	5.59
30	5.00	5.08	5.15	5.21	5.27	5.33	5.38	5.43	5.47
40	4.90	4.98	5.04	5.11	5.16	5.22	5.27	5.31	5.36
60	4.81	4.88	4.94	5.00	5.06	5.11	5.15	5.20	5.24
120	4.71	4.78	4.84	4.90	4.95	5.00	5.04	5.09	5.13
∞	4.62	4.68	4.74	4.80	4.85	4.89	4.93	4.97	5.01

TABLE XVI   Critical Values of the Studentized Range, $\alpha = .01$

v \ k	2	3	4	5	6	7	8	9	10	11
1	90.03	135.0	164.3	185.6	202.2	215.8	227.2	237.0	245.6	253.2
2	14.04	19.02	22.29	24.72	26.63	28.20	29.53	30.68	31.69	32.59
3	8.26	10.62	12.17	13.33	14.24	15.00	15.64	16.20	16.69	17.13
4	6.51	8.12	9.17	9.96	10.58	11.10	11.55	11.93	12.27	12.57
5	5.70	6.98	7.80	8.42	8.91	9.32	9.67	9.97	10.24	10.48
6	5.24	6.33	7.03	7.56	7.97	8.32	8.61	8.87	9.10	9.30
7	4.95	5.92	6.54	7.01	7.37	7.68	7.94	8.17	8.37	8.55
8	4.75	5.64	6.20	6.62	6.96	7.24	7.47	7.68	7.86	8.03
9	4.60	5.43	5.96	6.35	6.66	6.91	7.13	7.33	7.49	7.65
10	4.48	5.27	5.77	6.14	6.43	6.67	6.87	7.05	7.21	7.36
11	4.39	5.15	5.62	5.97	6.25	6.48	6.67	6.84	6.99	7.13
12	4.32	5.05	5.50	5.84	6.10	6.32	6.51	6.67	6.81	6.94
13	4.26	4.96	5.40	5.73	5.98	6.19	6.37	6.53	6.67	6.79
14	4.21	4.89	5.32	5.63	5.88	6.08	6.26	6.41	6.54	6.66
15	4.17	4.84	5.25	5.56	5.80	5.99	6.16	6.31	6.44	6.55
16	4.13	4.79	5.19	5.49	5.72	5.92	6.08	6.22	6.35	6.46
17	4.10	4.74	5.14	5.43	5.66	5.85	6.01	6.15	6.27	6.38
18	4.07	4.70	5.09	5.38	5.60	5.79	5.94	6.08	6.20	6.31
19	4.05	4.67	5.05	5.33	5.55	5.73	5.89	6.02	6.14	6.25
20	4.02	4.64	5.02	5.29	5.51	5.69	5.84	5.97	6.09	6.19
24	3.96	4.55	4.91	5.17	5.37	5.54	5.69	5.81	5.92	6.02
30	3.89	4.45	4.80	5.05	5.24	5.40	5.54	5.65	5.76	5.85
40	3.82	4.37	4.70	4.93	5.11	5.26	5.39	5.50	5.60	5.69
60	3.76	4.28	4.59	4.82	4.99	5.13	5.25	5.36	5.45	5.53
120	3.70	4.20	4.50	4.71	4.87	5.01	5.12	5.21	5.30	5.37
∞	3.64	4.12	4.40	4.60	4.76	4.88	4.99	5.08	5.16	5.23

(continued)

TABLE XVI Continued

ν \ k	12	13	14	15	16	17	18	19	20
1	260.0	266.2	271.8	277.0	281.8	286.3	290.0	294.3	298.0
2	33.40	34.13	34.81	35.43	36.00	36.53	37.03	37.50	37.95
3	17.53	17.89	18.22	18.52	18.81	19.07	19.32	19.55	19.77
4	12.84	13.09	13.32	13.53	13.73	13.91	14.08	14.24	14.40
5	10.70	10.89	11.08	11.24	11.40	11.55	11.68	11.81	11.93
6	9.48	9.65	9.81	9.95	10.08	10.21	10.32	10.43	10.54
7	8.71	8.86	9.00	9.12	9.24	9.35	9.46	9.55	9.65
8	8.18	8.31	8.44	8.55	8.66	8.76	8.85	8.94	9.03
9	7.78	7.91	8.03	8.13	8.23	8.33	8.41	8.49	8.57
10	7.49	7.60	7.71	7.81	7.91	7.99	8.08	8.15	8.23
11	7.25	7.36	7.46	7.56	7.65	7.73	7.81	7.88	7.95
12	7.06	7.17	7.26	7.36	7.44	7.52	7.59	7.66	7.73
13	6.90	7.01	7.10	7.19	7.27	7.35	7.42	7.48	7.55
14	6.77	6.87	6.96	7.05	7.13	7.20	7.27	7.33	7.39
15	6.66	6.76	6.84	6.93	7.00	7.07	7.14	7.20	7.26
16	6.56	6.66	6.74	6.82	6.90	6.97	7.03	7.09	7.15
17	6.48	6.57	6.66	6.73	6.81	6.87	6.94	7.00	7.05
18	6.41	6.50	6.58	6.65	6.72	6.79	6.85	6.91	6.97
19	6.34	6.43	6.51	6.58	6.65	6.72	6.78	6.84	6.89
20	6.28	6.37	6.45	6.52	6.59	6.65	6.71	6.77	6.82
24	6.11	6.19	6.26	6.33	6.39	6.45	6.51	6.56	6.61
30	5.93	6.01	6.08	6.14	6.20	6.26	6.31	6.36	6.41
40	5.76	5.83	5.90	5.96	6.02	6.07	6.12	6.16	6.21
60	5.60	5.67	5.73	5.78	5.84	5.89	5.93	5.97	6.01
120	5.44	5.50	5.56	5.61	5.66	5.71	5.75	5.79	5.83
∞	5.29	5.35	5.40	5.45	5.49	5.54	5.57	5.61	5.65

Source: Biometrika Tables for Statisticians, Vol. 1, 3rd ed., edited by E. S. Pearson and H. O. Hartley (Cambridge University Press, 1966). Reproduced by permission of Professor E. S. Pearson and the *Biometrika* Trustees.

Appendix B
Calculation Formulas for Analysis of Variance

B.1 Formulas for the Calculations in the Completely Randomized Design   914

B.2 Formulas for the Calculations in the Randomized Block Design   915

B.3 Formulas for the Calculations for a Two-Factor Factorial Experiment   915

B.4 Tukey's Multiple Comparisons Procedure (Equal Sample Sizes)   916

B.5 Bonferroni Multiple Comparisons Procedure (Pairwise Comparisons)   917

B.6 Scheffé's Multiple Comparisons Procedure (Pairwise Comparisons)   917

B.1 FORMULAS FOR THE CALCULATIONS IN THE COMPLETELY RANDOMIZED DESIGN

$$CM = \text{Correction for mean}$$

$$= \frac{(\text{Total of all observations})^2}{\text{Total number of observations}} = \frac{\left(\sum y_i\right)^2}{n}$$

$$SS(\text{Total}) = \text{Total sum of squares}$$

$$= (\text{Sum of squares of all observations}) - CM = \sum y_i^2 - CM$$

$$SST = \text{Sum of squares for treatments}$$

$$= \left(\begin{array}{c}\text{Sum of squares of treatments totals with}\\ \text{each square divided by the number of}\\ \text{observations for that treatment}\end{array}\right) - CM$$

$$= \frac{T_1^2}{n_1} + \frac{T_2^2}{n_2} + \cdots + \frac{T_k^2}{n_k} - CM$$

$$SSE = \text{Sum of squares for error} = SS(\text{Total}) - SST$$

$$MST = \text{Mean square for treatments} = \frac{SST}{k-1}$$

$$MSE = \text{Mean square for error} = \frac{SSE}{n-k}$$

$$F = \text{Test statistic} = \frac{MST}{MSE}$$

where

$$n = \text{Total number of observations}$$

$$k = \text{Number of treatments}$$

$$T_i = \text{Total for treatment } i \ (i = 1, 2, \ldots, k)$$

B.2   FORMULAS FOR THE CALCULATIONS IN THE RANDOMIZED BLOCK DESIGN

$$CM = \text{Correction for mean}$$

$$= \frac{(\text{Total of all observations})^2}{\text{Total number of observations}} = \frac{\left(\sum y_i\right)^2}{n}$$

$$SS(\text{Total}) = \text{Total sum of squares}$$

$$= (\text{Sum of squares of all observations}) - CM = \sum y_i^2 - CM$$

$$SST = \text{Sum of squares for treatments}$$

$$= \left(\begin{array}{c} \text{Sum of squares of treatment totals with} \\ \text{each square divided by } b\text{, the number of} \\ \text{observations for that treatment} \end{array} \right) - CM$$

$$= \frac{T_1^2}{b} + \frac{T_2^2}{b} + \cdots + \frac{T_k^2}{b} - CM$$

$$SST = \text{Sum of squares for blocks}$$

$$= \left(\begin{array}{c} \text{Sum of squares of block totals with} \\ \text{each square divided by } p\text{, the number} \\ \text{of observations in that block} \end{array} \right) - CM$$

$$= \frac{B_1^2}{k} + \frac{B_2^2}{k} + \cdots + \frac{B_b^2}{k} - CM$$

$$SSE = \text{Sum of squares for error} = SS(\text{Total}) - SST - SSB$$

$$MST = \text{Mean square for treatments} = \frac{SST}{k-1}$$

$$MSB = \text{Mean square for blocks} = \frac{SSB}{b-1}$$

$$MSE = \text{Mean square for error} = \frac{SSE}{n-k-b+1}$$

$$F = \text{Test statistic} = \frac{MST}{MSE}$$

where

$$n = \text{Total number of observations}$$

$$b = \text{Number of blocks}$$

$$k = \text{Number of treatments}$$

$$T_i = \text{Total for treatment } i \ (i = 1, 2, \ldots, k)$$

$$B_i = \text{Total for block } i \ (i = 1, 2, \ldots, b)$$

B.3   FORMULAS FOR THE CALCULATIONS FOR A TWO-FACTOR FACTORIAL EXPERIMENT

$$CM = \text{Correction for mean}$$

$$= \frac{(\text{Total of all } n \text{ measurements})^2}{n} = \frac{\left(\sum\limits_{i=1}^{n} y_i\right)^2}{n}$$

$$SS(\text{Total}) = \text{Total sum of squares}$$

$$= (\text{Sum of squares of all } n \text{ measurements}) - \text{CM} = \sum_{i=1}^{n} y_i^2 - \text{CM}$$

SS(A) = Sum of squares for main effects, factor A

$$= \left(\begin{array}{c} \text{Sum of squares of the totals } A_1, A_2, \ldots, A_a \\ \text{divided by the number of measurements} \\ \text{in a single total, namely } br \end{array} \right) - \text{CM}$$

$$= \frac{\sum_{i=1}^{a} A_i^2}{br} - \text{CM}$$

SS(B) = Sum of squares for main effects, factor B

$$= \left(\begin{array}{c} \text{Sum of squares of the totals } B_1, B_2, \ldots, B_b \\ \text{divided by the number of measurements} \\ \text{in a single total, namely } ar \end{array} \right) - \text{CM}$$

$$= \frac{\sum_{i=1}^{b} B_i^2}{ar} - \text{CM}$$

SS(AB) = Sum of squares for AB interaction

$$= \left(\begin{array}{c} \text{Sum of squares of the cell totals} \\ AB_{11}, AB_{12}, \ldots, AB_{ab} \text{ divided by} \\ \text{the number of measurements in} \\ \text{a single total, namely } r \end{array} \right) - \text{SS}(A) - \text{SS}(B) - \text{CM}$$

$$= \frac{\sum_{j=1}^{b} \sum_{i=1}^{a} AB_{ij}^2}{r} - \text{SS}(A) - \text{SS}(B) - \text{CM}$$

where

a = Number of levels of factor A

b = Number of levels of factor B

r = Number of replicates (observations per treatment)

A_i = Total for level i of factor A ($i = 1, 2, \ldots, a$)

B_i = Total for level i of factor B ($i = 1, 2, \ldots, b$)

AB_{ij} = Total for treatment (ij), i.e., for ith level of factor A and ith level of factor B

B.4   TUKEY'S MULTIPLE COMPARISONS PROCEDURE. (EQUAL SAMPLE SIZES)

Step 1 Select the desired experimentwise error rate, α.

Step 2 Calculate

$$\omega = q_\alpha(k, \nu) \frac{s}{\sqrt{n_t}}$$

where

k = Number of sample means (i.e., number of treatments)

$s = \sqrt{\text{MSE}}$

ν = Number of degrees of freedom associated with MSE

n_t = Number of observations in each of the k samples (i.e., number of observations per treatment)

$q_\alpha(k, \nu)$ = Critical value of the Studentized range (Tables XV and XVI of Appendix A)

Step 3 Calculate and rank the k sample means.

Step 4 Place a bar over those pairs of treatment means that differ by less than ω. A pair of treatments not connected by an overbar (i.e., differing by more than ω) implies a difference in the corresponding population means.

Note: The confidence level associated with all inferences drawn from the analysis is $(1 - \alpha)$.

B.5   BONFERRONI MULTIPLE COMPARISONS PROCEDURE (PAIRWISE COMPARISONS)

Step 1 Calculate for each treatment pair (i, j)

$$B_{ij} = t_{\alpha/(2c)}s\sqrt{\frac{1}{n_i} + \frac{1}{n_j}}$$

where

k = Number of sample (treatment) means in the experiment

c = Number of pairwise comparisons

[*Note:* If all pairwise comparisons are to be made, then $c = k(k-1)/2$]

$s = \sqrt{\text{MSE}}$

ν = Number of degrees of freedom associated with MSE

n_i = Number of observations in sample for treatment i

n_j = Number of observations in sample for treatment j

$t_{\alpha/(2c)}$ = Critical value of t distribution with ν df and tail area $\alpha/(2c)$ (Table VI in Appendix A)

Step 2 Rank the sample means and place a bar over any treatment pair (i, j) whose sample means differ by less than B_{ij}. Any pair of means not connected by an overbar implies a difference in the corresponding population means.

Note: The level of confidence associated with all inferences drawn from the analysis is at least $(1 - \alpha)$.

B.6   SCHEFFÉ'S MULTIPLE COMPARISONS PROCEDURE (PAIRWISE COMPARISONS)

Step 1 Calculate Scheffé's critical difference for each pair of treatments (i, j):

$$S_{ij} = \sqrt{(k-1)(F_\alpha)(\text{MSE})\left(\frac{1}{n_i} + \frac{1}{n_j}\right)}$$

where

k = Number of sample (treatment) means

MSE = Mean squared error

n_i = Number of observations in sample for treatment i

n_j = Number of observations in sample for treatment j

F_α = Critical value of F distribution with $k - 1$ numerator df and ν denominator df (Tables XIII, IX, X, and XI of Appendix A)

ν = Number of degrees of freedom associated with MSE

Step 2 Rank the k sample means and place a bar over any treatment pair (i, j) that differs by less than S_{ij}. Any pair of sample means not connected by an overbar implies a difference in the corresponding population means.

Short Answers to Selected Odd-Numbered Exercises

Chapter 1

1.11 qualitative; qualitative **1.13 a.** quantitative **b.** qualitative **c.** qualitative **d.** quantitative **1.15 b.** qualitative **e.** survey data **1.17 a.** CEOs of all U. S. companies **b.** (1) qualitative, (2) quantitative, (3) quantitative, (4) quantitative **c.** CEOs selected only from top-ranked companies **1.19 a.** qualitative; qualitative; qualitative; quantitative **b.** sample **1.21 a.** quantitative **b.** quantitative **c.** qualitative **d.** quantitative **e.** qualitative **f.** quantitative **g.** qualitative **1.23 a.** designed experiment **b.** smokers **c.** quantitative **d.** population: all smokers in the U.S.; sample: 50,000 smokers in trial **e.** the difference in mean age at which each of the scanning methods first detects a tumor. **1.25 a.** designed experiment **b.** amateur boxers **c.** heart rate (quantitative); blood lactate level (quantitative) **d.** no difference between the two groups of boxers **e.** no **1.27 a.** designed experiment **b.** inferential statistics **c.** all possible burn patients **1.29 b.** number of headers per game and IQ **c.** both quantitative **1.31 b.** answer to question posed; qualitative **d.** survey data

Chapter 2

2.5 a. $X - 8, Y - 9, Z - 3$ **b.** $X - .40, Y - .45, Z - .15$ **2.7 a.** $39/266 = .147$ **b.** level 2 $-.286$, level 3 $-.188$, level 4 $-.327$, level 5 $-.041$, level 6 $-.011$ **e.** level 4 **2.9 a.** relative frequencies: Black $-.207$; White $-.635$; Sumatran $-.017$; Javan $-.003$; Indian $-.137$ **c.** $.842; .157$ **2.11 a.** qualitative; infant, child, medical, infant & medical, child & medical, infant & child, infant & child & medical **b.** infant $-.061$; child $-.565$; medical $-.276$; infant & medical $-.001$; child & medical $-.030$; infant & child $-.062$; infant & child & medical $-.004$ **d.** $.312$ **2.13 a.** survey **b.** quantitative **c.** about 60% **2.15** 60% of sampled CEOs had advanced degrees **2.19** Over half of the whistle types were "Type a." **2.25 a.** 23 **2.27** frequencies: 50, 75, 125, 100, 25, 50, 50, 25

2.31 a.

Stem	Leaf
1	6
2	0 1 2 4 8
3	0 4 4 9
4	0 0 2
5	3

b. A students tend to read the most books

2.35 a.

Stem	Leaf
1	0000000
2	0
3	00
4	000
5	
6	
7	
8	
9	0
10	0
11	0
12	00

b. Yes **2.37** most of the PMI's range from 3 to 7.5

2.39 a.

Stem	Leaf
0	1 1 2 3 4 5 5 9
1	1 2 3
2	0 0
3	9
4	6
5	6
6	1 5
7	
8	
9	
10	0

c. eclipses **2.41 a.** Response rate of the familiarity group is higher. **b.** Familiarity group has highest rate; control group has lowest rate **2.43 a.** 23 **b.** 123 **c.** 18 **d.** 51 **e.** 529 **2.45 a.** 6 **b.** 50 **c.** 42.8 **2.47** mean, median, mode **2.49** sample size and variability of the data **2.51 a.** mean < median **b.** mean > median **c.** mean = median **2.53** mode = 15; mean = 14.545; median = 15 **2.55 a.** 8.5 **b.** 25 **c.** .78 **d.** 13.44 **2.57 a.** mean = 31.6; median = 32;mode = 34 and 40 **b.** little or no skewness **2.59 a.** 1.47 **b.** 1.49 **2.61 a.** mean = -4.86; median = -4.85; mode = -5.00 **2.63 b.** probably none **2.65 a.** qualitative, qualitative, quantitative, quantitative **c.** mean = 93.6; median = 91.5; mode = 86 **d.** mean = 95.3; median = 92; mode = 92 **e.** mean = 101.9; median = 103; mode = 113 **f.** three centers **g.** YND: mean = 46.88, median = 43.7, mode = 0; SLI: mean = 20.17, median = 32.5, mode = 0; OND: mean = 0, median = 0,mode = 0 **2.67 a.** mean = $-.15$; median = $-.11$; no mode **c.** mean = $-.12$; median = $-.105$; no mode **2.69** largest value minus smallest value **2.73** more variable **2.75 a.** 5, 3.7, 1.92 **b.** 99, 1,949.25, 44.15 **c.** 98, 1,307.84, 36.16 **2.77** data set 1: 1, 1, 2, 2, 3, 3, 4, 4, 5, 5; data set 2: 1, 1, 1, 1, 1,

5, 5, 5, 5, 5 **2.79 a.** 3, 1.3, 1.1402 **b.** 3, 1.3, 1.1402 **c.** 3, 1.3, 1.1402 **2.81 a.** 29, 75.7, 8.70 **b.** 24, 72.7, 8.53 **c.** A students **2.83 a.** .18
b. .0041 **c.** .064 **d.** Morning **2.85 a.** 12, 9.37, 3.06 **b.** 8, 5.15, 2.27; data less variable **c.** 8, 5.06, 2.25; data less variable **2.87 a.** dollars;
quantitative **b.** at least 3/4; at least 8/9; nothing; nothing **2.89 a.** ≈68% **b.** ≈95% **c.** ≈all **2.91** range/6 = 104.17, range/4 = 156.25; no
2.93 a. $\bar{x}$ = 94.42, s = 4.38 **b.** (90.04, 98.80); (85.66, 103.18); (81.28, 107.56) **c.** 68.4%, 96.6%, 97.1%; yes **2.95 a.** unknown **b.** ≈84%
2.97 a. (0, 300.5) **b.** (0, 546) **c.** handrubbing appears to be more effective **2.99 a.** at least 8/9 of the velocities will fall within 936 ± 3(10)
b. No **2.101 a.** 19 ± 195 **b.** 7 ± 147 **c.** SAT-Math **2.103 a.** 25%; 75% **b.** 50%; 50% **c.** 80%; 20% **d.** 16%; 84% **2.105** ≈95%
2.107 a. z = 2 **b.** z = −3 **c.** z = −2 **d.** z = 1.67 **2.109** 26.5th percentile **2.111 a.** z = −4.66 **b.** z = −.32 **2.113 a.** 23 **b.** z = 3.28
2.115 a. −0.2 **b.** −0.06 **c.** z = −4.65 **2.117 a.** z = 2.0: 3.7; z = −1.0: 2.2; z = .5: 2.95; z = −2.5: 1.45 **b.** 1.9 **c.** mound-shaped; symmetric **2.123 a.** no, z = .73 **b.** yes, z = −3.27 **c.** no, z = 1.36 **d.** yes, z = 3.73 **2.125 a.** 4 **b.** Q_U ≈ 6, Q_L ≈ 3 **c.** 3 **d.** skewed right
e. 50%; 75% **f.** 12, 13, and 16 **2.127 a.** −1.26 **b.** No **2.129 b.** variability for 2000 is slightly greater than 1990 **c.** No **2.131 b.** medians:
Familiar ≈45, Treatment ≈40, Control ≈30 **b.** c. IQR for Treatment appears to be largest **d.** yes **e.** no **2.133 a.** suspect outliers: 74, 79, 79,
81, and 81 **b.** levels with |z| > 3: 74, 79, 79, 81, and 81 **2.135** Group 1: M = 48, IQR = 12; group 2: M = 47.5, IQR = 12; group 3: M = 46,
IQR = 4 **2.139** slight positive linear trend **2.141** yes, positive linear trend **2.143 a.** nonlinear increasing **b.** nonlinear increasing
2.145 a. no **b.** yes, slight positive **c.** reliability is suspect (only 5 data points) **2.147 a.** negative trend **b.** positive trend **2.155 a.** −1, 1, 2
b. −2, 2, 4 **c.** 1, 3, 4 **d.** .1, .3, .4 **2.157 a.** 3.1234 **b.** 9.0233 **c.** 9.7857 **2.159 a.** $\bar{x}$ = 5.67, s^2 = 1.0667, s = 1.03 **b.** $\bar{x}$ = −$1.5, s^2 = 11.5,
s = $3.39 **c.** $\bar{x}$ = .4125%, s^2 = .0883, s = .30% **d.** 3; $10; .7375% **2.161** yes, positive **2.163** yes **2.165** z = −1.06 **2.167 a.** current:
42.0%; retired: 58.0% **b.** Most (40 of 50) Beanie babies have values less than $100. **c.** yes, positive **d.** unknown; at least 84%; at least 93.7%
e. 44%; 98%; 100% **f.** 90%; 98%; 98% **2.169 c.** 26.4 ± 21.2 **d.** 24.5 ± 22.4 **2.171 a.** "favorable/recommended"; .635 **b.** yes
2.173 a. 28.5% **b.** 71% **c.** female **2.175 a.** at most 25% **b.** ≈2.5% **2.177 b.** customers 238, 268, 269, and 264 **c.** z = 1.92, 2.06, 2.13,
3.14 **2.179 a.** Seabirds—quantitative; length—quantitative; oil—qualitative **b.** transect **c.** oiled: 38%; unoiled: 62% **e.** distributions are
similar **f.** 3.27 ± 13.4 **g.** 3.495 ± 11.936 **h.** unoiled **2.181 b.** yes **c.** A1775A: $\bar{x}$ = 19,462.2, s = 532.29; A1775B: $\bar{x}$ = 22,838.5,
s = 560.98 **d.** cluster A1775A **2.183 a.** quantitative: days and year **b.** lesser crimes **c.** yes **d.** mean = 41.4 days; median = 15 days
e. no; z = 2.38 **f.** no **2.185 a.** median **b.** mean **2.187** survey results biased, not reliable

Chapter 3

3.9 a. .5 **b.** .3 **c.** .6 **3.11** P(A) = .55; P(B) = .50; P(C) = .70 **3.13 a.** 10 **b.** 20 **c.** 15,504 **3.15 a.** (R_1R_2), (R_1R_3), (R_2R_3), (R_1B_1),
(R_1B_2), (R_2B_1), (R_2B_2), (R_3B_1), (R_3B_2), (B_1B_2) **b.** 1/10 for each sample point **c.** P(A) = 1/10, P(B) = 6/10, P(C) = 3/10 **3.17** .05
3.19 a. .01 **b.** yes **3.21 a.** .261 **b.** Trunk −.85, Leaves −.10, Branch −.05 **3.23 a.** a. 1, 2, 3, 4, 5, 6, 7, 8, 9 **b.** c. .147, .101, .104, .133, .097,
.157, .120, .083, .058 **d.** .248 **e.** .418 **3.25 a.** 6 **b.** .282, .0365, .339, .032, .008, .274 **c.** .686 **3.27 a.** 28 **b.** 1/28 **3.29** Probabilities are the
same **3.31 a.** 15 **b.** 20 **c.** 15 **d.** 6 **3.41 b.** P(A) = 7/8, P(B) = 1/2, P(A ∪ B) = 7/8, P(A^c) = 1/8, P(A ∩ B) = 1/2 **c.** 7/8 **d.** no
3.43 a. ³/₄ **b.** 13/20 **c.** 1 **d.** 2/5 **e.** ¼ **f.** 7/20 **g.** 1 **h.** ¼ **3.45 a.** .65 **b.** .72 **c.** .25 **d.** .08 **e.** .35 **f.** .72 **g.** .65 g. A and C, B and
C, C and D **3.47** A = {eighth-grader scores above 655 on mathematics assessment test}; P(A^c) = .95 **3.49 a.** {11, 13, 15, 17, 29, 31, 33, 35}
b. {2, 4, 6, 8, 10, 11, 13, 15, 17, 20, 22, 24, 26, 28, 29, 31, 33, 35, 1, 3, 5, 7, 9, 19, 21, 23, 25, 27} **c.** P(A) = 9/19, P(B) = 9/19, P(A ∩ B) =
4/19, P(A ∪ B) = 14/19, P(C) = 9/19 **d.** {11, 13, 15, 17} **e.** 14/19, no **f.** 2/19 **g.** {1, 2, 3, ..., 29, 31, 33, 35} **h.** 16/19 **3.51 a.** (PTW-R,
Jury), (PTW-R, Judge), (PTW-A/D, Jury), (PTW-A/D, Judge), (DTW-R, Jury), (DTW-R, Judge), (DTW-A/D, Jury), (DTW-A/D, Judge) **b.** .684
c. .124 **d.** no **e.** .316 **f.** .717 **g.** .091 **3.53 a.** .157 **b.** .029 **c.** .291 **3.55 a.** ½ **b.** 5/6 **3.63 a.** .5 **b.** .25 **c.** no **3.65 a.** .08 **b.** .40
c. .52 **3.67 a.** P(A) = .4; P(B) = .8; P(A ∩ B) = .3 **b.** P(E_1|A) = .25, P(E_2|A) = .25, P(E_3|A) = .5 **c.** .75 **3.69** no **3.71** 1/3, 0,
1/14, 1/7, 1 **3.73** .364 **3.75 a.** .1 **b.** .522 **c.** The person is guessing. **3.77 a.** .75 **b.** .5 **c.** .4 **3.79 a.** 38/132 = .2879 **b.** 29/123 = .236
3.81 a. P(A|I) = .9, P(B|I) = .95, P(A|N) = .2, P(B|N) = .1 **b.** .855 **c.** .02 **d.** .995 **3.83 a.** .333 **b.** .120
c. No **d.** probability of playing Center depends on race **3.85 b.** .147 **c.** .85 **d.** .65 **e.** yes **f.** African Americans are stopped for
speeding more often than expected **3.87 a.** .116 **b.** .728 **3.89 a.** .553 **b.** P(W|CA) = 1; P(W|CB) = .873; P(W|CC) = .559;
P(W|BA) = .741; P(W|BB) = .547; P(W|BC) = .342; P(W|AA) = .536; P(W|AB) = .216; P(W|AC) = .077 **c.** .856 **d.** .552
3.91 b. Worst −.250, 2nd worst −.200, 3rd worst −.157, 4th worst −.120, 5th worst −.089, 6th worst −.064, 7th worst −.044, 8th worst −.029,
9th worst −.018, 10th worst −.011, 11th worst −.007, 12th worst −.006, 13th worst −.005 **c.** 250/800 = .313 **d.** .297, .284, .274, .267, .262,
.257, .255, .253, .252, .252, .251 **e.** .288 **3.97 a.** 35,820,200 **b.** 1/35,820,200 **c.** highly unlikely **3.109 a.** 4 **b.** 8 **c.** 32 **d.** 2^n

3.111 a. 35 **b.** 15 **c.** 435 **d.** 45 **e.** $\binom{q}{r} = \dfrac{q!}{r!(q-r!)}$ **3.113 a.** 56 **b.** 1,680 **c.** 6,720 **3.115 a.** 24 **b.** 12 **3.117 a.** 30 **b.** 1,050

3.119 a. 6 **b.** 1/3 **3.121 a.** 3,003 **b.** .0186 **c.** .5734 **3.123 a.** 21/252 **b.** 21/252 **c.** 105/252 **3.125 a.** 2,598,960 **b.** .002 **c.** .00394
d. .0000154 **3.129 a.** .225 **b.** .125 **c.** .35 **d.** .643 **e.** .357 **3.131** .2 **3.133 a.** .5 **b.** .99 **c.** .847 **3.135** .966 **3.137 a.** #4 **b.** #4
or #6 **3.139 a.** A ∪ B **b.** B^c **c.** A ∩ B **d.** A^c|B **3.141 a.** 0 **b.** no **3.143** .5 **3.145 c.** P(A) = 1/4; P(B) = ½ **e.** P(A^c) = 3/4;
P(B^c) = 1/2; P(A ∩ B) = 1/4; P(A ∪ B) = 1/2; P(A|B) = 1/2; P(B|A) = 1 **f.** no, no **3.147 a.** no **b.** .3, .1 **c.** .37 **3.149 a.** false
b. true **c.** true **d.** false **3.151** .545 **3.153 a.** .02 **b.** .08 **3.155 c.** .6637, .1815, .1263, .0214, .0071 **d.** .2029 **3.157 a.** Total population,
Agricultural change, Presence of industry, Growth, Population concentration **b.** .18, .05, .27, .05, .45 **c.** .63 **3.159 a.** .385 **b.** .378 **c.** .183
3.161 a. .64, .32, .04 **b.** .72, .22, .06 **c.** dependent **3.163 a.** .4096 **b.** .0016 **c.** .9984 **3.165 a.** .7127 **b.** .2873 **c.** .9639 **d.** .3078
e. .0361 **f.** at least 3 **3.167 a.** 38,798,760 **b.** .105 **c.** .237 **3.169 a.** 1 to 2 **b.** .5 **c.** .4 **3.171 a.** .25 **b.** .0156 **c.** .4219 **d.** .001,
.000000001, .9970 **3.173** .993 **3.175** 4.4739×10^{-28} **3.177** yes **3.179** Marilyn

Chapter 4

4.3 a. discrete **b.** continuous **c.** continuous **d.** discrete **e.** continuous **f.** continuous **4.5 a.** continuous **b.** discrete **c.** discrete
d. discrete **e.** discrete **f.** continuous **4.7** 0, 1, 2, 3, ...; discrete **4.9** table, graph, formula **4.11 a.** .25 **b.** .40 **c.** .75 **4.13 a.** .7 **b.** .3
c. 1 **d.** .2 **e.** .8 **4.15 a.** a. P(0) = 1/8, P(1) = 3/8, P(2) = 3/8, P(3) = 1/8 **d.** 1/2 **4.17 a.** 1 **b.** .24 **c.** .39 **4.19 a.** .9985, .0015, 0, 0
c. 1 **4.21** P(−3) = .1, P(−1) = .105, P(5) = .795 **4.23 b.** .85 **c.** .6, 0, 0, 0, .7 **4.25** 7/8 **4.29** ≈.95 **4.31 a.** 3.8 **b.** 10.56 **c.** 3.2496
e. no **f.** yes **4.33 a.** μ_x = 1, μ_y = 1 **b.** distribution of x **c.** μ_x = 1, σ = .6; μ_y = 1, σ = .2 **4.35 b.** 4.65 **4.37 a.** a_1: 2.4; a_2: 1.5;

$a_3 - a_5$: .90; a_6: 1.65 **b.** a_1: .86, (.68, 4.12); a_2: .67, (.16, 2.84); $a_3 - a_5$: .3, (.3, 1.5); a_6: .57, (.51, 2.79) **4.39** $-\$0.263$ **4.41 a.** $p(x) = .05$ for all x-values **b.** 52.5 **c.** $(-5.16, 110.16)$ **f.** 33.25, 38.36 **g.** .525 **i.** .20 **j.** .65 **4.43 a.** mean = 2.9; median = 3 **b.** 3, 4 **d.** 3, 3

4.45 $p(x) = \binom{7}{x}.2^x.8^{7-x}$ $(x = 0, 1, 2, \ldots, 7)$ **4.47 a.** 15 **b.** 10 **c.** 1 **d.** 1 **e.** 4 **4.49 a.** .4096 **b.** .3456 **c.** .027 **d.** .0081

e. .3456 **f.** .027 **4.51 a.** $\mu = 12.5, \sigma^2 = 6.25, \sigma = 2.5$ **b.** $\mu = 16, \sigma^2 = 12.8, \sigma = 3.578$ **c.** $\mu = 60, \sigma^2 = 24, \sigma = 4.899$ **d.** $\mu = 63$, $\sigma^2 = 6.3, \sigma = 2.510$ **e.** $\mu = 48, \sigma^2 = 9.6, \sigma = 3.098$ **f.** $\mu = 40, \sigma^2 = 38.4, \sigma = 6.197$ **4.53 a.** 0 **b.** .998 **c.** .137 **4.55 a.** $p = .5$ **b.** $p < .5$ **c.** $p > .5$ **4.57 b.** .05 **c.** 10 **4.59 a.** .001 **b.** .322 **c.** .994 **4.61 a.** .9861 **b.** .000000384 **c.** 5 **4.63 a.** .7908 **b.** .0555 **4.65 a.** .1 **b.** .7 **c.** .4783 **d.** .0078 **e.** yes **4.67 b.** $\mu = 2.4, \sigma = 1.47$ **c.** $p = .9, q = .1, n = 24, \mu = 21.6, \sigma = 1.47$ **4.71** 3 **4.73 b.** $\mu = 3, \sigma = 1.7321$ **4.75 a.** .934 **b.** .191 **c.** .125 **d.** .223 **e.** .777 **f.** .001 **4.77 b.** $\mu = 3, \sigma = 1.7321$ **c.** .966 **4.79 a.** .368 **b.** .264 **c.** .920 **4.81 a.** .0224 **b.** .0850 **c.** $\mu = 3.8, \sigma = 1.9494$ **4.83 a.** 2 **b.** no, $p = .003$ **4.85 a.** $p(2) = .039, p(6) = .160$, $p(10) = .047$ **c.** $\mu = 6.2, \sigma = 2.490$ **d.** very unlikely **4.87** yes, .96 **4.91 a.** .3 **b.** .119 **c.** .167 **d.** .167 **4.93 b.** $\mu = 4, \sigma = .853$ **d.** .939 **4.95 a.** hypergeometric **b.** binomial **4.97 a.** .383 **b.** .0002 **4.99** .2693 **4.101 a.** .0883 **b.** .1585 **4.103** $P(x = 1) = .25$ **4.105 a.** $\mu = 113.24, \sigma = 4.194$ **b.** $z = 6.38$ **4.107 a.** Poisson **b.** binomial **c.** binomial **4.109 a.** .192 **b.** .228 **c.** .772 **d.** .987 **e.** .960 **f.** 14; 4.2; 2.05 **g.** .975 **4.111 a.** .243 **b.** .131 **c.** .36 **d.** .157 **e.** .128 **f.** .121 **4.113 a.** .180 **b.** .015 **c.** .076 **4.115 b.** 1/30 **c.** .1455 **d.** .1559 **4.117** binomial **4.119 a.** yes **b.** .051 **c.** .757 **d.** .192 **e.** 3.678 **4.121 a.** $\mu = 520, \sigma = 13.491$ **b.** no, $z = -8.895$ **4.123** .642 **4.125 a.** .383 **b.** .983 **c.** 20 **4.127 a.** .006 **b.** insecticide is less effective than claimed. **4.129 a.** A: 4.60; B: 3.70 **b.** A: $\$46,000$; B: $\$55,500$ **c.** A: 1.34, 1.16; B: 1.21, 1.10 **d.** A: .95; B: .95 **4.131** .0005 **4.133** NASA: .0004; Air Force: .5155; Air Force

Chapter 5

5.3 b. $\mu = 20, \sigma = 5.774$ **c.** $(8.452, 31.548)$ **5.5 b.** $\mu = 3, \sigma = .577$ **c.** .577 **d.** .61 **e.** .65 **f.** 0 **5.7 a.** 0 **b.** 1 **c.** 1 **5.9 a.** .1333, .5714 **b.** .2667, 0 **5.11** yes **5.13 a.** continuous **b.** $\mu = 7, \sigma = .2887$ **c.** .5 **d.** 0 **e.** .75 **f.** .0002 **5.15** .4444 **5.17** symmetric, bell-shaped curve **5.19** normal with $\mu = 0$ and $\sigma = 1$ **5.21 a.** .4772 **b.** .3413 **c.** .4545 **d.** .2190 **5.23 a.** 0 **b.** .8413 **c.** .8413 **d.** .1587 **e.** .6826 **f.** .9544 **g.** .6934 **h.** .6378 **5.25 a.** 1.645 **b.** 1.96 **c.** -1.96 **d.** 1.28 **e.** 1.28 **5.27 a.** 0 **b.** 1 **c.** 2.5 **d.** -3 **e.** 5 **f.** 1.4 **5.29 a.** .0456, .0026 **b.** .6826, .9544 **c.** 325.2; 261.6 **5.31 a.** 19.76 **b.** 36.72 **c.** 48.64 **5.33** 182 **5.35 a.** .9406 **b.** .9406 **c.** .1140 **5.37 a.** .1558 **b.** .2586 **c.** .0062 **d.** .9525 **5.39 a.** .4107 **b.** .1508 **c.** .9066 **d.** .0162 **e.** 841.8 **5.41 a.** .0735 **b.** .3651 **c.** 7.29 **5.43** $d = 56.24$ **5.45 a.** .3745 **b.** .7553 **5.47 a.** $z_L = -.675, z_U = .675$ **b.** $-2.68, 2.68$ **c.** $-4.69, 4.69$ **d.** .0074, 0 **5.51 a.** .68 **b.** .95 **c.** .997 **5.53** plot c **5.55 a.** not normal (skewed right) **b.** $Q_L = 37.5, Q_U = 152.8, s = 95.8$ **c.** IQR/s = 1.204 **5.57 a.** 7 **b.** 6.12 **c.** IQR/s = 1.14 **5.59** approx. normal **5.61** both distributions approx. normal **5.63** IQR/s = 1.3, histogram approx. normal **5.65** The lowest score of 0 is less than one standard deviation below the mean. **5.69 a.** yes **b.** $\mu = 10, \sigma^2 = 6$ **c.** .726 **d.** .7291 **5.71 a.** .1788 **b.** .5236 **c.** .6950 **5.73 a.** 40 **b.** 5.66 **c.** 1.86 **d.** .9686 **5.75 a.** 10 **b.** 3.082 **c.** .16 **d.** .4364 **5.77 a.** no **b.** yes **c.** yes **5.79** ≈ 0 **5.81 a.** 0 **b.** .4641 **c.** no **5.83 a.** 300 **b.** 800 **c.** 1 **5.89 a.** .367879 **b.** .950213 **c.** .223130 **d.** .993262 **5.91** .950213 **5.93 a.** .449329 **b.** .864665 **5.95** .434598 **5.97 a.** .367879 **b.** .606531 **c.** .135335 **d.** .814046 **5.99 a.** 17 **b.** .5862 **5.103 a.** exponential **b.** uniform **c.** normal **5.105 a.** .9821 **b.** .0179 **c.** .9505 **d.** .3243 **e.** .9107 **f.** .0764 **5.107 a.** .6915 **b.** .0228 **c.** .5328 **d.** .3085 **e.** 0 **f.** .9938 **5.109 a.** .3821 **b.** .5398 **c.** 0 **d.** .1395 **5.111** .8315 **5.113 a.** 0 **b.** 1 **5.115 a.** .5124 **b.** .2912 **c.** .0027 **5.117 a.** .667 **b.** .333 **c.** 82.5°F **5.119** .3125 **5.121** .0154; very unlikely **5.123 a.** .0764 **b.** $(65.024, 88.576)$ **5.125** approx. normal **5.127 a.** (i) .384, (ii) .49, (iii) .212, (iv) .84 **b.** (i) .3849, (ii) .4938, (iii) .2119, (iv) .8413 **c.** (i) .0029, (ii) .0038, (iii) .0001, (iv) .0013 **5.129** 52 minutes **5.131** .2676; no **5.133** 0; unlikely **5.135 a.** .05, .20, .50, .20, .05 **b.** z-scores **c.** identical

Chapter 6

6.3 c. 1/16 **6.5 c.** .05 **d.** no **6.13** unbiased, minimum variance **6.15 a.** 5 **b.** $E(\bar{x}) = 5$ **c.** $E(M) = 4.778$ **d.** $\bar{x}$ **6.19** **b.** 1.61 **c.** $E(s^2) = 1.61$ **e.** $E(s) = 1.004$ **6.21** mean and standard deviation of sampling distribution of $\bar{x}$ **6.23** smaller **6.27 a.** $\mu = 100, \sigma = 5$ **b.** $\mu = 100, \sigma = 2$ **c.** $\mu = 100, \sigma = 1$ **d.** $\mu = 100, \sigma = 1.414$ **e.** $\mu = 100, \sigma = .447$ **f.** $\mu = 100, \sigma = .316$ **6.29 a.** $\mu = 2.9, \sigma^2 = 3.29, \sigma = 1.814$ **c.** $\mu_{\bar{x}} = 2.9, \sigma_{\bar{x}} = 1.283$ **6.31 a.** $\mu_{\bar{x}} = 30, \sigma_{\bar{x}} = 1.6$ **b.** approx. normal **c.** .8944 **d.** .0228 **e.** .1292 **f.** .9699 **6.35 a.** 79 **b.** 2.3 **c.** approx. normal **d.** .43 **e.** .3336 **6.37** .0838 **6.39 a.** $\mu_{\bar{x}} = 5.1, \sigma_{\bar{x}} = .4981$ **b.** yes **c.** .2119 **d.** .4071 **6.41 a.** .0013 **b.** program did decrease the mean number of sick days **6.43** handrubbing: $P(\bar{x} < 30) = .2743$; handwashing: $P(\bar{x} < 30) = .0047$; sample used handrubbing **6.45** false **6.47** true **6.49 b.** $E(A) = \alpha$ **c.** choose estimator with smallest variance **6.51 a.** .5 **b.** .0606 **c.** .0985 **d.** .8436 **6.57 a.** $\mu_{\bar{x}} = 89.34, \sigma_{\bar{x}} = 1.3083$ **c.** .8461 **e.** .0367 **6.59 a.** $\mu_{\bar{x}} = 1.3, \sigma_{\bar{x}} = .240$ **b.** yes **c.** .1056 **d.** .0062 **6.61** .9772 **6.63 a.** .008 **b.** n large **6.65 a.** discrete **b.** approximately normal with $\mu_{\bar{x}} = 1.5, \sigma_{\bar{x}} = .01764$ **c.** .0023 **d.** no **6.67** .9332 **6.69 a.** .0031 **b.** more likely if $\mu = 156$; less likely if $\mu = 158$ **c.** less likely if $\sigma = 2$; more likely if $\sigma = 6$

Chapter 7

7.5 yes **7.7 a.** 1.645 **b.** 2.58 **c.** 1.96 **d.** 1.28 **7.9 a.** $28 \pm .784$ **b.** $102 \pm .65$ **c.** $15 \pm .0588$ **d.** $4.05 \pm .163$ **e.** no **7.11 a.** 83.2 ± 1.25 **c.** 83.2 ± 1.65 **d.** increases **e.** yes **7.13 a.** 19.3 **b.** 19.3 ± 3.44 **d.** random sample, large n **7.15 a.** mean egg length for all New Zealand birds **c.** $\bar{x} = 68.28, s = 55.65$ **d.** 68.28 ± 20.27 **7.17 a.** $1.13 \pm .672$ **b.** yes **7.19 a.** 19 ± 7.826 **b.** 7 ± 5.90 **c.** SAT-Math **7.21** $.422 \pm .067$ **7.23 a.** μ_Y: $4.17 \pm .095$; μ_{MA}: $4.04 \pm .057$; μ_O: $4.31 \pm .062$ **b.** more likely **7.25** Central Limit Theorem no longer applies; σ unknown **7.29 a.** 2.228 **b.** 2.567 **c.** -3.707 **d.** -1.771 **7.31 a.** 5 ± 1.876 **b.** 5 ± 2.394 **c.** 5 ± 3.754 **d.** (a) $5 \pm .780$, (b) $5 \pm .941$, (c) 5 ± 1.276; width decreases **7.33 a.** .009 **b.** 2.306 **c.** $.009 \pm .0037$ **7.35 a.** 2.8856 ± 4.034 **b.** $.4083 \pm .2564$ **7.37 c.** $(1,633.05, 2,778.85)$ **e.** $(1,532.39, 2,658.81)$ **7.39 a.** 7.3 ± 1.41 **c.** PMI values normally distributed **7.41 a.** 37.3 ± 7.70 **c.** One hour before: $\mu > 25.5$ **7.45 a.** yes **b.** $.64 \pm .067$ **7.47 a.** yes **b.** no **c.** yes **d.** no **7.49 a.** .03 **b.** $.03 \pm .015$ **7.51** $.219 \pm .024$ **7.53 a.** $.368 \pm .129$ **b.** $.605 \pm .130$ **7.55 a.** .636 **b.** $.636 \pm .167$ **7.57 a.** $.524 \pm .095$ **7.59** 95%

confident that proportion of health care workers with latex allergy who suspect he/she has allergy is between .327 and .541 **7.61** true **7.63** 519
7.65 a. 482 **b.** 214 **7.67** 34 **7.69 a.** $n = 16$: $W = .98$; $n = 25$: $W = .784$; $n = 49$: $W = .56$; $n = 100$: $W = .392$; $n = 400$: $W = .196$
7.71 a. .90 **b.** .05 **c.** 259 **7.73** 97 **7.75** 14,735 **7.77** 129 **7.79** 271 **7.81 a.** μ **b.** μ **c.** p **d.** p **e.** p **7.83 a.** $t = 2.086$ **b.** $z = 1.96$
c. $z = 1.96$ **d.** $z = 1.96$ **e.** neither t nor z **7.85 a.** .57 $\pm$ .049 **b.** 2,358 **7.87** (1) p; (2) μ; (3) μ; (4) μ **7.89 b.** no assumptions needed
c. 95% confident claim is false **7.91** 1.37 $\pm$ .76 **7.95 a.** .660 $\pm$ .029 **b.** .301 $\pm$ .035 **7.97 a.** .044 $\pm$ .162 **b.** no evidence to indicate that
this species has tendency to inbreed **7.99 a.** .81 $\pm$ .41 **b.** 140 **7.101 a.** .378 $\pm$ .156 **b.** .703 $\pm$ .147 **c.** 41.405 $\pm$ 21.493 **d.** .378 $\pm$ .156
7.103 a. .094 **b.** yes **c.** .094 $\pm$ .037 **7.105 a.** 49.3 $\pm$ 8.60 **c.** Population is normal. **d.** 60 **7.107 a.** 781 **7.109 a.** yes **b.** missing
measure of reliability **c.** 95% CI for μ: .932 $\pm$ .037

Chapter 8

8.1 null hypothesis **8.3** α **8.7** no **8.9** H_0: $p = .75$, H_a: $p \neq .75$ **8.11 a.** H_0: $p = .45$ **b.** H_0: $\mu = 2.5$ **8.13 a.** H_0: $p = .75$, H_a: $p > .75$
8.15 a. H_0: $\mu = 15$, H_a: $\mu < 15$ **b.** conclude mean mercury level is less than 15 ppm when mean equals 15 ppm **c.** conclude mean mercury
level equals 15 ppm when mean is less than 15 ppm **8.17 a.** H_0: No intrusion occurs **b.** H_a: Intrusion occurs **c.** $\alpha = .001$, $\beta = .5$
8.21 g. (a) .025, (b) .05, (c) $\approx$.005, (d) $\approx$.10, (e) .10, (f) $\approx$.01 **8.23 a.** $z = 1.67$, reject H_0 **b.** $z = 1.67$, fail to reject H_0 **8.25 a.** Type I:
conclude mean response for all New York City public school children is not 3 when mean equals 3; Type II: conclude mean response for all New
York City public school children equals 3 when mean is not equal to 3 **b.** $z = -85.52$, reject H_0 **c.** $z = -85.52$, reject H_0 **8.27** yes,
$z = 12.36$ **8.29 a.** H_0: $\mu = 16$, H_a: $\mu < 16$ **b.** $z = -4.31$, reject H_0 **8.31 a.** $z = 4.03$, reject H_0 **8.33 a.** no **b.** $z = .61$, do not reject H_0
d. no **e.** $z = -.83$, do not reject H_0 **8.35 a.** $z = -3.72$, reject H_0 **8.37** small p-values **8.39 a.** fail to reject H_0 **b.** reject H_0 **c.** reject H_0
d. fail to reject H_0 **e.** fail to reject H_0 **8.41** .0150 **8.43** p-value = .9279, fail to reject H_0 **8.45 a.** fail to reject H_0 **b.** fail to reject H_0
c. reject H_0 **d.** fail to reject H_0 **8.47 a.** .3446 **b.** do not reject H_0 **8.49** p-value < .0001; reject H_0 at $\alpha = .05$ **8.51 b.** reject H_0 at
$\alpha = .05$ **c.** reject H_0 at $\alpha = .05$ **8.53** small n, normal population **8.57 a.** $t < -2.160$ or $t > 2.160$ **b.** $t > 2.500$ **c.** $t > 1.397$
d. $t < -2.718$ **e.** $t < -1.729$ or $t > 1.729$ **f.** $t < -2.353$ **8.59 a.** $t = -2.064$; fail to reject H_0 **b.** $t = -2.064$; fail to reject H_0 **c.** (a)
.05 < p-value < .10; (b) .10 < p-value < .20 **8.61 a.** H_0: $\mu = 5.70$, H_a: $\mu < 5.70$ **b.** $t < -2.821$ **c.** $t = -4.33$ **d.** reject H_0
8.63 $t = -.43$; fail to reject H_0 **8.65** $t = 3.72$, p-value = .006, reject H_0 **8.67** $t = 2.97$, fail to reject H_0: $\mu = .100$ **8.69** yes, $t = 1.95$
8.71 qualitative **8.73 a.** yes **b.** no **c.** yes **d.** no **e.** no **8.75 a.** $z = -2.00$ **b.** reject H_0 **c.** .0228 **8.77 a.** $z = 1.13$, fail to reject H_0
b. .1292 **8.79 a.** .043 **b.** H_0: $p = .07$, H_a: $p \neq .07$ **c.** $z = -1.35$ **d.** $|z| > 1.96$. **e.** do not reject H_0 **f.** .177 **8.81** yes, $z = 1.74$
8.83 yes, $z = -2.71$ **8.85** $z = 15.46$, reject H_0: $p = .167$ **8.87** no, $z = 1.49$ **8.89** $z = 33.47$, reject H_0: $p = .5$ **8.91** power = $1 - \beta$
8.93 b. 1,032.9 **d.** .7422 **e.** .2578 **8.95 a.** approx. normal, $\mu_{\bar{x}} = 50$, $\sigma_{\bar{x}} = 2.5$ **b.** approx. normal, $\mu_{\bar{x}} = 45$, $\sigma_{\bar{x}} = 2.5$ **c.** .2358 **d.** .7642
8.97 a. approx. normal, $\mu_{\bar{x}} = 10$, $\sigma_{\bar{x}} = 0.1$ **b.** approx. normal, $\mu_{\bar{x}} = 9.9$, $\sigma_{\bar{x}} = 0.1$ **c.** .8300 **d.** .8300 **8.99** power increases **8.101** .1075
8.105 false **8.107 a.** $\chi^2 < 6.26214$ or $\chi^2 > 27.4884$ **b.** $\chi^2 > 40.2894$ **c.** $\chi^2 > 21.0642$ **d.** $\chi^2 < 3.57056$ **e.** $\chi^2 < 1.63539$ or
$\chi^2 > 12.5916$ **f.** $\chi^2 < 13.8484$ **8.109 a.** $\chi^2 = 182.16$, reject H_0 **8.111 a.** H_0: $\sigma^2 = 225$, H_a: $\sigma^2 > 225$ **b.** $\chi^2 = 187.896$ **c.** p-value =
.9938, do not reject H_0 **8.113** $\chi^2 = 12.61$, fail to reject H_0 **8.115** $\chi^2 = 2.16$, fail to reject H_0 **8.117 a.** no, $\chi^2 = 2.09$ **b.** The population of
CO_2 amounts are normally distributed. **8.119** alternative **8.121** H_0, H_a, α **8.123** null **8.125 a.** $z = -1.78$, fail to reject H_0 **b.** $z = -1.78$,
fail to reject H_0 **c.** .29 $\pm$ .063 **d.** .29 $\pm$ .083 **e.** 549 **8.127 a.** $\chi^2 = 63.48$, reject H_0 **b.** $\chi^2 = 63.48$, reject H_0 **8.129 a.** H_0: Drug is
unsafe, H_a: Drug is safe **b.** α **8.131 a.** $t = -3.46$, reject H_0 **b.** normal population **8.133 a.** H_0: $p = .5$, H_a: $p \neq .5$ **b.** $z = 5.99$
c. yes **d.** reject H_0 **8.135 a.** H_0: $\mu = 10$, H_a: $\mu > 10$; one-tailed **b.** $z > 1.645$ **c.** $z = 1.29$, fail to reject H_0 **8.137 a.** $t = 1.44$,
p-value = .169, fail to reject H_0 **b.** yes **8.139 a.** $z = .70$, fail to reject H_0 **b.** yes **8.141 a.** no, $z = 1.41$ **b.** small α **8.143 a.** no **b.** $\beta = .5910$,
power = .4090 **c.** power increases **8.145** $z = 21.66$, reject H_0 **8.147 b.** .37, .24 **8.149 a.** yes, $z = 4.55$ **b.** unknown; Type II error
c. .01; Type I error **d.** .94 **e.** .352

Chapter 9

9.1 normally distributed with mean $\mu_1 - \mu_2$ and standard deviation $\sqrt{\dfrac{\sigma_1^2}{n_1} + \dfrac{\sigma_2^2}{n_2}}$ **9.3 a.** no **b.** no **c.** no **d.** yes **e.** no **9.5** b **9.7 a.** 14; .4
b. 10; .3 **c.** 4; .5 **d.** yes **9.9 a.** .5989 **b.** $t = -2.39$, reject H_0 **c.** $-1.24 \pm .98$ **9.11 a.** fail to reject H_0 at $\alpha = .10$ **b.** p-value = .0575,
reject H_0 at $\alpha = .10$ **9.13 a.** $\mu_1 - \mu_2$ **b.** 12.5 $\pm$ 10.2 **9.15 a.** $z = -2.64$, reject H_0 **b.** $z = .27$, fail to reject H_0 **9.17 a.** H_0: $\mu_1 - \mu_2 = 0$,
H_a: $\mu_1 - \mu_2 \neq 0$ **b.** reject H_0 **c.** fail to reject H_0 **9.19 a.** (−.60, 7.96) **b.** independent random samples from normal populations with
equal variances **9.21 a.** $t = -7.24$, p-value = 0; reject H_0 **b.** $t = -.50$, p-value = .62; fail to reject H_0 **c.** $t = -1.25$, p-value = .21; fail
to reject H_0 **d.** independent random samples **9.23** no, $t = .18$ **9.25 a.** $\mu_1 - \mu_2$ **b.** no **c.** .2262 **d.** fail to reject H_0 **9.27** $t = -.46$, fail
to reject H_0 **9.29 a.** no standard deviations reported **b.** $s_1 = s_2 = 5$ **c.** $s_1 = s_2 = 6$ **9.31** before **9.33 a.** $t > 1.833$ **b.** $t > 1.328$
c. $t > 2.776$ $t > 2.896$ **9.35 a.** $\bar{x}_D = 2$, $s^2_D = 2$ **b.** $\mu_D = \mu_1 - \mu_2$ **c.** 2 $\pm$ 1.484 **d.** $t = 3.46$, reject H_0 **9.37 a.** $z = 1.79$, fail to reject
H_0 **b.** .0734 **9.39 a.** μ_D **b.** paired difference **c.** H_0: $\mu_D = 0$, H_a: $\mu_D > 0$ **d.** $t = 2.19$ **e.** reject H_0 **9.41 a.** 749.5 $\pm$ 278.1 **9.43 a.**
H_0: $\mu_D = 0$, H_a: $\mu_D \neq 0$ **b.** $z = 2.08$, p-value = .0376 **c.** reject H_0 **9.45 a.** b. 95% CI for μ_D: 1.95 $\pm$ 1.91; control group has larger mean
9.47 $t = -2.306$, p-value = .0163, reject H_0 at $\alpha = .05$ **9.49 a.** both have binomial distributions **b.** approx. normal with mean $p_1 - p_2$ and
standard deviation $\sqrt{\dfrac{p_1 q_1}{n_1} + \dfrac{p_2 q_2}{n_2}}$ **9.53 a.** $z < -2.33$ **b.** $z < -1.96$ **c.** $z < -1.645$ **d.** $z < -1.28$ **9.55 a.** .07 $\pm$ .067 **b.** .06 $\pm$ .086
c. −.15 $\pm$ .131 **9.57** $z = 1.16$, fail to reject H_0 **9.59 a.** .153 **b.** .215 **c.** −.062 $\pm$ .070 **9.61 a.** .143 **b.** .049 **c.** $z = 2.27$, fail to reject
d. reject H_0 **9.63** $z = -1.201$, fail to reject H_0 **9.65** yes; $z = 2.13$, reject H_0 at $\alpha = .05$ **9.67** $z = 5.47$, reject H_0: $p_1 - p_2 = 0$ in favor of
H_a: $p_1 - p_2 > 0$ **9.69 a.** at least 18 **b.** sample may not be representative of the population **9.73** $n_1 = n_2 = 24$ **9.75 a.** $n_1 = n_2 = 29,954$
b. $n_1 = n_2 = 2,165$ **c.** $n_1 = n_2 = 49$ **9.77** $n_1 = n_2 = 1,113$ **9.79** $n_1 = n_2 = 130$ **9.81** $n_1 = n_2 = 1,729$ **9.83** $n_1 = n_2 = 136$ **9.87** false
9.89 a. .025 **b.** .90 **c.** .99 **d.** .05 **9.91 a.** $F > 2.36$ **b.** $F > 3.04$ **c.** $F > 3.84$ **d.** $F > 5.12$ **9.93 a.** $F = 3.43$, reject H_0 **b.** $F = 3.43$,
reject H_0 **9.95 a.** H_0: $\sigma_M^2 = \sigma_F^2$, H_a: $\sigma_M^2 < \sigma_F^2$ **b.** $F = 1.06$ **c.** $F > 1.26$ **d.** p-value > .10 **e.** fail to reject H_0 **9.97** $F = 1.16$, fail
to reject H_0 **9.99 a.** $F = 1.44$, fail to reject H_0 **b.** $F = 5.25$, fail to reject H_0 **c.** no differences **9.101** $F = 1.045$, fail to reject H_0 **9.103**
a. $\mu_1 - \mu_2$ **b.** $\mu_1 - \mu_2$ **c.** $p_1 - p_2$ **d.** σ_1^2 / σ_2^2 **e.** $p_1 - p_2$ **9.105 a.** $t = .78$, fail to reject H_0 **b.** 2.5 $\pm$ 8.99 **c.** $n_1 = n_2 = 225$

9.107 a. $3.9 \pm .31$ **b.** $z = 20.60$, reject H_0 **c.** $n_1 = n_2 = 346$ **9.109 a.** $t = 5.73$, reject H_0 **b.** 3.8 ± 1.84 **9.111 a.** p-value $= .871$, fail to reject H_0: $\mu_{no} - \mu_{yes} = 0$ **9.113 a.** time needed **b.** climbers **c.** paired experiment **9.115 a.** H_0: $\mu_D = 0$, H_a: $\mu_D > 0$, **b.** paired difference test **d.** leadership: fail to reject H_0 at $\alpha = .05$; popularity: reject H_0 at $\alpha = .05$; intellectual self-confidence: reject H_0 at $\alpha = .05$ **9.117** $z = 1.21$, fail to reject H_0 at $\alpha = .01$ **9.119 a.** H_0: $\mu_1 - \mu_2 = 0$, H_a: $\mu_1 - \mu_2 \neq 0$ **b.** hours of work: fail to reject H_0; free time: reject H_0 at $\alpha = .05$; breaks: reject H_0 at $\alpha = .01$ **9.121 a.** t test **b.** yes **c.** no **d.** fail to reject H_0 **e.** reject H_0 at $\alpha = .05$ **9.123** $t = 1.77$, fail to reject H_0 at $\alpha = .01$ **9.125** $z = -2.55$, reject H_0 **9.127** $-.33 \pm .22$ **9.129 a.** yes, $F = 10$ **b.** both populations normal **9.131** $z = -3.55$, reject H_0: $p_1 - p_2 = 0$ **9.133** yes, $t = -2.19$ **9.135** use of creative ideas ($z = 8.85$); good use of job skills ($z = 4.76$)

Subject Index

A

Accuracy score, 53
Additive rule of probability, 139–141
Adjusted confidence interval procedure for p, applying, 347
Adjusted multiple coefficient of determination, 674
Agent Orange, 821
  comparing the TCDD levels in fat and plasma of Vietnam Vets, 843–844
  testing correlation of the TCDD levels in fat and plasma of Vietnam Vets, 865
  testing the median TCDD level of Vietnam Vets, 827
Alternative hypothesis, 370
  steps for selecting, 377
  symbol for, 418
Analysis of variance (ANOVA), 512–589, 578
  checking the assumptions, 529–531
  completely randomized design, 520–537
  for a completely randomized design: steps for conducting, 531
  defined, 527
  designed experiment:
    elements of, 514–520
    two-factor experiment, 517
  factorial experiments, 560–577
  F-test, 675
  guidelines for selecting a multiple comparisons method in, 541
  multiple comparisons of means, 537–545
  randomized block design, 545–560
ANOVA F-test:
  to compare k treatment means: randomized block design, 548
  to compare k treatment means for a completely randomized design, 525
  in a completely randomized design, 579
  conducting, 525–528
  in a factorial design, 579
  in a randomized block design, 579
Anscombe, Francis J., 741
Aphasia study, 30–31
Arithmetic mean, 55–56
Ars Conjectandi (Bernoulli), 205

B

Balanced design, 520, 564, 579
Bar graph, 32–33
Base level, 709, 710
Bayes, Thomas, 174, 176
Bayesian statistical methods, 174
Bayes's rule, 174–179
  applying, 174–175
  defined, 175
Bayes's theorem, 176
Bell curve, 243
Bell-shaped probability distribution, 243
Bernoulli, Jacob, 205
Biased estimate, 299–301
Binomial experiment, 204

Binomial model, using to solve the cocaine sting case, 215
Binomial probability distributions:
  applying, 209
  defined, 208
  deriving, 206–209
Binomial random variables, 204–219
  finding the mean, variance, and standard deviation, 210
Binomial tables, using, 210–213
Bivariate data, graphing, 96–98
Bivariate relationships, 624
  defined, 95
  graphing, 95–98
Blocking, 456
Blocks, 545
Bonferroni, Carlo E., 538
Bonferroni's method, 538, 579
Bootstrap, 437
Bound on an estimation error, 10
Box plots, 86
  aids to the interpretation of, 88
  comparing, 89–90
  elements of, 88
  using the computer, 88–89

C

Categorical data, and multinomial experiment, 783–785
Categorical data analysis, 782–819
  chi-square test, caution about, 811
  one-way table, 785–794
  one-way X^2 test, conducting, 788–789
  two-way contingency table, 794–811
    finding expected cell counts for, 796
    general form of analysis, 799
Categorical variable, 709
Categories, 784
Cell counts, 784
Cells, 784
Census, 7
Central Limit Theorem, 304–305, 312, 436
  practical application of, 307–309
  using to find a probability, 305–307
Central tendency, 823
  defined, 55
  measures of, 55–63
Chebyshev, P. L., 73
Chebyshev's Rule, 73, 76
Chi-square statistic, 812
Chi-square tests, 786, 812
  caution about, 811
Chi-square (X^2) distribution, 412–413
Clark, David, 734
Class, 31
Class frequency, 30–31
Class intervals, 43
Class percentage, 31
Class relative frequency, 30–31
Classes, 784

Cluster sampling, 205
CNN poll, 14, 204
Cockroach study, 513
  one-way analysis, 531–532
  ranking the means of the cockroach groups, 541–542
  two-way analysis of the cockroach data, 571–572
Coded variable, 663
Coefficient of correlation, 624–628, 625
  defined, 625
  finding, 626–628
  population correlation coefficient, 628
Coefficient of determination, 628–635, 649
  defined, 630
Combinations Rule, 129–130
  applying, 168–169
  defined, 169
Combinatorial mathematics, 129
Comparisonwise error rate, 538
Complement, defined, 137
Complementary events, 137–139
  finding the probability of, 138
  rule of complements, applying, 138–139
Complete 4×2 factorial, 561
Complete factorial design, 579
Complete factorial experiment, defined, 560
Complete model, 725, 769
Complete (nested) model, 725
Complete second-order model, 703
  defined, 703
  in two xs, 704–705
  with two quantitative independent variables, 703
Completely randomized design, 520–537, 579
  assigning treatments in, 520–525
Compound events, 133
Conditional probability, 145–148
  finding, 148
Conditional probability formula:
  applying, 146–147
  defined, 146
Condominium sale price:
  building a model for, 730–731
  residual analysis for, 756–758
Condominium sale price modeling, 661–662
  first-order model for, 687–688
Confidence coefficient, 359
  defined, 324
Confidence interval, 11, 359, 637
  defined, 324
  estimation with, 320–367
  for mean of y, 636
  for a paired difference, TI-83 graphing calculator, 460–462
  for a population mean, interpretation of, 327
Confidence level:
  defined, 324
Contingency tables, 794, 812
  TI-83 graphing calculator, 801–803

Continuous probability distributions, 237–238
Continuous random variables, 236–289
  cumulative probabilities for:
    using MINITAB, 286–289
  uniform probability distribution, 238–241
  values of, 191–192
Contrasts, 538
Control group, 53
Correction for continuity, 270
Correlated errors, 763
Correlation, 624
Correlation coefficient, 649
Corrosion baths, 734
Countable list, 191
Counting rules, 165
  applying, 169–172
  summary of, 169
Counts, 784
Coupon users study, 783
  testing category proportions for customer type in, 790–791
  testing coupon customer characteristics, 803–805
Critical thinking, role of statistics in, 17–19
Cumulative binomial probabilities, 211

D
Data, 4
Data collection, 14–16
Data collection method:
  examples, 15–16
  identifying, 16
Data sets, 28–117
Data types, 12–13
  identifying, 16
De Moivre, Abraham, 271
Degrees of freedom (df), 333, 436
Dependence, 797
Dependent events, 151, 153
Dependent variable, 594, 648
Descriptive statistical problems, elements of, 11
Descriptive statistics, 5
  interpreting, 78
  misleading, 101–104
Designed experiments, 14, 513, 579
  defined, 515
  elements of, 514–520
  randomization in, 163
Deterministic model, 592
Deterministic relationship, 592
Dichotomous responses, 204
Dimensions, 794
Discrete random variables, 191
  binomial random variable, 204–219
  Chebyshev's Rule for, 200
  Empirical Rule for, 200
  expected values, 198–204
    finding, 198–200
  hypergeometric random variables, 224–228
  Poisson random variables, 218–224
  probability distributions for, 193–198
Distribution-free tests, 821–823, 822, 870
  defined, 822
Doctrine of Chances, The (De Moivre), 271
Dot plots, 41–42, 47
Dowsing study, 591
  assessing the straight-line model fit with the dowsing data, 621

estimating a straight-line regression model for dowsing data, 603–605
  predicting pipe location using the straight-line model, 640–641
  using correlation coefficient to assess dowsing data, 628
Dummy variables, 709

E
Efron, Bradley, 437
Empirical Rule, 74, 76, 83
Error of estimation, 10, 298
Errors of prediction, 597
Estimated standard error of the regression model, 613
Estimators, variance of, 301
Ethics, of a statistical study, critically assessing, 18–19
Events, 120–121
  complementary, 137–139
  compound, 133
  defined, 125
  probability of, 126–127
Expected value:
  defined, 198
  of the squared distance from the mean, 199
Experimental units, 6, 515
Experiments, 120
  defined, 121
  and sample spaces, 122
Experimentwise error rate, 538, 579
Exponential distribution, 276–279
Exponential probability, finding, 277
Exponential probability distribution, 276
Exponential random variables:
  mean and variance of, 278–279
  probability distribution for, 276
Extrapolation, 763, 769
"Eye Cue" test, 29

F
Factor Interaction component, 562
Factor levels, 514
Factor Main Effect components, 562
Factorial ANOVA:
  conducting, 565–575
    ranking of means, 570
    test for brand main effect, 569–570
    test for club main effect, 570
    test for equality of treatment means, 568–569
Factorial experiments, 560–577
  conditions required for valid F-tests in, 565
  tests conducted in analyses of, 564–565
    test for factor interaction, 564
    test for main effect of factor A, 564
    test for main effect of factor B, 565
    test for treatment means, 564
  two-factor factorial experiment, procedure of analysis of, 562–564
Factors, 514
Familiarity group, 53
F-distribution, 483
First-order model, 664
First-order multiple regression model, 664–670
  fitting, 665–669
  in five quantitative independent variables, 664
First-order (straight-line) model, 648
Fisher, Ronald A., 516, 810

Fishers exact test, 810
Frequency, 44
Frequency function, 238
Friedman F_r-statistic:
  conditions required for, 855
  defined, 854
  for a randomized block design, 854–855
Friedman F_r-test, 853, 869, 870
F-test, 525
  conducting, 485–487
  for equal population variances, 488
  equal variance:
    checking the assumption of, 489–490
    normality of the population frequency distributions, 490
  p-value of, 487–488

G
Gallup poll, 14, 204
Galton, Francis, 593
Gauss, Carl Friedrich, 243
General population parameter, symbol for, 358
Global F-test, 675
Global test, 673
Gosset, William S., 333
Grammer of Science, The (Pearson), 786
Graphical method for describing qualitative data, 30

H
Harris poll, 14, 204
Hecht, Heiko, 29
Helmert, Friedrich R., 414
Higher-order term, 663
Hinges, 86, 88
Histograms, 43–44, 47
  determining the number of classes in, 45
  interpreting, 49
Hypergeometric distribution, applying, 225–226
Hypergeometric model, using to solve the cocaine sting case, 226–227
Hypergeometric probability distribution, 224
Hypergeometric random variables, 206, 224–228
  characteristics of, 225
  probability distribution, mean and variance of, 225
Hypothesis test for a paired difference, TI-83 graphing calculator, 462–464

I
Independence, checking for, 152–153
Independent events:
  occurring simultaneously, finding the probability of, 154–155
  probability of intersection of, 154
Independent sampling, 430–441, 468–479
  conditions required for valid large-sample inferences, 471
  large samples, 431–435
    conditions required for large-sample inferences about $\mu_1 - \mu_2$, 434
    confidence interval for $(\mu_1 - \mu_2)$, 433
    properties of the sampling distribution $(x_1 - x_2)$, 433
    test of hypothesis for $(\mu_1 - \mu_2)$, 433–434
  large-sample confidence interval, 470
  large-sample test of hypothesis, 470
  properties of the sampling distribution, 469

p-value for a test of $\mu 1 - \mu 2$, 435–436
small samples, 436–441
  approximate small-sample procedures for unequal sample sizes, 445–446
  conditions required for valid small-sample inferences about, 438
  confidence interval for $(\mu 1 - \mu 2)$, 437
  test of hypothesis for $(\mu 1 - \mu 2)$, 437
Independent variable, 594, 648
Indicator variable, 709
Indicator variables, 709
Inferences, 5
  identifying, 12
  reliability of, 11
  using normal probabilities to make, 251–252
  z-scores using, 91
Inferences based on a single sample, 320–367, 368–427
  large-sample confidence interval: for a population proportion, 343–348
  large-sample confidence interval for a population mean, 322–329
  sample size: determining, 350–357
  small-sample confidence interval for a population mean, 332–339
  target parameter: defined, 321
    determining, 321–322
    identifying, 321–322
Inferences based on two samples, 428–511
  comparing two population means: independent sampling, 430–441
    paired difference experiments, 453–460
  comparing two population proportions: independent sampling, 468–479
  comparing two population variances: independent sampling, 483–492
  sample size: determining, 479–482
    for estimating $p1 - p2$, 480–481
    for estimating $\mu 1 - \mu 2$, 479–480
Inferential statistical problems, elements of, 11
Inferential statistics, 5
Inner fences, 87, 88
Insomnia pill, 291
  making an inference about the mean sleep time for pill takers, 309
Interaction, 691
Interaction models, 690–698
  evaluating, 691–694
  relating $E(y)$ to two quantitative independent variables, 691
Interaction term, 691
Internet (World Wide Web), and data from published sources, 14
Interquartile range (IQR), 86, 106
Intersection, 133–137, *See also* Union and intersection
  defined, 134
Interval data, 13
Interval estimator, defined, 324
Inverse probability, 176
Inverted-U theory, 774

K
KLEENEX® survey, 369
  identifying key elements of a hypothesis test relevant to, 375

testing a population mean in, 388
testing a population proportion in, 401
Kruskal-Wallis H-test, 847
Kruskal-Wallis test, 869, 870

L
Language lab, 105–106, 178, 229, 358, 498–499, 578–579, 648, 768
Laplace, Pierre-Simon, 305
Large-sample confidence interval:
  for p, 359
    conditions required for, 344
    finding, 345–346
  for a population proportion, 343–348
  for a population mean, 322–329
  for u, 359
    conditions required for, 326
    finding, 326–328
Large-sample test for population mean, 418
Large-sample test for population proportion, 418
Large-sample test of hypothesis:
  about a population proportion, 397–404
    conditions required for, 399
    conducting, 399–400
    p-value, finding, 400–401
Large-sample test of hypothesis about a population mean, 376–383
  conditions required for, 380
  hypothesis test: carrying out, 379–380
    setting up, 378–379
Law of Large Numbers, 123
Law of universal regression, 593
Least squares approach, 595–611
Least squares estimates, 598
  formulas for, 598
Least squares line, 597, 603
  defined, 598
Least squares prediction equation, 597, 665
Level of a variable, 709
Level of significance, 374
Levels, 514, 709
Line of means, 594
Lot acceptance sampling, 272
Lottery, probability of winning, 155
Lottery Buster, 119
Lower quartile, 86, 106
Lower-tailed test, 418

M
Main effect terms, 717
Mann-Whitney U-statistic, 832
Marginal probabilities, 795
Matched sets, 545
Mean, 55–56, 198
  comparing median and mode, 61–62
  comparing to the median: to detect skewness, 59–60
  defined, 56
  finding on a printout, 56–57
  of a sample, 56
Mean Square for A X B interaction (MS(AB)), 579
Mean Square for Blocks (MSB), 578
Mean square for error, 667
Mean Square for Error (MSE), 523–524, 578
Mean square for error (MSE), 667
Mean Square for Factor A (MS(A)), 579
Mean Square for Factor B (MS(B)), 579
Mean Square for Treatments (MST), 523–524, 578

Measure of reliability, 10
Measure of sampling variability (MSE), 561
Measure of the variability, 67–71
Measure of treatment mean variability (MST), 561
Measurement, 7, 120
Measurement error, 18
Measures of central tendency, 55–63
Median, 57–58, 823
  comparing mean and mode, 61–62
  comparing to the mean: to detect skewness, 59–60
  computing (example), 58
  finding on a printout, 59
Method of least squares, 597, 649
  applying, 598–602
Middle quartile, 86, 106
Minimum variance unbiased estimator (MVUE), 302, 303, 312
MINITAB:
  analysis of variance (ANOVA) using, 586–589
    completely randomized design, 586–588
    randomized block and factorial designs, 588–589
  binomial, Poisson and hypergeometric probabilities using, 234–235
  chi-square analyses using, 818–819
  creating/listing data in, 24–27
  describing data using, 114–117
    graphing data, 114
    numerical descriptive statistics, 114–115
  dot plots, 41–42, 47
  generating a random sample using, 186–187
  multiple regression using, 779–781
  nonparametric tests using, 876–880
    Friedman test, 879
    Kruskal-Wallis test, 878–879
    rank sum test, 877–878
    sign test, 876–877
    signed-rank test, 878
    Spearman's rank correlation, 880
  simple linear regression using, 657–659
  simulating a sampling distribution using, 317–319
  stem-and-leaf display, 42–43, 47
  tests of hypothesis using, 424–427
  two sample inferences using, 508–511
  using technology confidence intervals using, 364–367
Miscellanea Analytica (De Moivre), 271
Misleading descriptive statistics, 101–104
Misspecified model, detecting, 769
Modal class, 61
Mode, 60
  comparing mean and median, 61–62
  finding (example), 60–61
Model building, 664
  complete second-order model: with two quantitative independent variables, 703
    in two xs, 704–705
    interaction models, 690–698
  models with both quantitative and qualitative variables, 716–725
    interpreting the B's in, 718–719
    testing for two different slopes, 719–723
  nested models, comparing, 725–734

quadratic model, 698–708
  in a single quantitative independent
      variable, 698
  qualitative (dummy) variable models,
      709–716
  second-order model, 698
  stepwise regression, 735–740
Mound-shaped distributions of data:, 73
  interpretation of z-scores for, 83
Multicollinearity, 759, 759–760, 769
  detecting:
      example, 760–762
      in the regression model, 760
  in regression:
      solutions to problems created by, 763
Multinomial data, 812
Multinomial experiment, 812
  identifying, 784–785
  properties of, 784
Multiple coefficient of determination, 674
Multiple comparisons, defined, 538
Multiple comparisons methods, 579
Multiple comparisons of means, 537–545
  ranking treatment means, 539–541
Multiple regression, residual analysis,
      740–758
Multiple regression model, 662
  first-order, fitting, 665–669
Multiple regression models, 662–664
  analyzing, 663
  assessing overall adequacy of a model,
      676–677
  checking the utility of, recommendation
      for, 677
  estimator of s2 for, with k independent
      variables, 667
  first-order model, 664–670
  general, 663
  individual parameter coefficient in, test of,
      670
  inferences about the bparameters,
      671–676
  inferences about the bparameters and the
      overall model utility, 670
  interpreting the bestimates, 669–670
  using the model for estimation and
      prediction, 684–686
Multiplicative rule:
  applying, 165–166
  defined, 169
Multiplicative rule of probability, 149
  applying, 149–151
  defined, 149
  and independent events, 151–155
Mutually exclusive events, 140–141
  as dependent events, 153
  probability of union of, 140
  union of, 141
  Venn diagram of, 140

N
n factorial, 167
Negative slope, 594
Nested model F-test, 725
Nested models, 725, 769
  comparing, 725–734
  complete second-order model:
      analyzing, 726–734
  defined, 725
  F-test for comparing, 726
Neyman, Jerzey, 325

Nielsen survey, 14
Nightingale, Florence, 5
Nominal data, 12
Nonconstant error variance, 769
Non-normal errors, 769
Nonparametric statistical tests, 446
Nonparametric statistics, 820–880
  comparing three or more populations:
      completely randomized design,
          847–853
      randomized block design, 853–859
  comparing two populations, 838–47
  distribution-free tests, 821–823
  independent samples, 830–838
      conditions required for a valid rank
          sum test, 433
      Wilcoxon Rank Sum Test, 830–835
  paired difference experiment, 838–47
      applying the signed rank test, 841–842
      conditions required for a valid signed
          rank test, 840
      Wilcoxon signed rank test for, 840
  rank correlation, 859–68
  single population inferences, 823–826
Nonparametrics, defined, 822
Nonrandom samples, 18
Nonresponse bias, 16, 18
Nonstandard normal probabilities, T1–83
      graphing calculator, 252–253
Normal data, checking for, 262–264
Normal distributions, 243–254
  property of, 248
Normal probabilities:
  finding, 249–250
  TI-83 graphing calculator, 250
  using to make an inference, 251–252
Normal probability distribution:
  approximating a binomial distribution
      with, 269–274
  approximating a binomial probability
      with, 272–274
      steps in, 272–274
Normal probability plots, 264–265
  defined, 261
  cumulative probabilities for, using
      MINITAB, 286–289
Normal random variable, 243
  steps for finding a probability
      corresponding to, 249–250
Normal table in reverse:
  application of, 255–256
  using, 254–255
Normality, descriptive methods for assessing,
      261–265
Null distribution, 404
Null hypothesis, 370
  steps for selecting, 377
  symbol for, 418
Numerical descriptive measures, 55
Numerical measures:
  of central tendency, 55–63
  of relative standing, 81–85
Numerical measures of variability, 67–71
Numerical method for describing qualitative
      data, 30

O
Observation, 120
Observational experiment, defined, 515
Observational sampling experiments, 513
Observational studies, 14

Observed count, 796
Observed significance levels (p-values),
      383–388, 418
  application using, 386
  computing, 385–386
  steps for calculating:
      for a test of hypothesis, 384
Odds, 183
One-tailed (one-sided) statistical test, 376–377
One-variable descriptive statistics:
  and TI-83 graphing calculator, 63
One-way table, 785–794, 812
Ordinal data, 12, 822
Outer fences, 87, 88
Outliers:
  defined, 85, 745
  detecting, 93
  detection methods, 85–92
  identifying, 745–748, 769

P
Paired difference experiment, 456, 546
Paraboloid, 703
Parameter estimability, 758
Parameters, 292
Parametric statistical tests, 821
Pareto, Vilfredo, 33
Pareto diagram, 32–33
Parsimonious model, 730, 769
Parsimony principle, 729
Partitions rule:
  defined, 168, 169
Partitions rule applying, 167–168
Pascal, Blaise, 152
Pearson, Egon, 373
  Pearson, Karl, 373, 786
Pearson correlation coefficient, 625
Pearson product moment coefficient of
      correlation, 624
Percentile rankings, 81
Percentiles, finding/interpreting, 82
Perfect negative correlation, 859, 860
Perfect positive correlation, 859, 860
Permutations, defined, 166
Permutations rules:
  applying, 166–167
  defined, 169
Piaget, Jean, 29
Pie chart, 32–33
  interpreting, 35–36
Point estimator, 298, 322
Poisson, Siméon, 218–219
Poisson distribution, 218
Poisson probabilities, finding, 219–221
Poisson random variables, 218–224
  characteristics of, 218
  probability distribution, mean, and
      variance for, 219
Polls, 204
Pooled sample estimator, 436
Population, 7, 8
  census of, 7
  identifying, 12
Population correlation coefficient, 628
Population data sets, 8
Population mean, 105, 823
  confidence interval for:
      interpretation of, 327
      estimating, 351–352
      large-sample confidence interval for,
          322–329

small-sample confidence for, 332–339
symbol for, 57, 358
Population proportion:
  large-sample confidence interval for, 343–348
  symbol for, 358
Population rank correlation coefficient, 863
Population standard deviation, 105
  symbol for, 69, 358
Population variance, 105, 199
  symbol for, 69
Population z-score, 82
Positive slope, 594
Potential outliers, 87
Power of a test:
  defined, 407
  finding, 407–410
Prediction interval, 637
Predictor variable, 594
Primary source, 14
Probabilistic modela, 592–595, 648
  first-order, 594
  general form of, 593
Probabilistic relationship, 592
Probability, 118–187
  conditional, 145–148
  of events, 126–127
    steps for calculating, 127–128
  and inference making, 120
  inverse, 176
  of a sample point, 123–124
  of winning lotto,
    computing/understanding, 130
Probability density function, 238
Probability distributions, 238
  defined, 194
  for discrete random variables, 193–198
  for an exponential random variable, 276
  finding, 193–194
  for a normal random variable, 244
  for a uniform random variable, 239
  using a formula, 194–195
Probability of the contingency table, 810
Proffitt, Dennis R., 29
pth percentile, 81
Published source, 14
Punnett, Reginald, 198
Punnett square, 198
Pupillometer, 502
p-values, 383–388
  application using, 386
  computing, 385–386
  steps for calculating:
    for a test of hypothesis, 384

Q

Quadratic model, 698
  analyzing, 698–704
  in a single quantitative independent
    variable, 698
Quadratic term, 698
Qualitative data, 12–13
  defined, 13
  describing, 30–40
  graphing/summarizing, 30–33
  examples, 33–36
Qualitative factors, 514
Qualitative independent variables, 709–716
  with k levels, procedure for writing a
    model with, 710
Qualitative variable, 709

Quantitative data, 12
  graphing, 41–54
    dot plots, 41–42, 47
    example, 45–47
    histograms, 43–44, 47
    stem-and-leaf display, 42–43, 47
Quantitative factors, 514
Quartiles, 86

R

Random error, 592
Random number generators, 161
Random number tables, 162
Random sample, 15, 161
Random sampling, 161–165
  selecting a random sample, 161–163
Randomization, in a designed experiment, 163
Randomized block design, 545–560, 579, 853
  ANOVA for, 550–552
  defined, 545
  experimental design principles, 549–550
  ranking means in, 552–554
  steps for conducting an ANOVA for, 554
Randomized block experiment, 456
Randomness distribution, *See* Uniform
  probability distribution:
Range, 67
Rank correlation, 859–868
  Spearman's nonparametric test for, 864
Rank statistics, 822, 870
Rank sums, 831
Rank tests, 822
Rare-event approach, 91
Ratio data, 12
Reduced model, 725, 769
Regression analysis, 594
  robust, 750
Regression line, 597
Regression model, origin of term, 593
Regression modeling, 594
Regression residuals, 769
  constant error variance, checking, 751–755
  defined, 741
  normal errors, checking for, 748–749
  outliers, identifying, 745–748
  properties of, 742
Rejection region, 371
Relative standing, numerical measures of, 81–85
Reliability, 10
  of an inference, 11
Replicates, 564
Representative sample, 15
Research hypothesis, 370
  symbol for, 418
Residual analysis, 740–758, 741
  steps in, 754–755
Residual plots, 750
Residuals, 741
  analyzing, 742–745
  defined, 741
  TI-83 graphing calculator, 755–756
Resource constraints, 10
Response surface, 728
Response variable, 594
Ridge regression, 763
Rigged milk price detection, 429
  comparing the dispersion of bid prices in
    two milk markets, 490–492

comparing the incumbency rates of two
  milk markets, 476
comparison of mean winning bid prices of
  two milk markets, 446
Robust method, 529, 579, 750
Roper poll, 14

S

Saddle-shaped surface, 703
Sample, 7, 8
  identifying, 12
Sample data sets, 8
Sample mean, 105
  computing, 56
  defined, 56
  symbol for, 57
Sample median, calculating, 58
Sample points:
  assigning probabilities to, 124–125
  defined, 121
  finding the probability of a collection of, 125
  listing (example), 121
Sample size, 57
  determining, 350–357
  population mean:
    estimating, 351–352
    finding, 352–353
  population proportion:
    estimating, 353–354
    finding, 354–355
Sample spaces, 120–121
  defined, 122
Sample standard deviation, 70, 105
Sample statistics, 292
Sample variance, 68, 105
  symbol for, 69
Sample z-score, 82
Sampling, 5
  lot acceptance, 272
  random, 161–165
Sampling distributions, 290–319
  biased estimate, 299–302
  concept of, 292–298
  defined, 293
  estimators, variance of, 301
  finding, 294–295
  properties of, 298–302
  simulating, 296–297
  unbiased estimate, 299–301
  of x:
    and Central Limit Theorem, 303–309
    properties of, 304
Sampling error, 352
  symbol for, 358
Scale break, 101
Scales of classification, 794
Scanner panel, 815
Scattergrams, 95–98, 624, 596
Scheffé's method, 538–539, 579
Secondary source, 14
Second-order model, 698
Second-order term, 698
Selection bias, 18
Self-selected respondents, 15–16, 18
Sign test, 823, 869, 870
Simple linear regression, 590–659
  assessing model utility, 616–624
    sampling distribution of the least
      squares estimator, 617–620
  coefficient of correlation, 624–628
  coefficient of determination, 628–635

complete example, 644–647
estimator of o2, 613
fitting the model, 595–611
least squares approach, 595–611
model assumptions, 611–612
probabilistic models, 592–595
steps in, 648
TI-83 graphing calculator, 602–603, 631–632
using MINITAB, 657–659
using the model for estimation and prediction, 635–644
Simple linear regression analysis, 592
Simple random sample, 161
Single population inferences, 823–826
    sign test for a population median n, 825
        conditions required for valid application of, 825
Single-factor experiments, 560
Skewed data set, 59
Skewness, 59
    detecting by comparing the mean and the median, 59–60
Slope(s), 594, 648
    testing for two different, 719–723
Small-sample confidence interval:
    for a population mean, 332–339
    for u, 359
        conditions required for, 336
        finding, 337–339
Small-sample test for population mean, 418
Small-sample test of hypothesis:
    about a population mean, 390–397
        conditions required for, 391
        conducting, 392–393
        p-value for, 393–394
Snedecor, George W., 484
Spearman, Charles E., 861
Spearman rank correlation, 869
Spearman's rank correlation coefficient, 860, 861
Spearman's rank correlation test, 870
    applying, 862–865
Sporting News, The, 14
Spread, 57, 67
Sprint times:
    determining number of athletes to participate in training program, 355
    estimating the mean decrease in, 328
    estimating proportion of sprinters improved after speed training, 347–348
    improving, 321
Standard deviation, 69
    checking the calculation of, 75–76
    of a discrete random variable, 200
    interpreting, 72–74
        Chebyshev's Rule, 73
        Empirical Rule, 74
        example, 74–75
    origin of term, 786
    symbol for, 69
Standard error, 433
    of the estimated slope, 617
    of the mean, 304
    of the regression model, 613
    of the statistic, 300
Standard normal distribution, 244
    definition, 245
Standard normal random variable, 245

Standard normal table, using, 246–249
Statistical inference, 8
    making, 76–78
Statistical Methods for Research Workers (Fisher), 516
Statistical problem, key elements of, 9–10
Statistical science, 4
Statistical thinking, 17–18
Statistics:
    defined, 4
    fundamental elements of, 6–7
    role in critical thinking, 17–19
    science of, 4
Stem-and-leaf display, 42–43, 47
Stepwise regression, 735, 735–740, 769
    running, 737–738
Straight-line model, 592, 594
Subset, 7
Sum of Square A X B interaction (SS(AB)), 579
Sum of Squares for Blocks (SSB), 546–547, 578
Sum of Squares for Error (SSE), 522–523, 578
Sum of Squares for Factor B (SS(B)), 579
Sum of Squares for Factor (SS(A)), 579
Sum of Squares for Treatments (SST), 522, 578
Summation notation, 54–55, 105
    meaning of, 55
Super weapons:
    hit data, assessing normal distribution appropriateness for modeling, 265–266
    using the normal model to maximize hit probability with, 256–257
Super weapons development, 237
Survey of Current Business, 14
Surveys, 14, 16

T

Target parameter:
    defined, 322, 430
    determining, 322, 374, 430
    identifying, 321–322, 430
TCDD file, 821
Test of hypothesis, 369
    about a population variance, 412–417
    alternative hypothesis, 370, 374
    assumptions, 374
    conclusion, 374
    conclusions and consequences for, 373
    elements of, 369–376
    experiment and calculation of test statistic, 374
    null hypothesis, 370, 374
    possible conclusions for, 380–381
    rejection region, 371, 374
    research hypothesis, 370, 374
    test statistic, 370
Test statistic, 370
Tests for main effects, 579
Time series model, 763
TI-83 graphing calculator:
    analysis of variance (ANOVA), 528–529
    box plots, 92
    binomial probabilities, 213–214
    confidence interval:
        for a paired difference, 460–462
        for a population mean, 328–329, 338–339

for a population proportion, 348
    for p1 – p1, 473–474
    for μ1 - μ2, 441–443
contingency tables, 801–803
histograms, 47–49
hypothesis test:
    for a paired difference, 462–464
    for p1 - p2, 474–475
    for two population variance, 493–495
    for μ1 - μ2, 443–445
hypothesis testing, 387
nonstandard normal probabilities, 252–253
normal probability plot, 264–265
one-variable descriptive statistics, 63
Poisson probabilities, 221–222
quadratic regression, 701
residuals, 755–756
scatterplots, 98
simple linear regression, 602–603, 631–632
standard normal probabilities, 250
Treatment group, 53
Treatments, 515
Tree diagrams, 150
t-statistic, 333
Tukey, John, 43
Tukey's method, 538–539, 579
Two-factor factorial experiment, procedure of analysis of, 562–564
Two-tailed hypothesis, 377
Two-tailed test, 418
Two-way classification, 561
Two-way contingency table, 794–811
    analysis:
        conducting, 799–801
        general form of, 799
    finding expected cell counts for, 796
Two-way table, 812
    defined, 136
    finding probabilities from, 136
Type I errors, 371, 418
Type II errors, 372–373, 418
Type II error probabilities:
    calculating, 404–412
    symbol for, 418

U

Unbiased estimate, 299–301
Unbiased estimators, 69, 312
Uncertainty in inferences, 10
Unconditional probabilities, 145
Unethical statistical practice, 18
Uniform probability distribution, 238–241
    applying, 240–241
Union, defined, 134
Union and intersection, 133–137
    of three events, 132
    of two events, 134–135
    of two mutually exclusive events, 141
Upper quartile, 86, 106
Upper-tailed test, 418
USA Weekend:
    Annual Teen, 16
    teen survey, 3

V

Variability, 55
    of data, 57
Variables, 7
Variance:

of a random variable, 200
  -stabilizing transformation, 751, 752
  symbols for, 69
Variation:
  computing measures of, 70
  finding measures of, on a printout
    (example), 70–71
Venn, John, 122
Venn diagrams, 122
  for die-toss experiment, 152
  of mutually exclusive events, 140
  of union, 139

W

Waiting time distribution, 276
Wall Street Journal, The, 14

Wells, H. G., 17
Wheel system, probability of winning lotto
    with, 141–142
Whiskers, 87, 88
Wilcoxon, Frank, 830
Wilcoxon rank sum test, 830–835, 869, 870
  applying, 833–835
  conditions required for a valid rank sum
    test, 833
Wilcoxon signed rank test, 840, 869
  for large samples, 843
  for paired difference experiment, 840
Wilson point estimator of p, 346
Wilson's adjusted estimate of p, symbol for,
    358

X

x_2 goodness-of-fit test, 817
x_2_test, 812

Y

y-intercept, 594, 648

Z

z-scores, 105
  finding, 82–83
  inference using, 91

Photo Credits

Florence Nightingale, Corbis/Bettmann; H.G. Wells, Getty Images, Inc.-Hulton Archive Photos; Wilfredo Pareto, The Granger Collection; John Tukey, Alfred Eisenstaedt/Getty Images/Time-Life Pictures; Pafnuty L. Chebyshev, Sovfoto/Eastfoto; John Venn, Maull and Fox/Gonville and Caius College; Blaise Pascal, The Granger Collection; Thomas Bayes, Prof. Stephen M. Stigler; Simeon Denis Poisson, Photo Researchers, Inc.; Carl F. Gauss, The Granger Collection; Abraham de Moivre, Picture Desk, Inc./Kobal Collection; Pierre-Simon Marquis de LaPlace, Picture Desk, Inc./Kobal Collection; Jerzey Neyman, Paul Bishop/University of California-Berkeley; William Sealy Gosset, The Granger Collection; Egon Sharpe Pearson, Biometrika; Friedrich R. Helmert, Bibliothek des GeoForschungsZentrums GFZ; Bradley Efron, Stanford University; Sir Ronald A. Fisher, Library of Congress; Francis Galton, Corbis/Bettmann; Francis J. Anscombe, Phyllis R. Anscombe; Karl Pearson, University College, London; Frank Wilcoxon, Florida State University, Department of Statistics; Charles E. Spearman, University College, London Department of Psychology

Chapter Opening Photos: Chapter 1, Getty Images; Chapter 2, Left Lane Productions/Corbis/Bettmann; Chapter 3, Morton Beebe/Corbis/Bettmann; Chapter 4, Alan Schein Photography/Corbis/Bettmann; Chapter 5, DiMaggio/Kalish/Corbis/Bettmann; Chapter 6, Neil Rabinowitz/Corbis/Bettmann; Chapter 7, Bryan Pickering/Eye Ubiquitous/Corbis/Bettmann; Chapter 8, Alan Schein Photography/Corbis/Bettmann; Chapter 9, Duomo/Corbis/Bettmann; Chapter 10, Lester Lefkowitz/Getty Images, Inc.-Image Bank; Chapter 11, Corbis Digital Stock; Chapter 12, Freelance Consulting Services Pty. Ltd./Corbis/Bettmann; Chapter 13, Grafton Marshall Smith/Corbis/Bettmann; Chapter 14, Kelly/Mooney Photography/Corbis/Bettmann

McClave/Sincich
Statistics, 10th Edition, Student Data CD
0-13-149827-4
© **2006 Pearson Education, Inc.**
Pearson Prentice Hall
Pearson Education, Inc.
Upper Saddle River, NJ 07458
Pearson Prentice Hall™ is a trademark of Pearson Education, Inc.